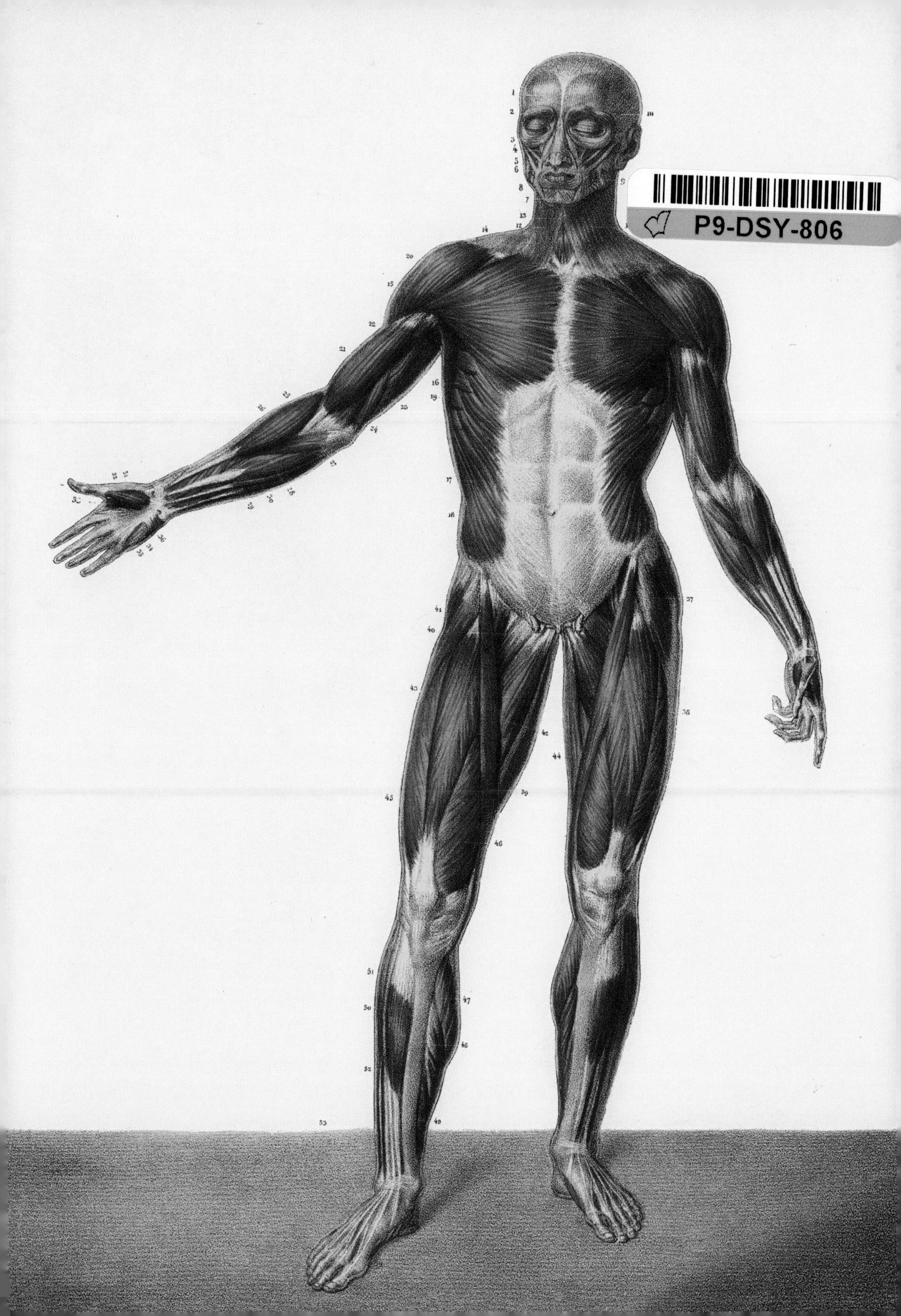

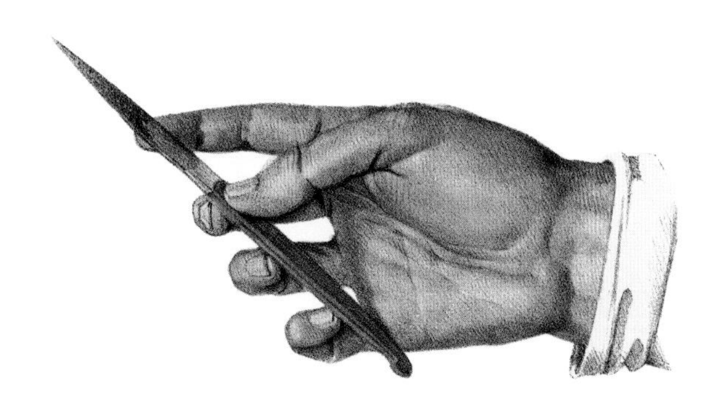

J. M. Bourgery & N. H. Jacob

THE COMPLETE

ATLAS OF HUMAN ANATOMY AND SURGERY

Atlas d'anatomie humaine et de chirurgie

Atlas de anatomía humana y cirugía

Traité complet de l'anatomie de l'homme
Complete edition of the coloured plates / Édition complète des planches coloriées / Edición completa con láminas en color

Edited by / commenté par / Editado por
JEAN-MARIE LE MINOR & HENRI SICK

TASCHEN

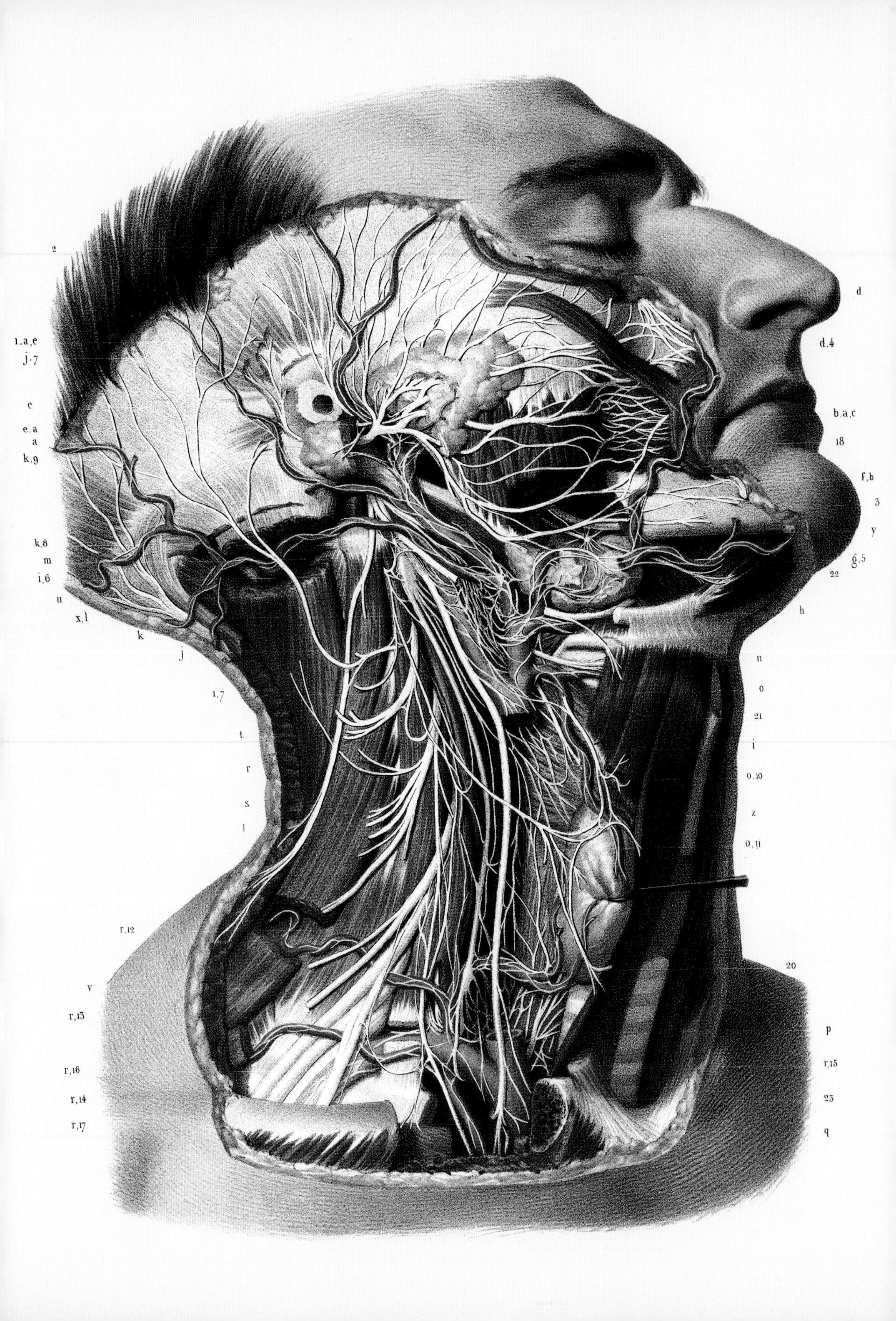

2
1.a,e
j.7
e
e.a
a
k.9
k,8
m
i,6
u
x,l
k
j
1,7
t
r
s
l
r,12
v
r,13
r,16
r,14
r,17
d
d.4
b,a,c
18
f,b
3
y
g.5
22
h
n
o
21
i
o,10
z
o,11
20
p
r,15
23
q

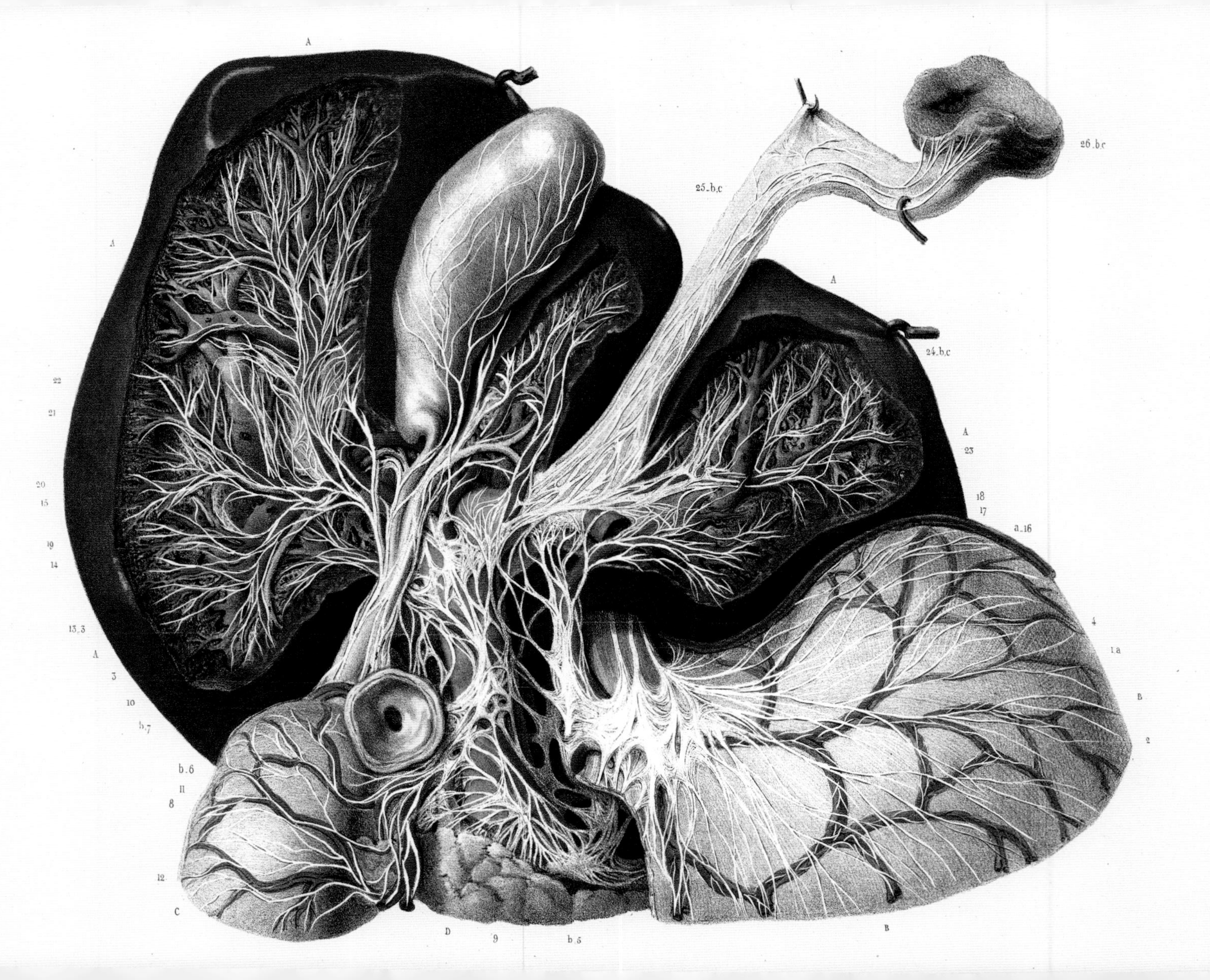

A
26.b.c
25.b.c
A
A
24.b.c
22
21
A
23
20
15
18
17
a.16
19
14
13.3
A
4
1a
5
B
10
b.7
2
b.6
11
8
12
C
D
9
b.5
B

Dessiné d'après nature
par
Rosselin, éditeur, 21, quai Voltaire, à Paris.
Lith. de Grégoire et Deneux, 15, r. de l'Abbaye

J.-M. BOURGERY.

THE ATLAS OF ANATOMY AND SURGERY BY J. M. BOURGERY AND N. H. JACOB – A MONUMENTAL WORK OF THE 19TH CENTURY

Human anatomy, the morphological study of the architecture of the human body, based on dissection, has given rise to the publication of some outstanding illustrated books. *The Complete treatise of human anatomy* by J. M. Bourgery and N. H. Jacob, published in Paris between 1831 and 1854, while joining a long list of illustrated works, at the same time represents one of the most remarkable works in the whole history of anatomy, and in any case is the most outstanding to be published in the 19th century. The work is monumental: In large folio format, it comprises eight volumes of text totalling 2108 pages, and atlas volumes with 725 plates, representing a total of 3750 figures.

THE MAJOR WORKS OF ANATOMY PRIOR TO THE 19TH CENTURY

Anatomical knowledge was for a long time limited to data gathered from the dissection of animals by Galen (c. 130–c. 200), a Greek physician who practised in Pergamon and Rome, and whose influence was considerable right up until the 16th century.

In the Middle Ages, the only work on anatomy truly worthy of the name was that of Mondino dei Luzzi (c. 1275–1326), written in 1319 and titled *Anathomia*; taking up the data of Galen, he made some interesting observations on the basis of human dissections he had undertaken in 1315.

These works were disseminated in the form of manuscript copies and were very sparsely illustrated. With the invention of printing by Johannes Gensfleisch alias Gutenberg (c. 1397–1468) in about 1450, the dissemination of knowledge was to increase by leaps and bounds. The so-called incunabula, in other words works printed before 1500, include the first edition of the *Anathomia of dei Luzzi*, printed in 1478; this work underwent several subsequent editions, in particular one with a commentary by Berengario da Carpi (1460?–1530), professor in Bologna, which was published in Venice in 1521.

The anatomical drawings of Leonardo da Vinci (1452–1519), 228 hand-drawn plates of extraordinary scientific quality, occupy a very marginal place, because they were never edited, and were ignored by the scholars of the day. Published for the first time in 1898, they had no impact on the development of the subject.

In 1543, the work by André Vésale (1514–1564), *De humani corporis fabrica*, was published in Basle; it is indisputably the most outstanding book in the whole history of anatomy both in respect of its concept and of its aesthetic qualities (ill. p. 13). The publication of this work represented a veritable scientific revolution, providing a new vision of Man by replacing Galen's speculative studies and his extrapolations from animal anatomy by systematic dissections of the human body. Vésale's work comprises 25 superb plates separate from the text, and numerous figures within the text, all of them

Jean Marc Bourgery (1797–1849)
Drawn by Maurin, lithographed by Grégoire and Deneux and edited by Rosselin in Paris.
Dessiné par Maurin, lithographié par Grégoire et Deneux, et édité par Rosselin à Paris.
Dibujado por Maurin, litografiado por Grégoire y Deneux, y editado por Rosselin en París.

woodcuts, probably the work of Jan Stephan von Calcar, who belonged to Titian's circle. This book, of which a second improved edition appeared in 1555, and which went through several more, had a considerable impact and was copied by numerous authors. It would henceforth no longer be possible to think of anatomy without illustrations.

Among the most outstanding anatomical works of the 16th century, we might mention that by Charles Estienne (c. 1504–1564), *De dissectione partium corporis humani*, which was published in Paris in 1545, with a French edition published in 1546, comprising 62 woodcut plates, and numerous vignettes in the text; although published two years after the work by Vésale, Estienne's had been in the making since 1530. In 1556, Juan Valverde de Hamusco (c. 1525–c. 1587) published in Rome a work in Spanish copied from Vésale; a Latin edition of this work, entitled *Vivae imagines partium corporis humani*, was published in 1566 by C. Plantin in Antwerp, with, for almost the very first time, the use of copperplate engraving for the illustrations; this new technique, allowing a precision and half-tone finesse impossible to achieve with woodcuts, opened up new and unheard-of possibilities, and was destined to be used until the beginning of the 19th century. Finally, in 1600, André Du Laurens (1558?–1609), professor at Montpellier, published in Paris and Frankfurt an *Historia anatomica humani corporis* illustrated by 26 splendid copperplate engravings.

For the 17th century, we should mention the work of Giulio Casserio alias Julius Casserius (c. 1550–1616), *Tabulae anatomicae*, published posthumously in Venice in 1627 with 97 copperplate engravings by Francesco Valesio after Odoardo Fialetti, a painter in Tintoretto's circle; the plates in this book also serve to illustrate the works of his successor in Padua, Adrian van der Spieghel (c. 1578–1625). The work of Govert Bidloo (1649–1713), *Anatomia humani corporis*, published in Amsterdam in 1685, comprises 105 very original copperplate engravings by Pieter van Gunst based on drawings by Gérard de Lairesse (1640?–1711).

In the 18th century, numerous outstanding works on anatomy illustrated with copperplate engravings appeared, but often they were confined to some specialized aspect of the subject. The most remarkable is that by Bernhard Siegfried Weiss alias Albinus (1697–1770), professor of anatomy and surgery at Leyden, devoted to osteology and myology, or the study of bones and muscles: *Tabulae sceleti et musculorum corporis humani*, published in Leyden in 1747, with 40 plates by Jean Wandelaer (1690–1759), a former pupil of Gérard de Lairesse (ills. pp. 17, 19, 20, 22). This work enjoyed great success and opened up a new path in scientific anatomical depiction and was much copied as a result.

Among other remarkable works, we might also mention those by William Cowper (1666–1709), *Myotomia reformata* (London, 1724); Albrecht von Haller (1708–1777), *Icones anatomicae*, published in eight instalments in Göttingen between 1743 and 1756, with 46 admirable plates; Paolo Mascagni (1752–1815), on the lymphatic system, *Vasorum lymphaticorum corporis humani historia* (Siena, 1787); and Antonio Scarpa (1752–1832), on the nerves, *Tabulae nevrologicae* (Pavia, 1794). The magnificent work by Jacques Gamelin (1738–1803), painter, graphic artist and engraver, *Nouveau recueil d'ostéologie et de myologie*, published in Toulouse in 1779 with 79 plates, is somewhat different in that it treats anatomy artistically rather than medically. Finally we should mention the extraordinary works printed in colour by Jacques Fabien Gautier d'Agoty (1710–1785), in part in collaboration with the surgeon J. F. Duverney: *Myologie complette en couleur et grandeur naturelle*, with 20 plates (Paris, 1746; ill. p. 32), *Anatomie de la tête*, with 8 plates (Paris, 1748; ill. p. 29), *Anatomie générale des viscères et de la névrologie, angéologie et ostéologie du corps humain*, with 18 plates (Paris, 1754), and *Exposition anatomique de la structure du corps humain*, with 20 plates (Marseille, 1759).

INTRODUCTION INTO THE "TREATISE" OF J. M. BOURGERY AND N. H. JACOB

"Now that lithography allows us to publish, at relatively low cost, very extensive illustrated works, it would be a service to physicians to make available to everybody all those works which have anatomy as their subject. However, for a work of this kind to satisfy all its potential uses, not only has the science to be presented in its most advanced state, it also has to appear with all its applications. Therefore, we must not slavishly copy a previous work, as none exists to which new facts could not be added; but, above all, it is essential for the plates of such a work, created with new intentions, to be drawn from nature, whilst using as guides renowned figures amongst those that have been published to date. This is the task that M. Jacob and myself have decided to accomplish. We will spare no effort to honourably complete the immense work that we have undertaken." (Bourgery, vol. 1, pp. 1–2)

The above quotation, taken from the introduction written by Jean Marc Bourgery in October 1830 and published in the first volume of this work, published in 1831–1832, sums up the entire philosophy that informed the creation of the *Complete treatise of human anatomy*, including operative medicine, by Dr J. M. Bourgery, with lithographic plates from nature by N. H. Jacob.

In his work *Les médecins de Paris jugés par leurs œuvres*, published in 1845, C. Sachaile de la Barre writes: "...it was reserved to M. Bourgery not only to give the most satisfactory answer to this question, but to astonish us by the perfection of the means employed to achieve this task. There is indeed nothing more beautiful than the plates which form the anatomical works to which principally his name is attached. The biographical note written by E. Beaugrand in 1876 for the famous *Dictionnaire encyclopédique des sciences médicales*, published under the direction of A. Dechambre, therefore justly describes Dr J. M. Bourgery as the author of one of the most beautiful monuments to the science of the structure of the human body."

In Bourgery's day, Paris was a city of reference for anatomy. The Dean of the Faculty of Medicine, Matthieu Orfila (1787–1853), appointed in 1832, undertook the complete renovation of the faculty and initiated the creation of a new and remarkably rich anatomical museum, which was opened in 1844. The numerous dissections performed in the Practical School attached to the faculty were enviously admired everywhere.

The publication of the *Complete treatise of human anatomy* took place at a time when anatomy was at its height, and in the introduction to his work Bourgery could therefore write: "Without anatomy, physiology is only a tissue of more or less imaginative tales, surgery is without a guide, and medicine is reduced to blind empiricism" (vol. 1, p. 1). Throughout his work, Bourgery reasserts several times the primacy of anatomy amongst the medical specialities and in the evolution of scientific concepts.

THE INITIATOR AND AUTHOR: JEAN MARC BOURGERY

Jean Marc Bourgery, born in Orléans on 8 Prairial year V of the revolutionary calendar (27 May, 1797), was the son of Marc Claude Bourgery, haberdasher, and Madeleine Marthe Delaboulaye; the birth took place at the family home at 1, rue du Tabourg, at eleven o'clock in the morning; present were Jean Claude Vignolet, haberdasher, and Nicolas Bergerac, second-hand clothes dealer.

Bourgery chose to study medicine. In 1815, he also enrolled to attend the course of the famous naturalist Jean Baptiste de Lamarck (1744–1829), then professor at the Museum of Natural History in Paris. Following the internship competition, Bourgery was accepted as an intern at the Hospitals from 1817 to 1820, and in 1819 received the Gold Internship Medal.

At the end of his medical course, Bourgery did not take his doctorate, apparently because of a lack of funds, and instead served as medical officer at the copper foundries in Romilly-sur-Seine (Aube department) for several years. There he was involved in the establishment of a copper sulphate factory. It was probably during this time that he conducted research into the colouring of wood: "M. Bourgery has again used his knowledge of organic chemistry to give growing wood a colour different from what is natural: the experiments he has conducted on this subject have already produced beautiful results and give rise to great hopes" (Sachaile de la Barre, 1845).

In 1827, at the age of 30, Bourgery's career took a decisive turn when he decided to return to Paris. He finally received his doctorate in medicine, for a thesis defended in Paris on 27 August 1827, on circular ligatures of the limbs. Two years later, in 1829, he published a *Traité de petite chirurgie*, a remarkable reference work, although not illustrated, which had great success, as a second French edition was published in 1835, and it was translated into English (as *A treatise on lesser surgery or the minor surgical operations*) in 1834, and into German in 1836.

In 1830, in collaboration with the illustrator N. H. Jacob, Bourgery established the project for his *Complete treatise of human anatomy*, which was to occupy him for more than 20 years, until his death. The first volumes were published in 1831. Following the success of these first volumes, in 1834–1835 Bourgery and Jacob published an *Anatomie élémentaire* in large folio format with 20 lithographic plates and a small separate text volume. The work went into a second edition (1836–1839) and was translated into German (1837). The publication of the *Complete treatise of human anatomy* continued, but the labour remained considerable. An English version of the first volumes, with texts translated by Robert Willis, was published from 1833 to 1837, confirming the significance of the work accomplished thus far.

From 1840, Bourgery used personal observations to write original scientific articles, mainly in the form of essays, published between 1842 and 1848 in the *Comptes-Rendus de l'Académie des Sciences de Paris*. These essays are often illustrated by beautiful lithographic plates, and several of them were also published as small individual reprints.

Bourgery was also associated with the creation of anatomical models from carton-pierre and pulpboard by Félix Thibert, as witnessed by a presentation brochure: "Musée Thibert d'anatomie pathologique et d'histoire naturelle par la méthode plastique du Dr Félix Thibert ... sous la direction scientifique du Dr J. M. Bourgery", published in Paris in 1847. These models, moulded in relief from nature and then painted, met with great success, as reflected in the numerous pieces mentioned in the printed catalogues of anatomical museums, in particular of that in Strasbourg, written by C. H. Ehrmann (1843), or of the Orfila Museum in Paris, written by M. Houel (1881).

Andreas Vesalius, *De humani corporis fabrica*, Basel, 1543
Wood engraving probably by Jan Stephan von Calcar. The most outstanding work in the history of anatomy.
Gravure sur bois vraisemblablement due à Jan Stephan von Calcar. L'ouvrage le plus exceptionnel de l'histoire de l'anatomie. / Xilografía probablemente realizada por Jan Stephan von Calcar. La obra más excepcional en la historia de la anatomía.

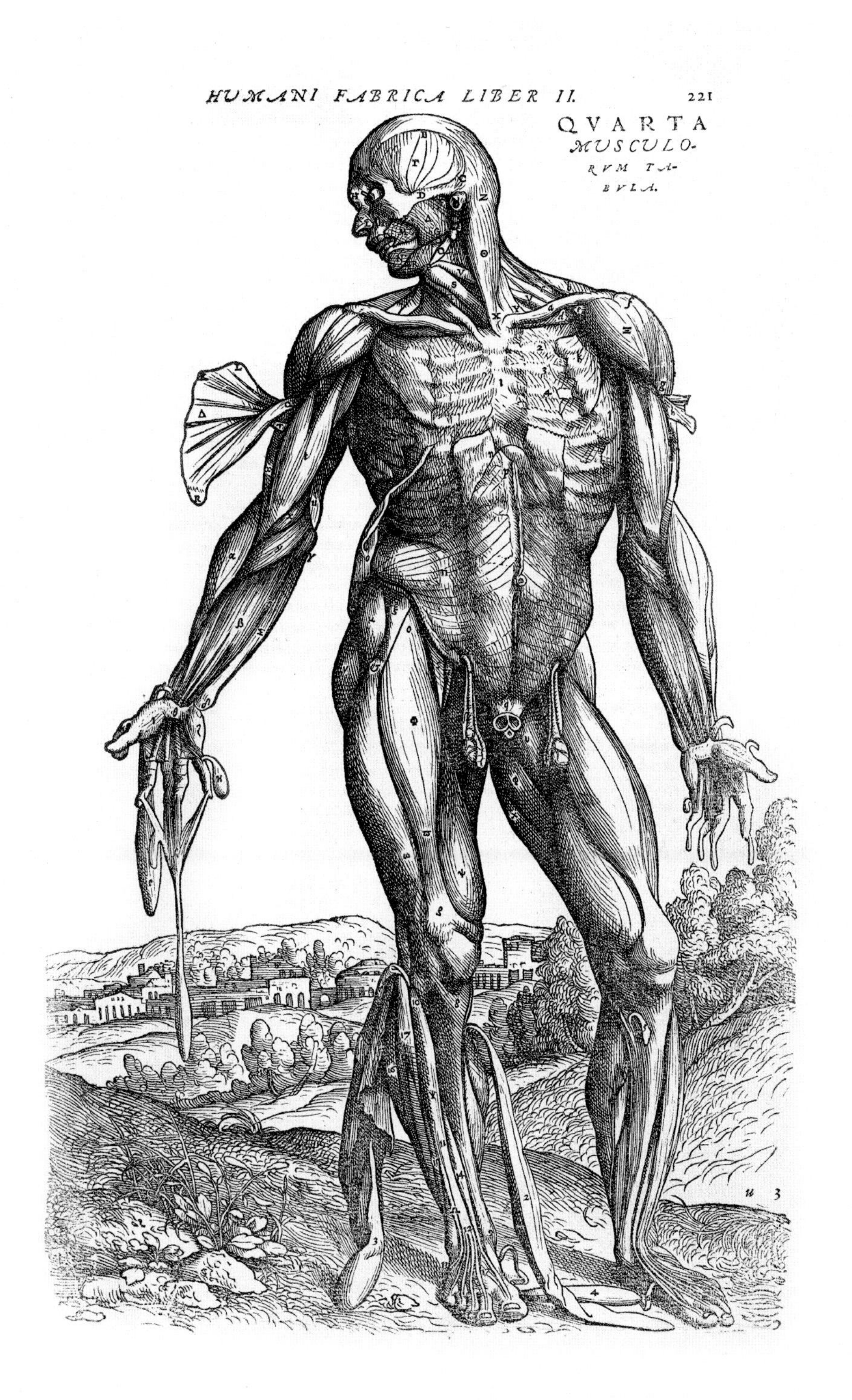
HUMANI FABRICA LIBER II. 221

QVARTA MUSCULORVM TABULA.

The extent of Bourgery's work led him to apply for different university and academic posts and to enter different competitions, but every time without success. In particular he presented himself as a candidate for the post of professor of anthropology at the Natural History Museum in Paris, for membership of the Academy of Sciences in Paris in 1843, and for the chair of anatomy at the Faculty of Medicine in Paris in 1846; in this context he presented a thesis, defended on 13 February, 1846, on the subject of the appendages of the foetus and their development.

Bourgery's repeated failures as a candidate for university and academic posts, despite the solid fame he had acquired, made him bitter; a certain exhaustion also seems to show through. The confession he made on this subject in the introduction to the eighth and final volume of his *Treatise*, which was published posthumously, is unique in the history of medical and scientific publishing, and particularly poignant: "And now, on the point of completing my work for which I possess all the material, coming close to achieving what I wanted to do, may the public recognize that I have not failed in my task, although fortune has cheated me out of the success a great man had predicted for me. Alas! Cuvier judged the heart and intelligence of others by his own. But does everybody have the heart and mind of Cuvier! When I lost him, I lost everything. Instead of the happy career that he saw smiling at me, what have I found? Loathing, obstacles, intrigues, a hidden league of tenacious opposition. During the 20 years that I have worked relentlessly, I do not have to blame myself for not helping myself. I have done everything that was honourable to attain something. I have presented myself everywhere I could. But to no avail. I have seen everybody pass in front of me, both those who had some right, but particularly those who had none. Having so much to say about a science that I have worked on so much, it seemed to me that there should be a place for me somewhere: but no. Academies, faculties, colleges of higher education, I have presented myself everywhere: Everywhere there were always others who presented themselves. Two facts sum up everything: today, after 20 years, I am nothing, and I do not expect anything anymore; my name even fails to be quoted in any of the modern books, although many of them are indebted to mine. I finish with this single statement: It is the cry of 20 years of oppression that escapes from me. I might as well hold myself up as an example, so that any unwary person, in danger of being seduced, as I was, by an inconsiderate love for science, might escape this fate. At least they will learn from me that conscientious work leads to nothing. Please forgive me for this complaint! It is the first; it will also be the last." (vol. 8, p. III)

Bourgery died in Paris, at the early age of 52, in June 1849, apparently a victim of a cholera epidemic. His life's work, the eight volumes of the *Treatise*, had just been completed, but it was only posthumously, in 1854, that the last volume was published in its entirety.

Until eponymous terms disappeared with the progressive introduction of the international anatomical nomenclature, Bourgery's name remained attached to several anatomical structures, in particular: Bourgery's superior and inferior semicircular bands, Bourgery's ligament, Bourgery's vulvar arteries, and Bourgery's quadrilateral space.

There are few known portraits of Bourgery. One of these, drawn from life by Maurin, was lithographed by Grégoire and Deneux and distributed by the editor Rosselin in Paris. It shows a bust of the young Bourgery; the ribbon attached to a buttonhole on the left lapel of his coat is in all probability the insignia of a knight of the Order of the Legion of Honour (ill. p. 8).

FROM THE PROJECT OF THE "TREATISE" AS JUDGED BY GEORGES CUVIER TO THE COMPLETE WORK: A LABOUR OF 20 YEARS

About the origin of his *Treatise*, Bourgery recalled: a programme written in 1829 (vol. 8, p. 1); at the time, he was 32 years old. The projected outline was laid out in the introduction of the first volume of the work, published in 1831–1832, not dated in the first edition, and dated October 1830 in the reprint of 1840. It was, from the start, very ambitious and aimed to be encyclopaedic, hence the choice of the first two words of the title: *Complete treatise*.

The detailed plan had been clearly announced in the introduction of 1830: "When all of it has been published, the work will consist of eight volumes. The first five will deal with descriptive anatomy; the sixth and seventh will contain surgical anatomy and the surgical manual; the eighth will cover general anatomy and philosophical anatomy." (vol.1, p. 3)

In 1830, Bourgery had submitted the manuscript of his introduction to the famous Georges Cuvier (1769–1832), professor of natural history at the Collège de France, professor of comparative anatomy at the Natural History Museum in Paris, Councillor of State, and founder of the science of the comparative anatomy and palaeontology of vertebrates. After reading the manuscript of the introduction, Cuvier made comments which Bourgery only made public in the eighth volume of his work: "The work that you undertake, he said to me, is colossal, but it is not impossible. However, you have to know in advance, and believe my long experience, that this work will take you much further than you might think, it will be your life's work. However, as you have conceived this plan and as you envisage it without fear, follow your instincts. The odds are in your favour. You have the firm resolution to do well; you are gifted with a physical strength without which I would advise you against undertaking such a great work, and as a helper for the creation of your figures, you have had the luck of finding in M. Jacob an artist whose talent as an illustrator is seminal in this field. You have the goal and the means. Courage then! And keep right on without letting any obstacle stop you.

Your plan seems good to me; I approve of it. It is rich in applications of all kinds. But before applying, one must look carefully and well. Devote yourself mainly to the study of positive facts and get them drawn with great precision in such a way as to make their spirit come alive and so that they can be found and recognized in nature without effort...

I am not at all concerned about what you can make of the first five volumes of anatomy. Here the certain facts, be they reproduced or original, but always well observed and well illustrated, can be placed on all pages. This entirely depends on you... I believe that you will succeed. I should be very cautious about the two volumes of surgical anatomy, which do not fall into my field of competence... But from the general point of view of the science of organization, I have to admit that it bothers me to see it embrace such a large, purely practical subject, and one which interrupts the scientific link between descriptive anatomy and philosophical anatomy. But a much more serious drawback is that here your subject no longer belongs to you; you are no longer its master. In anatomy, in the field of science, you were at home, on the solid ground of nature and truth, seeing for yourself, sure of your information, and free in your judgements. In surgery, in the field of practical art, you are in someone else's house, on the fickle platform of opinions and interests, floating on error, illusion, and fashion, often obliged to see only through the suspicious eyes of others, and without certainty how to distinguish truth from lies. I know that authors are rarely free to do as they like, and that these surgical illustrations have been imposed on you; but if you cannot dispense with them, in my opinion it would be better perhaps to consign them to a separate book.

The last volume of your work, which you will have to derive completely from your own resources, and which, depending on how you understand it, could be very good or very bad, is the one which causes me most worry on your behalf... I regret that for this volume you have, in your introduction, taken up commitments which are too detailed. You yourself do not know what you will do then... You cannot know from the first day what will be your last word. Let the collaborative enterprise ripen over time: What you will have to say in the end will reveal itself of its own accord. Your subject is beautiful; do not spoil it..." (vol. 8, pp. I–II)

Unfortunately, Cuvier, the patron, died in 1832, shortly after the complete publication of the first volume (1831–1832) of Bourgery's treatise, though not before he had presented a eulogistic report to the Academy of Sciences in Paris during the session of 12 March, 1832.

The writing of the whole work was initially planned to be completed within five years, by 1835. In fact, Bourgery required 20 years to complete his *Treatise*, which he did, miraculously, just before his premature death in June 1849, at the age of 52. In the advertisement for the eighth and final volume, he wrote: "After a long interruption, imposed by *force majeure*, I take this work up again in order to complete it. During the bitter and unrewarding scientific career I have pursued over the past 20 years, the thought of this last volume never left me; this means that year after year it has seen, in my mind, numerous modifications..." (vol. 8, p. I)

Bourgery's monumental work required a titanic effort; he was the master builder at all times, writing texts, carrying out remarkable syntheses, and supervising all details. The initial plan was respected and methodically executed and the course was steadfastly maintained. The unusual traits of Bourgery's character show through across the result of these 20 years' work; he had an unshakable belief in his project, somehow feeling he was invested with a mission, and he was concerned about scientific honesty, accuracy of ideas, and perfection.

Unusually, Bourgery's work was conducted outside the university and academic structures. In addition to Cuvier's support, which we have already mentioned, Bourgery, who worked in relatively solitary fashion, also mentions the help of several other well-known scientists, "...and their influence to obtain for us the books, items, or different scientific objects which we needed to consult," (vol. 2, p. II), in particular Constant André Marie Duméril (1774–1860), Etienne Geoffroy-Saint-Hilaire (1772–1844), François Magendie (1783–1855), Henri Ducrotay de Blainville (1777–1850), and Mathieu Orfila (1787–1853), from 1832 Dean of the Faculty of Medicine in Paris.

BOURGERY'S SCIENTIFIC AND PHILOSOPHICAL APPROACH

For his *Treatise*, Bourgery was not satisfied with a simple compilation. He personally conducted meticulous observations, based on numerous dissections and original anatomical preparations. He particularly devoted himself to the exact study of aspects of morphology which were still neglected, for reasons related to length of observation and methodological difficulty: "... let us say that here, in anatomy, there are a multitude of subjects which

B. S. Weiss, dit Albinus, *Tabulae sceleti et musculorum corporis humani*, Leyden, 1747
Myology, plate 7, copperplate engraving by Jean Wandelaer. One of the most remarkable works on anatomy of the 18th century. / Myologie, planche 7, gravure sur cuivre par Jean Wandelaer. Un des plus remarquables ouvrages d'anatomie du dix-huitième siècle. / Miología, lámina 7, grabado en cobre de Jean Wandelaer. Una de las obras de anatomía más notables del siglo XVIII.

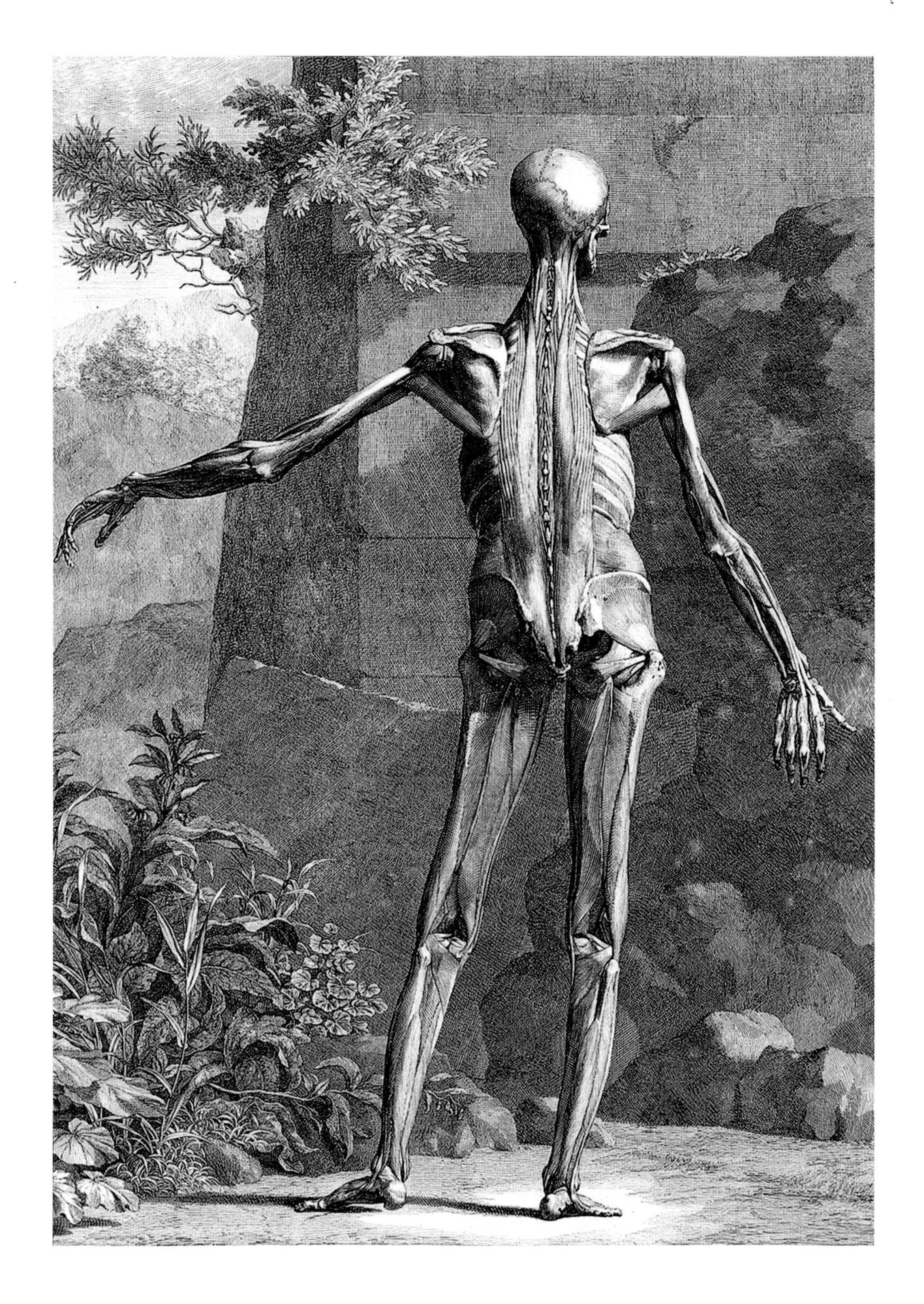

nobody has studied in depth. All those which demand long and difficult preparations belong to this category." (vol. 5, p. 5) Bourgery also developed several methods and new approaches in order to solve various questions that had remained in abeyance; in his *Treatise*, he described them systematically and in detail.

At all times during his work Bourgery kept himself perfectly informed about recent research, and in the eighth volume, he again wrote: "To be sure, the knowledgeable public do not expect me to keep to a programme written in 1829. My task is not to reproduce the state of science as it was or as I understood it then, but as it is or as I understand it today; and how much have all its aspects changed over the last 20 years!" (vol. 8, p. I) He undertook, for the first time, numerous noteworthy syntheses, in particular on the anatomy of the nervous system and in embryology and organogenesis.

But the project that Bourgery aimed for was much more than an encyclopaedic account of morphological observations. He stated: "We hope to be able to show how knowledge of the organism should serve as the basis for ethics, legislation, and political economy. His reflections encompassed all the sciences and philosophy: Science is criticized for being materialistic; this is a great mistake. This imputation... is only valid for the unintelligent opinion... of some of those called scholars. But science... can only lead to the first cause of all beings... on the contrary, it is science that provides the most positive arguments in favour of the spiritual world... If the scholars lack all social interests, they have only themselves to blame: It is they who bury their science... The knowledgeable bodies who only judge the reality of physical facts regulate the world of material instincts without otherwise worrying about doctrines; and, conversely, the men who have taken the path of doctrine are only scholars by dint of the ideas they create themselves... None of these want to accept the world as it has pleased the Creator to make it, and each remakes it according to his own fancy..." (vol. 3, pp. 33–34)

Bourgery's scientific approach and intellectual development had all the character of a metaphysical quest: "Deprived of a guide in this philosophical survey, where books could not help me, I had to fill in by drawing on my personal inspirations... But, even when I had hardly begun to explore the pathways of the organism, I did not hesitate to recognize that from all quarters they lose themselves in the metaphysical. As the traveller who crosses unknown regions suddenly finds himself stopped by bottomless abysses or inaccessible cliffs which force him to retrace his steps, at every step I faced questions which attracted me in the most powerful way, but were sufficiently deep and obscure to give me vertigo... When I thought I could catch sight of something, I said so; otherwise I have passed over it, without feeling obliged to find a meaning for something our weak minds cannot reach." (vol.3, p. 2)

Taking up a philosophical thought of Joseph de Maistre (1753–1821), Bourgery also wrote: "All science, said de Maistre, begins with a mystery. To complete the idea of this great thinker, one would have to say: All science begins and ends with a mystery, or rather is nothing but a mystery... The notion which seems clearest to us is only a shimmer of light between two abysses..." (vol. 3, p. 33)

B. S. Weiss, dit Albinus, *Tabulae sceleti et musculorum corporis humani*, Leyden, 1747
Myology, plate 8, copperplate engraving by Jean Wandelaer. / Myologie, planche 8, gravure sur cuivre par Jean Wandelaer. / Miología, lámina 8, grabado en cobre de Jean Wandelaer.

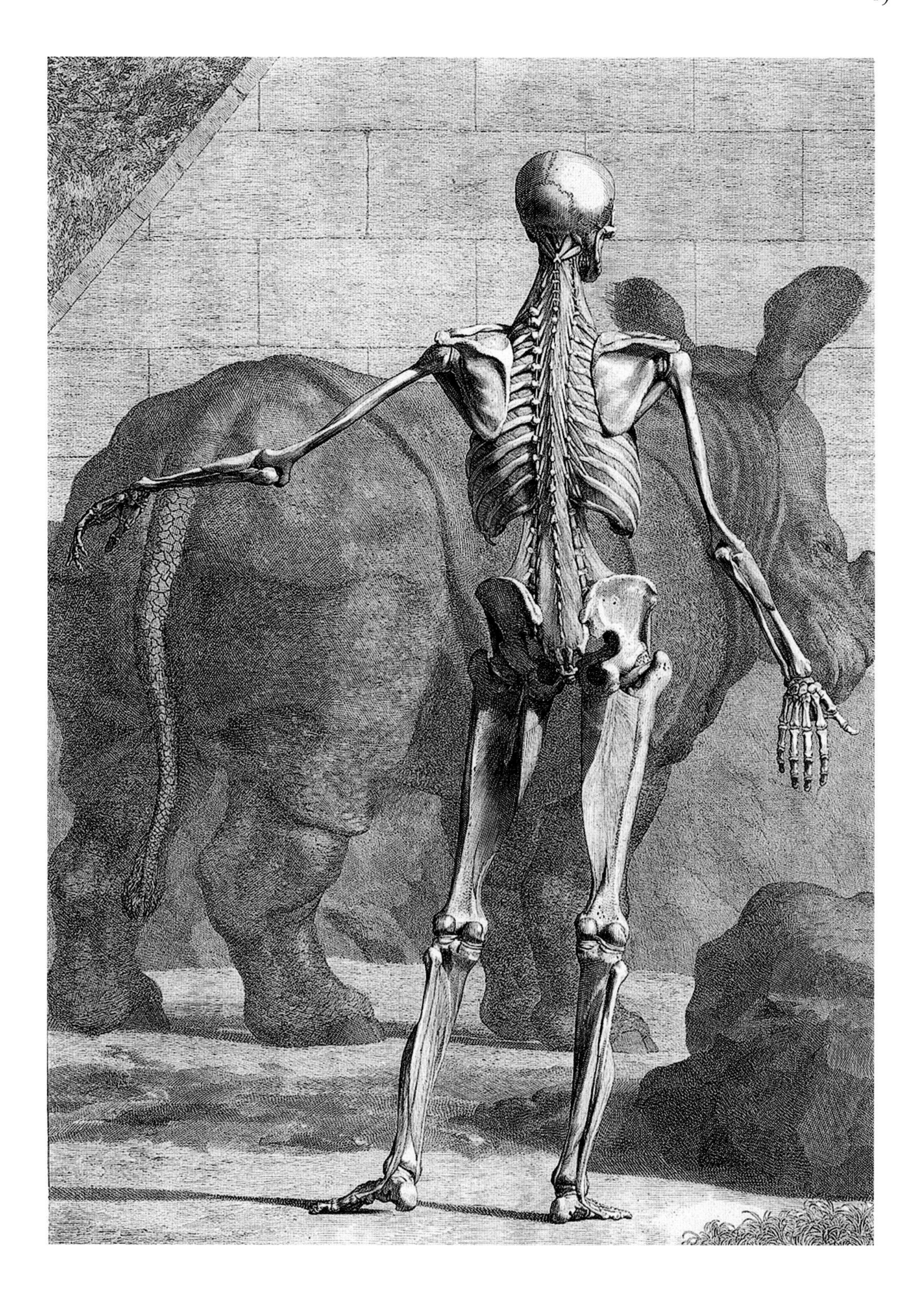

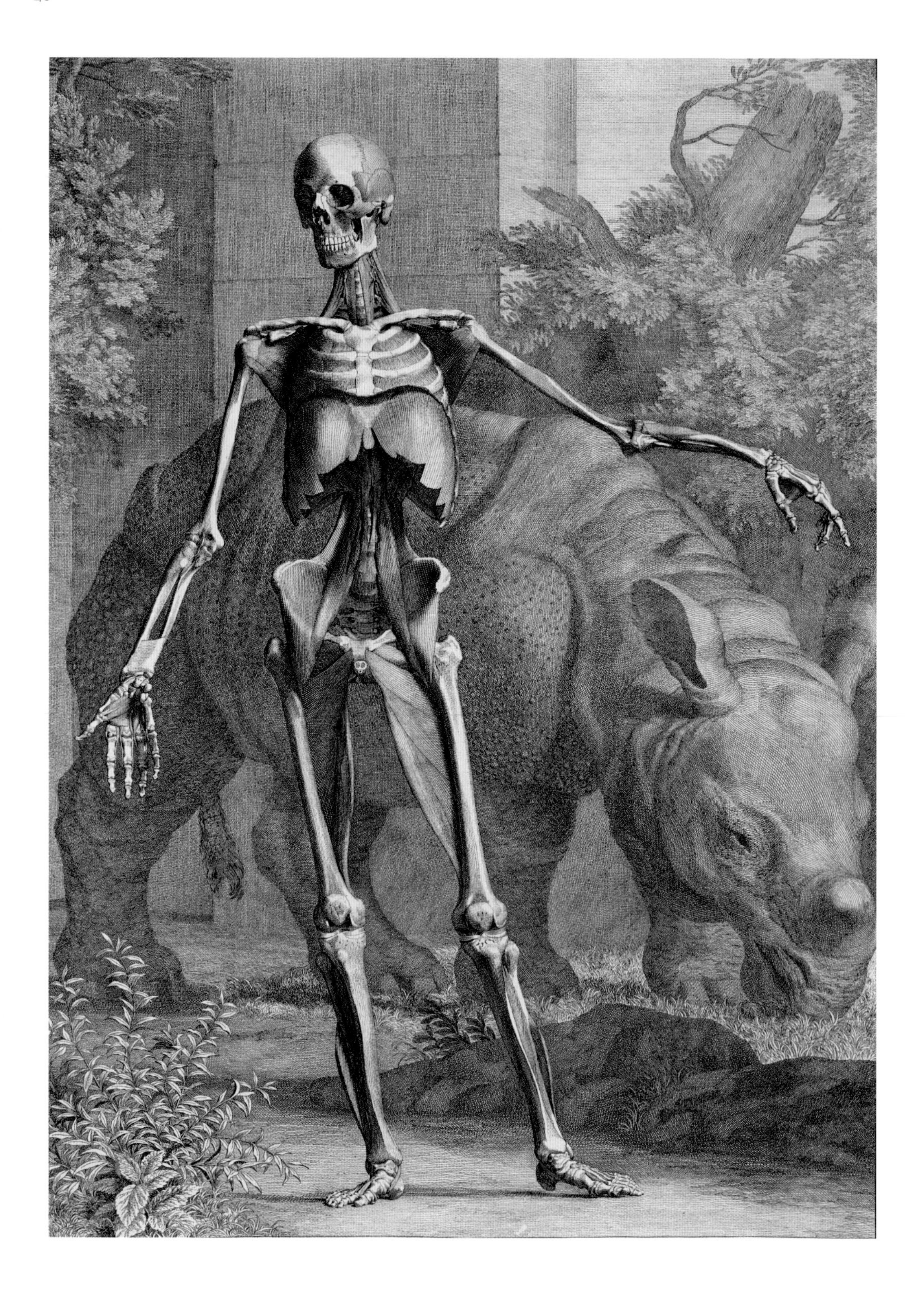

LITHOGRAPHY AND THE ILLUSTRATIONS OF THE "TREATISE"

All the plates of the *Treatise* were made and printed using the technique of lithography. In order to place the making of these plates in their context and to appreciate their very particular importance, we need to draw attention to some points of the lithography technique. A correct analysis of these illustrations cannot be dissociated from the study of the technique, which imposes its own restrictions and a particular style.

Etymologically, the word lithography means stone-writing or drawing. This technique, invented by Aloys Senefelder, born in Prague, between 1796 and 1798, which its author called *Steindruck* or *Steindruckerey* or *chemische Druckerey*, was first called "gravure chimique" or "impression chimique" ("chemical engraving" or "chemical printing") in French, then, from 1810 onwards, lithography. Senefelder gave this definition: "... the application, on to a suitably polished stone, of an oily mark, burned in by an acid, which can only retain an oil-based ink. The discovery of lithography was a real revolution, as until then, the only means of reproducing an image was hollow engraving, in particular on copper, or in relief, essentially on wood: long, difficult, and expensive procedures. The ease of use of lithography and its reduced cost explains the speedy multiplication of lithographs and lithographic printers who produced illustrations for books as well as musical score, popular images, or smaller, ephemeral items (headed paper, labels for industry, advertisements).

In 1802, Philippe André obtained a patent to introduce this technique in France, but it only took off with the foundation of a workshop by Godefroy Engelmann (1788–1839) in Mulhouse in 1814, then in Paris in 1816, and Count Charles de Lasteyrie's workshop, also in Paris and in the same year. The year 1816 marked the true takeoff of lithography in France. It was to become the preferred technique for illustrations in the Romantic period.

The first anatomical work to use lithography for its illustrations was that of Jules Germain Cloquet (1790–1883), *Anatomie de l'homme ou description et figures lithographiées du corps humain*, published in Paris in 1821 (ill. p. 37). As the large folio format made this work difficult to handle and expensive, Cloquet then decided to execute a *Manuel d'anatomie descriptive du corps humain* in quarto, published in Paris in 1825–1826, with 340 lithographic plates in black and white, which has been recently re-issued (ills. pp. 38, 43). At the same time, François Antommarchi (1780–1838), who had been physician to the Emperor Napoleon on Saint Helena, published under his name, based on drawings by Paolo Mascagni (1752–1815), the work *Planches anatomiques du corps humain exécutées d'après les dimensions naturelles...*, comprising 80 lithographic plates, and edited from 1823 to 1826 in Paris by C. de Lasteyrie. Lithography brought a certain precision to the drawing, whilst maintaining softness and allowing numerous shades of grey, and was characterized by a texture, a feel, and a rendering closer to anatomical reality than previous engraved interpretations, and it handsomely replaced the old procedures of anatomical illustration. However, a practical inconvenience was the fact that it could not be incorporated into the body of the text; on the other hand, this might have given it an aesthetic advantage. Therefore, in 1830, when Bourgery and Jacob began the production of their *Treatise*, lithography was both a novel and yet already a perfectly mastered technique.

B. S. Weiss, dit Albinus, *Tabulae sceleti et musculorum corporis humani*, Leyden, 1747
Myology, plate 4, copperplate engraving by Jean Wandelaer. / Myologie, planche 4, gravure sur cuivre par Jean Wandelaer. / Miología, lámina 4, grabado en cobre de Jean Wandelaer.

The underlying principle of lithography as invented by Senefelder was essentially based on the phenomenon of repulsion between water and a greasy layer on the surface on a limestone slab. The design, drawn by a greasy pencil, or letters written by pen and oil-based ink on this previously grained or polished support, was then prepared with a mixture of gum arabic and nitric acid. This acidulation modified the nature of the oil contained in the markers, causing it to penetrate into and strongly adhere to the stone. As gum arabic induces water retention by those parts of the stone surface not covered by designs, these retain the moisture and cannot take up any oily particles such as printing ink. Conversely, the ink laid down by the ink roller adheres to the oily parts, corresponding exactly to the original design, placing the black outline onto the printed proof and reproducing the image on the paper.

The lithographic stone was a limestone of very compact structure and great purity. It was quarried in slabs of seven to ten-centimetres thickness to resist the strains of the press. The compactness and regular nature of its grain gave it ideal properties for lithography. The most commonly used stones and those of the best quality came from quarries in Bavaria, in particular from Solnhofen. The stone was never used in its raw state, but had to undergo, on one of its surfaces, a procedure of refinement and graining, which allowed the pencil or the ink to adhere to the surface of the stone. This preparation consisted in rubbing two stones one against the other, with an abrasive mixed with water in between. It was the grain of the stone that gave lithographic illustrations their characteristic texture. But lithographic stones had several inconveniences: they were heavy, bulky, difficult to handle, brittle, expensive, and the large formats slowed down the printing speed.

The greasy pencils used were made of wax, black soap, tallow, and lamp-black, allowing a great diversity of half-tones, ranging from the lightest greys to the deepest blacks, reminiscent of the grain of a lead pencil or black chalk drawing.

The printing of the plates was a particularly important and delicate step. Entrusted to a specialized printer, it required great care. The lithographic presses underwent numerous refinements. The stone, wedged into the press, was covered in ink with the ink roller. Following guide marks, the lithographer applied a moistened sheet of paper and passed everything under the press, whose carriage was moved without stopping all in one go, to avoid edge blurring. When the carriage had been moved back to its point of departure, the printer delicately lifted up the proof adhering to the stone. The lithographic print was then flattened out and allowed to dry.

To start with, the artist had to draw on the stone in reverse, but from 1817, Senefelder developed a transfer paper on which the artist drew with pencil or lithographic ink. This transfer paper or lithographic paper was a specially prepared paper which was mechanically grained and coated with a thin adhesive layer. Amongst the most notable advantages, the artist could work at home on a light and easily portable support and could draw on the spot. The paper with the drawing was then given to the printer who transferred the drawing on to the stone by moistening the paper and repeatedly pressing it onto the stone. The process had the advantage of eliminating the inversion: when the drawing, made the right way around, is transferred onto the stone, the proof obtained after printing is also the right

B. S. Weiss, dit Albinus, *Tabulae sceleti et musculorum corporis humani*, Leyden, 1747
Osteology, plate 1, copperplate engraving by Jean Wandelaer. / Ostéologie, planche 1, gravure sur cuivre par Jean Wandelaer. / Osteología, lámina 1, grabado en cobre de Jean Wandelaer.

Frontispiece

Following the classical tradition, the work opens with a frontispiece, a page which illustrates or symbolizes the subject of the work (ill. p. 2). The top of the plate states, in capital letters: Frontispiece of the general treatise of human anatomy by Bourgery and Jacob. At the bottom of the plate appears the caption: Composed and drawn by N. H. Jacob.

On the left stands a naked adult man, athletic, with curly black hair and a black beard, the right hand on the hip, and with the other hand holding the hand of the woman at his side; a casually draped cloth hides his genitals. On the right, a young woman, completely naked, with long hair, holds a child on her right arm. At their feet sits a meditative old man, also naked, partly bald, and with a long, white beard. In the background a sculpture, representing a flayed human figure, is placed on a pedestal, below which appears an anatomized foetus.

This allegory of the stages of human life is a very academic work and shows the affinity to Jacques Louis David, under whom Jacob studied. The subject is also reminiscent of one of Jacob's very first works, exhibited at the Salon of 1802, *The three principal stages of human life*.

Text Volumes and Atlas

For each of the eight volumes of the *Treatise* a specific text volume was published, written in encyclopaedic style and practically independent of the illustrations, to which it never refers. The eight text volumes represent a total of 2108 pages.

For each of the eight volumes of the *Treatise* an atlas or specific volume devoted to the illustrations and to bringing together the plates was published. Before each plate there is a sheet with descriptive text and legends. The eight volumes of the atlas make up a total of 725 plates.

The title page of each atlas volume is lithographed. On a column to the left appears the list of 30 fundamental authors in anatomy, the choice of whom is a revelation: Aristotle, Herophilus, Mondini, Vesal, Fallope, Eustache, Servet, Varole, Casserius, Harvey, Aselli, Rudbeck, T. Bartholin, Malpighi, Willis, Ruysch, Leuwenhoeck, Duverney, Albinus, Winslow, Haller, Meckel, Buffon, Walter, W. Hunter, Mascagni, Caldani, Bichat, Soemmering, Gall. To the right appears, in symmetrical fashion, a list of 30 famous physicians and surgeons: Empedocles, Hippocrates, Areteus, Galen, Avicenna, Albucasis, Guy de Chauliac, Fernel, A. Paré, Franco, Fabrice de Hilden, Severin, Sydenham, J. L. Petit, Stahl, Boerhaave, Hoffmann, Cheselden, Sauvage, A. Louis, Senac, Morgagni, Cullen, Brown, Desault, Sabatier, Jenner, Pinel, Corvisart, Laennec.

NOTES ON THE PRESENT EDITION OF THE PLATES

The present work contains reproductions of all 725 lithographic plates, in their colour version, of the *Complete treatise of human anatomy, including operative medicine, by Doctor J. M. Bourgery, with lithographic plates from nature by N. H. Jacob*. The 467 plates of descriptive anatomy are of exceptional artistic value, and have likewise retained a scientific value of prime importance; indeed, unlike the descriptive text, which has lost much of its interest for today's reader, the illustrations, based on original dissections, have remained very modern; the result of rigorous observation and accurate depiction, these anatomical illustrations continue to convey, even today, a wealth of scientific information: Morphological reality does not go out of fashion. The plates of the section on surgery, whose aesthetic quality is also superb, are of great interest for the history of medicine and surgery; the plates of surgical instruments constitute a remarkable documentation, which is still useful.

For the present edition, each plate has been given a title in Latin. These titles did not exist in the original edition, which was written completely in

French. For the description of the plates and the figure legends, no original text has been preserved or reproduced.

The French captions fulfil the current requirements of scientific and medical language and vocabulary. In particular, the names of all anatomical structures have been rendered in the French version of the international anatomical nomenclature, directly inspired by the Latin international nomenclature of the *Nomina anatomica* which is used as reference today. Similarly, a current French nomenclature, essentially derived from the nomenclature validated by the International Commission on Zoological Nomenclature, has been used systematically for the names of zoological species quoted in the comparative anatomy. For the plates on operative medicine, the modernization of the captions was more difficult, as the majority of the operations described are no longer performed and have been forgotten; their names therefore no longer appear in current dictionaries.

It is these modern French texts that underlie the translation used for the English edition, where the corresponding English terminology has of course been used.

L'ATLAS D'ANATOMIE ET DE CHIRURGIE DE J. M. BOURGERY ET N. H. JACOB – UNE ŒUVRE MONUMENTALE DU 19e SIECLE

L'anatomie humaine, science morphologique de l'étude de l'architecture du corps humain basée sur la dissection, a donné lieu à la publication de livres illustrés exceptionnels. Le *Traité complet de l'anatomie de l'homme de J. M. Bourgery et N. H. Jacob*, paru à Paris de 1831 à 1854, s'inscrit dans une longue tradition d'ouvrages illustrés, mais constitue un des ouvrages les plus remarquables de toute l'histoire de l'anatomie, et, en tous les cas, le plus exceptionnel du dix-neuvième siècle. L'ouvrage est monumental, de grand format in-folio, constitué de huit tomes, totalisant 2 108 pages pour les volumes de texte, et 725 planches regroupant 3 750 figures pour les volumes d'atlas.

LES GRANDS OUVRAGES D'ANATOMIE JUSQU'AU 19e SIECLE

Les connaissances anatomiques furent longtemps limitées aux données réunies à partir de dissections d'animaux par Galien (vers 130–vers 200), médecin grec qui exerça à Pergame et à Rome, et dont l'influence fut considérable jusqu'au seizième siècle.

Au Moyen Age, le seul ouvrage d'anatomie vraiment digne de ce nom fut celui de Mondino dei Luzzi (vers 1275–1326) rédigé en 1319 et intitulé *Anathomia* ; reprenant les données de Galien, il apportait d'intéressantes précisions dues aux dissections humaines que l'auteur avait réalisées en 1315.

Ces ouvrages étaient diffusés par des copies manuscrites et ne contenaient que de rares illustrations. Avec l'invention de l'imprimerie ou typographie par Johannes Gensfleisch dit Gutenberg (vers 1397–1468) vers 1450, la diffusion des connaissances allait connaître un essor toujours croissant. Parmi les incunables ou ouvrages imprimés avant 1500, figure l'édition princeps de l'*Anathomia* de dei Luzzi imprimée en 1478 ; cet ouvrage connut de nombreuses rééditions, en particulier celle commentée par Berengario da Carpi (1460 ? –1530), professeur à Bologne, parue à Venise en 1521.

Les dessins anatomiques de Léonard de Vinci (1452–1519), correspondant à 228 planches manuscrites d'une extraordinaire qualité scientifique, occupent une place très marginale puisqu'ils restèrent inédits et ignorés des savants de l'époque. Publiés pour la première fois en 1898, ils n'eurent aucun impact sur l'évolution de la discipline.

En 1543, parut à Bâle l'ouvrage d'André Vésale (1514–1564), *De humani corporis fabrica*, qui est sans conteste le livre le plus exceptionnel de toute l'histoire de l'anatomie tant sur le plan conceptuel que sur le plan esthétique (ill. p. 11). La publication de cet ouvrage constitua une véritable révolution scientifique, offrant une nouvelle vision de l'Homme, en remplaçant les études spéculatives de Galien et les extrapolations à partir de l'anatomie animale par des dissections humaines

J. F. Gautier d'Agoty, *Anatomie de la tête*, Paris, 1748
Plate 4, copperplate engraving printed in colour. One of the most famous works on anatomy of the 18th century. / Planche 4, gravure sur cuivre imprimée en couleur. Un des plus magnifiques ouvrages d'anatomie du dix-huitième siècle. / Lámina 4, grabado en cobre impreso en color. Una de las obras de anatomía más magníficas del siglo XVIII.

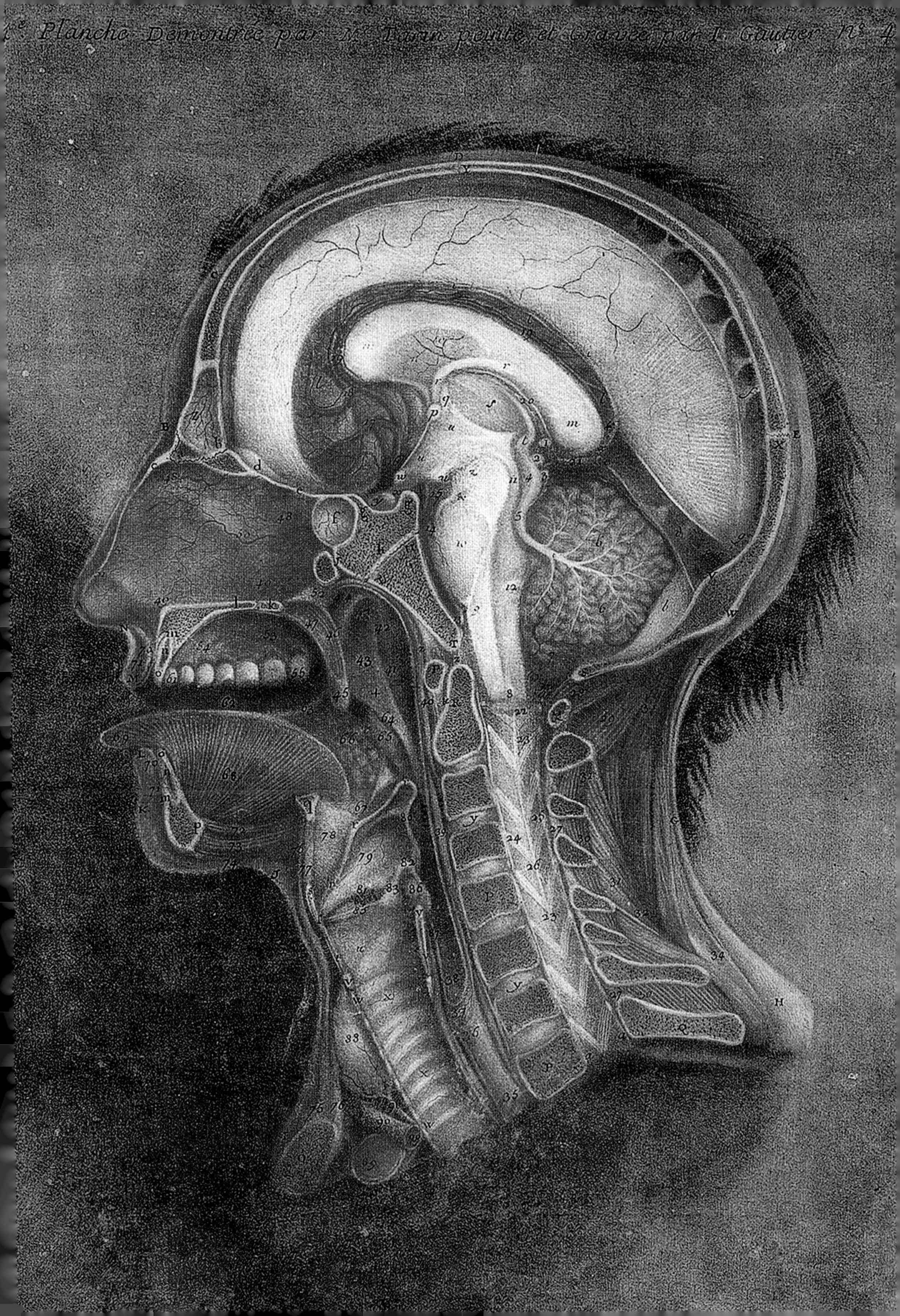
Planche Demontrée par M. Tarin peinte et Gravée par I. Gautier N° 4

systématiques. L'ouvrage de Vésale comporte 25 planches hors-texte superbes et de nombreuses figures dans le texte, toutes gravées sur bois, vraisemblablement dues à Jan Stephan von Calcar de l'entourage du Titien. Cet ouvrage, dont une deuxième édition améliorée parut en 1555 et qui connut de multiples éditions, eut un impact considérable et fut copié par de nombreux auteurs. Il n'était désormais plus possible de penser l'anatomie sans illustrations.

Parmi les ouvrages d'anatomie les plus exceptionnels du seizième siècle, il convient de citer celui de Charles Estienne (vers 1504–1564), *De dissectione partium corporis humani*, paru à Paris en 1545, avec une édition française en 1546, comprenant 62 planches gravées sur bois et de nombreuses vignettes dans le texte ; bien que publié deux ans après l'ouvrage de Vésale, l'ouvrage de C. Estienne était en chantier depuis 1530. Juan Valverde de Hamusco (vers 1525–vers 1587) publia à Rome en 1556 un ouvrage en espagnol copié de Vésale ; une édition latine de cet ouvrage, intitulée *Vivae imagines partium corporis humani*, fut publiée en 1566 par C. Plantin à Anvers, avec pour une des toutes premières fois l'utilisation de la taille-douce ou gravure sur cuivre pour les illustrations ; cette nouvelle technique, permettant une précision et des finesses de demi-teintes impossibles à obtenir avec la gravure sur bois, ouvrait de nouvelles possibilités incomparables et allait être utilisée jusqu'au début du dix-neuvième siècle. Enfin, André Du Laurens (1558 ? – vers 1609), professeur à Montpellier, publia en 1600 à Paris et à Francfort une Historia anatomica humani corporis ornée de 26 splendides planches gravées sur cuivre.

Pour le dix-septième siècle, il convient de citer l'ouvrage de Giulio Casserio ou Julius Casserius (vers 1550–1616), *Tabulae anatomicae*, paru de manière posthume à Venise en 1627 avec 97 planches gravées sur cuivre par Francesco Valesio d'après Odoardo Fialetti, un peintre de l'entourage du Tintoret ; les planches de ce livre servirent aussi à illustrer des ouvrages de son successeur à Padoue, Adrian van der Spieghel (vers 1578–1625). L'ouvrage de Govert Bidloo (1649–1713), *Anatomia humani corporis*, paru à Amsterdam en 1685 comporte 105 planches très originales gravées sur cuivre par Pieter van Gunst d'après des dessins de Gérard de Lairesse (1640 ?–1711).

Au dix-huitième siècle, paraissent de multiples ouvrages d'anatomie illustrés de planches gravées sur cuivre exceptionnelles, mais souvent sur un aspect précis seulement. Le plus remarquable est celui de Bernhard Siegfried Weiss dit Albinus (1697–1770), professeur d'anatomie et de chirurgie à Leyde, consacré à l'ostéologie et à la myologie ou étude des os et des muscles : *Tabulae sceleti et musculorum corporis humani*, paru à Leyde en 1747, avec 40 planches par Jean Wandelaer (1690–1759), ancien élève de Gérard de Lairesse (ill. p. 15–17) ; cet ouvrage, qui connut un grand succès, ouvrit un chemin nouveau aux représentations anatomiques scientifiques et fut grandement copié par la suite. Parmi les ouvrages remarquables peuvent encore être cités ceux de William Cowper (1666–1709), *Myotomia reformata* (Londres, 1724) ; de Albrecht von Haller (1708–1777), *Icones anatomicae*, en huit fascicules parus à Goettingen de 1743 à 1756, avec 46 admirables planches ; de Paolo Mascagni (1752–1815), sur les lymphatiques, Vasorum lymphaticorum corporis humani historia (Sienne, 1787) ; ou d'Antonio Scarpa (1752–1832), sur les nerfs, *Tabulae nevrologicae* (Pavie 1794). Le magnifique ouvrage de Jacques Gamelin (1738–1803), peintre, dessinateur, et graveur, Nouveau recueil d'ostéologie et de myologie, paru à Toulouse en 1779 avec 79 planches, est un peu à part car il relève de l'anatomie artistique et non médicale. Il convient enfin de citer les extraordinaires ouvrages imprimés en couleur par Jacques Fabien Gautier d'Agoty (1710–1785), en partie en collaboration avec le chirurgien J. F. Duverney : *Myologie complette en couleur et grandeur naturelle*, avec 20 planches (Paris, 1746 ; ill. p. 23), *Anatomie de la tête*, 8 planches (Paris, 1748 ; ill. p. 21), *Anatomie générale des viscères et de la névrologie, angéologie et ostéologie du corps humain*, avec 18 planches (Paris, 1754), et *Exposition anatomique de la structure du corps humain*, avec 20 planches (Marseille, 1759).

PRESENTATION DU « TRAITE » DE J. M. BOURGERY ET N. H. JACOB

« Maintenant que la lithographie permet de publier, sans trop de frais, des ouvrages iconographiques très volumineux, ce serait rendre un service aux médecins que de mettre à la portée de tous l'ensemble des travaux qui ont eu l'anatomie pour objet. Mais, pour qu'un ouvrage de ce genre puisse offrir toute l'utilité dont il est susceptible, il faut non seulement que la science y soit présentée dans son état le plus avancé, mais encore qu'elle y paraisse avec toutes ses applications. Ainsi on ne devrait copier servilement aucun travail antécédent, dès lors qu'il n'en est pas auquel on ne puisse ajouter des faits nouveaux ; mais surtout il est indispensable que les planches d'un pareil ouvrage, exécutées dans une intention nouvelle, soient dessinées d'après nature, en se servant toutefois comme indication des figures reconnues parmi celles qui ont été publiées jusqu'à ce jour. C'est cette tâche que M. Jacob et moi nous nous sommes proposé de remplir. Aucun travail ne nous coûtera pour terminer honorablement l'immense travail que nous avons entrepris. » (Bourgery, t. 1, pp. 1–2)

Toute la philosophie ayant présidé à la réalisation du *Traité complet de l'anatomie de l'homme* comprenant la médecine opératoire par le Docteur J. M. Bourgery avec planches lithographiées d'après nature par N. H. Jacob se trouve résumée dans la citation précédente, extraite de l'introduction rédigée par Jean Marc Bourgery en octobre 1830 et publiée dans le premier tome de cet ouvrage paru en 1831–1832.

C. Sachaile de la Barre, dans son ouvrage *Les médecins de Paris* jugés par leurs œuvres, paru en 1845 écrit : « ... il était réservé à M. Bourgery non seulement de donner à cette question la solution la plus satisfaisante, mais de nous étonner par la perfection des moyens employés à cet égard. Rien, en effet, n'est plus beau que les planches qui forment les ouvrages d'anatomie auxquels se rattache principalement son nom. » Le Docteur J. M. Bourgery est qualifié, à juste titre, *d'auteur de l'un des plus beaux monuments qui aient été élevés à la science de la structure de l'homme* dans la notice biographique rédigée en 1876 par E. Beaugrand dans le fameux *Dictionnaire encyclopédique des sciences médicales* publié sous la direction de A. Dechambre.

Paris était, à l'époque de Bourgery, une ville de référence pour l'anatomie. Le Doyen de la Faculté de Médecine Matthieu Orfila (1787–1853), nommé en 1832, entreprit de rénover complètement la faculté et fut à l'origine de la création d'un nouveau musée anatomique, remarquablement riche, ouvert en 1844. Les très nombreuses dissections réalisées dans l'Ecole Pratique annexée à la Faculté de Médecine étaient partout admirées et enviées.

La publication du *Traité complet de l'anatomie de l'homme* eut lieu à une époque où l'anatomie était à son apogée, et Bourgery pouvait écrire ainsi dans l'introduction de son ouvrage : « Sans l'anatomie, la physiologie n'est qu'un tissu de fables plus ou moins ingénieuses, la chirurgie est sans guide, et la médecine est réduite à un aveugle empirisme. » (t. 1, p. 1) Bourgery réaffirme à plusieurs reprises, tout au long de son ouvrage, la primauté de l'anatomie parmi les disciplines médicales et dans l'évolution des concepts scientifiques.

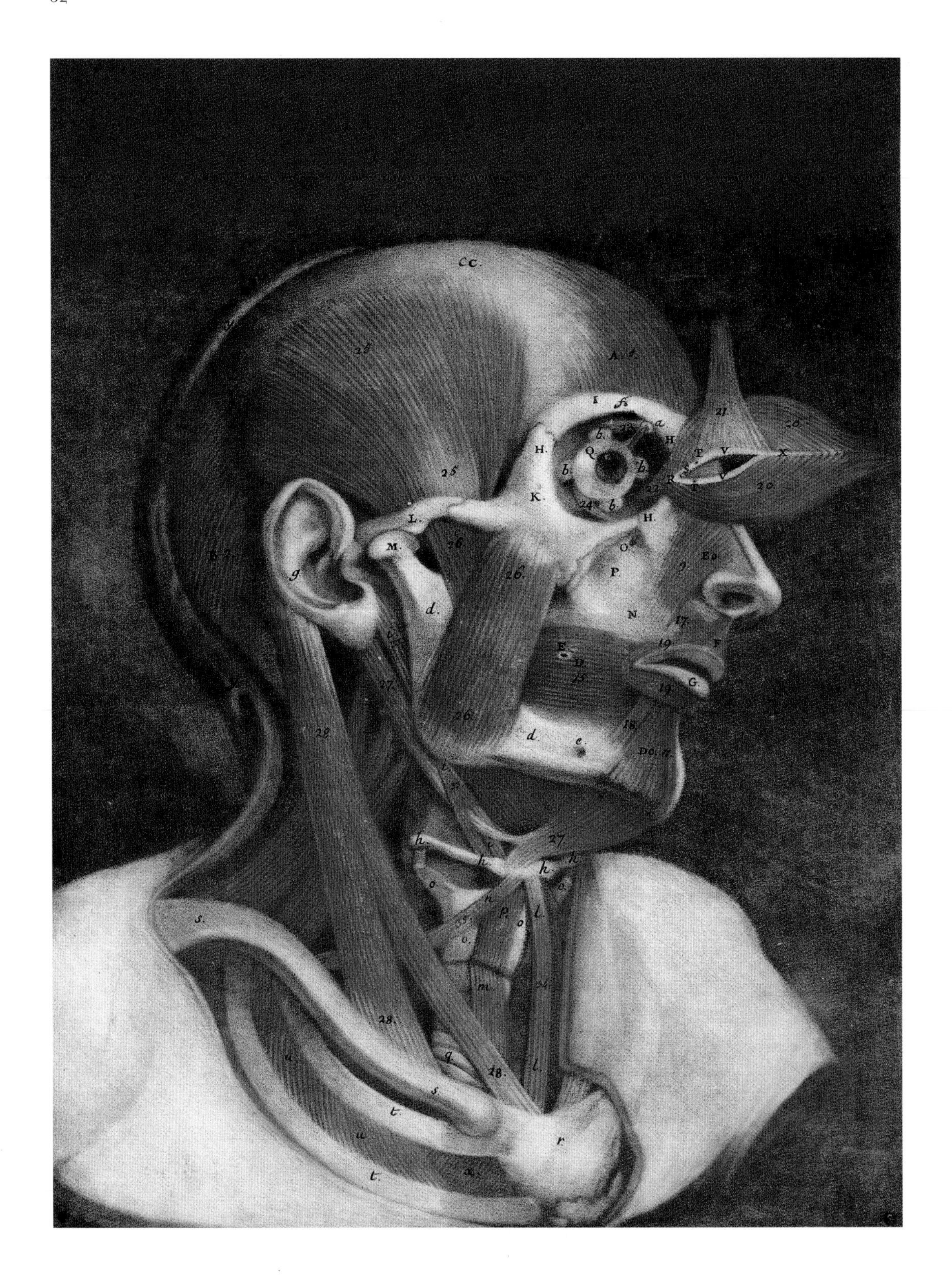

Cc.
A.
25
25
21.
20
20.
T
V
X
H.
H.
H.
Q
K.
L.
M.
26
26.
O.
P.
N.
E.
D.
15
17.
19.
19.
F
G.
18.
d.
d.
e.
g.
27.
27
28
28.
h.
h.
h.
h.
o.
n
p.
l.
l.
m.
34.
q.
s.
s.
t.
t.
u
r.
x.

LE CONCEPTEUR ET AUTEUR : J. M. BOURGERY

Jean Marc Bourgery, né le 8 Prairial an V du calendrier révolutionnaire ou 27 mai 1797 à Orléans, était le fils de Marc Claude Bourgery, marchand mercier, et de Madeleine Marthe Delaboulaye ; la naissance eut lieu au domicile familial au n° 1 rue du Tabourg à onze heures du matin ; les témoins étaient Jean Claude Vignolet, mercier, et Nicolas Bergerac, fripier.

Bourgery s'orienta vers des études de médecine. En 1815, il s'inscrivit aussi comme auditeur aux cours du célèbre naturaliste Jean Baptiste de Lamarck (1744–1829), alors professeur au Muséum d'Histoire Naturelle de Paris. Reçu au concours de l'Internat, Bourgery fut Interne des Hôpitaux de 1817 à 1820, et distingué par la médaille d'Or de l'Internat en 1819.

A la fin de son cursus médical, Bourgery ne passa pas de doctorat, semble-t-il par manque de fortune, et exerça pendant plusieurs années comme Officier de Santé auprès des fonderies de cuivre de Romilly-sur-Seine (département de l'Aube). Il participa alors à la création d'une fabrique de sulfate de cuivre. C'est à cette époque, très vraisemblablement, qu'il mena des recherches sur la coloration des bois : « M. Bourgery s'est encore servi de ses connaissances en chimie organique pour donner aux bois encore sur pied une couleur différente de celle qui leur est propre : les essais qu'il a tentés à ce sujet ont déjà fourni de beaux résultats et donnent de grandes espérances. » (Sachaile de la Barre, 1845)

En 1827, âgé de 30 ans, la carrière de Bourgery connut un tournant décisif lorsqu'il se décida à revenir à Paris. Il fut enfin reçu docteur en médecine avec une thèse de doctorat soutenue à Paris, le 27 août 1827, sur les ligatures circulaires des membres.

Deux ans plus tard, en 1829, il publia un *Traité de petite chirurgie*, remarquable ouvrage de référence, bien que non illustré, qui eut un succès certain puisqu'il connut une deuxième édition française en 1835, et fut traduit en anglais en 1834 et en allemand en 1836.

En 1830, Bourgery mit en place le projet de son *Traité complet de l'anatomie de l'homme*, qui allait l'occuper pendant près de vingt ans jusqu'à sa mort, en collaboration avec l'illustrateur N. H. Jacob. Les premières livraisons parurent en 1831. Devant le succès des premiers tomes, Bourgery et Jacob publièrent en 1834–1835 une *Anatomie élémentaire*, de grand format in-folio avec 20 planches lithographiées, et avec un petit volume séparé de texte. Cet ouvrage connut une deuxième édition (1836–1839), et fut traduit en allemand (1837). La publication du *Traité complet de l'anatomie de l'homme* se poursuivait progressivement mais le travail restait considérable. Une version anglaise des premiers tomes, avec des textes traduits par Robert Willis, fut publiée de 1833 à 1837 attestant la portée de l'œuvre déjà réalisée.

A partir de 1840, Bourgery allait utiliser des observations personnelles pour rédiger des articles scientifiques originaux, principalement sous forme de mémoires, parus dans les *Comptes-Rendus de l'Académie des Sciences de Paris*, de 1842 à 1848. Ces mémoires sont souvent illustrés par de belles planches lithographiées et plusieurs ont été aussi publiés sous forme d'opuscules tirés à part.

Bourgery fut aussi associé à la réalisation des modèles anatomiques en carton-pierre ou carton-pâte de Félix Thibert comme en témoigne un prospectus présentant des pièces : *Musée Thibert d'anatomie pathologique et d'histoire naturelle*

J. F. Gautier d'Agoty, *Myologie complète en couleur et grandeur naturelle*, Paris, 1746
Plate 2, copperplate engraving printed in colour. / Planche 2, gravure sur cuivre imprimée en couleur.
Lámina 2, grabado en cobre impreso en color.

par la méthode plastique du Dr Félix Thibert... sous la direction scientifique du Dr J. M. Bourgery, paru à Paris en 1847. Ces modèles, moulés en relief sur nature et ensuite peints, connurent un grand succès attesté par les nombreuses pièces recensées dans les catalogues imprimés de musées anatomiques, en particulier celui de Strasbourg rédigé par C. H. Ehrmann (1843) ou du Musée Orfila de Paris rédigé par M. Houel (1881).

L'ensemble des travaux de Bourgery l'amenèrent alors à postuler à différents postes universitaires et académiques et à se présenter à différents concours, mais à chaque fois sans succès. Il présenta en particulier sa candidature comme professeur d'anthropologie au Muséum d'Histoire Naturelle de Paris, comme membre de l'Académie des Sciences de Paris en 1843, et comme professeur titulaire de la chaire d'anatomie de la Faculté de Médecine de Paris en 1846, présentant dans ce cadre une thèse soutenue le 13 février 1846 sur le thème *Les annexes du fœtus et leur développement*.

Les échecs successifs de Bourgery comme candidat à des postes universitaires et académiques, malgré une solide notoriété acquise, le rendirent amer ; un certain épuisement semble transparaître aussi. La confession qu'il fit à ce sujet dans le discours préliminaire du tome 8 et dernier de son *Traité*, et qui parut de manière posthume, est exceptionnelle dans l'histoire de l'édition médicale et scientifique, et particulièrement poignante : « Et maintenant, sur le point de terminer mon travail dont je possède tous les matériaux, rapprochant ce que j'ai fait de ce que je m'étais proposé de faire, puisse le public reconnaître que je n'ai pas failli à ma tâche comme la fortune a menti aux succès qu'un homme supérieur m'en avait prédit. Hélas ! Cuvier jugeait du cœur et de l'intelligence des autres par les siens propres. Mais tout le monde a-t-il le cœur et l'intelligence de Cuvier ! Avec lui j'ai tout perdu. Au lieu de cette heureuse carrière qui lui avait souri pour moi, qu'ai-je trouvé ? Des dégoûts, des obstacles, des intrigues, une ligue occulte de répulsions tenaces. Depuis vingt ans que je travaille sans relâche, je n'ai pas à me reprocher de ne m'être point aidé moi-même. J'ai fait tout ce qui était honorable pour arriver à quelque chose. Je me suis produit partout où je l'ai pu. Mais c'est en vain. J'ai vu passer tout le monde devant moi, et ceux qui avaient quelques droits et ceux surtout qui n'en avaient pas. Ayant tant à dire sur une science que j'avais tant travaillée, il me semblait qu'il devait y avoir place pour moi quelque part : mais non. Académies, Facultés, Collèges de haut enseignement, je me suis présenté partout : partout il y en avait toujours d'autres à produire. Deux faits résument tout : aujourd'hui, après vingt ans, je ne suis rien et je n'attends plus rien ; mon nom même n'est cité dans aucun des livres modernes, quoique beaucoup d'entre eux soient faits avec le mien. J'en ai fini de cette révélation singulière : c'est le cri de vingt ans d'oppression qui m'échappe. Aussi bien je donne mon exemple à fuir, s'il se trouvait quelque imprudent prêt à se laisser séduire, comme je l'ai fait, par un amour inconsidéré de la science. Au moins il apprendra de moi que le travail consciencieux ne mène à rien. Qu'on me pardonne cette plainte ! c'est la première, ce sera aussi la dernière. » (t. 8, p. III)

Bourgery mourut, de manière prématurée, en juin 1849, à Paris, à l'âge de 52 ans, victime, semble-t-il, d'une épidémie de choléra. La rédaction de l'œuvre de sa vie, les huit tomes du *Traité*, venait tout juste de s'achever, mais le dernier tome ne parut complètement que de manière posthume en 1854.

Le nom de Bourgery resta attaché à plusieurs structures anatomiques jusqu'à la disparition des éponymes avec l'introduction progressive de la nomenclature anatomique internationale, et en particulier : aux bandelettes semi-circulaires supérieure et inférieure de Bourgery, au ligament de Bourgery, aux artères vulvaires de Bourgery, ou à l'espace quadrilatère de Bourgery.

Les portraits connus de Bourgery sont rares. L'un d'entre eux, dessiné d'après nature par Maurin, a été lithographié par Grégoire et Deneux et diffusé par l'éditeur Rosselin à Paris. Bourgery y est représenté en buste, encore jeune ; la bande de tissu fixée à une boutonnière du revers gauche de son costume correspond, selon toute vraisemblance, à l'insigne de Chevalier de l'Ordre de la Légion d'Honneur (ill. p. 6).

DU PROJET DU « TRAITE » JUGE PAR GEORGES CUVIER A LA REALISATION COMPLETE : UNE ŒUVRE DE VINGT ANS

Concernant l'origine de son traité, Bourgery évoquait « un programme écrit en 1829 » (t. 8, p. 1) ; il était alors âgé de 32 ans. Le projet en fut exposé dans l'introduction du premier tome de l'ouvrage publié en 1831–1832, non datée dans la première édition, et datée d'octobre 1830 dans le retirage de 1840. Il était, dès l'origine, très ambitieux et se voulait encyclopédique comme le choix des deux premiers mots du titre : *Traité complet...*, le démontrait déjà.

Le plan précis fut clairement annoncé dès l'introduction de 1830 : « L'ouvrage, lorsqu'il aura paru dans son entier, devra composer huit volumes. Les cinq premiers appartiendront à l'anatomie descriptive ; les 6e et 7e contiendront l'anatomie chirurgicale et le manuel opératoire ; le 8e comprendra l'anatomie générale et l'anatomie philosophique. » (t. 1, p. 3)

Bourgery avait soumis, en 1830, le manuscrit de son introduction à l'illustre Georges Cuvier (1769–1832), professeur d'histoire naturelle au Collège de France, professeur d'anatomie comparée au Muséum d'Histoire Naturelle de Paris, Conseiller d'Etat, membre de l'Institut de France, et fondateur de l'anatomie comparée et de la paléontologie des Vertébrés.

G. Cuvier, après avoir lu le manuscrit d'introduction, fit des commentaires que Bourgery ne rendit publics que dans le huitième tome de son ouvrage : « Le travail que vous entreprenez, me dit-il, est colossal, mais il n'est pas impossible. Toutefois, sachez le bien à l'avance, et, croyez-en ma vieille expérience, cet ouvrage vous entraînera beaucoup plus loin que peut-être vous ne le pensez, ce sera l'emploi de votre vie. Toutefois, puisque vous avez conçu ce plan et que vous l'envisagez sans effroi, suivez votre instinct. Les probabilités sont en votre faveur. Vous avez la ferme résolution de bien faire ; vous êtes doué d'une force physique sans laquelle je vous détournerais d'un si grand travail, et comme auxiliaire pour l'exécution de vos figures, vous avez eu le bonheur de rencontrer, dans M. Jacob, un artiste dont le talent de dessinateur fait école en ce genre. Vous tenez la fin et les moyens. Courage donc ! et marchez droit devant vous sans vous laisser arrêter par aucun obstacle.

Votre plan me paraît bon, je l'approuve. En embrassant tous les aspects, il est riche en applications de toutes sortes. Mais avant d'appliquer il faut beaucoup et bien voir. Attachez-vous principalement à la recherche de faits bien positifs et faites-les dessiner avec une grande netteté de manière à éclairer vivement l'esprit et qu'on puisse les retrouver sans peine sur la nature...

Je ne suis point inquiet de ce que vous pourrez faire dans les cinq premiers volumes d'anatomie de votre ouvrage. Ici les faits certains, soit reproduits, soit originaux, mais partout bien observés et bien dessinés peuvent se trouver à toutes les pages. Cela dépend de vous entièrement... Je crois que vous réussirez.

Je devrais être très circonspect concernant vos deux volumes d'anatomie chirurgicale qui ne sont pas de ma compétence... Mais au point de vue général de la science de l'organisation, je suis fâché, je l'avoue, d'y voir encadrer un sujet purement pratique aussi vaste et qui interrompt le lien scientifique entre l'anatomie descriptive et l'anatomie philosophique. Mais ce qui est un inconvénient bien plus grave, c'est que, ici, votre sujet ne vous appartient plus ; vous n'en êtes plus le maître. En anatomie, dans le domaine de la science, vous étiez chez vous sur le terrain solide de la nature et de la vérité, voyant par vous-même, certain de vos informations et libre de vos jugements. En chirurgie, dans le domaine de l'art pratique, vous êtes chez les autres, sur le plancher mobile des opinions et des intérêts, flottant au gré de l'erreur, de l'illusion et de la vogue, souvent obligé de ne voir que par les yeux suspects d'autrui, et sans certitude pour distinguer la vérité du mensonge. Je sais que les auteurs sont rarement libres de faire ce qu'ils voudraient et que cette iconographie chirurgicale vous a été imposée ; mais si vous ne pouviez vous dispenser de la faire, à mon avis, mieux eût valu peut-être en composer un livre à part.

Le dernier volume de votre ouvrage, qu'il vous faudra extraire en entier de votre propre fonds, et qui, suivant que vous l'aurez compris, pourra être si bon ou si mauvais, est celui qui me préoccupe le plus pour vous... Je regrette que vous ayez pris à cet égard, dans votre introduction, des engagements trop nettement spécifiés. Ce que vous ferez alors, vous l'ignorez vous même... Vous ne pouvez savoir dès le premier jour quel sera votre dernier mot. Laissez le temps mûrir l'œuvre commune : ce que vous aurez à dire à la fin se présentera de soi-même. Votre sujet est beau ; ne le gâtez pas. » (t. 8, pp. I–II)

G. Cuvier, le protecteur, allait malheureusement mourir en 1832, peu après la parution complète du premier tome du traité de Bourgery, dont il put encore faire un rapport élogieux à l'Académie des Sciences de Paris le 12 mars 1832.

La rédaction complète de l'ouvrage était initialement prévue comme devant être achevée en cinq ans, soit en 1835. Vingt années furent en réalité nécessaires pour que Bourgery achève la rédaction de son traité et ce, comme par miracle, juste avant sa mort prématurée en juin 1849, à l'âge de 52 ans. Il écrit dans l'avertissement du huitième et dernier tome : « Après une longue interruption, commandée par des évènements de force majeure, je reprends le cours de cet ouvrage pour le finir. Dans la pénible et ingrate carrière scientifique que j'ai parcourue depuis vingt ans, la pensée de ce dernier volume ne m'a pas quitté ; c'est dire qu'elle a subi d'année en année, dans mon esprit, de nombreuses modifications... » (t. 8, p. I)

L'œuvre monumentale de Bourgery a nécessité un travail titanesque dont il a été le maître d'œuvre de tous les instants, rédigeant les textes, effectuant des synthèses remarquables, et supervisant tous les détails. Le plan initial a été respecté et mis en œuvre avec méthode et le cap a été maintenu avec obstination. A travers le résultat de ce travail de vingt années, transparaissent des traits de caractère hors du commun de Bourgery qui avait une foi inébranlable dans son projet, se sentant en quelque sorte investi d'une mission, qui avait le souci de l'honnêteté scientifique, de la justesse des idées, et de la perfection.

Le travail de Bourgery a été mené, et ce n'est pas commun, en dehors des structures universitaires et académiques. Bourgery, qui a travaillé de manière relativement solitaire, évoque toutefois, outre le soutien de Georges Cuvier, déjà cité, l'aide de plusieurs scientifiques réputés... « et de leur influence pour nous procurer les livres, les pièces ou les

J. G. Cloquet, *Anatomie de l'homme ou description et figures lithographiées du corps humain*, Paris, 1821
Plate 86, drawn by Haincelin and lithographed by C. de Lasteyrie. First work on anatomy with lithographed plates. / Planche 86, dessinée par Haincelin et lithographiée par C. de Lasteyrie. Premier ouvrage d'anatomie avec des planches lithographiées. / Lámina 86, dibujada por Haincelin y litografiada por C. de Lasteyrie. Primera obra de anatomía con láminas litografiadas.

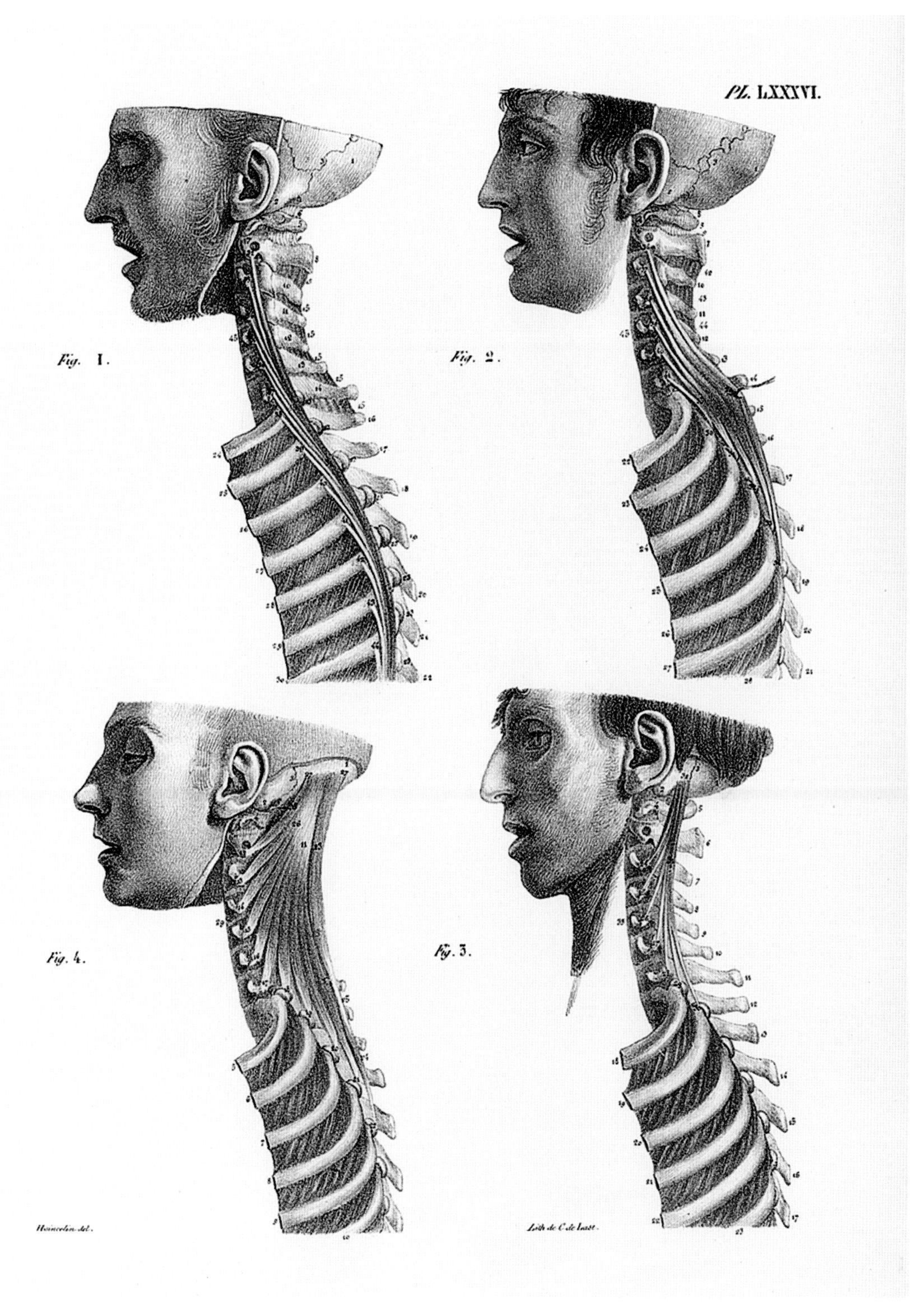
Pl. LXXXVI.
Fig. 1.
Fig. 2.
Fig. 4.
Fig. 3.
Heincelin del.
Lith. de C. de Last.

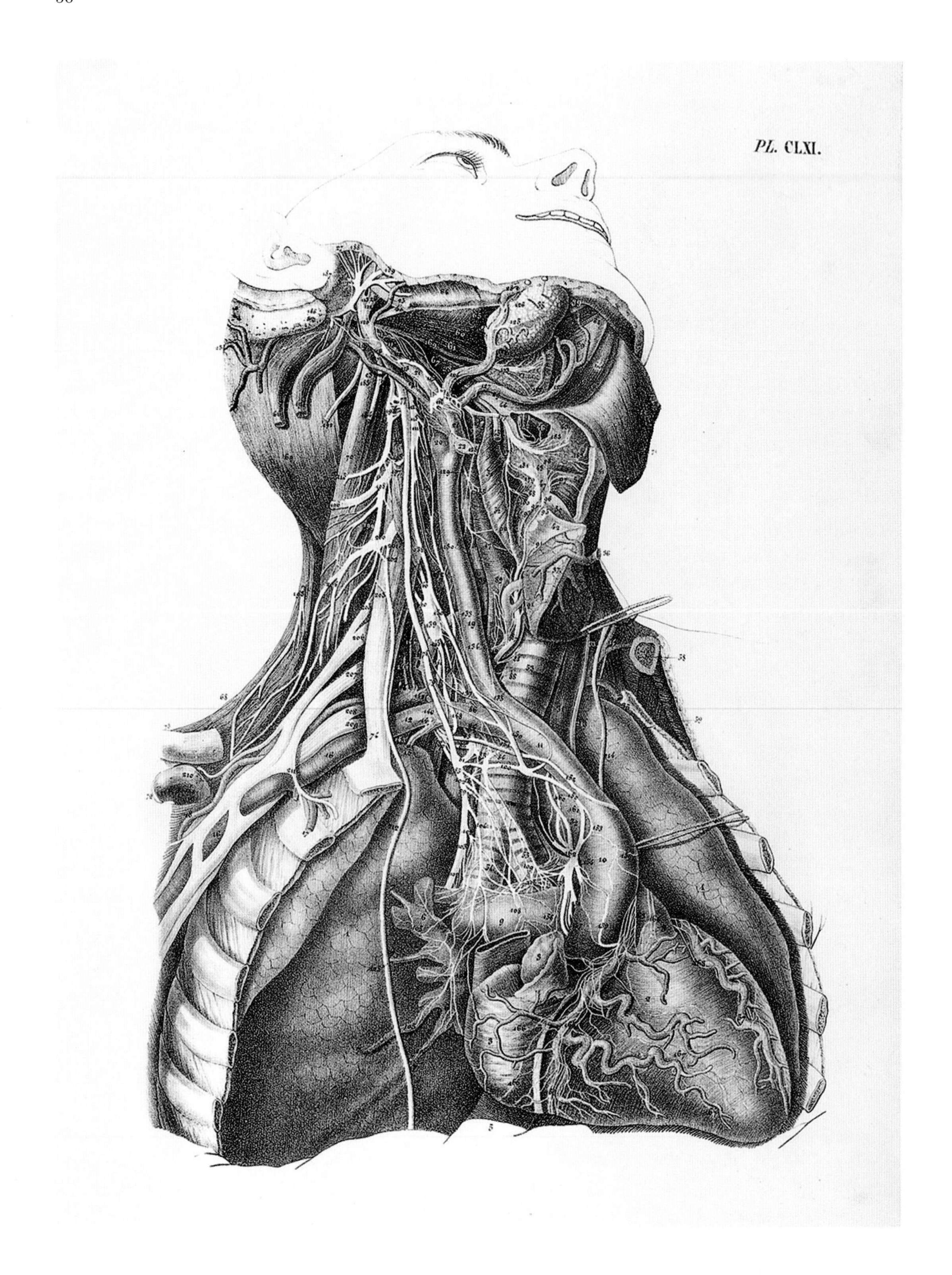
PL. CLXI.

divers objets scientifiques que nous avons si fréquemment besoin de consulter. » (t. 2, p. II), mentionnant, en particulier, Constant André Marie Duméril (1774–1860), Etienne Geoffroy-Saint-Hilaire (1772–1844), François Magendie (1783–1855), Henri Ducrotay de Blainville (1777–1850), ou Matthieu Orfila (1787–1853), Doyen de la Faculté de Médecine de Paris depuis 1832.

LA DEMARCHE SCIENTIFIQUE ET PHILOSOPHIQUE DE J. M. BOURGERY

Pour son *Traité complet de l'anatomie de l'homme*, Bourgery ne se contenta pas d'une simple compilation. Il procéda personnellement à des observations méticuleuses basées sur de nombreuses dissections et préparations anatomiques originales.

Il s'attacha plus particulièrement à l'étude précise d'aspects encore délaissés de la morphologie en raison de la longueur des observations et des difficultés méthodologiques : « ...disons qu'il y a ainsi, en anatomie, une foule de sujets que personne n'étudie profondément. Tous ceux qui exigent de longs apprêts et des préparations difficiles sont dans ce cas. » (t. 5, p. 5) De multiples méthodes et approches nouvelles furent également mises au point par Bourgery pour résoudre différentes questions restées en suspens ; il les décrivit systématiquement de manière détaillée dans son traité.

Tout au long de son travail, Bourgery se tint parfaitement informé des recherches récentes, et dans le huitième tome, il écrit encore : « Sans doute le public savant n'attend pas de moi que je m'en tienne à un programme écrit en 1829. Ma tâche n'est pas de reproduire l'état de la science, tel qu'il était ou que je le comprenais alors, mais tel qu'il est ou que je le comprends aujourd'hui ; et combien tous ses aspects n'ont-ils pas changé depuis vingt ans ! » (t. 8, p. I) Il réalisa, pour la première fois, de nombreuses synthèses remarquables, en particulier sur l'anatomie du système nerveux ou en embryologie et organogenèse.

Mais le projet que s'était fixé Bourgery était bien plus vaste qu'un recueil encyclopédique d'observations morphologiques ; ainsi confiait-il : « Nous espérons pouvoir démontrer comment la connaissance de l'organisme devrait servir de base à la morale, à la législation et à l'économie politique. » Sa réflexion englobait l'ensemble des sciences et de la philosophie : « On reproche à la science d'être matérialiste ; c'est une grande erreur. Cette imputation... ne s'adresse qu'à l'opinion inintelligente... de quelques-uns de ceux que l'on appelle savants. Mais la science... ne peut mener qu'à la cause première de tous les êtres... c'est elle au contraire qui renferme les arguments les plus positifs en faveur du spiritualisme... Si les savants sont en dehors de tous les intérêts sociaux, ils ne doivent s'en prendre qu'à eux-mêmes : à eux qui enfouissent leur science... Les corps savants, qui ne jugent que de la réalité des faits physiques, gouvernent le monde des instincts matériels sans s'inquiéter autrement des doctrines ; et au contraire, les hommes qui ont pris la direction des doctrines, ne sont savants que par les idées qu'ils se créent à eux-mêmes... Aucun d'eux ne veut accepter le monde, comme il a plu au Créateur de le faire, et chacun le refait à sa fantaisie... » (t. 3, pp. 33–34)

La démarche scientifique et le cheminement intellectuel de Bourgery eurent tout d'une quête métaphysique : « Dépourvu de guide dans cet aperçu philosophique, où les livres ne pouvaient m'être d'aucun secours, il m'a fallu y suppléer en puisant dans mes inspirations personnelles... Mais, à peine

J. G. Cloquet, *Anatomie de l'homme ou description et figures lithographiées du corps humain*, Paris, 1821
Plate 161, drawn by Haincelin and lithographed by C. de Lasteyrie./ Planche 161, dessinée par Haincelin et lithographiée par C. de Lasteyrie. / Lámina 161, dibujada por Haincelin y litografiada por C. de Lasteyrie.

engagé dans ces voies inexplorées de l'organisme, je n'ai pas tardé à reconnaître qu'elles se perdent de toutes parts dans la métaphysique. Comme le voyageur qui parcourt des régions inconnues, se voit arrêté tout à coup par des abîmes sans fond, ou des escarpements inaccessibles qui le forcent à rebrousser chemin, à chaque pas se dressaient devant moi des questions de l'attrait le plus imposant, mais profondes et obscures à donner le vertige. Quand j'ai cru entrevoir quelque chose, je l'ai dit ; autrement j'ai passé outre, sans me croire obligé de trouver un sens à ce que ne peut atteindre la faiblesse de notre esprit. » (t. 3, p. 2)

Reprenant une pensée du philosophe Joseph de Maistre (1753–1821), Bourgery écrivait encore : « Toute science, a dit de Maistre, commence par un mystère. Pour compléter l'idée de ce grand penseur, il faudrait dire : toute science commence et finit par un mystère, ou plutôt n'est que mystère... La notion qui nous paraît la plus claire n'est qu'une lueur entre deux abîmes... » (t. 3, p. 33)

LA LITHOGRAPHIE ET LES ILLUSTRATIONS DU TRAITE

Toutes les planches du *Traité* furent réalisées et imprimées grâce à la lithographie. Afin de situer la réalisation de ces planches dans leur contexte et d'apprécier leur aspect très particulier, il convient d'attirer l'attention sur quelques points de la technique lithographique. Une analyse correcte de ces illustrations ne peut être dissociée de l'étude de la technique qui impose des contraintes et un style.

Le mot lithographie signifie étymologiquement écriture ou dessin sur pierre. Cette technique inventée par Aloys Senefelder, né à Prague, entre 1796 et 1798, appelée par son auteur *Steindruck* ou *Steindruckerey* ou *chemische Druckerey*, fut d'abord appelée en français gravure chimique ou impression chimique, puis lithographie à partir de 1810. Une définition que Senefelder en donna est : « ...produire sur une pierre convenablement polie une tâche grasse, isolée par un acide et susceptible de retenir seule un encrage gras. » La découverte de la lithographie fut une véritable révolution car, jusqu'alors, le seul moyen de reproduire une image était la gravure en creux, en particulier sur cuivre, ou en relief, essentiellement sur bois, procédés longs, difficiles et coûteux. La facilité d'emploi de la lithographie et son coût réduit expliquèrent la multiplication rapide des lithographes et des imprimeries lithographiques produisant aussi bien des illustrations pour des livres que des partitions de musique, de l'imagerie populaire, ou des travaux de ville du registre des éphémères (papier à en-tête, étiquettes pour l'industrie, publicités).

Un brevet pour introduire cette technique en France fut obtenu par Philippe André en 1802, mais elle ne fut lancée qu'avec la fondation des ateliers de Godefroy Engelmann (1788–1839) à Mulhouse en 1814, puis Paris en 1816, et du comte Charles de Lasteyrie également en 1816 à Paris. L'année 1816 marquait le véritable départ de l'essor de la lithographie en France. Elle allait être la technique privilégiée pour les illustrations de la période romantique.

Le premier ouvrage d'anatomie ayant fait appel à la lithographie pour ses illustrations est celui de Jules Germain Cloquet (1790–1883), *Anatomie de l'homme ou description et figures lithographiées du corps humain*, paru à Paris en 1821 (ill. p. 27). Comme le grand format in-folio rendait cet ouvrage peu maniable et cher, J. G. Cloquet se décida ensuite à réaliser un *Manuel d'anatomie descriptive du corps humain*, de format in-quarto, paru à Paris en 1825–1826, avec 340 planches lithographiées en noir et blanc, et réédité récemment (ill. pp. 29, 35). Au même moment, François Antommarchi (1780–1838), qui avait été le médecin de l'Empereur Napoléon Ier à Sainte-Hélène, publiait sous son nom, d'après les dessins de Paolo Mascagni (1752–1815), l'ouvrage *Planches anatomiques du corps humain* exécutées d'après les dimensions naturelles..., comprenant 80 planches lithographiées, et édité à Paris par C. de Lasteyrie de 1823 à 1826. La lithographie apportait une certaine précision dans le dessin tout en redonnant de la souplesse, permettait de nombreuses nuances de gris, et se caractérisait par une matière, un toucher, et un rendu plus proches de la réalité anatomique que dans les interprétations gravées antérieures, et elle vint avantageusement remplacer les anciens procédés d'illustration anatomique. Un inconvénient pratique toutefois, mais qui lui conféra sans doute un avantage esthétique, était sa contrainte à demeurer hors-texte. Ainsi, en 1830, lorsque Bourgery et Jacob mettaient en route la réalisation de leur traité, la lithographie était une technique à la fois récente mais déjà devenue parfaitement maîtrisée.

Le principe de base de la lithographie, tel qu'il a été mis en évidence par Senefelder, consistait pour l'essentiel, dans le phénomène de répulsion entre l'eau et les corps gras sur la surface d'une dalle de calcaire. Le dessin exécuté au crayon gras, ou le texte par le biais d'une plume et de l'encre grasse sur ce support préalablement grainé ou poli, était ensuite préparé avec un mélange de gomme arabique et d'acide nitrique. Ce traitement chimique ou acidulation modifiait la nature de la graisse contenue dans les marqueurs en la faisant pénétrer et adhérer fortement à la pierre. Par l'action de la gomme arabique, favorisant la rétention de l'eau dans les parties non dessinées à la surface de la pierre, celles-ci demeuraient humides et insensibles aux corps gras comme l'encre d'imprimerie. En revanche, l'encre déposée par le rouleau encreur adhérait sur les parties grasses correspondant très exactement au dessin original, donnant les noirs sur l'épreuve imprimée et restituant l'image sur le papier.

La pierre lithographique était une pierre calcaire présentant une structure très compacte et d'une grande pureté. Elle était débitée en dalles épaisses de 7 à 10 centimètres pour résister aux contraintes de la presse. La nature serrée et régulière de son grain lui conférait les propriétés idéales pour la lithographie. Les pierres les plus utilisées et de meilleure qualité venaient de carrières de Bavière, en particulier de Solnhofen. La pierre n'était jamais utilisée à l'état brut, mais devait subir sur l'une de ses faces une opération d'affinage et de grainage permettant l'adhérence du crayon ou de l'encre sur la surface de la pierre. Cette préparation consistait à frotter deux pierres l'une contre l'autre en y interposant un abrasif mélangé à de l'eau. Le grain de la pierre était à l'origine de la texture caractéristique des illustrations lithographiées. Mais les pierres lithographiques avaient plusieurs inconvénients : elles étaient lourdes, encombrantes, difficiles à manier, cassantes, d'un coût élevé, et, pour les grands formats, ralentissaient la vitesse du tirage.

Les crayons gras utilisés étaient composés de cire, de savon noir, de suif et de noir de fumée permettant d'obtenir une grande diversité de demi-teintes, allant des gris les plus légers aux noirs les plus profonds, et rappelant le grain d'un dessin à la mine de plomb ou à la craie noire.

L'impression des planches était une étape particulièrement importante et délicate. Confiée à un imprimeur spécialisé, elle exigeait un soin attentif. Les presses lithographiques connurent d'importants perfectionnements. La pierre, calée dans la presse, était encrée au rouleau. Le lithographe y déposait, en suivant des repères, une feuille de papier humectée et passait le tout sous la presse dont le chariot devait être déplacé sans arrêt et sans à-coups pour éviter les flous. Une fois le chariot ramené à son point de départ, l'imprimeur soulevait délicatement l'épreuve qui adhérait à la pierre. Le tirage lithographique était alors posé à plat et mis à sécher.

A l'origine, l'artiste avait l'obligation de dessiner à l'envers sur la pierre, mais, dès 1817, A.

Senefelder mettait au point le papier-report sur lequel l'artiste dessinait au crayon ou à l'encre lithographique. Ce papier-report ou papier autographique à grain ou papier lithographique était un papier spécialement préparé qui était grainé mécaniquement et enduit d'une légère couche adhésive. Parmi les avantages notables, l'artiste pouvait travailler chez lui sur un support léger et facilement transportable, et pouvait dessiner à l'endroit. Le papier avec le dessin était alors remis à l'imprimeur qui reportait le dessin sur la pierre par humidification du papier et pressions répétées. Ce procédé a l'avantage de supprimer l'inversion : le dessin exécuté à l'endroit est reporté à l'envers sur la pierre, on obtient au tirage une épreuve à l'endroit. Suivant les cas, le dessin était lithographié par l'artiste lui-même ou confié à un lithographe spécialisé.

Mais la lithographie, au débit lent mal adapté à la grande production, était condamnée à n'être qu'une technique de transition. Dès 1860, la lithographie connaissait une crise importante. Elle fut alors rapidement détrônée par la zincographie, où le zinc remplaçait la pierre lithographique et pouvait s'adapter à la rotative (1868), puis apparut, à partir de 1885, la photogravure industrielle. Un des derniers grands ouvrages d'anatomie avec des planches lithographiées est celui de C. L. Bonamy, P. Broca et E. Beau, *Atlas d'anatomie descriptive du corps humain*, paru à Paris en 1866 (ill. p. 39).

LA MISE EN COULEURS DES PLANCHES

En 1831, lors de la publication du premier volume de planches du traité de Bourgery et Jacob, seule une impression en noir était possible en lithographie. La plupart des exemplaires du *Traité* avaient ainsi des planches imprimées uniquement en noir et blanc. Mais, si l'impression en noir suffisait à restituer les os du squelette, en revanche, elle donnait une image imparfaite d'une région disséquée que la couleur permettait de délimiter et préciser (ill. p. 42–44). La mise en couleur ou coloriage des planches pouvait alors être faite soit librement à l'aide d'un pinceau soit à l'aide de pochoirs.

Pour les planches de la première édition du traité de Bourgery et Jacob, la mise en couleur fut réalisée à la main en utilisant la technique du coloriage au pochoir ou coloriage au patron. Cette technique permettait de poser facilement des couleurs semblables en des endroits semblables sur de multiples exemplaires d'une même planche. Les différentes zones de couleurs de l'original étaient tout d'abord isolées, puis reportées pour chacune d'entre elles par calque et décalque sur une feuille de métal, de bristol, ou de tissu rigide. En principe, une feuille par teinte était réalisée. La partie correspondante à la couleur était ensuite évidée et l'on obtenait ainsi une découpe ; le travail de la découpe était extrêmement délicat, si l'on voulait obtenir des contours fidèles et nets et si les contours étaient complexes. Les couleurs étaient ensuite appliquées les unes après les autres avec une brosse spéciale à poils raides, appelée pompon, ou avec une éponge. Les teintes appliquées étaient, en général, légères et de type aqueux ou aquarelle, mais des couleurs opaques et gouachées pouvaient parfois être utilisées. Il fallait éviter les bavures et attendre qu'une couleur soit sèche pour passer la suivante. Le passage de couleurs différentes était réalisé en juxtaposition et parfois en superposition ; parfois aussi,

J. G. Cloquet, *Manuel d'anatomie descriptive du corps humain*, Paris, 1825–1826
Plate 247, drawn by Haincelin and lithographed by Frey. Another example of a work of anatomy by Cloquet with lithographed plates. / Planche 247, dessinée par Haincelin et lithographiée par Frey. Autre exemple d'ouvrage d'anatomie par Cloquet avec des planches lithographiées. / Lámina 247, dibujada por Haincelin y litografiada por Frey. Otro ejemplo de obra de anatomía de Cloquet con láminas litografiadas.

PL. 247.

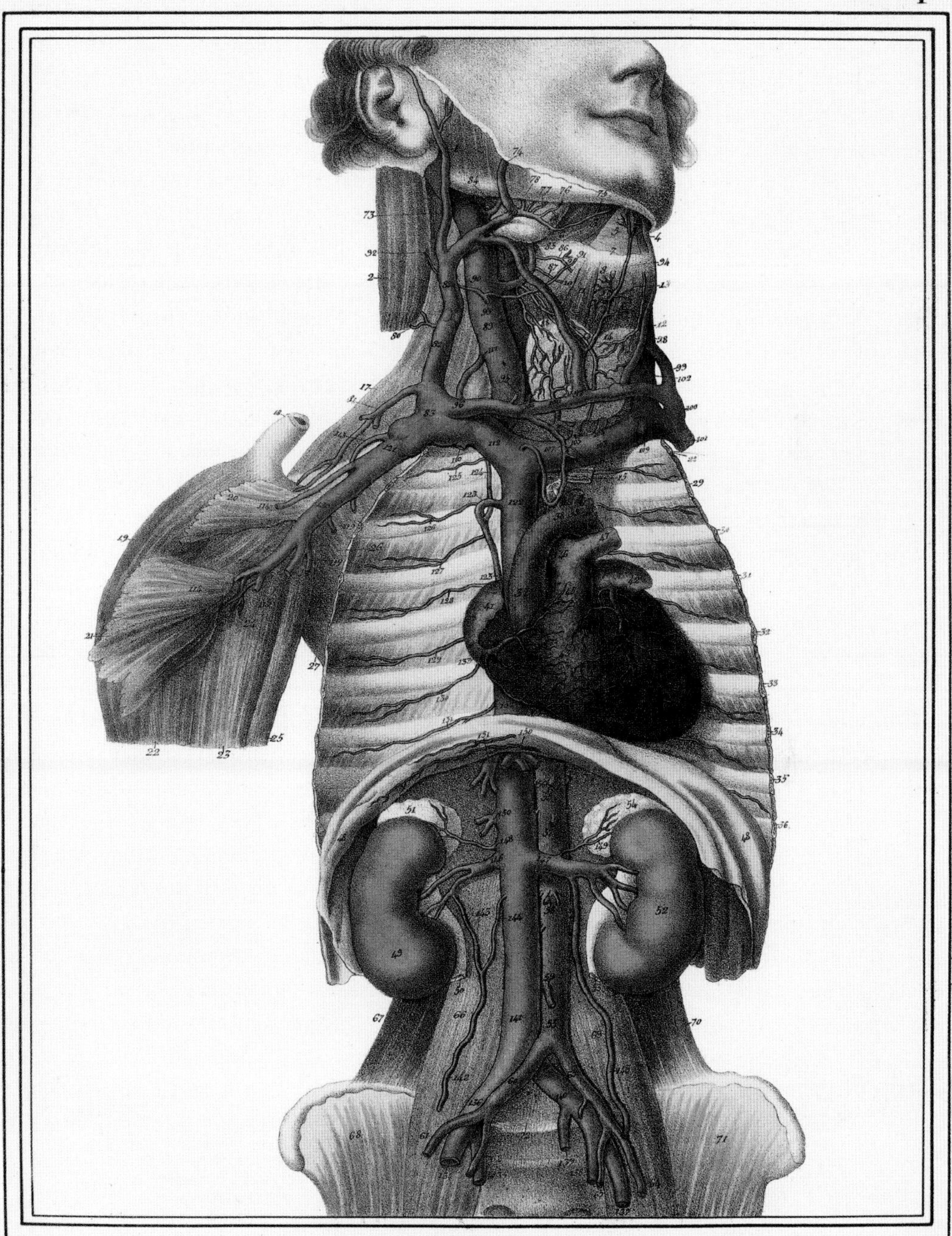

Haincelin del^t. *Lith. de Frey.*

les couleurs étaient appliquées sur des fonds humides afin d'obtenir des fondus. Certains détails pouvaient être rehaussés à la gouache. Les couleurs pouvaient être multipliées à volonté avec un pompon par couleur ; aidés par des coloristes habiles, certains ateliers possédaient plusieurs centaines de pompons afin de pouvoir assurer toutes les nuances. On arrivait souvent à obtenir des prix de revient assez bas avec de bons praticiens et des couleurs simples. Bien que manuel, le pochoir était un travail relativement rapide pour une technique d'estampe, et on estimait qu'un praticien bien entraîné pouvait colorier environ 500 feuilles de petit format à l'heure. Cette technique de coloriage au pochoir a été très utilisée au dix-neuvième siècle pour la mise en couleur de gravures isolées ou d'illustrations de livres ou de revues.

Le brevet pour la lithographie en couleur fut déposé par G. Engelmann en 1837. Le brevet de G. Engelmann reposait sur trois points essentiels : utilisation d'un nombre réduit de couleurs faisant appel au principe de la trichromie (rouge, jaune, bleu), avec l'impression séparée de trois couleurs ou quatre avec le noir nécessitant donc la réalisation d'autant de pierres lithographiques, mise au point et utilisation systématique d'un cadre à repérer, impression à sec sur papier laminé par glaçage. Mais la lithographie en couleur restait encore une technique difficile et d'un maniement lourd pour la réalisation d'un livre, et ce n'est qu'avec la deuxième édition du traité de Bourgery et Jacob que les planches pouvaient être imprimées en couleurs grâce à la chromolithographie.

L'EDITION DU « TRAITE »

La réalisation d'un ouvrage comme le *Traité* constitua une gigantesque aventure éditoriale. L'éditeur eut en effet aussi un rôle déterminant dans un tel projet, et Bourgery soulignait : « Notre éditeur, mon collaborateur, M. Jacob, et moi, nous n'y avons épargné ni le temps, ni les sacrifices, sans nous inquiéter des obstacles et des lenteurs toujours inévitables quand on veut bien faire. » (t. 5, p. 7)

L'éditeur de l'ensemble de la première édition du traité fut C. A. Delaunay, *Librairie Anatomique*, 13 rue de l'Ecole de Médecine à Paris. Les raisons du choix de cet éditeur restent obscures. Il peut paraître étonnant que l'édition n'en ait pas été réalisée par le grand éditeur parisien Jean Baptiste Baillière (1797–1885), qui avait déjà assuré auparavant celle du *Traité de petite chirurgie* de Bourgery, paru en 1829, et qui assura sa réédition en 1835, ainsi que l'édition de l'*Anatomie élémentaire* en 20 planches de Bourgery et Jacob publiée en 1834–1835.

La parution des volumes d'iconographie ou atlas fut réalisée progressivement sous forme de livraisons, c'est-à-dire de parties délivrées périodiquement aux souscripteurs, au fur et à mesure de l'impression. Chaque livraison était composée de 8 planches et de 8 feuilles de texte descriptif et de légendes, de format in-folio. De 1831 à 1844, furent ainsi réalisées 70 livraisons. Cette publication sous formes de livraisons volantes, reliées seulement en un second temps, explique que la plupart des exemplaires conservés soient hétéroclites dans leur composition, réunissant des fascicules portant des dates variées ; plusieurs réimpressions furent en effet réalisées, en particulier de 1850 à 1854.

Les imprimeurs étaient aussi lourdement mis à contribution. Pour les volumes de texte, il s'agissait, suivant les tomes et les années, de Paul Renouard puis W. Remquet et Cie, au 5 rue Garancière à Paris, et de l'Imprimerie de Jules Didot

J. G. Cloquet, *Manuel d'anatomie descriptive du corps humain*, Paris, 1825–1826
Plate 245, drawn by Haincelin and lithographed by Frey. / Planche 245, dessinée par Haincelin et lithographiée par Frey. / Lámina 245, dibujada por Haincelin y litografiada por Frey.

PL. 245.

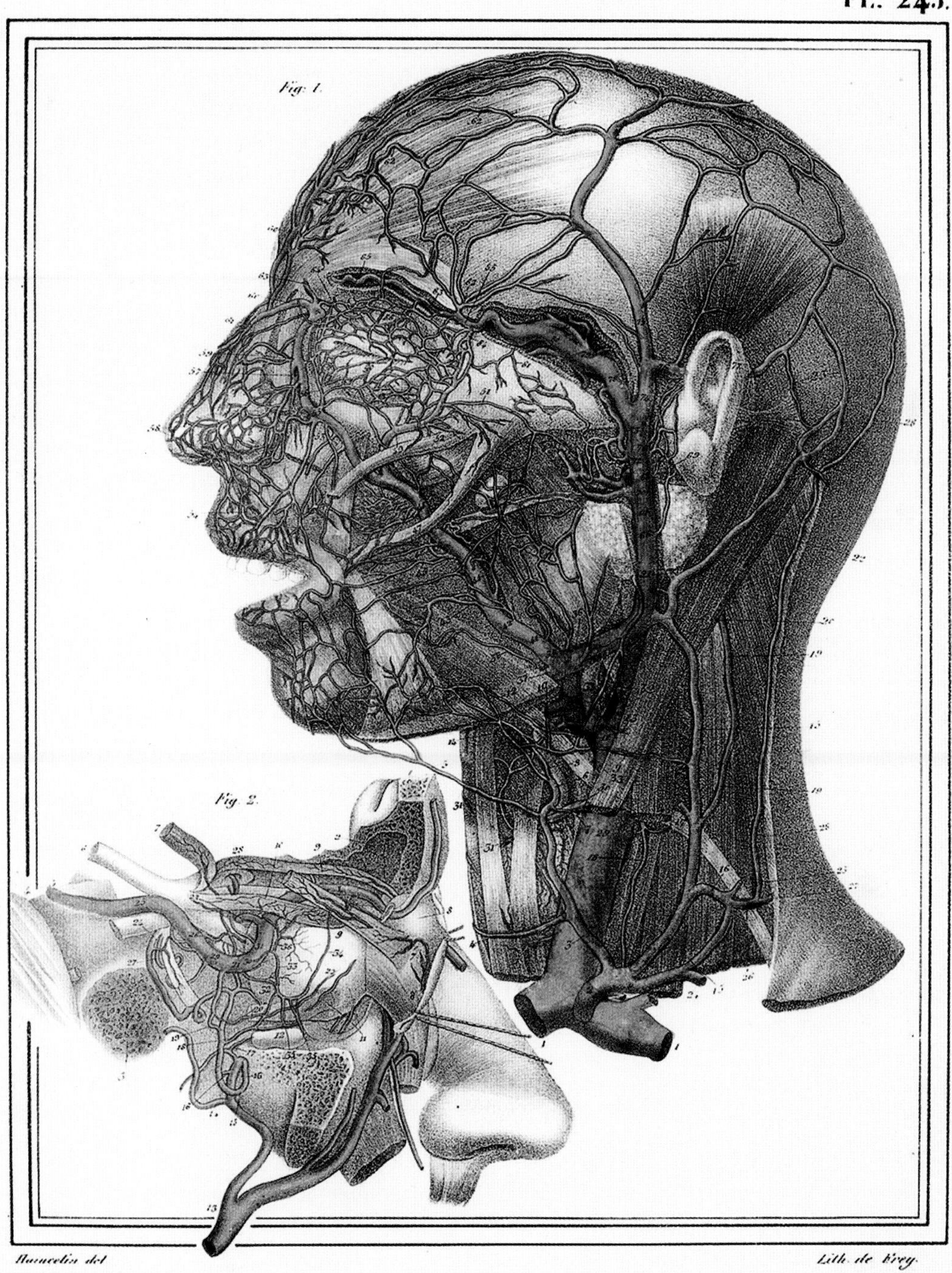

l'Aîné au 4 boulevard d'Enfer (devenu Denfert-Rochereau), également à Paris.

Pour les planches lithographiées, l'impression fut assurée par Bénard, puis Lemercier Bénard et Cie, et enfin Lemercier à Paris ; leur nom est mentionné au bas de chaque planche ; l'imprimerie de Rose Joseph Lemercier (1803–1887), ancien ouvrier de l'atelier de Senefelder-Knecht, installée rue de Seine, était le haut lieu de la lithographie parisienne avec une centaine de presses en 1838.

Le prix d'un exemplaire en noir et blanc était de 800 francs, somme déjà considérable, alors qu'il était du double, soit 1 600 francs pour un exemplaire en couleur, ce qui explique leur plus grande rareté déjà à l'époque. Ce prix élevé paraît avoir été un frein à la diffusion de l'ouvrage, la notice concernant Bourgery parue en 1853 dans la *Nouvelle biographie universelle* mentionne au sujet de son traité qu'il s'agit d'un « ouvrage d'une exécution remarquable, et qui, s'il n'était pas si cher, se trouverait entre les mains de tous les élèves de médecine. »

Une édition anglaise partielle, traduite par Robert Willis, *The whole anatomy of the human body, with its various practical applications, including a system of operative surgery, by J. M. Bourgery, ...illustrated by lithographic plates drawn from nature by N. H. Jacob*, fut assurée 1833–1837 par C. A. Delaunay.

La seconde édition du traité de Bourgery et Jacob fut réalisée de 1866 à 1871 par l'éditeur L. Guérin. Le retirage des planches fut effectué avec les pierres matrices originales qui étaient alors conservées de manière systématique.

L'ORGANISATION GENERALE DU TRAITE

Le traité se compose d'un frontispice, de volumes de textes, et d'atlas dont l'organisation générale est évoquée ici.

Frontispice

Suivant la tradition classique, l'ouvrage s'ouvre par un frontispice, page composée d'une planche illustrant ou symbolisant le thème de l'ouvrage (ill. p. 2). Le haut de la planche mentionne en lettres capitales : Frontispice du traité général de l'anatomie de l'homme par MM. Bourgery et Jacob. Au bas de la planche figure la mention : Composé et dessiné par N. H. Jacob.

Sur la gauche, un homme adulte nu, athlétique, aux cheveux bouclés noirs, portant une barbe noire, la main droite sur la hanche, et tenant de l'autre la main de la femme à ses côtés ; un drap cache sa région pubienne. Sur la droite, une jeune femme, complètement dénudée, à la longue chevelure, tient un enfant dans son bras droit. A leurs pieds est assis un vieillard méditatif, également nu, chauve en partie et à la longue barbe blanche. A l'arrière-plan, une sculpture représentant un écorché est posée sur un socle, et en dessous apparaît un fœtus anatomisé.

Cette allégorie des passages de la vie humaine est un ouvrage académique et montre l'affinité de J. L. David dont N. H. Jacob avait été l'élève. Le thème n'est pas non plus sans rappeler une des toutes premières œuvres de Jacob, exposée au Salon de 1802, *Les trois principaux passages de la vie humaine*.

Volumes de texte et Atlas

Pour chacun des huit tomes du traité a paru un volume spécifique de texte, rédigé de manière encyclopédique et indépendamment de l'iconographie à laquelle il n'est jamais fait de renvoi. Les huit volumes de texte représentent un total de 2 108 pages. Pour chacun des huit tomes du traité a paru un atlas ou volume spécifique consacré à l'iconographie et regroupant les planches. Avant chaque planche est placée une feuille de texte descriptif et de légendes. Les huit volumes d'atlas totalisent 725 planches.

La page de titre de chaque volume d'atlas est lithographiée. Sur une colonne à gauche figure la liste de 30 auteurs fondamentaux en anatomie dont le choix est révélateur : Aristote, Hérophile, Mondini, Vésale, Fallope, Eustache, Servet, Varole, Casserius, Harvey, Aselli, Rudbeck, T. Bartholin, Malpighi, Willis, Ruysch, Leuwenhoeck, Duverney, Albinus, Winslow, Haller, Meckel, Buffon, Walter, W. Hunter, Mascagni, Caldani, Bichat, Soemmering, Gall. De manière symétrique figure, à droite, la liste de 30 médecins et chirurgiens illustres : Empédocle, Hippocrate, Aretée, Galien, Avicenne, Albucasis, Guy de Chauliac, Fernel, A. Paré, Franco, Fabrice de Hilden, Severin, Sydenham, J. L. Petit, Stahl, Boerhaave, Hoffmann, Cheselden, Sauvage, A. Louis, Senac, Morgagni, Cullen, Brown, Desault, Sabatier, Jenner, Pinel, Corvisart, Laennec.

NOTES SUR LA PRESENTE EDITION DES PLANCHES

Le présent ouvrage contient la reproduction de la totalité des 725 planches lithographiées, dans leur version en couleurs, du *Traité complet de l'anatomie de l'homme comprenant la médecine opératoire par le Docteur J. M. Bourgery avec planches lithographiées d'après nature par N. H. Jacob*. Les 467 planches d'anatomie descriptive, d'une valeur artistique exceptionnelle gardent également une valeur scientifique de premier plan ; en effet, contrairement au texte descriptif qui a perdu une grande partie de sa force et de son intérêt pour le lecteur actuel, l'iconographie, basée sur des dissections originales, est restée, quant à elle, très moderne ; résultat de la rigueur de l'observation et de la précision de la représentation, ces illustrations anatomiques transmettent encore aujourd' hui de nombreuses et riches informations scientifiques : la réalité morphologique ne se démode pas. Les planches de médecine opératoire, à l'esthétique également superbe, présentent un grand intérêt pour l'histoire de la médecine et de la chirurgie ; les planches d'instruments chirurgicaux constituent une documentation remarquable toujours utile.

Pour la présente édition, un titre latin a été donné à chacune des planches. Ces titres donnés n'existaient pas dans l'édition originale, rédigée entièrement en français.

Aucun texte d'origine n'a été conservé, ou reproduit, pour les descriptions des planches et les légendes des figures. Les titres français répondrent aux exigences actuelles du langage et du vocabulaire scientifique et médical. En particulier, pour toutes les structures anatomiques, il était nécessaire d'utiliser la nomenclature anatomique internationale francisée, directement inspirée de la nomenclature latine internationale des *Nomina anatomica* faisant référence actuellement. De même, pour les noms d'espèces zoologiques citées pour l'anatomie comparée, une nomenclature française actuelle, essentiellement issue de celle validée par l'*International Commission on Zoological Nomenclature*, a été systématiquement utilisée. Pour les planches de médecine opératoire, la modernisation des titres a été plus difficile, puisque la plupart des opérations décrites n'existent plus et sont tombées dans l'oubli ; leurs dénominations mêmes ne figurent plus dans les dictionnaires actuels.

EL ATLAS DE ANATOMÍA Y CIRUGÍA DE J. M. BOURGERY Y N. H. JACOB – UNA OBRA MONUMENTAL DEL SIGLO XIX

La anatomía humana, ciencia morfológica dedicada al estudio de la arquitectura del cuerpo humano basada en la disección, ha dado lugar a la publicación de libros ilustrados excepcionales. El *Traité complet de l'anatomie de l'homme* de J. M. Bourgery y N. H. Jacob, publicado en París entre 1831 y 1854, se enmarca en una larga tradición de obras ilustradas, pero constituye uno de los libros más destacables de toda la historia de la anatomía y, sin lugar a dudas, el más excepcional del siglo XIX. La obra es monumental, de gran formato *in folio*, formada por ocho tomos y un total de 2.108 páginas en el caso de los volúmenes de texto y 725 láminas con 3.750 figuras en el de los tomos del atlas.

LAS GRANDES OBRAS DE ANATOMÍA HASTA EL SIGLO XIX

Los conocimientos anatómicos se limitaron durante mucho tiempo a los datos recogidos a partir de disecciones de animales realizadas por Galeno (c 130-c 200), médico griego que ejerció en Pérgamo y Roma y que tuvo una considerable influencia hasta el siglo XVI.

En la Edad Media, la única obra de anatomía realmente digna de recibir tal nombre fue la de Mondino dei Luzzi (c 1275-1326), redactada en 1319 y titulada *Anathomia*. En dicha obra, partiendo de los datos de Galeno, el autor aporta interesantes precisiones extraídas de disecciones humanas que había realizado en 1315.

Estas obras se difundían mediante copias manuscritas y contenían muy pocas ilustraciones. Con la invención de la imprenta o tipografía por Johann Gensfleisch, conocido como Gutenberg (c 1397-1468), hacia 1450, la difusión de los conocimientos iba a experimentar un crecimiento imparable. Entre los incunables (obras impresas antes de 1500) figura la edición príncipe de la *Anathomia* de Dei Luzzi impresa en 1478; dicha obra fue objeto de numerosas reediciones, entre las que destaca la comentada por Berengario da Carpi (1460?-1530), profesor en Bolonia, publicada en Venecia en 1521.

Los dibujos anatómicos de Leonardo da Vinci (1452-1519), correspondientes a 228 láminas manuscritas de una calidad científica extraordinaria, ocupan un lugar muy marginal y permanecieron inéditos e ignorados por los sabios de la época. Fueron publicados por primera vez en 1898 y no tuvieron repercusión alguna en la evolución de la disciplina.

En 1543, apareció en Basilea la obra de Andrés Vesalio (1514-1564) *De humani corporis fabrica*, que es, sin duda alguna, el libro más excepcional de toda la historia de la anatomía tanto desde el punto de vista conceptual como estético (il. pág. 11). La publicación de dicha obra constituyó una auténtica revolución científica, ya que ofreció una nueva visión del hombre, pues sustituyó los estudios especulativos de Galeno y las extrapolaciones a partir de la anatomía animal por disecciones humanas sistemáticas.

C. L. Bonamy, P. Broca & E. Beau, *Atlas d'anatomie descriptive du corps humain*, Paris, 1866
Volume 2, plate 28, drawn by Emile Beau, lithographed and printed in colour by Lemercier.
Tome 2, planche 28, dessinée par Emile Beau, lithographiée et imprimée en couleur par Lemercier.
Tomo 2, lámina 28, dibujada por Emile Beau, litografiada e impresa en color por Lemercier.

Tome. 2me. Pl.28.
C
A
D
B
E
10
F
6
9
H
G
11
18
9
P
17
R
23
21
29
U
S
4
7
J
L
N
12
8
M
19
3
16
20
14
O
13
15
Q
V
28
30
24
7
28
22
X
25
26
26'
Y
Z
Emile Beau ad naturam del.
Offic. litho Artus.

La obra de Vesalio incluye 25 magníficas láminas fuera del texto y numerosas figuras en el texto, todas ellas grabadas en madera, probablemente obra de Jan Stephan von Calcar (quien pertenecía al círculo de Tiziano). Esta obra, de la que apareció una segunda edición mejorada en 1555 y que sumó múltiples impresiones, tuvo una repercusión considerable y fue copiada por numerosos autores. A partir de entonces, ya no era posible pensar en la anatomía sin ilustraciones.

Entre las obras de anatomía más excepcionales del siglo XVI, cabe citar la de Charles Estienne (c 1504-1564), *De dissectione partium corporis humani*, publicada en París en 1545, con una edición francesa en 1546, que incluía 62 xilografías y numerosas viñetas en el texto; a pesar de que se publicó dos años después de la obra de Vesalio, la de Estienne había empezado a elaborarse en 1530. Juan Valverde de Hamusco (c 1525-c 1587) publicó en Roma en 1556 una obra en español copiada de Vesalio; una edición latina de dicha obra, titulada *Vivae imagines partium corporis humani*, fue publicada en 1566 por C. Plantin en Amberes y para sus ilustraciones se utilizó (una de las primeras veces que se hizo) el grabado en dulce o en cobre. Esta nueva técnica, que permitía una precisión y una finura en las medias tintas imposibles de obtener con la xilografía, abría nuevas posibilidades incomparables y se utilizó hasta principios del siglo XIX. Por último, André Du Laurens (1558?-c 1609), profesor en Montpellier, publicó en 1600 en París y en Fráncfort una *Historia anatomica humani corporis* adornada con 26 espléndidas láminas grabadas en cobre.

En el siglo XVII, cabe destacar la obra de Giulio Casserio o Julius Casserius (c 1550-1616) *Tabulae anatomicae*, publicada de manera póstuma en Venecia en 1627, con 97 láminas grabadas en cobre por Francesco Valesio a la manera de Odoardo Fialetti, un pintor del círculo de Tintoretto; las láminas de este libro también sirvieron para ilustrar obras de su sucesor en Padua, Adrian van der Spieghel (c 1578-1625). La obra de Govert Bidloo (1649-1713) *Anatomia humani corporis*, aparecida en Ámsterdam en 1685, contiene 105 láminas muy originales grabadas en cobre por Pieter van Gunst según unos dibujos de Gérard de Lairesse (1640?-1711).

En el siglo XVIII, aparecieron numerosas obras de anatomía ilustradas con láminas grabadas en cobre excepcionales, pero a menudo trataban únicamente un aspecto concreto. La más destacable es la de Bernhard Siegfried Weiss, conocido como Albinus (1697-1770) y profesor de anatomía y cirugía en Leiden, dedicada a la osteología y la miología, o estudio de los huesos y los músculos: *Tabulae sceleti et musculorum corporis humani*, aparecida en Leiden en 1747, con 40 láminas de Jean Wandelaer (1690-1759), ex alumno de Gérard de Lairesse (ils. págs. 15-17); esta obra, que alcanzó un gran éxito, abrió un nuevo camino a las representaciones anatómicas científicas y posteriormente fue objeto de numerosas copias. Entre las obras destacables también cabe citar las de William Cowper (1666-1709), *Myotomia reformata* (Londres, 1724); Albrecht von Haller (1708-1777), *Icones anatomicae*, en ocho fascículos aparecidos en Gotinga entre 1743 y 1756, con 46 láminas admirables; Paolo Mascagni (1752-1815), *Vasorum lymphaticorum corporis humani historia* (Siena, 1787), sobre los vasos linfáticos; o Antonio Scarpa (1752-1832), sobre los nervios, *Tabulae nevrologicae* (Pavia, 1794). La magnífica obra de Jacques Gamelin (1738-1803), pintor, dibujante y grabador, *Nouveau recueil d'ostéologie et de myologie*, aparecida en Toulouse en 1779, con 79 láminas, se encuentra algo apartada, ya que trata la anatomía desde el punto de vista artístico y no médico. Por último, hay que destacar las extraordinarias obras impresas en color por Jacques Fabien Gautier d'Agoty (1710-1785), en parte en colaboración con el cirujano J. F. Duverney: *Myologie complette en couleur et grandeur naturelle*, con

20 láminas (París, 1746; il. pág. 23), *Anatomie de la tête*, con 8 láminas (París, 1748; il. pág. 21), *Anatomie générale des viscères et de la névrologie, angéologie et ostéologie du corps humain*, con 18 láminas (París, 1754), y *Exposition anatomique de la structure du corps humain*, con 20 láminas (Marsella, 1759).

PRESENTACIÓN DEL TRATADO DE J. M. BOURGERY Y N. H. JACOB

Ahora que la litografía permite publicar, sin incurrir en gastos excesivos, obras iconográficas muy voluminosas, sería hacer un favor a los médicos el poner al alcance de todos ellos el conjunto de los trabajos realizados sobre anatomía. Pero, para que una obra de este tipo pueda ofrecer toda la utilidad posible, no solo es necesario que la ciencia esté presente en ella en su estado más avanzado, sino también que aparezca con todas sus aplicaciones. Así, no debería copiarse servilmente ningún trabajo anterior, ya que no existe ninguno al que no puedan añadirse nuevos conocimientos; pero sobre todo es indispensable que las láminas de una obra tal, elaboradas con nuevas intenciones, se dibujen del natural, tomando en cualquier caso como referente las figuras reconocidas entre las que se han publicado hasta la fecha. Esa es la tarea que el señor Jacob y yo nos hemos propuesto llevar a cabo. Haremos todo lo posible para concluir de forma honrosa el inmenso trabajo que hemos iniciado (Bourgery, tomo 1, págs. 1-2).

Toda la filosofía que preside la elaboración del *Traité complet de l'anatomie de l'homme comprenant la médecine opératoire par le Docteur J. M. Bourgery avec planches lithographiées d'après nature par N. H. Jacob* se encuentra resumida en la cita anterior, extraída de la introducción redactada por Jean Marc Bourgery en octubre de 1830 y contenida en el primer tomo de esta obra publicado en 1831-1832.

C. Sachaile de la Barre, en su obra *Les médecins de Paris jugés par leurs œuvres*, publicada en 1845, escribe: *[...] estaba reservado al señor Bourgery no solo el hecho de dar a esta cuestión la solución más satisfactoria, sino el de sorprendernos por la perfección de los medios utilizados al respecto. En efecto, no hay nada más bello que las láminas que forman las obras de anatomía a las que se vincula principalmente su nombre.* El doctor J. M. Bourgery está considerado, con justicia, *el autor de uno de los monumentos más bellos erigidos a la ciencia de la estructura del hombre* en la nota biográfica redactada en 1876 por E. Beaugrand para el famoso *Dictionnaire encyclopédique des sciences médicales*, publicado bajo la dirección de A. Dechambre.

París era, en la época de Bourgery, una ciudad de referencia para la anatomía. El decano de la Facultad de Medicina Matthieu Orfila (1787-1853), nombrado en 1832, se encargó de renovar por completo la facultad e inició la creación de un nuevo museo anatómico, sumamente rico, inaugurado en 1844. Las numerosísimas disecciones realizadas en la Escuela Práctica aneja a la Facultad de Medicina despertaron admiración y envidia en todo el mundo.

La publicación del *Traité complet de l'anatomie de l'homme* tuvo lugar en una época de pleno auge de la anatomía, y Bourgery afirmaba en la introducción de su obra lo siguiente: *Sin la anatomía, la fisiología no es más que un tejido de fábulas más o menos ingeniosas, la cirugía carece de guía y la medicina se reduce a un empirismo ciego* (tomo 1, pág. 1). Bourgery reafirma en varias ocasiones a lo largo de su obra la primacía de la anatomía entre las disciplinas médicas y en la evolución de los conceptos científicos.

EL IDEADOR Y AUTOR: J. M. BOURGERY

Jean Marc Bourgery, nacido el 8 de pradial del año V del calendario revolucionario (27 de mayo de 1797) en Orleans, era hijo de Marc Claude Bourgery, mercero, y de Madeleine Marthe Delaboulaye; el nacimiento se produjo en el domicilio familiar sito en el n.° 1 de la rue du Tabourg a las once de la mañana; los testigos fueron Jean Claude Vignolet, mercero, y Nicolas Bergerac, ropavejero.

Bourgery optó por estudiar medicina. En 1815, se matriculó como oyente en las clases del famoso naturalista Jean Baptiste de Lamarck (1744-1829), por aquel entonces profesor en el Museo de Historia Natural de París. Tras aprobar la oposición de ingreso, Bourgery fue admitido como interno de los Hospitales de 1817 a 1820, y se le concedió la Medalla de Oro del Internado en 1819.

Al finalizar los estudios médicos, Bourgery no realizó ningún doctorado, al parecer por falta de recursos financieros, y trabajó durante algunos años como responsable sanitario en varias fundiciones de cobre de Romilly-sur-Seine (departamento de Aube). Participó entonces en la creación de una fábrica de sulfato de cobre. Es muy probable que en aquella época realizara diversos estudios sobre la coloración de las maderas:

El señor Bourgery ha utilizado sus conocimientos de química orgánica para dar a las maderas de los árboles aún arraigados un color diferente del que las caracteriza: los experimentos realizados al respecto ya han dado resultados favorables y despiertan grandes esperanzas (Sachaile de la Barre, 1845).

En 1827, con 30 años, la trayectoria profesional de Bourgery dio un giro decisivo cuando decidió regresar a París. Fue entonces cuando recibió el título de doctor en medicina con la defensa de su tesis sobre las ligaduras circulares de los miembros el 27 de agosto de 1827 en París.

Dos años más tarde, en 1829, publicó un *Traité de petite chirurgie*, obra de referencia notable, pese a no estar ilustrada, que alcanzó gran éxito, ya que se publicó una segunda edición en francés en 1835 y se tradujo al inglés en 1834 y al alemán en 1836.

En 1830, Bourgery comenzó el proyecto de su *Traité complet de l'anatomie de l'homme*, que le mantendría ocupado durante casi 20 años (hasta su muerte), en colaboración con el ilustrador N. H. Jacob. Las primeras entregas aparecieron en 1831. Dado el éxito de los primeros tomos, Bourgery y Jacob publicaron en 1834-1835 una *Anatomie élémentaire* de gran formato *in folio* con 20 láminas litografiadas y con un pequeño volumen separado de texto. Dicha obra tuvo una segunda edición (1836-1839) y se tradujo al alemán (1837). La publicación del *Traité complet de l'anatomie de l'homme* avanzaba lentamente pero quedaba un trabajo considerable. Entre 1833 y 1837, se publicó una versión en inglés de los primeros tomos, con textos traducidos por Robert Willis, lo cual confirmaba la relevancia del trabajo realizado hasta esa fecha.

A partir de 1840, Bourgery utilizó observaciones personales para redactar artículos científicos originales, en forma de memorias principalmente, aparecidos en los *Comptes-Rendus de l'Académie des Sciences de Paris*, entre 1842 y 1848. Dichas memorias están ilustradas a menudo por bellas litografías y varias de ellas también se publicaron en forma de opúsculos impresos aparte.

También se asoció a Bourgery con la realización de los modelos anatómicos en cartón piedra de Félix Thibert, tal como atestigua un folleto que presenta unas piezas, aparecido en París en 1847: *Musée Thibert d'anatomie pathologique et d'histoire naturelle par la méthode plastique du Dr Félix Thibert [...] sous la direction scientifique du Dr J. M. Bourgery*. Esas figuras, modeladas en relieve del natural y pintadas a continuación, tuvieron un gran éxito, tal como muestran las numerosas piezas recogidas en los catálogos impresos de museos anatómicos, en particular el de Estrasburgo, redactado por C. H. Ehrmann (1843), o el del Museo Orfila de París, firmado por M. Houel (1881).

El conjunto de los trabajos de Bourgery le llevó entonces a postularse para distintos puestos univer-

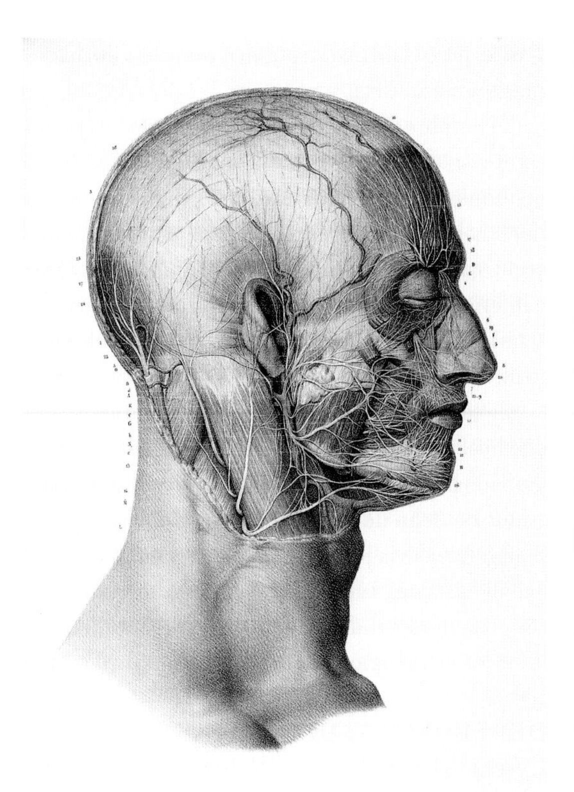

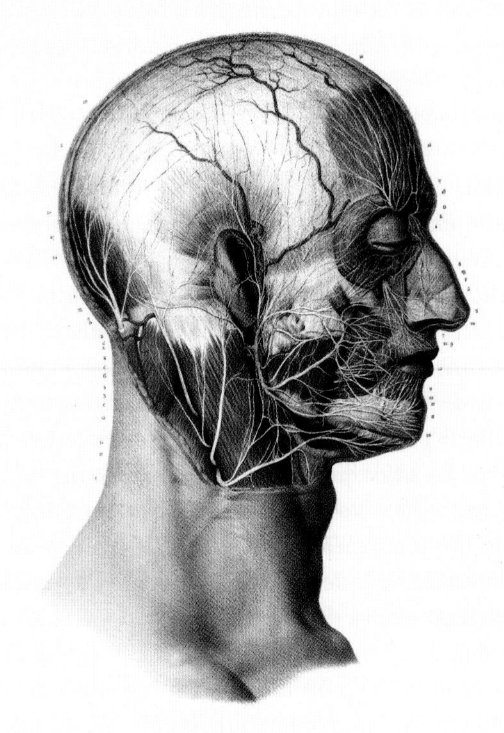

Comparison of the lithographed plates of the volume 3, plate 40 of the *Traité complet de l'anatomie de l'homme* by J. M. Bourgery and N. H. Jacob (1844) printed in black-and-white and lithographed in colour using stencil; drawn by N. H. Jacob. / Comparaison des planches lithographiées du tome 3, planche 40 imprimée en noir et blanc et mise en couleur au pochoir du *Traité complet de l'anatomie de l'homme* de J. M. Bourgery et N. H. Jacob (1844) ; dessinée par N. H. Jacob. / Comparación de las láminas litografiadas del tomo 3, lámina 40 impresa en blanco y negro y coloreada con patrón estarcido del *Traité complet de l'anatomie de l'homme* de J. M. Bourgery y N. H. Jacob (1844); dibujada por N. H. Jacob.

sitarios y académicos y a presentarse a diversos concursos, aunque siempre sin éxito. En concreto, presentó su candidatura como profesor de antropología en el Museo de Historia Natural de París, como miembro de la Academia de las Ciencias de París en 1843 y como profesor titular de la cátedra de anatomía de la Facultad de Medicina de París en 1846, defendiendo para ello una tesis el 13 de febrero de 1846 sobre los anejos del feto y su desarrollo.

Los sucesivos fracasos de Bourgery como candidato a puestos universitarios y académicos, a pesar de la sólida notoriedad adquirida, dejaron en él un poso de amargura; también parece vislumbrarse cierto agotamiento. Su confesión al respecto en el discurso preliminar del octavo y último tomo de su *Traité*, y que apareció de manera póstuma, es excepcional en la historia de la edición médica y científica, y especialmente desgarradora: *Y ahora, a punto de terminar mi trabajo, del que poseo todo el material, comparando lo que he hecho con lo que me había propuesto realizar, ojalá pueda el público reconocer que no he faltado a mi deber,*

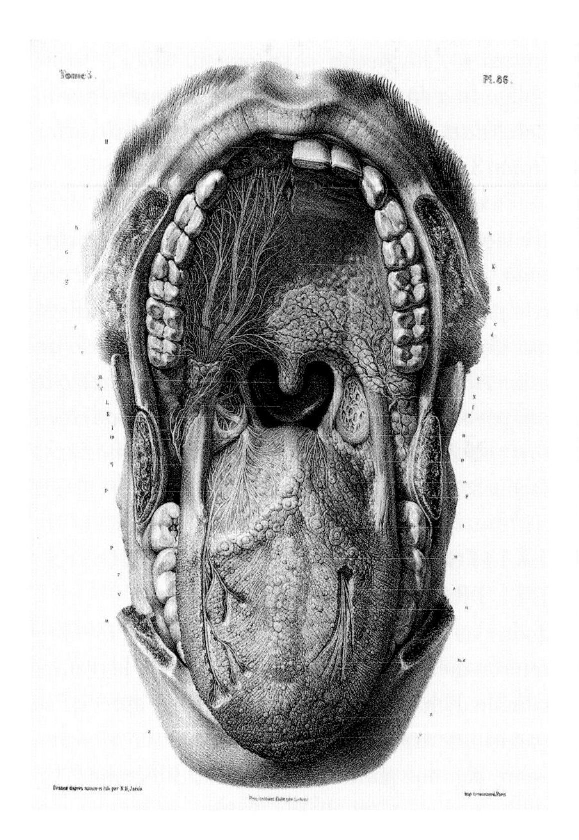

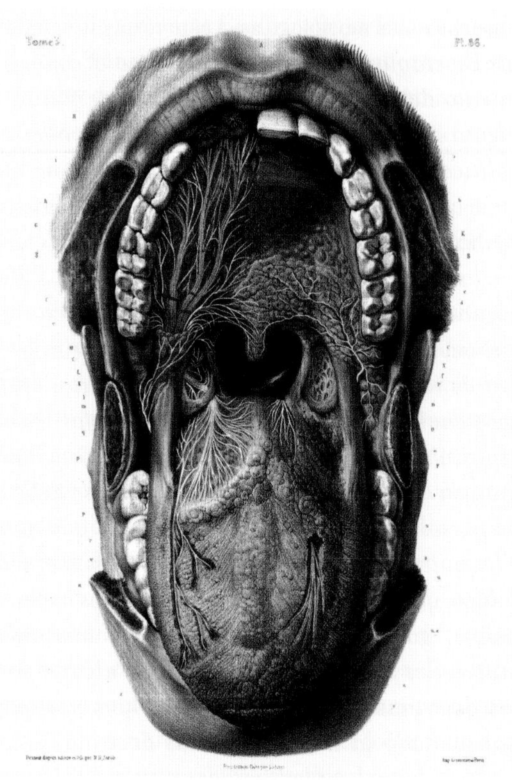

Comparison of the lithographed plates of volume 3, plate 86 of the *Traité complet de l'anatomie de l'homme* by J. M. Bourgery and N. H. Jacob (1844) printed in black-and-white and lithographed in colour using stencil; drawn by N. H. Jacob. / Comparaison des planches lithographiées du tome 3, planche 86 imprimée en noir et blanc et mise en couleur au pochoir du *Traité complet de l'anatomie de l'homme* de J. M. Bourgery et N. H. Jacob (1844) ; dessinée par N. H. Jacob. / Comparación de las láminas litografiadas del tomo 3, lámina 86 impresa en blanco y negro y coloreada con patrón estarcido del *Traité complet de l'anatomie de l'homme* de J. M. Bourgery y N. H. Jacob (1844); dibujada por N. H. Jacob.

explicaron la rápida multiplicación de los litógrafos y de las imprentas litográficas que producían tanto ilustraciones para libros como partituras musicales, estampas populares o trabajos mundanos de tipo efímero (papel con encabezado, etiquetas para la industria, publicidad).

Philippe André obtuvo en 1802 una licencia para introducir esta técnica en Francia, aunque no sería presentada hasta la fundación de los talleres de Godefroy Engelmann (1788-1839) en Mulhouse en 1814, y después en París en 1816, y del conde Charles de Lasteyrie, también en 1816 en París. El año 1816 marcó el auténtico auge de la litografía en Francia. Más adelante se convertiría en la técnica favorita para las ilustraciones del Romanticismo. La primera obra de anatomía en la que se recurrió a la litografía para sus ilustraciones fue la de Jules Germain Cloquet (1790-1883), *Anatomie de l'homme ou description et figures lithographiées du corps humain*, aparecida en París en 1821 (il. pág. 27). Dado que el gran formato *in folio* hacía esta obra poco manejable y cara, J. G. Cloquet decidió realizar un *Manuel d'anatomie descriptive du corps humain*, en un formato *in quarto*, publicado en París en 1825-1826, con 340 láminas litografiadas en blanco y negro, y reeditado recientemente (ils. págs. 29, 35). Por aquel entonces, François Antommarchi (1780-1838), que había sido el médico del emperador Napoléon I en Santa Elena, publicó con su nombre, a partir de los dibujos de Paolo Mascagni (1752-1815), la obra *Planches anatomiques du corps humain exécutées d'après les dimensions naturelles [...]*, que contenía 80 láminas litografiadas, y que fue editada en París por C. de Lasteyrie de 1823 a 1826. La litografía aportaba cierta precisión al dibujo al tiempo que introducía flexibilidad, ya que posibilitaba numerosos matices de gris, y se caracterizaba por un realismo, un toque y una expresión más próximos a la realidad anatómica que en las interpretaciones grabadas anteriores, y acabó sustituyendo de manera ventajosa a los antiguos procedimientos de ilustración anatómica. Un inconveniente práctico, que sin embargo le confería a todas luces una ventaja estética, residía en que debía mantenerse fuera del texto. Así, en 1830, cuando Bourgery y Jacob comenzaron la realización de su tratado, la litografía era una técnica reciente pero ya perfectamente dominada.

El principio básico de la litografía, tal como destacó Senefelder, consistía fundamentalmente en el fenómeno de repulsión entre el agua y los cuerpos grasos en la superficie de la piedra caliza. El dibujo realizado con el lápiz graso o la escritura con una pluma y tinta grasa sobre dicho soporte previamente graneado o pulido se preparaban a continuación con una mezcla de goma arábiga y ácido nítrico. Dicho tratamiento químico, o acidulación, modificaba la naturaleza de la grasa contenida en los marcadores y hacía que esta penetrara y se adhiriera con firmeza a la piedra. Mediante la acción de la goma arábiga, que favorecería la retención del agua en las partes no dibujadas de la superficie de la piedra, estas permanecían húmedas e insensibles a los cuerpos grasos como la tinta de imprenta. Por el contrario, la tinta depositada por el rodillo entintador se adhería a las partes grasas correspondientes de manera muy fiel al dibujo original, daba los negros en la prueba impresa y transfería la imagen al papel.

La piedra litográfica era piedra caliza, con una estructura muy compacta y una gran pureza. Se extraía en losas de 7 a 10 centímetros de grosor para resistir las presiones de la prensa. La naturaleza compacta y regular de su grano le confería las propiedades idóneas para la litografía. Las piedras más utilizadas y de mejor calidad procedían de las canteras de Baviera, en particular de Solnhofen. Nunca se utilizaba la piedra en bruto, sino que se debía someterse una de sus caras a un proceso de pulido y graneado que permitiera la adherencia del lápiz o la tinta a la superficie de la piedra. Dicho proceso consistía en frotar dos piedras una con otra interponiendo un abrasivo mezclado con agua. El grano de la piedra originaba la textura característica de las ilustraciones litográficas. No obstante, las piedras litográficas presentaban varios inconvenientes: eran pesadas, voluminosas, difíciles de manejar, quebradizas, caras y, en el caso de los grandes formatos, ralentizaban la velocidad de la impresión.

Los lápices grasos utilizados contenían cera, jabón negro, sebo y negro de humo que permitían obtener una gran variedad de medias tintas, que iban de los grises más suaves a los negros más intensos, y recordaban el grano de un dibujo hecho con lápiz de grafito o tiza negra.

La impresión de las láminas era una etapa especialmente importante y delicada. Se confiaba a un impresor especializado y exigía gran cuidado. Las prensas litográficas experimentaron notables perfeccionamientos. La piedra, calzada en la prensa, se entintaba con el rodillo. Siguiendo unas marcas, el litógrafo colocaba una hoja de papel humedecida y lo pasaba todo bajo la prensa, cuyo carro debía desplazarse sin detenerse y sin sacudidas para evitar imágenes borrosas. Una vez que el carro se situaba de nuevo en su punto de partida, el impresor levantaba con cuidado la prueba, que se adhería a la piedra. A continuación, la prueba litográfica se colocaba plana y se ponía a secar.

Al principio, el artista se veía obligado a realizar el dibujo al revés en la piedra, pero, en 1817, A. Senefelder perfeccionó el papel autográfico, en el que el artista realizaba el dibujo a lápiz o con tinta litográfica. Este papel reporte o autográfico graneado o litográfico estaba especialmente preparado, graneado de forma mecánica y recubierto con una fina capa adhesiva.

Entre las principales ventajas, el artista podía trabajar en su casa sobre un soporte ligero y fácil de transportar, y dibujar en cualquier sitio. A continuación, se entregaba el papel con el dibujo al impresor, que lo transfería a la piedra mediante la humidificación del papel y presiones repetidas. Este procedimiento permitía suprimir la inversión, ya que el dibujo realizado tal cual se transfería al revés a la piedra y, por lo tanto, la prueba obtenida estaba en el sentido correcto. Según los casos, el propio artista litografiaba el dibujo o bien se encomendaba dicha tarea a un litógrafo especializado.

Pero la litografía, cuya impresión lenta no se adaptaba a la producción en serie, estaba condenada a no ser más que una técnica de transición. A partir de 1860, la litografía experimentó una crisis importante. Se vio rápidamente destronada por la cincografía, técnica en la que el zinc sustituía a la piedra litográfica y podía adaptarse a la rotativa (1868), y en 1885 apareció el fotograbado industrial. Una de las últimas grandes obras de anatomía elaborada con láminas litografiadas es la de C. L. Bonamy, P. Broca y E. Beau, el *Atlas d'anatomie descriptive du corps humain*, publicado en París en 1866 (il. pág. 39).

LA COLORACIÓN DE LAS LÁMINAS

En 1831, cuando se publicó el primer volumen de láminas del tratado de Bourgery y Jacob, la litografía solo permitía hacer una impresión en negro. Así pues, la mayor parte de los ejemplares del *Traité* tenían láminas impresas únicamente en blanco y negro. Pero, si bien la impresión en negro bastaba para plasmar los huesos del esqueleto, ofrecía en cambio una imagen imperfecta de una región diseccionada que el color permitía delimitar y precisar (ils. págs. 42-44). En tales casos, la coloración o iluminación de las láminas podía hacerse libremente con ayuda de un pincel o bien utilizando patrones de estarcido.

En el caso de las láminas de la primera edición del tratado de Bourgery y Jacob, la coloración se realizó a mano utilizando la técnica de la coloración con plantilla o con patrón de estarcido. Dicha técnica permitía aplicar fácilmente colores similares en lugares parecidos en múltiples ejemplares de una misma lámina. Primero se aislaban las distintas zonas de color del original y después se calcaba cada una de ellas a una lámina de metal, una cartulina o una tela rígida. En principio, se realizaba una hoja por cada color. A continuación, la parte correspondiente al color se cortaba y se obtenía así un recorte; el trabajo de corte era muy delicado si se querían obtener contornos fieles y nítidos, o bien si estos eran complejos.

A continuación se aplicaban los colores unos tras otros con un pincel especial de pelo rígido, llamado borla, o bien con una esponja. Los colores empleados eran, por lo general, suaves y de tipo acuoso o acuarela, aunque en ocasiones podían utilizarse colores opacos y aguadas. Había que impedir que el color se corriera y era preciso esperar a que un tono se hubiera secado por completo para pasar al siguiente. El paso de un tono a otro se realizaba por yuxtaposición y, a veces, por superposición; en ocasiones, también se aplicaban los colores sobre fondos húmedos para degradarlos. Algunos detalles podían realzarse con pintura a la aguada. Los colores podían multiplicarse a placer utilizando una borla por tono; ayudados por iluminadores hábiles, algunos talleres poseían centenares de borlas para garantizar todos los matices. Normalmente, se obtenían precios de coste bastante bajos con buenos técnicos y colores simples. Pese a ser manual, el estarcido era un trabajo relativamente rápido para un técnico en estampación y se calculaba que un profesional bien preparado podía colorear unas 500 hojas de formato pequeño por hora. Esta técnica de coloración con patrón se utilizó mucho en el siglo XIX en grabados aislados e ilustraciones de libros o revistas.

G. Engelmann registró la patente de la litografía en color en 1837. La patente de Engelmann se basaba en tres puntos fundamentales: utilización de un número reducido de colores que apelaban al principio de la tricromía (rojo, amarillo y azul), con la impresión separada de tres colores (o cuatro, con el negro) que precisaba la elaboración de otras tantas piedras litográficas; fabricación y utilización sistemática de un marco de señalamiento, e impresión en seco en papel laminado por glaseado. Pero la litografía en color seguía siendo una técnica difícil y de manejo pesado para la elaboración de un libro, y no fue hasta la segunda edición del tratado de Bourgery y Jacob cuando pudieron imprimirse las láminas en color gracias a la cromolitografía.

LA EDICIÓN DEL TRATADO

La realización de una obra como el *Traité* constituyó una gigantesca aventura editorial. Efectivamente, el editor desempeñó un papel determinante en el proyecto, y Bourgery subrayaba: *Nuestro editor, mi colaborador, el señor Jacob, y yo no hemos escatimado tiempo ni en sacrificios, sin preocuparnos por los obstáculos y las ralentizaciones inevitables cuando se quiere hacer bien las cosas* (tomo 5, pág. 7).

El editor del conjunto de la primera edición del tratado fue C. A. Delaunay, Librairie Anatomique, sito en el número 13 de la rue de l'École de Médecine, en París. Los motivos de la elección de dicho editor no están claros. Puede resultar sorprendente que el encargado de realizar la edición no fuera el gran editor parisino Jean Baptiste Baillière (1797-1885), que ya había editado anteriormente el *Traité de petite chirurgie* de Bourgery, aparecido en 1829, y que se ocupó de su reedición en 1835, así como de la producción de la *Anatomie élémentaire en 20 planches* de Bourgery y Jacob publicada en 1834-1835.

La aparición de los volúmenes de iconografía o atlas tuvo lugar progresivamente en forma de entregas, es decir, de partes entregadas periódicamente a los suscriptores, a medida que se iban imprimiendo. Cada entrega se componía de 8 láminas y de 8 hojas de texto descriptivo y pies, en formato *in folio*. Entre 1831 y 1844, se realizaron así 70 entregas. Esta publicación en forma de entregas sueltas, encuadernadas únicamente en una segunda etapa, explica que la mayor parte de los ejemplares conservados sean heteróclitos en su composición, ya que reúnen fascículos con fechas variadas; en efecto, se realizaron varias reimpresiones, en particular entre 1850 y 1854.

También se utilizaron los servicios de varios impresores. Por lo que respecta a los volúmenes de texto, fueron impresos, según los tomos y los años, por Paul Renouard (posteriormente W. Remquet et Cie), sito en el número 5 de la rue Garancière de París, y por la imprenta de Jules Didot padre, en el número 4 del boulevard d'Enfer (después Denfert-Rochereau), también en París.

En cuanto a las láminas litografiadas, se encargó de la impresión Bénard (posteriormente Lemercier Bénard et Cie, y por último Lemercier), de París; su nombre se menciona al pie de cada lámina; la imprenta de Rose Joseph Lemercier (1803-1887), antiguo obrero del taller de Senefelder-Knecht, instalada en la rue de Seine, era el súmmum de la litografía parisina y en 1838 ya contaba con un centenar de prensas.

El precio de un ejemplar en blanco y negro era de 800 francos, suma ya considerable, mientras que costaba el doble, es decir, 1.600 francos, si se trataba de uno en color, lo cual explica por qué eran tan escasos en aquella época. Ese elevado precio parece haber constituido una rémora para la difusión de la obra, puesto que la nota relativa a Bourgery aparecida en 1853 en la *Nouvelle biographie universelle* dice con relación a su tratado que se trata de una *obra de una ejecución notable que, si no fuera tan cara, estaría en manos de todos los estudiantes de medicina.*

C. A. Delaunay realizó en 1833-1837 una edición parcial en inglés, traducida por Robert Willis, *The whole anatomy of the human body, with its various practical applications, including a system of operative surgery, by J. M. Bourgery [...] illustrated by lithographic plates drawn from nature by N. H. Jacob.*

El editor L. Guérin realizó la segunda edición del tratado de Bourgery y Jacob entre 1866 y 1871. La reimpresión de las láminas se efectuó con las piedras matrices originales, que por entonces se conservaban de manera sistemática.

LA ORGANIZACIÓN GENERAL DEL TRATADO

El tratado está compuesto por un frontispicio, volúmenes de texto y atlas cuya organización general se explica a continuación.

Frontispicio

Según la tradición clásica, la obra comienza con un frontispicio, página compuesta por una lámina que ilustra o simboliza el tema de la obra (il. pág. 2). La parte superior de la lámina reza, en letras mayúsculas: *Frontispicio del tratado general de anatomía humana de los señores Bourgery y Jacob.* Al pie de la lámina consta la mención: *Compuesto y dibujado por N. H. Jacob.*

A la izquierda aparece un hombre adulto desnudo, atlético, de pelo negro rizado, con barba negra, con la mano derecha en la cadera y sujetando con la otra la mano de la mujer que está a su lado; una sábana cubre su región púbica. A la derecha, una joven de pelo largo, completamente desnuda, sostiene a un niño en su brazo derecho. A sus pies está sentado un anciano meditabundo, también desnudo, un poco calvo y con una larga barba blanca. En segundo plano, sobre un zócalo hay una escultura que representa un desollado y debajo puede verse un feto anatomizado.

Esta alegoría de los cambios de la vida humana es una obra académica y muestra la afinidad de J. L. David, de quien Jacob había sido alumno. También recuerda una de las primeras obras de Jacob, sobre el mismo tema, expuesta en el Salón de 1802, *Les trois principaux passages de la vie humaine.*

Volúmenes de texto y atlas

Para cada uno de los ocho tomos del tratado se publicó un volumen específico de texto, redactado de forma enciclopédica e independiente de la iconografía, a la que nunca se hace referencia. Los ocho volúmenes de texto tienen un total de 2.108 páginas.

Para cada uno de los ocho tomos del tratado se publicó un atlas o volumen específico dedicado a la iconografía y que agrupaba las láminas. Antes de cada lámina se colocó una hoja con texto descriptivo y pies. Los ocho volúmenes de atlas contienen un total de 725 láminas.

La portadilla de cada volumen del atlas está litografiada. En una columna que hay a la izquierda figura la lista de 30 autores fundamentales en la anatomía, cuya selección resulta reveladora: *Aristóteles, Herófilo, Mondini, Vesalio, Falopio, Eustaquio, Servet, Varolio, Casserius, Harvey, Aselli, Rudbeck, T. Bartholin, Malpighi, Willis, Ruysch, Leuwenhoeck, Duverney, Albinus, Winslow, Haller, Meckel, Buffon,*

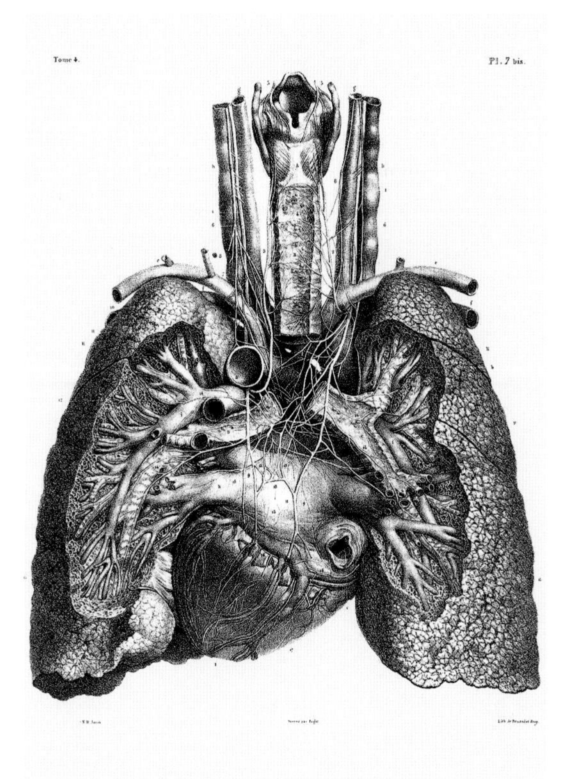

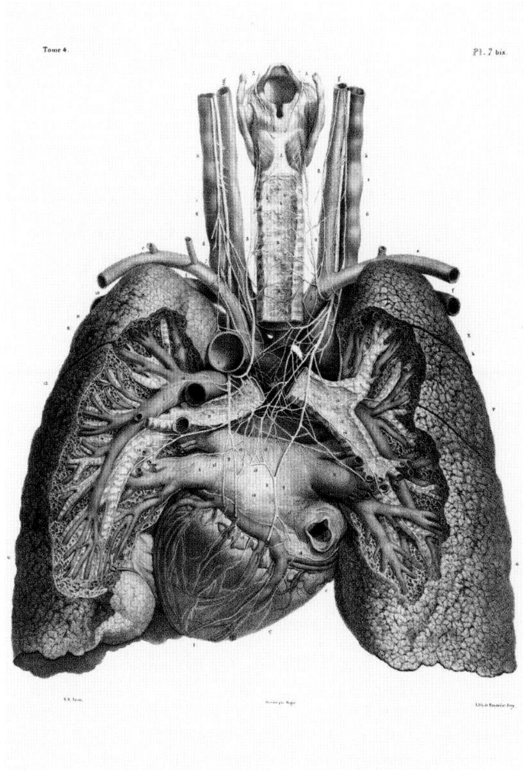

Comparison of the lithographed plates of volume 4, plate 7 bis of the *Traité complet de l'anatomie de l'homme* by J. M. Bourgery and N. H. Jacob (1835–1836) printed in black-and-white and lithographed in colour using stencil; drawn by Rogat. / Comparaison des planches lithographiées du tome 4, planche 7 bis imprimée en noir et blanc et mise en couleur au pochoir du *Traité complet de l'anatomie de l'homme* de J. M. Bourgery et N. H. Jacob (1835–1836) ; dessinée par Rogat. / Comparación de las láminas litografiadas del tomo 4, lámina 7 bis impresa en blanco y negro y coloreada con patrón estarcido del *Traité complet de l'anatomie de l'homme* de J. M. Bourgery y N. H. Jacob (1835-1836); dibujada por Rogat.

Walter, W. Hunter, Mascagni, Caldani, Bichat, Soemmering y *Gall*. Dispuesta de forma simétrica a la derecha, se encuentra la lista de 30 médicos y cirujanos ilustres: *Empédocles, Hipócrates, Areteo, Galeno, Avicena, Albucasis, Guy de Chauliac, Fernel, A. Paré, Franco, Fabrice de Hilden, Severin, Sydenham, J. L. Petit, Stahl, Boerhaave, Hoffmann, Cheselden, Sauvage, A. Louis, Senac, Morgagni, Cullen, Brown, Desault, Sabatier, Jenner, Pinel, Corvisart* y *Laennec*.

NOTAS SOBRE LA PRESENTE EDICIÓN DE LAS LÁMINAS

La presente obra contiene la reproducción de la totalidad de las 725 láminas litografiadas, en su versión en color, del *Traité complet de l'anatomie de l'homme comprenant la médecine opératoire par le Docteur J. M. Bourgery avec planches lithographiées d'après nature par N. H. Jacob*. Las 467 láminas de anatomía descriptiva, de un valor artístico excepcional, atesoran también un valor científico de primer orden;

en efecto, contrariamente al texto descriptivo, que ha perdido gran parte de su fuerza e interés para el lector actual, la iconografía, basada en disecciones originales, sigue estando plenamente vigente; resultado del rigor de la observación y de la precisión en la representación, estas ilustraciones anatómicas transmiten todavía hoy numerosos y preciados datos científicos: la realidad morfológica no pasa de moda. Las láminas de medicina operatoria, de estética igualmente magnífica, presentan un gran interés para la historia de la medicina y de la cirugía; las de instrumentos quirúrgicos constituyen una documentación notable siempre útil.

Para la presente edición, se ha dado un título en latín a cada una de las láminas. Dichos títulos no existían en la edición original, redactada íntegramente en francés.

No se ha conservado ni reproducido ningún texto original en el caso de las descripciones de las láminas y los pies de las figuras. Dichos textos satisfacen las exigencias actuales del idioma y del vocabulario científico y médico. En particular, para todas las estructuras anatómicas, era necesario utilizar la versión francesa de la nomenclatura anatómica internacional, inspirada directamente en la latina de la *Nomina anatomica* que se utiliza como referencia en la actualidad. Del mismo modo, para los nombres de las especies zoológicas citadas en la anatomía comparada, se ha utilizado sistemáticamente una nomenclatura francesa actual, fundamentalmente extraída de la validada por la International Commission on Zoological Nomenclature. Por lo que respecta a las láminas de medicina operatoria, la modernización de los pies de las figuras ha sido más complicada, ya que la mayor parte de las intervenciones descritas ya no existen y han caído en el olvido; incluso sus denominaciones han dejado de figurar en los diccionarios actuales. Es en esta nomenclatura francesa actual en la que se ha basado la traducción de la edición en español, en la que, evidentemente, se ha utilizado la correspondiente terminología en español.

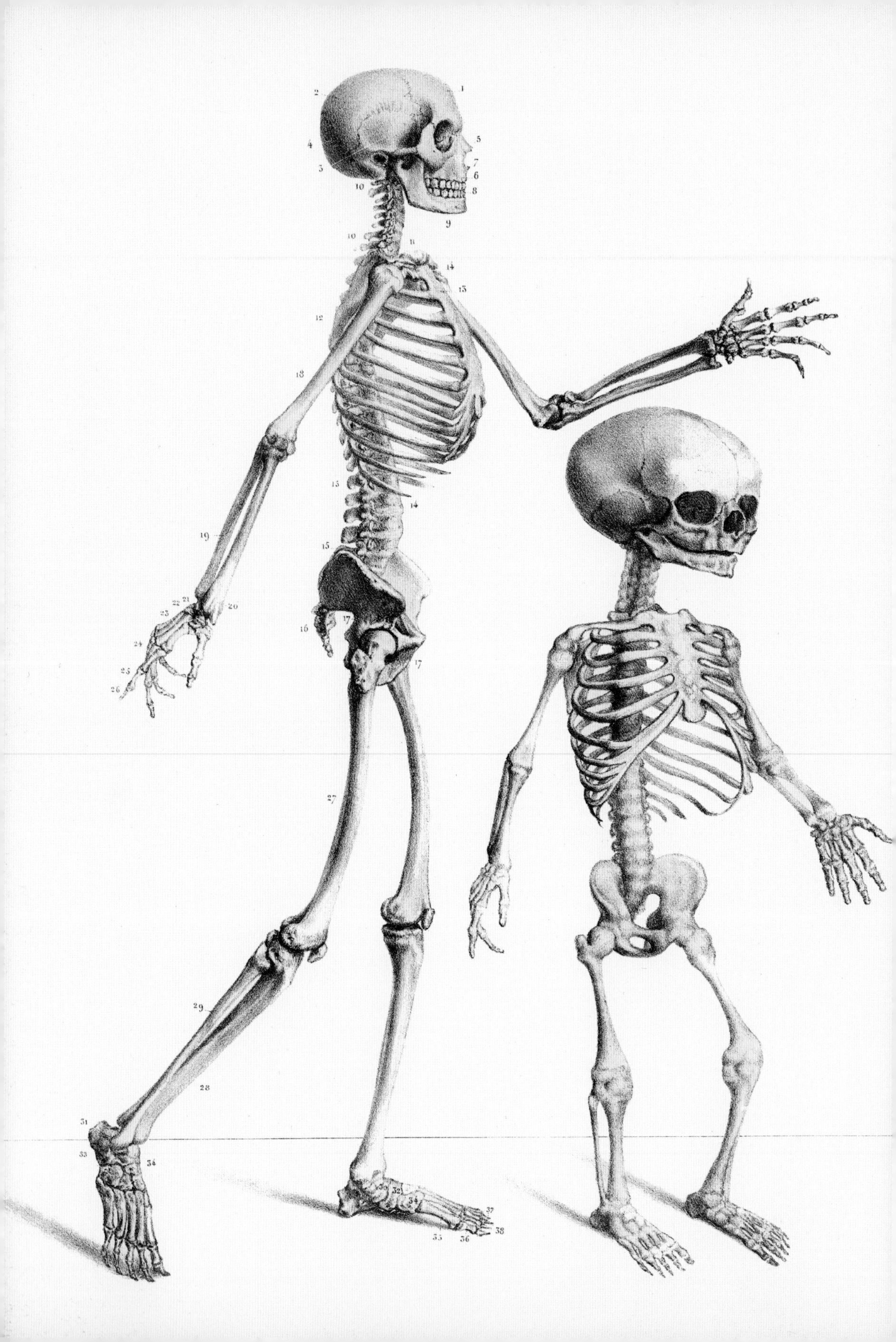
2
1
4
5
3
7
6
10
8
9
10
11
14
13
12
18
15
14
19
15
22
21
20
23
16
17
24
17
25
26
27
29
28
31
33
34
30
32
37
35
36
38

VOL. 1

OSTEOLOGIA ET SYNDESMOLOGIA: OSSA, ARTICULATIONES, ET LIGAMENTA

OSTEOLOGY AND SYNDESMOLOGY: BONES, JOINTS, AND LIGAMENTS

OSTÉOLOGIE ET SYNDESMOLOGIE : OS, ARTICULATIONS ET LIGAMENTS

OSTEOLOGÍA Y SINDESMOLOGÍA: HUESOS, ARTICULACIONES Y LIGAMENTOS

Left page / Ci-contre / Página contigua:
Skeleton / Squelette / Esqueleto

CONFIGURATIO ET PROPORTIONES PARTIUM CORPORIS HUMANIS

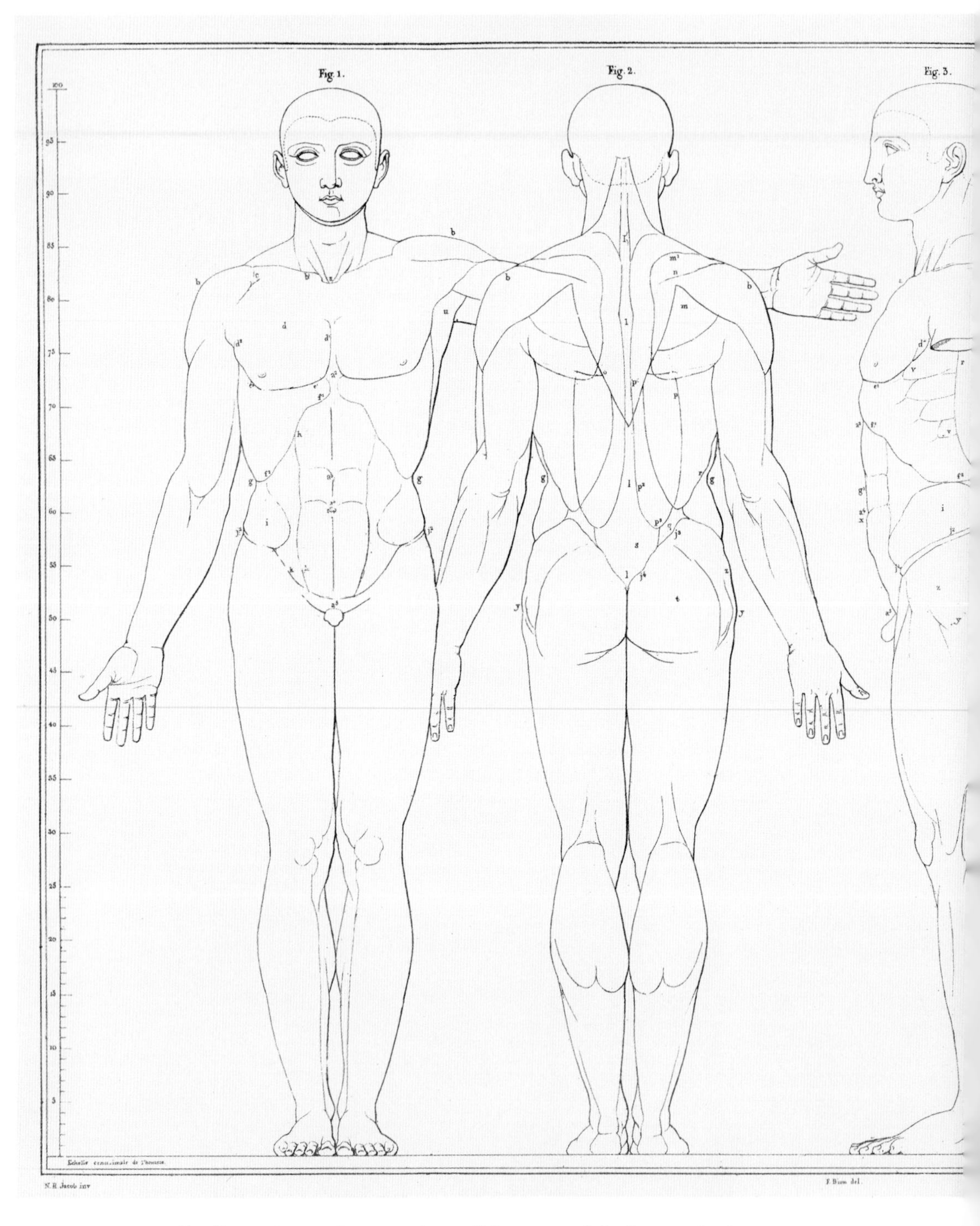

Configuration and proportions of the parts of the human body
Configuration et proportions des parties du corps humain
Configuración y proporciones de las regiones del cuerpo humano

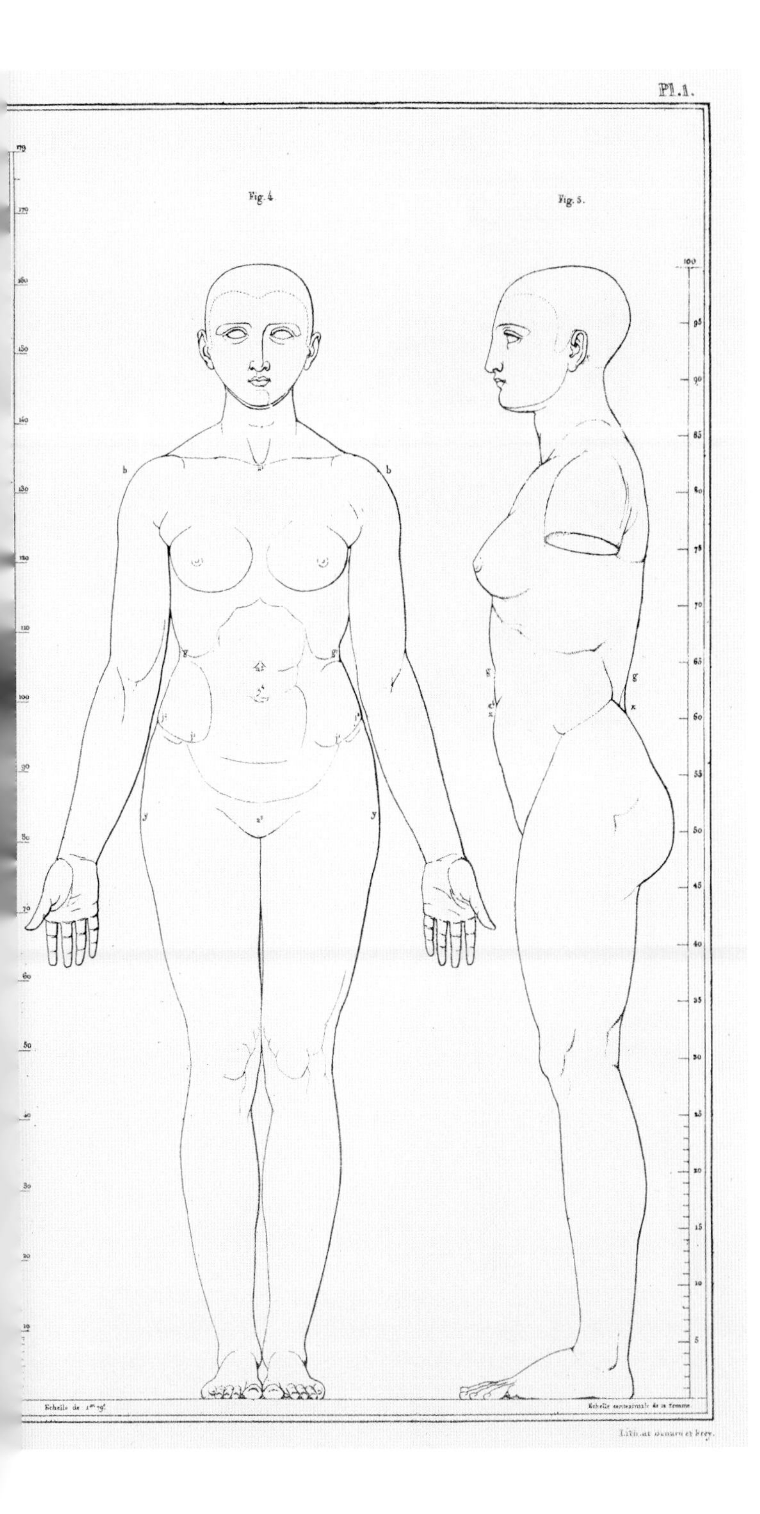
Pl. 1.
Fig. 4.
Fig. 5.
Echelle de 1m 79c
Echelle centésimale de la femme

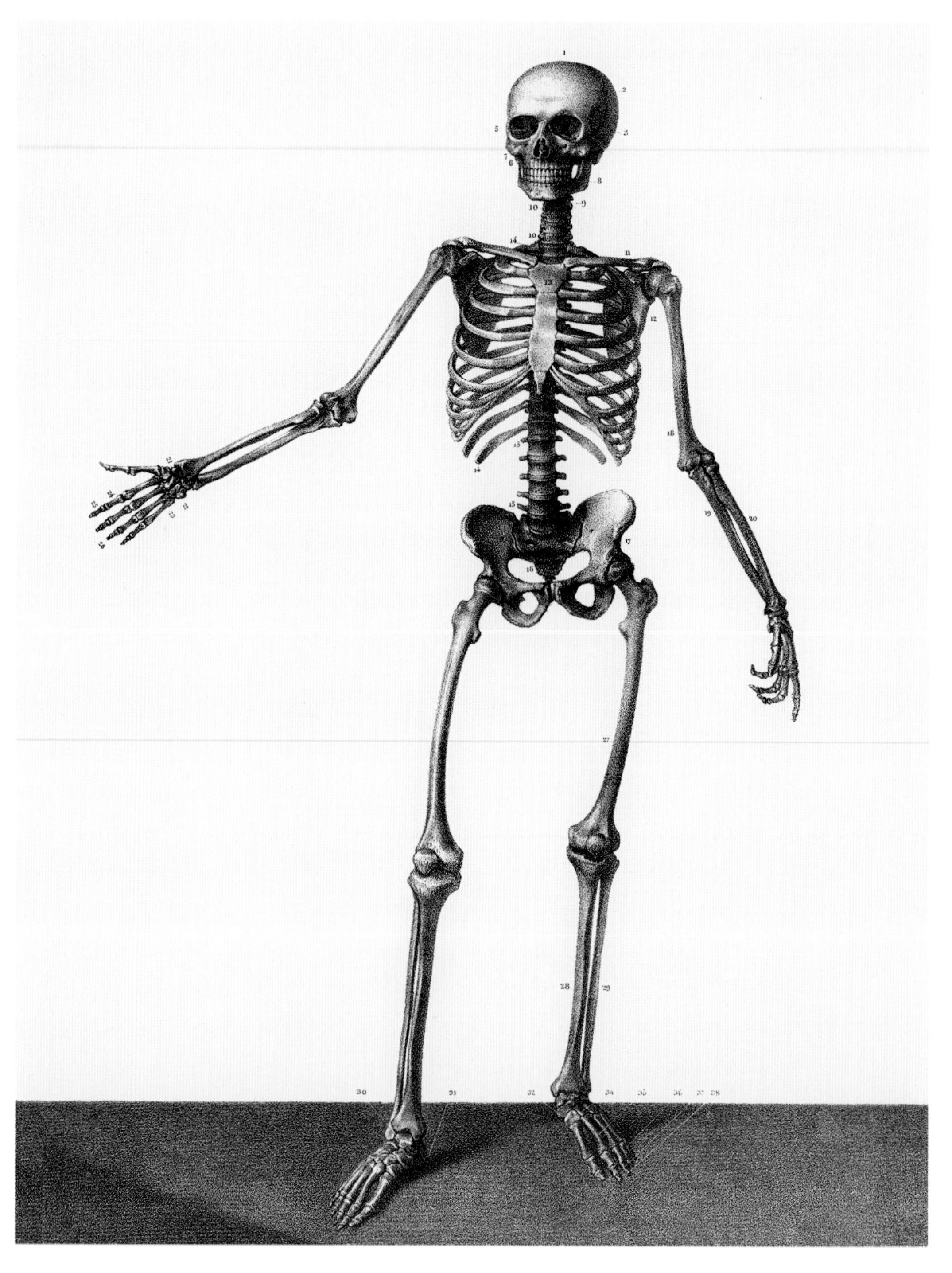

Skeleton / Squelette / Esqueleto

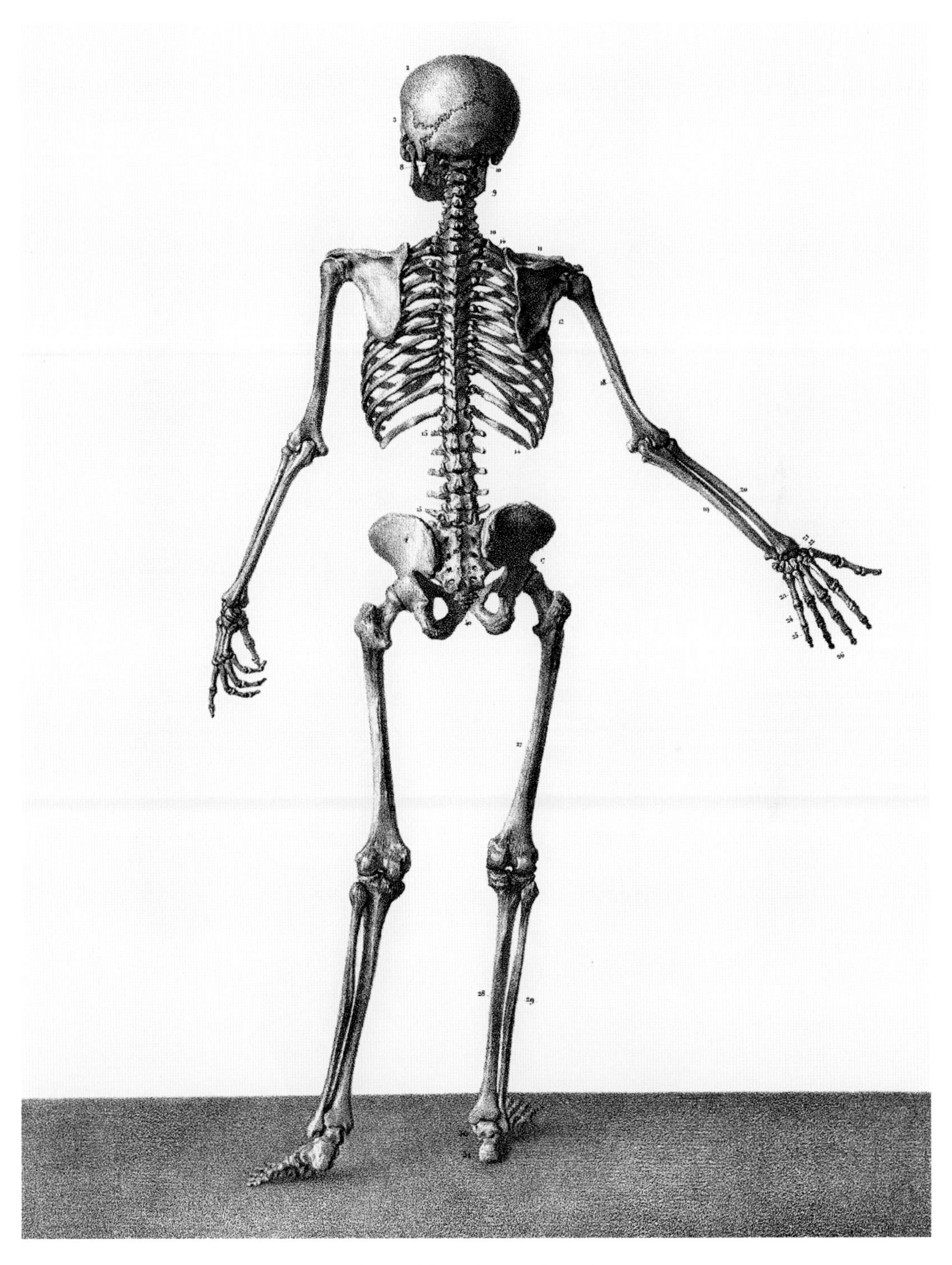

Skeleton / Squelette / Esqueleto

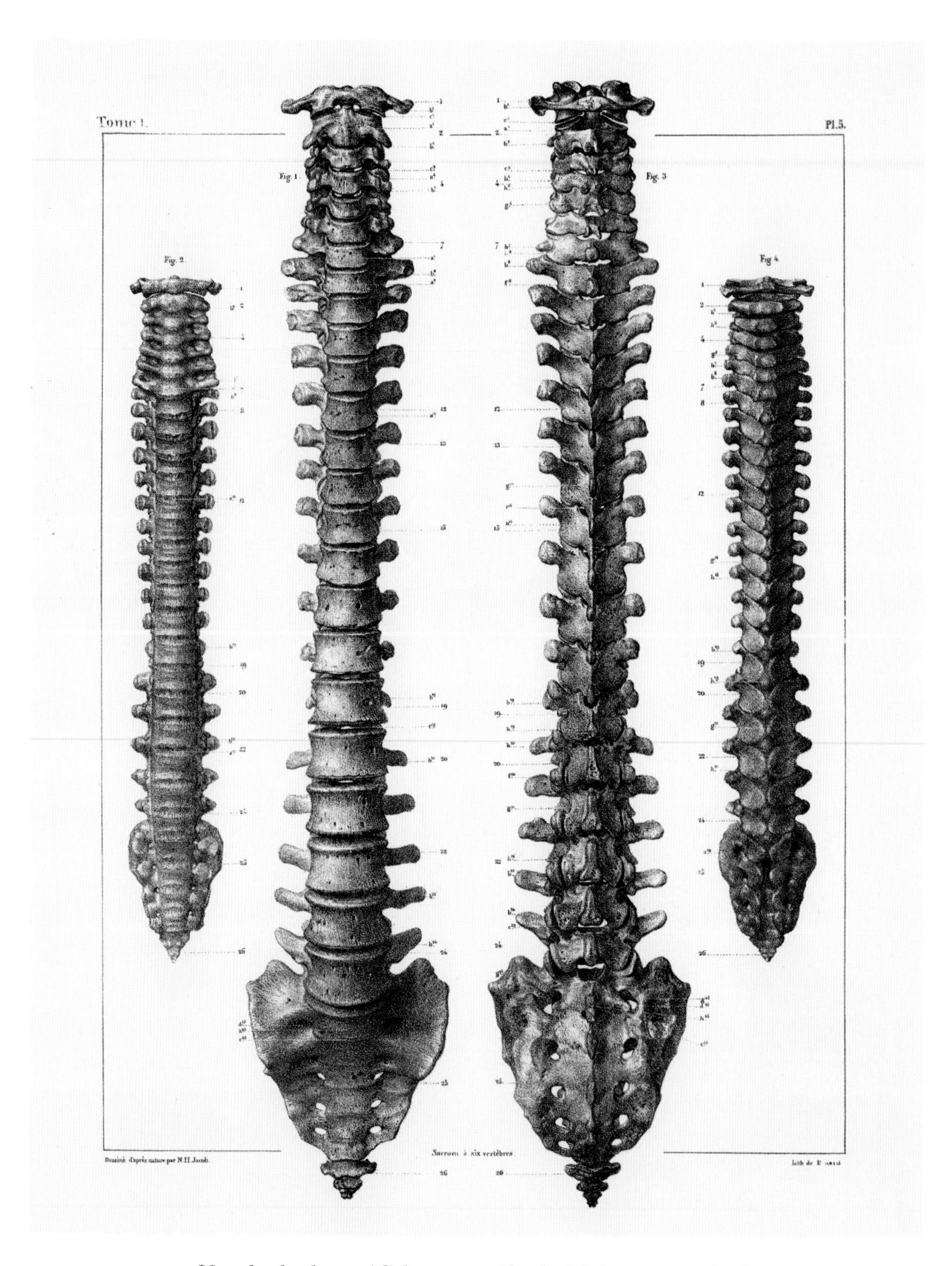

Vertebral column / Colonne vertébrale / Columna vertebral

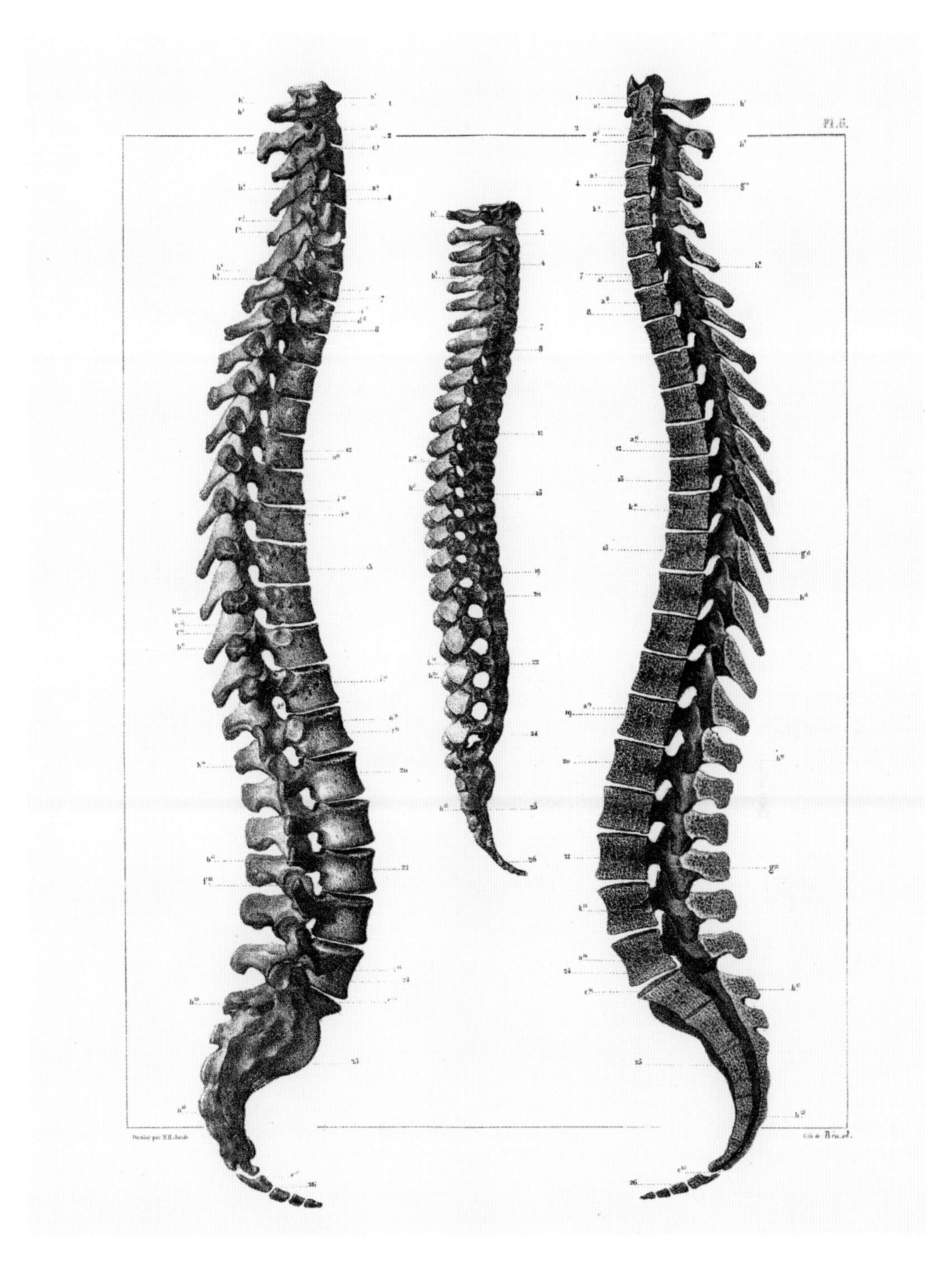

Vertebral column / Colonne vertébrale / Columna vertebral

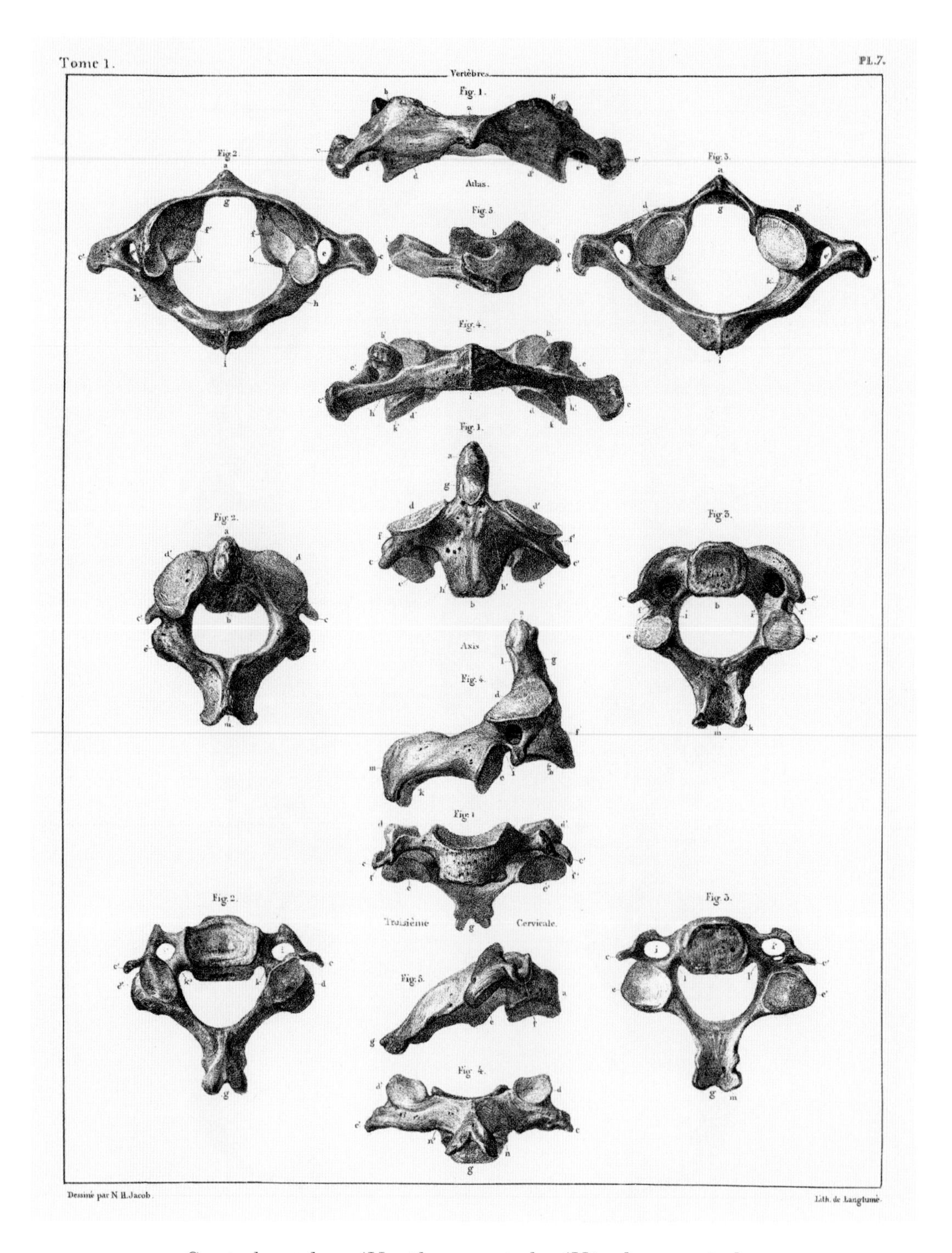

Cervical vertebrae / Vertèbres cervicales / Vértebras cervicales

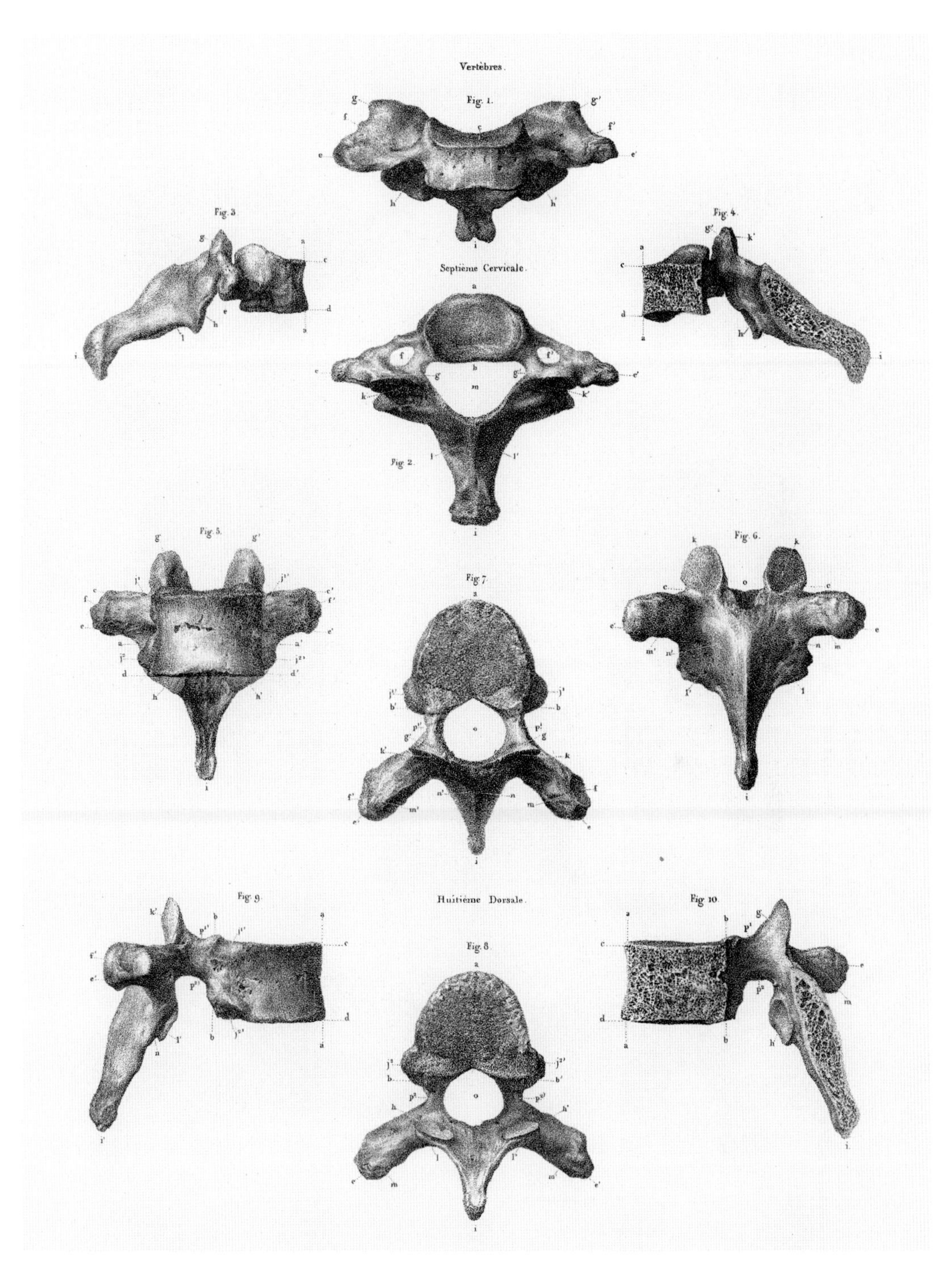

Cervical and thoracic vertebrae / Vertèbres cervicale et thoracique
Vértebras cervicales y torácicas

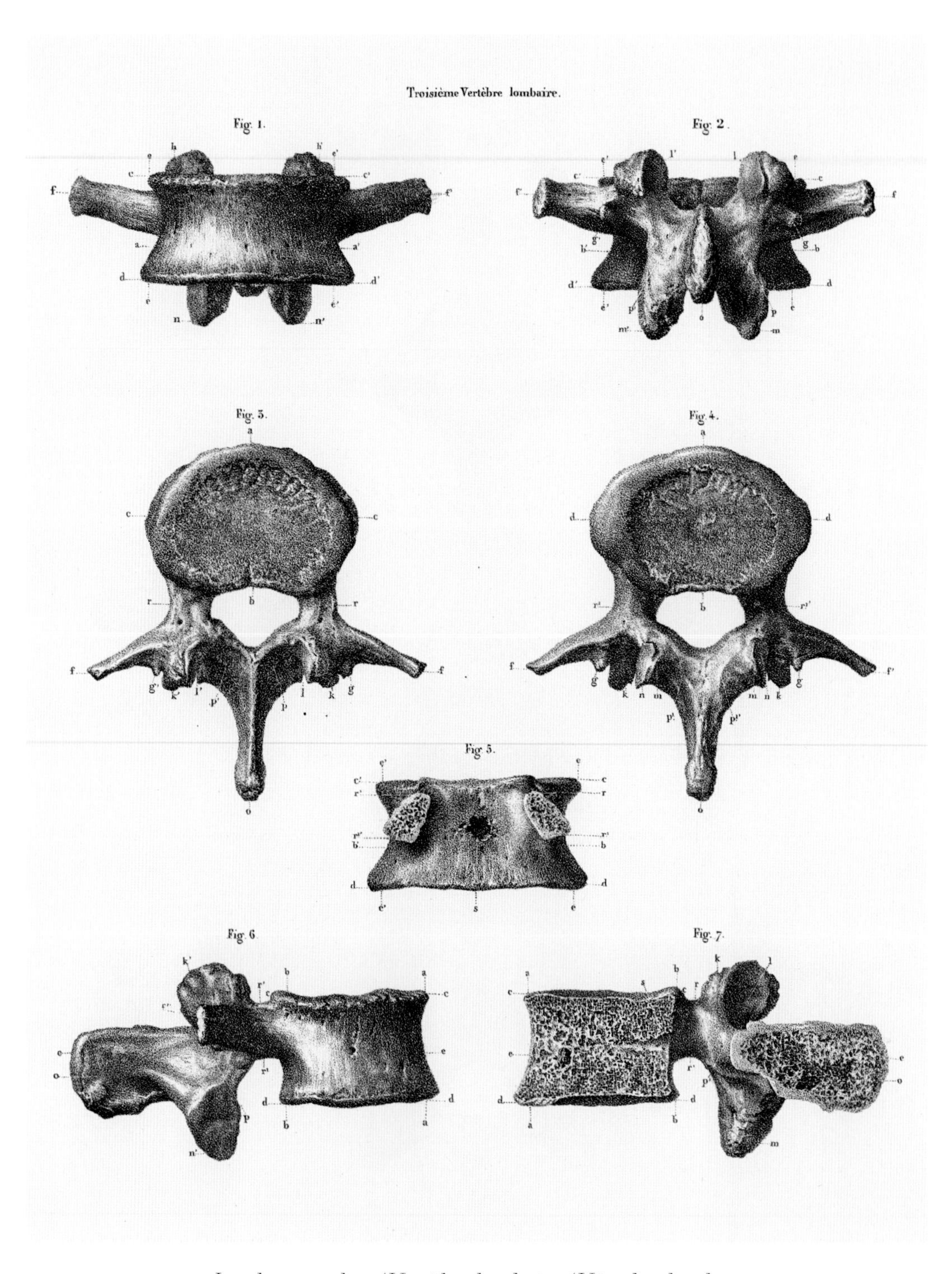

Lumbar vertebra / Vertèbre lombaire / Vértebra lumbar

THORAX - COMPAGES THORACIS.
COSTAE ET STERNUM

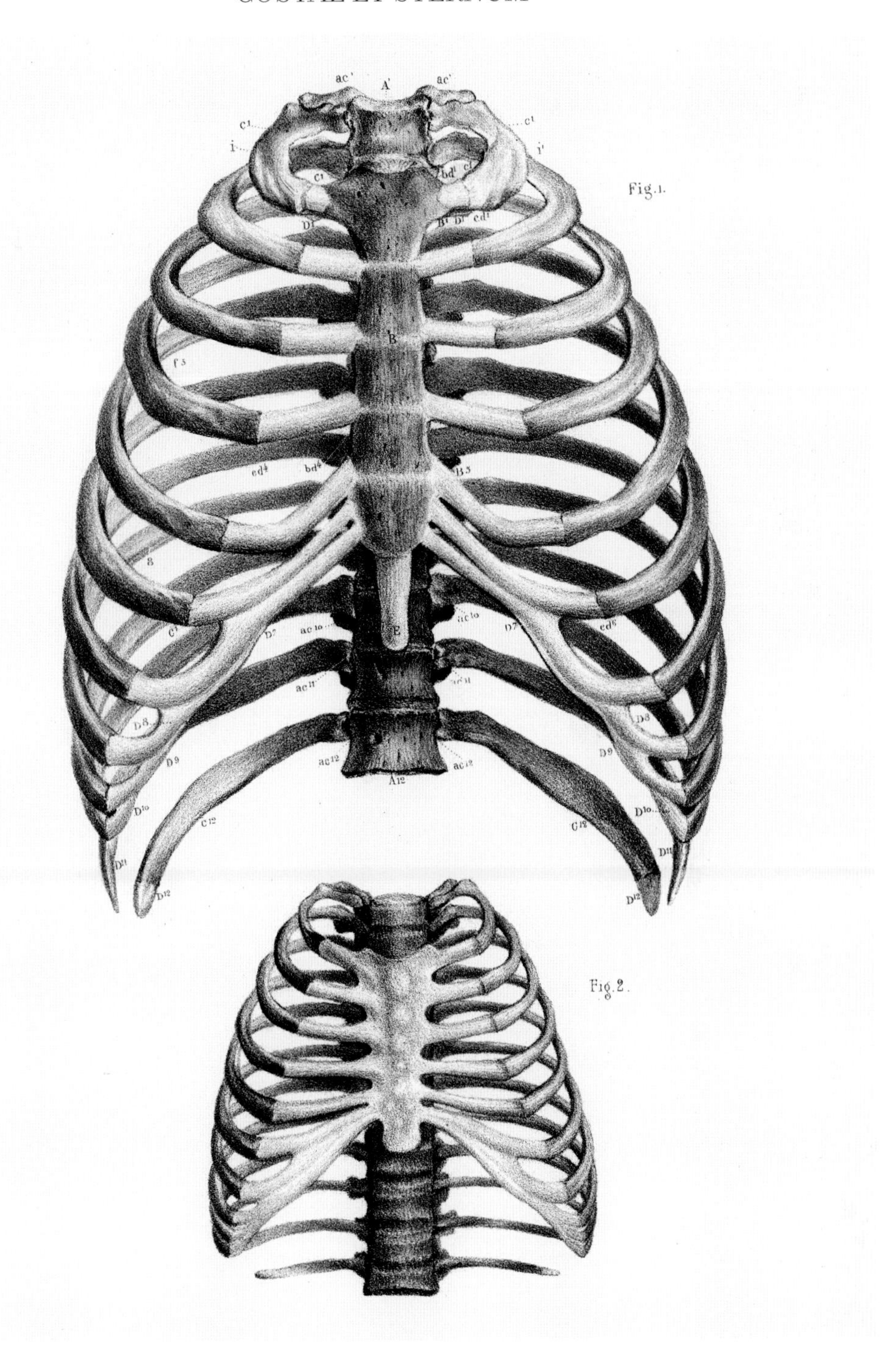

Thorax – thoracic cavity / Thorax – Cage thoracique / Tórax – Caja torácica

THORAX – COMPAGES THORACIS. COSTAE ET STERNUM

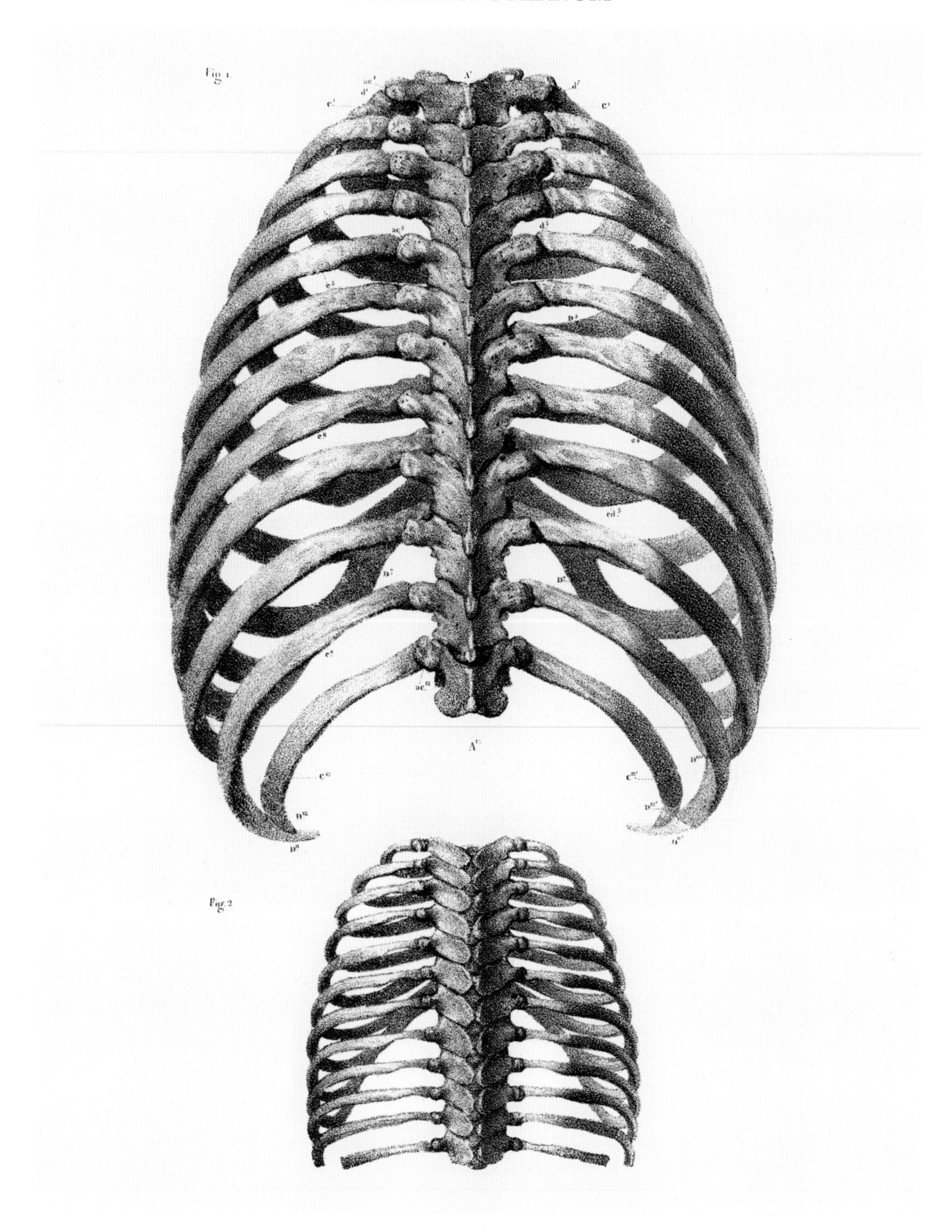

Thorax – thoracic cavity / Thorax – Cage thoracique / Tórax – Caja torácica

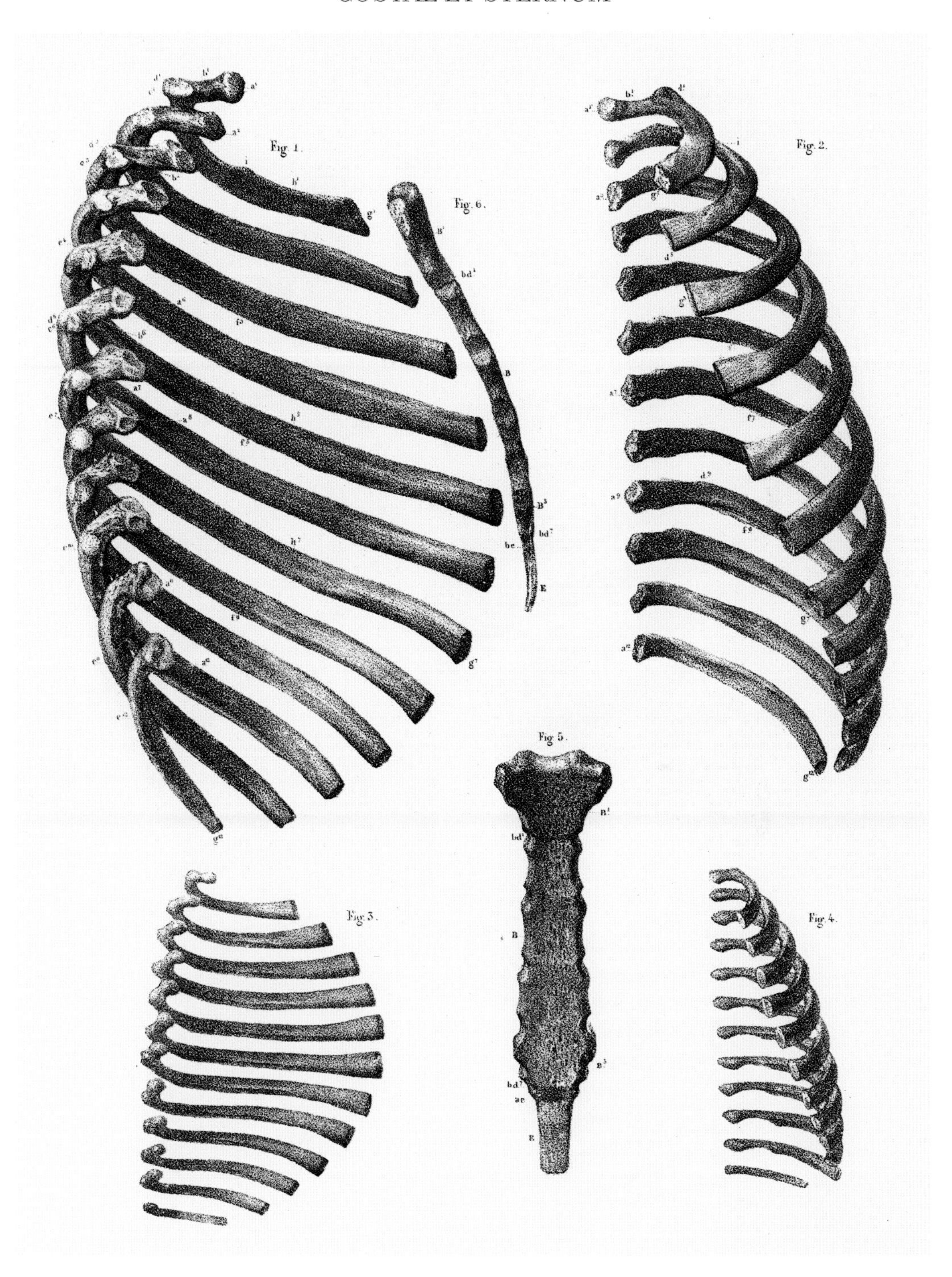

Ribs and sternum / Côtes et sternum / Costillas y esternón

THORAX – COMPAGES THORACIS. COSTAE ET STERNUM

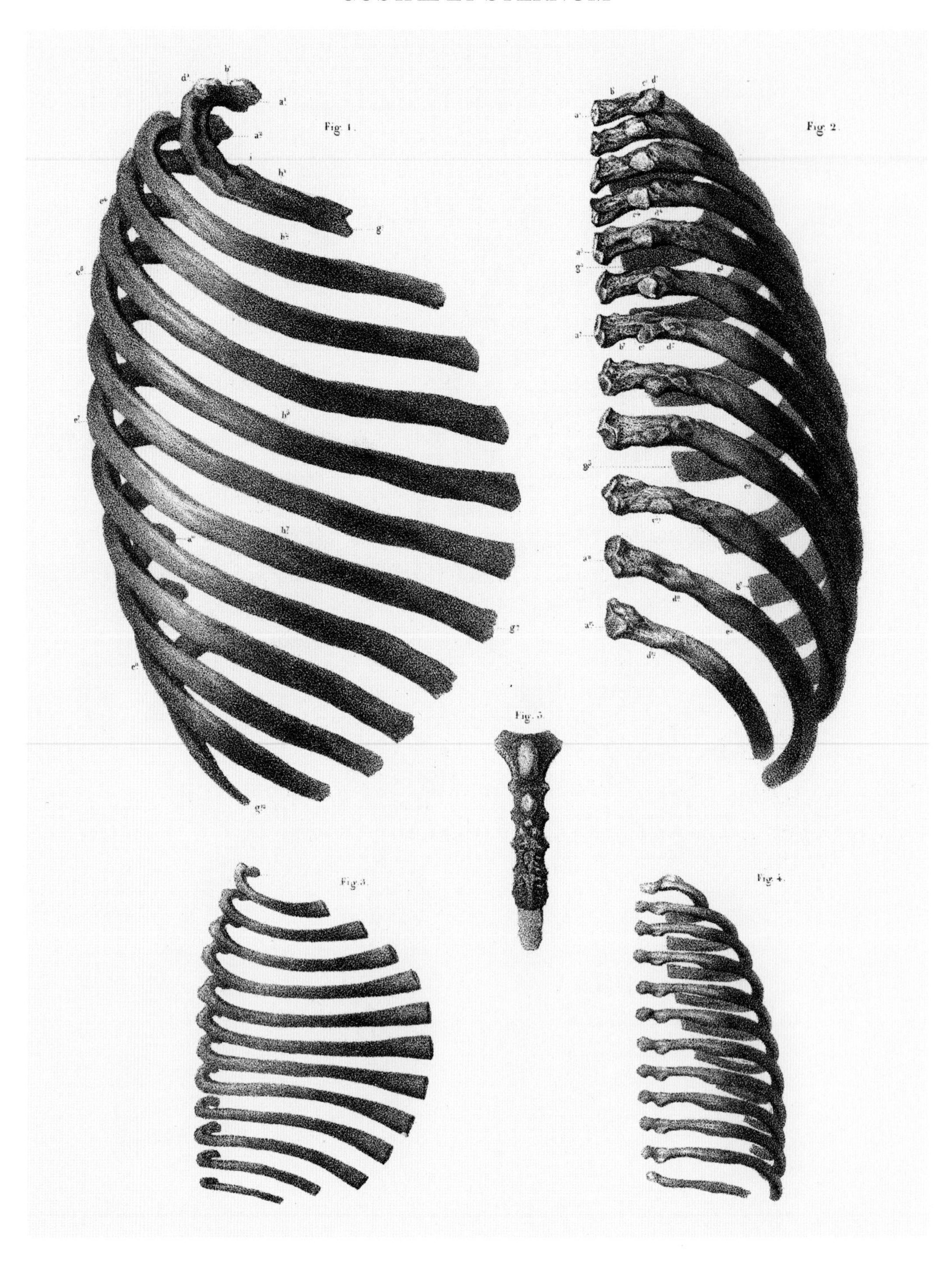

Ribs and sternum / Côtes et sternum / Costillas y esternón

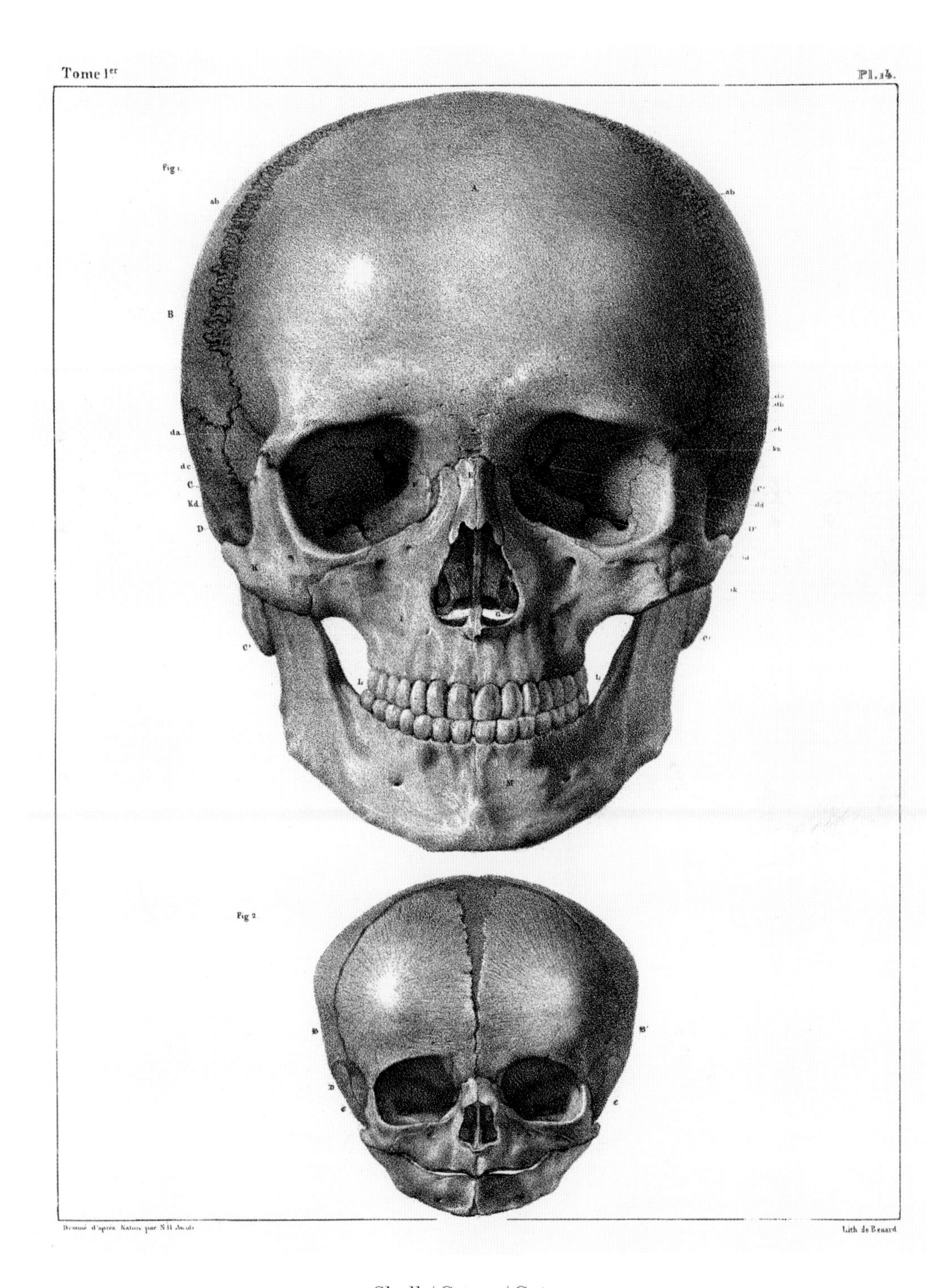

Skull / Crâne / Cráneo

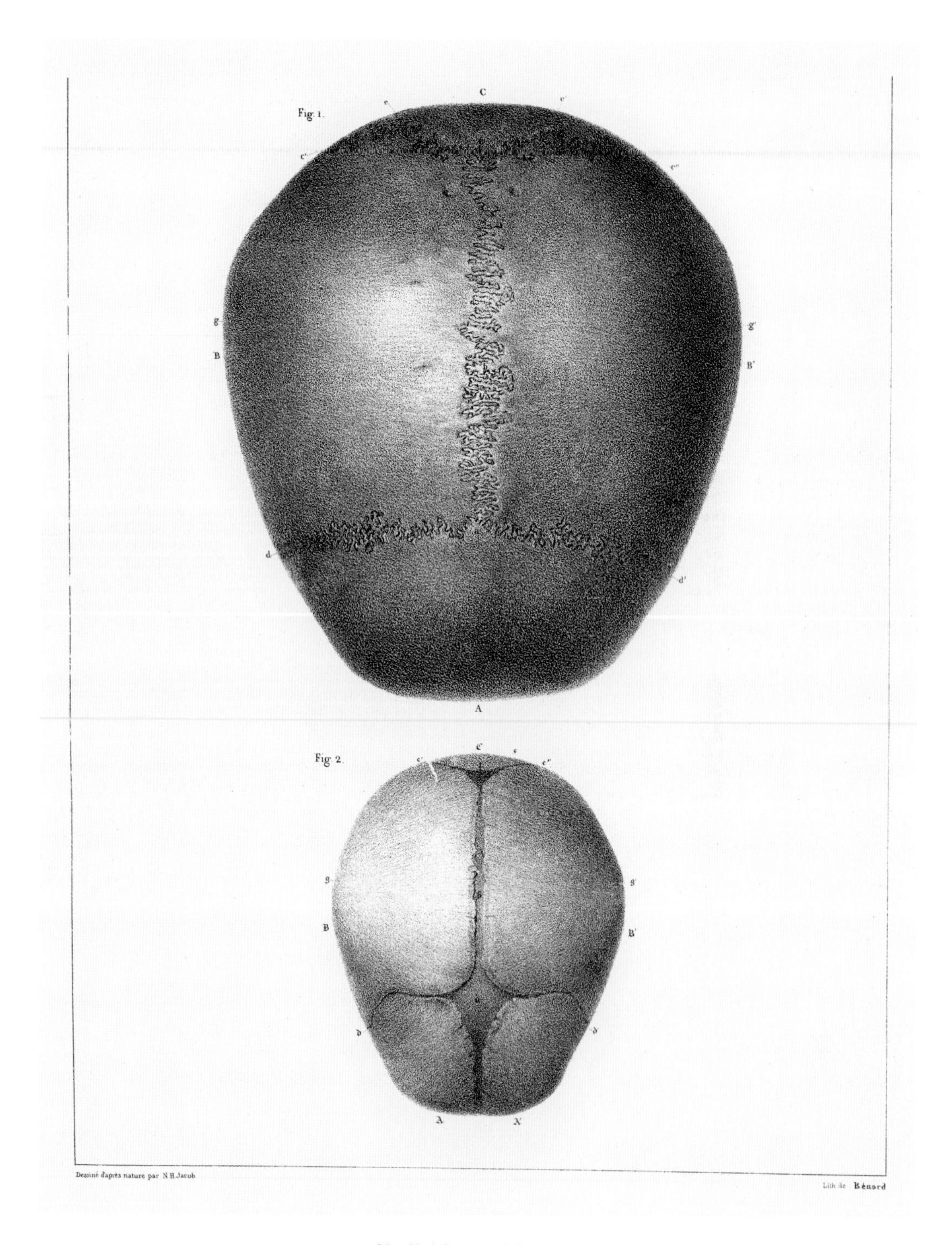

Skull / Crâne / Cráneo

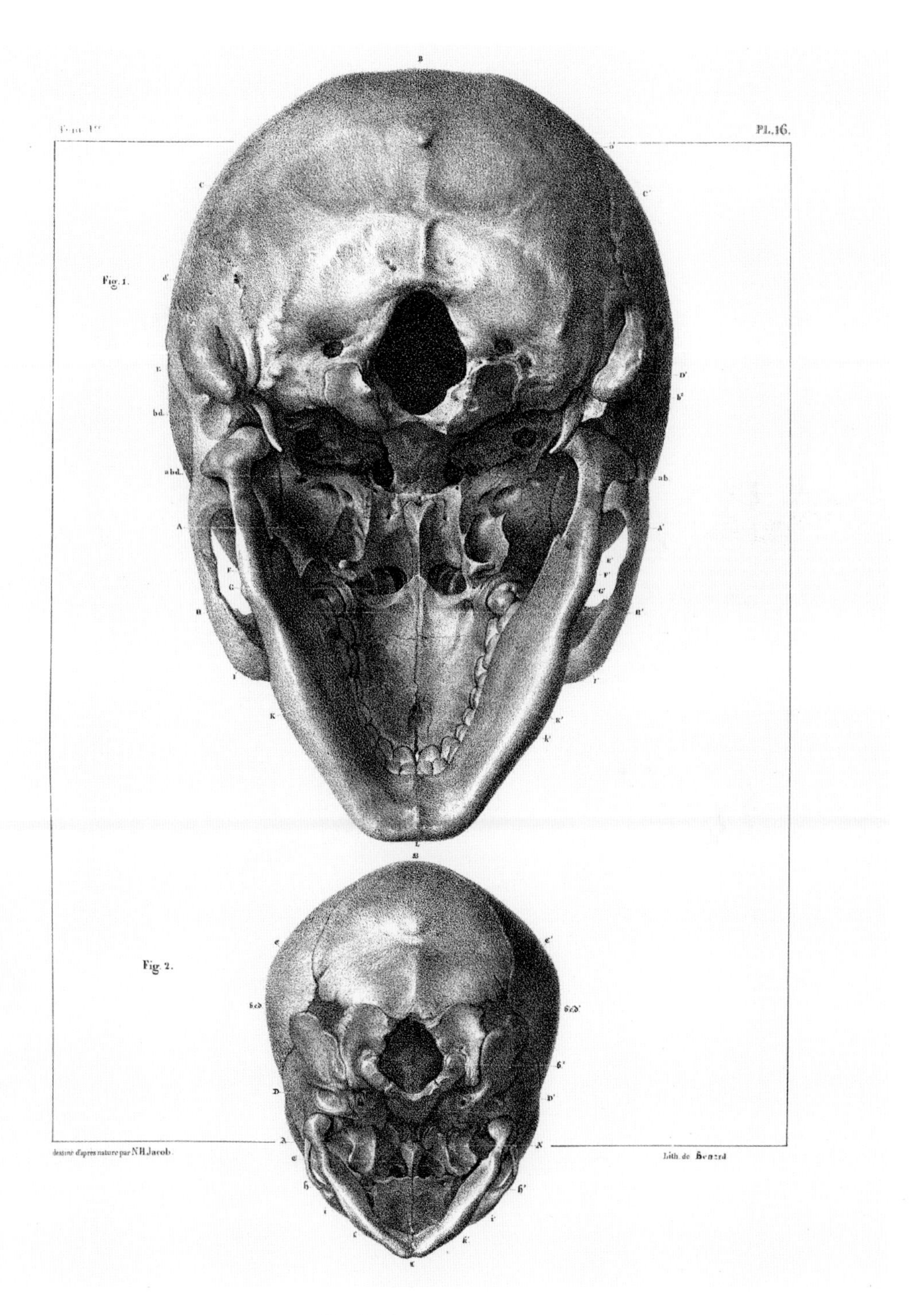

Skull / Crâne / Cráneo

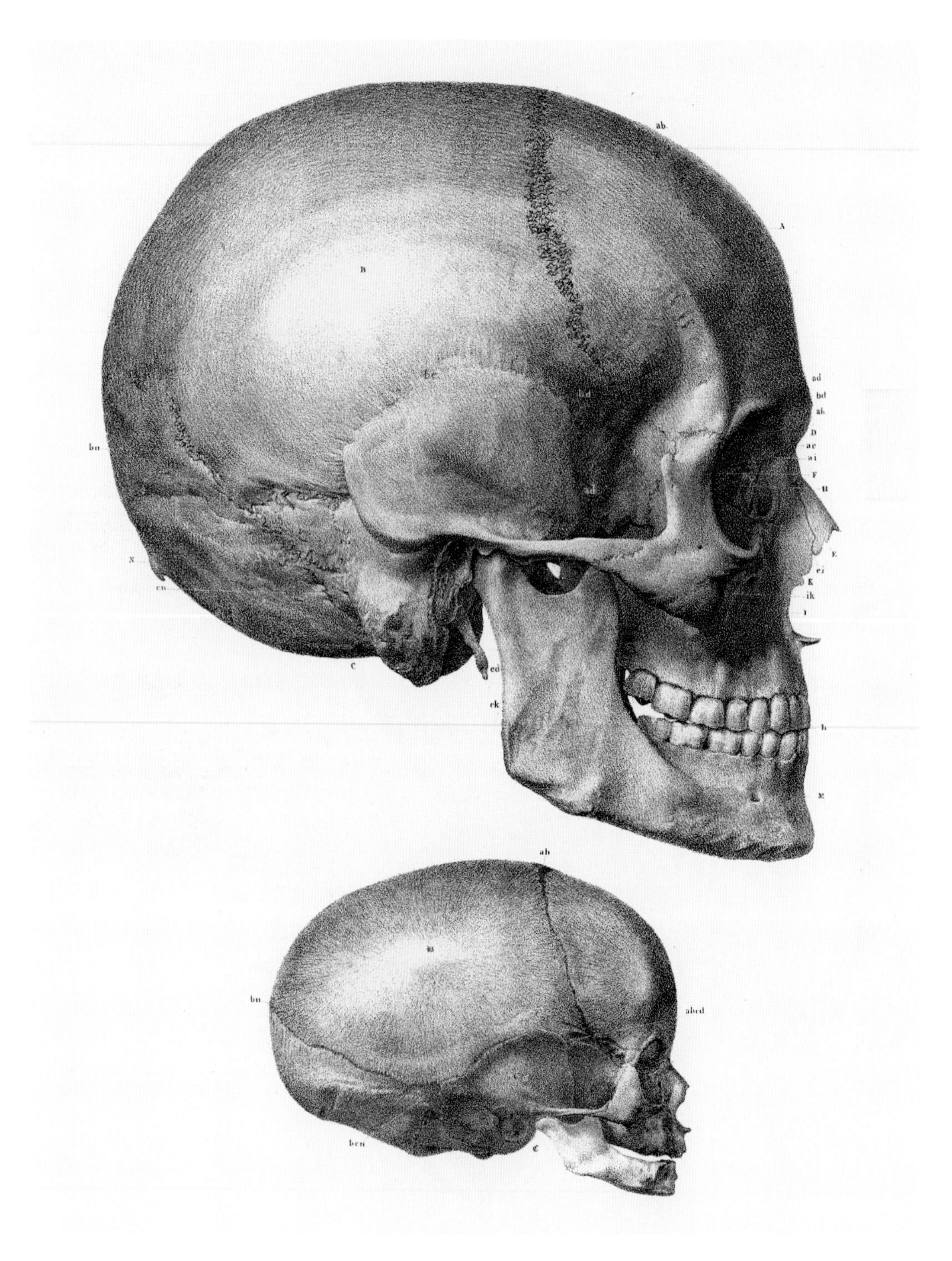

Skull / Crâne / Cráneo

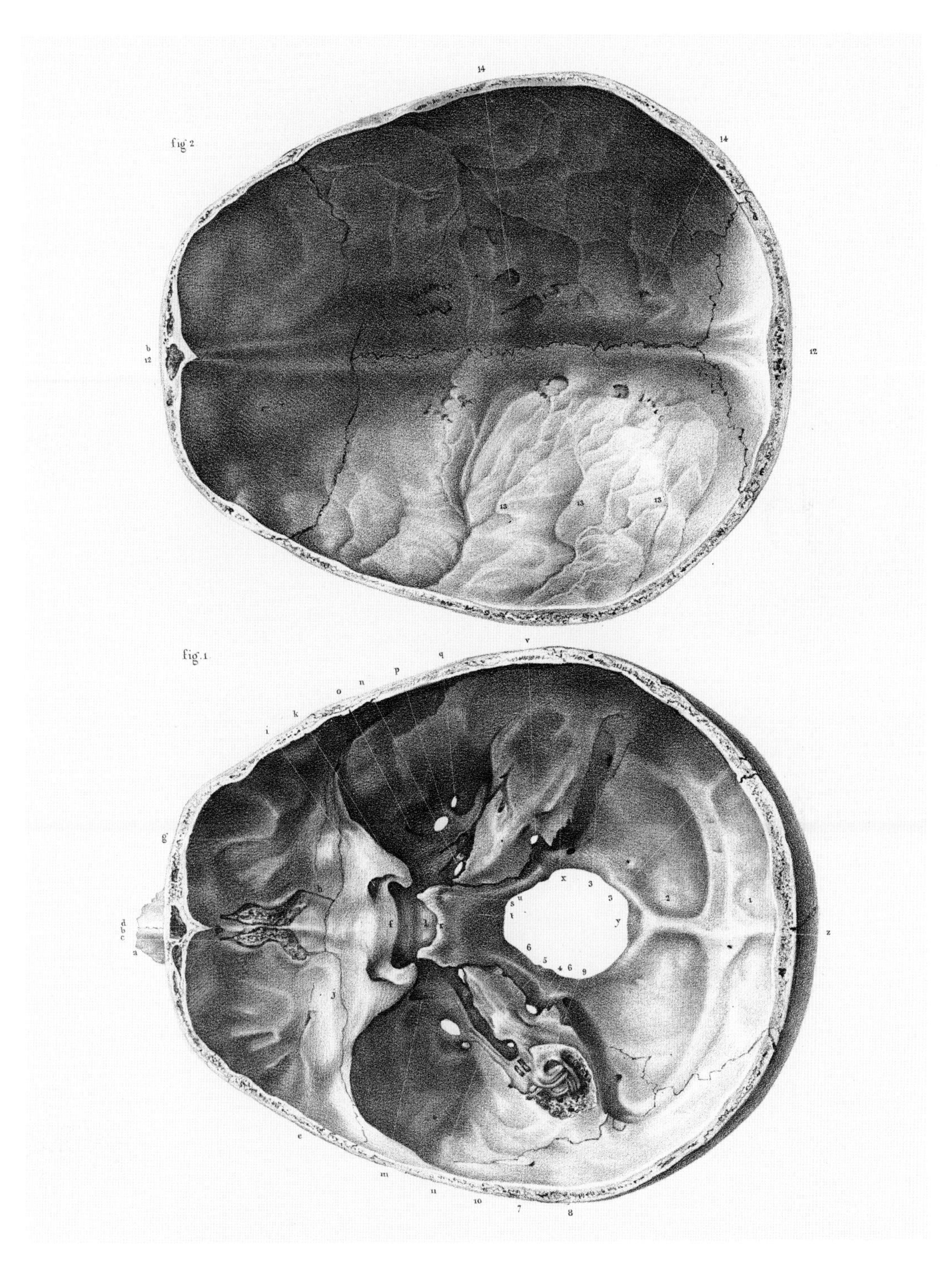

Skull cavity / Cavité crânienne / Cavidad craneal

OSSA CRANII ET FACIEI: OS FRONTALE, OS PARIETALE, ET OS OCCIPITALE

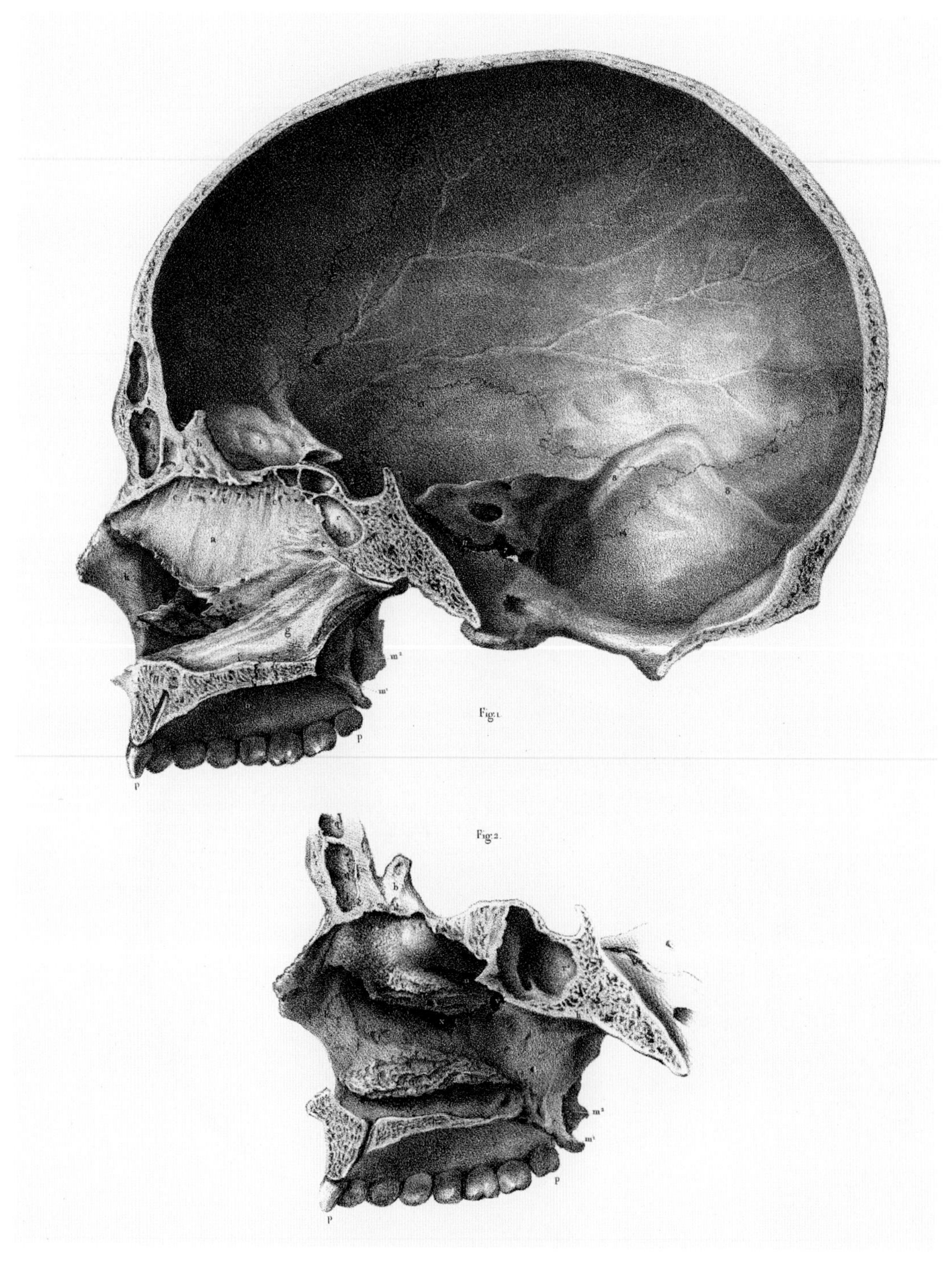

Bones of the skull and of the face / Os du crâne et de la face
Huesos del cráneo y de la cara

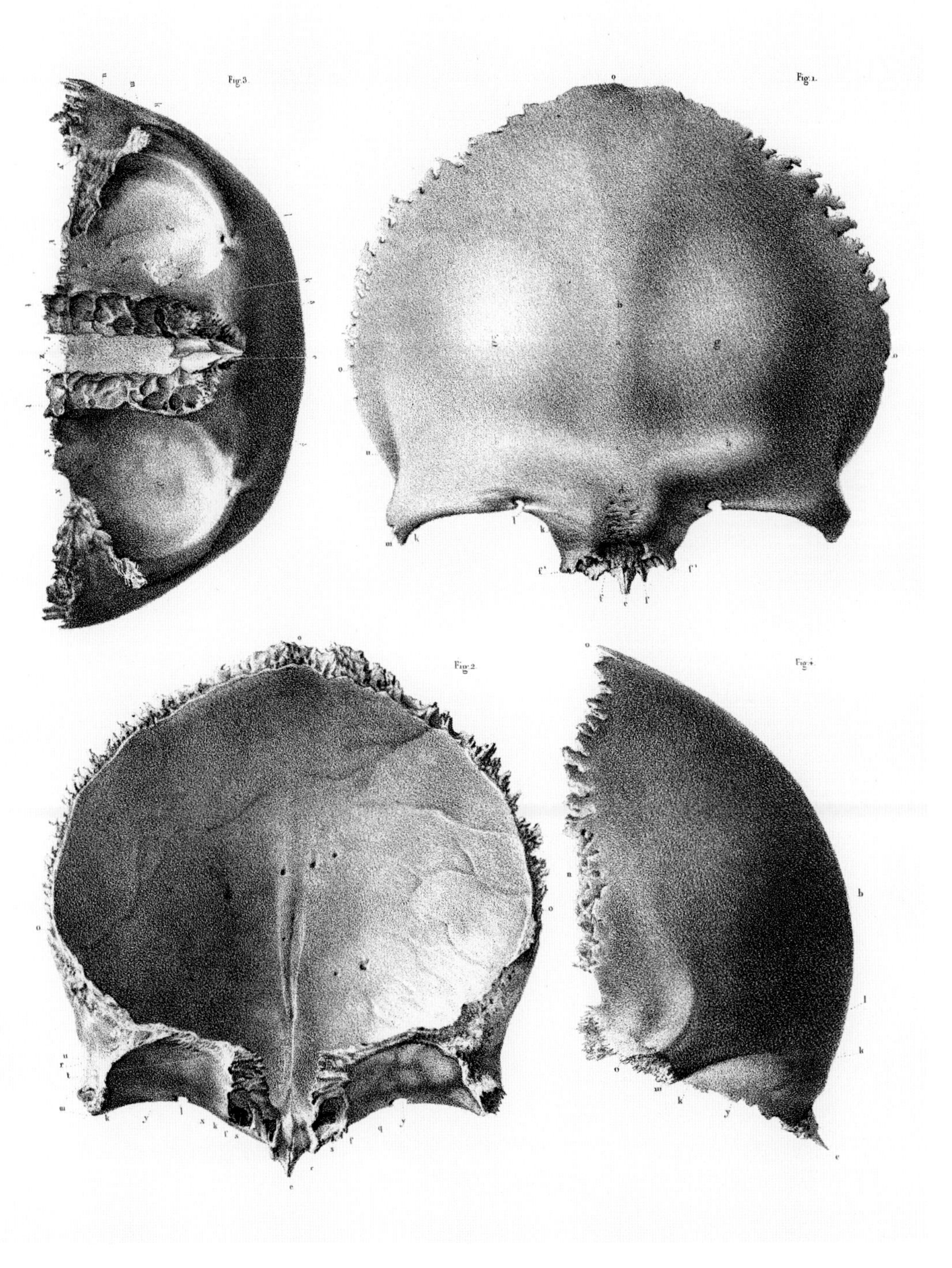

Skull bones: Frontal bone / Os du crâne : Os frontal
Huesos del cráneo: hueso frontal

OSSA CRANII ET FACIEI: OS FRONTALE, OS PARIETALE, ET OS OCCIPITALE

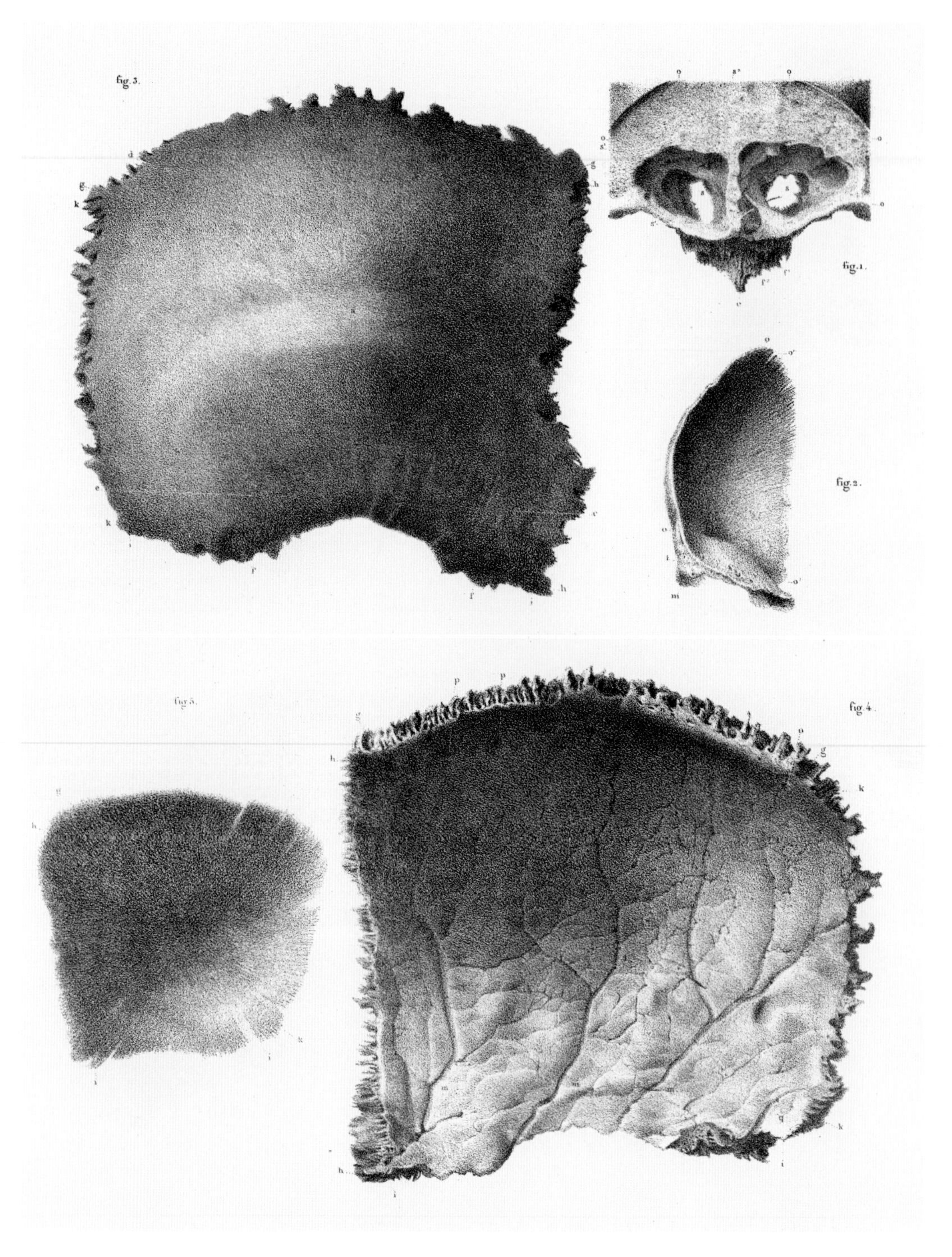

Skull bones: Frontal and parietal bone / Os du crâne : Os frontal et os pariétal
Huesos del cráneo: huesos frontal y parietal

OSSA CRANII ET FACIEI: OS FRONTALE, OS PARIETALE, ET OS OCCIPITALE

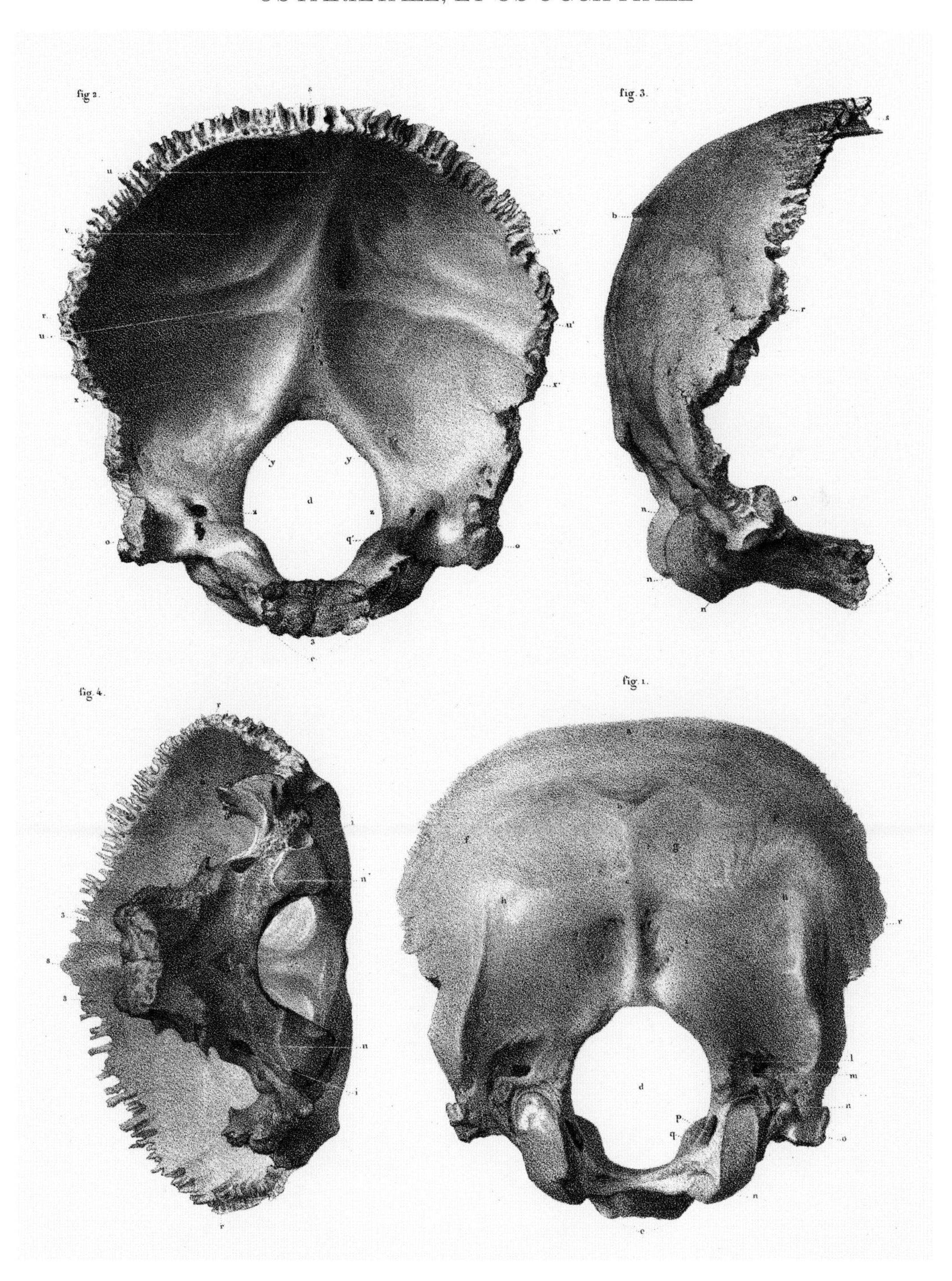

Skull bones: Occipital bone / Os du crâne : Os occipital
Huesos del cráneo: hueso occipital

OSSA CRANII: OS OCCIPITALE, OSSA SUTURALIA, ET OS TEMPORALE

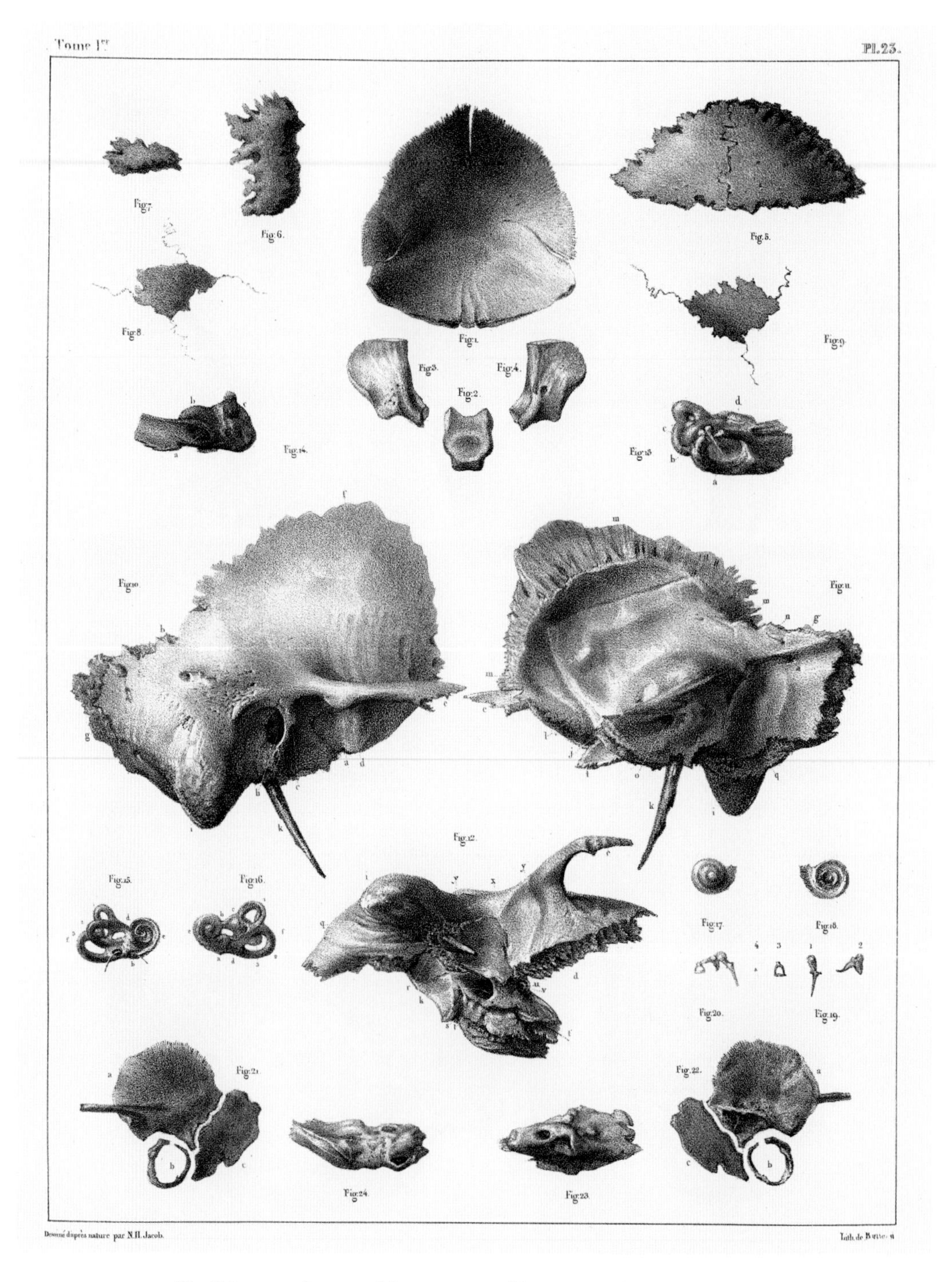

Skull bones: Occipital bone, sutural bones, and temporal bone
Os du crâne : Os occipital, os suturaux et os temporal
Huesos del cráneo: huesos occipital, suturales y temporal

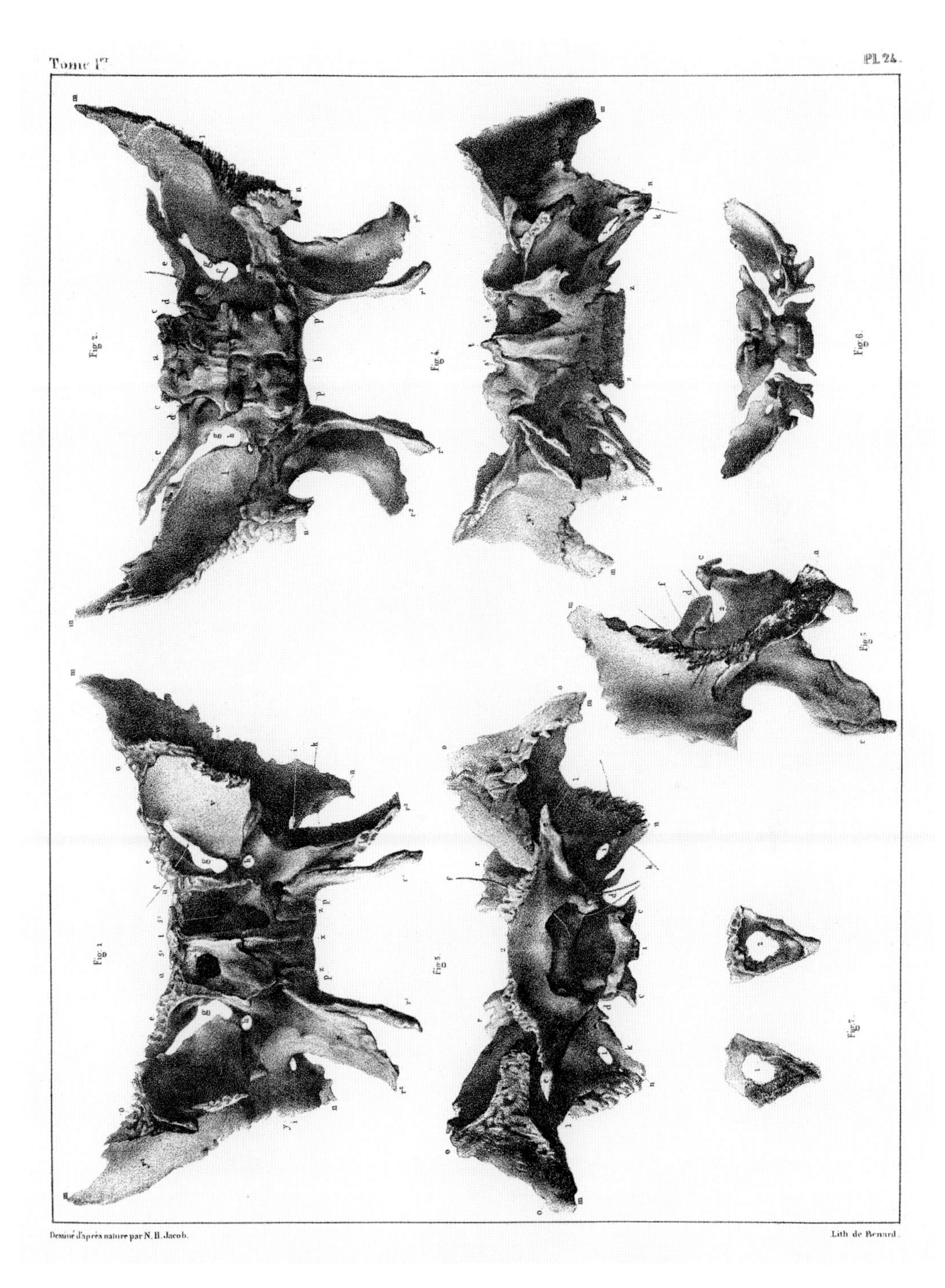

Skull bones: Sphenoid bone / Os du crâne : Os sphénoïde
Huesos del cráneo: hueso esfenoides

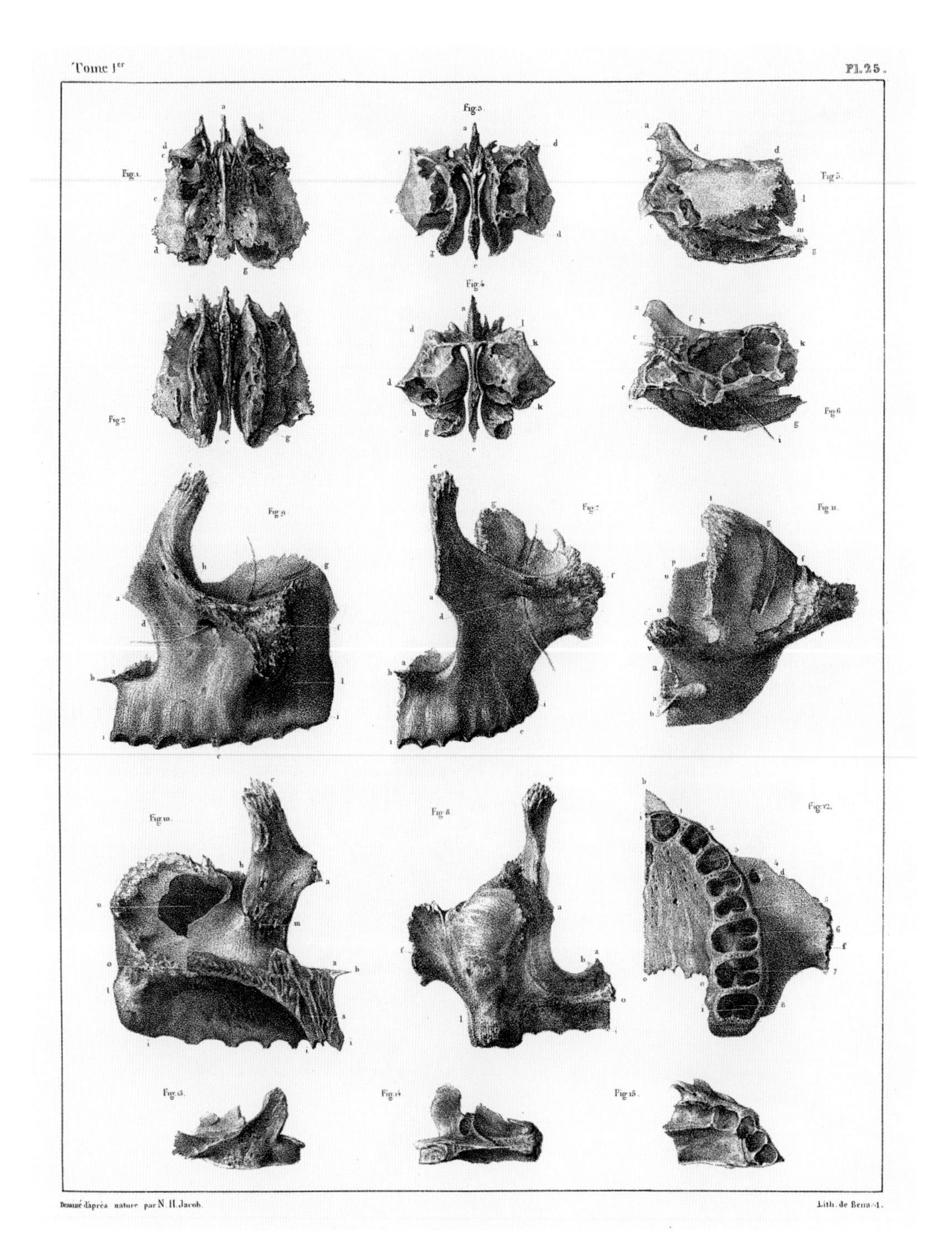

Bones of the skull and of the face: Ethmoid bone and maxillary bone
Os du crâne et de la face : Os ethmoïde et os maxillaire
Huesos del cráneo y de la cara: huesos etmoides y maxilar

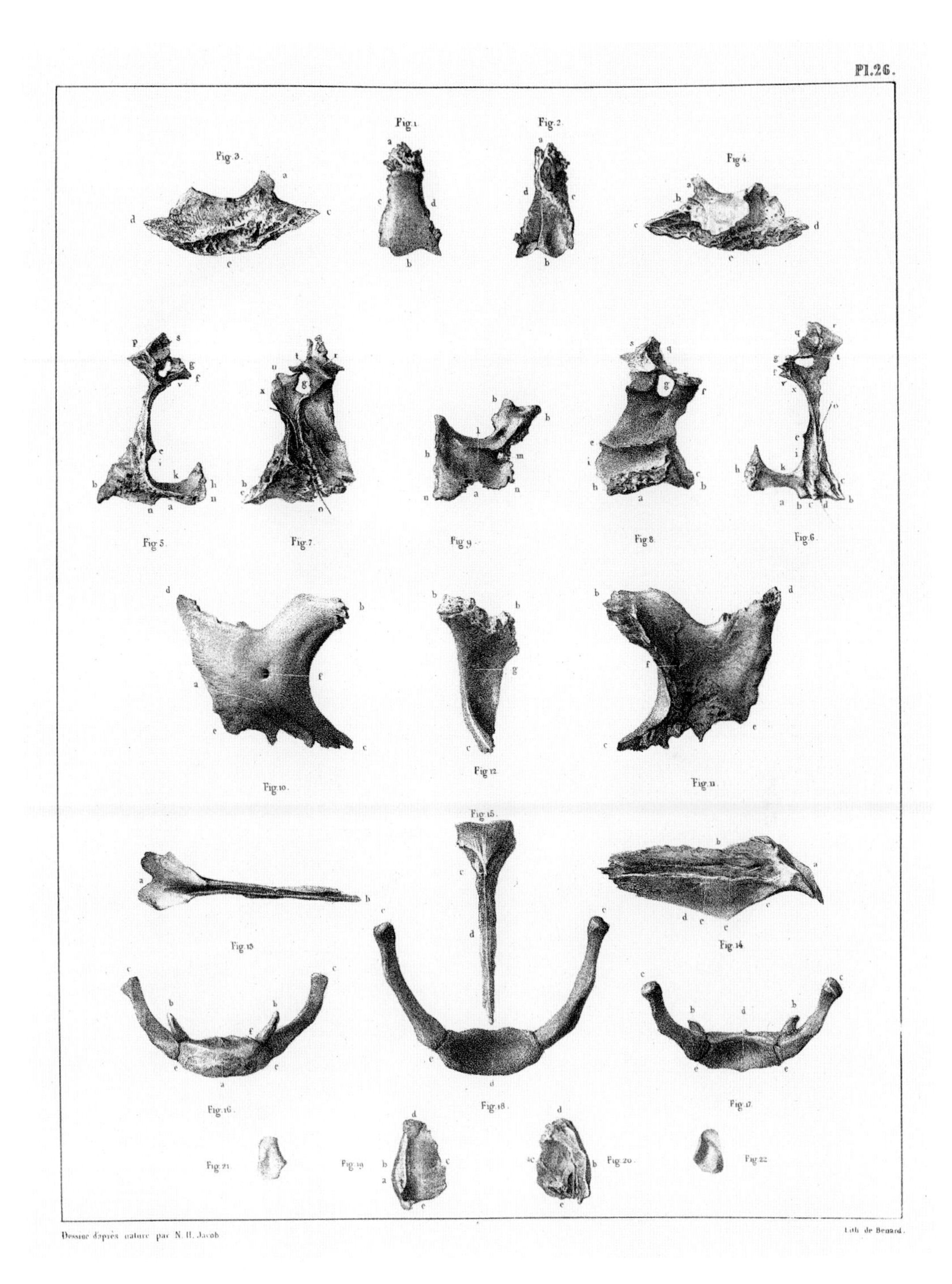

Bones of the face and hyoid bone / Os de la face et os hyoïde
Huesos de la cara y hueso hioides

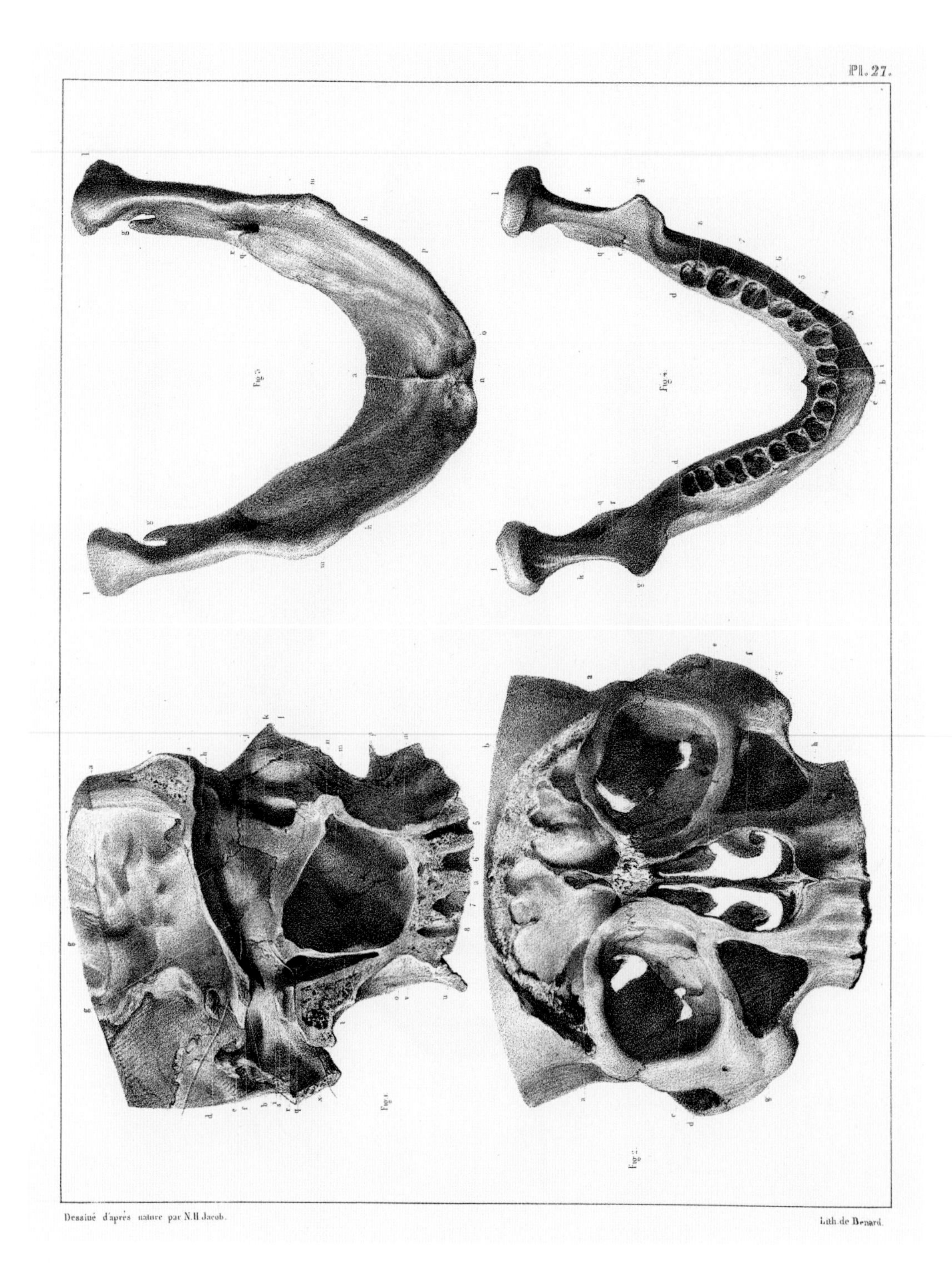

Bones of the face and paranasal sinuses. Mandible
Os de la face et sinus paranasaux. Mandibule
Huesos de la cara y senos paranasales. Mandíbula

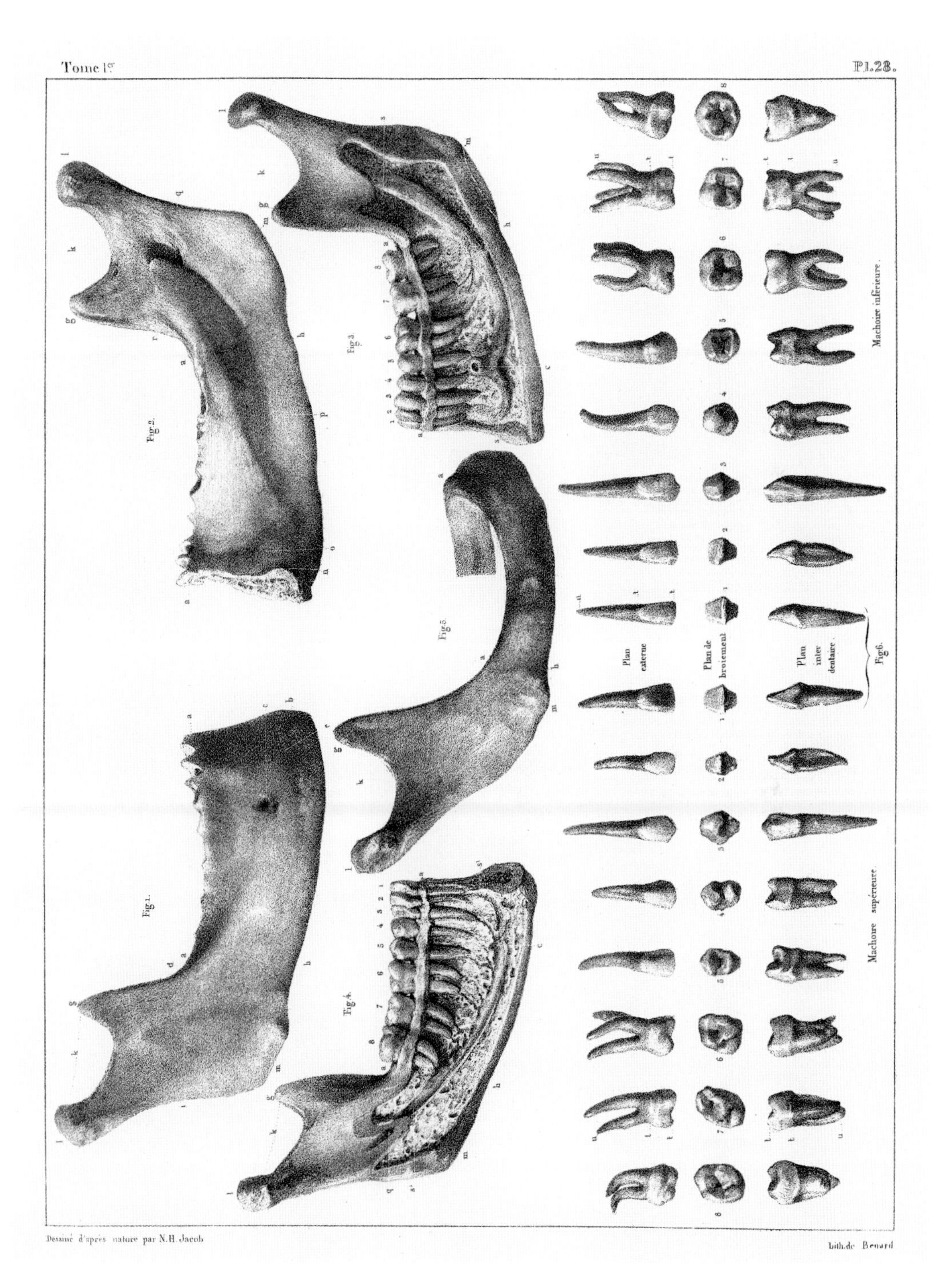

Mandible and teeth / Mandibule et dents / Mandíbula y dientes

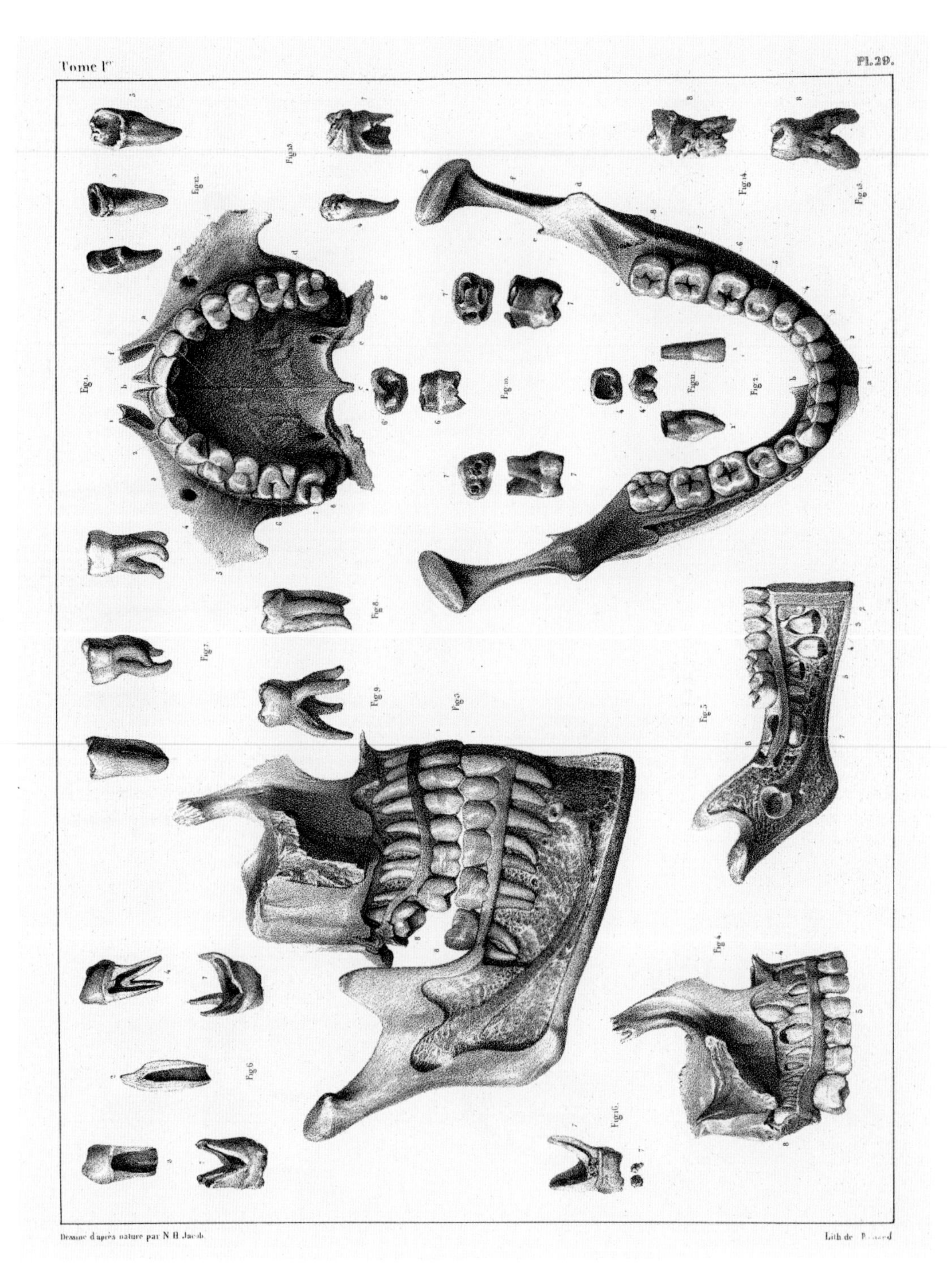

Dental arcades and teeth / Arcades dentaires et dents
Arcadas dentales y dientes

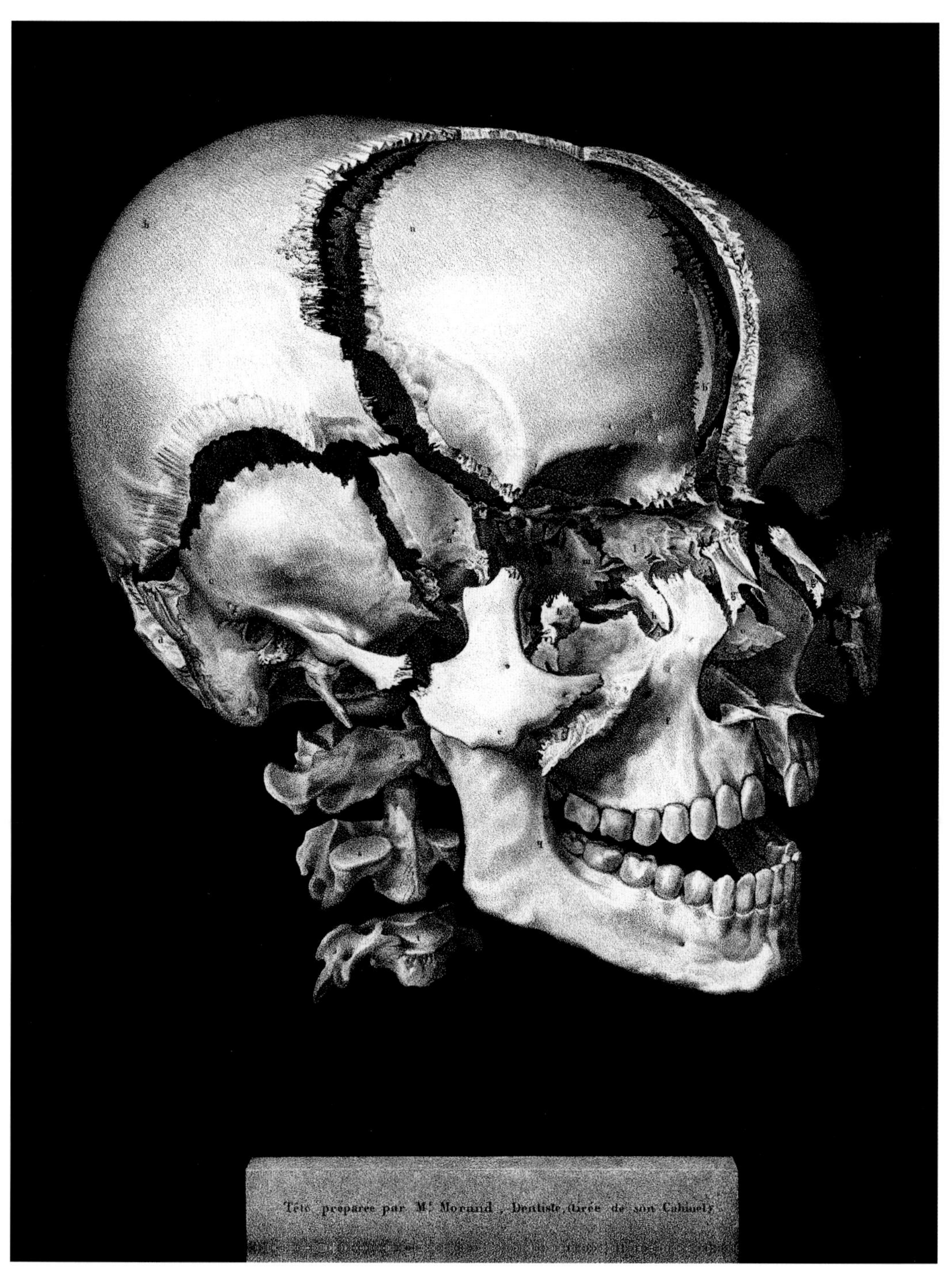

Bones of the skull and of the face, separated / Os du crâne et de la face séparés
Huesos del cráneo y de la cara separados

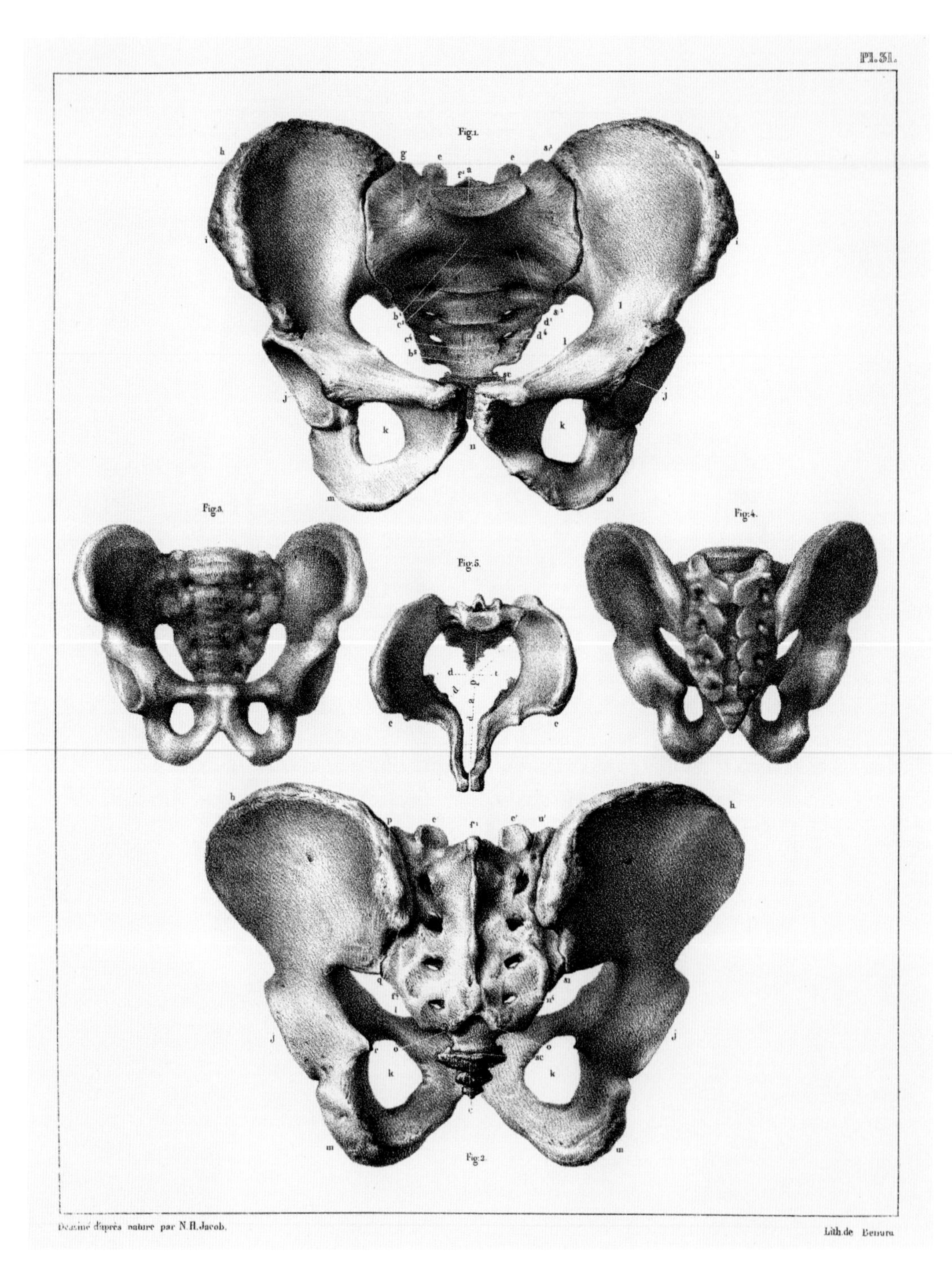

Girdle of the lower limb. Bony pelvis
Ceinture du membre inférieur. Bassin osseux ou pelvis
Cintura pélvica. Pelvis ósea

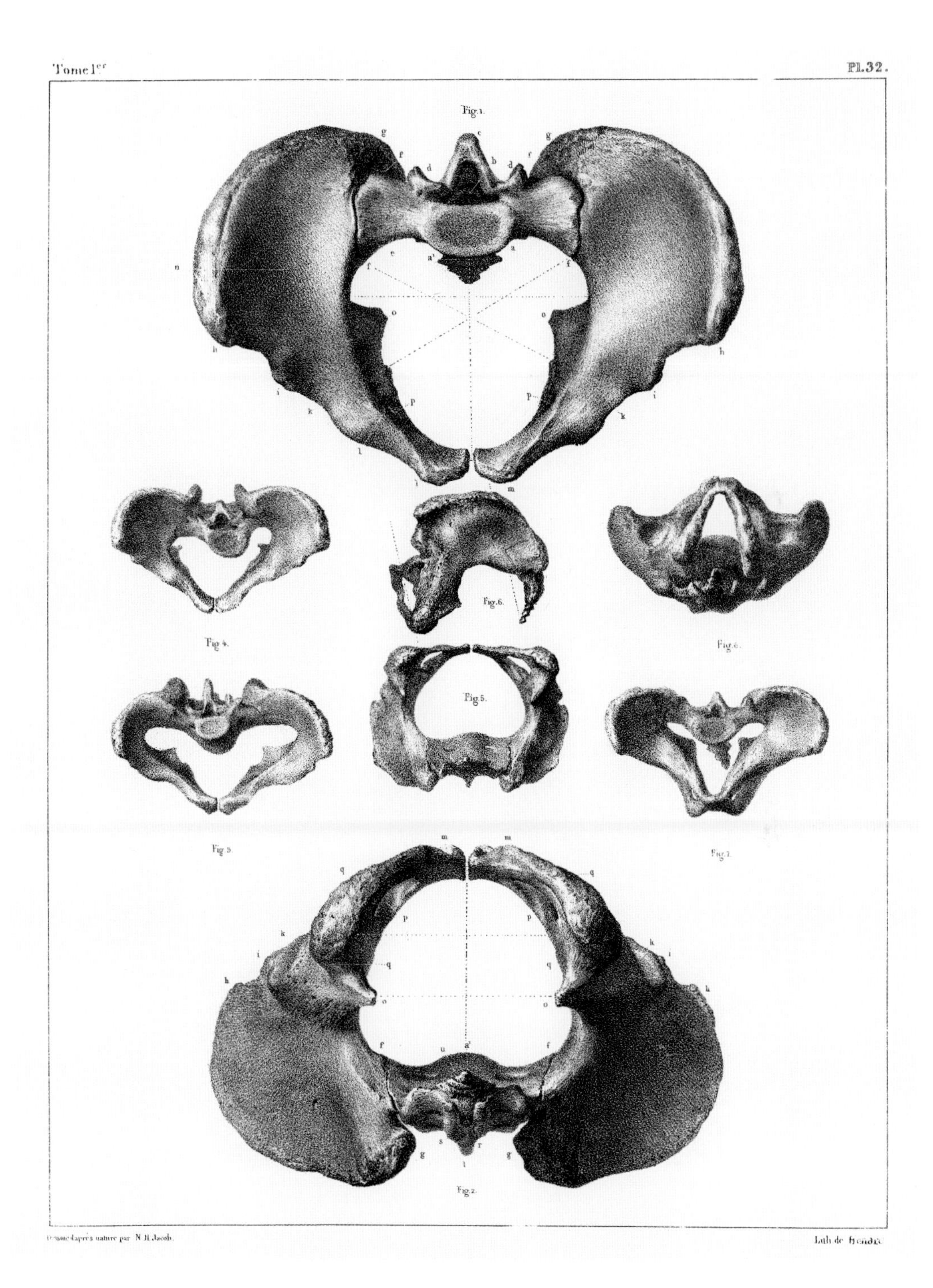

Girdle of the lower limb. Bony pelvis
Ceinture du membre inférieur. Bassin osseux ou pelvis
Cintura pélvica. Pelvis ósea

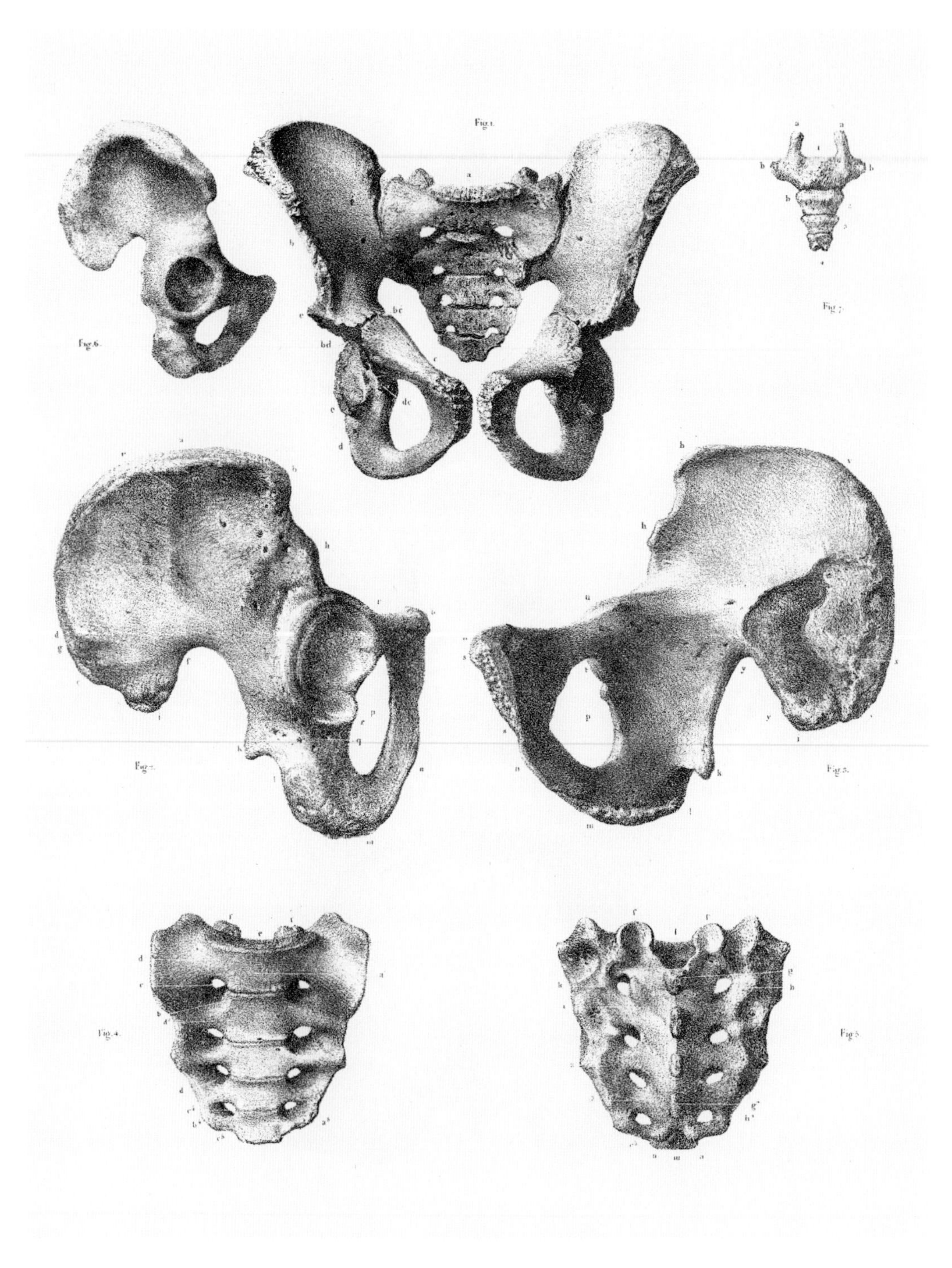

Pelvic bones: Hip bone, sacrum, and coccyx
Os du bassin : Os coxal, sacrum et coccyx
Huesos de la pelvis: hueso coxal, sacro y cóccix

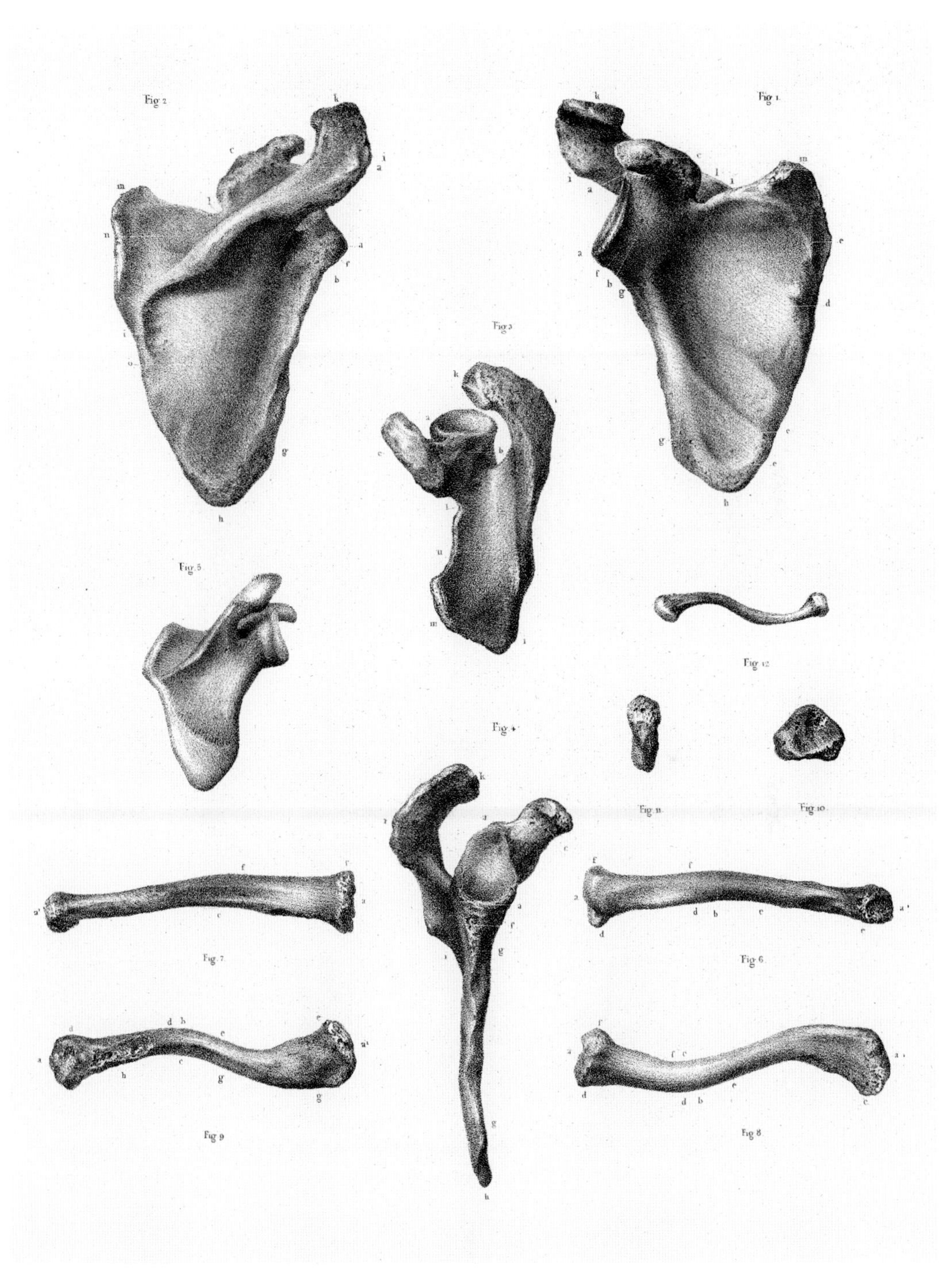

Girdle of the upper limb: Scapula and collarbone
Ceinture du membre supérieur : Scapula et clavicule
Cintura escapular: escápula y clavícula

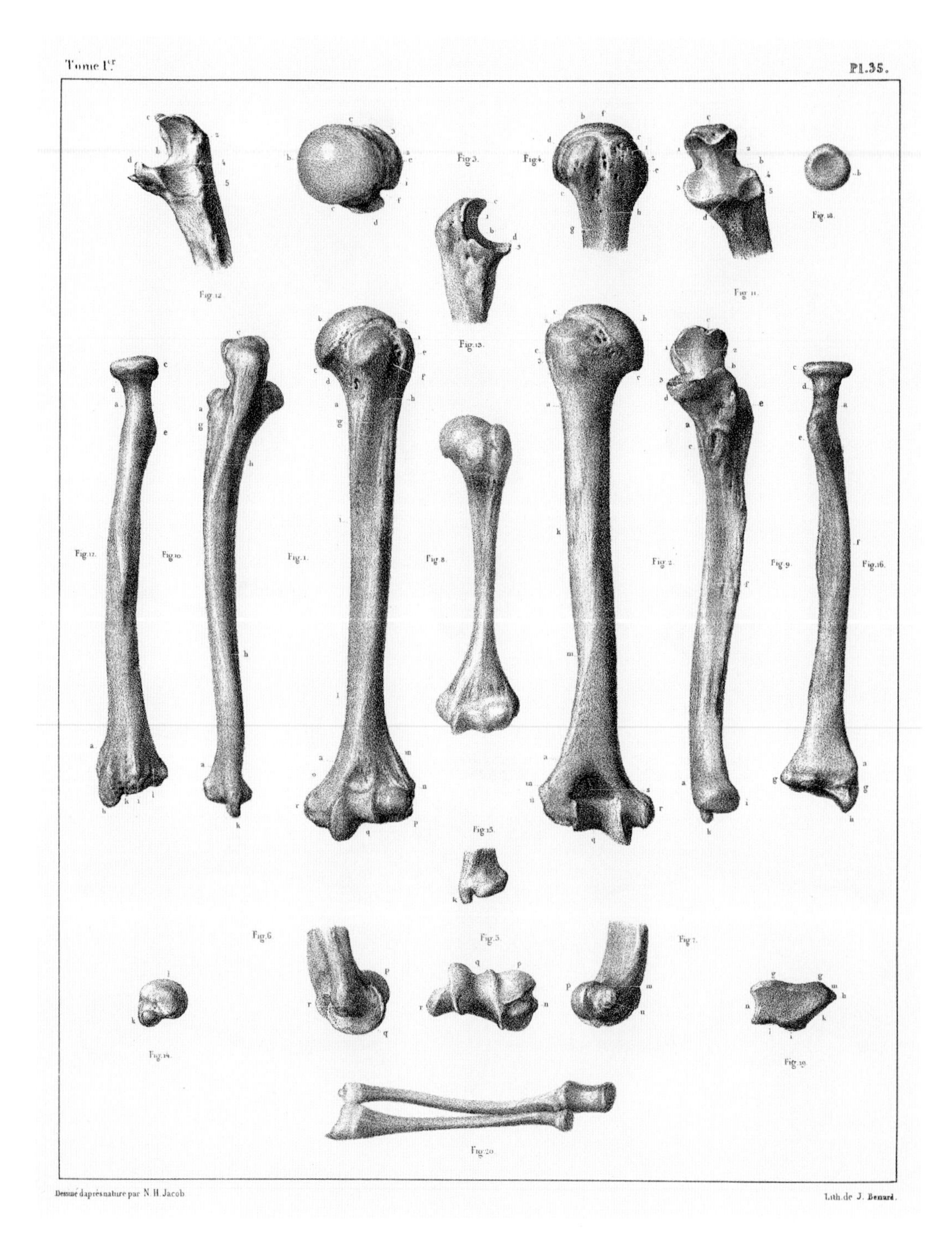

Bones of the upper limb: Humerus, radius, and ulna
Os du membre supérieur : Humérus, radius et ulna
Huesos del miembro superior: húmero, radio y cúbito

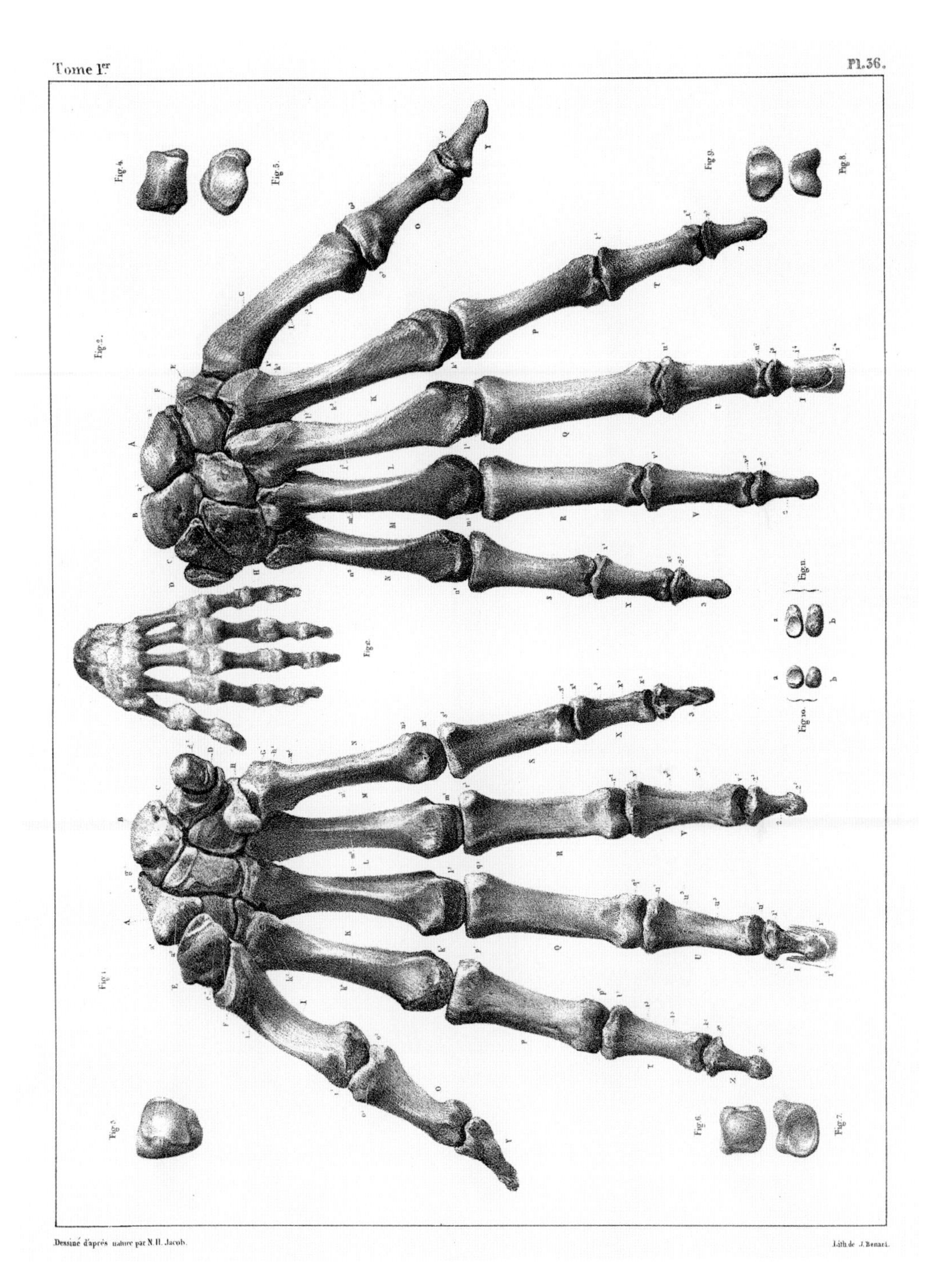

Bones of the upper limb: Bones of the hand
Os du membre supérieur : Squelette de la main
Huesos del miembro superior: esqueleto de la mano

OSSA MEMBRI INFERIORIS: FEMUR ET PATELLA, TIBIA ET FIBULA, ET SKELETON PEDIS. STRUCTURA INTERNA OSSIUM

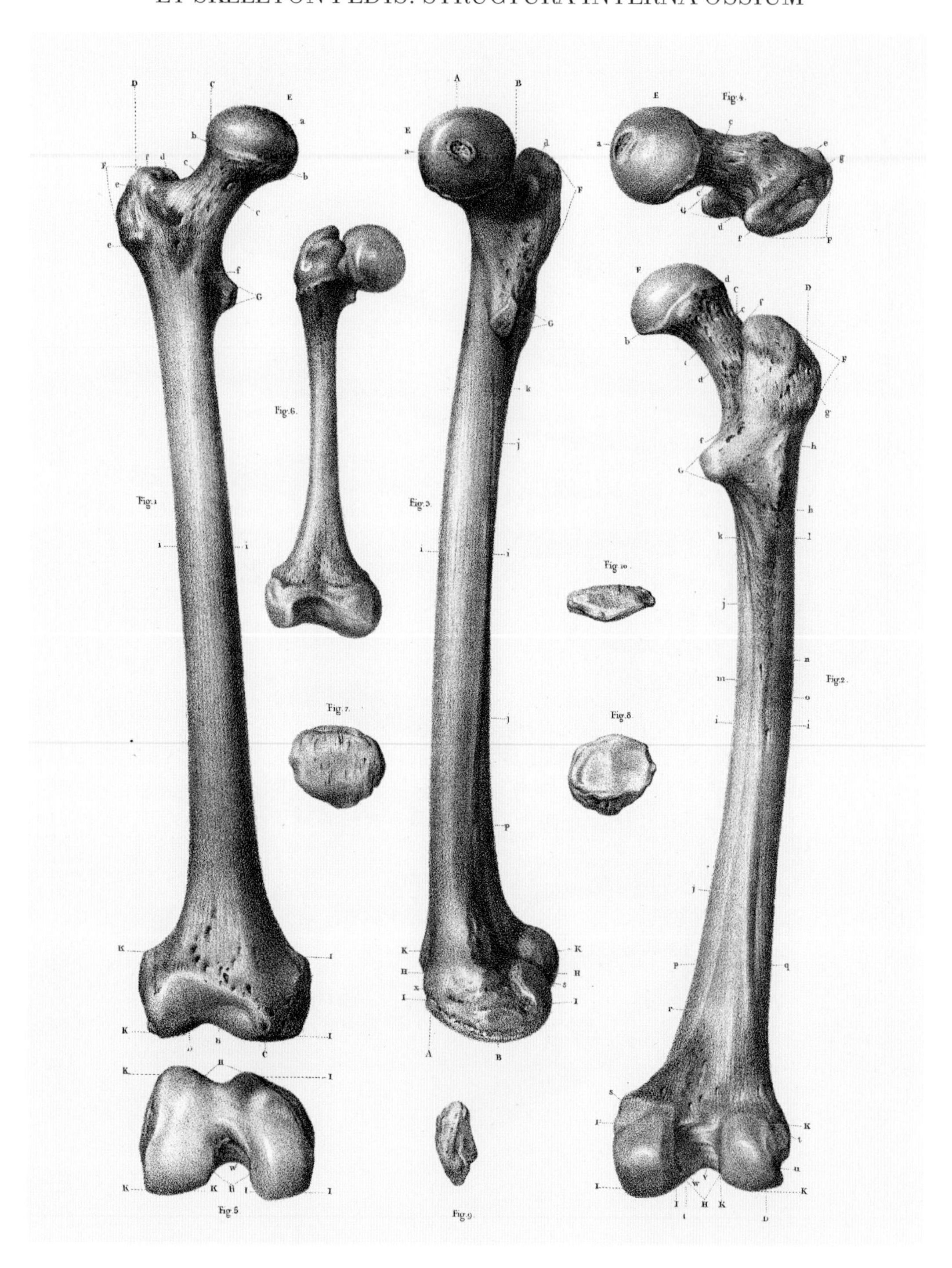

Bones of the lower limb: Femur and patella / Os du membre inférieur : Fémur et patella
Huesos del miembro inferior: fémur y rótula

OSSA MEMBRI INFERIORIS: FEMUR ET PATELLA, TIBIA ET FIBULA, ET SKELETON PEDIS. STRUCTURA INTERNA OSSIUM

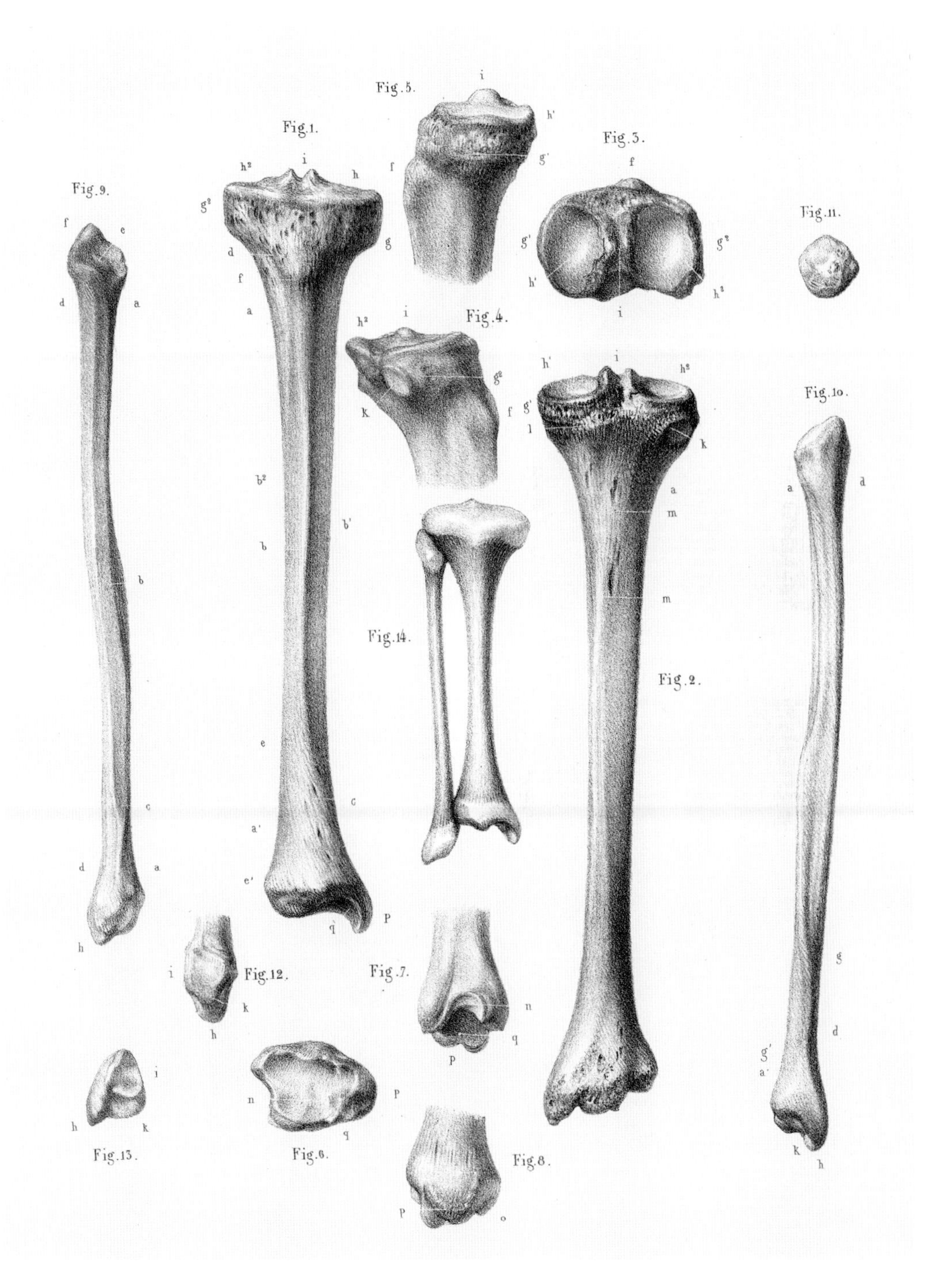

Bones of the lower limb: Tibia and fibula / Os du membre inférieur : Tibia et fibula
Huesos del miembro inferior: tibia y peroné

OSSA MEMBRI INFERIORIS: FEMUR ET PATELLA, TIBIA ET FIBULA, ET SKELETON PEDIS. STRUCTURA INTERNA OSSIUM

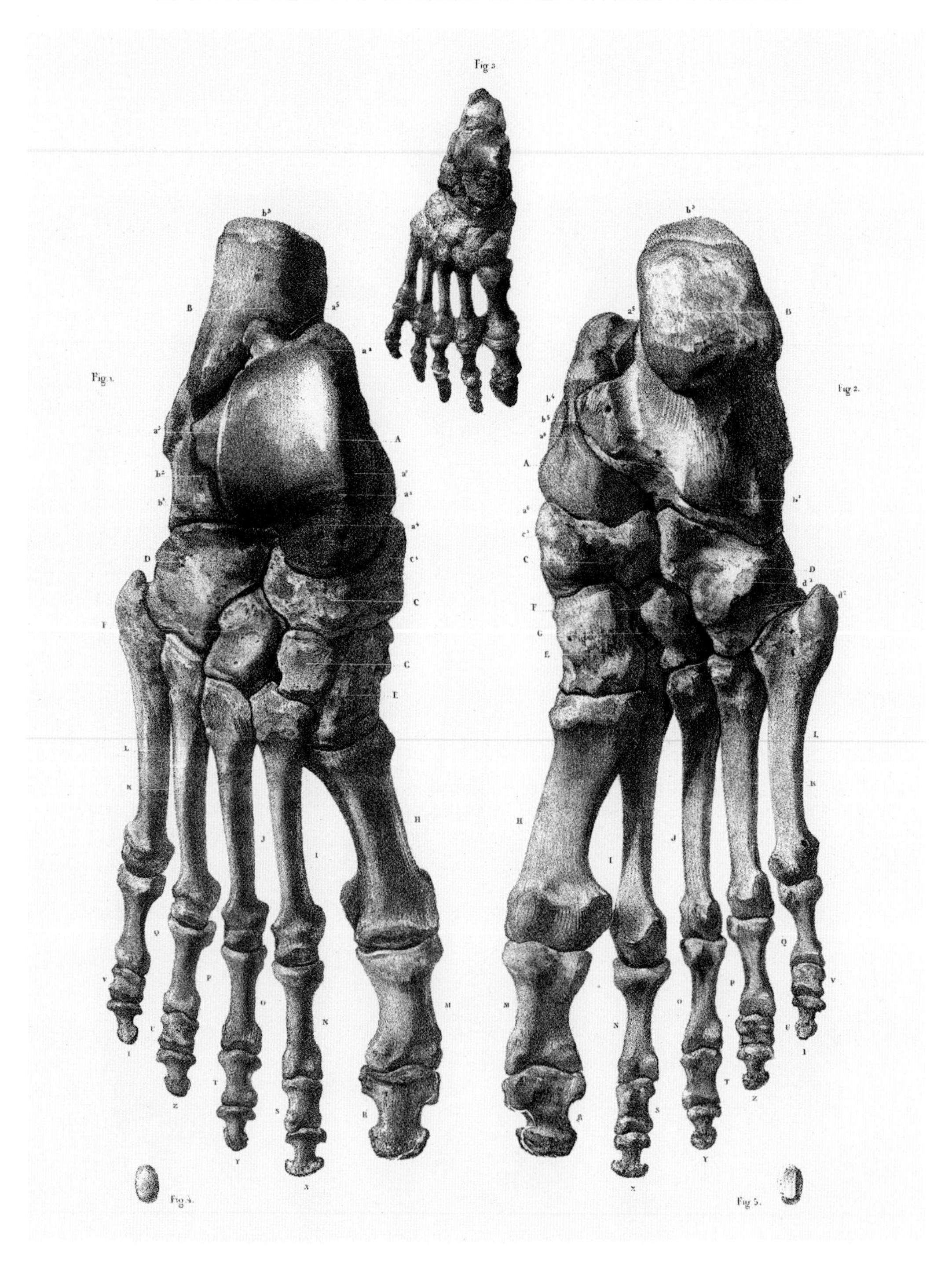

Bones of the lower limb: Bones of the foot / Os du membre inférieur : Squelette du pied
Huesos del miembro inferior: esqueleto del pie

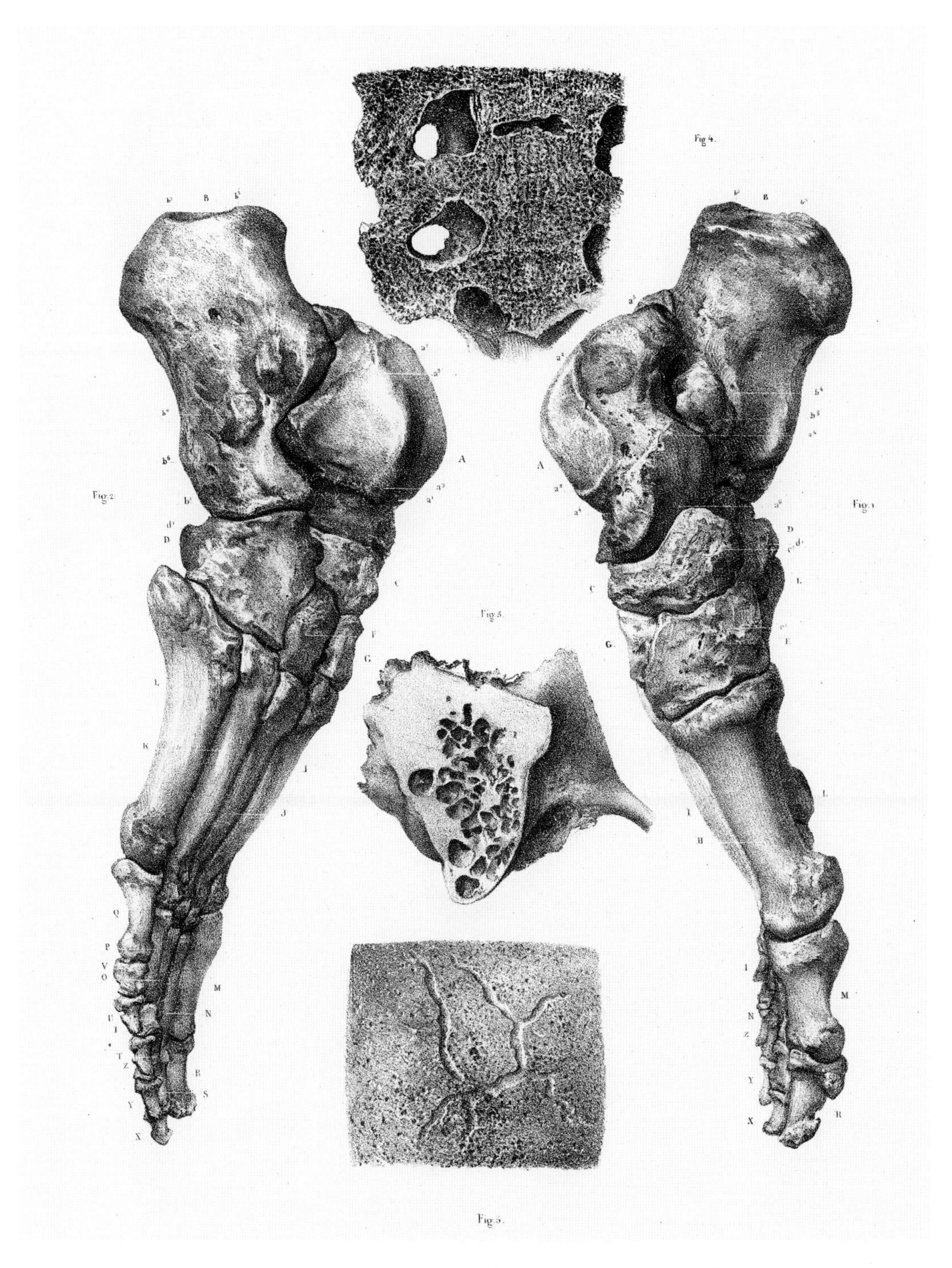

Bones of the lower limb: Bones of the foot – inner structure of the bones
Os du membre inférieur : Squelette du pied – Structure interne des os
Huesos del miembro inferior: esqueleto del pie – Estructura interna de los huesos

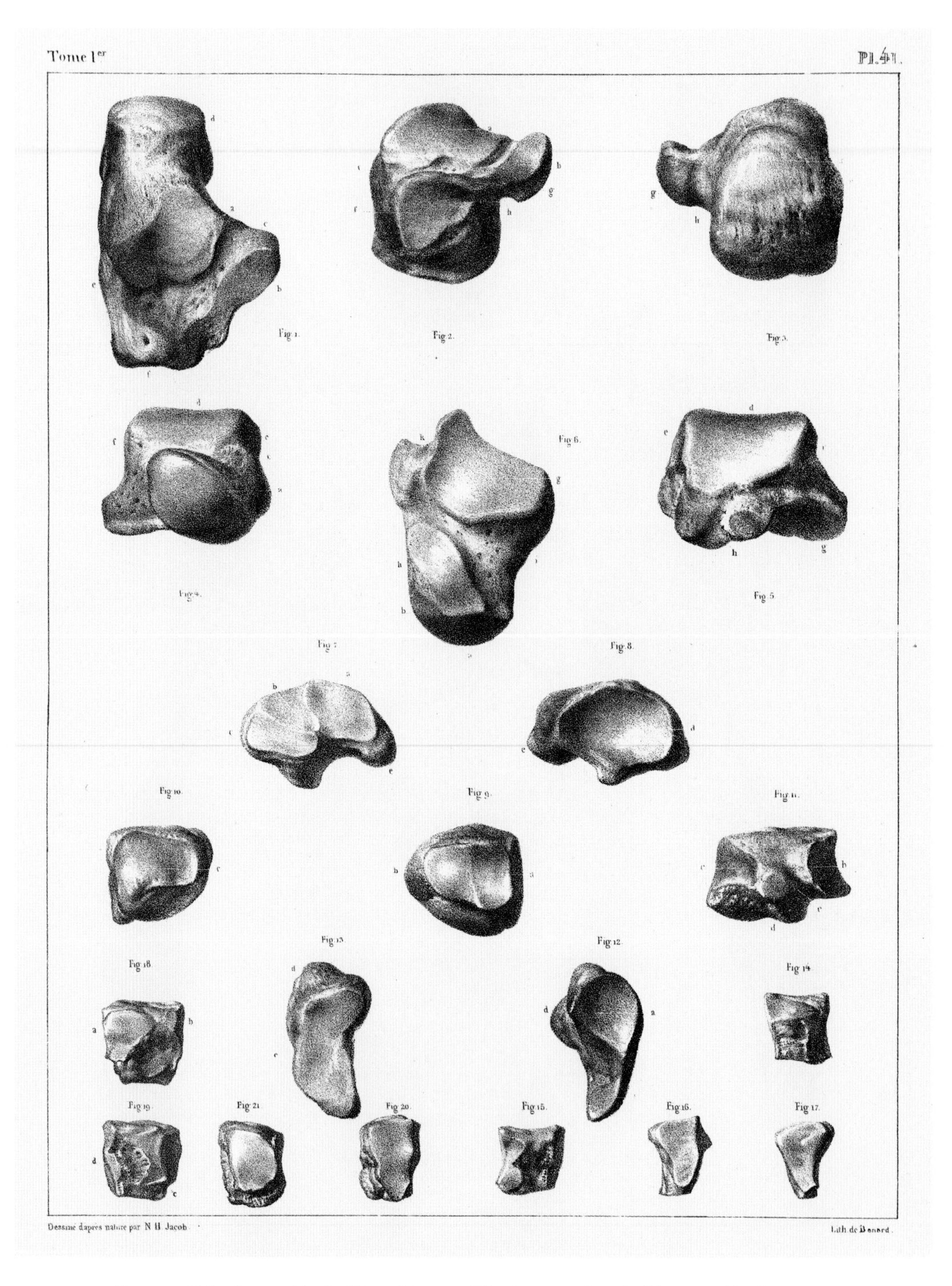

Bones of the lower limb: Tarsal bone / Os du membre inférieur : Os du tarse
Huesos del miembro inferior: huesos del tarso

STRUCTURA INTERNA OSSIUM –
SUBSTANTIA COMPACTA ET SPONGIOSA

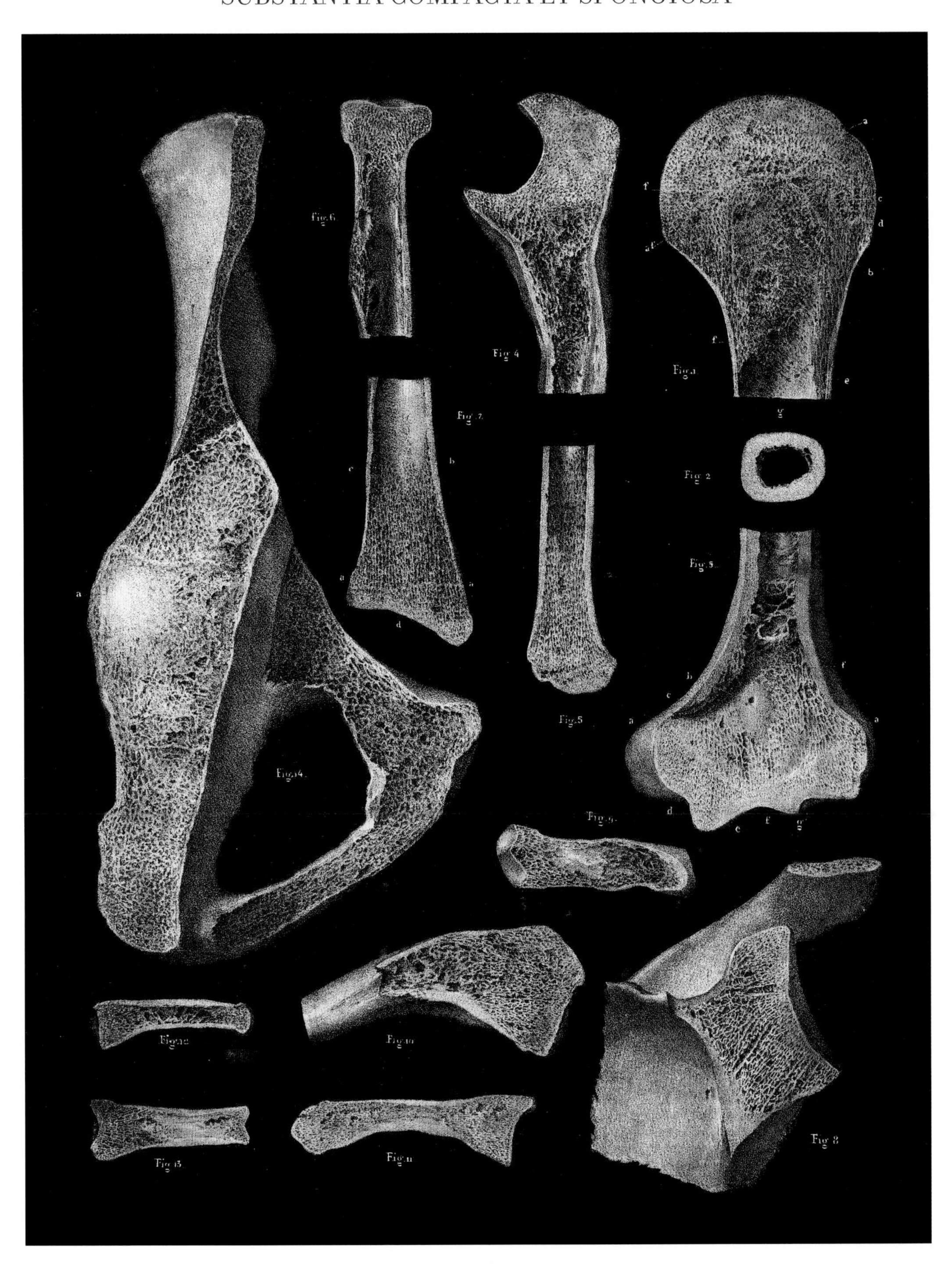

Inner structure of the bones – compact bone and spongy bone
Structure interne des os – Os compact et os spongieux
Estructura interna de los huesos – Huesos compacto y esponjoso

STRUCTURA INTERNA OSSIUM – SUBSTANTIA COMPACTA ET SPONGIOSA

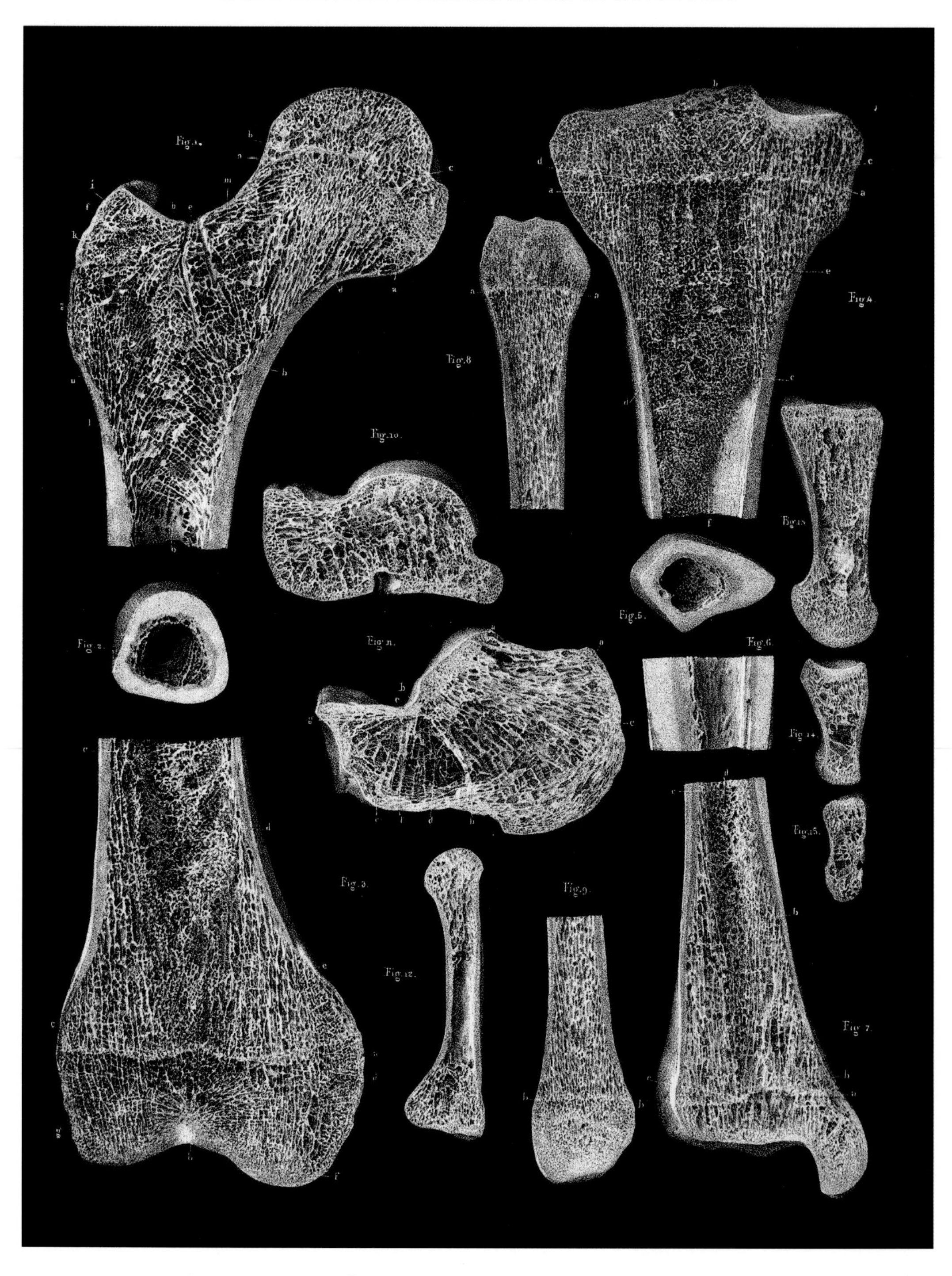

Inner structure of the bones – compact bone and spongy bone
Structure interne des os – Os compact et os spongieux
Estructura interna de los huesos – Huesos compacto y esponjoso

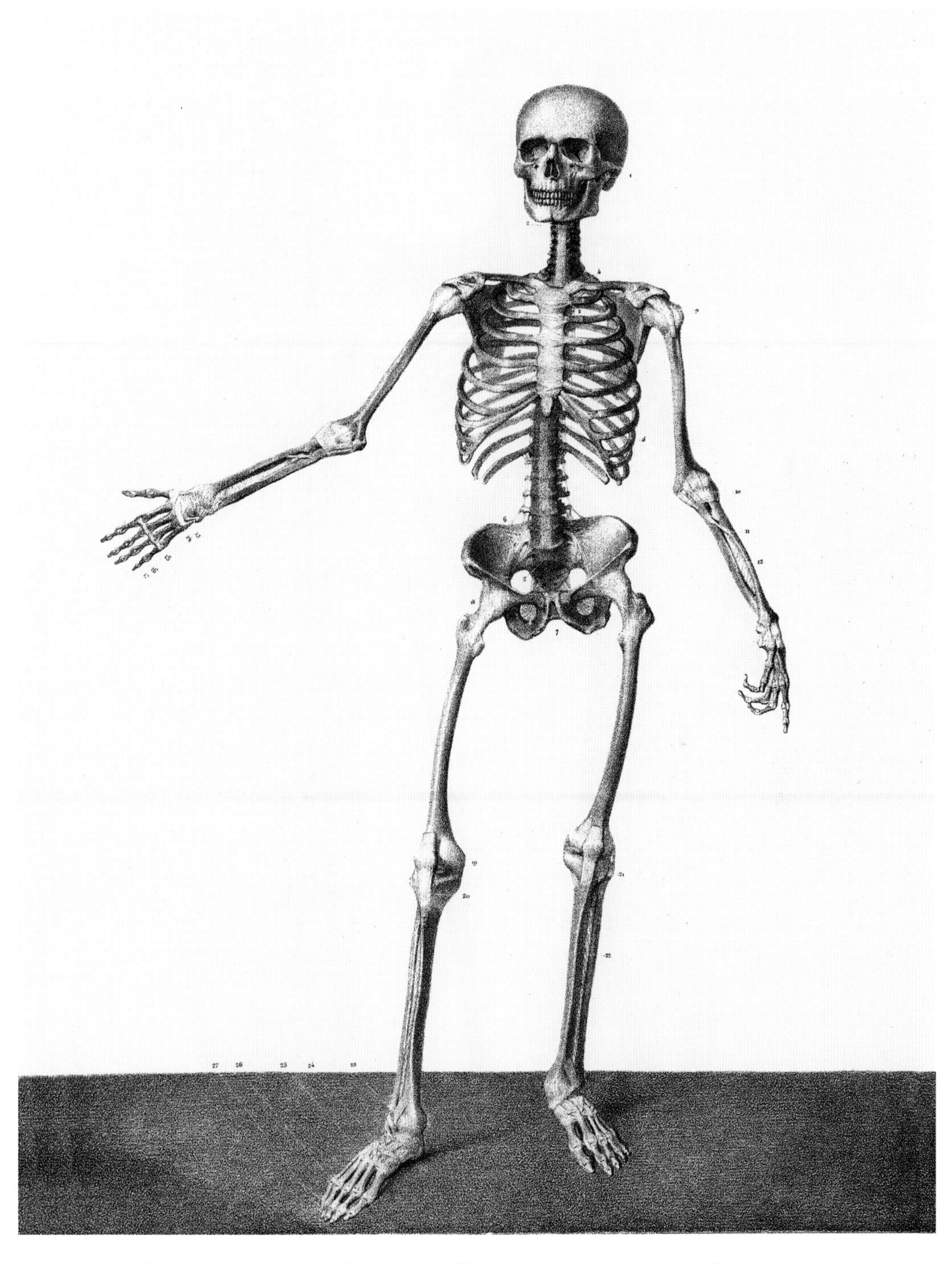

Skeleton, joints, and ligaments / Squelette, articulations et ligaments
Esqueleto, articulaciones y ligamentos

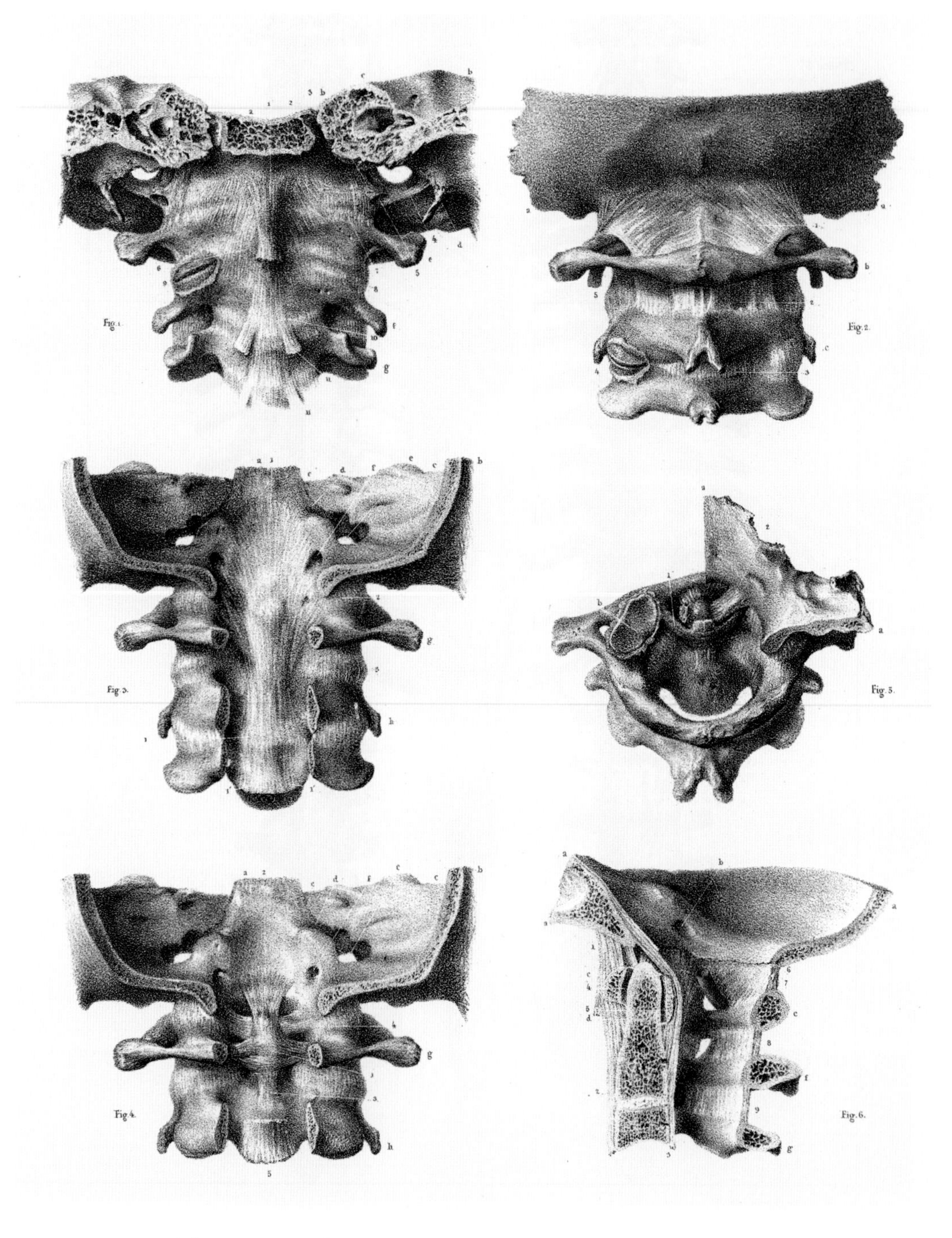

Atlanto-occipital and atlanto-axial joints. Craniovertebral joint
Articulations atlanto-occipitale et atlanto-axoïdiennes. Charnière cranio-vertébrale
Articulaciones atlanto-occipital y atlanto-axoideas. Charnela craneovertebral

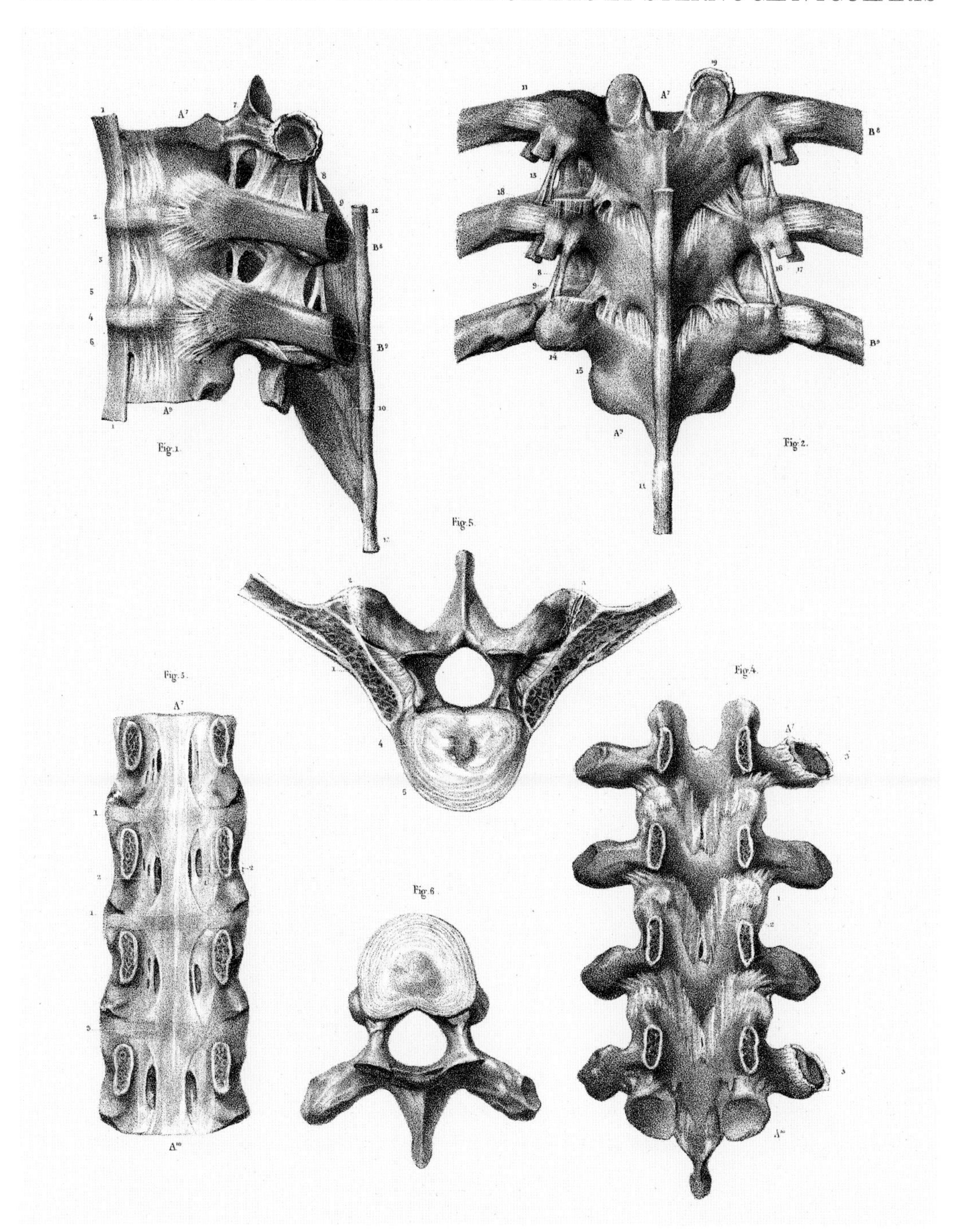

Joints of the thoracic vertebral column and costovertebral joints
Articulations de la colonne vertébrale thoracique et articulations costo-vertébrales
Articulaciones de la columna vertebral torácica y costovertebrales

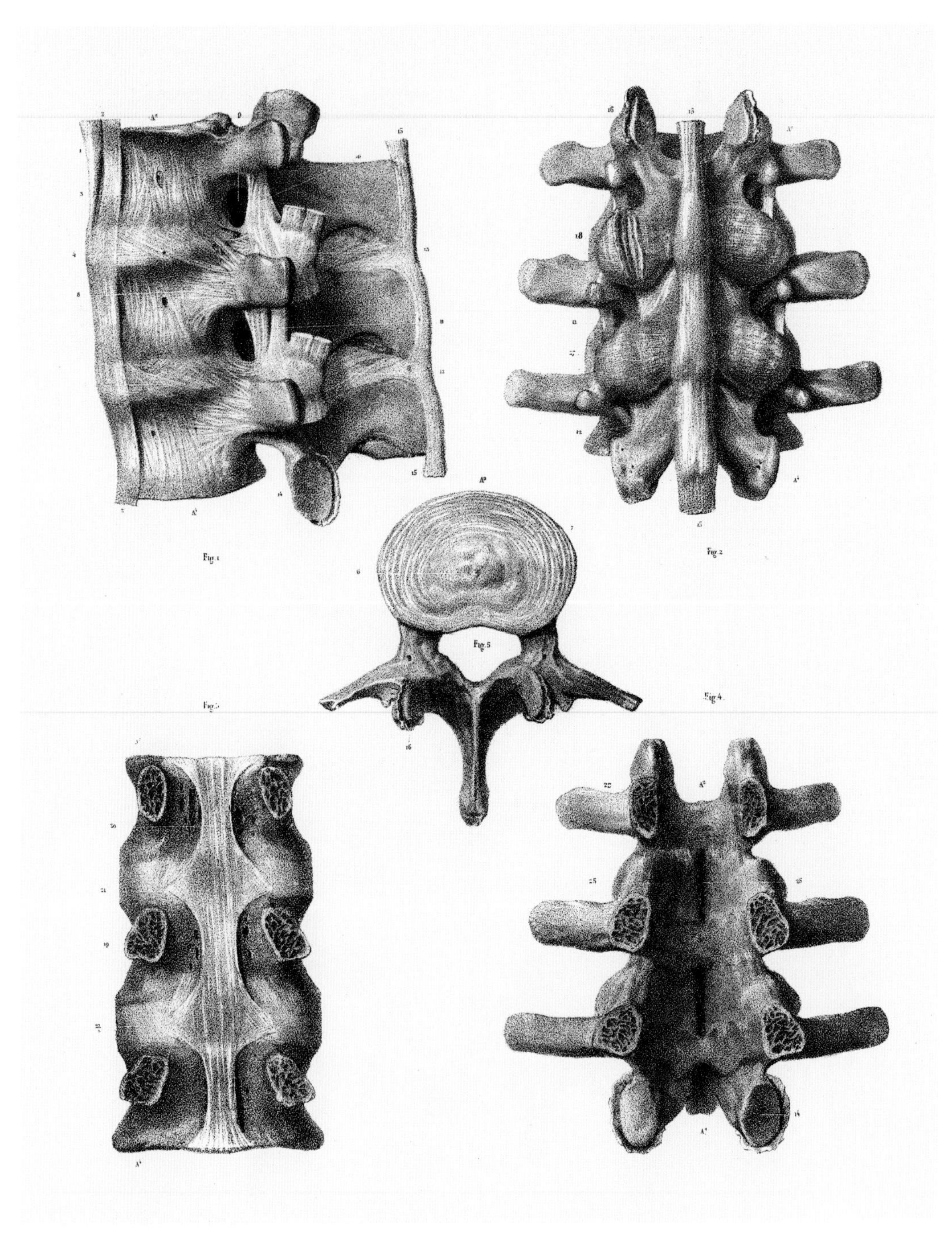

Joints of the lumbar vertebral column
Articulations de la colonne vertébrale lombaire
Articulaciones de la columna vertebral lumbar

ARTICULATIONES ATLANTOOCCIPITALIS ET ATLANTO AXIALIS. ARTICULATIONES COLUMNAE VERTEBRALIS ET THORACIS. ARTICULATIONES TEMPOROMANDIBULARIS ET STERNOCLAVICULARIS

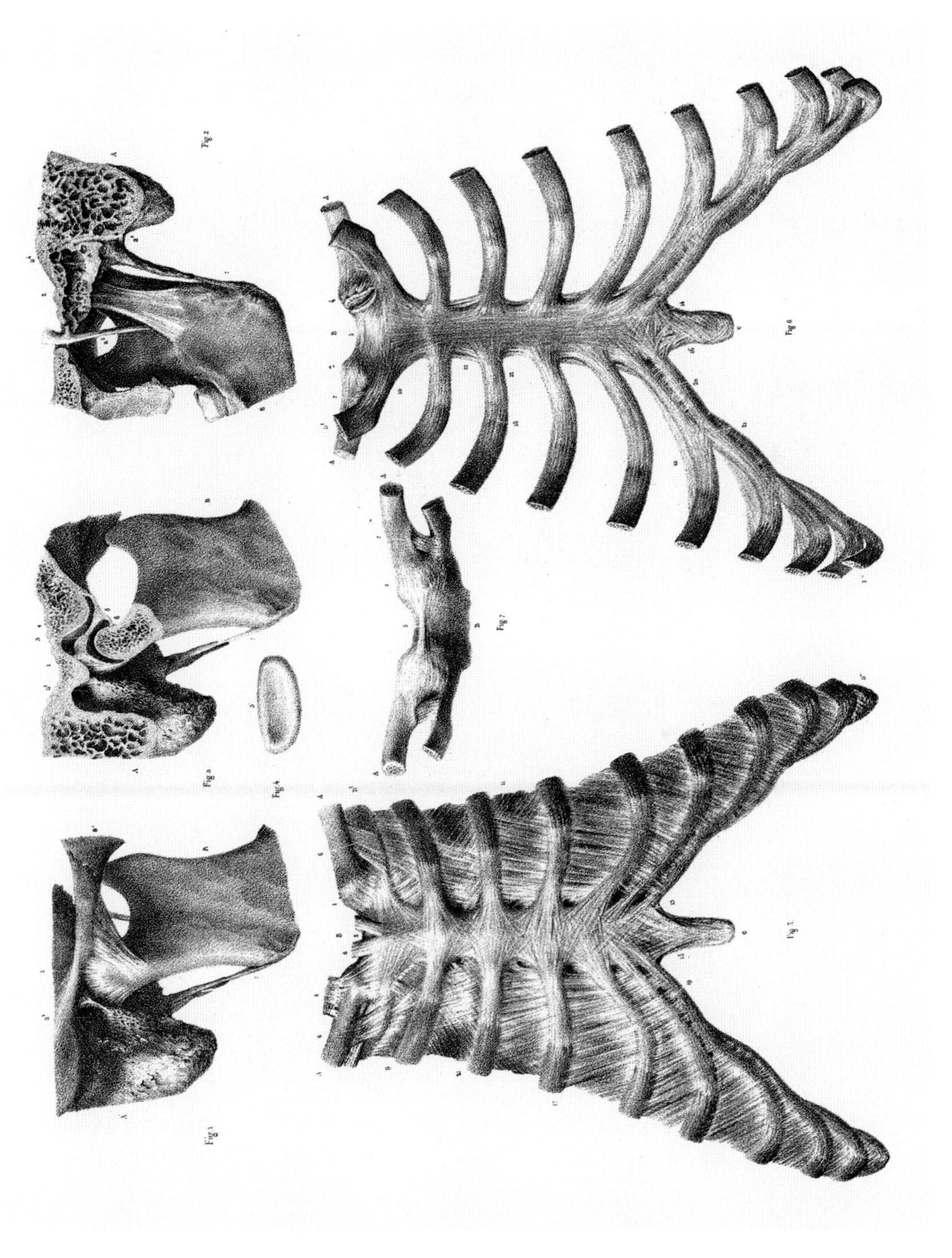

Temporomandibular, sternoclavicular, and sternocostal joints
Articulations temporo-mandibulaire, sterno-claviculaire et sterno-costales
Articulaciones temporomandibular, esternoclavicular y esternocostales

ARTICULATIONES CINGULI MEMBRI INFERIORIS ET ARTICULATIO COXAE

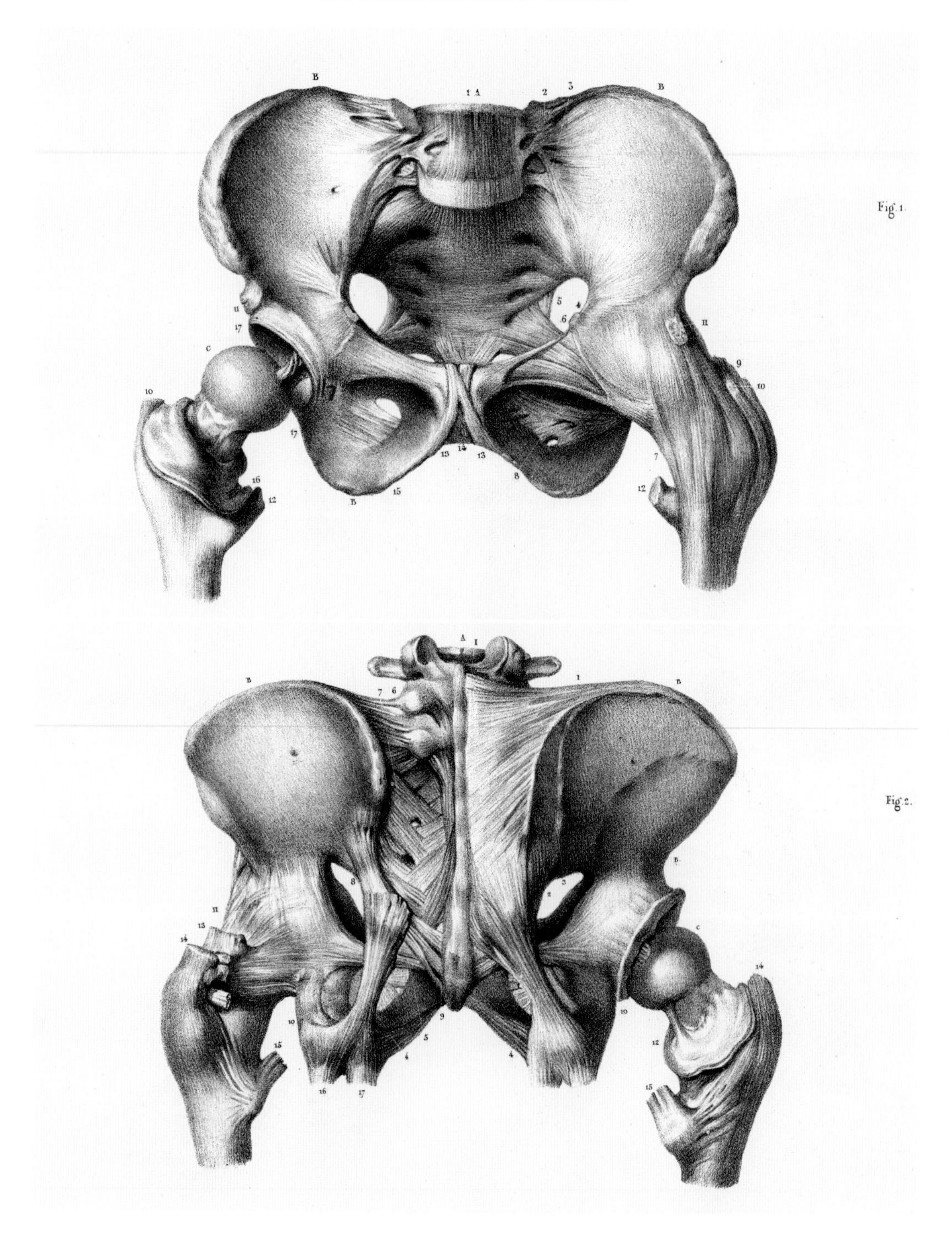

Pelvic joints and hip joint
Articulations du bassin et articulation de la hanche (coxo-fémorale)
Articulaciones de la pelvis y de la cadera (coxofemoral)

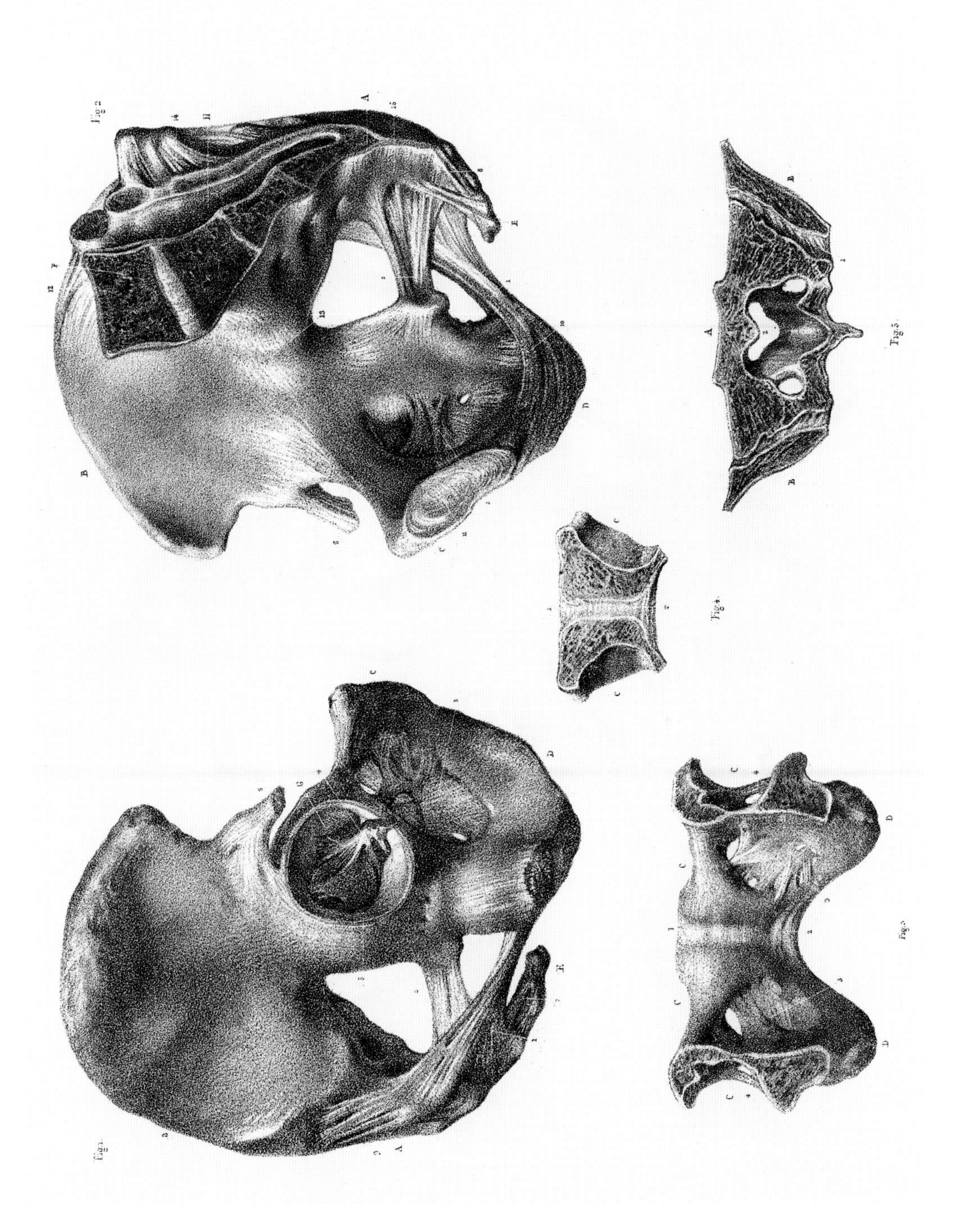

Pelvic joints and hip joint
Articulations du bassin et articulation de la hanche (coxo-fémorale)
Articulaciones de la pelvis y de la cadera (coxofemoral)

ARTICULATIONES MANUS ET DIGITORUM MANUS

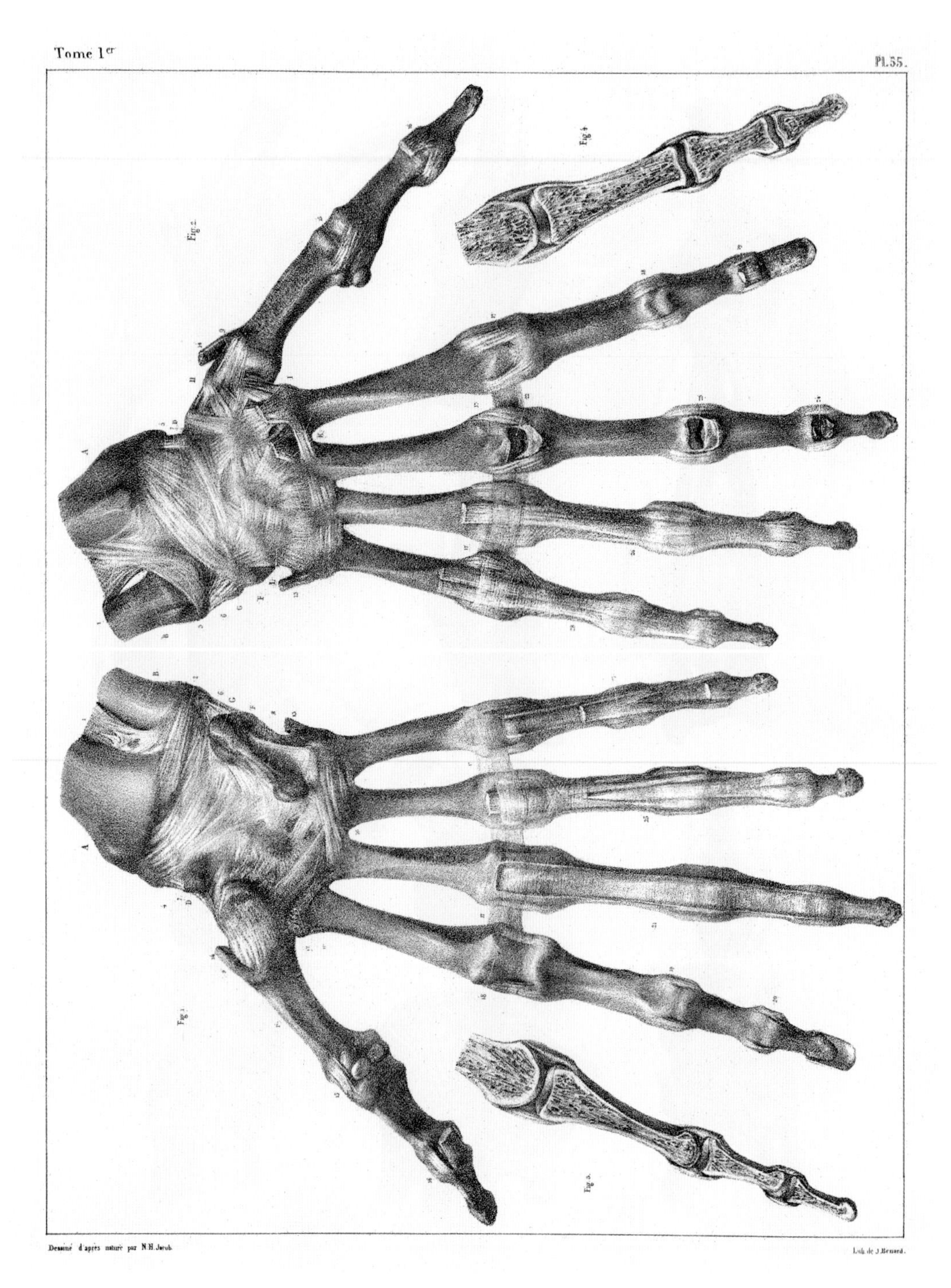

Joints of the hand and fingers / Articulations de la main et des doigts
Articulaciones de la mano y de los dedos

ARTICULATIO GENUS. ARTICULATIONES TIBIOFIBULARES, TALOCRURALIS, SUBTALARIS, ET TALOCALCANEA. ARTICULATIONES PEDIS ET DIGITORUM PEDIS

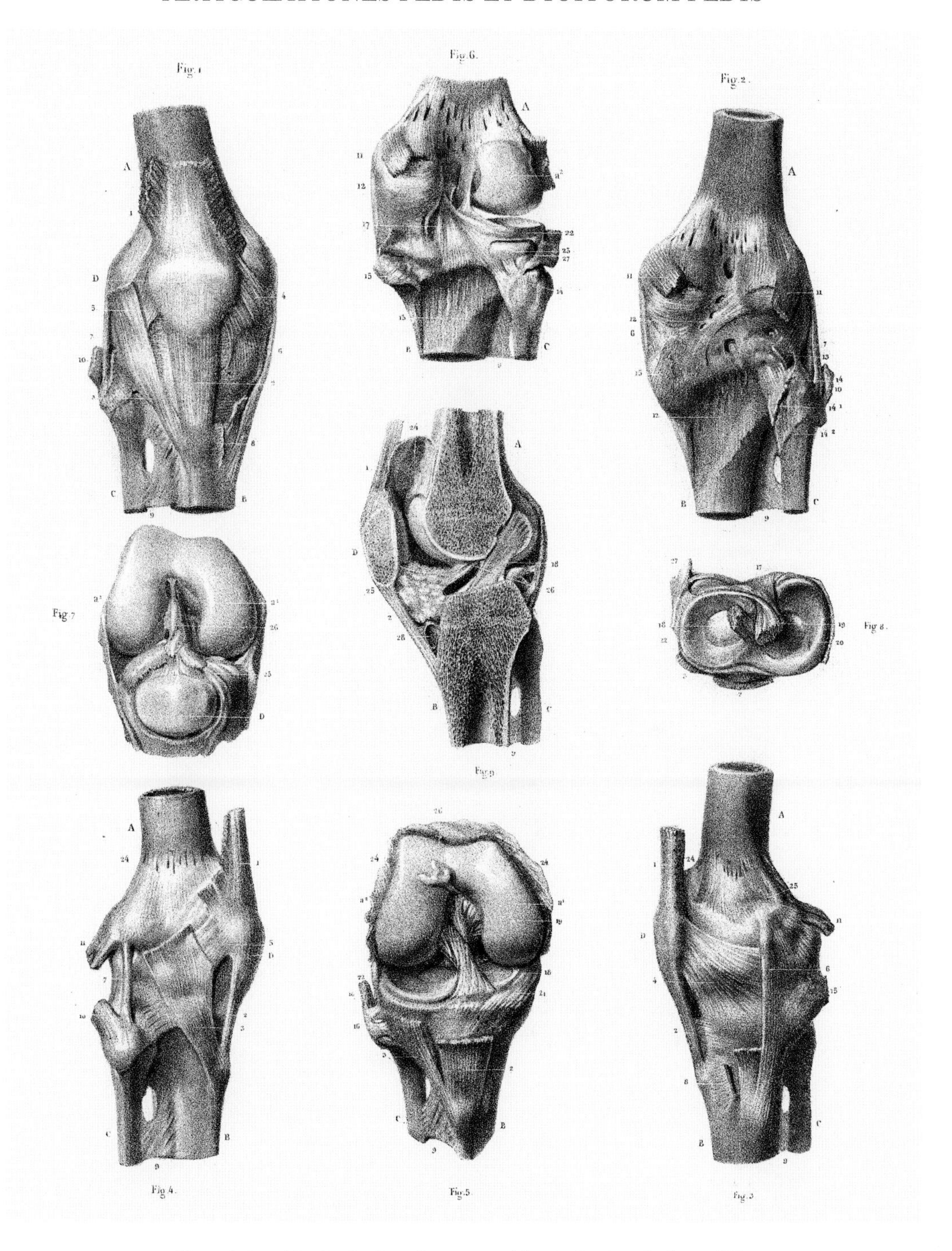

Knee joint / Articulation du genou / Articulación de la rodilla

ARTICULATIO GENUS. ARTICULATIONES TIBIOFIBULARES, TALOCRURALIS, SUBTALARIS, ET TALOCALCANEA. ARTICULATIONES PEDIS ET DIGITORUM PEDIS

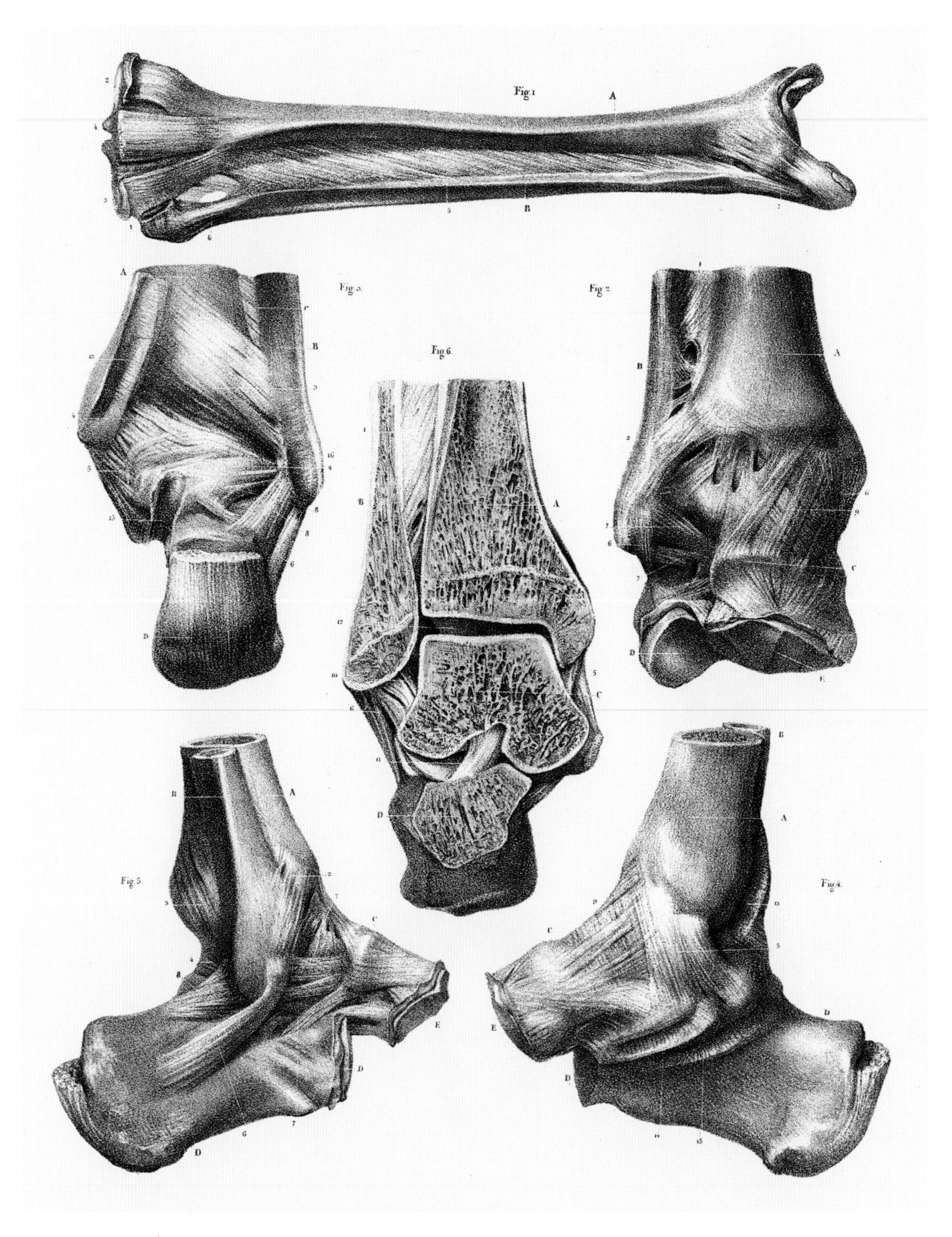

Tibiofibular joints and ankle joints / Articulations tibio-fibulaires et articulations de la cheville (talo-crurale, subtalaire et talo-calcanéenne)
Articulaciones tibioperoneales y del tobillo (tibioastragalina, subastragalina y astragalocalcánea)

ARTICULATIO GENUS. ARTICULATIONES TIBIOFIBULARES, TALOCRURALIS, SUBTALARIS, ET TALOCALCANEA. ARTICULATIONES PEDIS ET DIGITORUM PEDIS

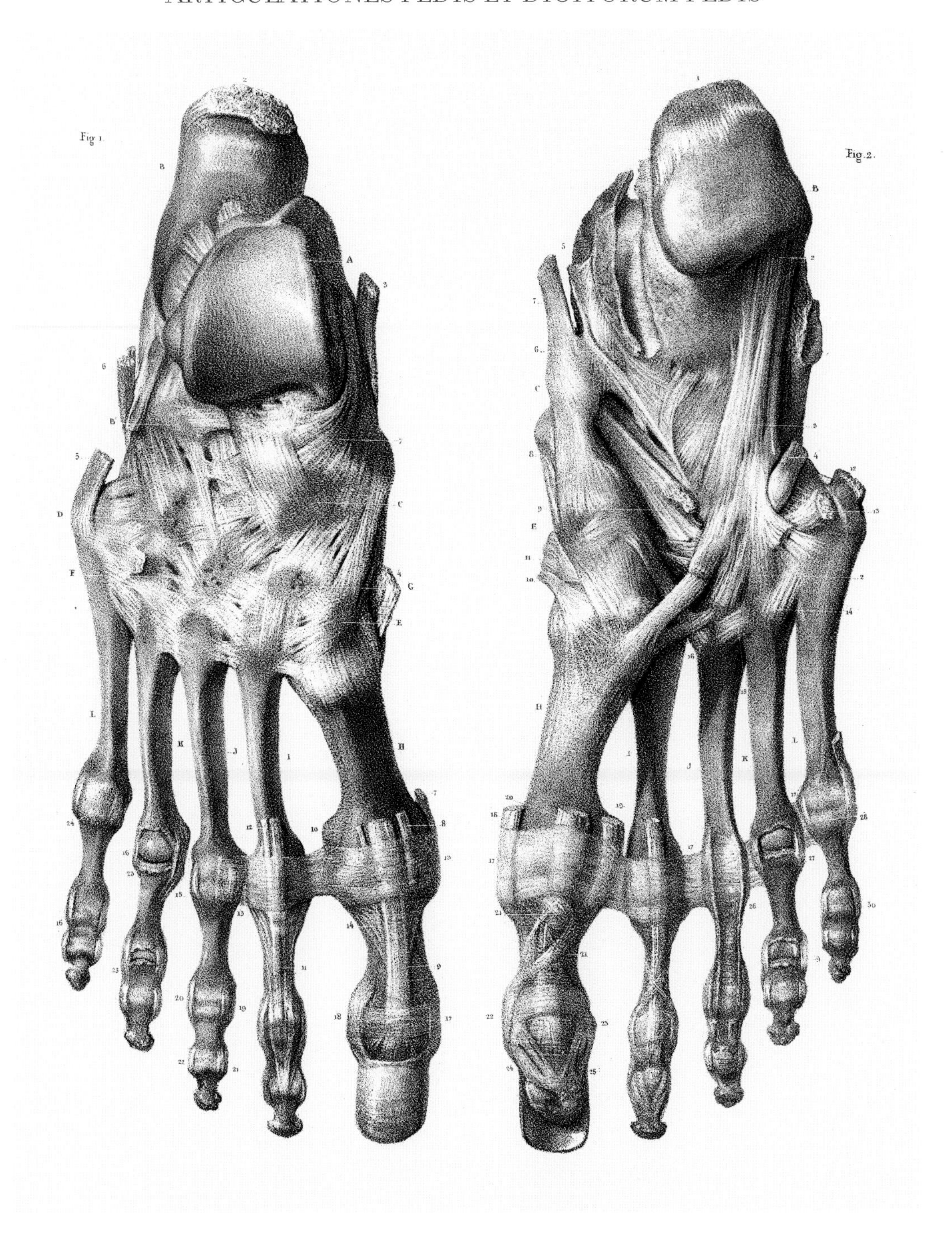

Joints of the foot / Articulations du pied / Articulaciones del pie

ARTICULATIO GENUS. ARTICULATIONES TIBIOFIBULARES, TALOCRURALIS, SUBTALARIS, ET TALOCALCANEA. ARTICULATIONES PEDIS ET DIGITORUM PEDIS

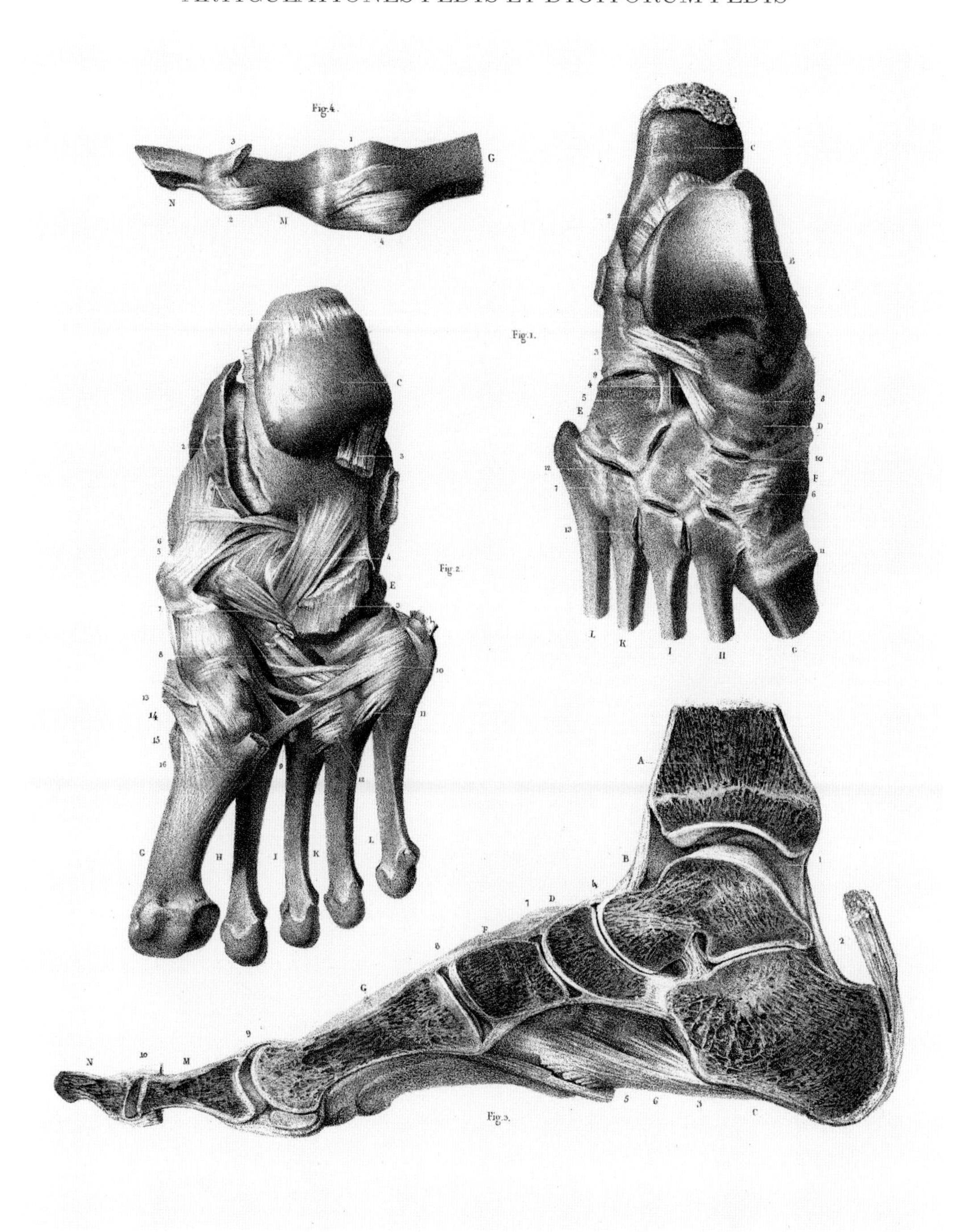

Joints of the foot and toes / Articulations du pied et des orteils
Articulaciones del pie y de los dedos del pie

Dessiné d'après nature par N. H. Jacob.

Litho. de Benard.

VOL. 2

Myologia: Musculi, Tendines, et Fasciae

MYOLOGY: MUSCLES, TENDONS, AND FASCIAS

MYOLOGIE : MUSCLES, TENDONS ET FASCIAS

MIOLOGÍA: MÚSCULOS, TENDONES Y FASCIAS

Left page / Ci-contre / Página contigua:
Thoracic and abdominal muscles / Muscles thoraciques et abdominaux
Músculos torácicos y abdominales

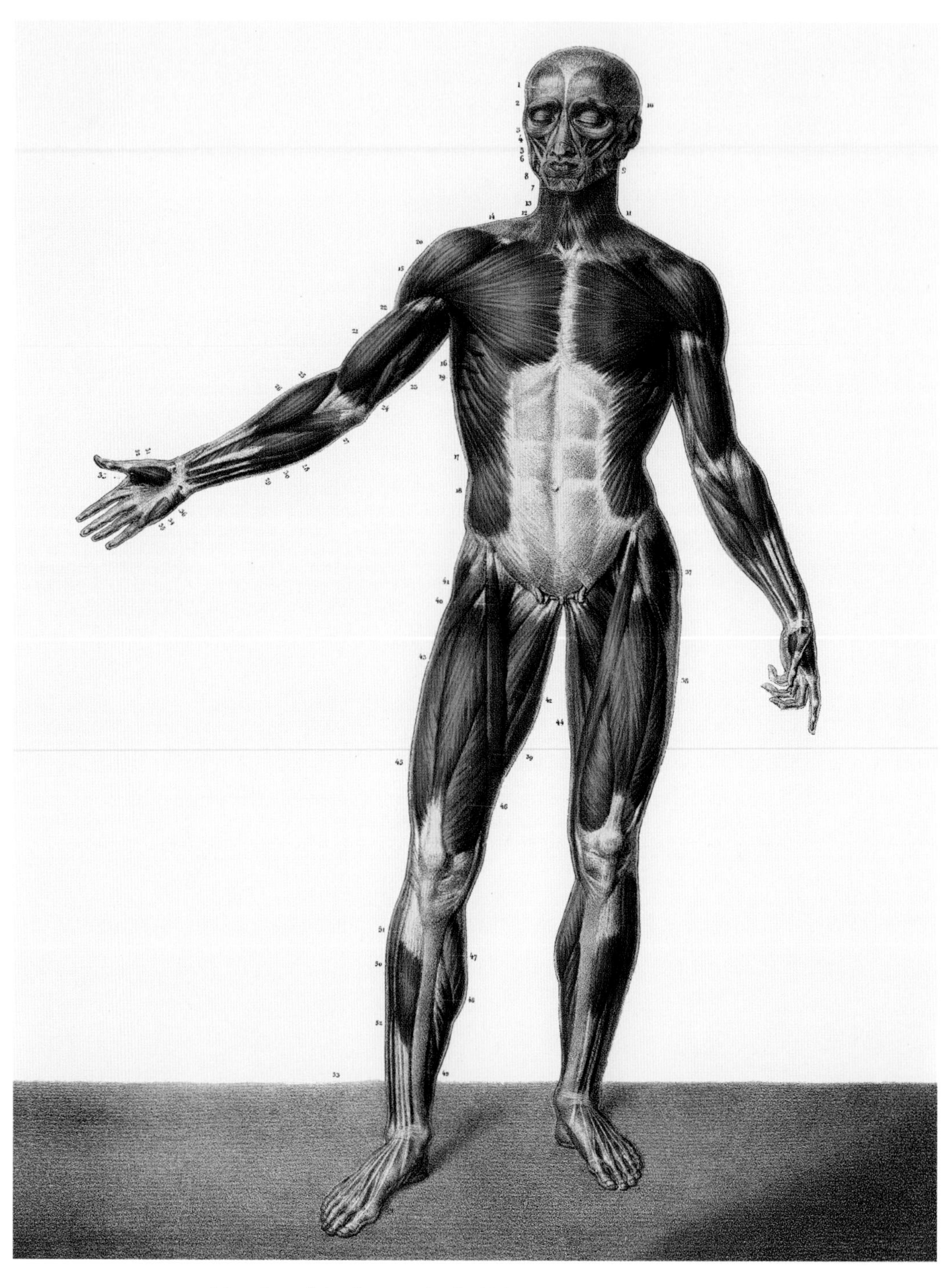

Muscles of the human body / Muscles du corps humain
Músculos del cuerpo humano

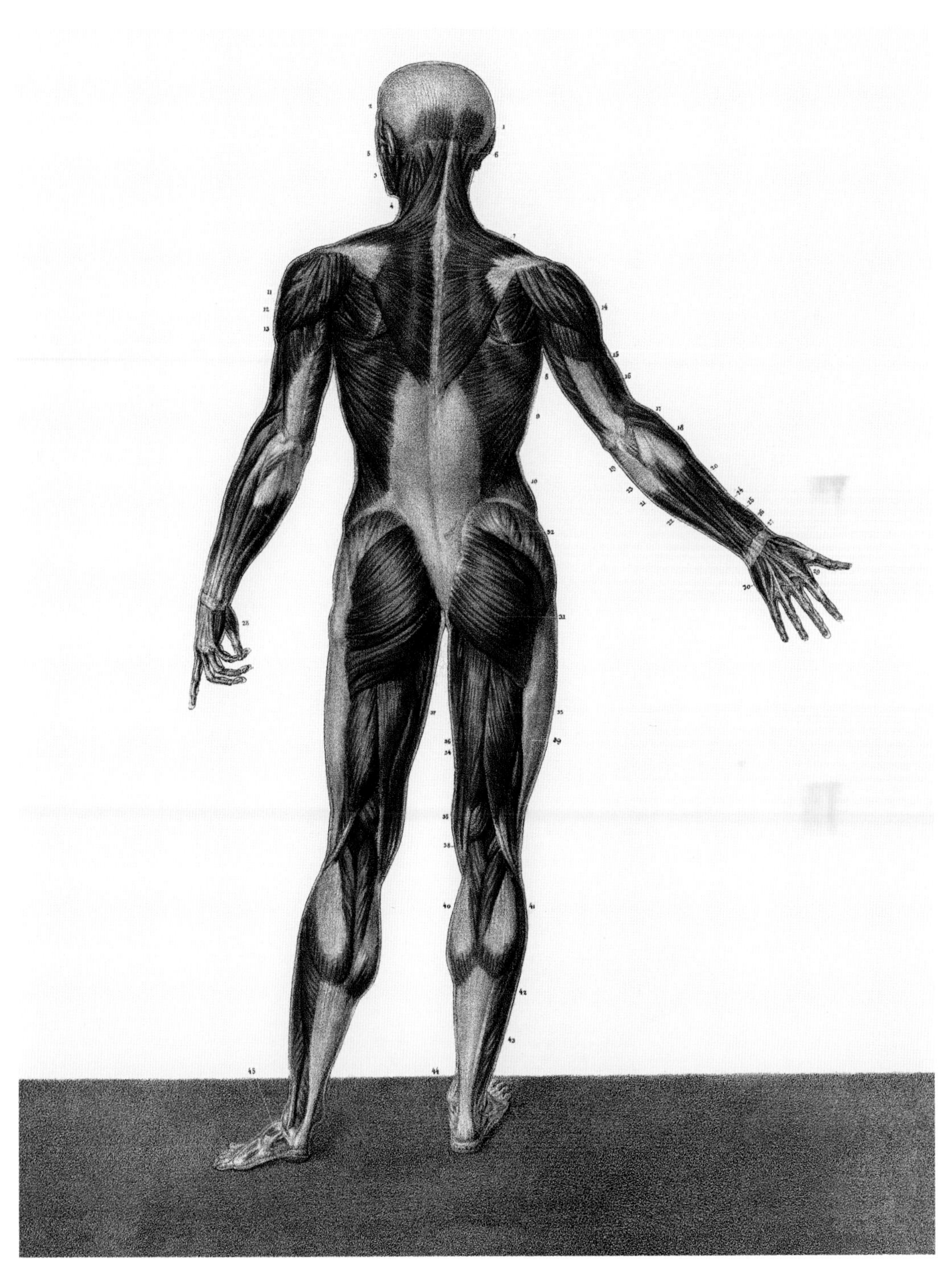

Muscles of the human body / Muscles du corps humain
Músculos del cuerpo humano

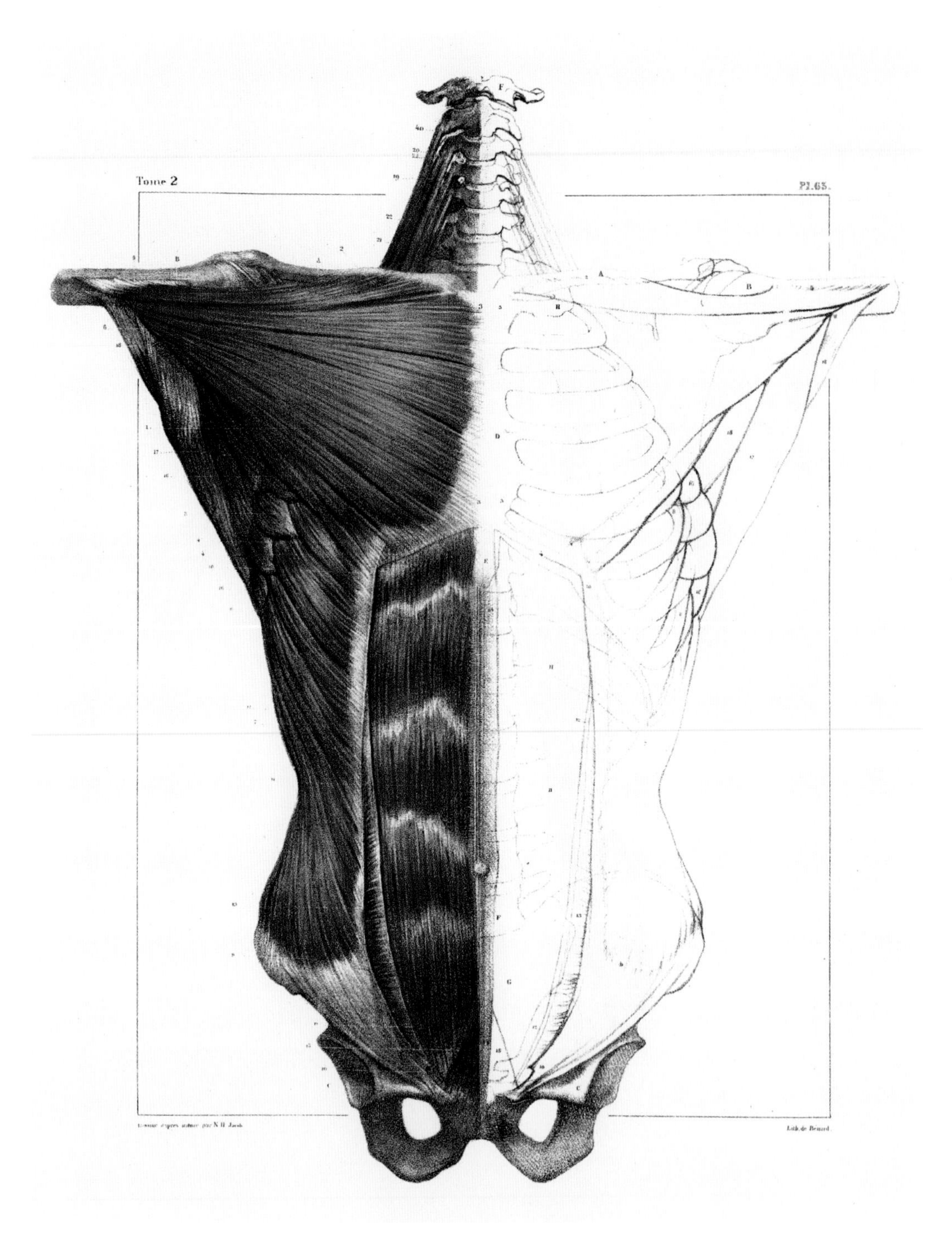

Thoracic and abdominal muscles / Muscles thoraciques et abdominaux
Músculos torácicos y abdominales

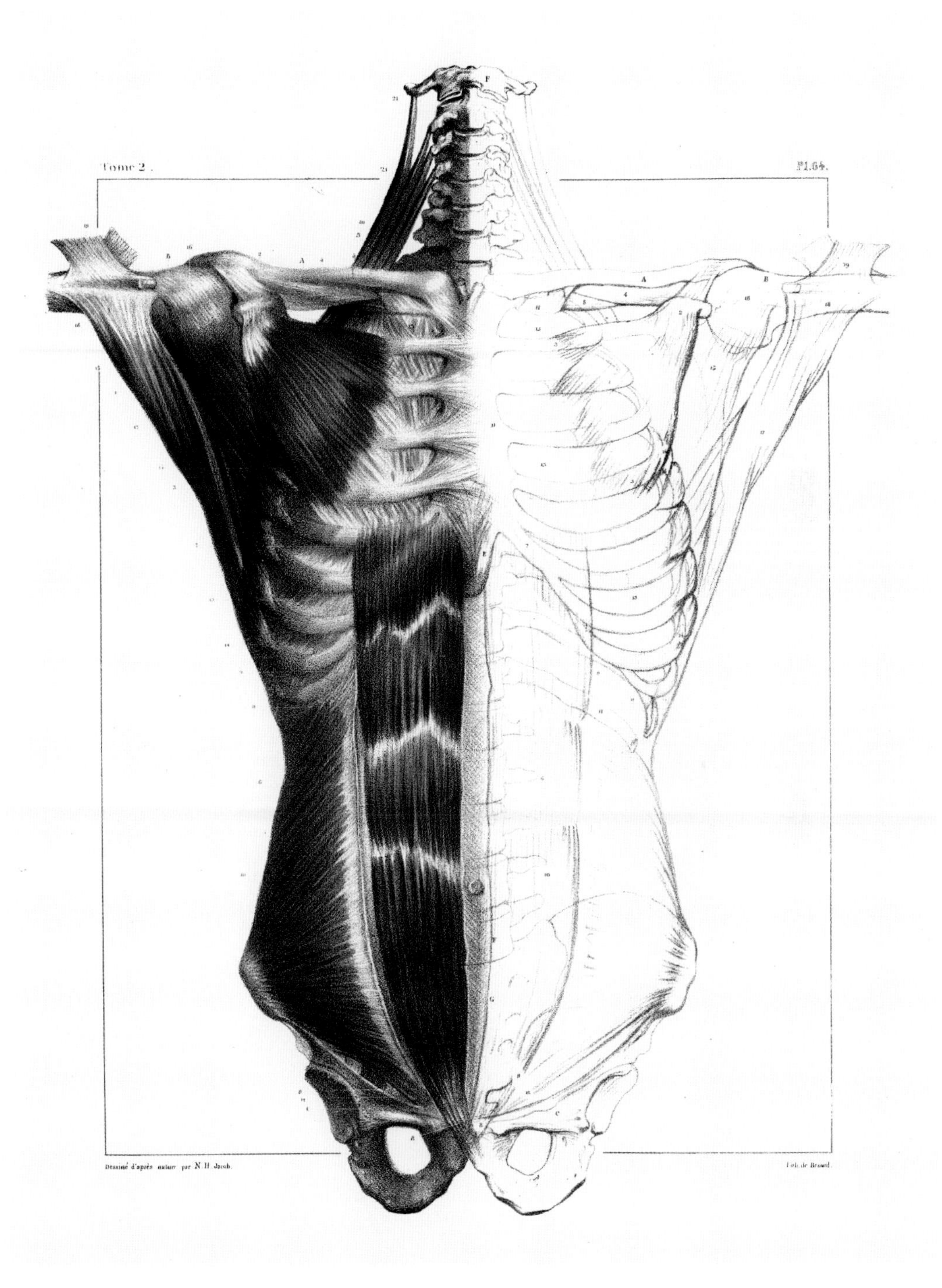

Thoracic and abdominal muscles / Muscles thoraciques et abdominaux
Músculos torácicos y abdominales

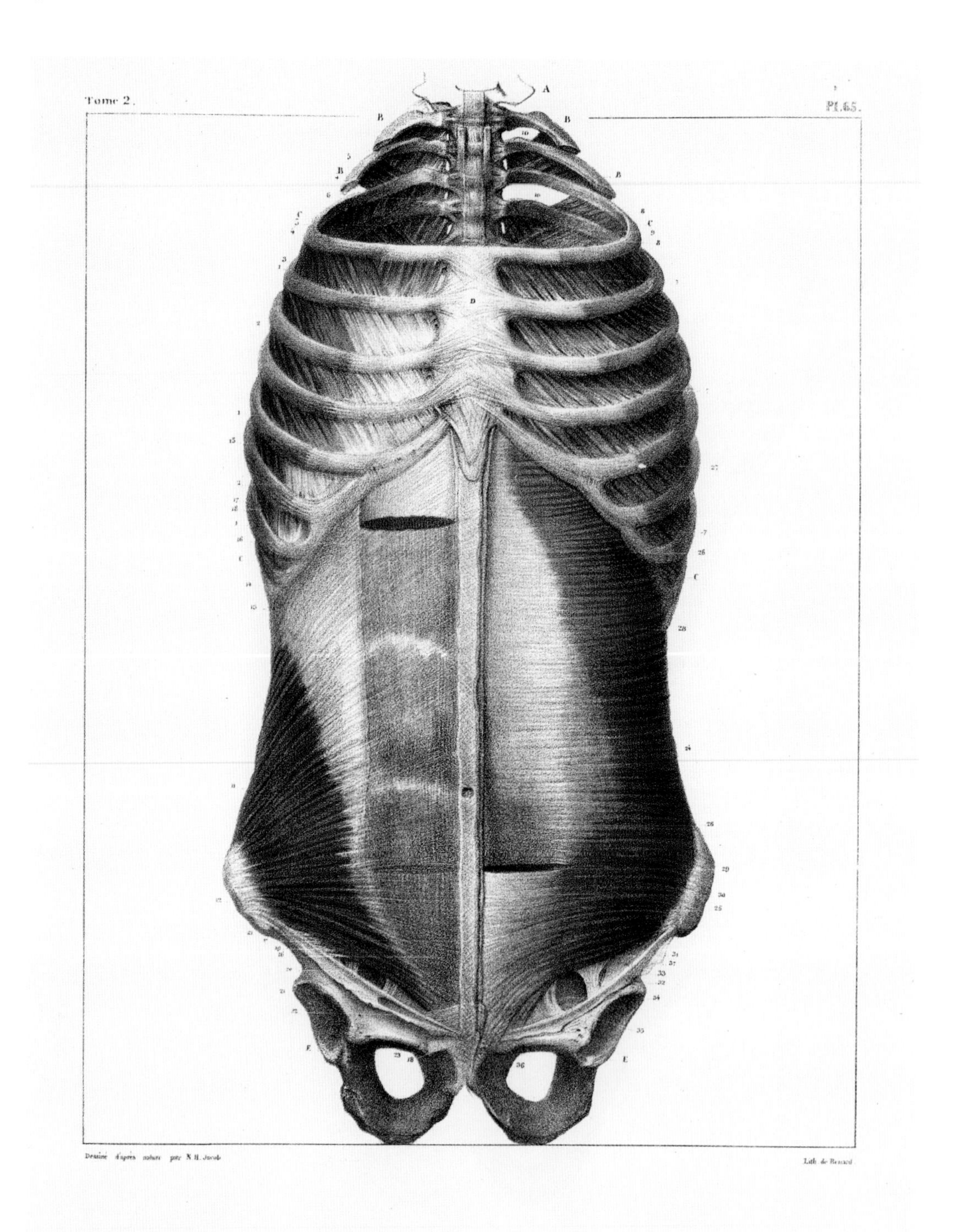

Thoracic and abdominal muscles / Muscles thoraciques et abdominaux
Músculos torácicos y abdominales

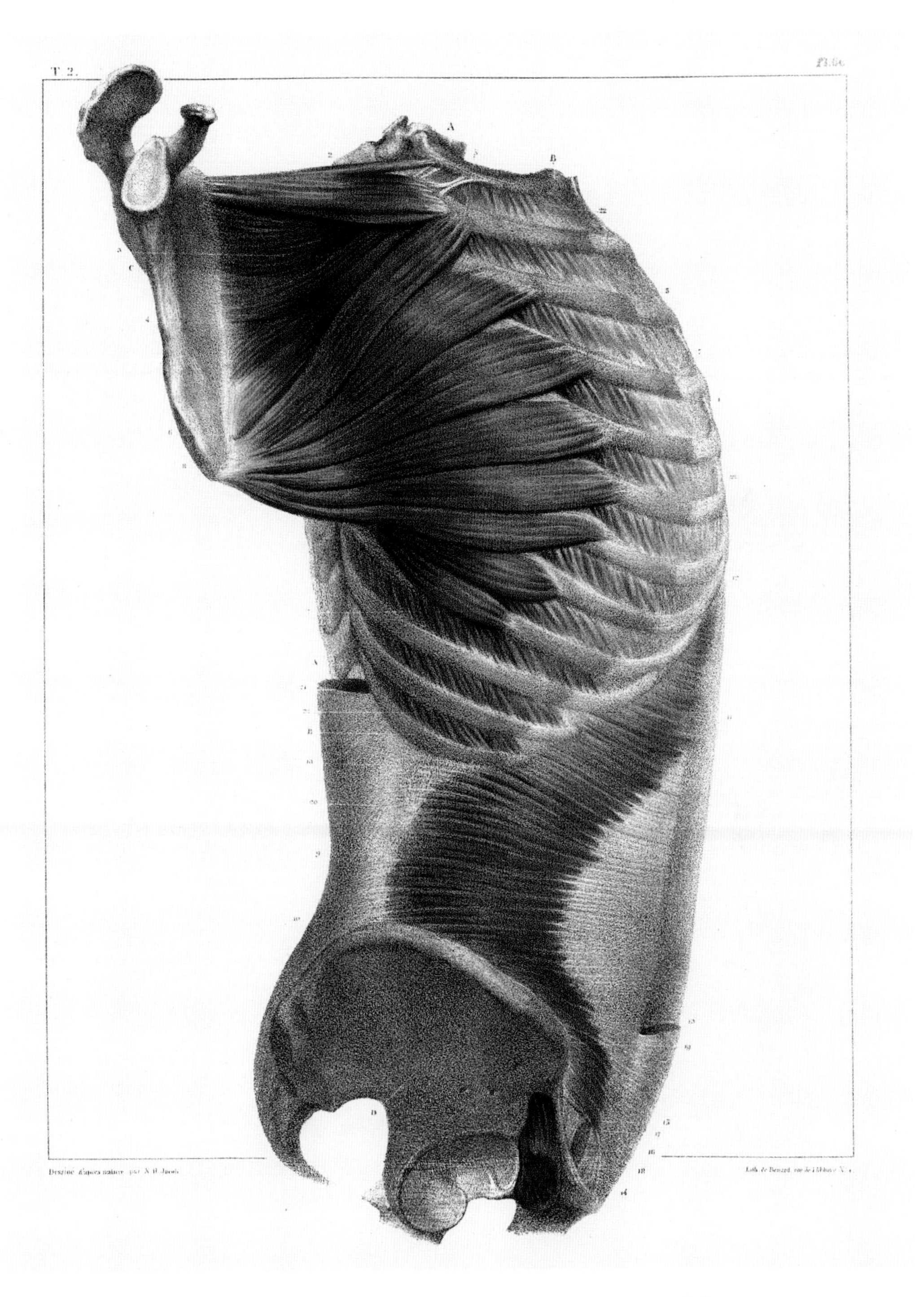

Thoracic and abdominal muscles / Muscles thoraciques et abdominaux
Músculos torácicos y abdominales

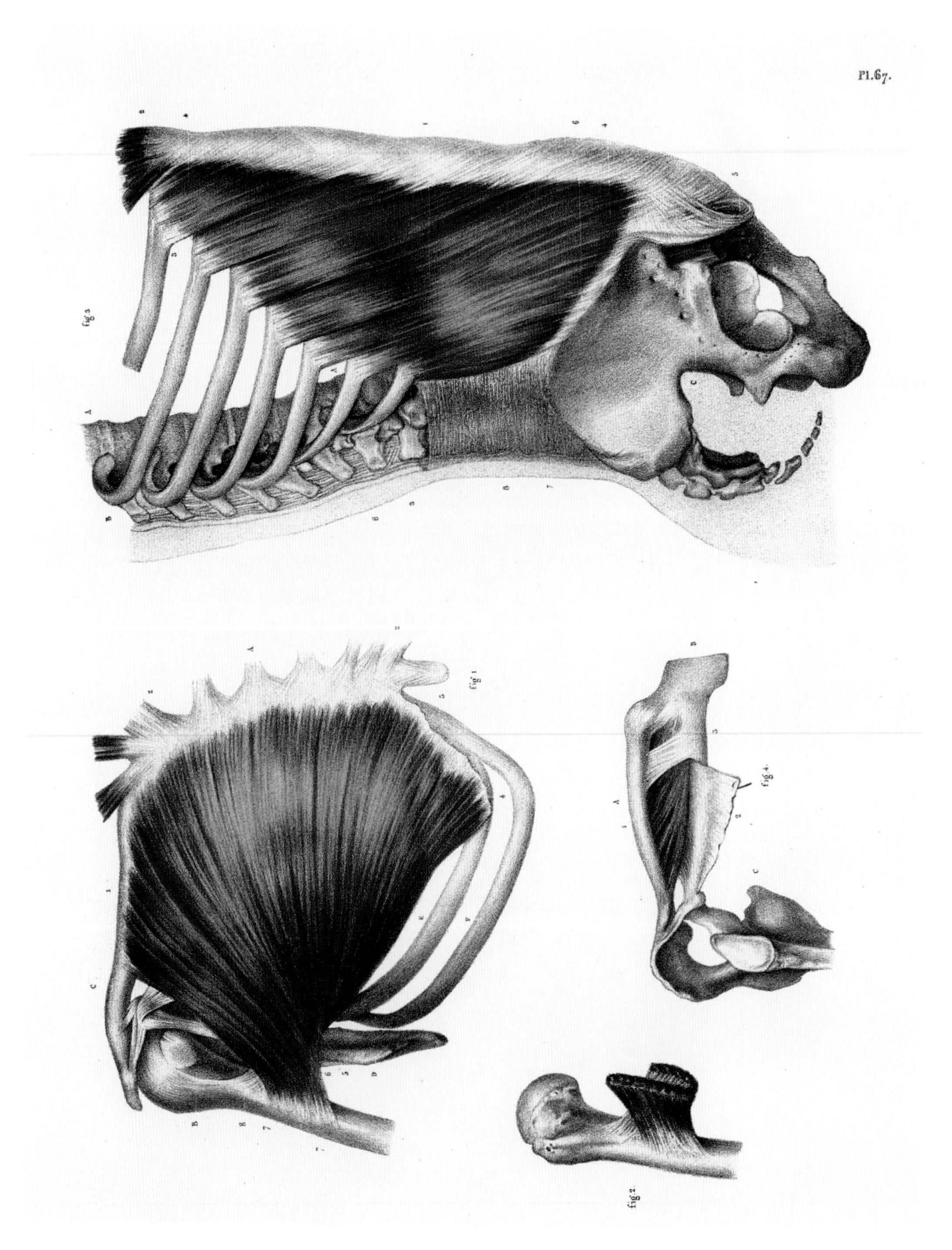

Thoracic and abdominal muscles / Muscles thoraciques et abdominaux
Músculos torácicos y abdominales

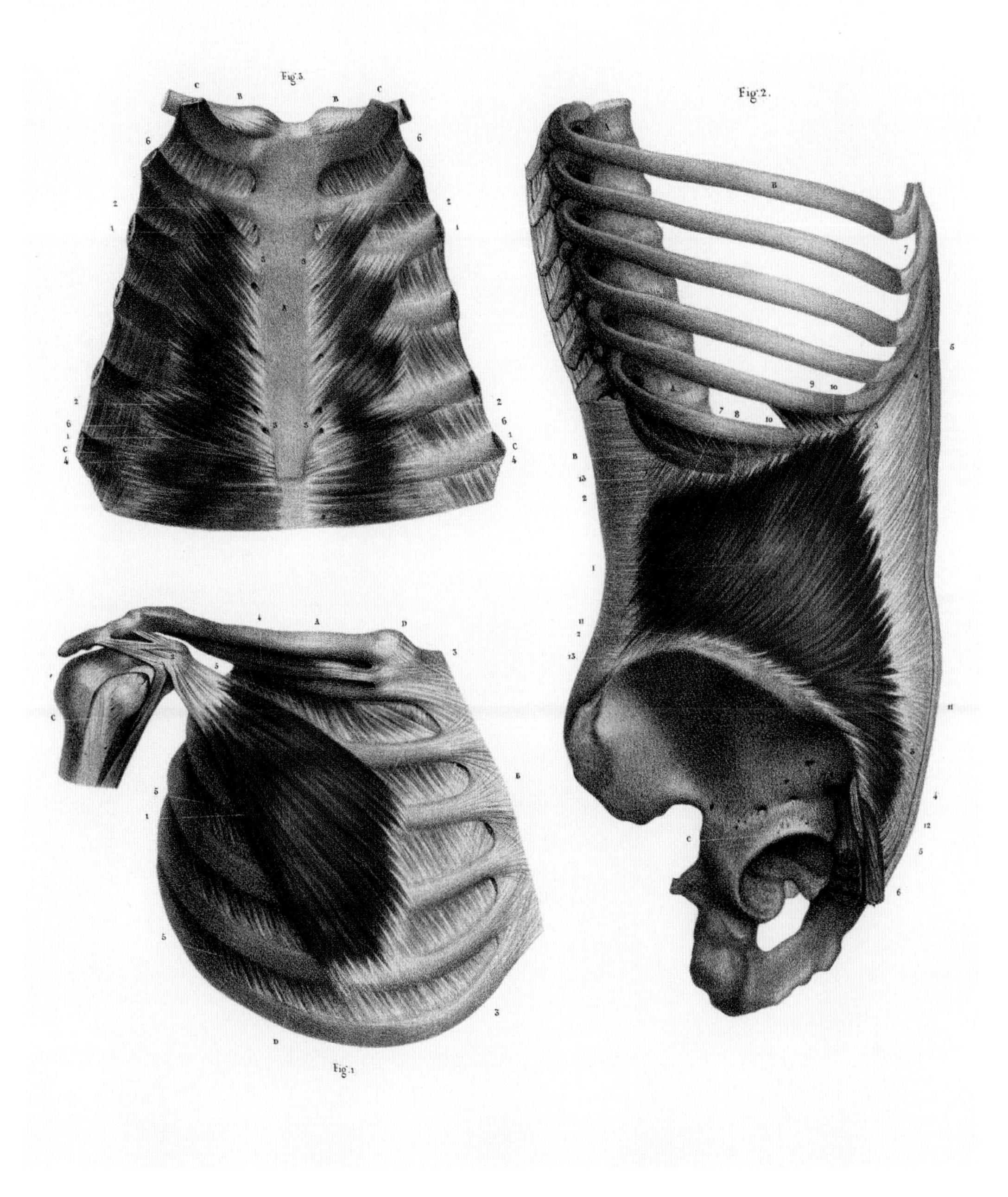

Thoracic and abdominal muscles / Muscles thoraciques et abdominaux
Músculos torácicos y abdominales

Abdominal muscles. Inguinal canal / Muscles abdominaux. Canal inguinal
Músculos abdominales. Conducto inguinal

Abdominal muscles. Inguinal canal / Muscles abdominaux. Canal inguinal
Músculos abdominales. Conducto inguinal

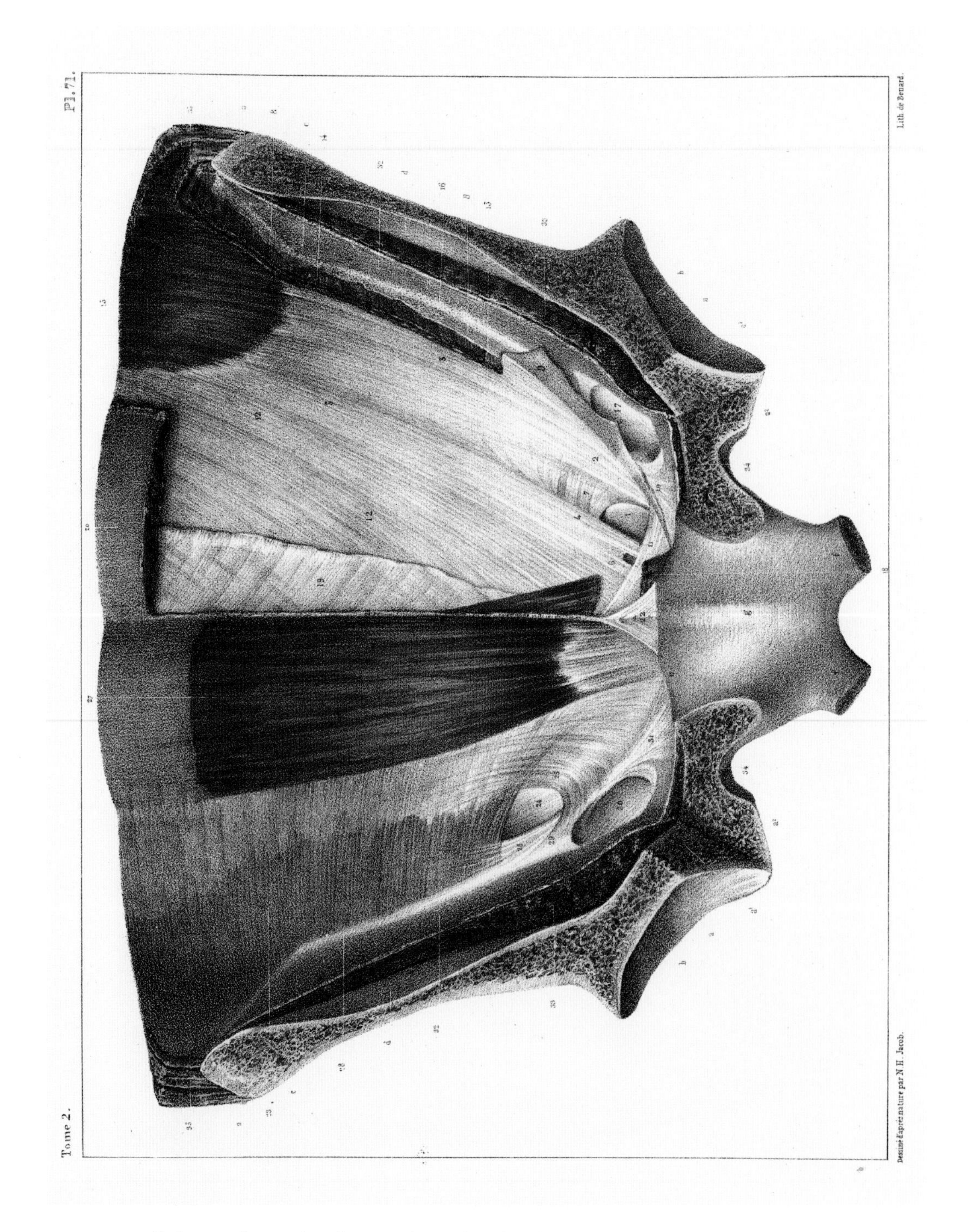

Abdominal muscles. Inguinal canal / Muscles abdominaux. Canal inguinal
Músculos abdominales. Conducto inguinal

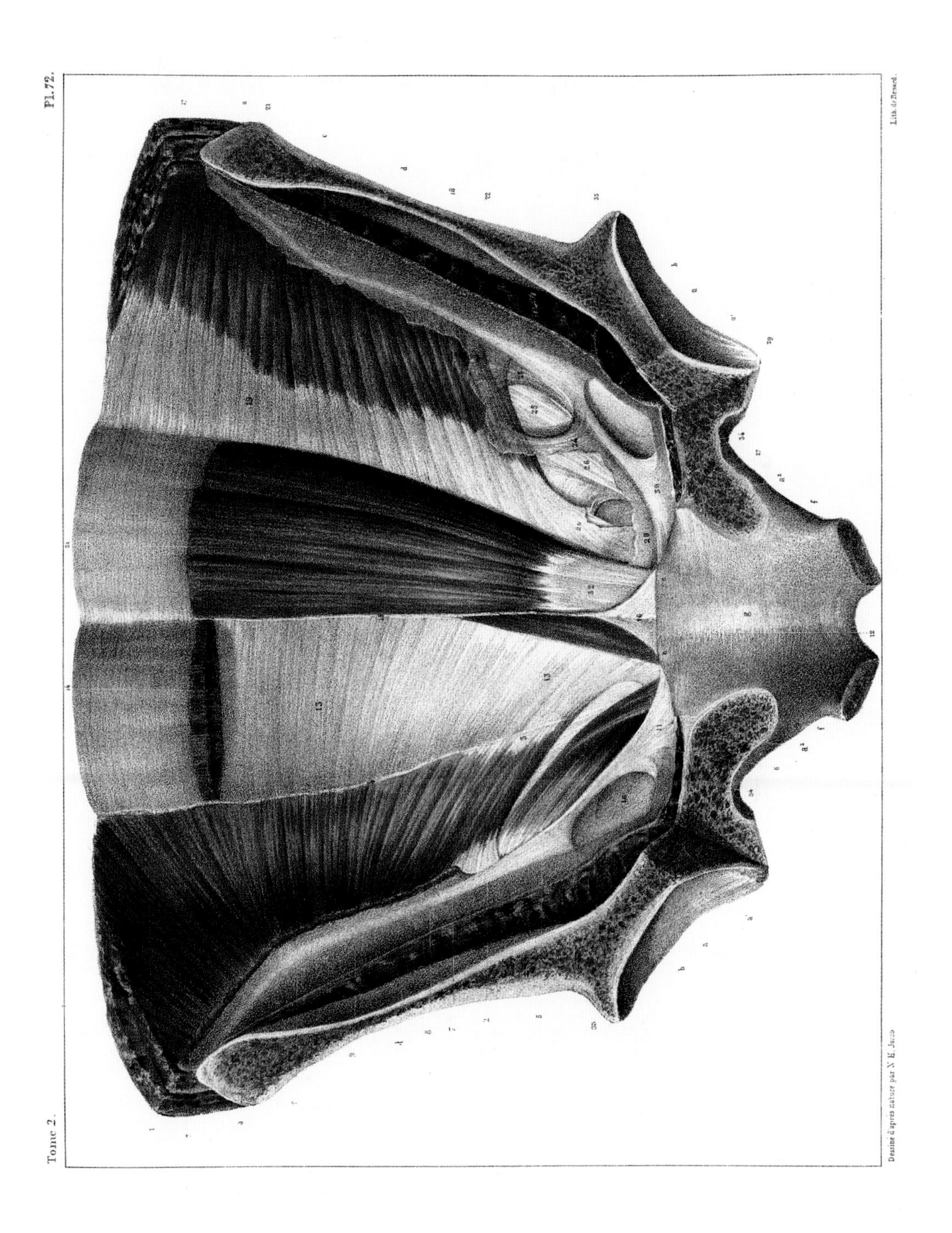

Abdominal muscles. Inguinal canal / Muscles abdominaux. Canal inguinal
Músculos abdominales. Conducto inguinal

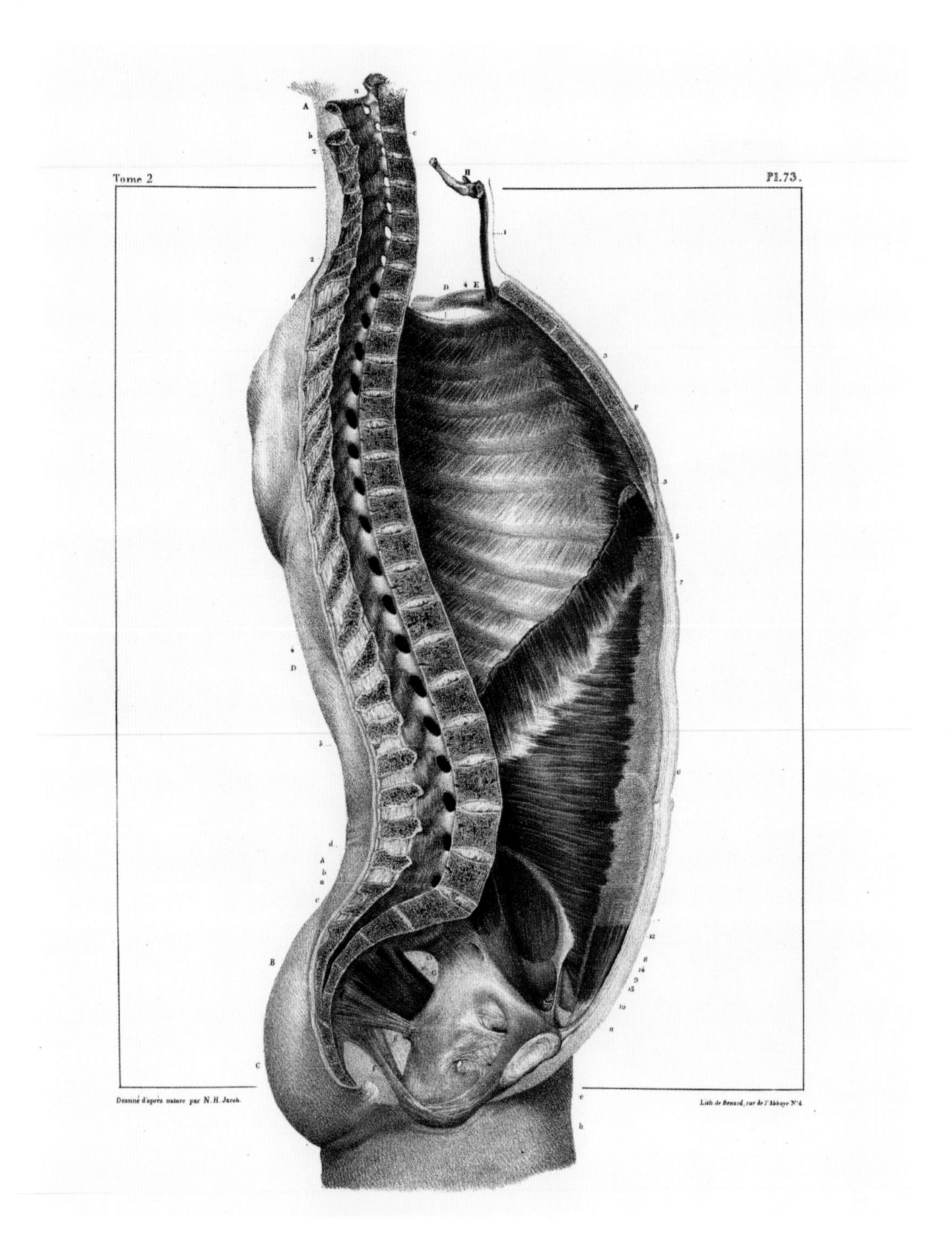

Thoracic and abdominal muscles / Muscles thoraciques et abdominaux
Músculos torácicos y abdominales

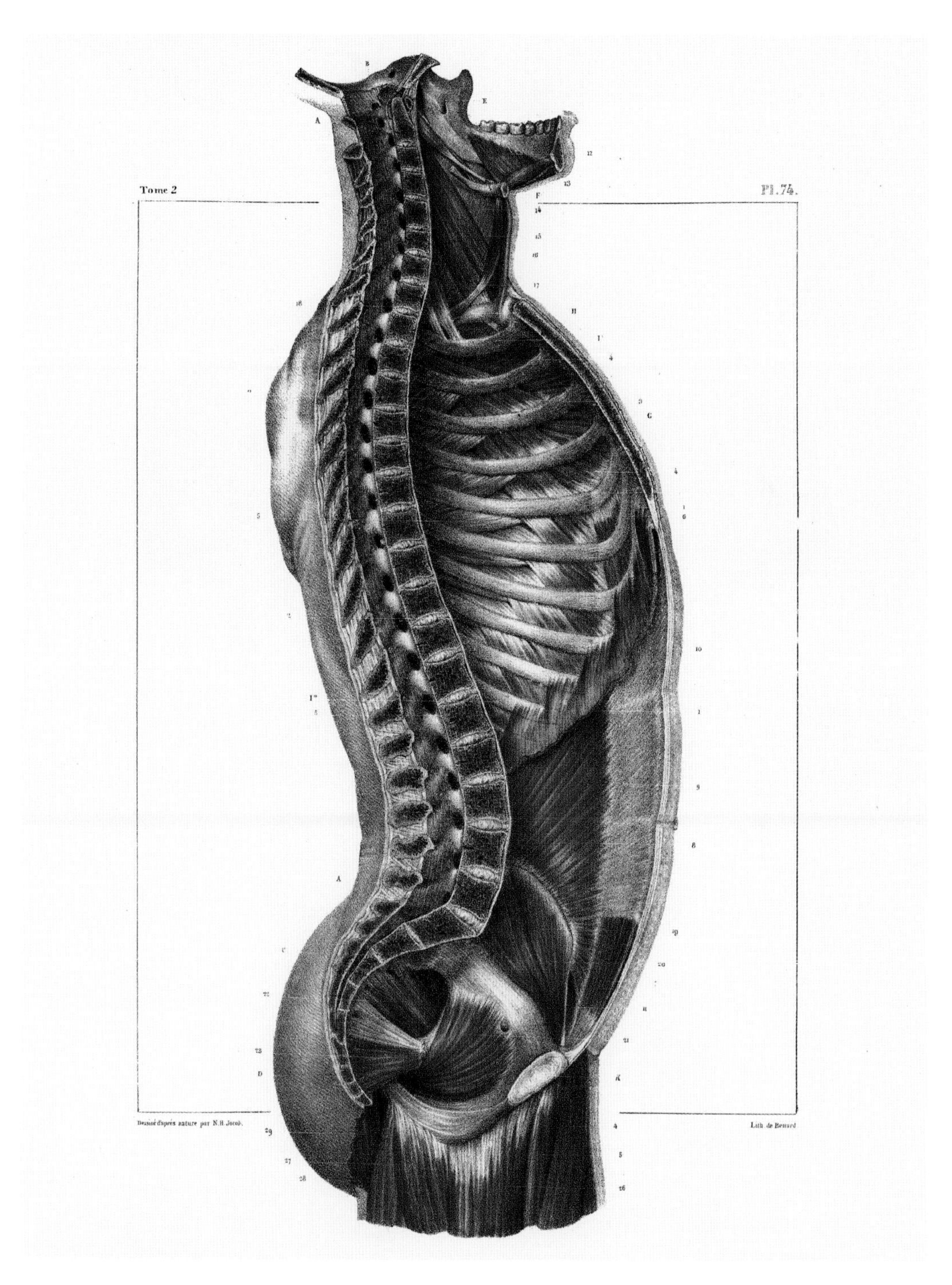

Thoracic and abdominal muscles / Muscles thoraciques et abdominaux
Músculos torácicos y abdominales

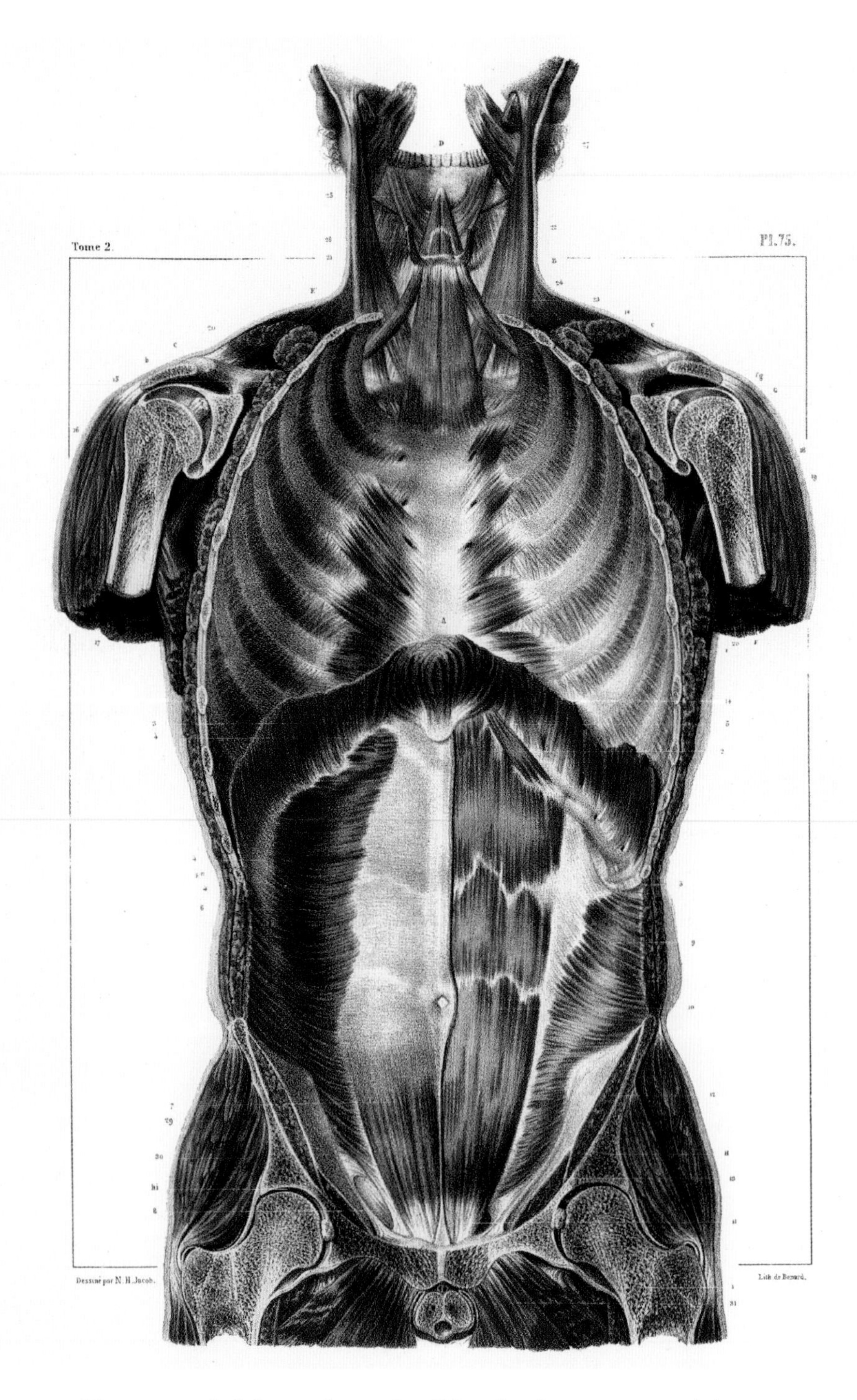

Thoracic and abdominal muscles / Muscles thoraciques et abdominaux
Músculos torácicos y abdominales

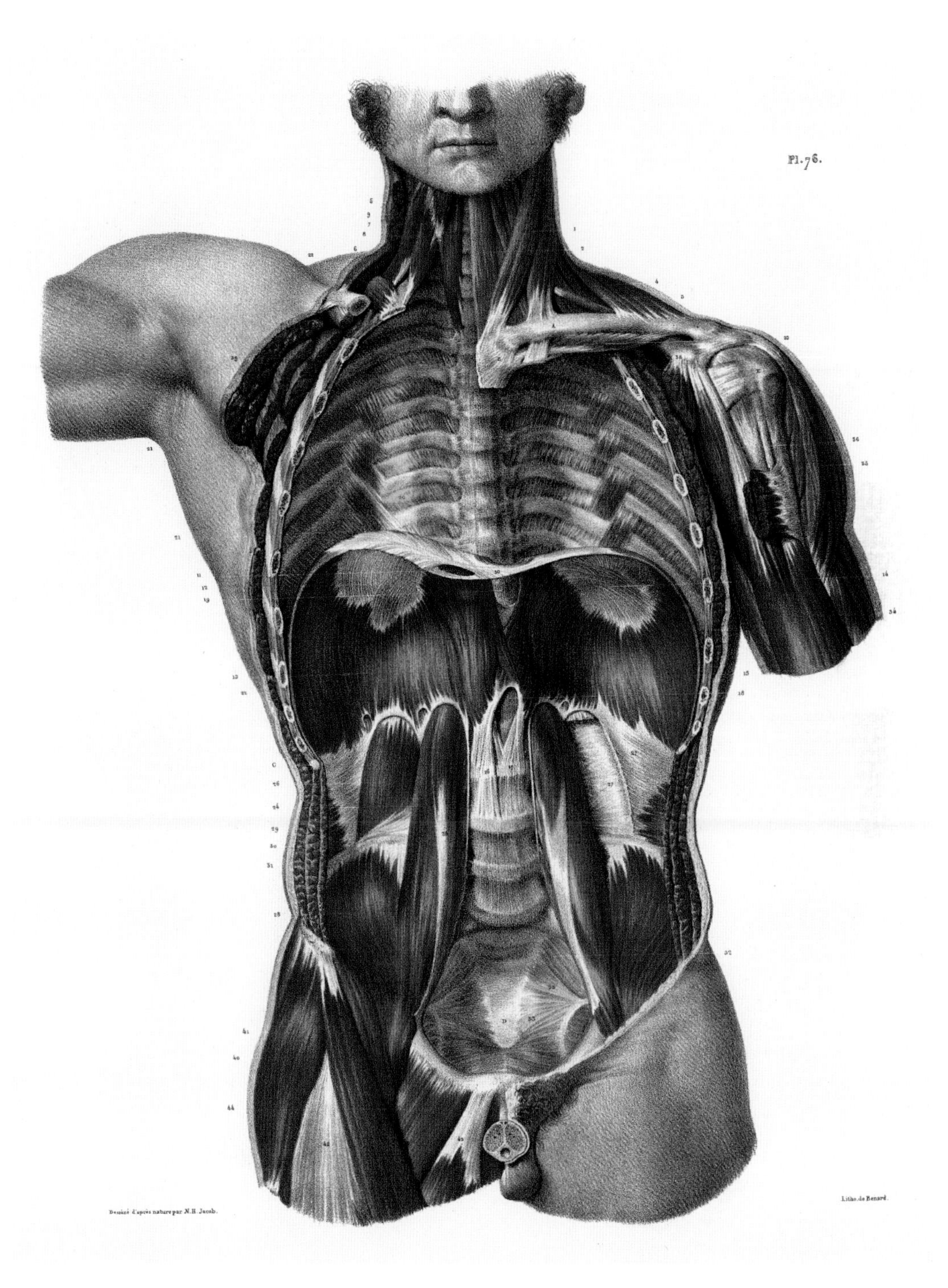

Thoracic and abdominal muscles / Muscles thoraciques et abdominaux
Músculos torácicos y abdominales

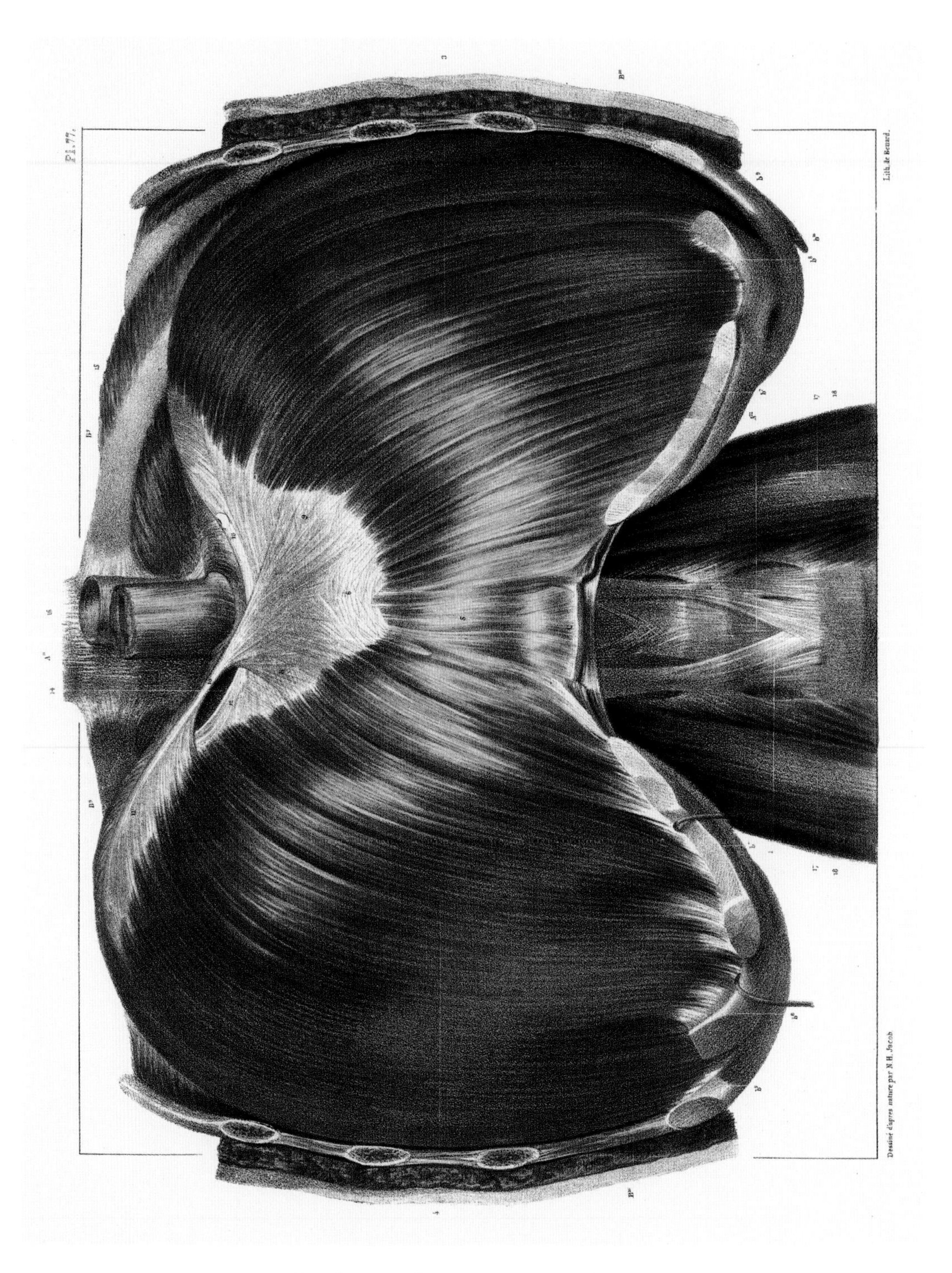

Diaphragm / Diaphragme / Diafragma

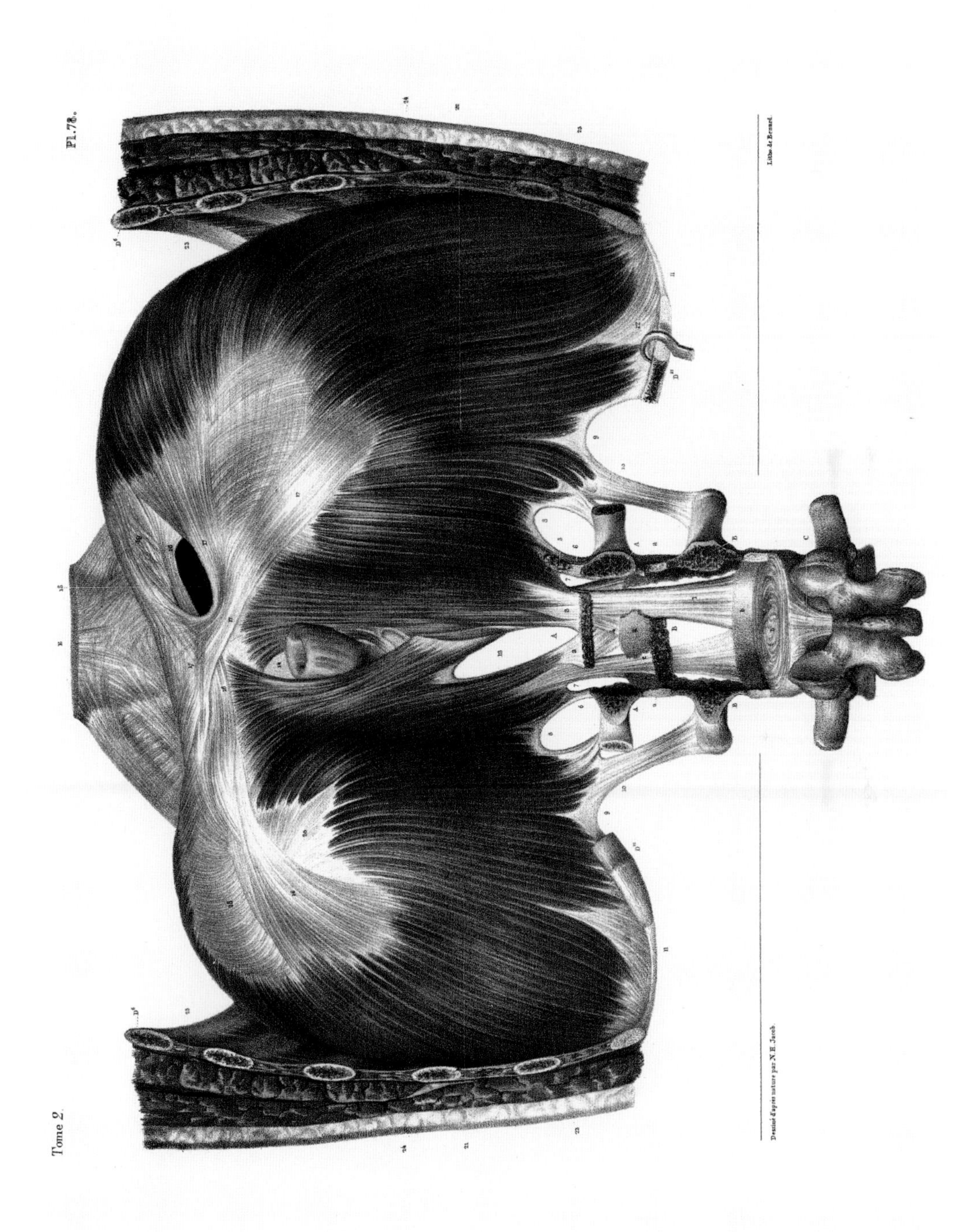

Diaphragm / Diaphragme / Diafragma

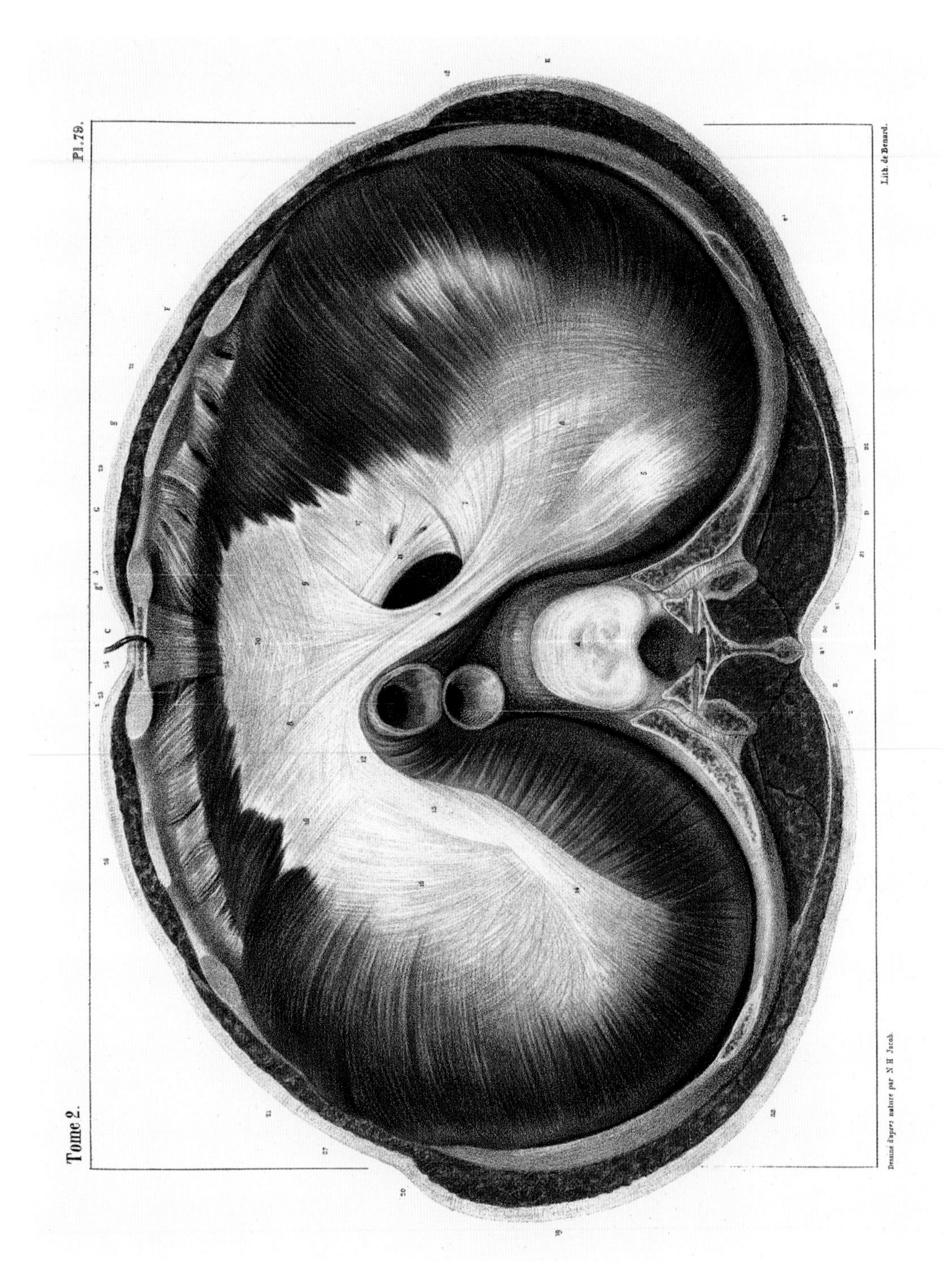

Diaphragm / Diaphragme / Diafragma

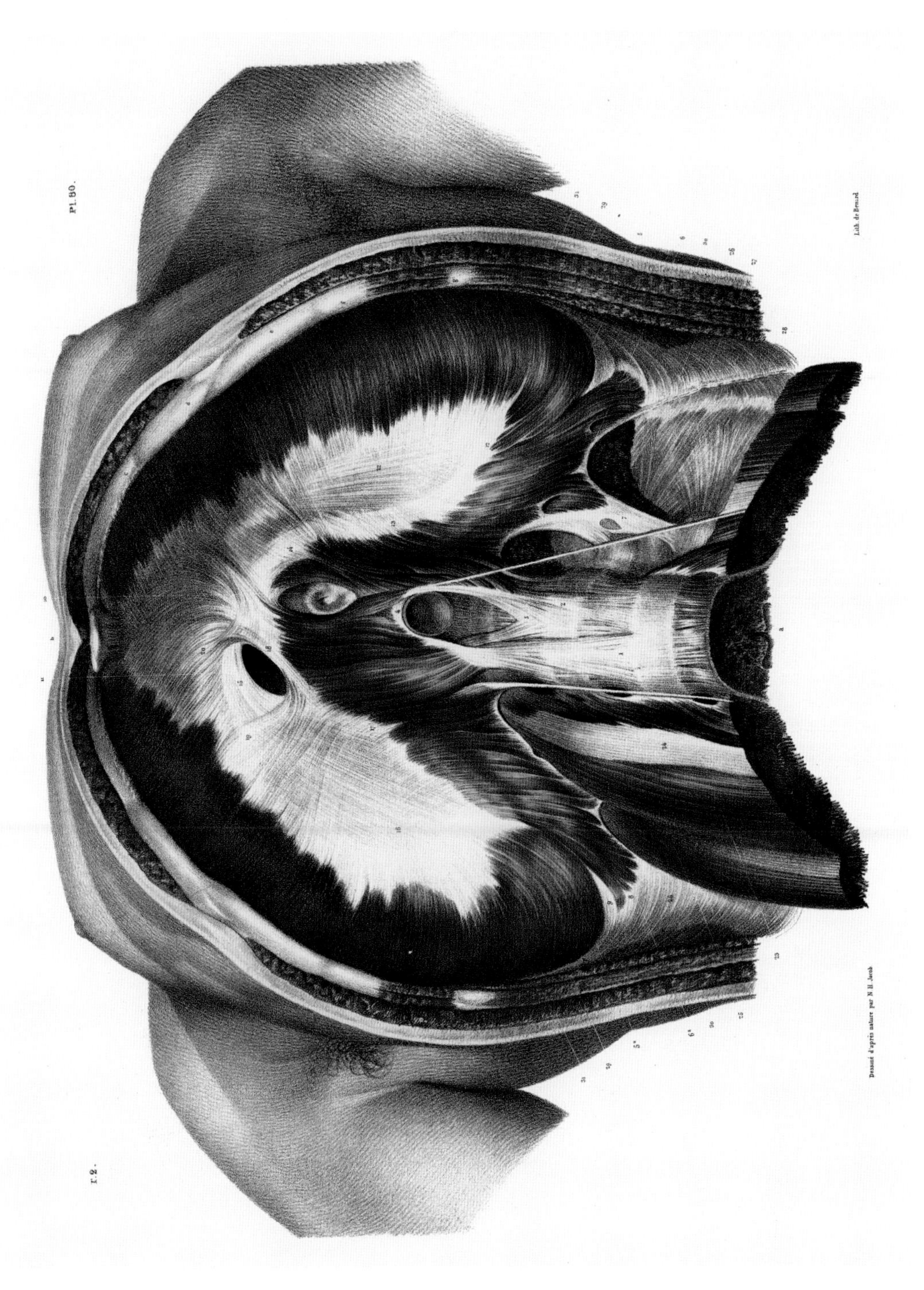

Diaphragm / Diaphragme / Diafragma

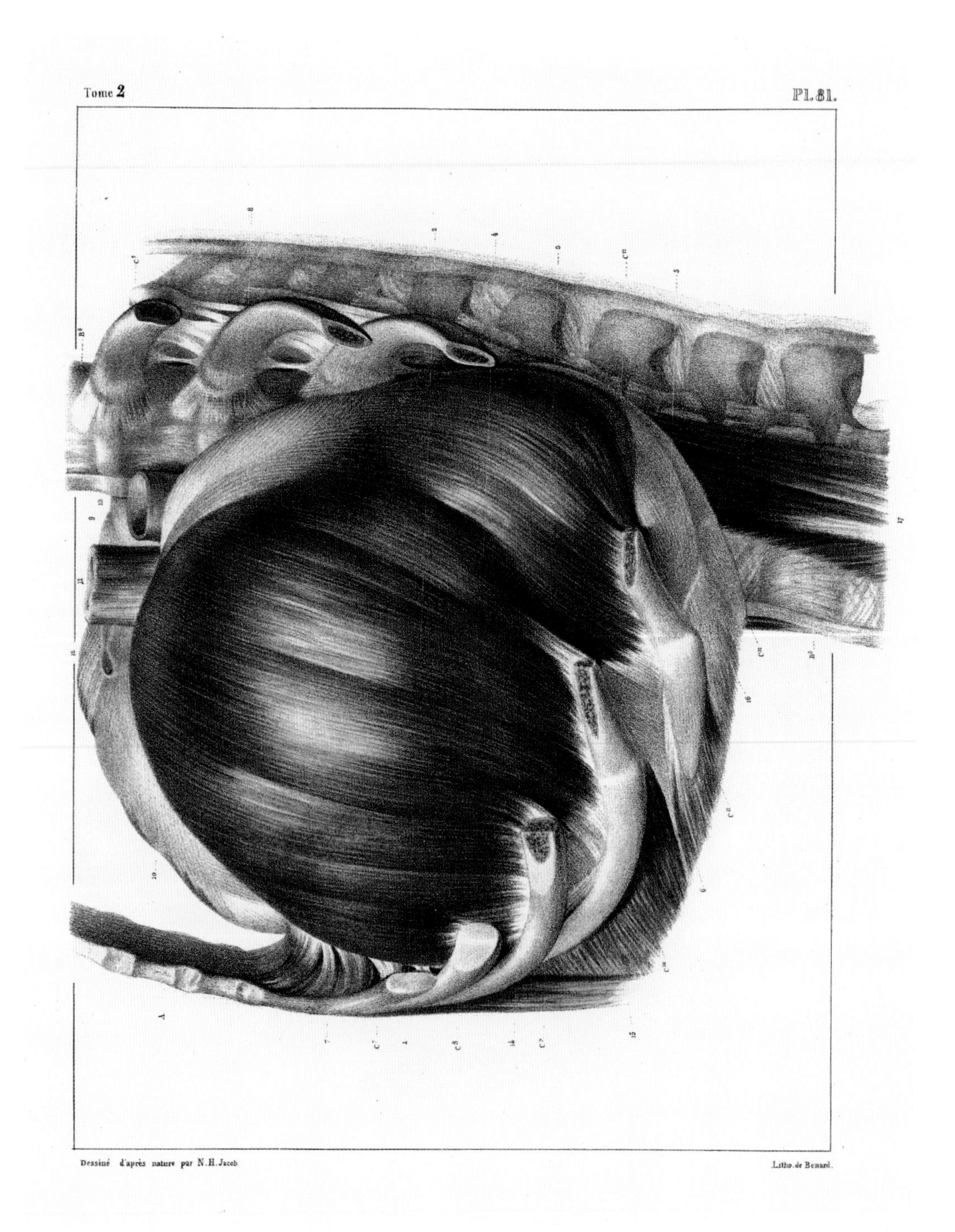

Diaphragm / Diaphragme / Diafragma

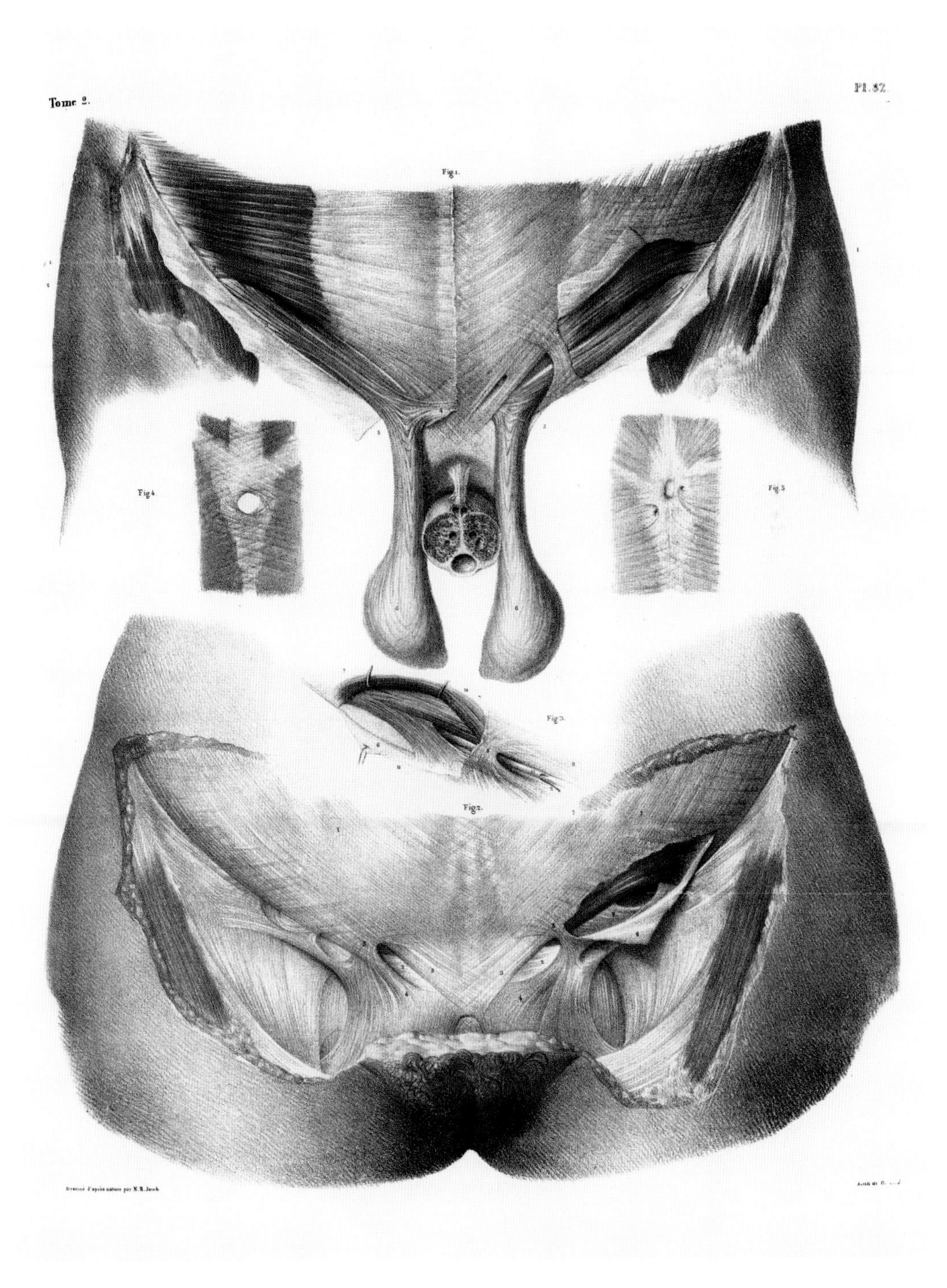

Inguinal canal. Umbilical ring / Canal inguinal. Anneau ombilical
Conducto inguinal. Anillo umbilical

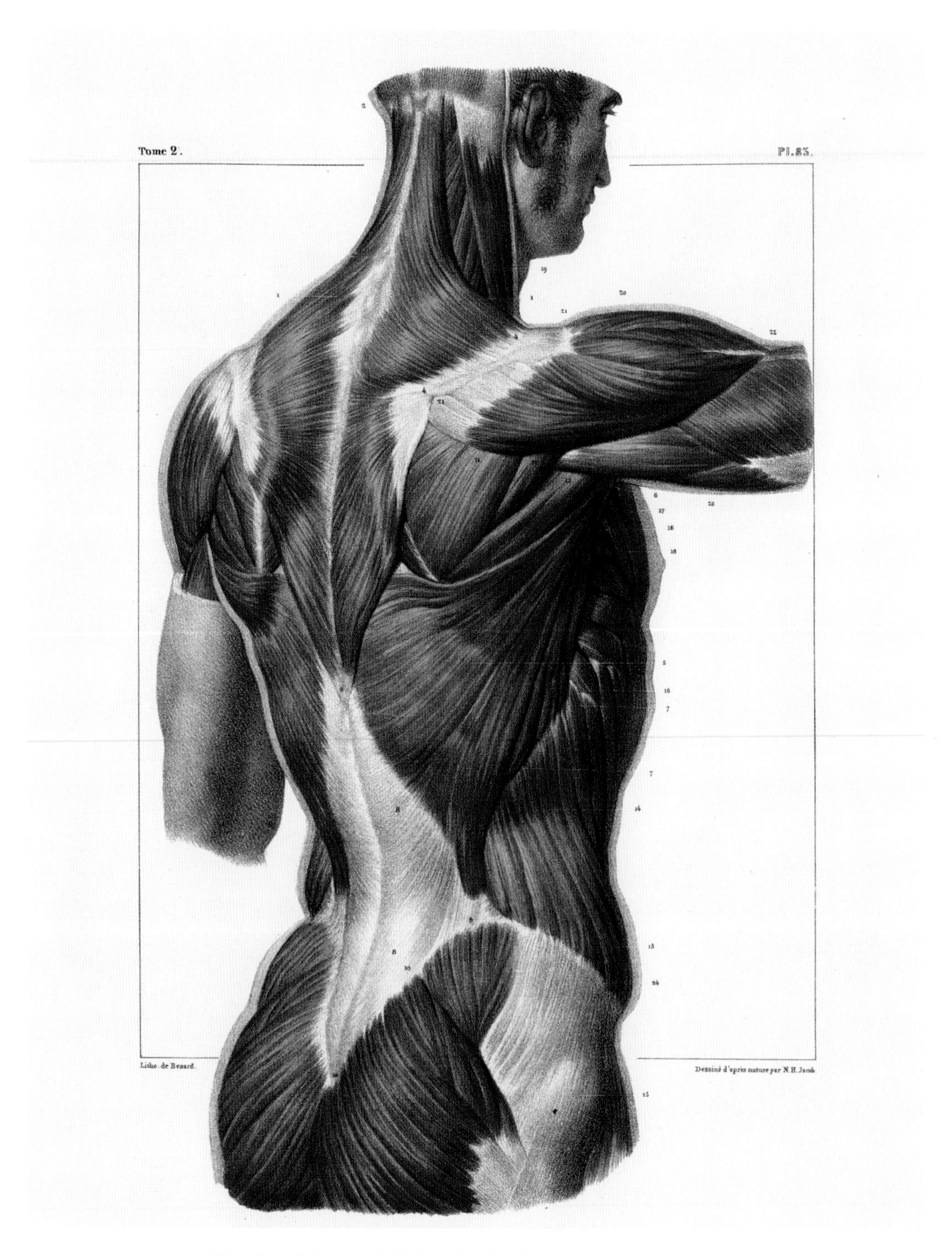

Muscles of the back / Muscles du dos / Músculos del dorso

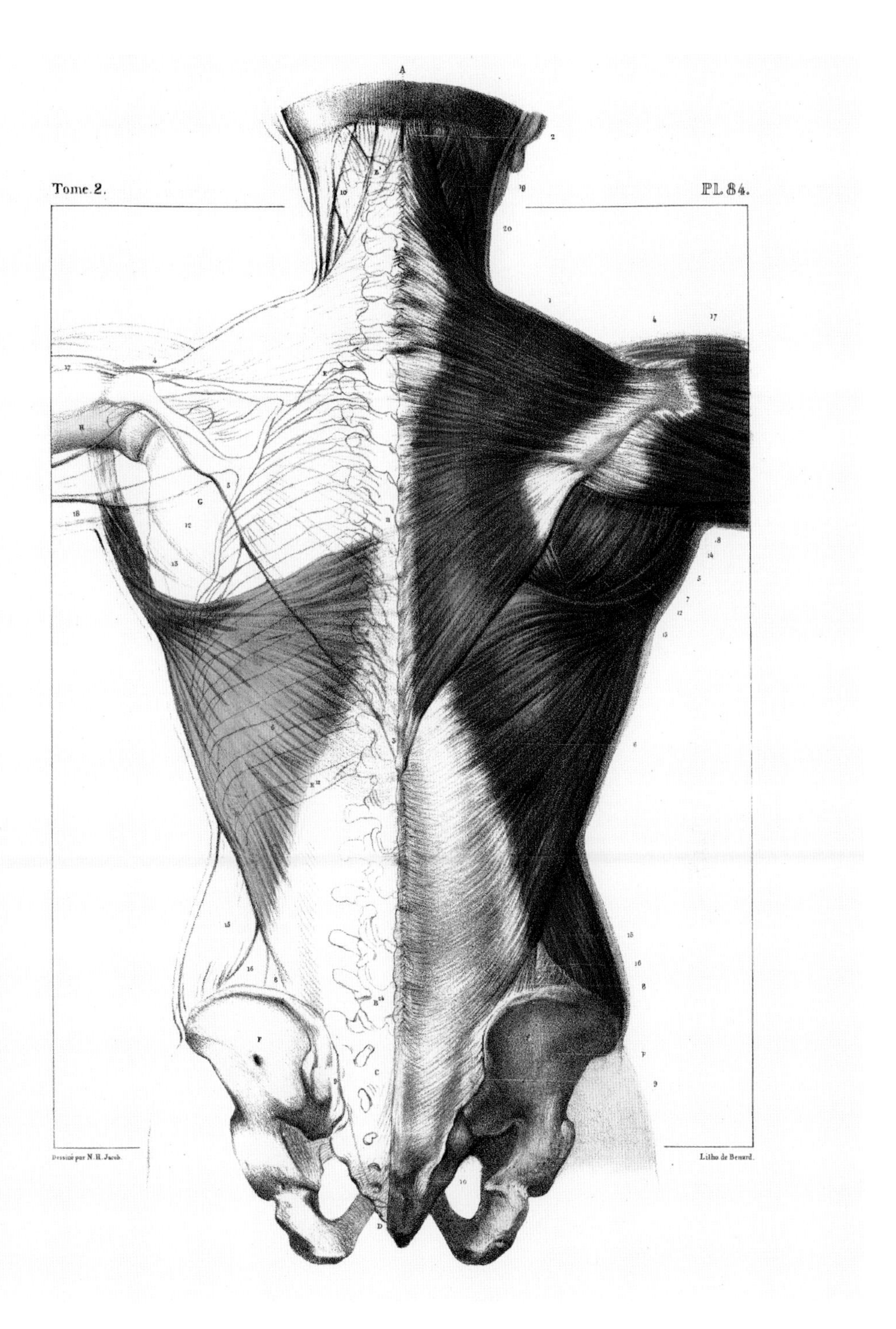

Muscles of the back / Muscles du dos / Músculos del dorso

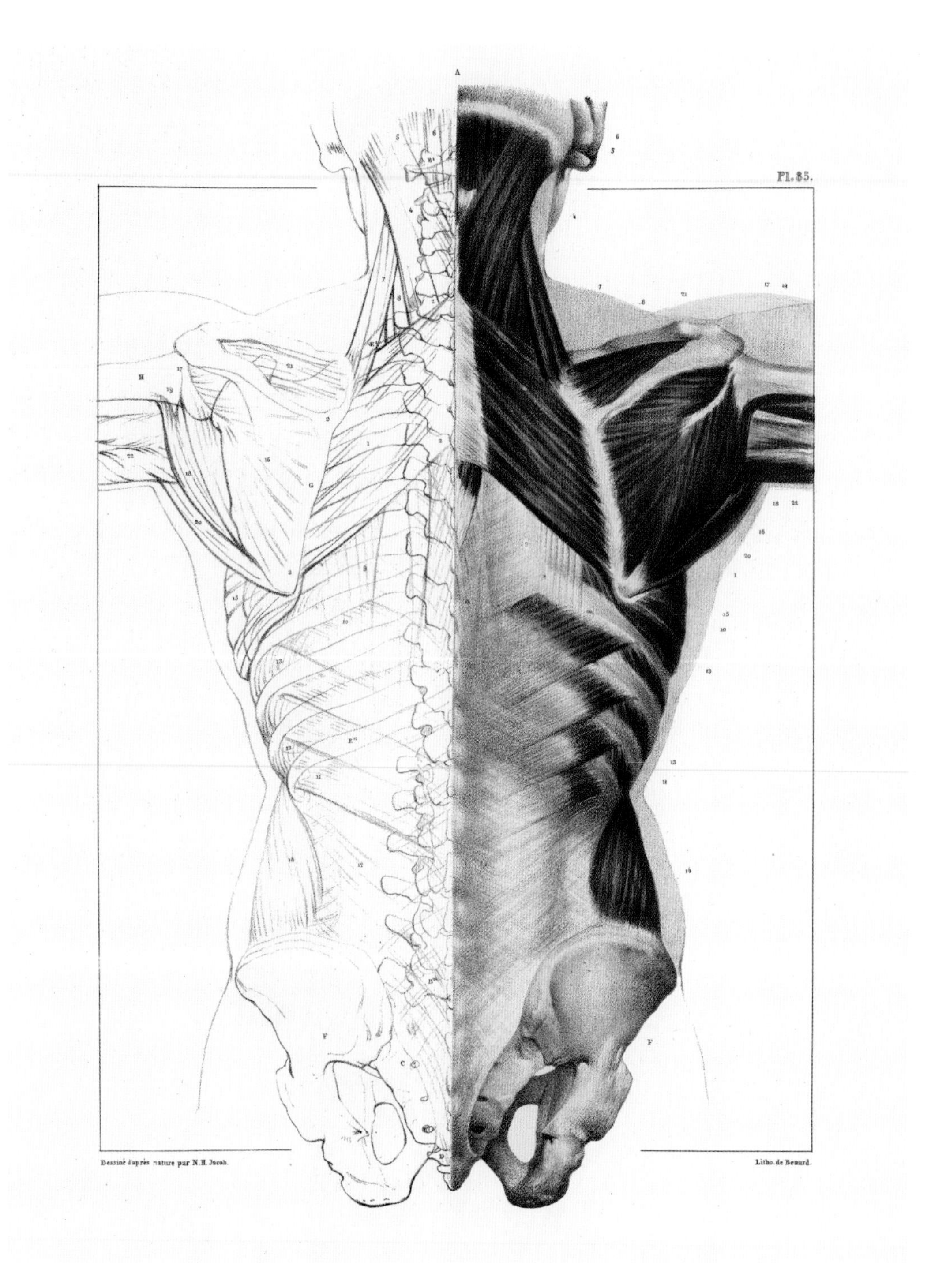

Muscles of the back / Muscles du dos / Músculos del dorso

Muscles of the erector spinae / Muscles érecteurs spinaux
Músculos erectores de la columna

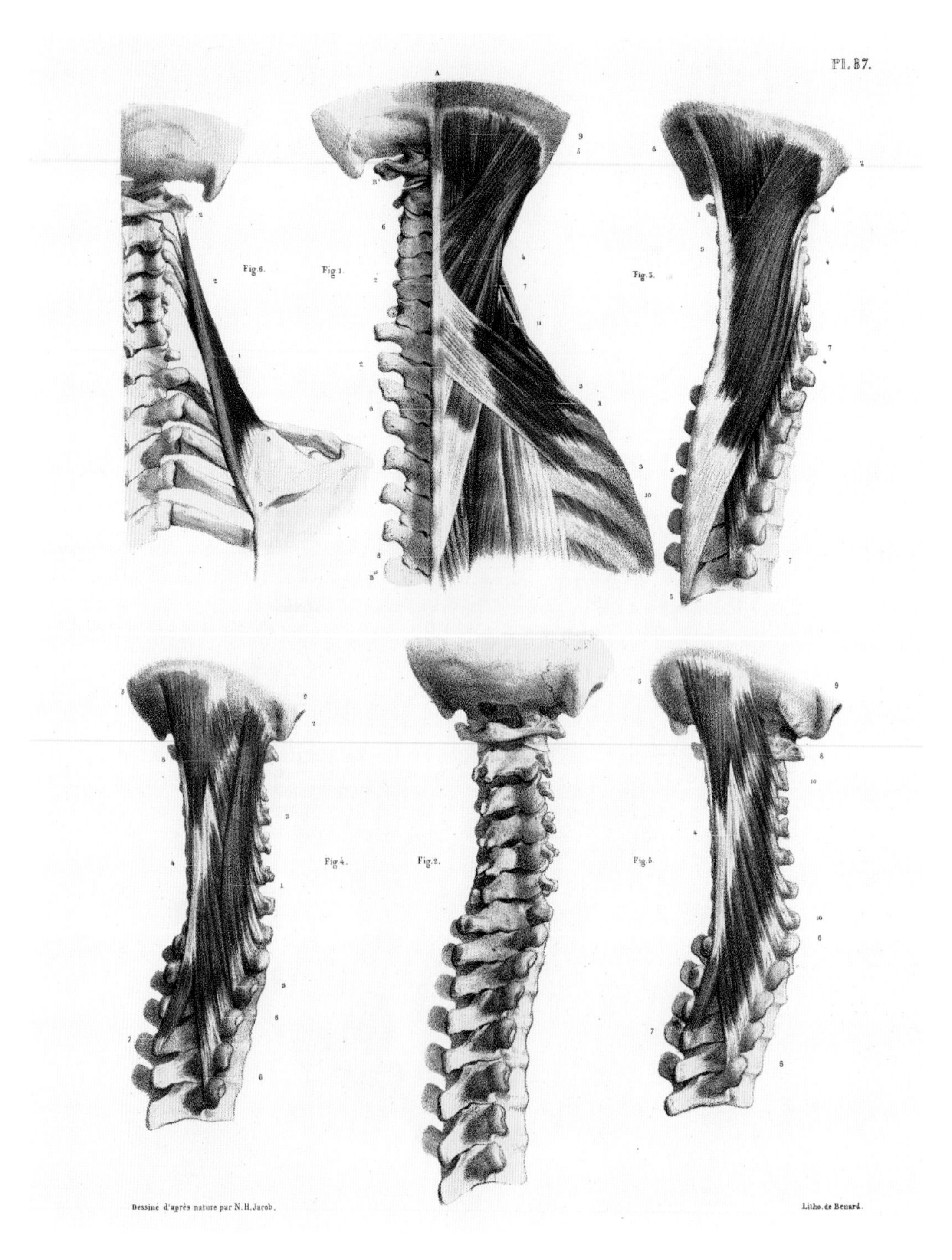

Muscles of the erector spinae: Muscles of the nape of the neck
Muscles érecteurs spinaux : Muscles de la nuque
Músculos erectores de la columna: Músculos de la nuca

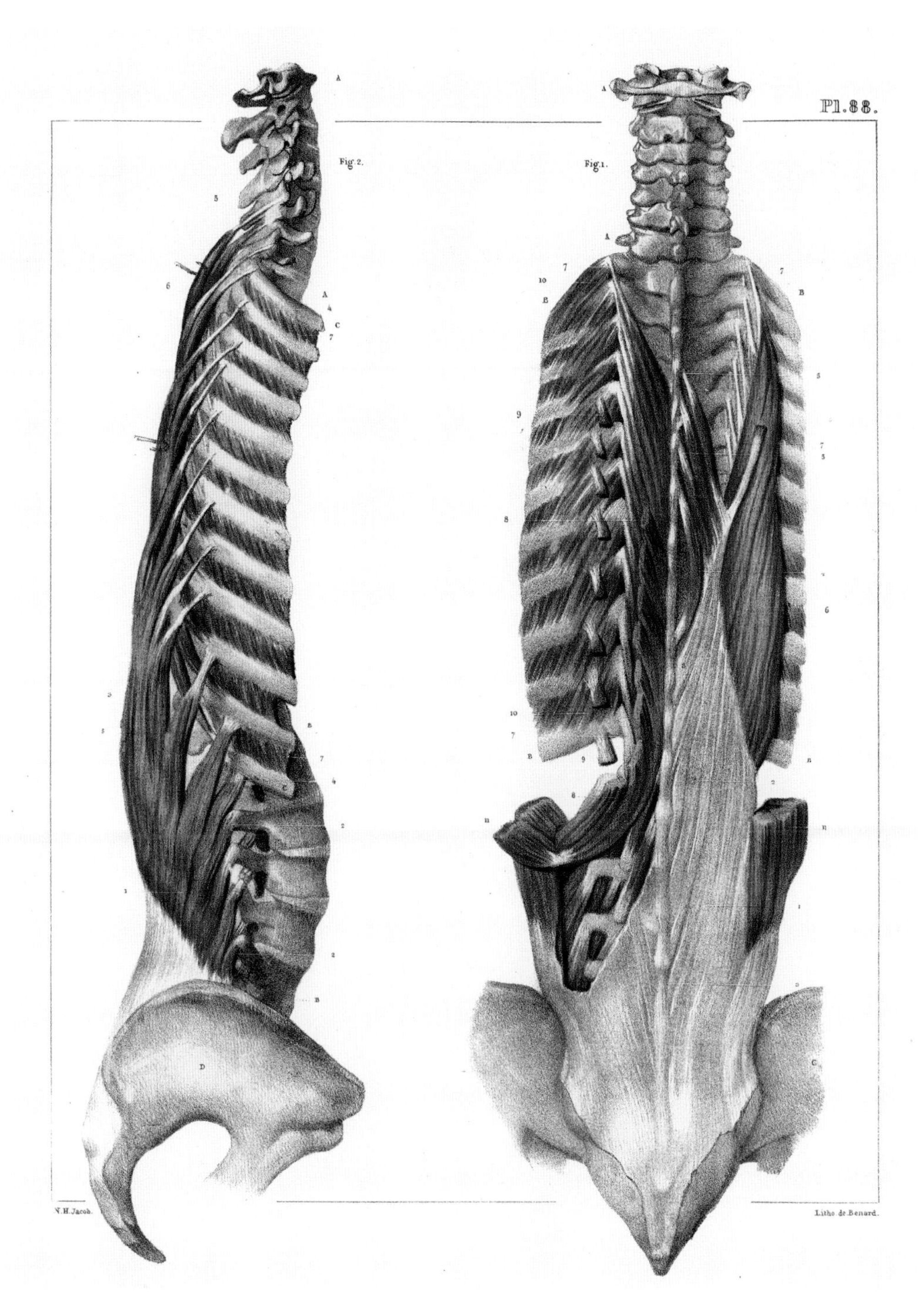

Muscles of the erector spinae
Muscles érecteurs spinaux
Músculos erectores de la columna

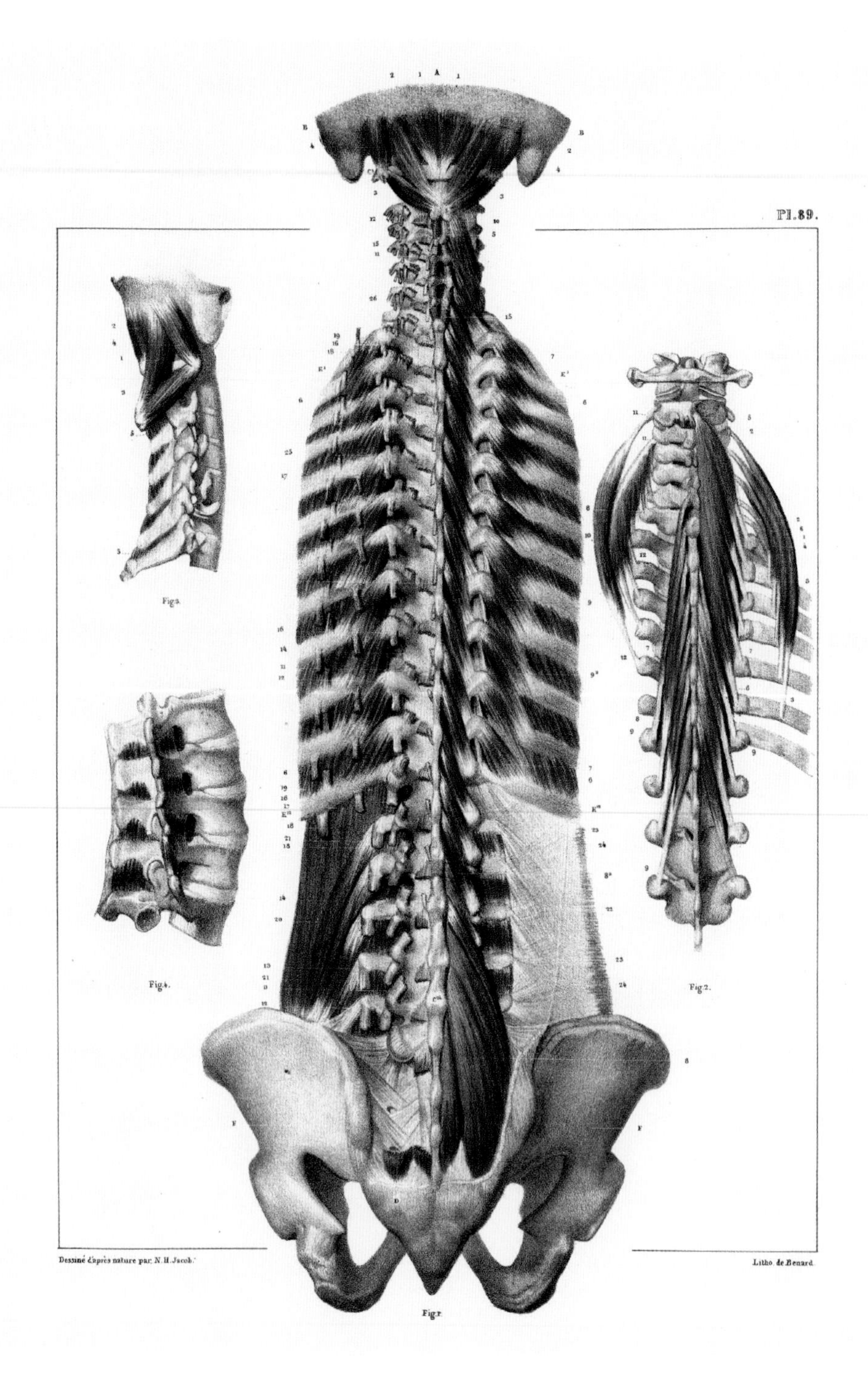

Muscles of the erector spinae / Muscles érecteurs spinaux
Músculos erectores de la columna

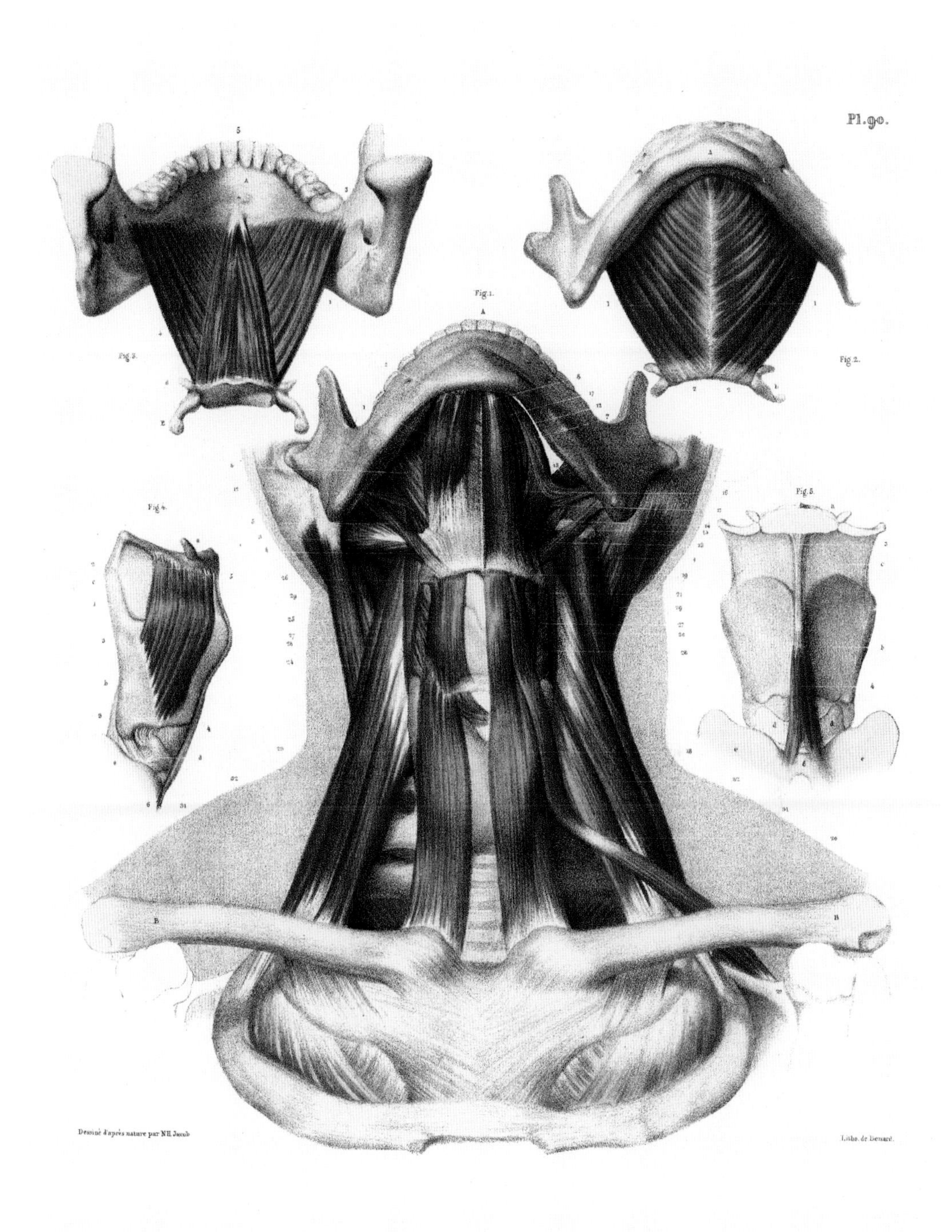

Muscles of the neck / Muscles du cou / Músculos del cuello

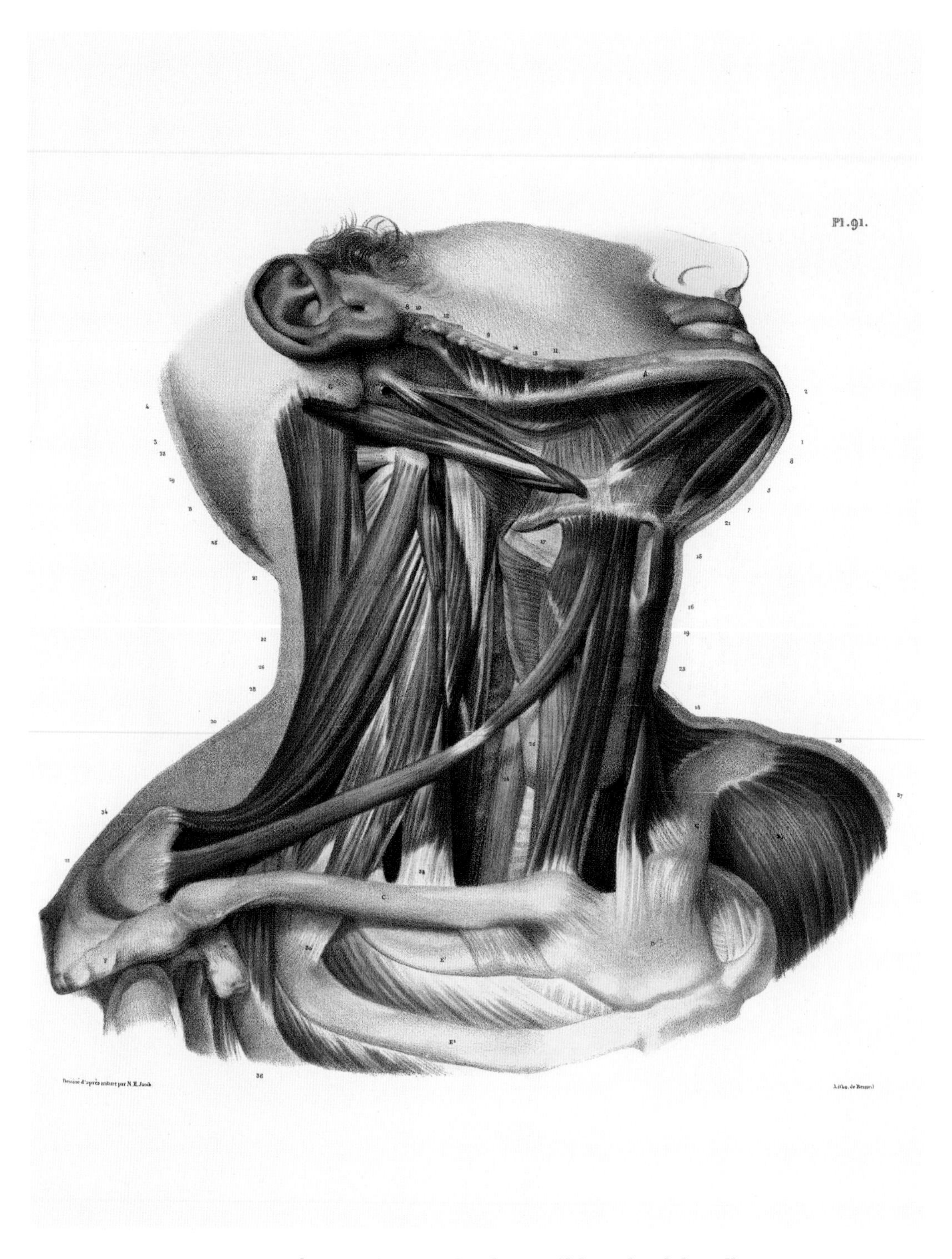

Muscles of the neck / Muscles du cou / Músculos del cuello

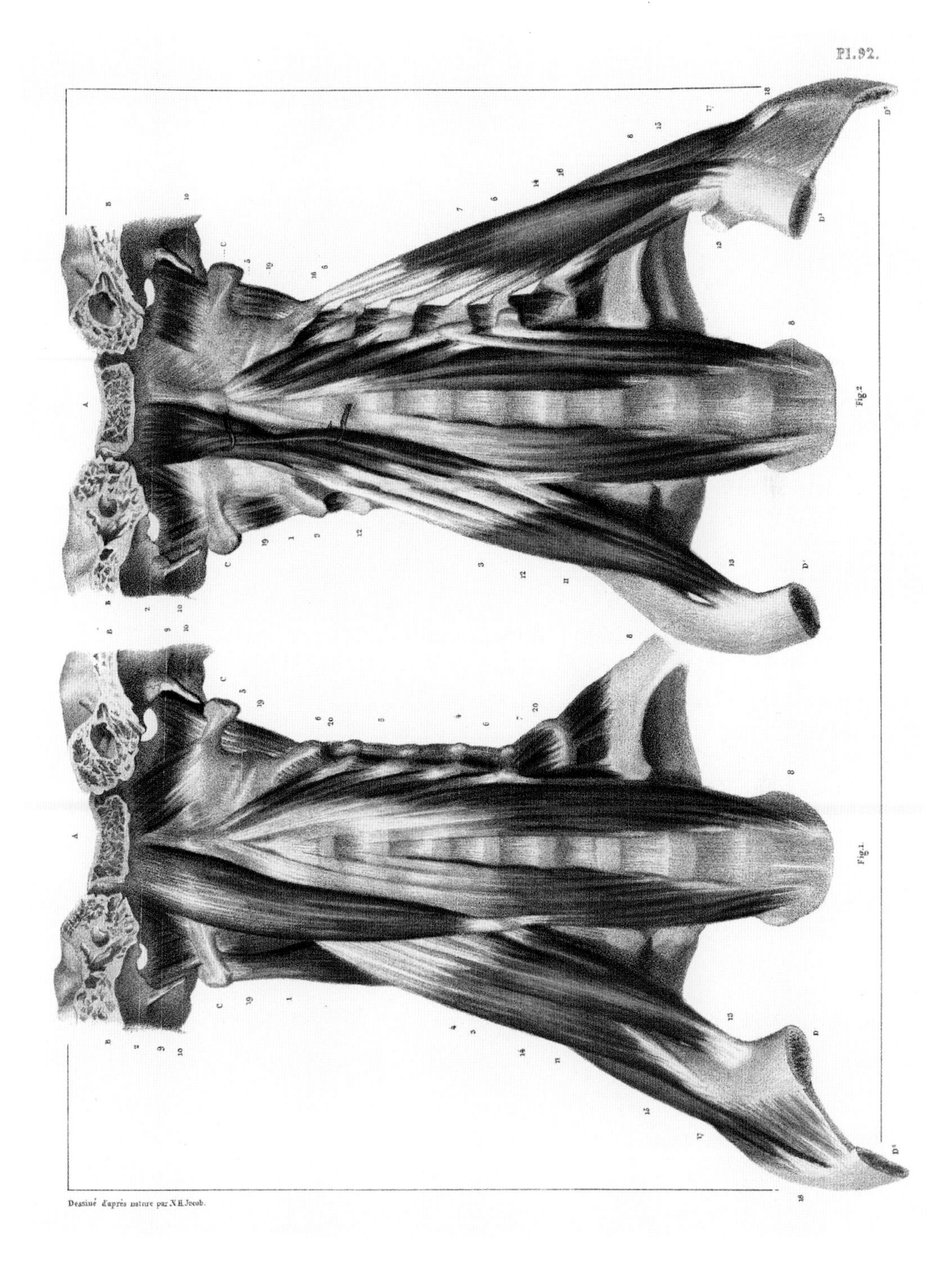

Muscles of the neck / Muscles du cou / Músculos del cuello

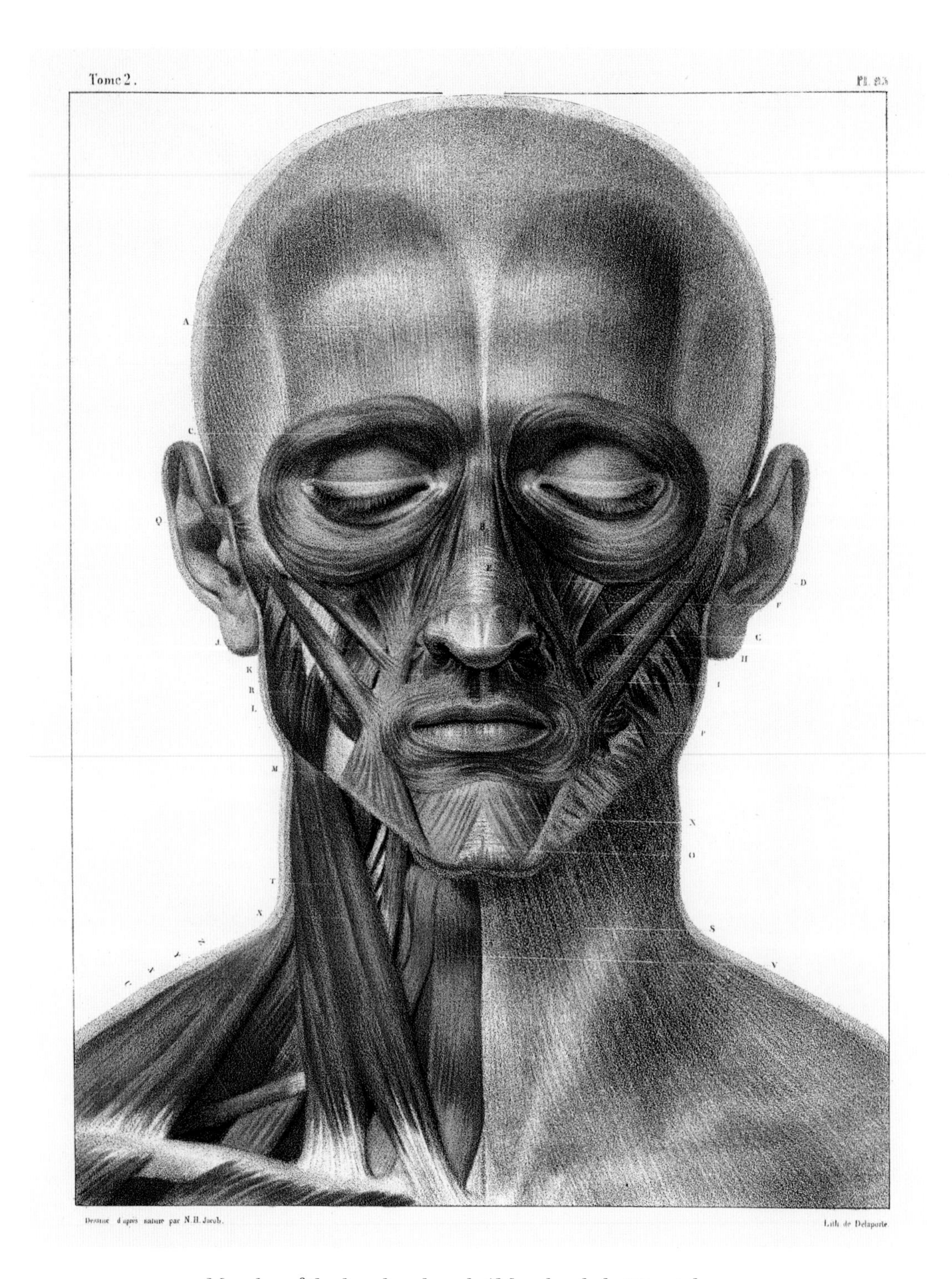

Muscles of the head and neck / Muscles de la tête et du cou
Músculos de la cabeza y del cuello

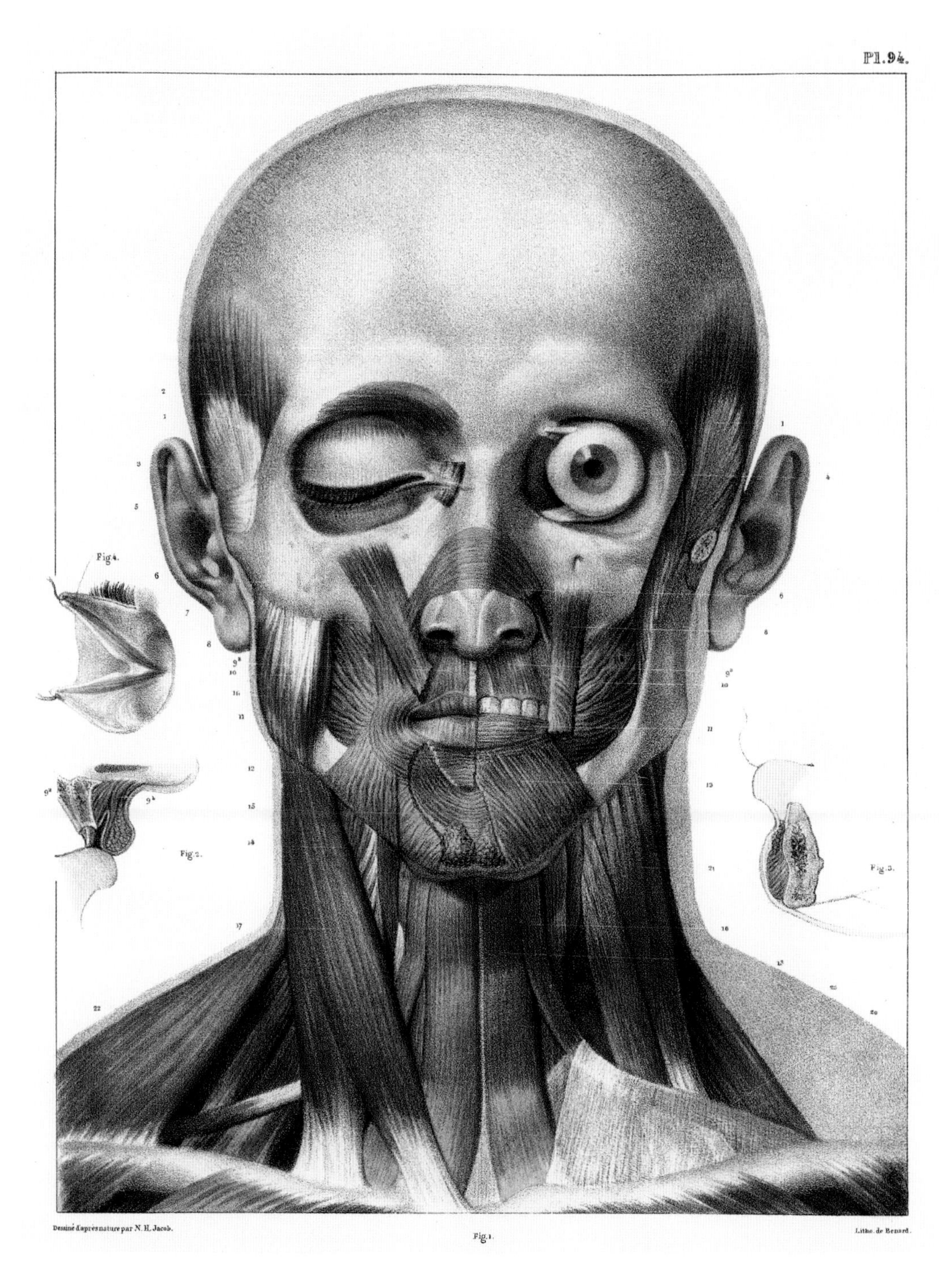

Muscles of the head and neck / Muscles de la tête et du cou
Músculos de la cabeza y del cuello

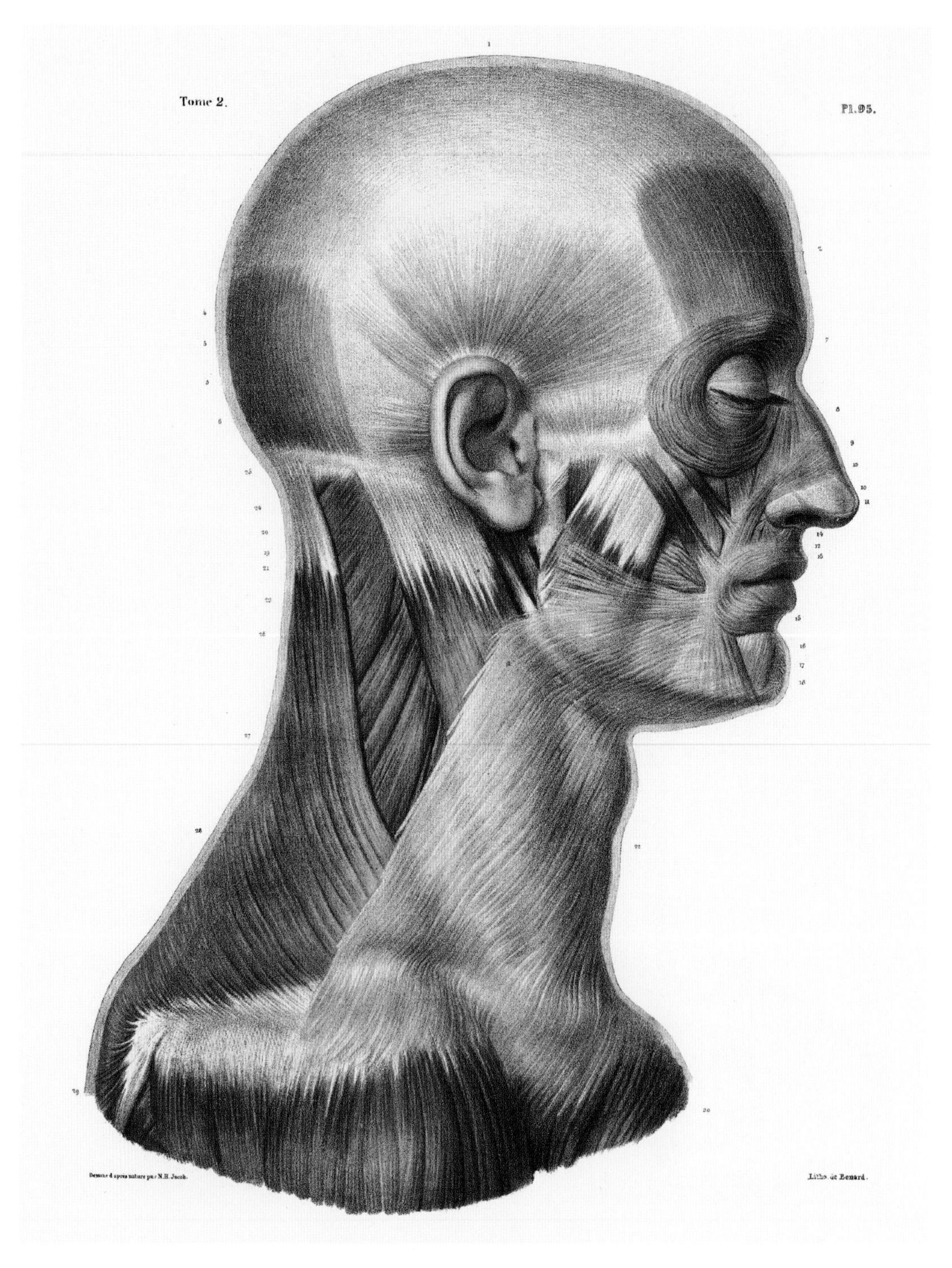

Muscles of the head and neck / Muscles de la tête et du cou
Músculos de la cabeza y del cuello

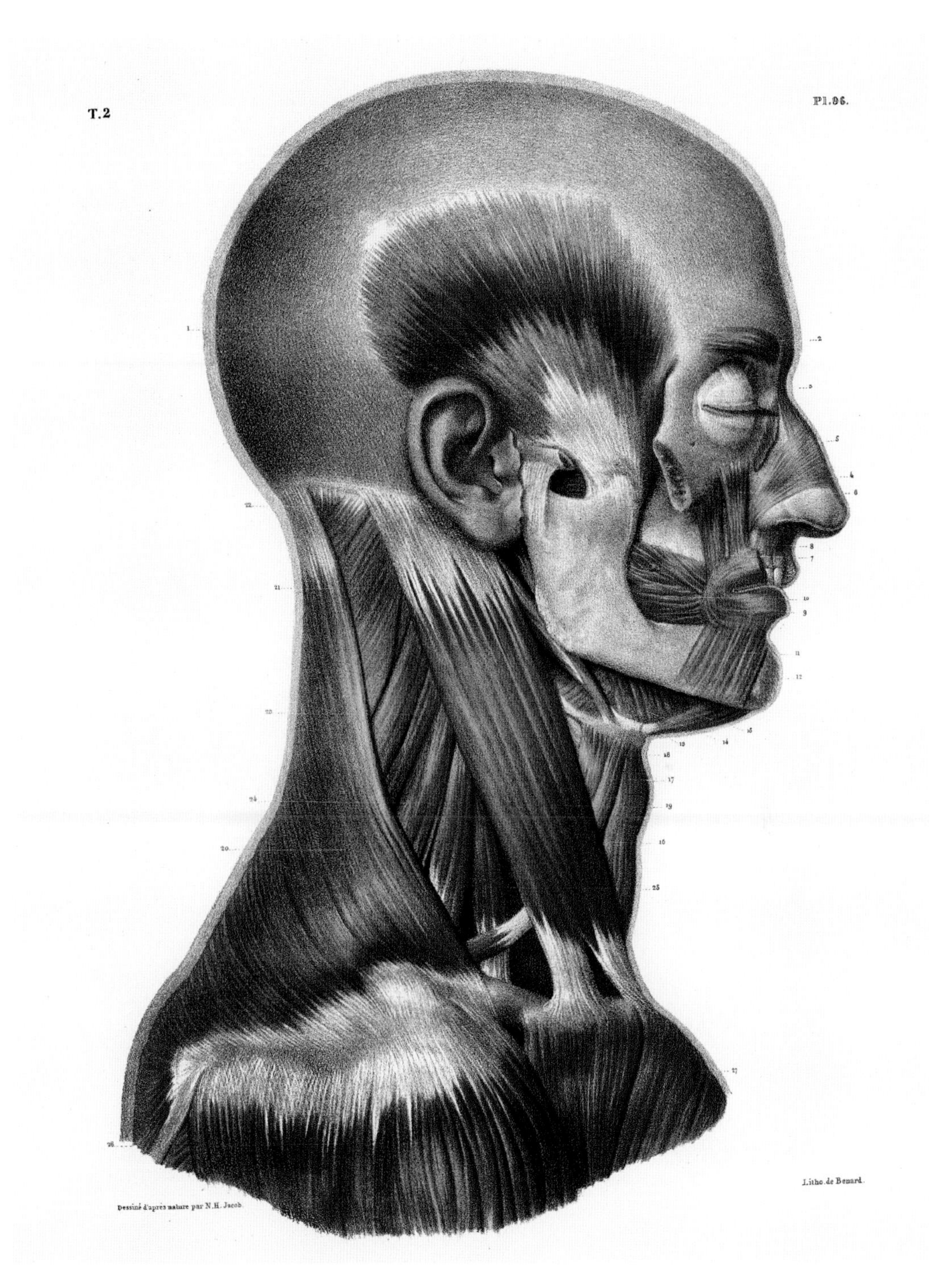

Muscles of the head and neck / Muscles de la tête et du cou
Músculos de la cabeza y del cuello

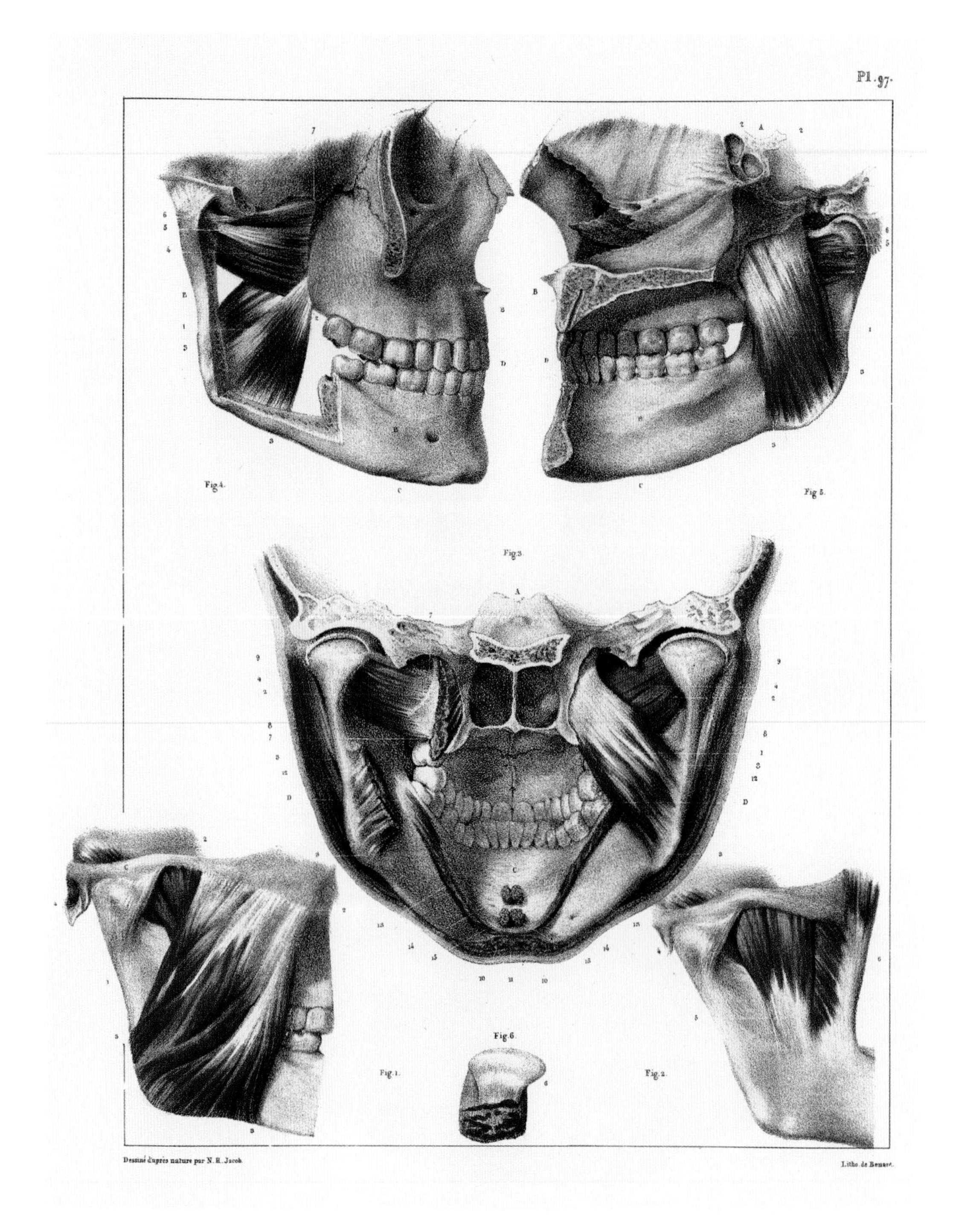

Muscles of the head / Muscles de la tête / Músculos de la cabeza

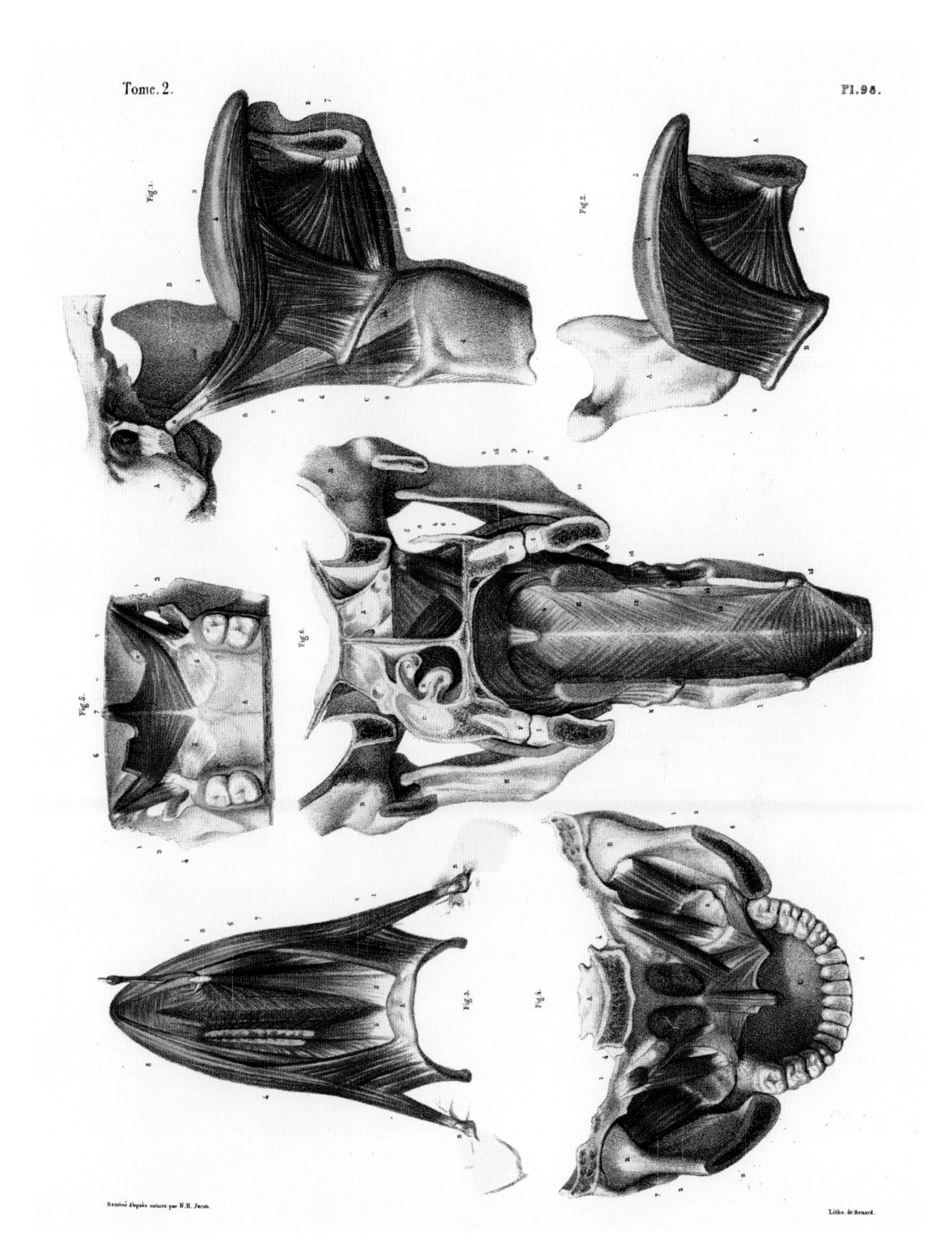

Muscles of the tongue, the palate, and the pharynx
Muscles de la langue, du palais et du pharynx
Músculos de la lengua, del paladar y de la faringe

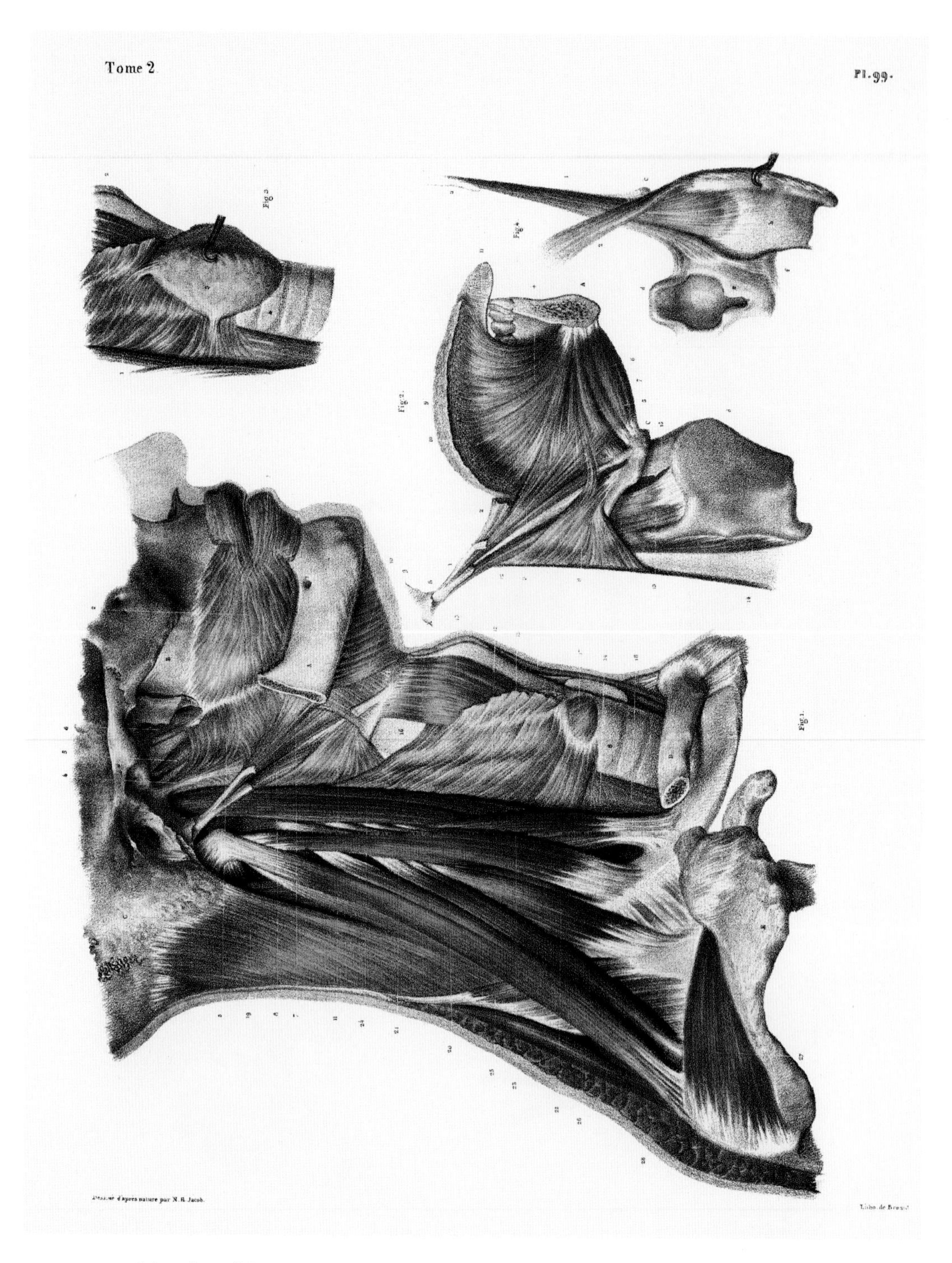

Muscles of the tongue and pharynx / Muscles de la langue et du pharynx
Músculos de la lengua y de la faringe

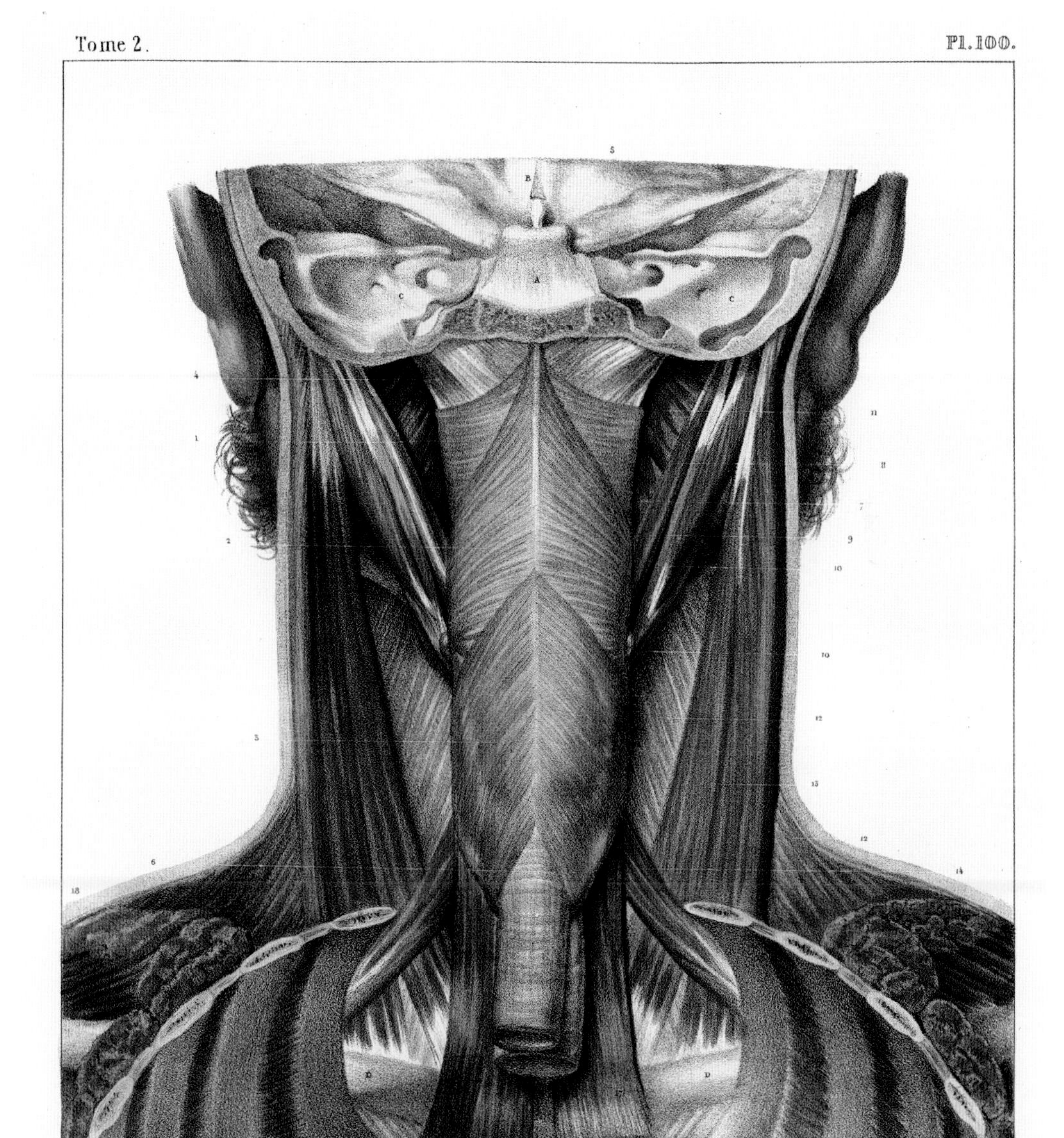

Muscles of the pharynx / Muscles du pharynx
Músculos de la faringe

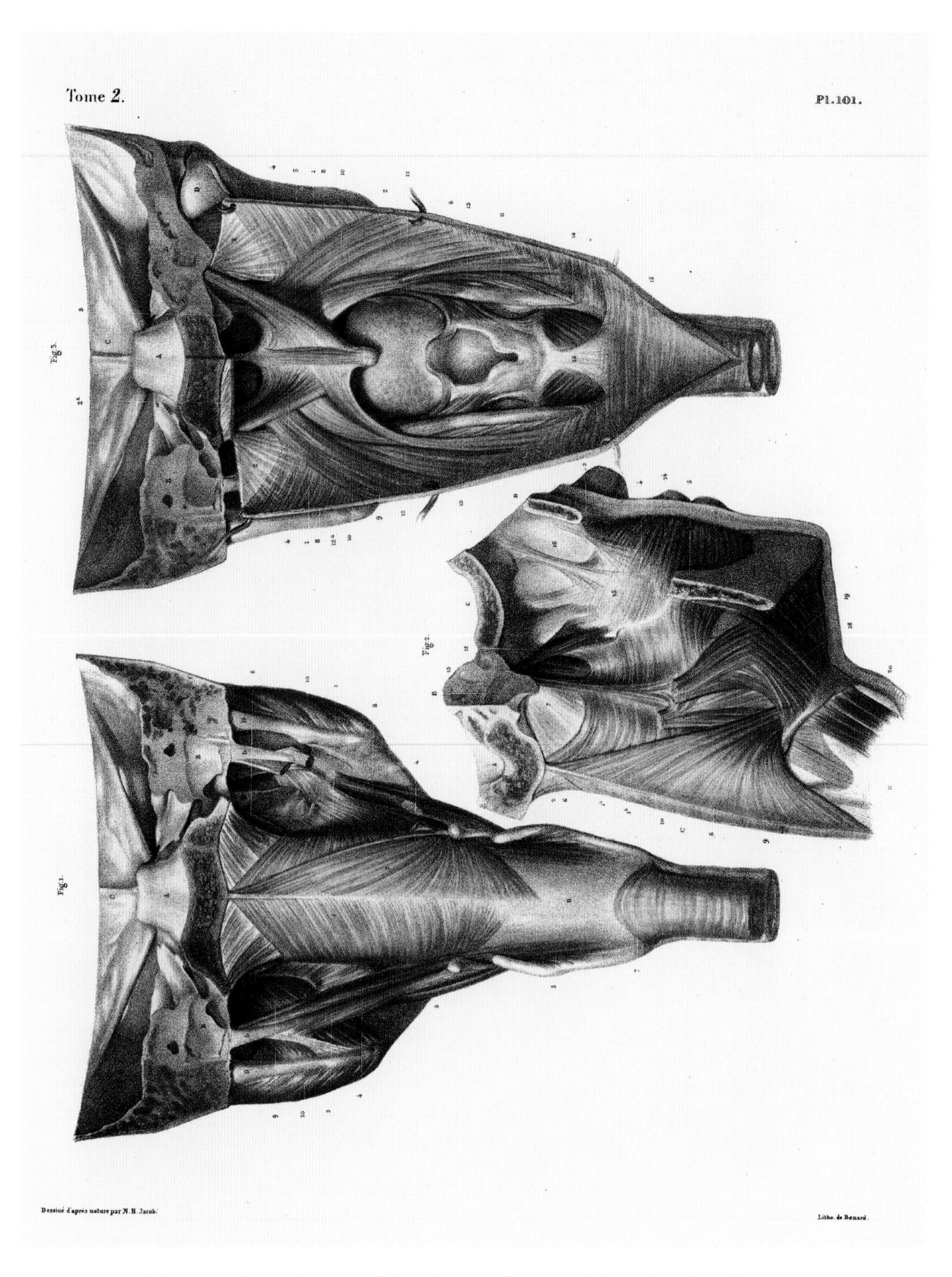

Muscles of the pharynx / Muscles du pharynx / Músculos de la faringe

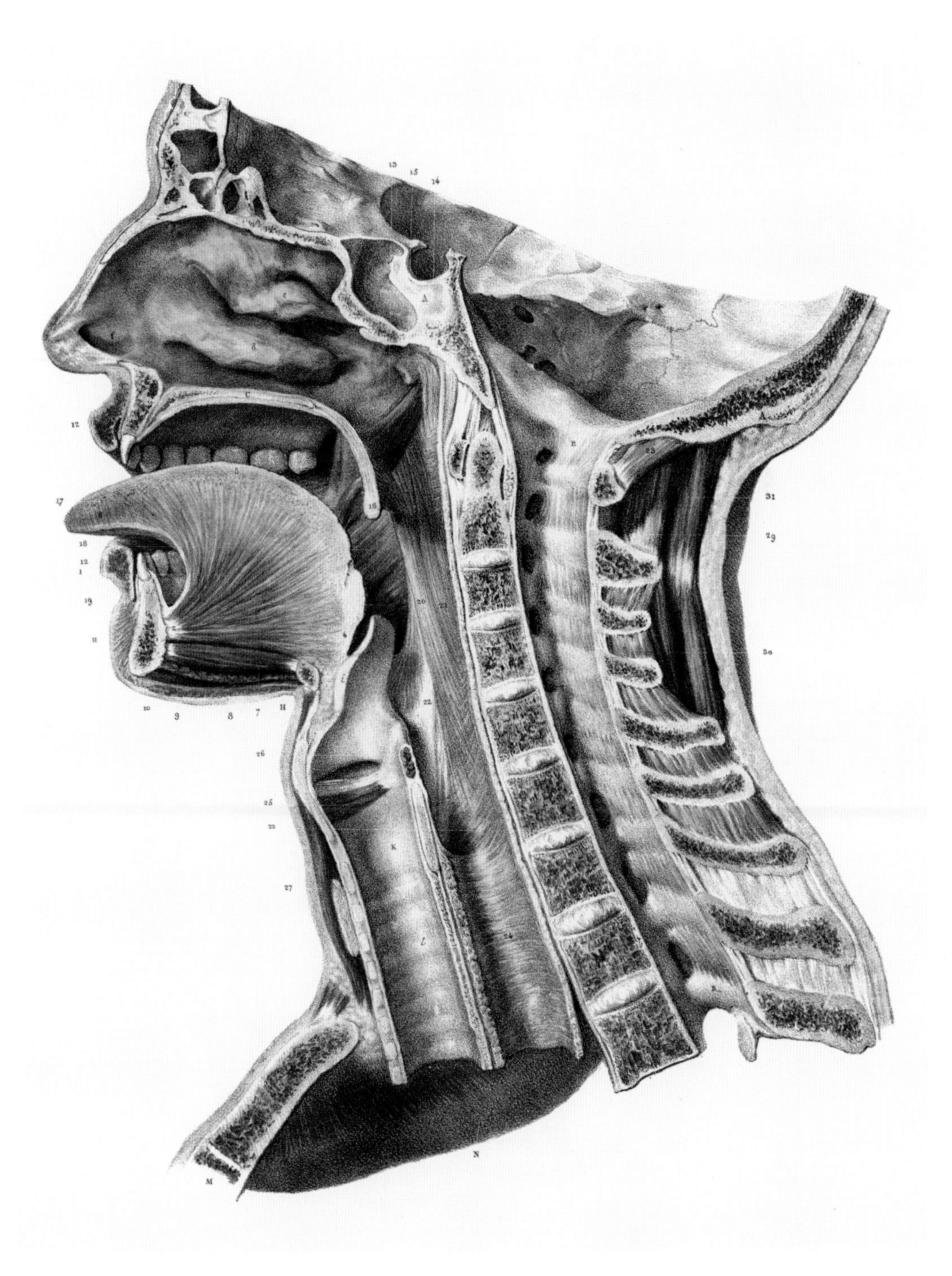

Muscles of the tongue, the palate, the larynx, and the pharynx
Muscles de la langue, du palais, du larynx et du pharynx
Músculos de la lengua, del paladar, de la laringe y de la faringe

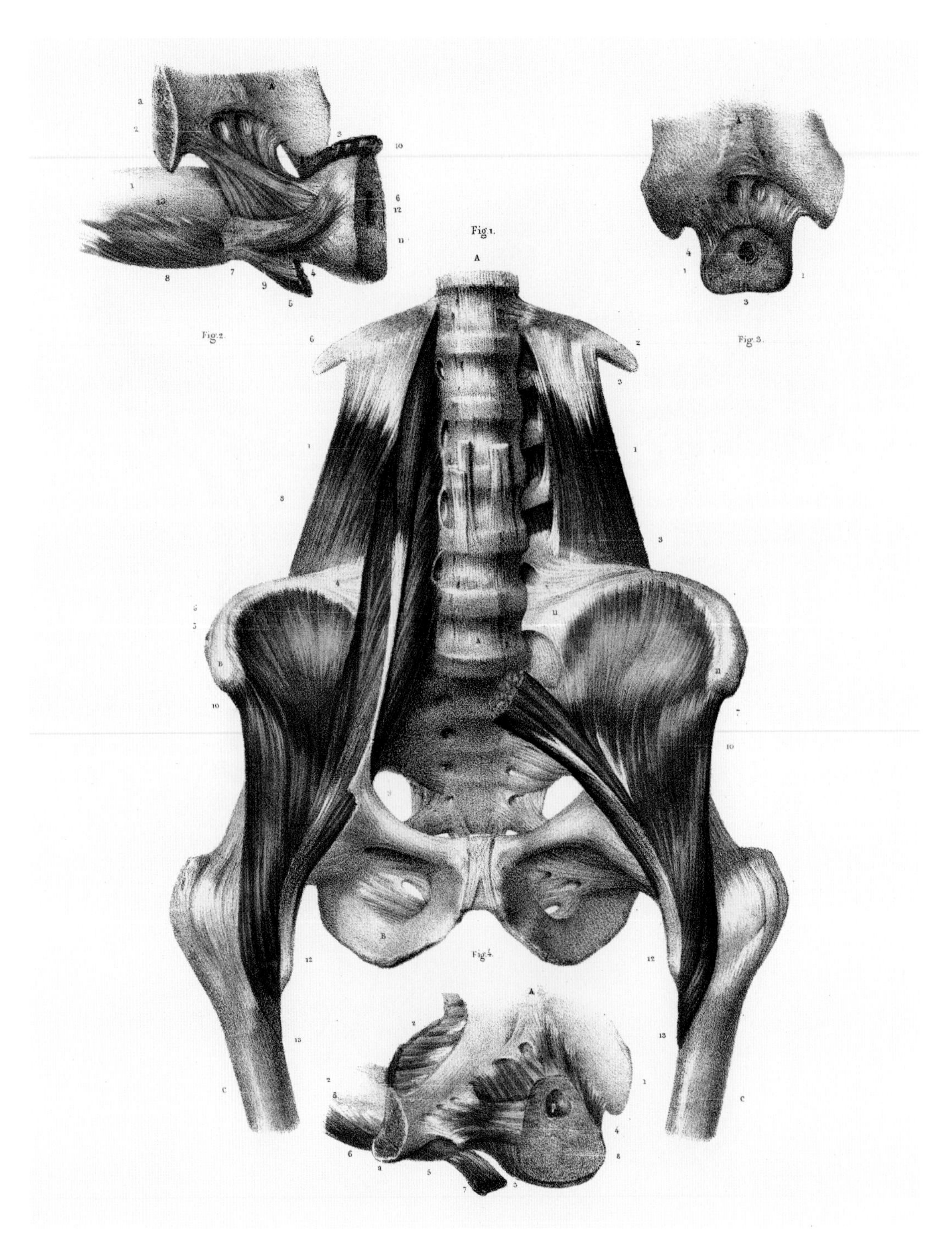

Muscles of the lumbar region and the pelvis
Muscles des lombes et du bassin
Músculos lumbares y de la pelvis

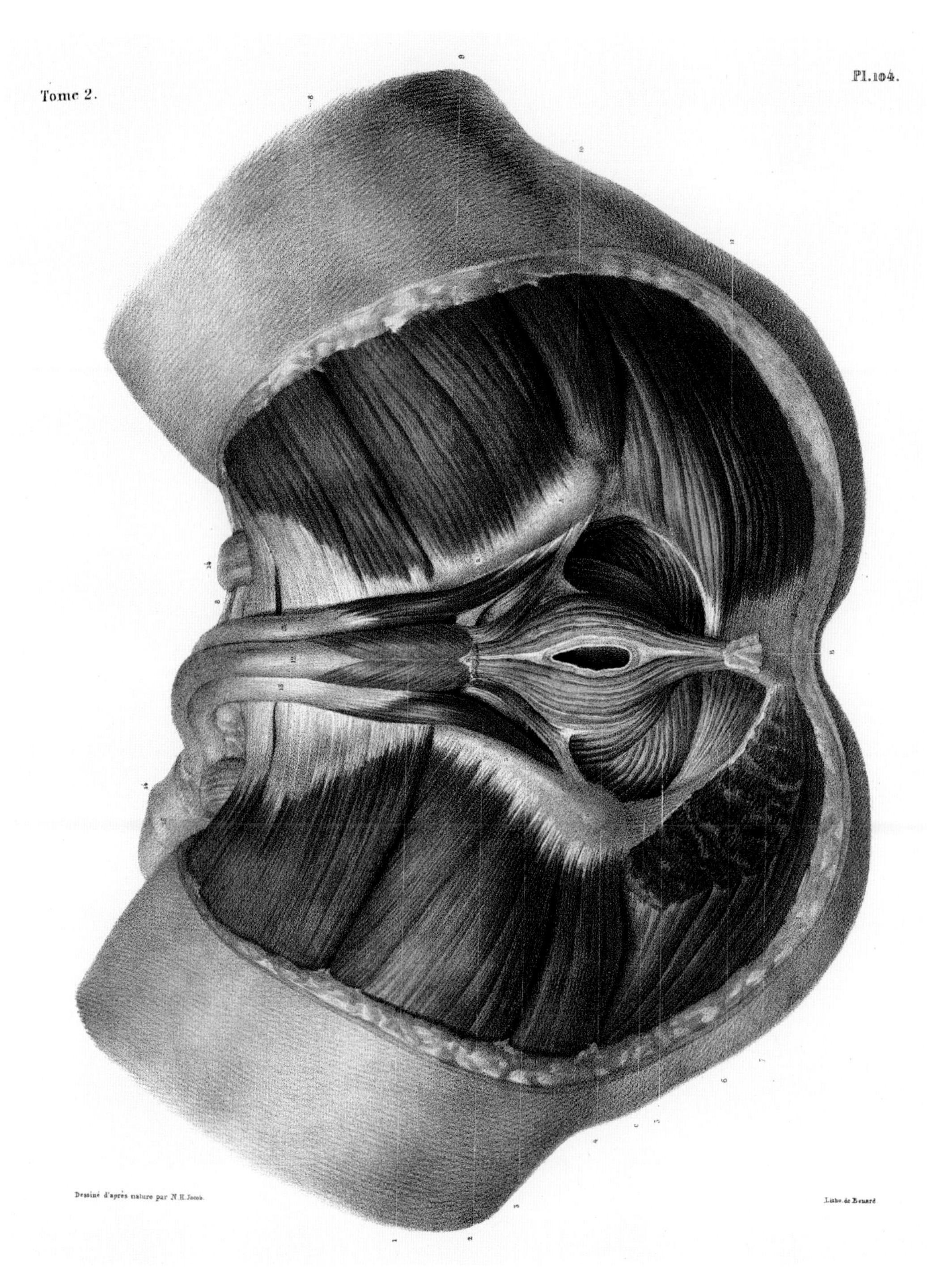

Muscles of the perineum – pelvic diaphragm
Muscles du périnée – Diaphragme pelvien
Músculos del periné – Diafragma pélvico

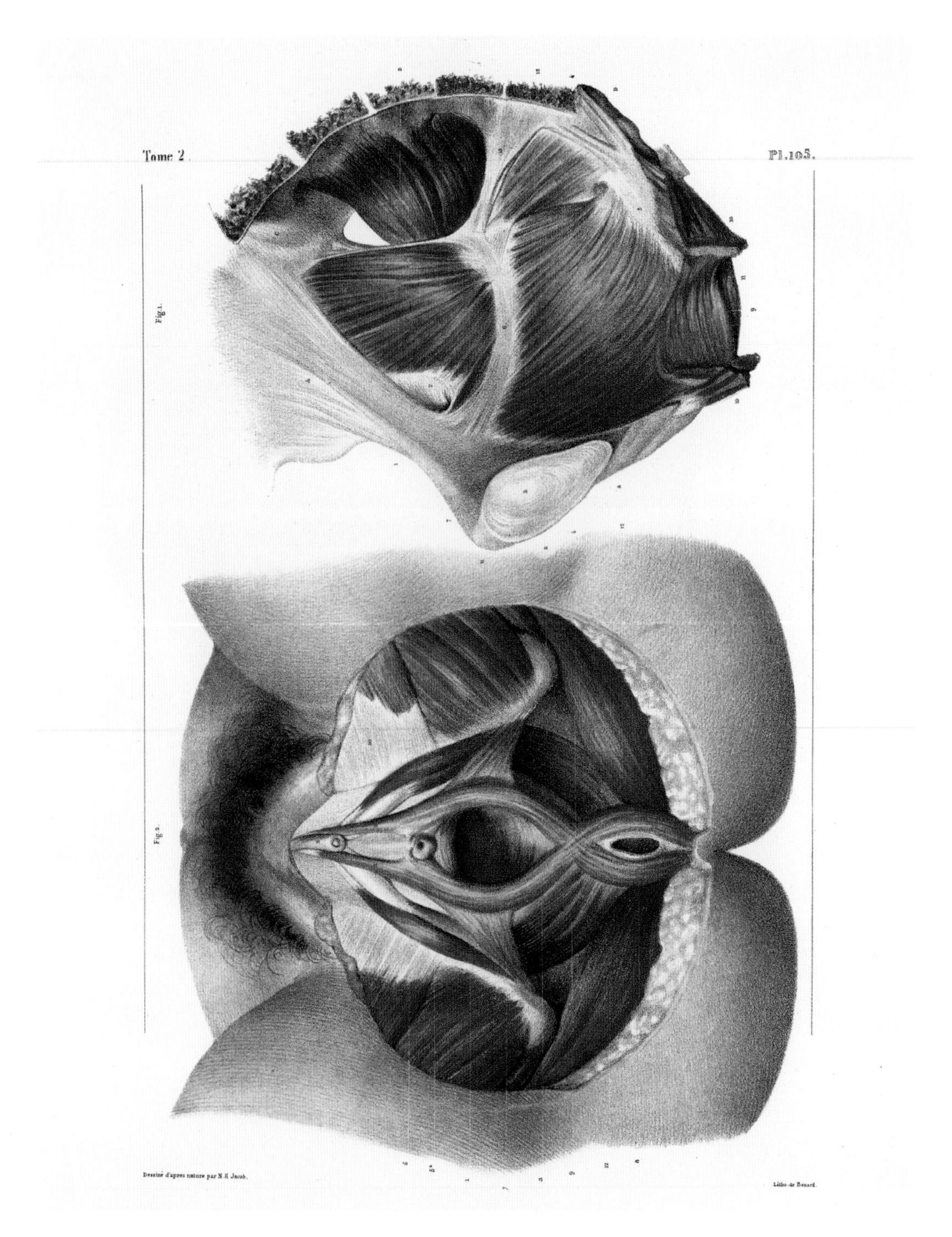

Muscles of the perineum and the pelvis – pelvic diaphragm
Muscles du périnée et du bassin – Diaphragme pelvien
Músculos del periné y de la pelvis – Diafragma pélvico

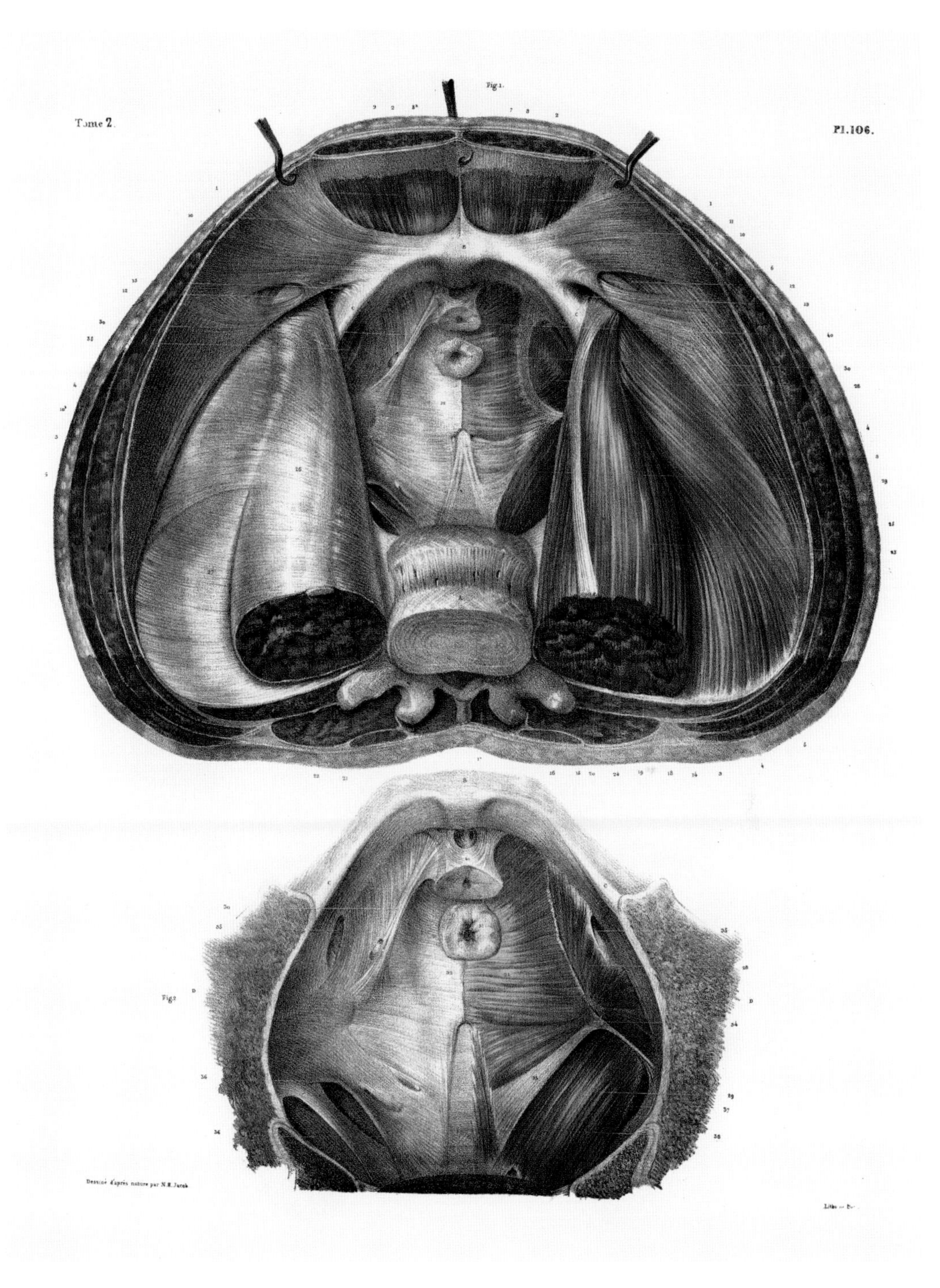

Muscles of the perineum and the pelvis – pelvic diaphragm
Muscles du périnée et du bassin – Diaphragme pelvien
Músculos del periné y de la pelvis – Diafragma pélvico

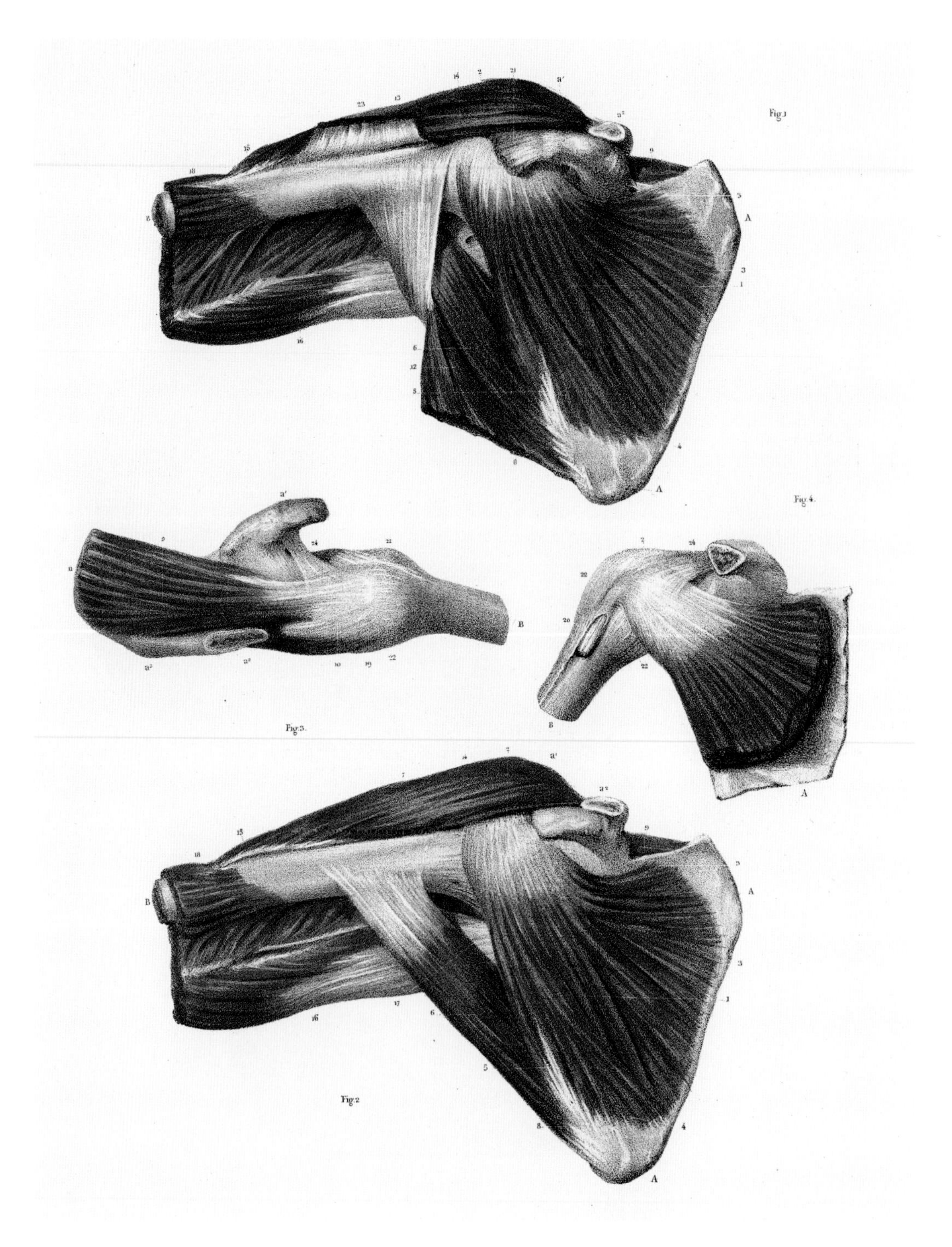

Shoulder muscles / Muscles de l'épaule / Músculos del hombro

Shoulder muscles / Muscles de l'épaule / Músculos del hombro

Muscles of the axillary region / Muscles de la région axillaire
Músculos de la región axilar

Muscles of the axillary region / Muscles de la région axillaire
Músculos de la región axilar

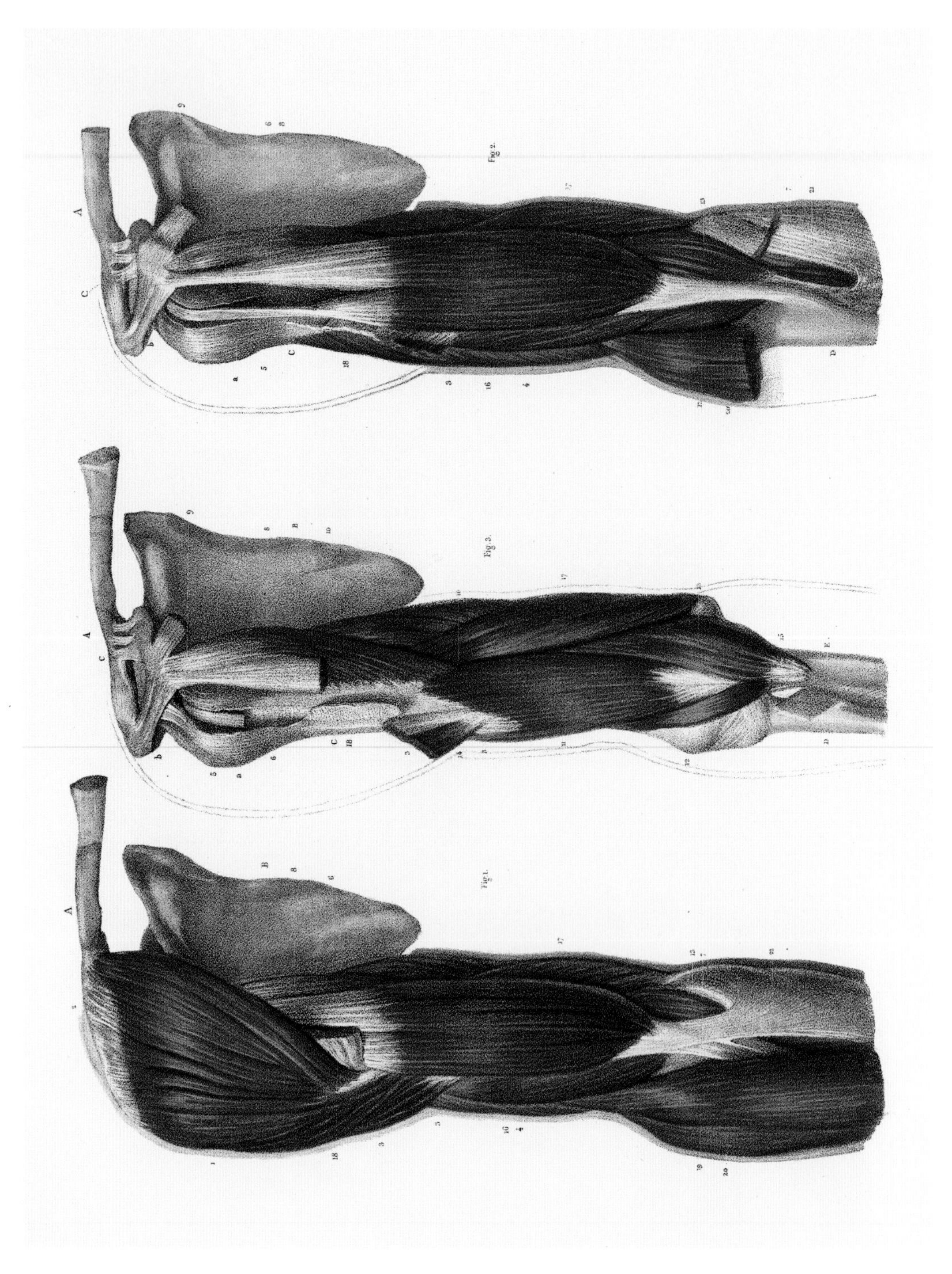

Muscles of the arm / Muscles du bras / Músculos del brazo

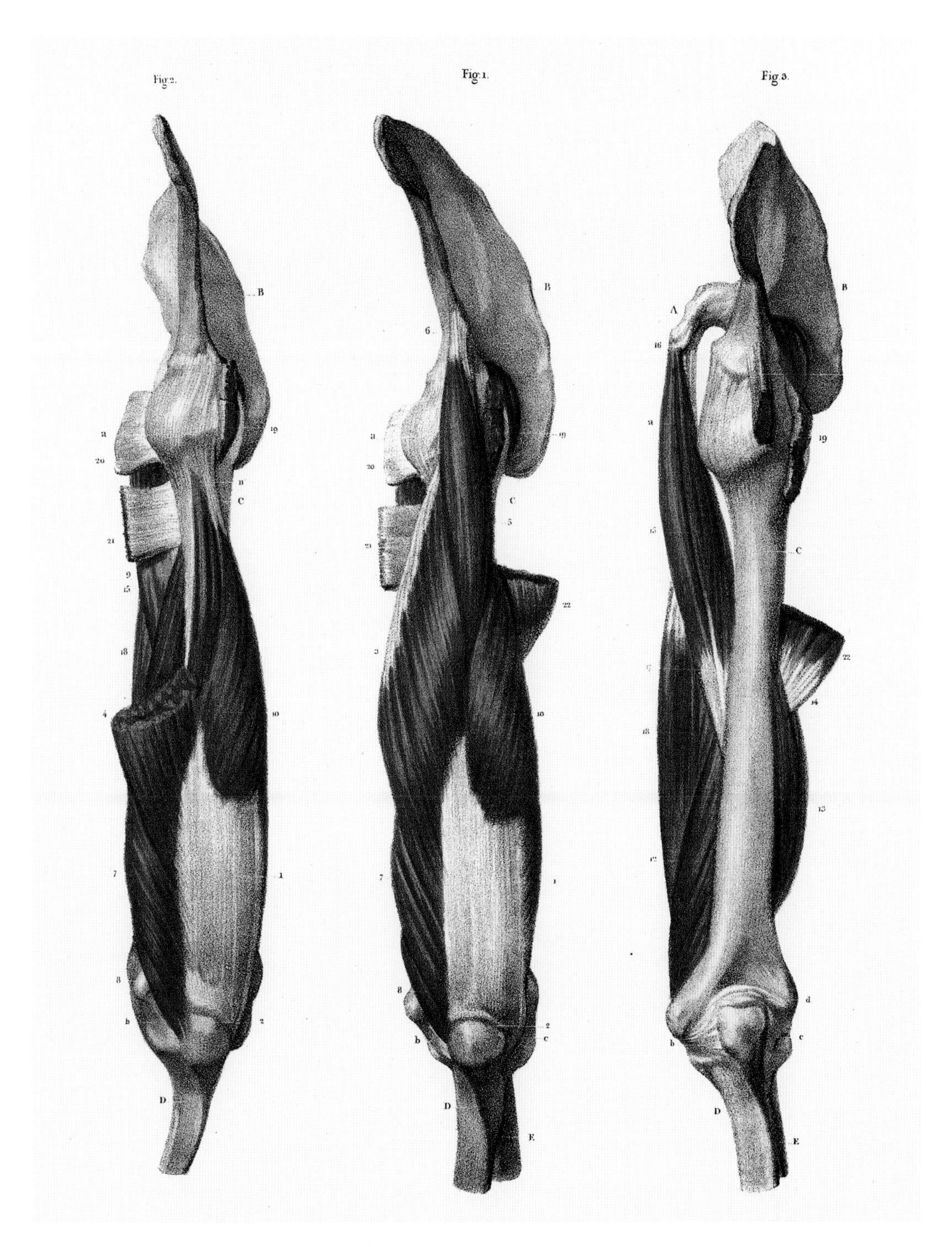

Muscles of the arm / Muscles du bras / Músculos del brazo

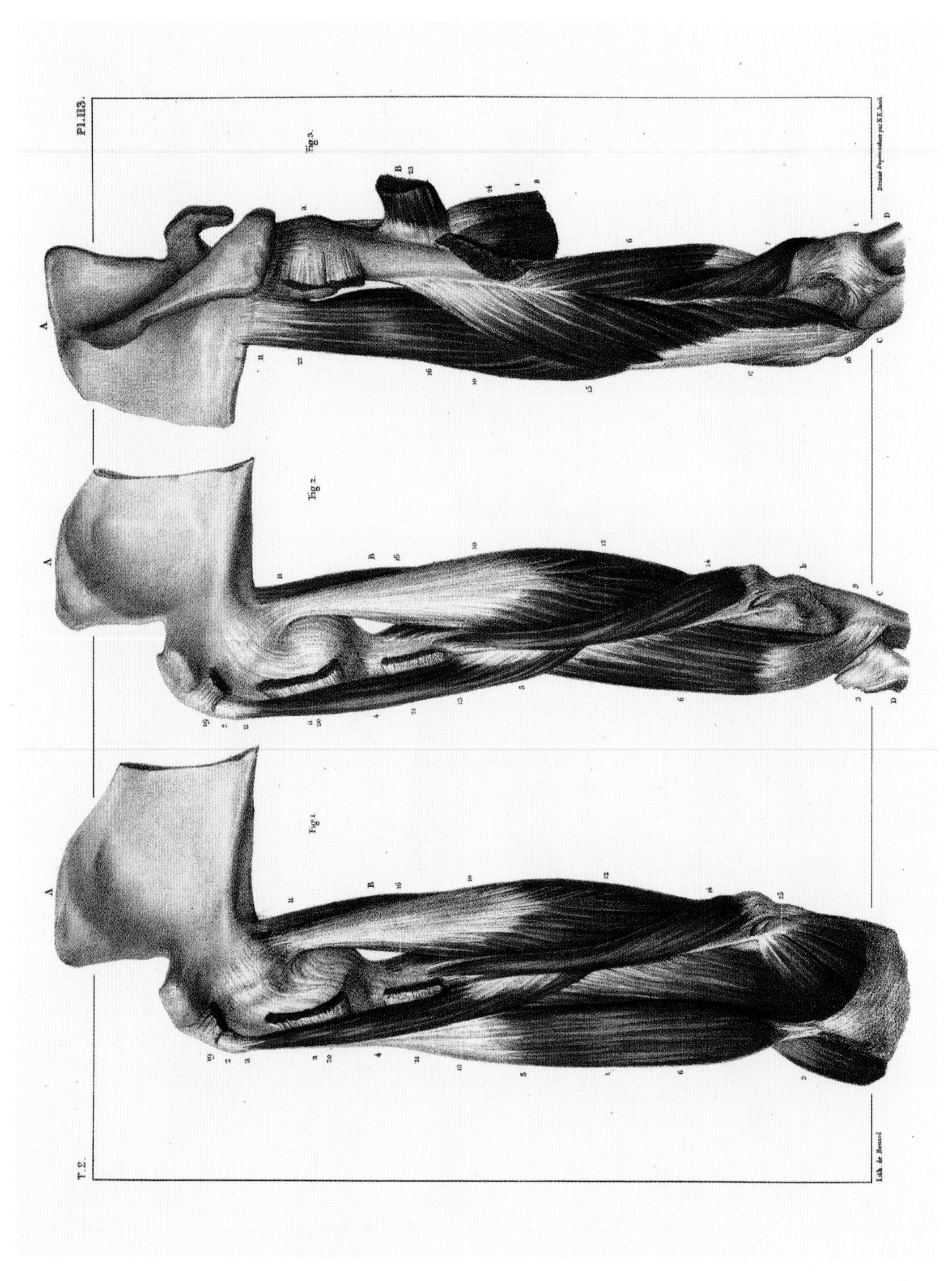

Muscles of the arm / Muscles du bras / Músculos del brazo

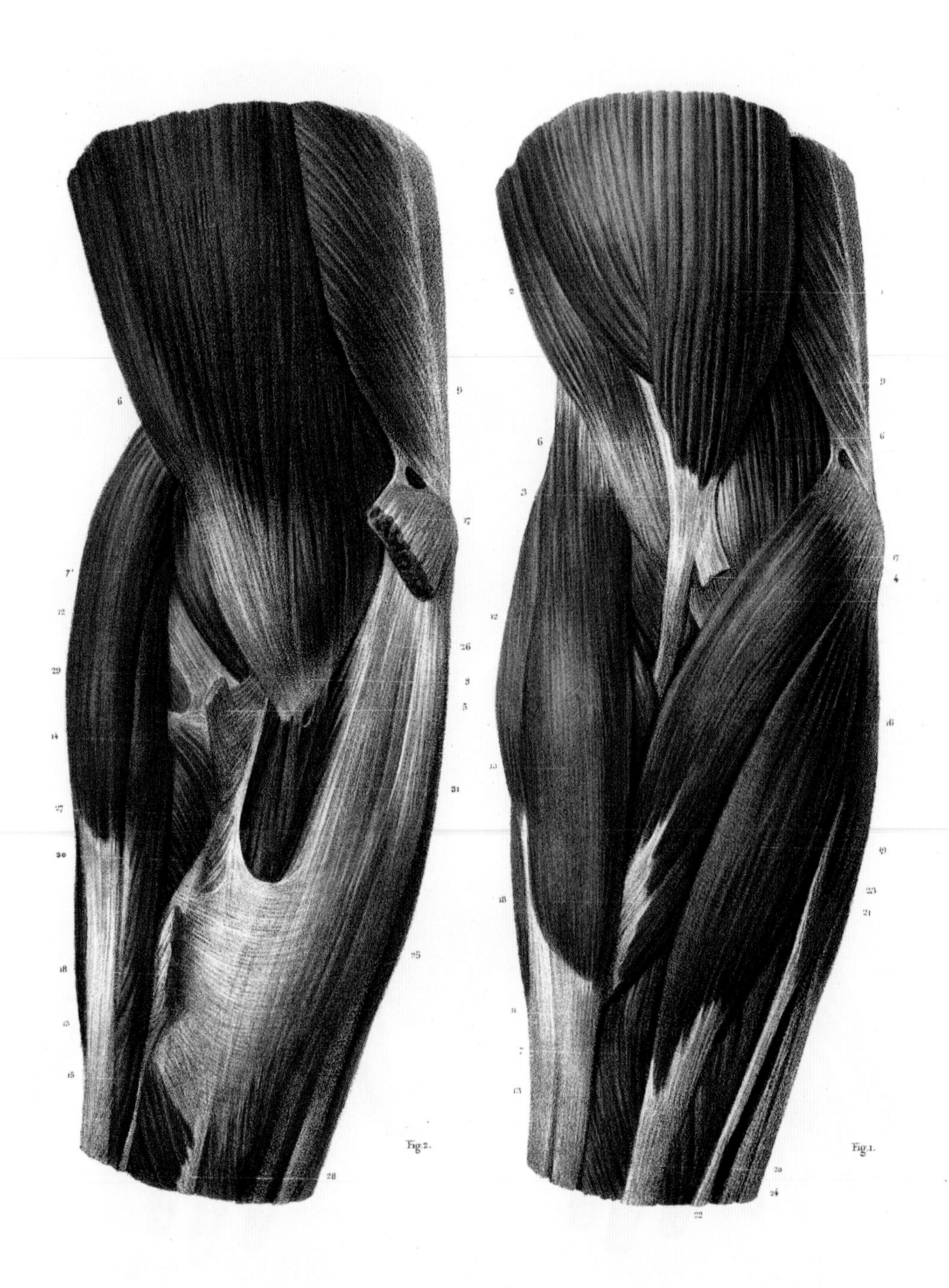

Muscles of the ventral side of the elbow / Muscles de la région du pli du coude
Músculos de la región del pliegue cubital

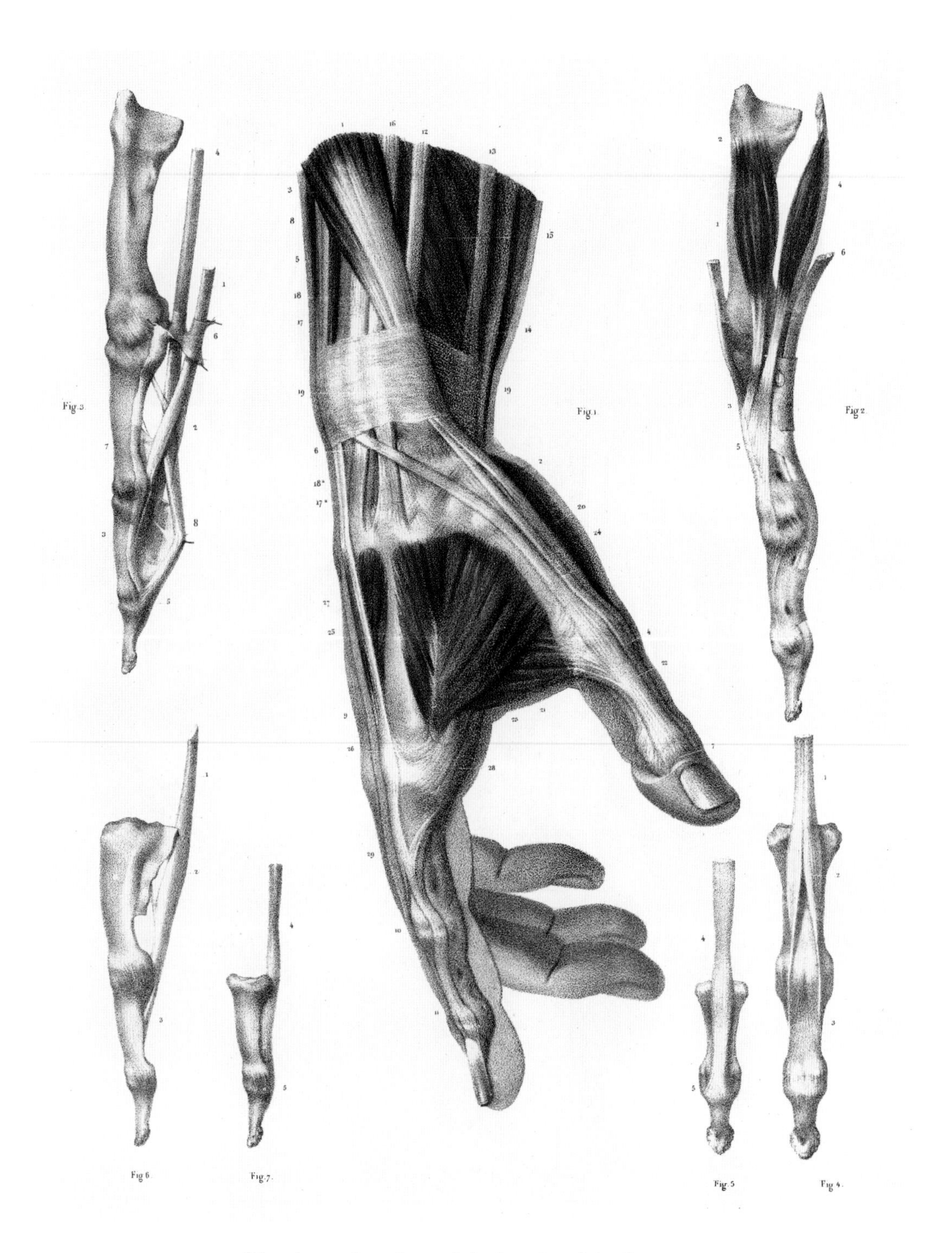

Muscles and tendons of the hand and the fingers
Muscles et tendons de la main et des doigts
Músculos y tendones de la mano y de los dedos de la mano

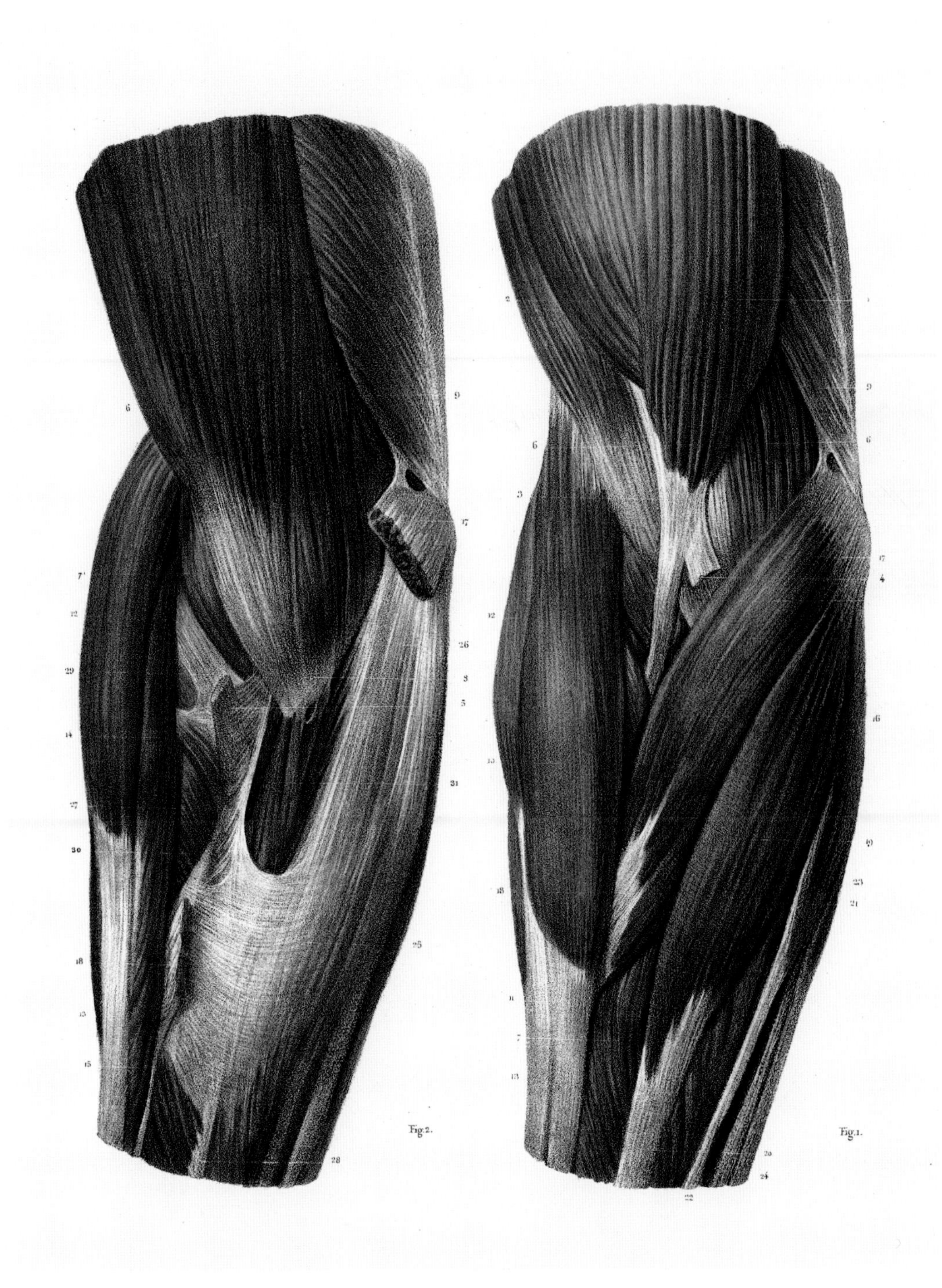

Muscles of the ventral side of the elbow / Muscles de la région du pli du coude
Músculos de la región del pliegue cubital

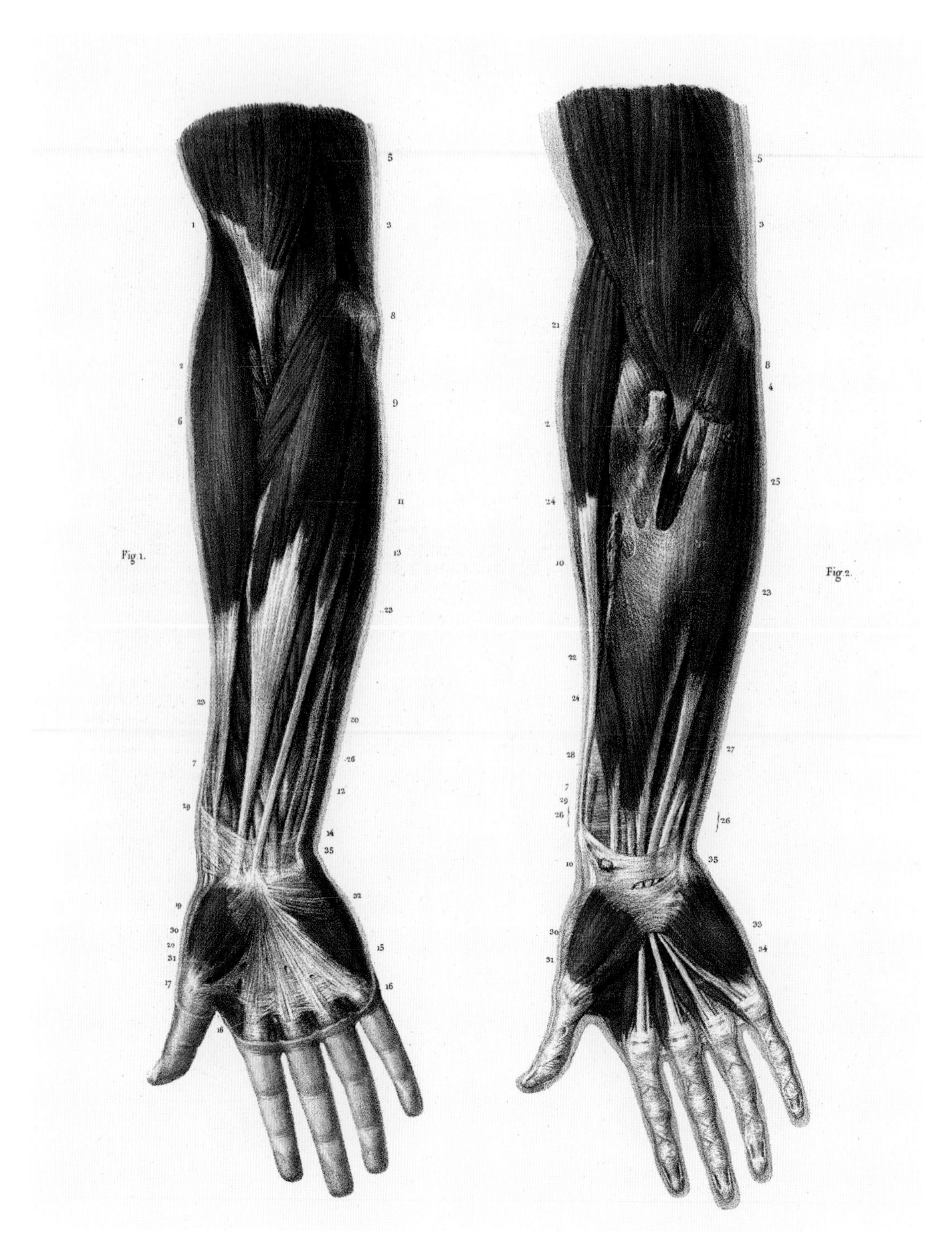

Muscles of the forearm and the hand / Muscles de l'avant-bras et de la main
Músculos del antebrazo y de la mano

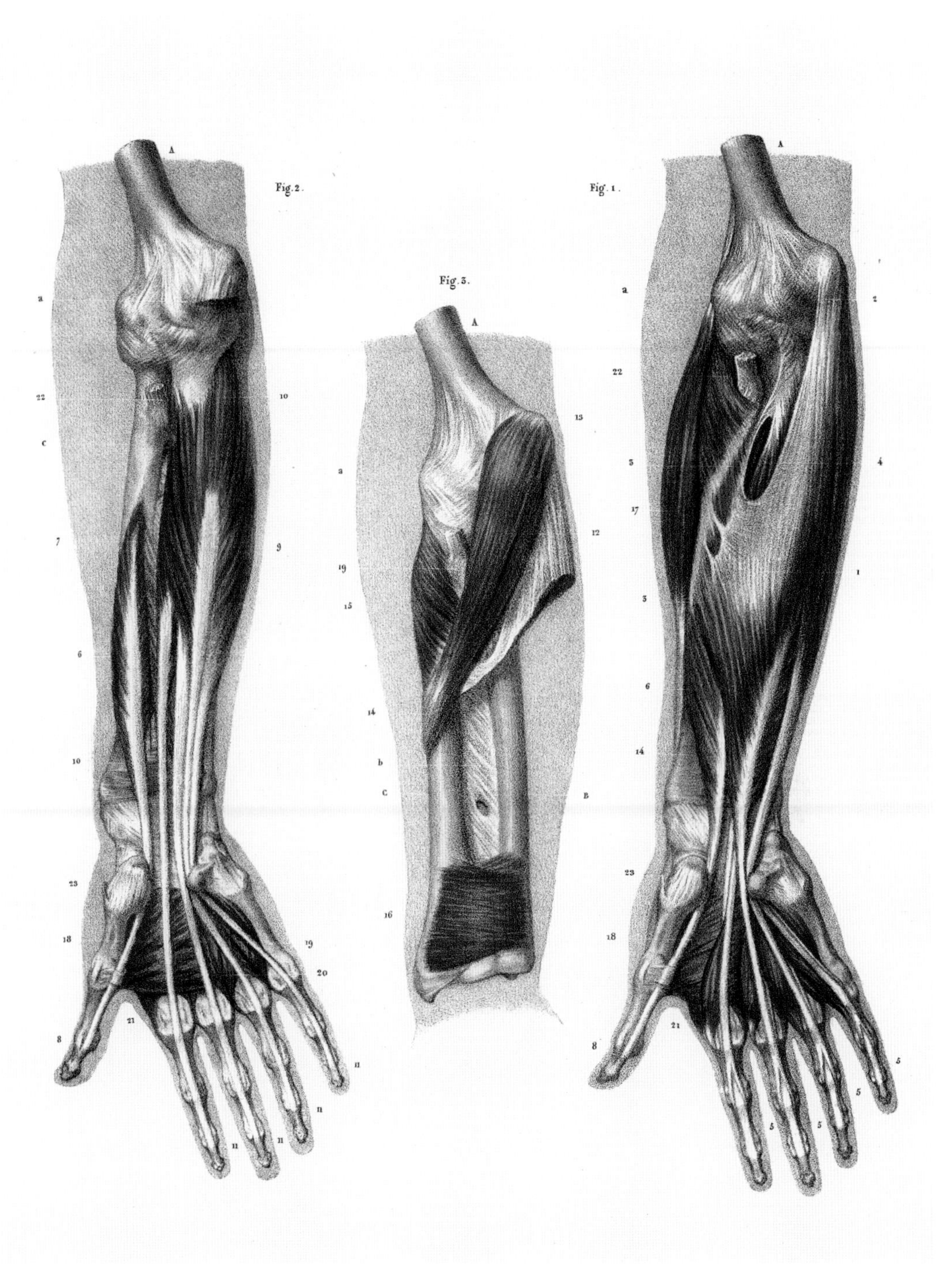

Muscles of the forearm and the hand / Muscles de l'avant-bras et de la main
Músculos del antebrazo y de la mano

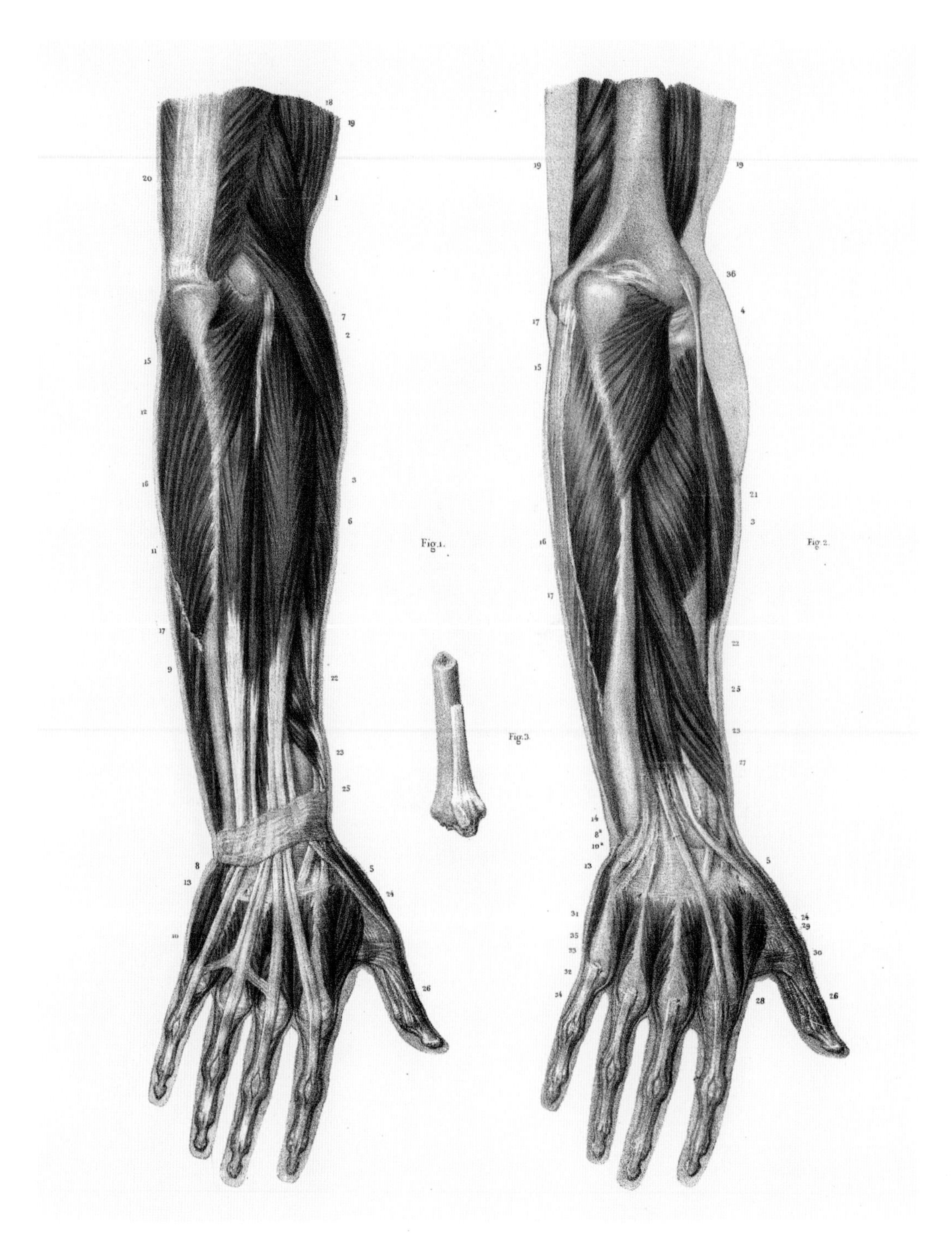

Muscles of the forearm and the hand / Muscles de l'avant-bras et de la main
Músculos del antebrazo y de la mano

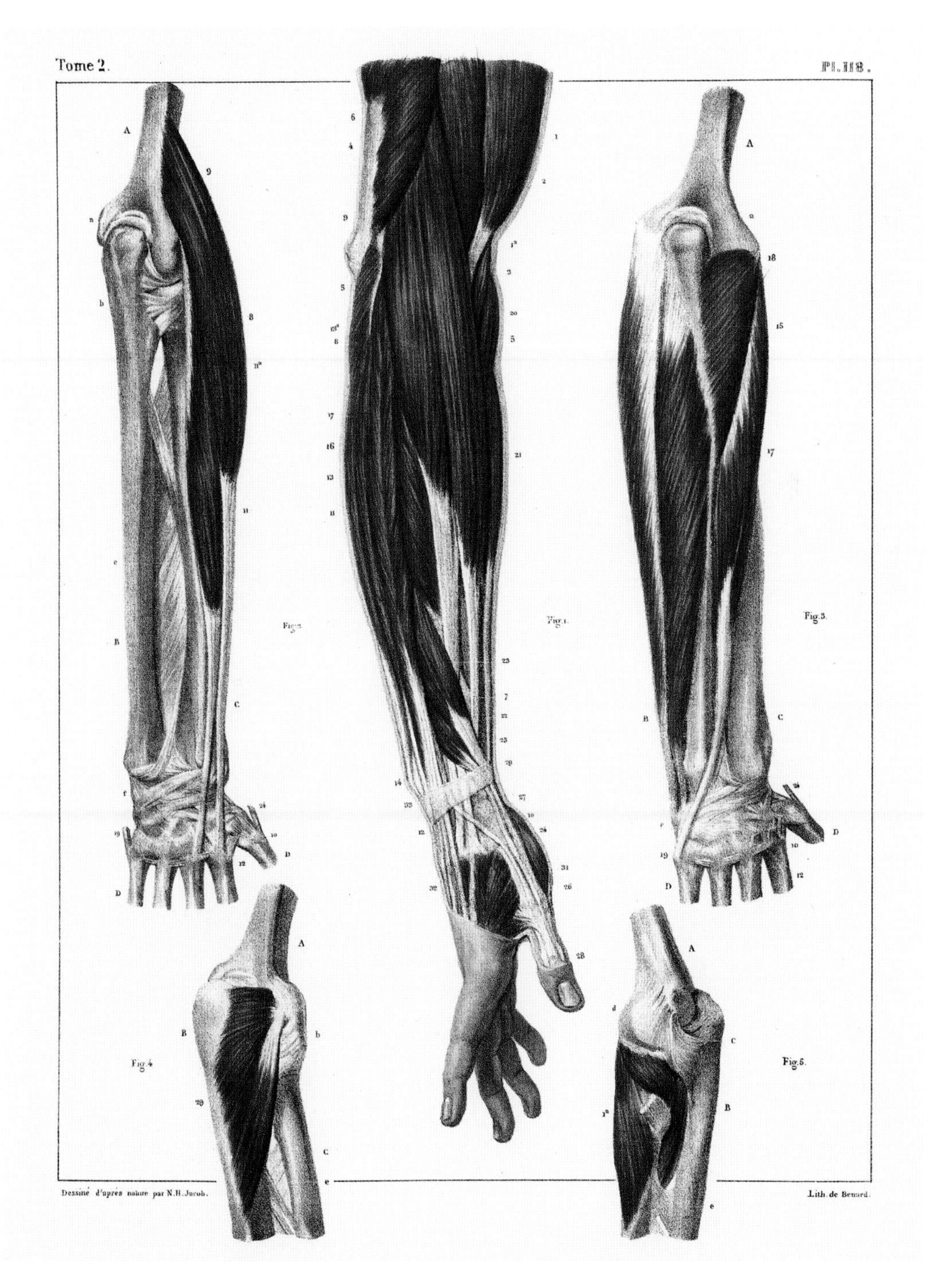

Muscles of the forearm and the hand / Muscles de l'avant-bras et de la main
Músculos del antebrazo y de la mano

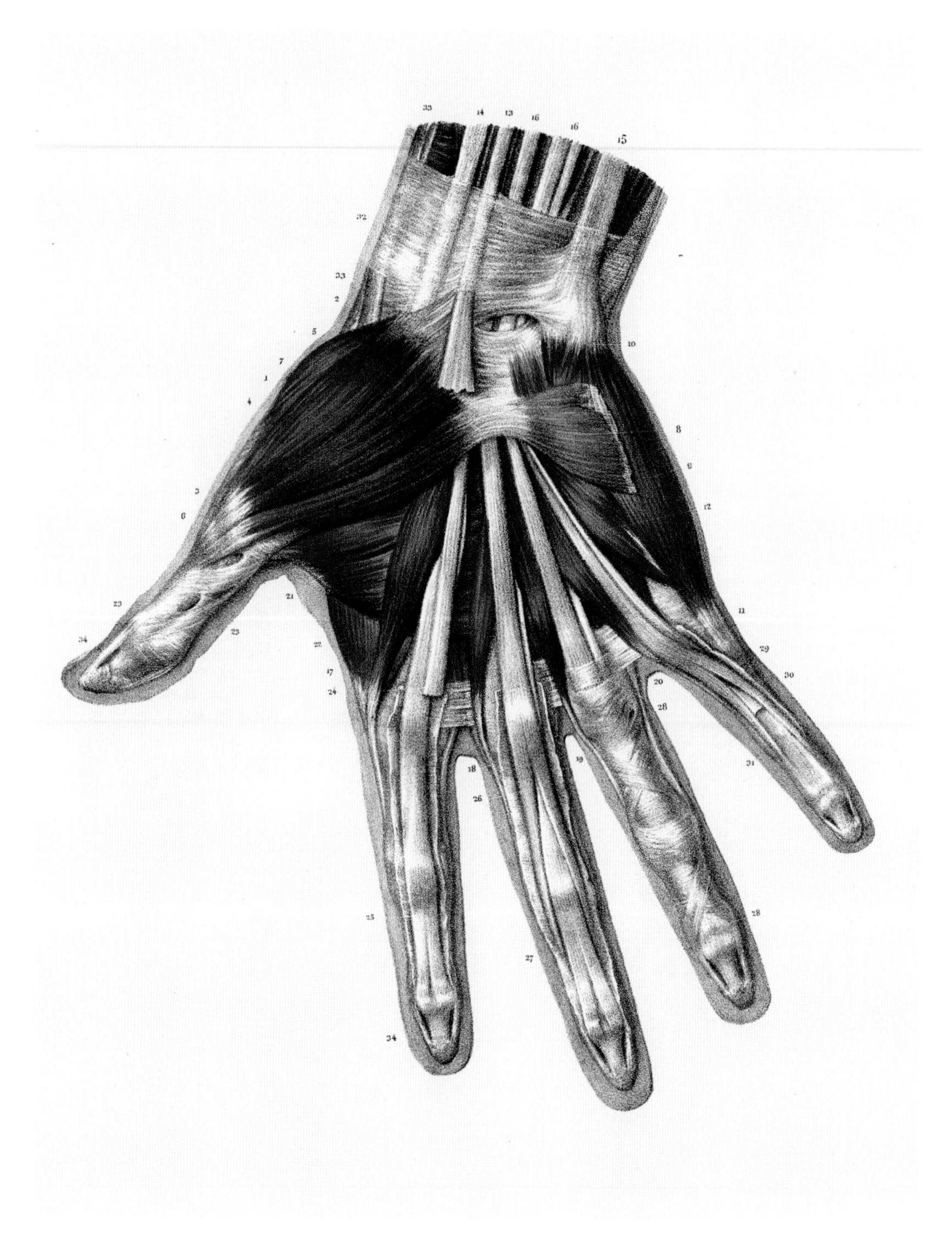

Muscles and tendons of the hand / Muscles et tendons de la main
Músculos y tendones de la mano

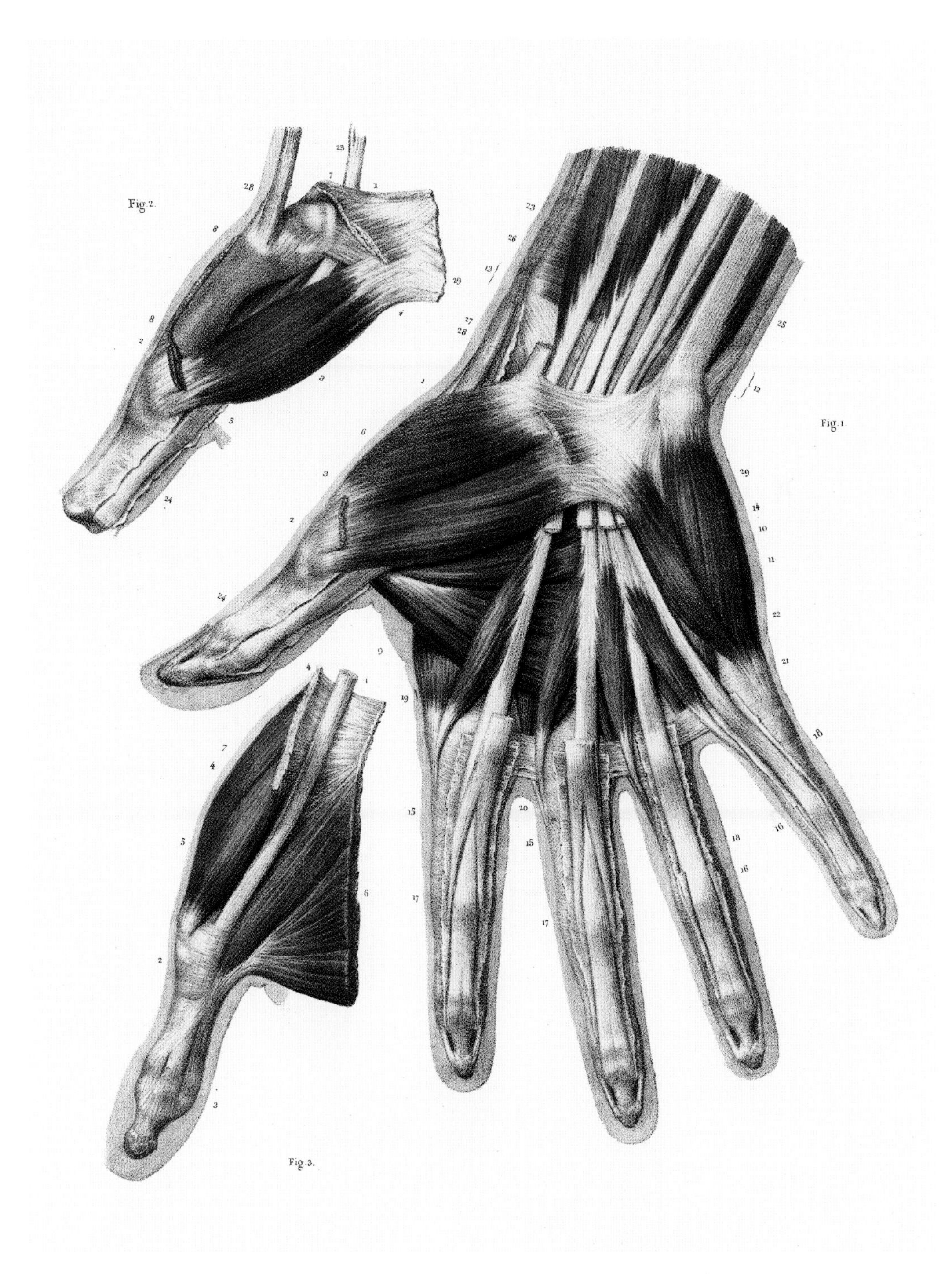

Muscles and tendons of the hand / Muscles et tendons de la main
Músculos y tendones de la mano

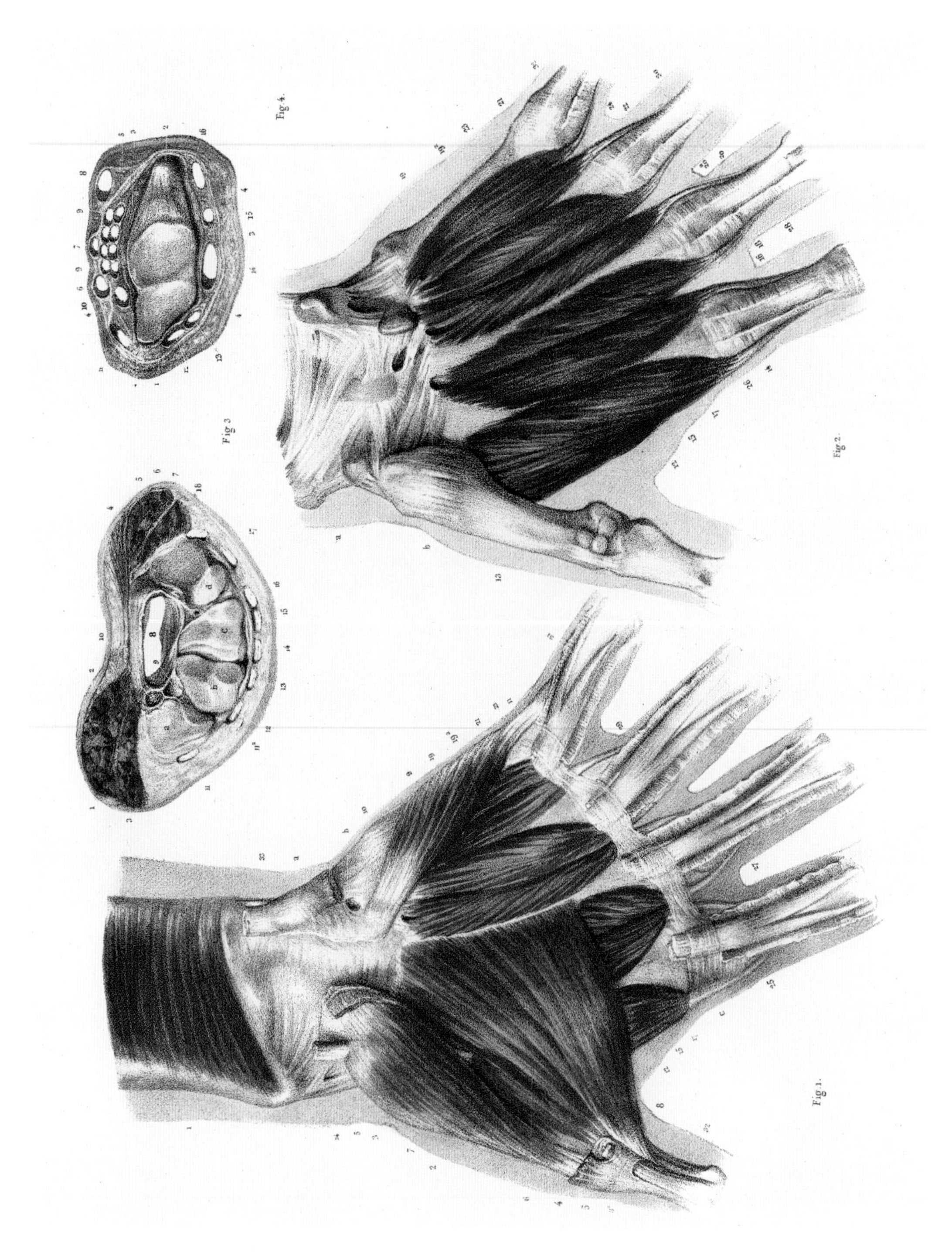

Muscles of the hand / Muscles de la main / Músculos de la mano

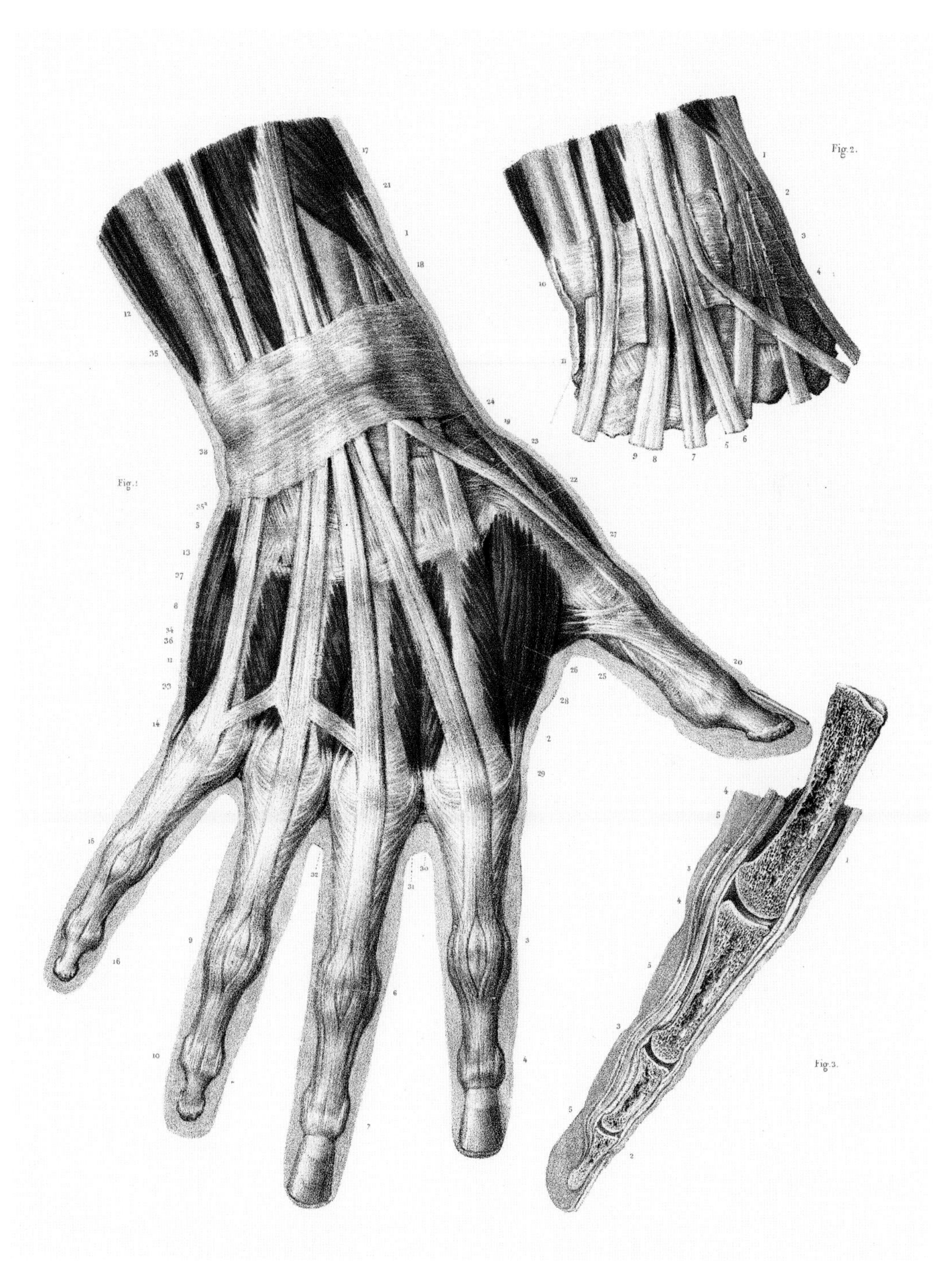

Muscles and tendons of the hand and the fingers
Muscles et tendons de la main et des doigts
Músculos y tendones de la mano y de los dedos de la mano

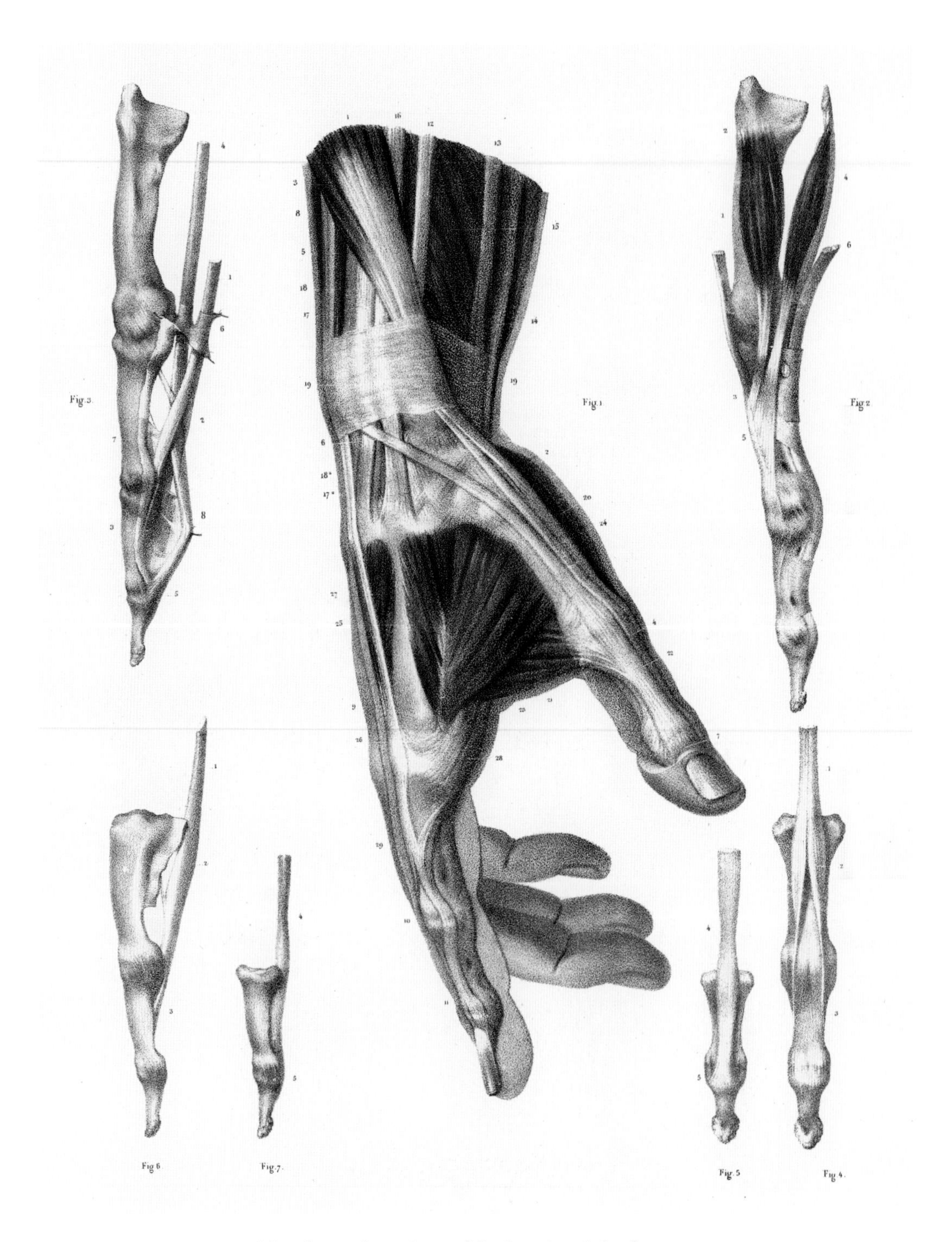

Muscles and tendons of the hand and the fingers
Muscles et tendons de la main et des doigts
Músculos y tendones de la mano y de los dedos de la mano

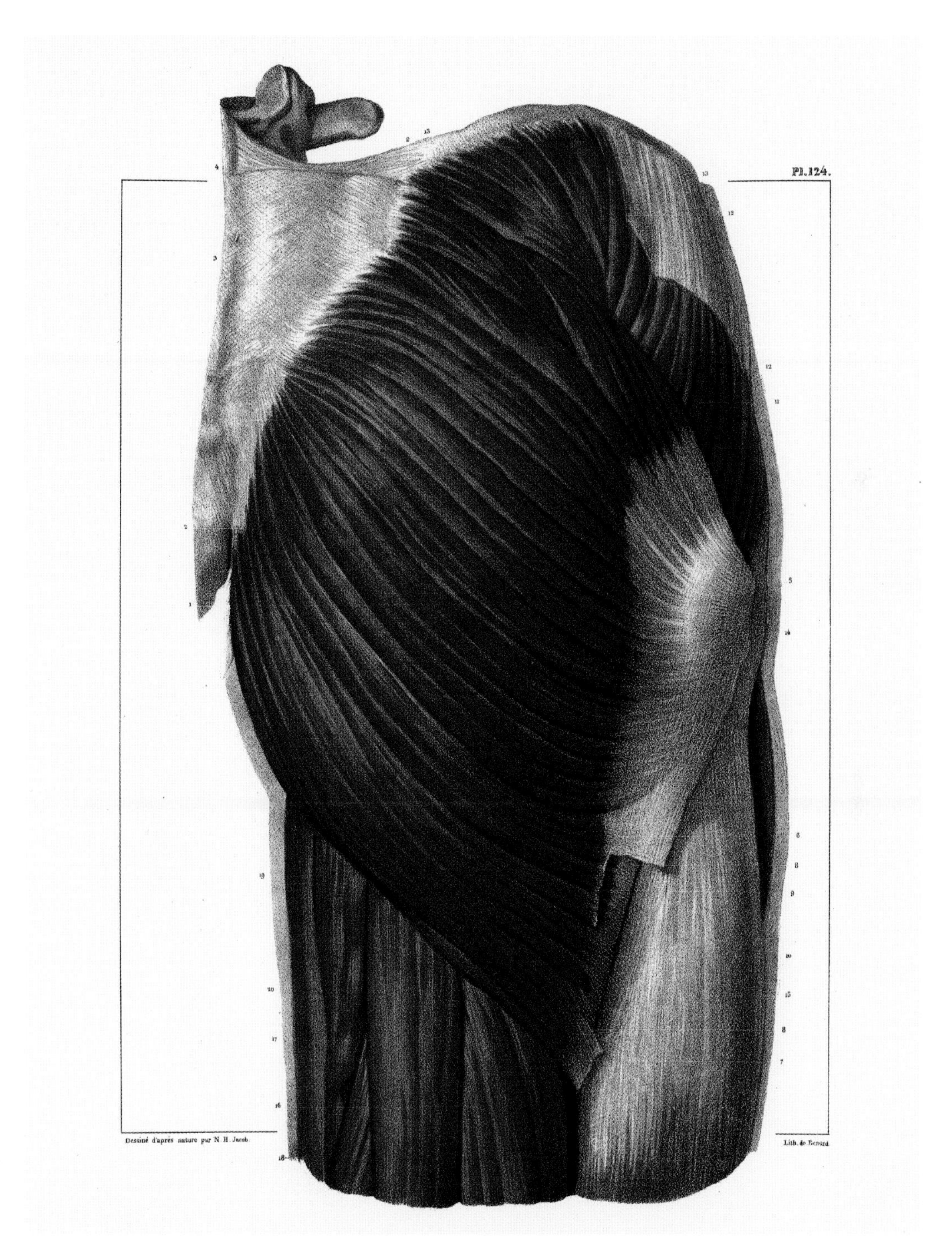

Buttock muscles / Muscles de la région fessière
Músculos de la región glútea

Buttock muscles / Muscles de la région fessière
Músculos de la región glútea

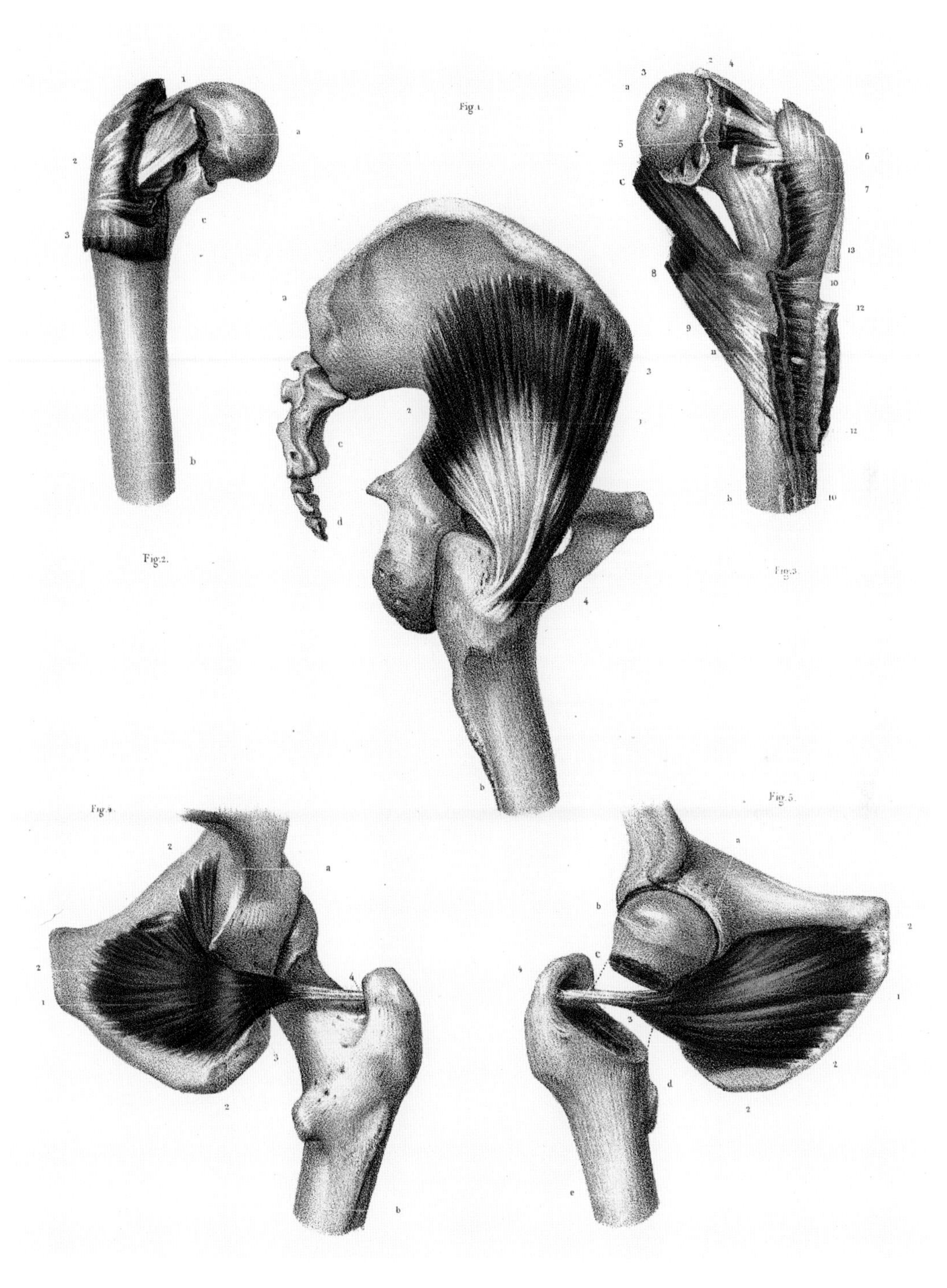

Muscles of the hip / Muscles de la hanche
Músculos de la cadera

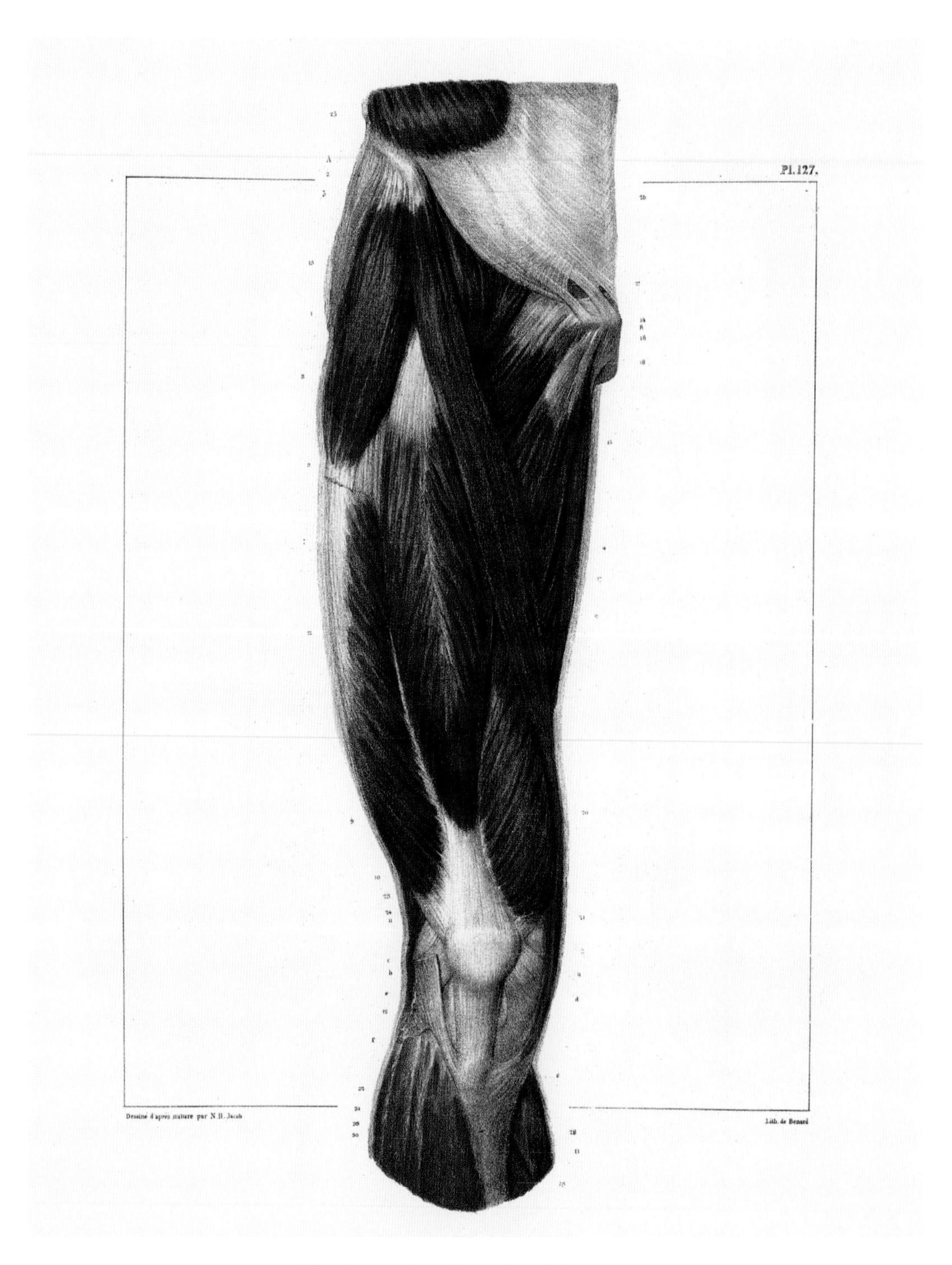

Thigh muscles / Muscles de la cuisse
Músculos femorales

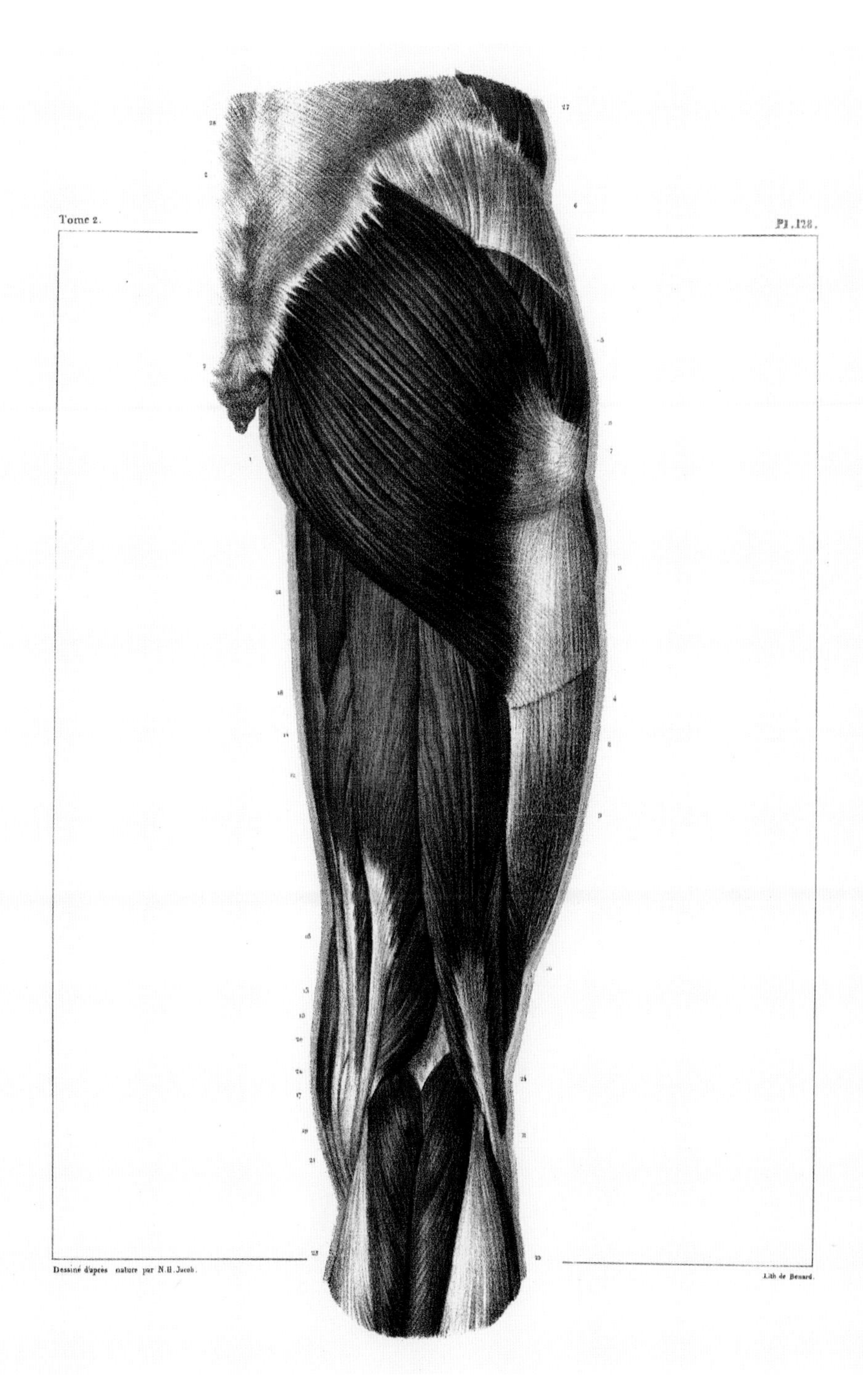

Thigh muscles / Muscles de la cuisse
Músculos femorales

Thigh muscles / Muscles de la cuisse
Músculos femorales

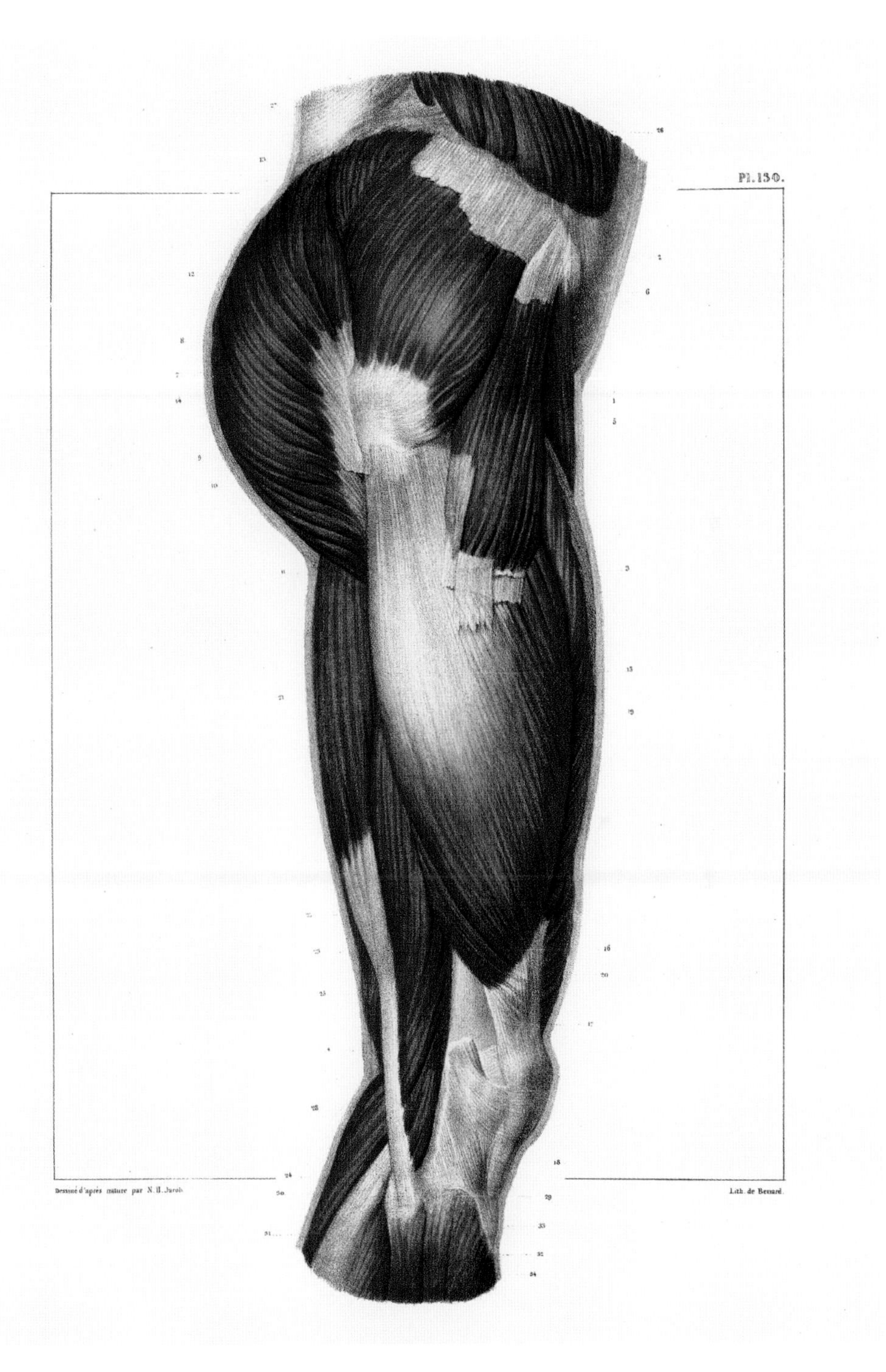

Thigh muscles / Muscles de la cuisse
Músculos femorales

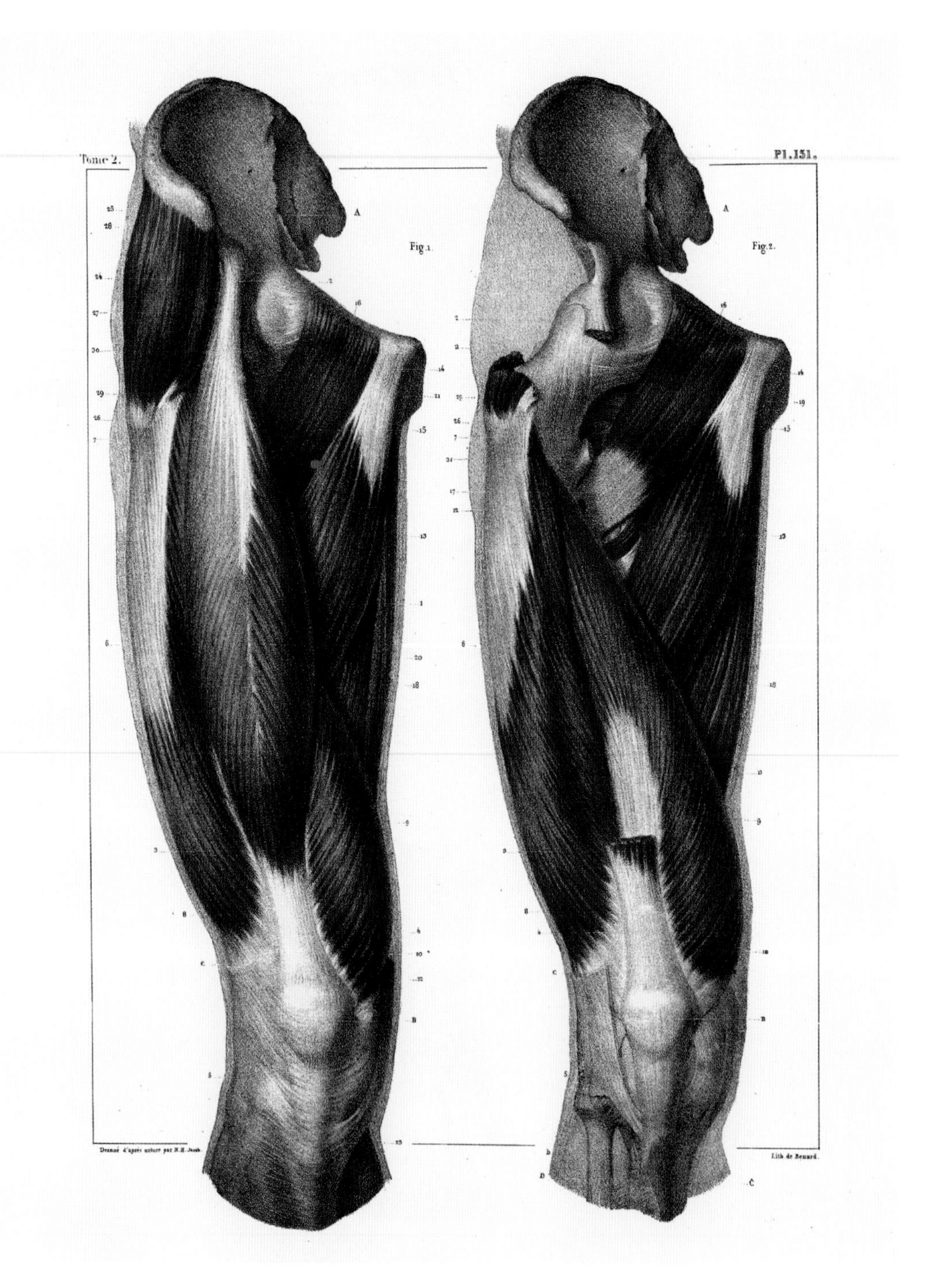

Thigh muscles / Muscles de la cuisse
Músculos femorales

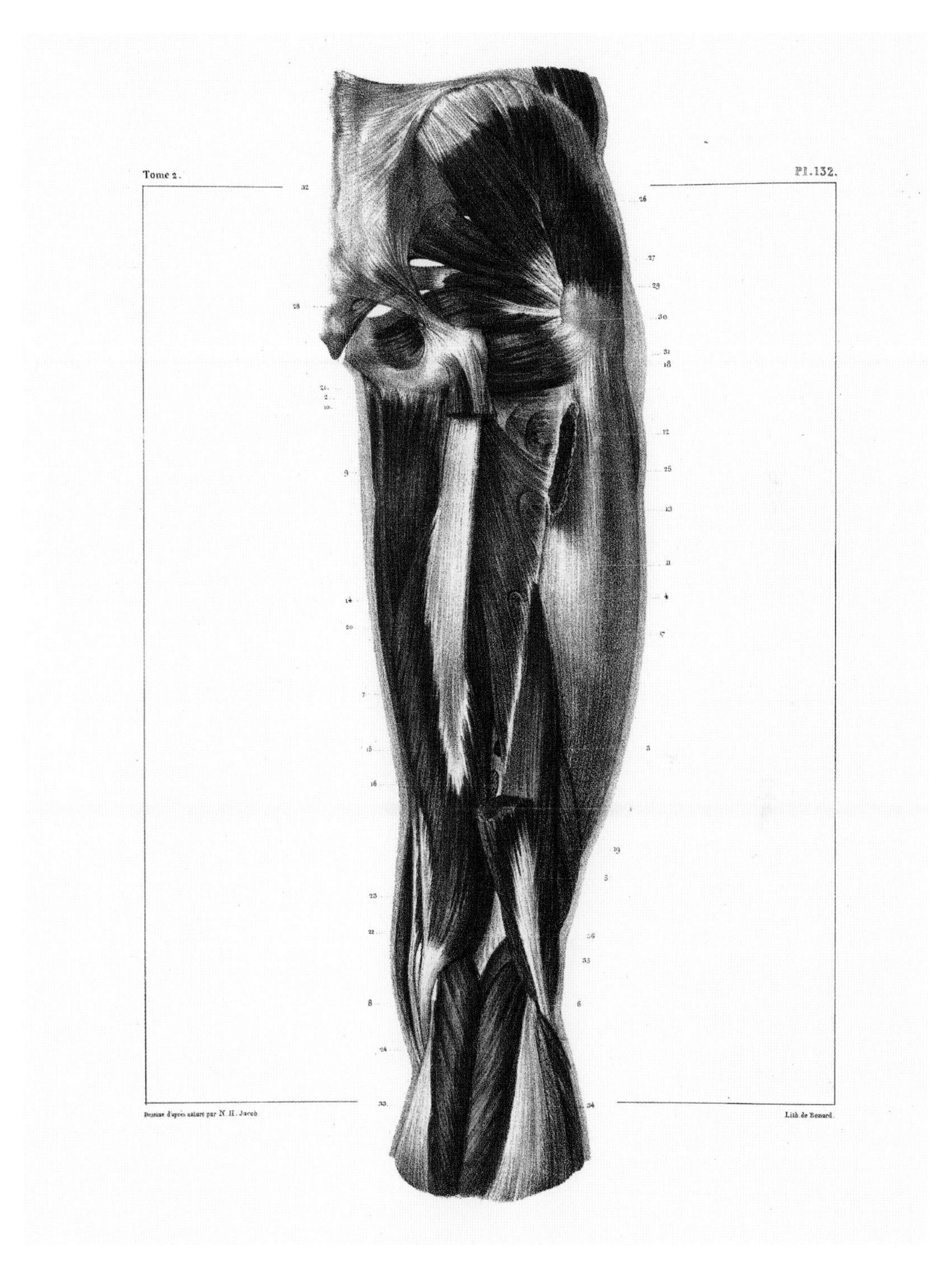

Thigh muscles / Muscles de la cuisse
Músculos femorales

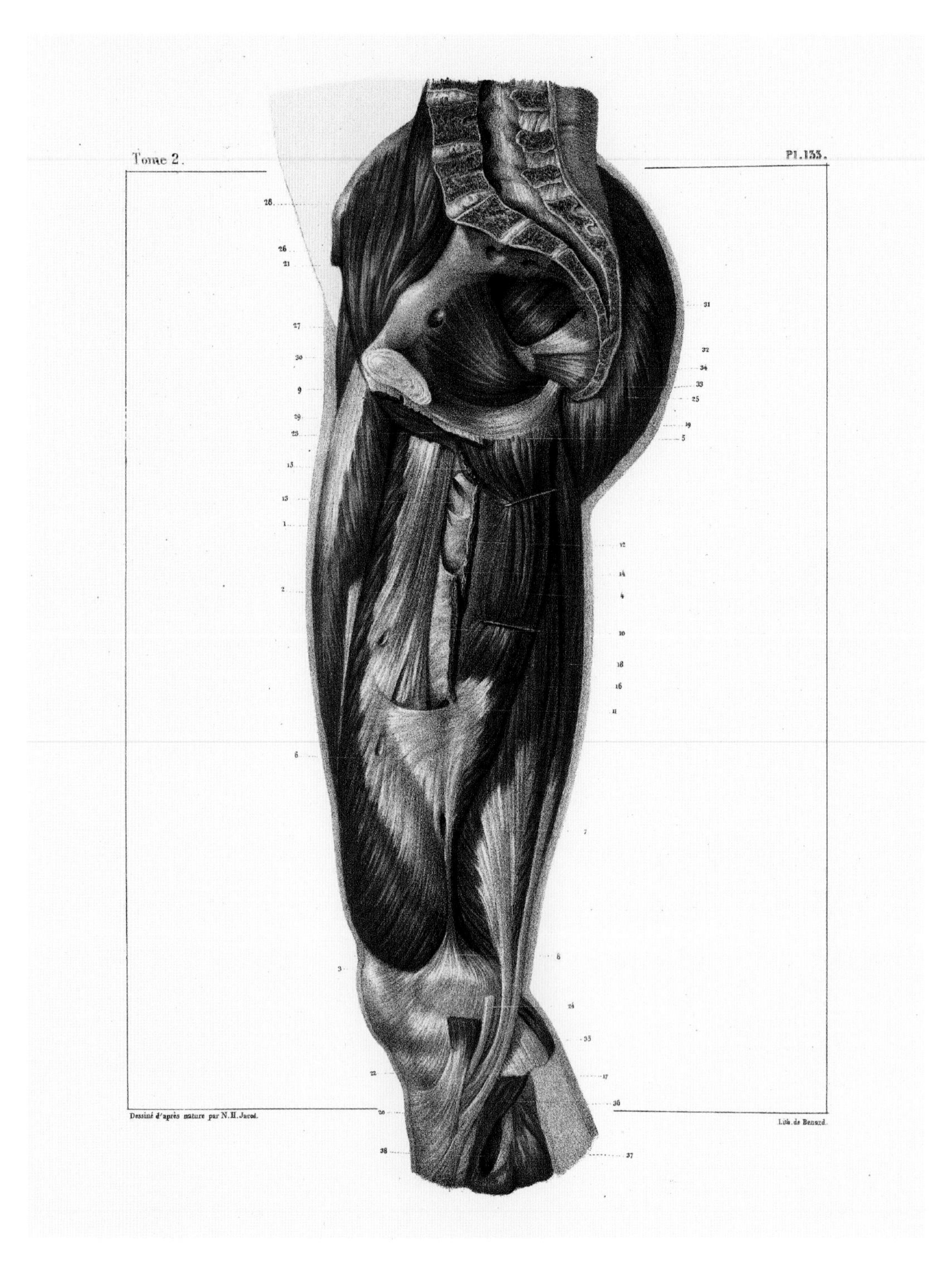

Thigh muscles / Muscles de la cuisse
Músculos femorales

MUSCULI FEMORIS. MUSCULI ET TENDINES REGIONIS GENUS POSTERIORIS

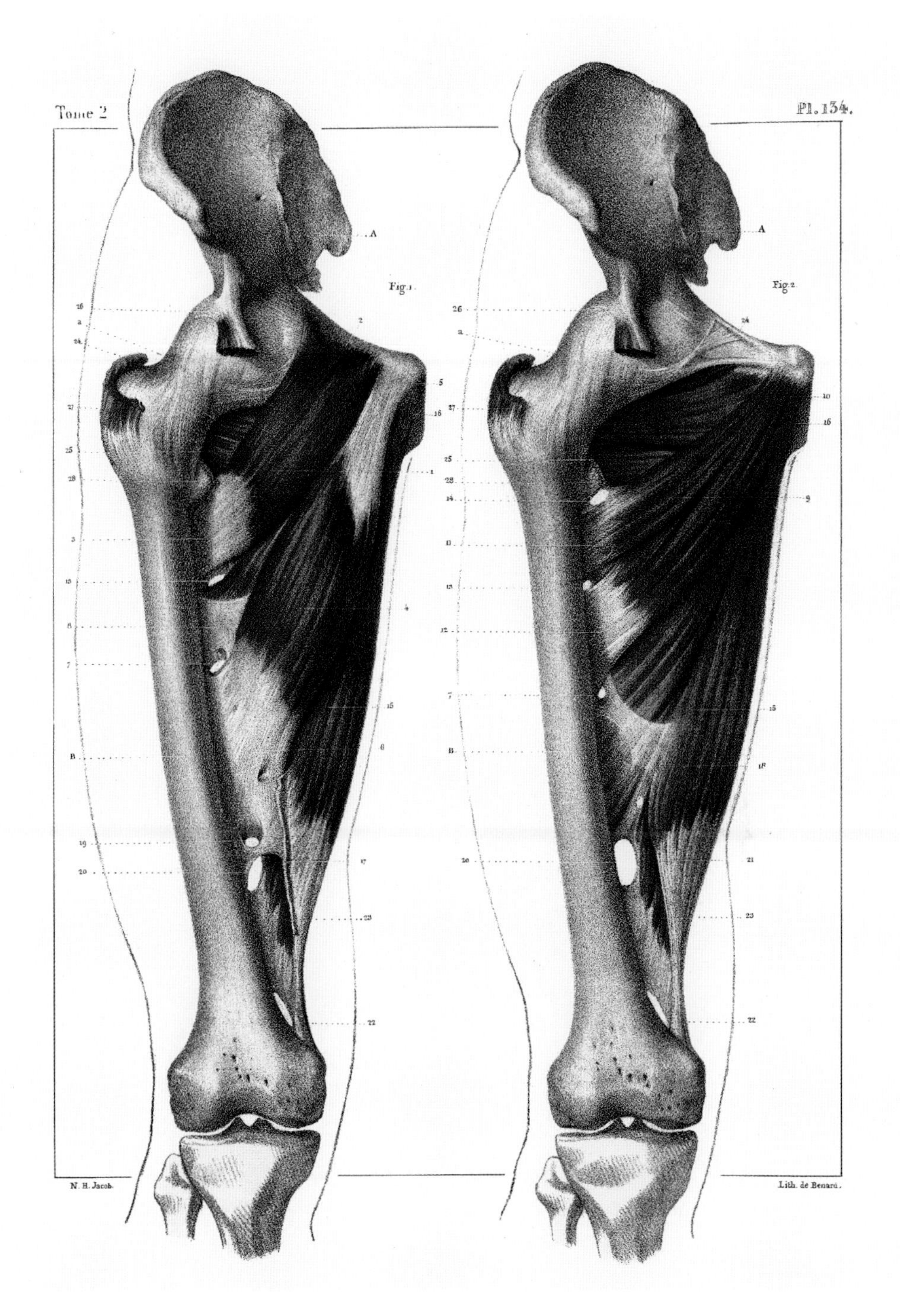

Thigh muscles / Muscles de la cuisse
Músculos femorales

MUSCULI FEMORIS. MUSCULI ET TENDINES REGIONIS GENUS POSTERIORIS

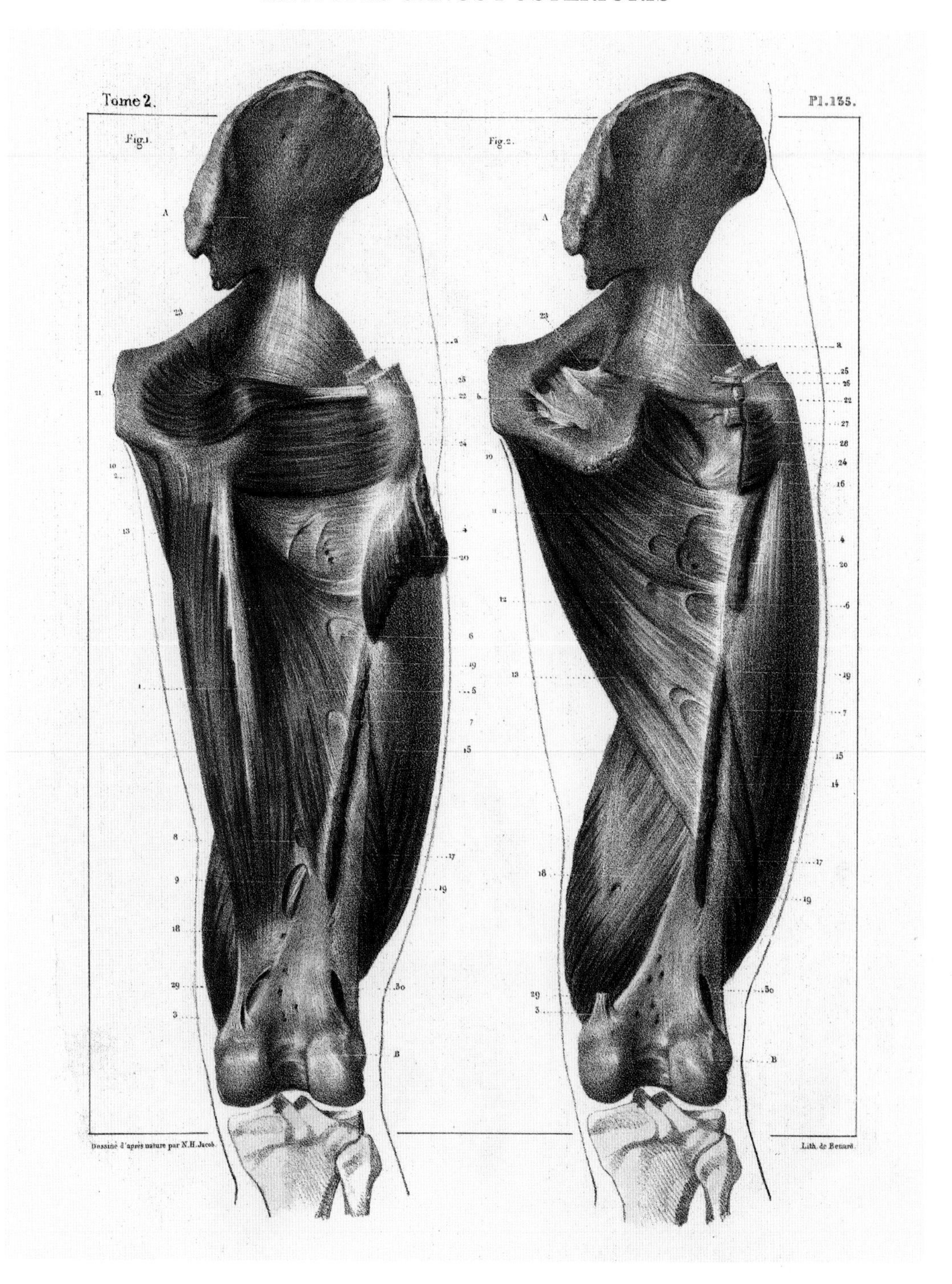

Thigh muscles / Muscles de la cuisse
Músculos femorales

MUSCULI FEMORIS. MUSCULI ET TENDINES REGIONIS GENUS POSTERIORIS

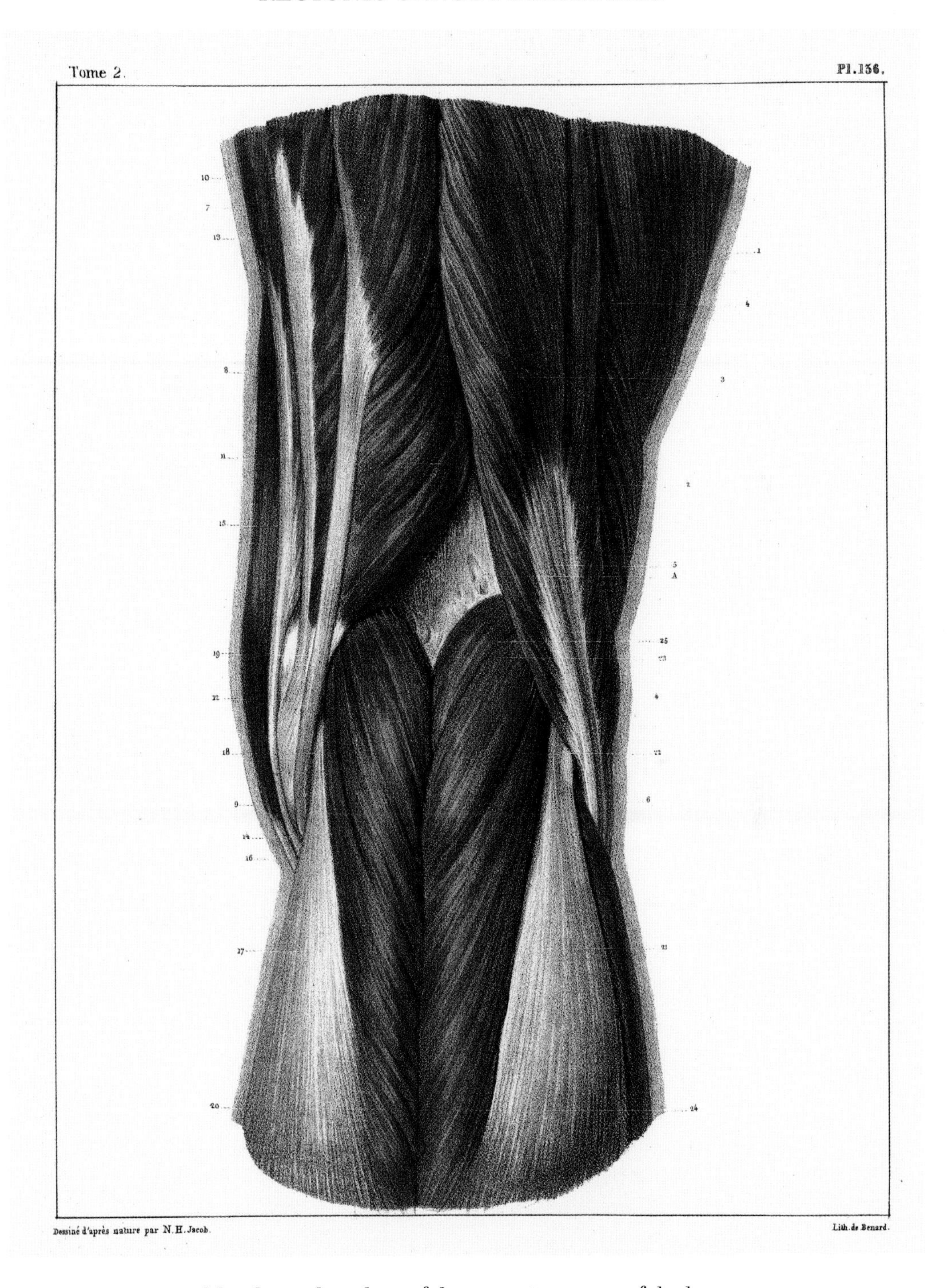

Muscles and tendons of the posterior aspect of the knee
Muscles et tendons de la région postérieure du genou
Músculos y tendones de la región posterior de la rodilla

MUSCULI FEMORIS. MUSCULI ET TENDINES REGIONIS GENUS POSTERIORIS

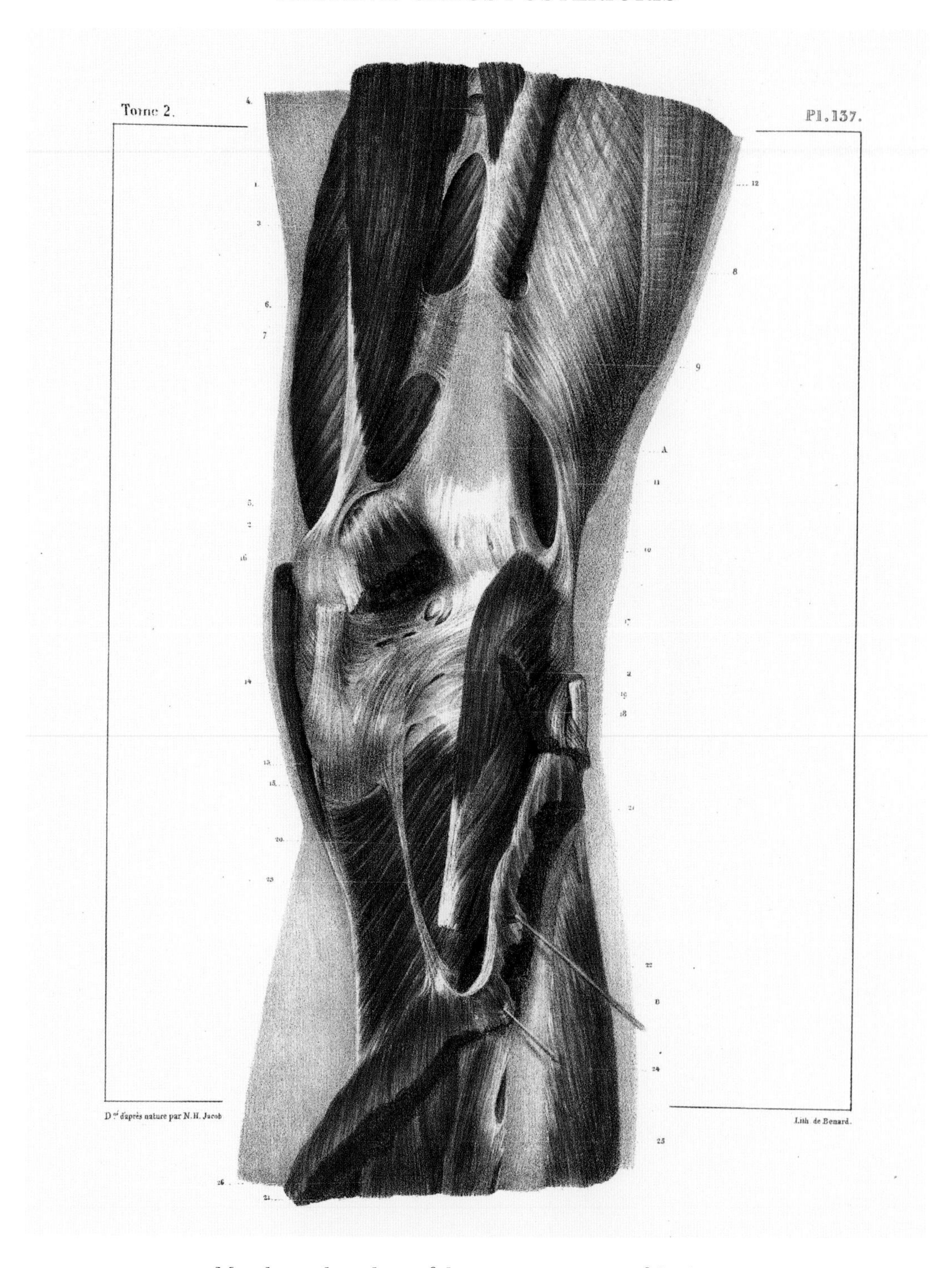

Muscles and tendons of the posterior aspect of the knee
Muscles et tendons de la région postérieure du genou
Músculos y tendones de la región posterior de la rodilla

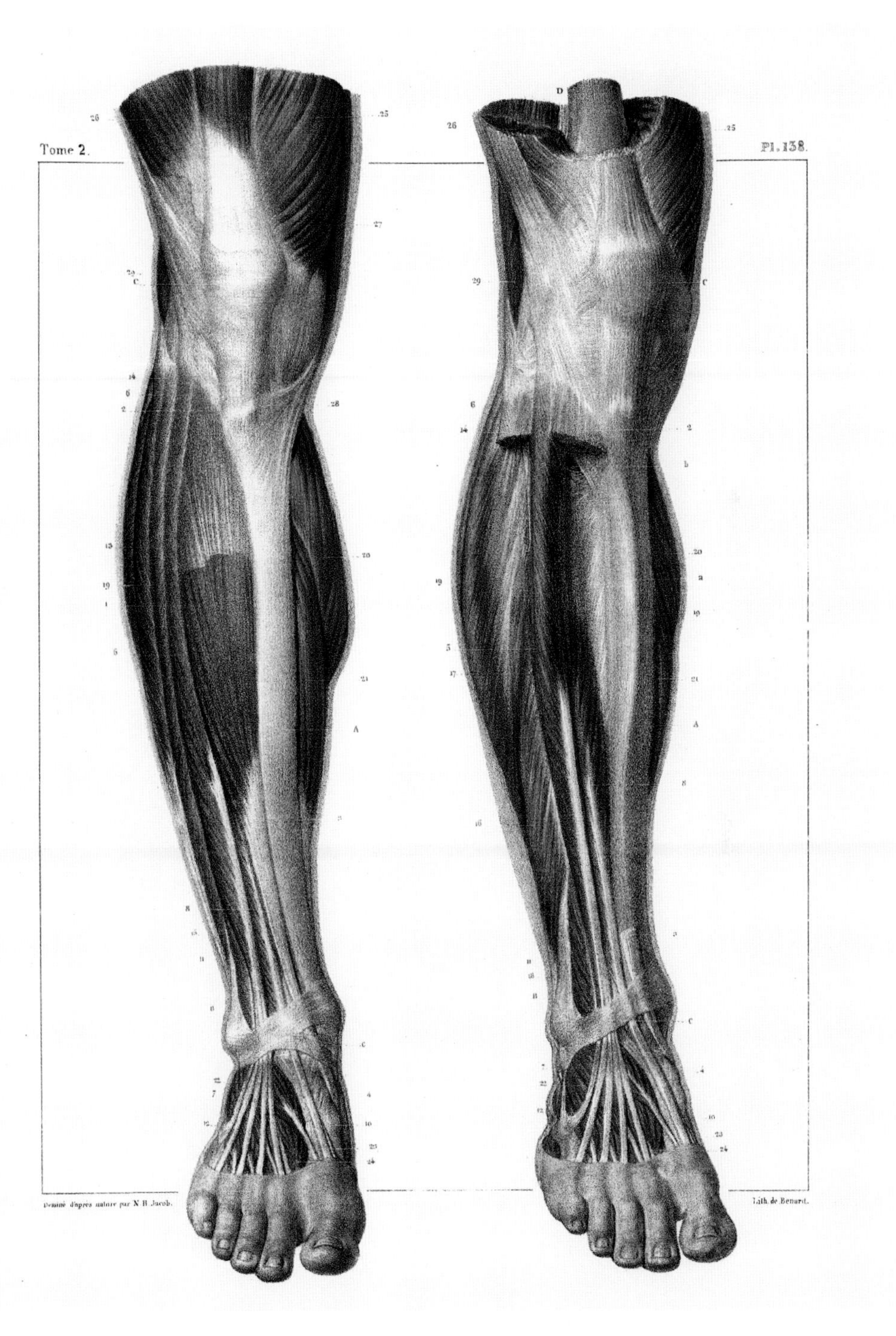

Muscles of the lower leg and the foot
Muscles de la jambe et du pied
Músculos de la pierna y del pie

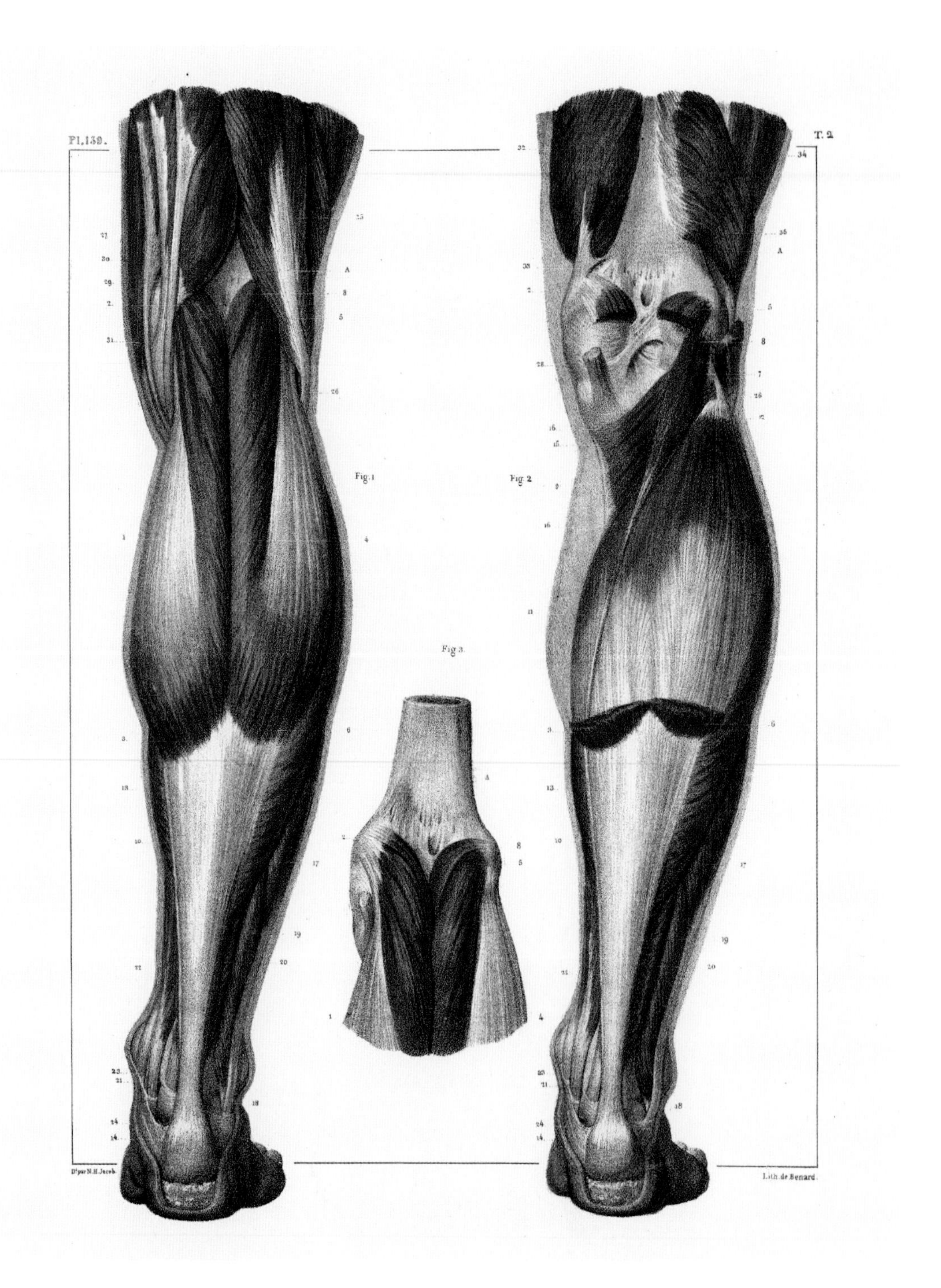

Muscles of the lower leg and the foot / Muscles de la jambe et du pied
Músculos de la pierna y del pie

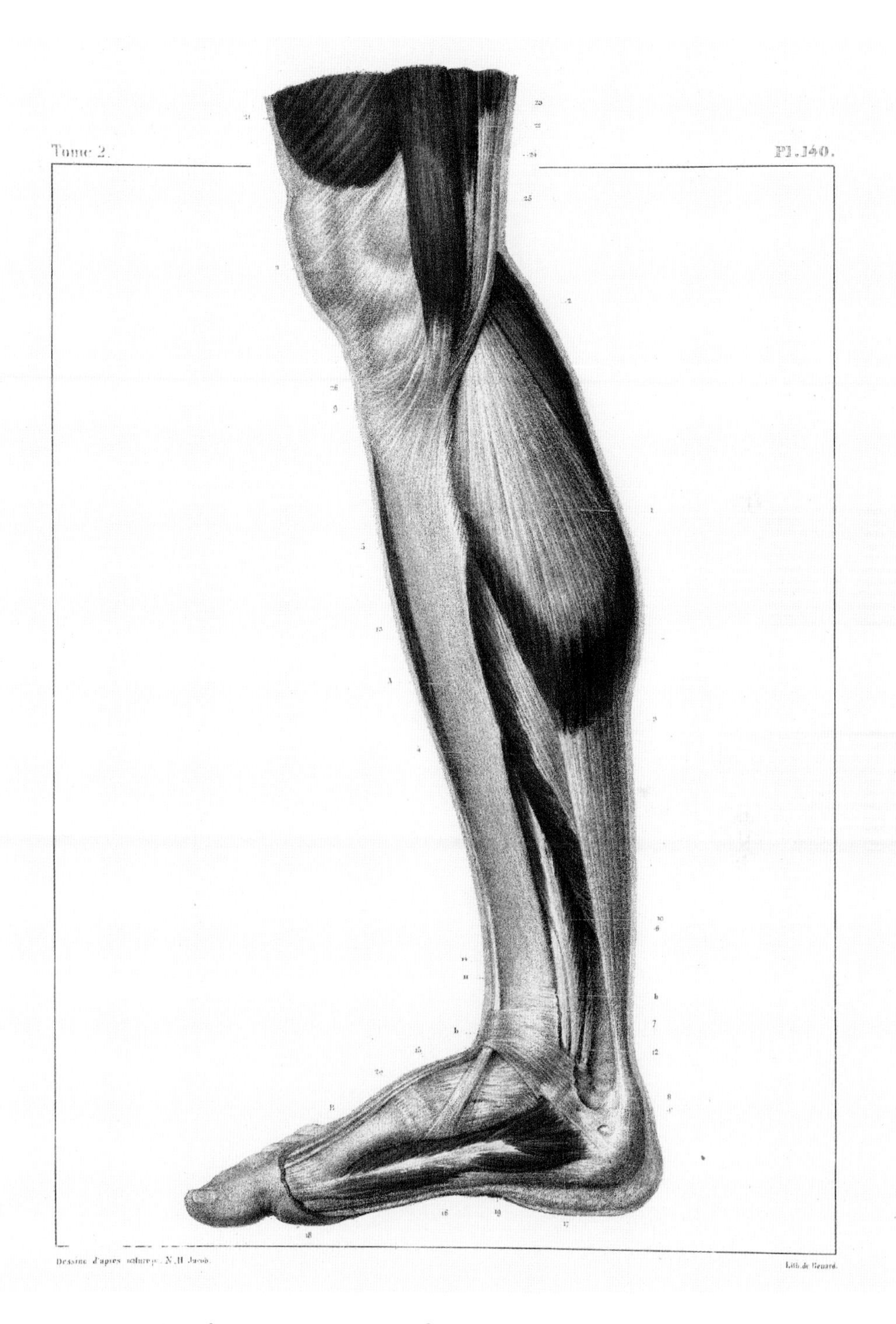

Muscles of the lower leg and the foot / Muscles de la jambe et du pied
Músculos de la pierna y del pie

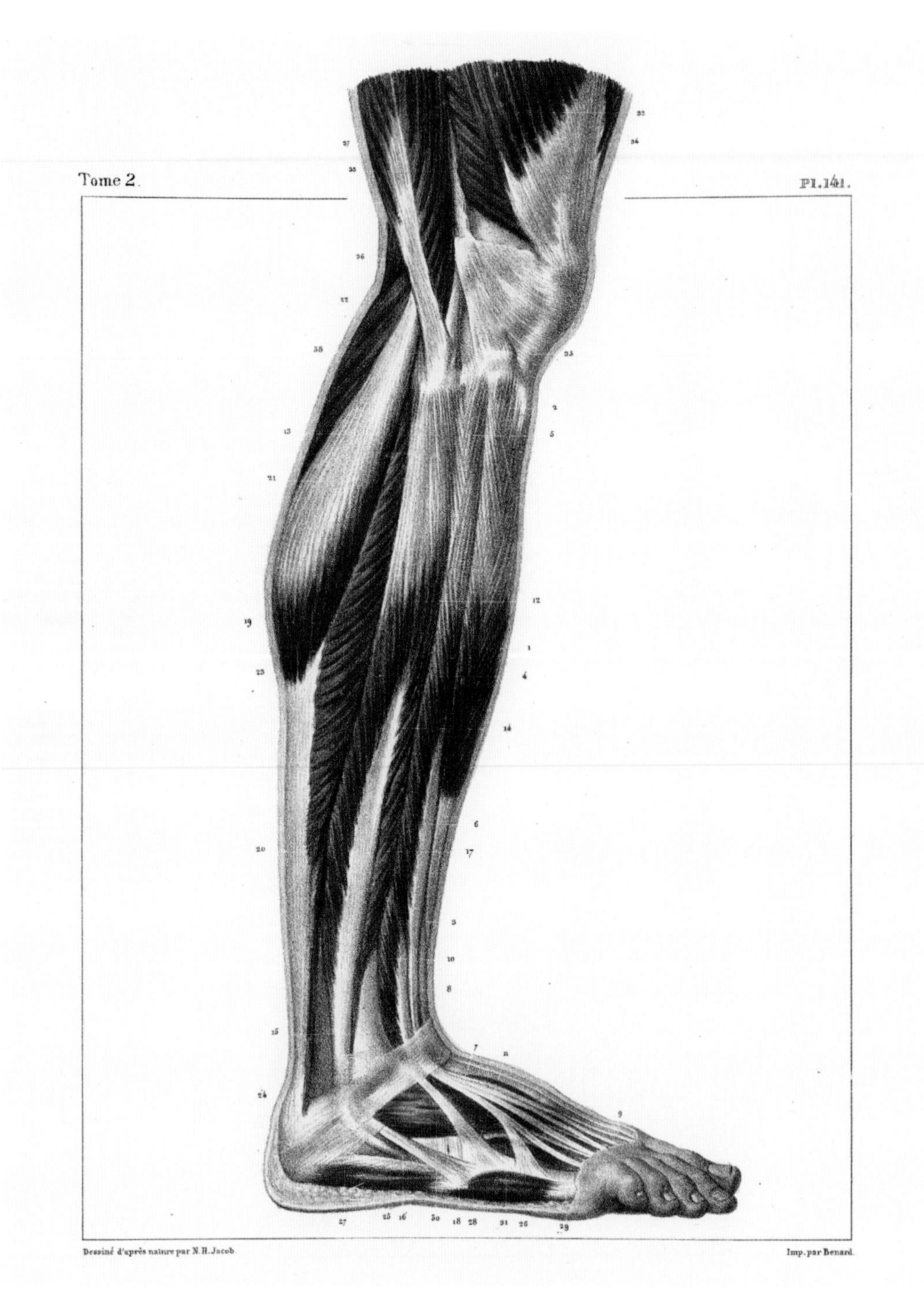

Muscles of the lower leg and the foot / Muscles de la jambe et du pied
Músculos de la pierna y del pie

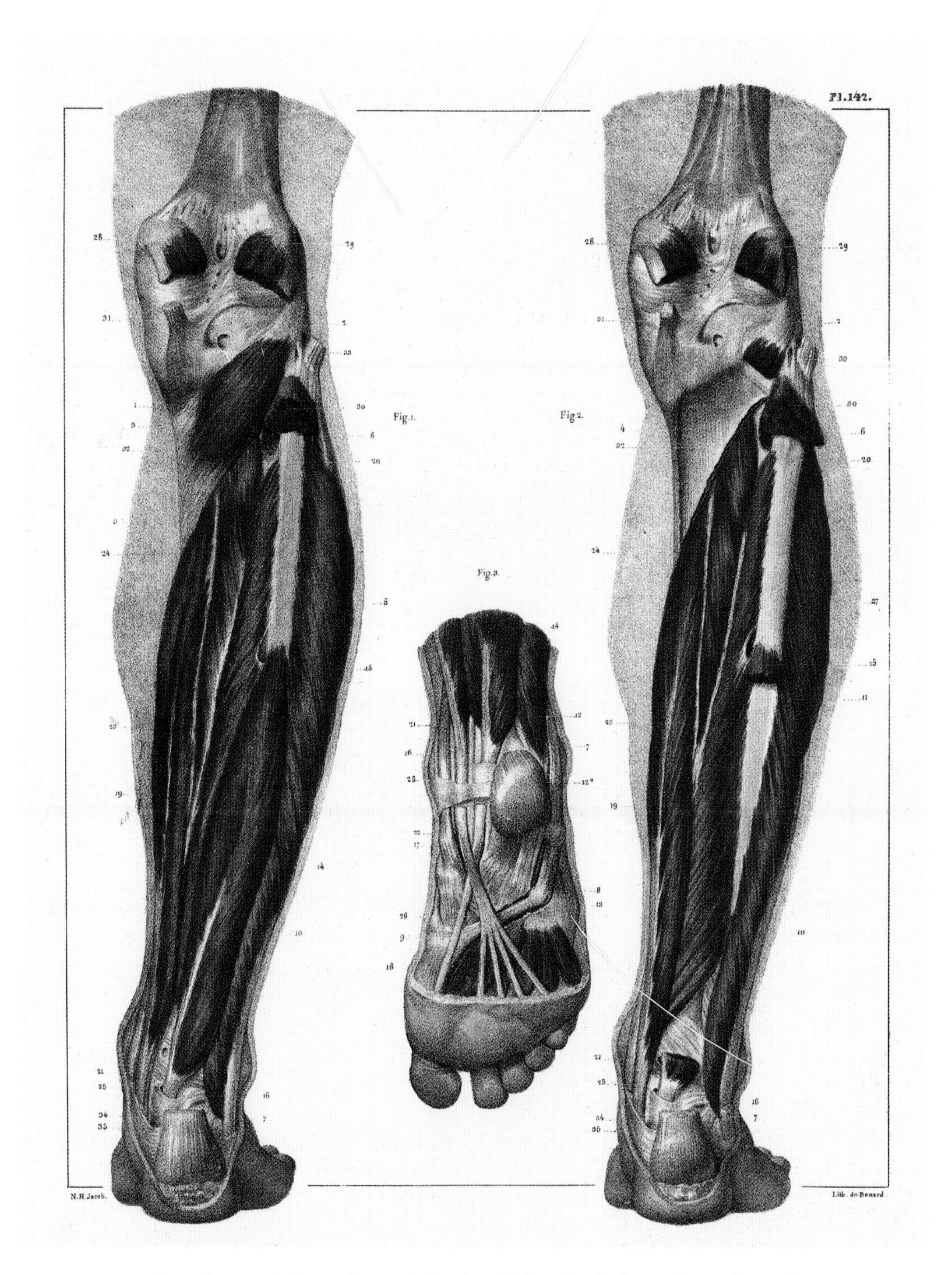

Muscles of the lower leg and the foot / Muscles de la jambe et du pied
Músculos de la pierna y del pie

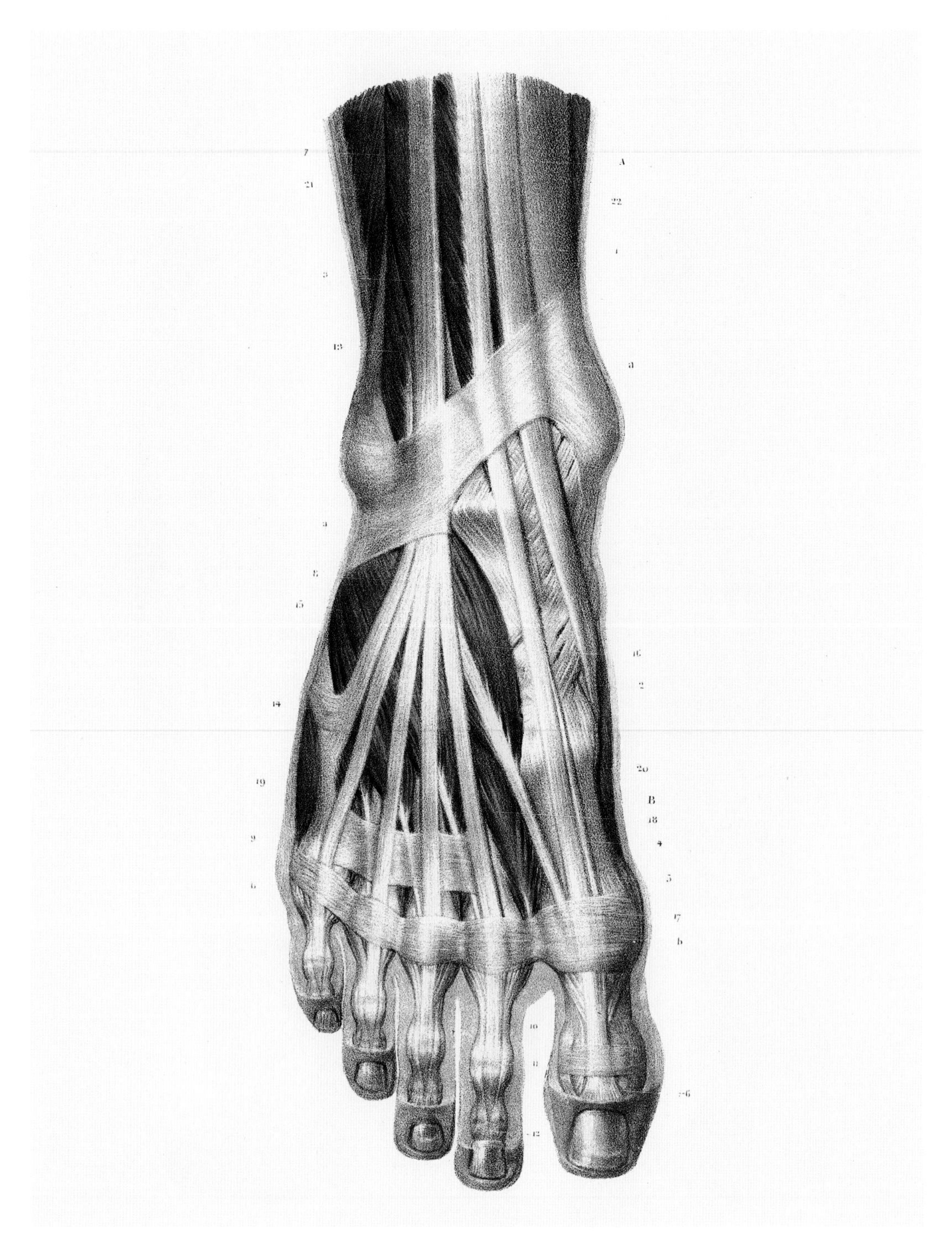

Muscles and tendons of the foot / Muscles et tendons du pied
Músculos y tendones del pie

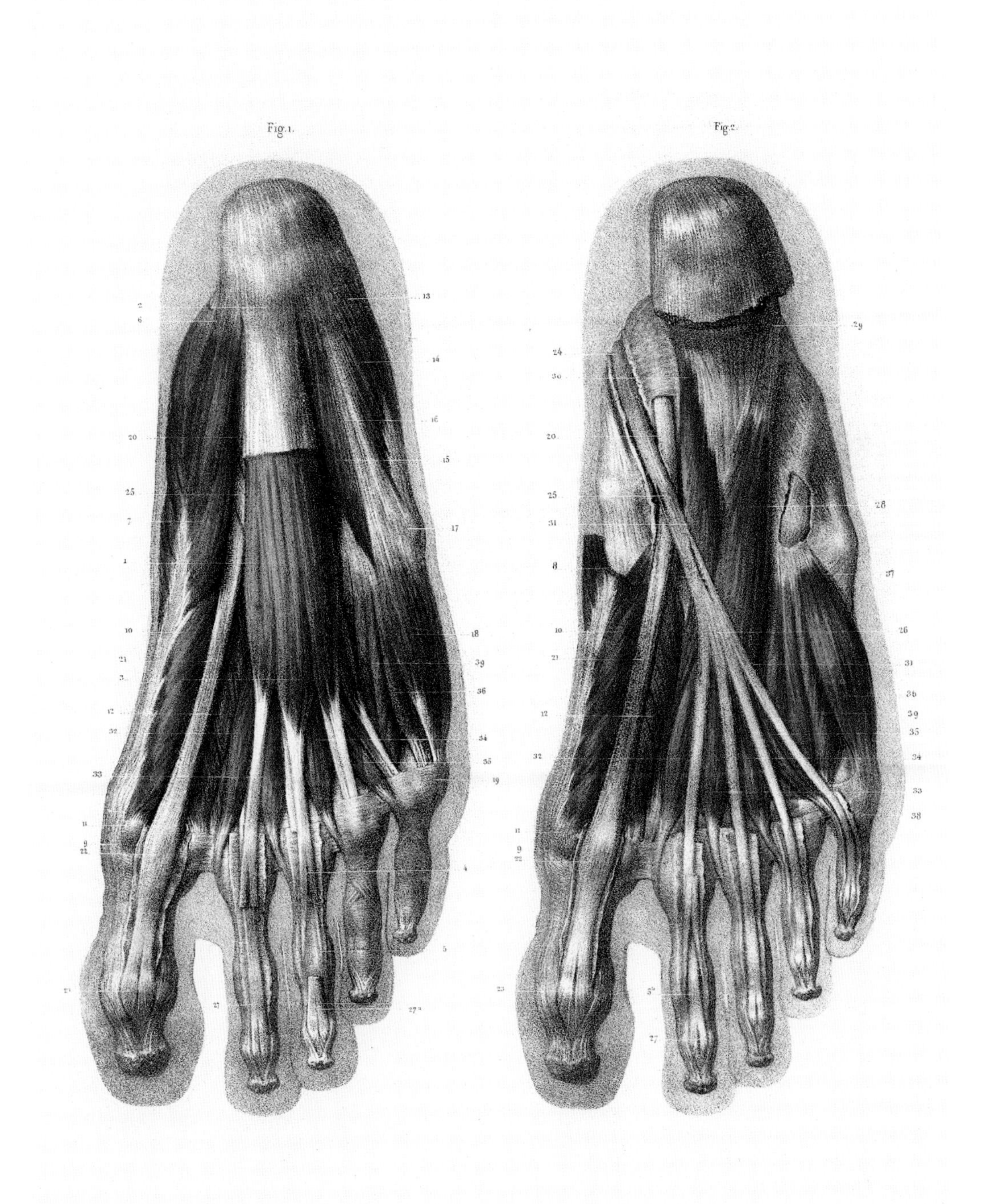

Muscles and tendons of the foot / Muscles et tendons du pied
Músculos y tendones del pie

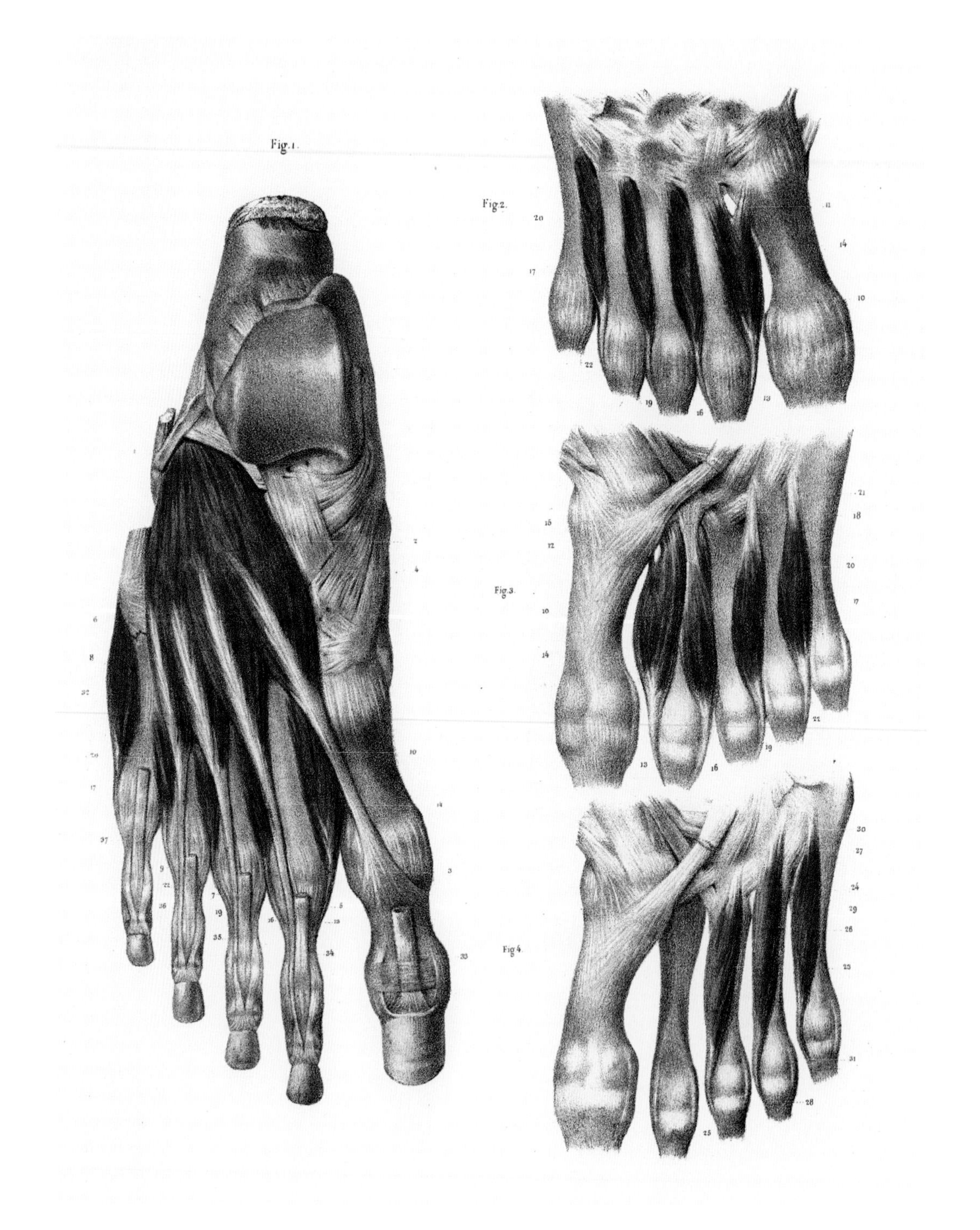

Muscles of the foot / Muscles du pied / Músculos del pie

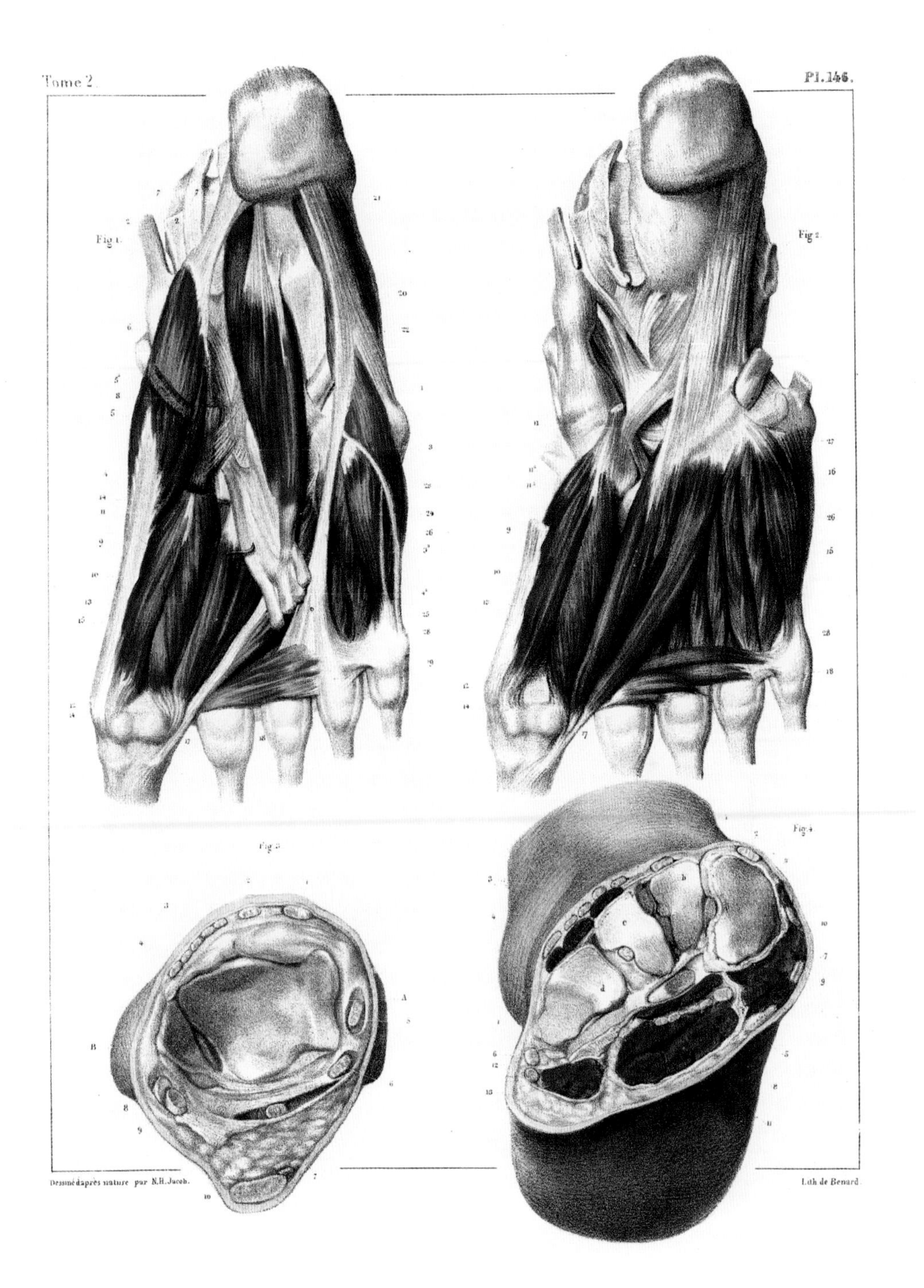

Muscles of the foot / Muscles du pied / Músculos del pie

FASCIAE PALMAE MANUS. FASCIAE ET SEPTA INTERMUSCALARIA BRACHII ET ANTEBRACHII

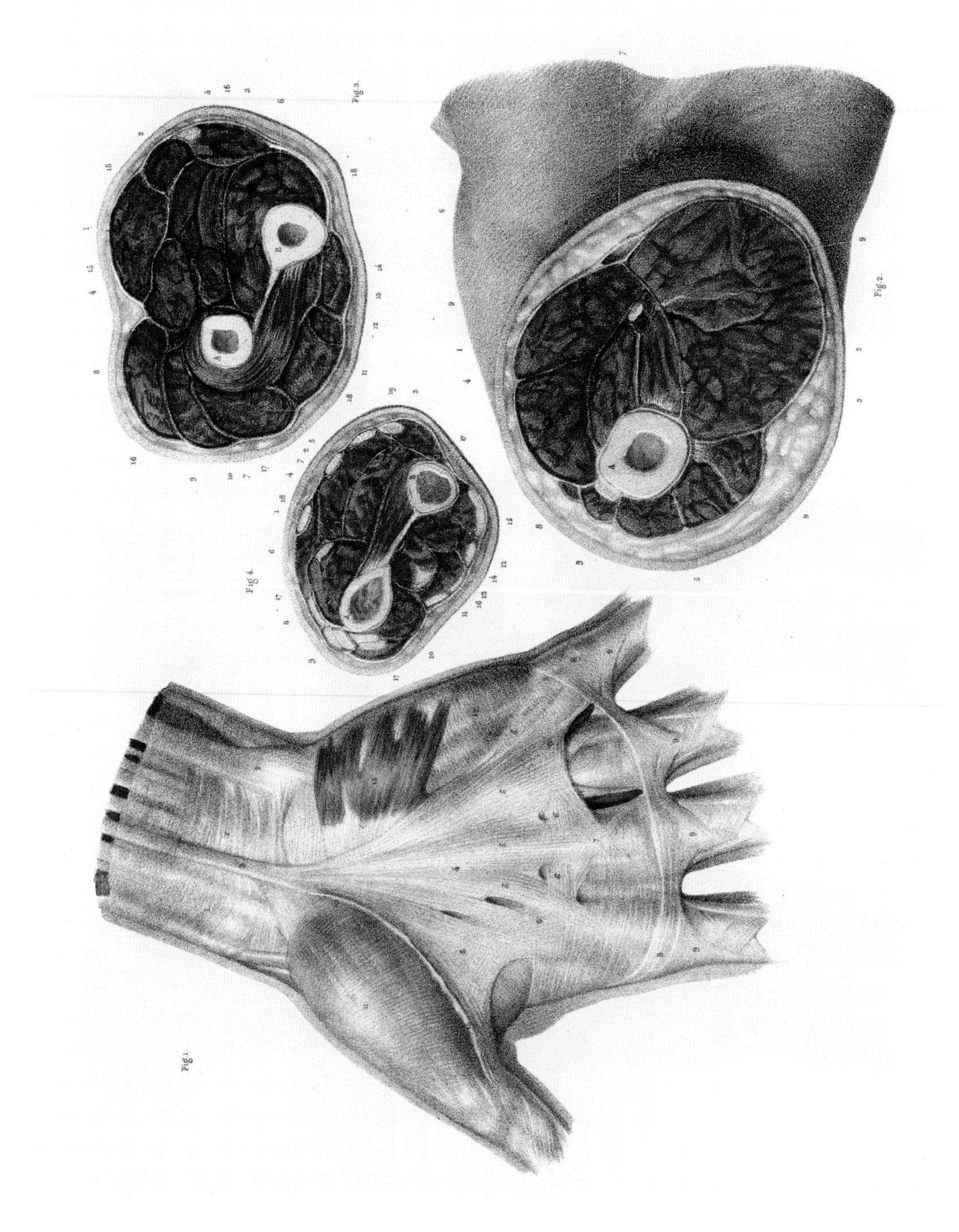

Fascias of the palm of the hand. Fascias and intermuscular septa of the upper arm and forearm
Fascias de la paume de la main. Fascias et septums intermusculaires du bras et de l'avant-bras
Fascias palmares. Fascias y tabiques intermusculares del brazo y del antebrazo

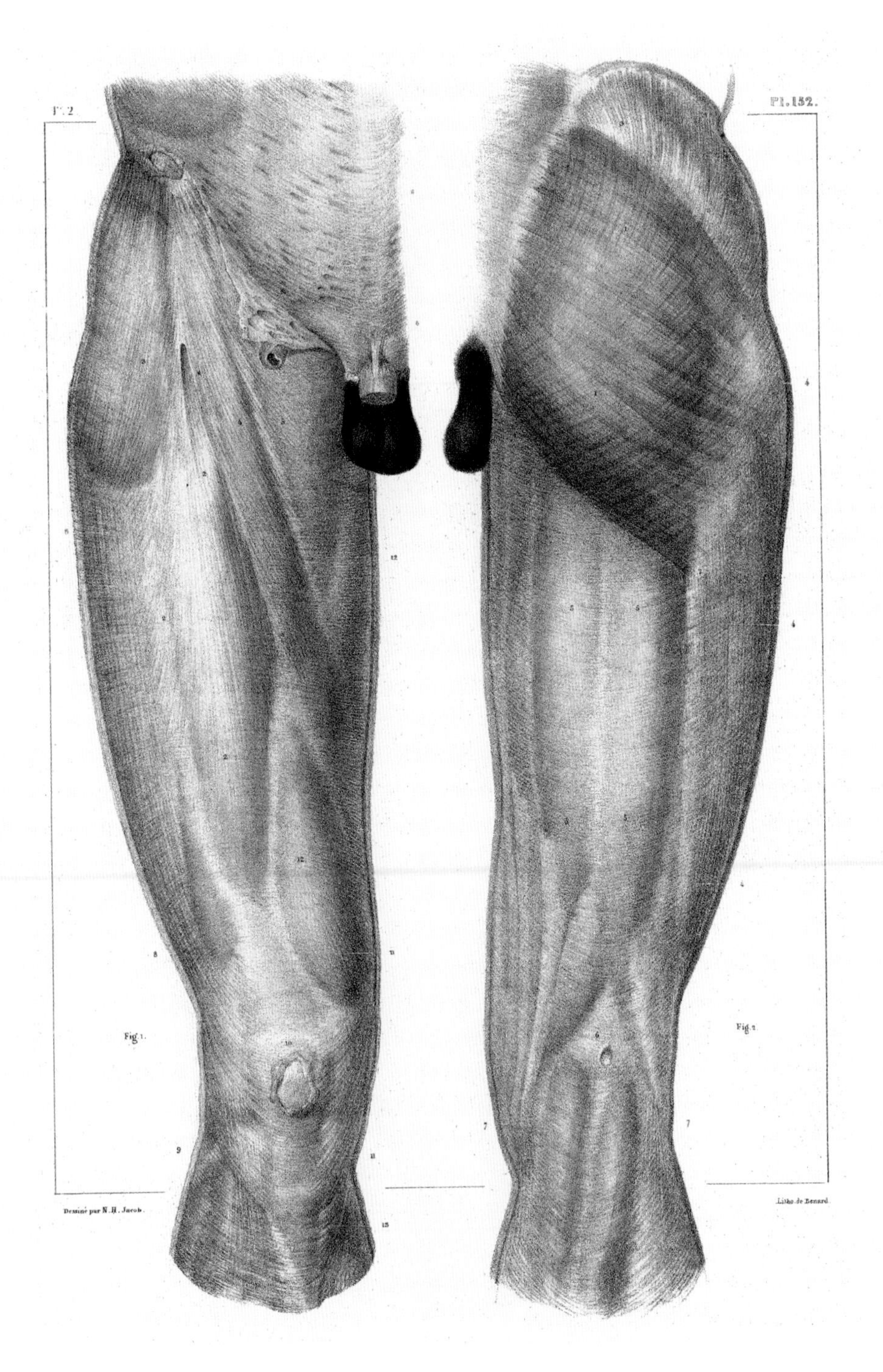

Fascias of the buttocks and the thigh
Fascias de la région fessière et de la cuisse
Fascias de la región glútea y femoral

FASCIAE PLANTAE PEDIS. FASCIAE ET SEPTA INTERMUSCALARIA FEMORIS ET CRURIS

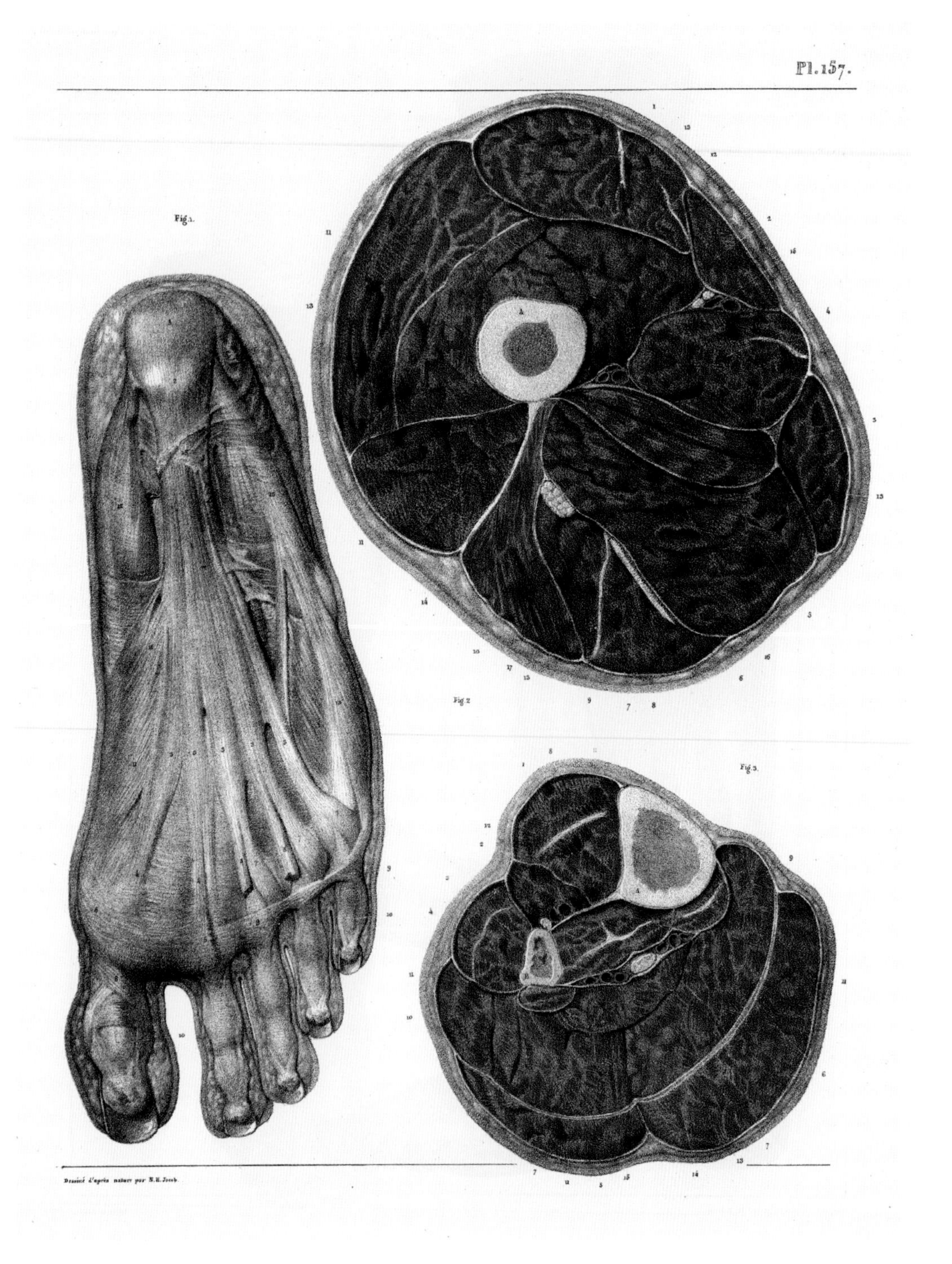

Fascias of the sole of the foot. Fascias and intermuscular septa of the thigh and the lower leg
Fascias de la plante du pied. Fascias et septums intermusculaires de la cuisse et de la jambe
Fascias plantares. Fascias y tabiques intermusculares del muslo y de la pierna

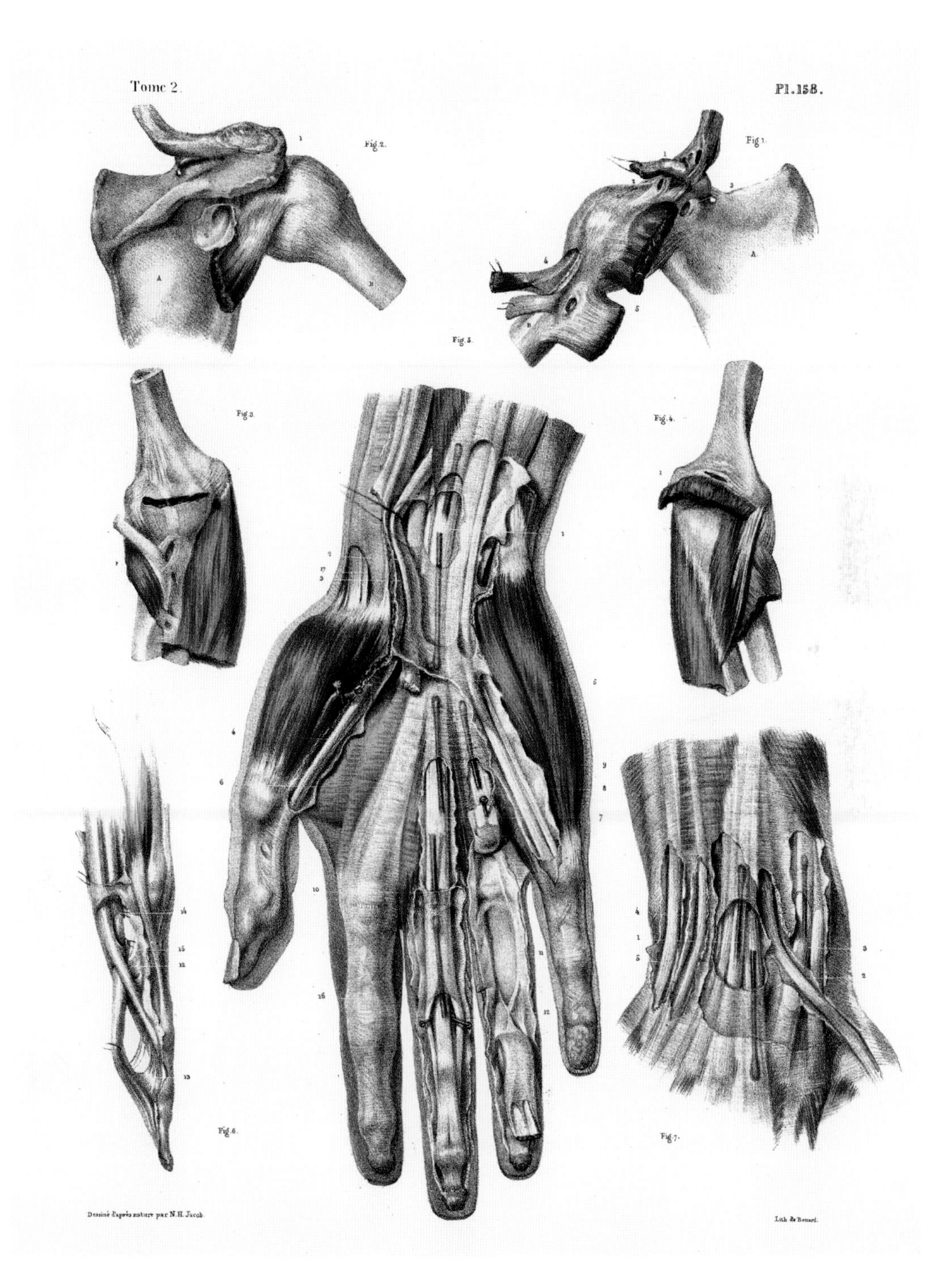

Bursae and synovial sheaths of the upper limb
Bourses et gaines synoviales du membre supérieur
Bolsas y vainas sinoviales del miembro superior

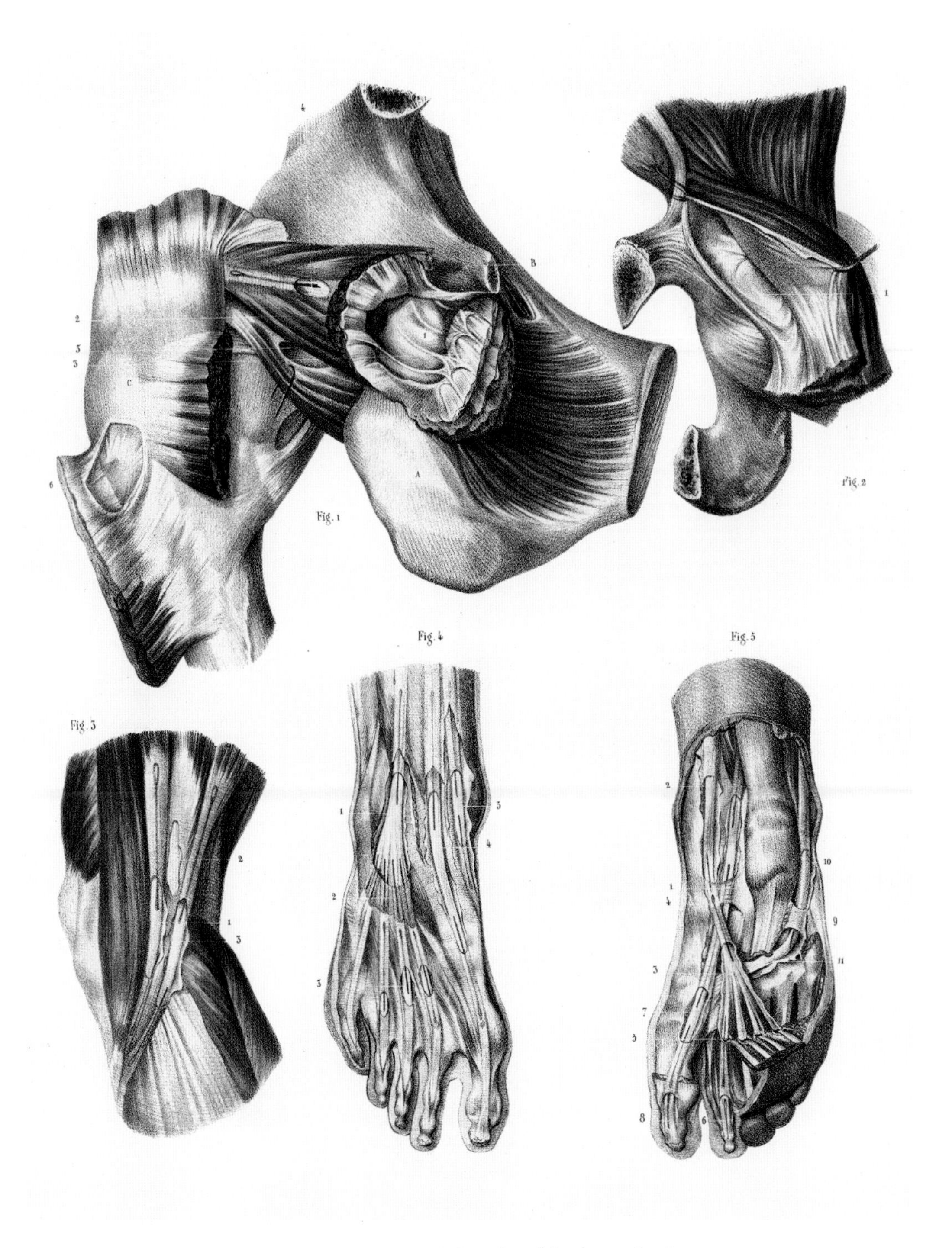

Bursae and synovial sheaths of the lower limb
Bourses et gaines synoviales du membre inférieur
Bolsas y vainas sinoviales del miembro inferior

VOL. 3

NEVROLOGIA:
SYSTEMA NERVOSUM CENTRALE,
PERIPHERICUM, ET AUTONOMICUM.
ORGANA SENSUUM

NEUROLOGY:
CENTRAL, PERIPHERAL,
AND VEGETATIVE NERVOUS SYSTEM.
SENSORY ORGANS

NEVROLOGIE :
SYSTEME NERVEUX CENTRAL,
PERIPHERIQUE ET AUTONOME.
ORGANES DES SENS

NEUROLOGÍA:
SISTEMA NERVIOSO CENTRAL,
PERIFÉRICO Y VEGETATIVO.
ÓRGANOS DE LOS SENTIDOS

Left page / Ci-contre / Página contigua:
Meninges / Méninges / Meninges

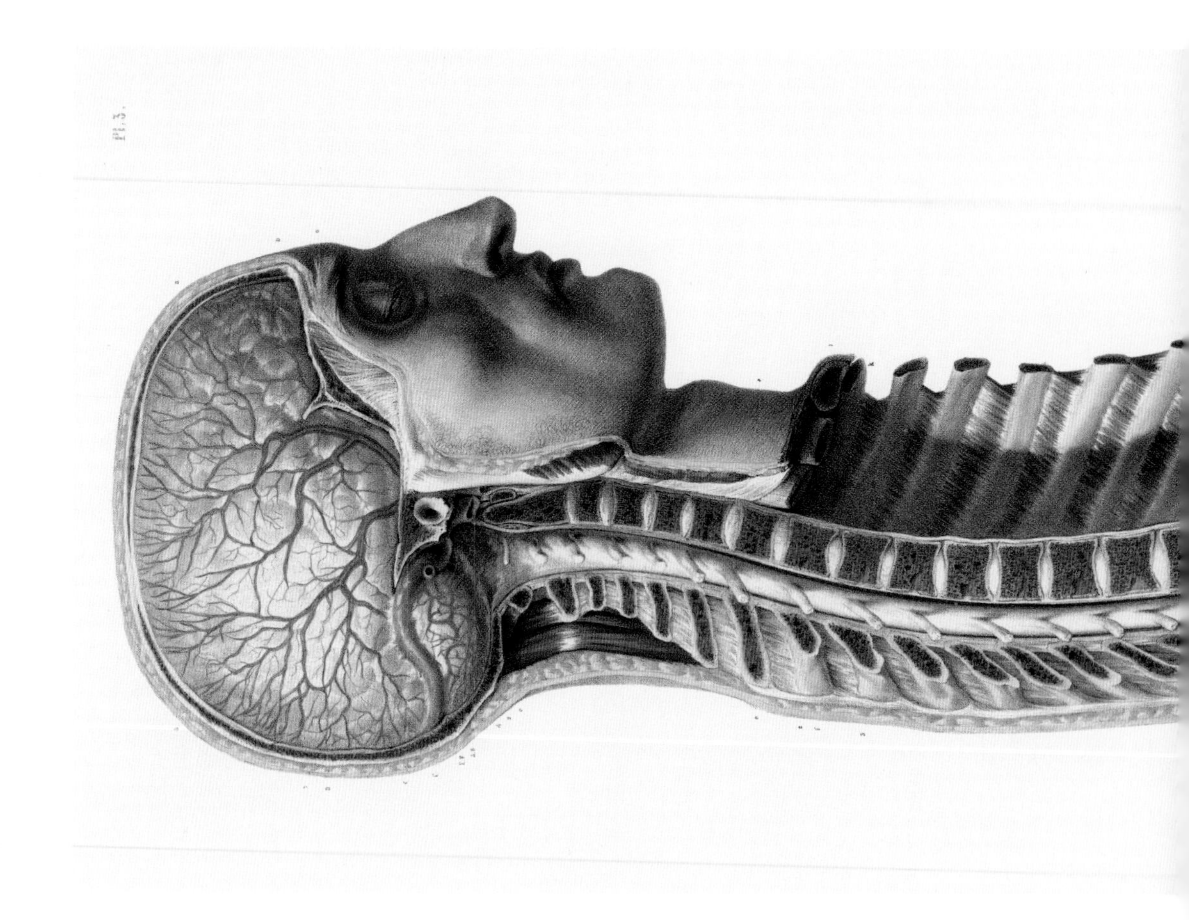

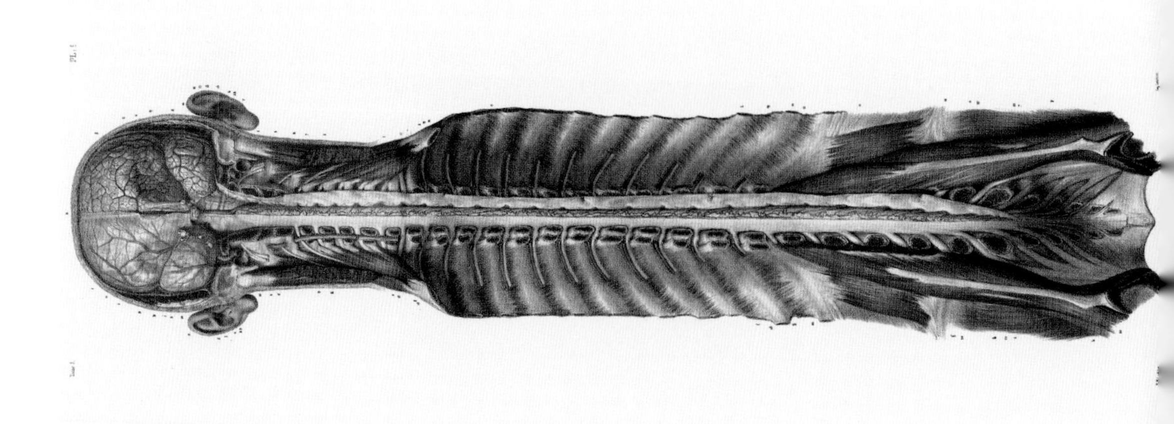

Meninges / Méninges / Meninges

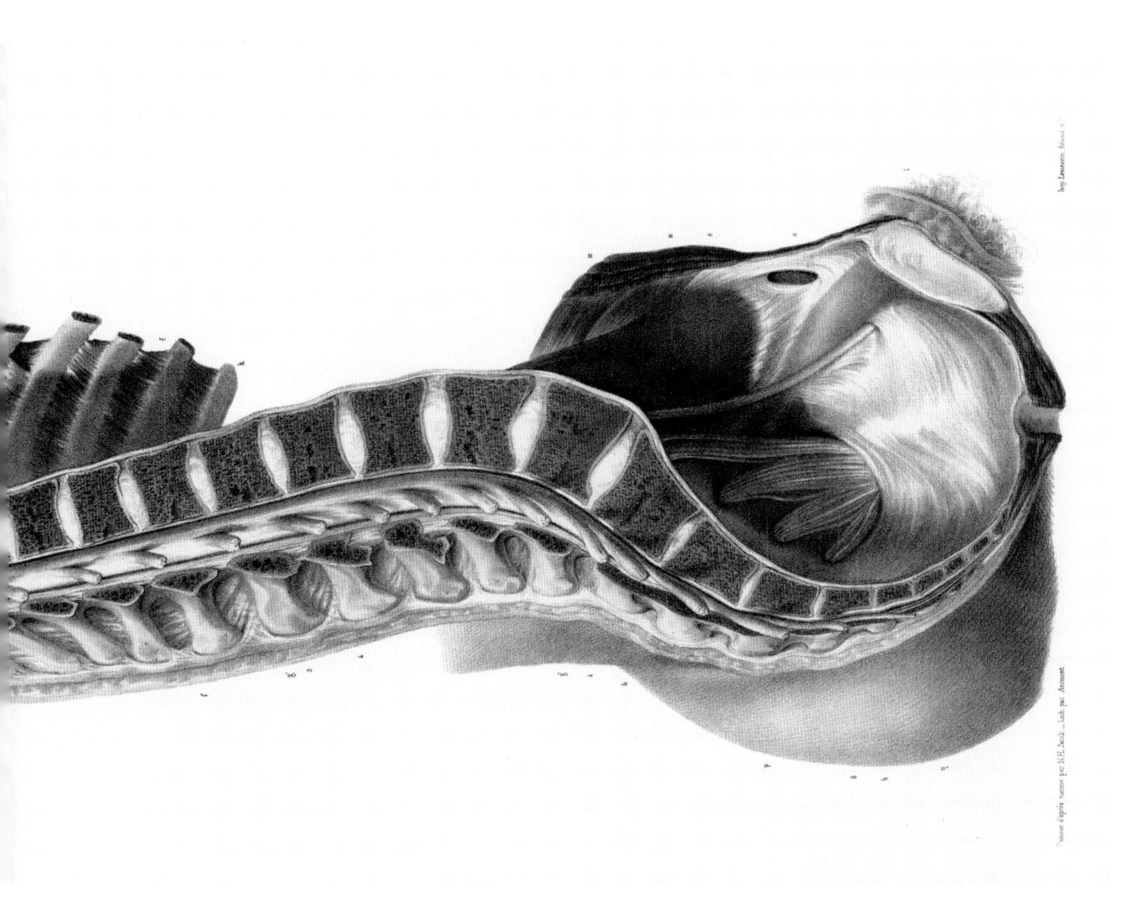

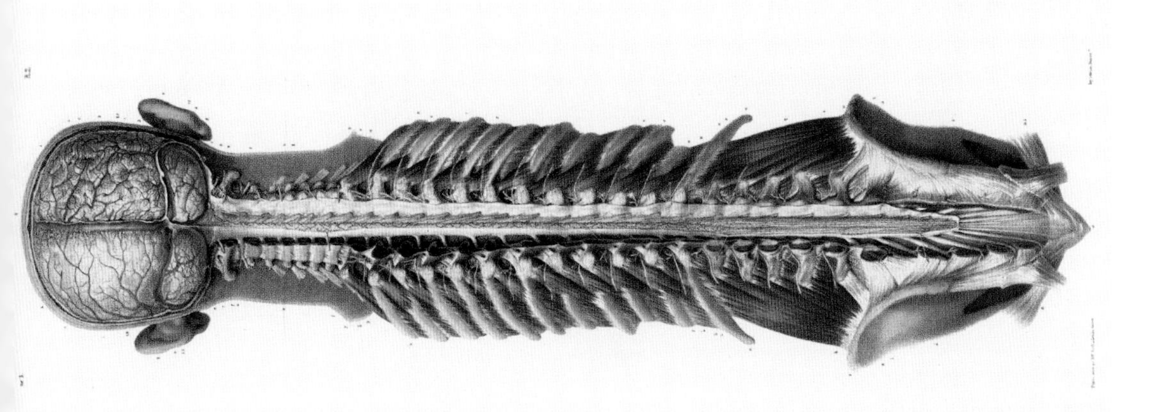

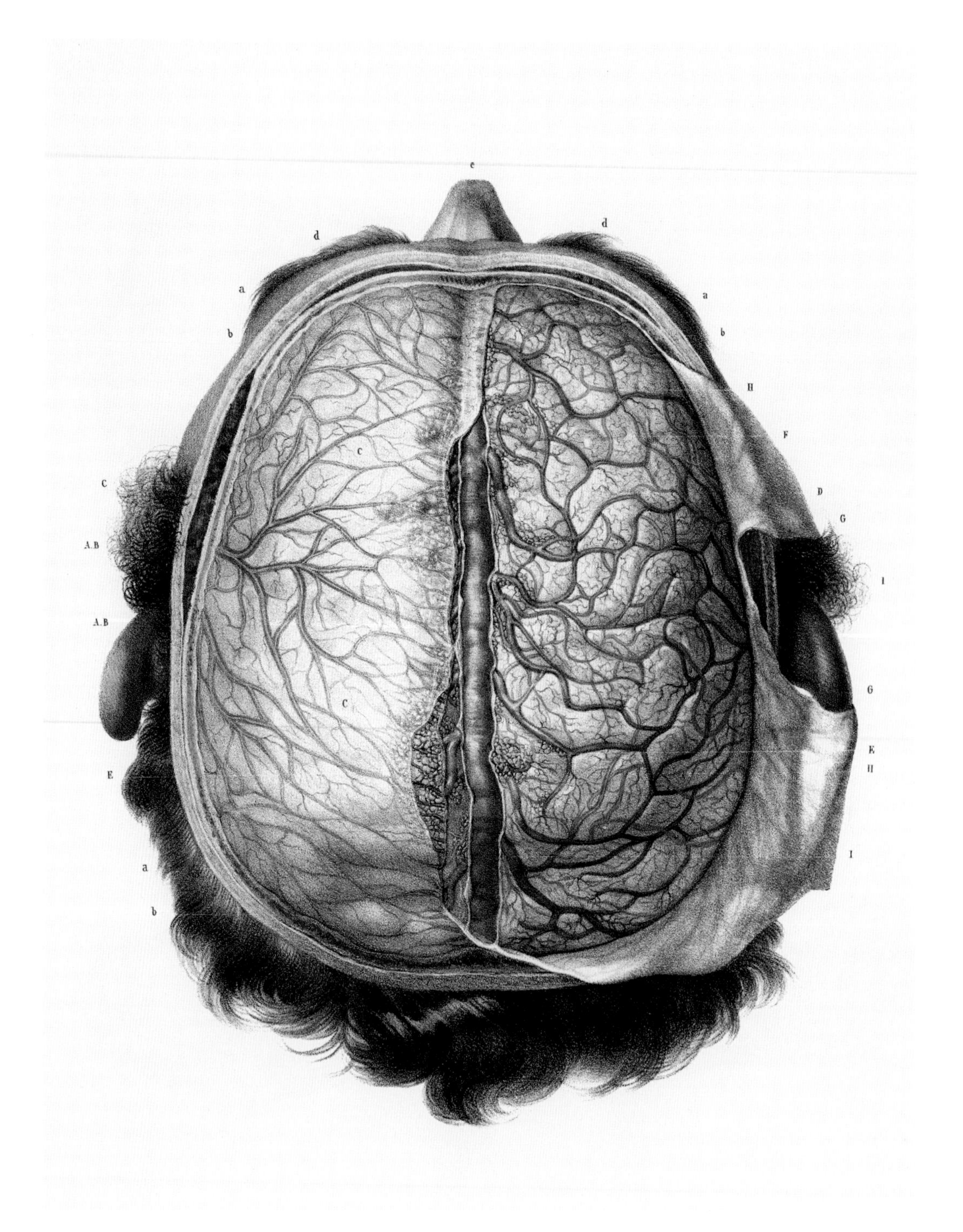

Meninges of the brain or cranial meninges
Méninges de l'encéphale ou crâniennes
Meninges del encéfalo o craneales

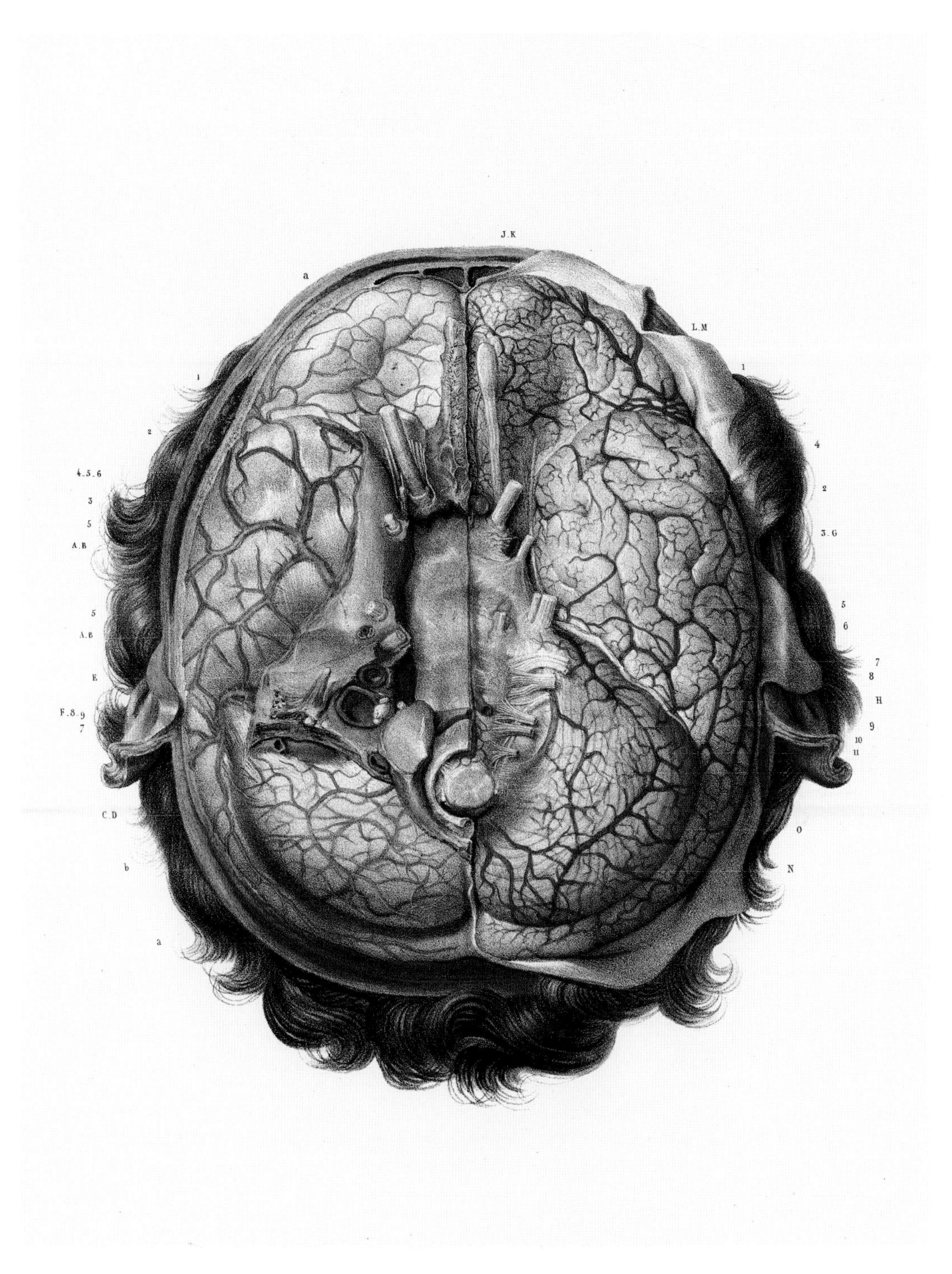

Meninges of the brain or cranial meninges
Méninges de l'encéphale ou crâniennes
Meninges del encéfalo o craneales

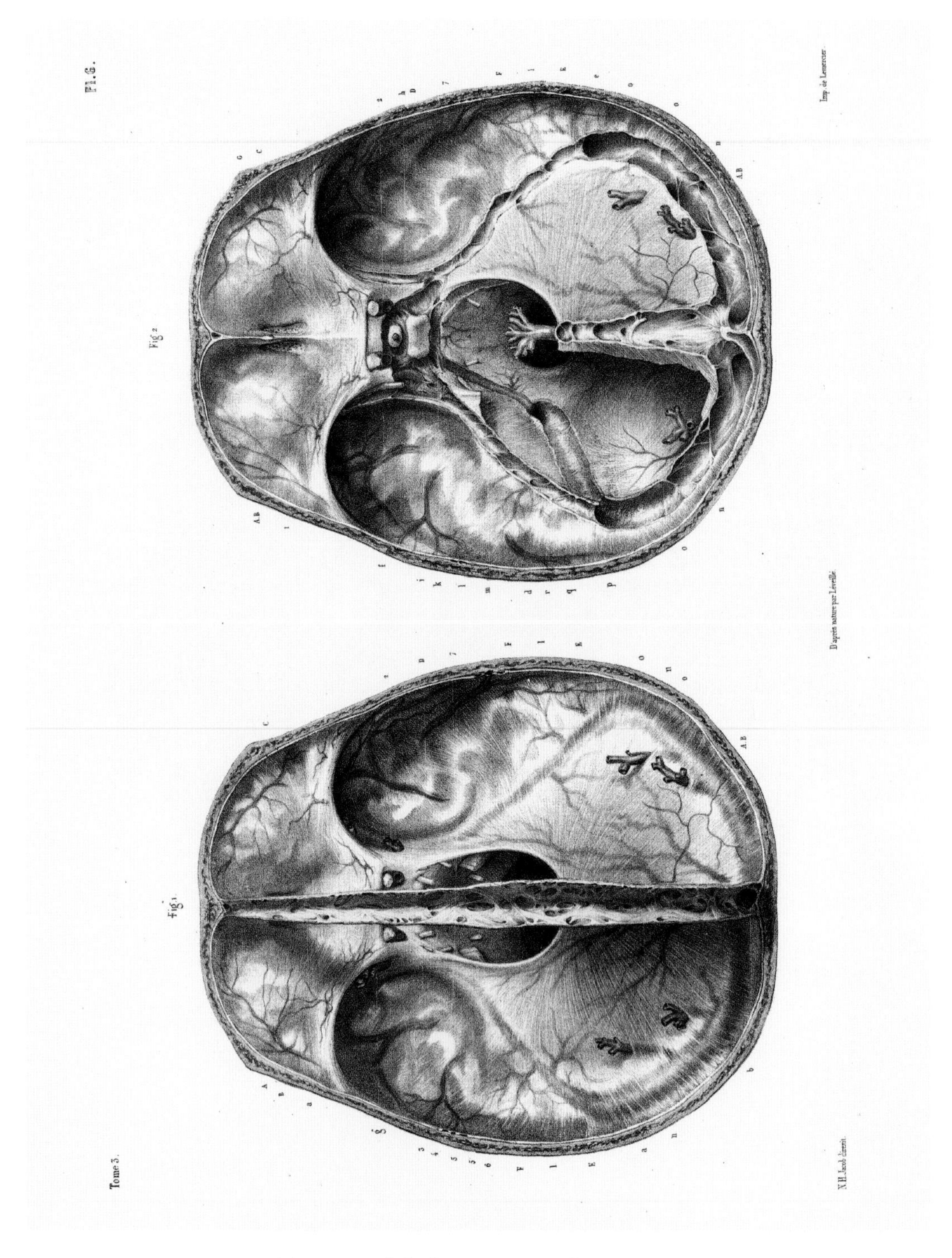

Meninges of the brain or cranial meninges
Méninges de l'encéphale ou crâniennes
Meninges del encéfalo o craneales

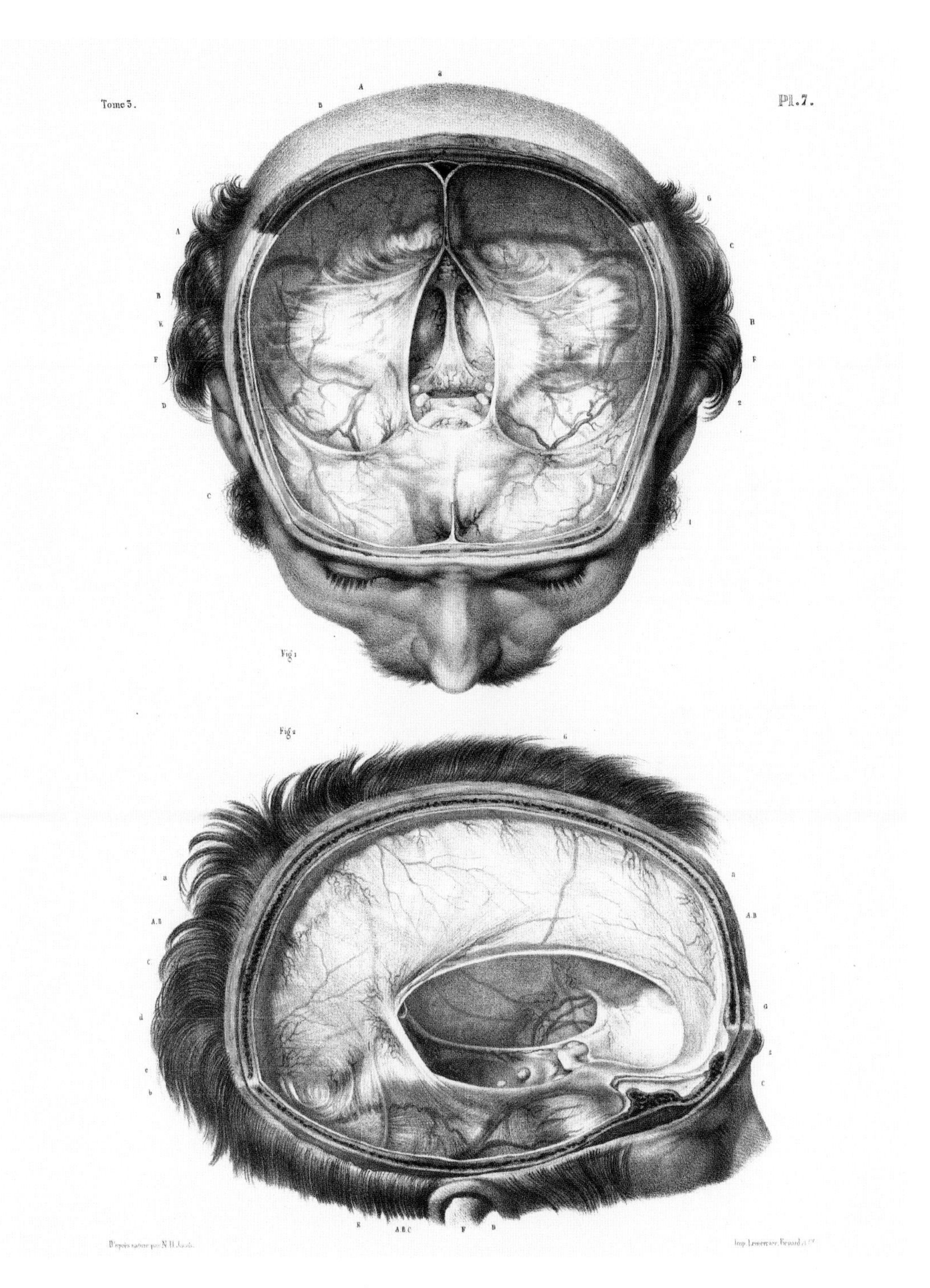

Meninges of the brain or cranial meninges
Méninges de l'encéphale ou crâniennes
Meninges del encéfalo o craneales

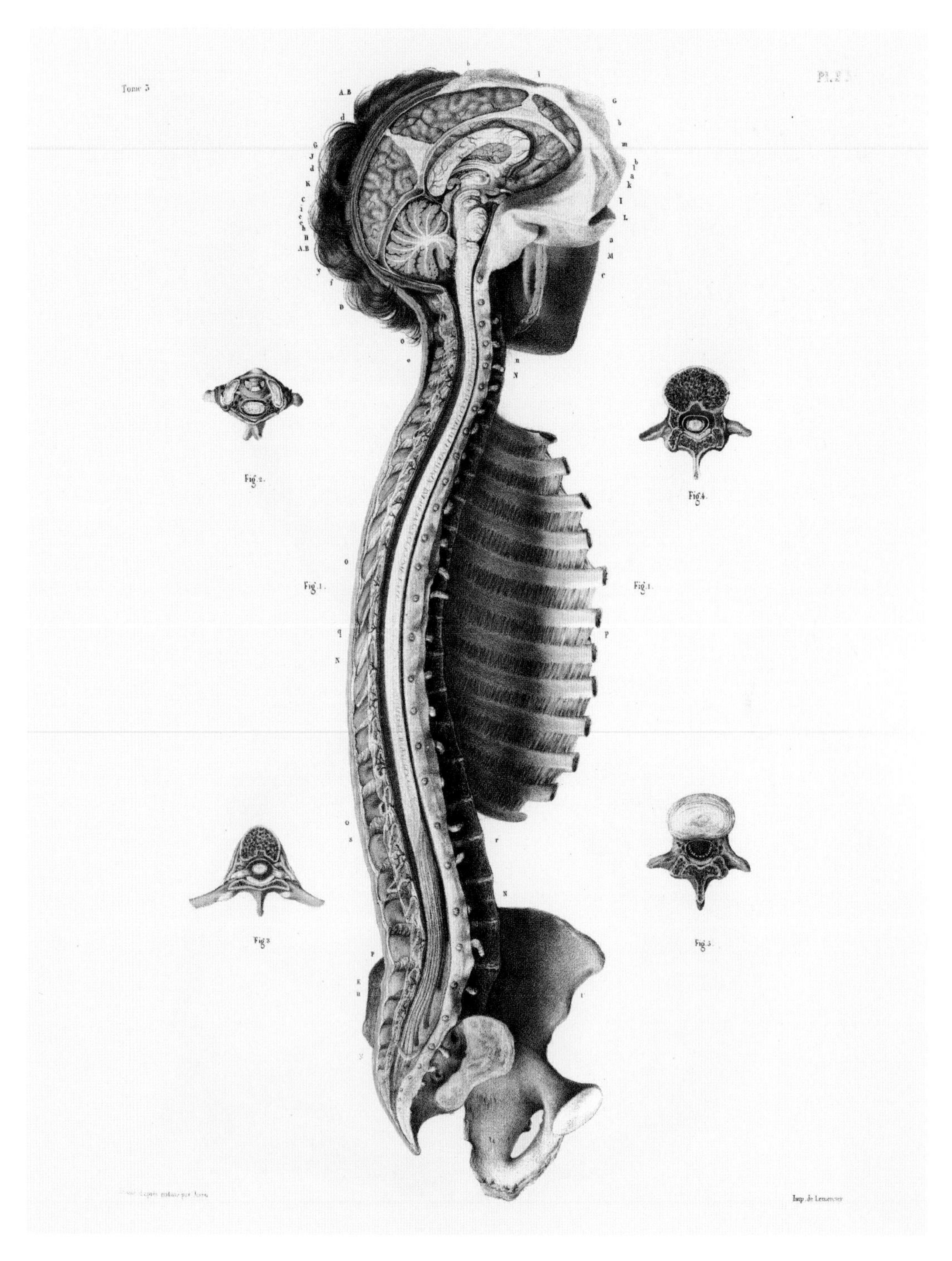

Meninges / Méninges / Meninges

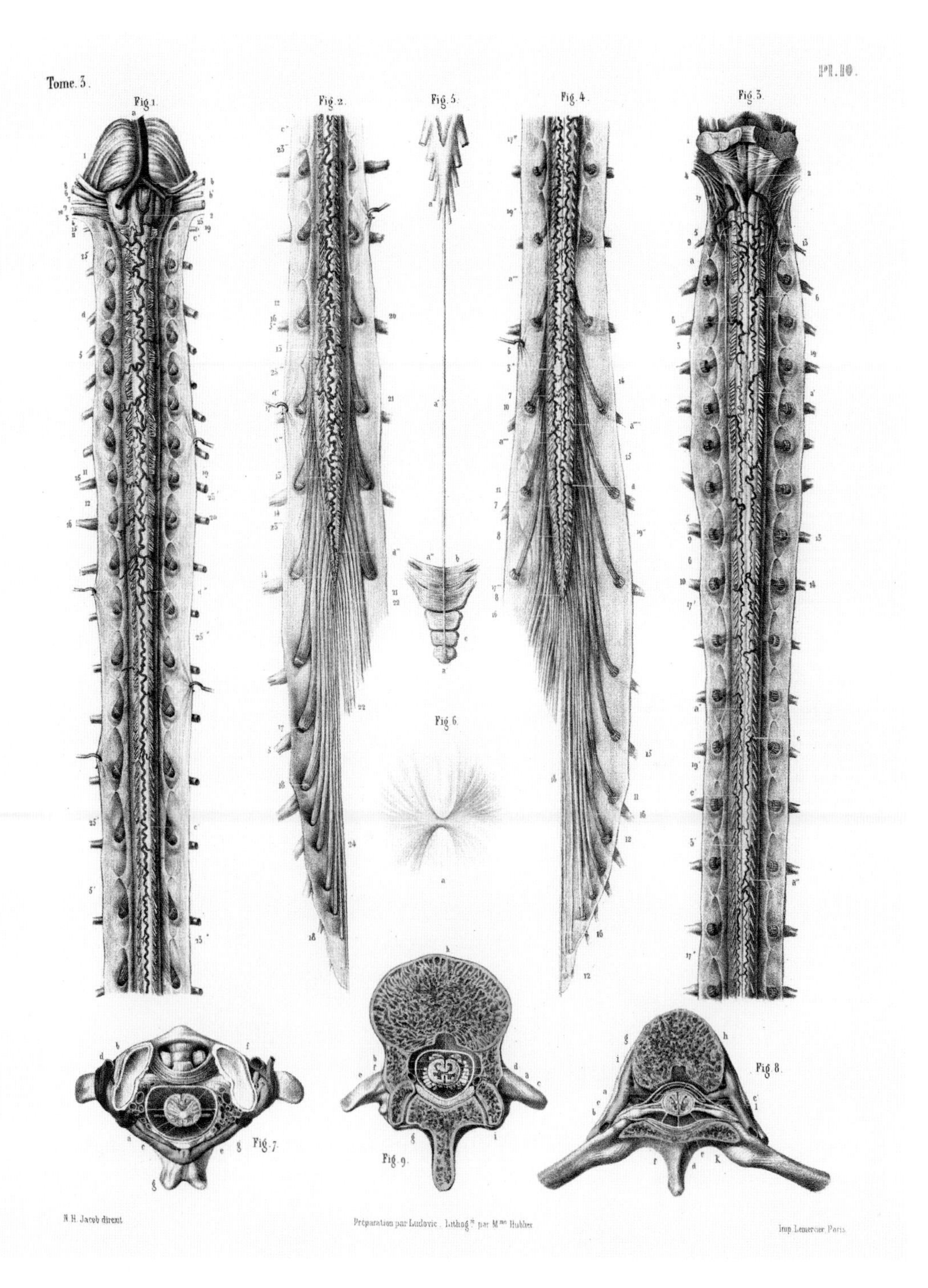

Spinal meninges / Méninges spinales / Meninges raquídeas

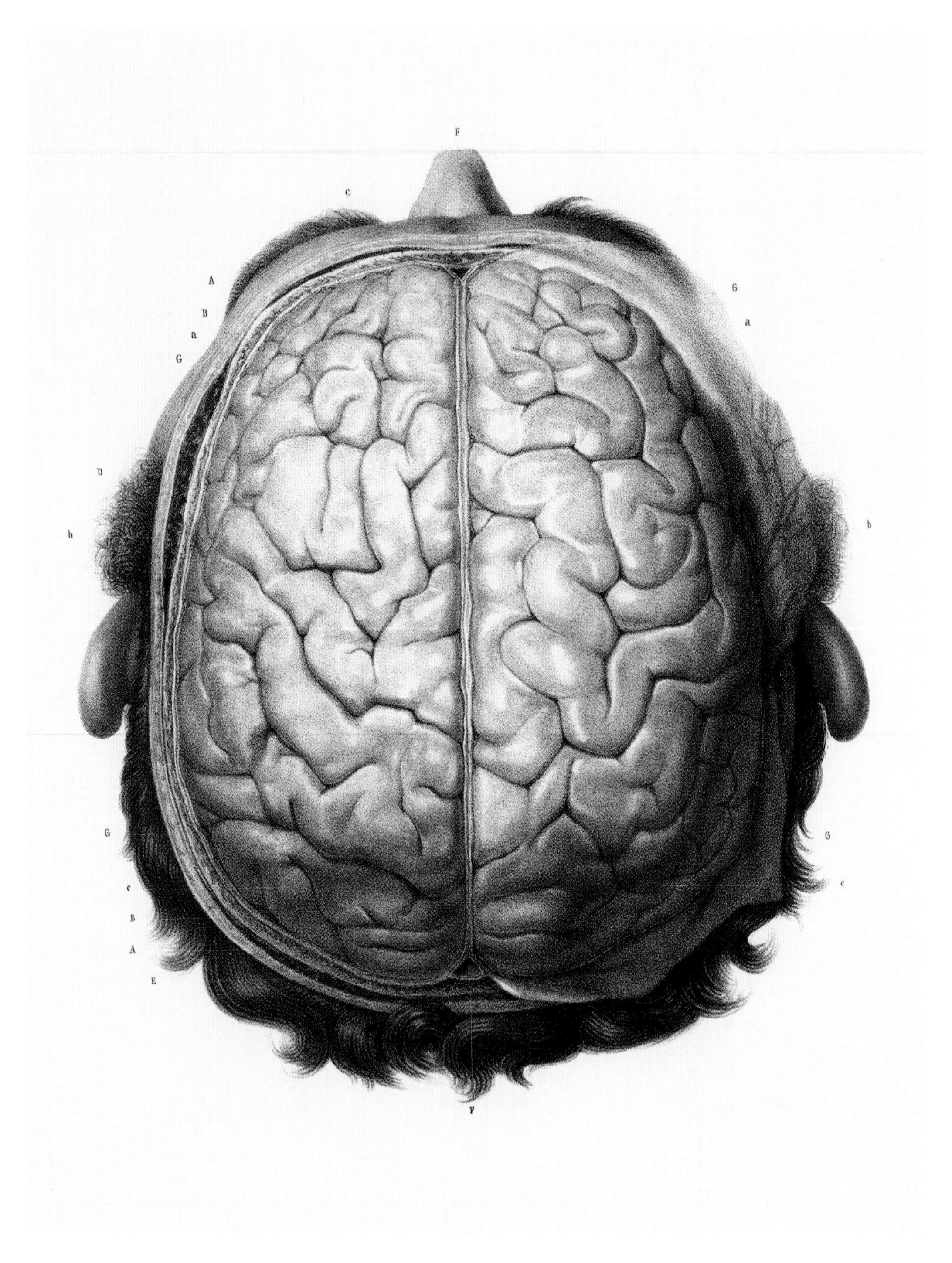

Encephalon / Encéphale / Encéfalo

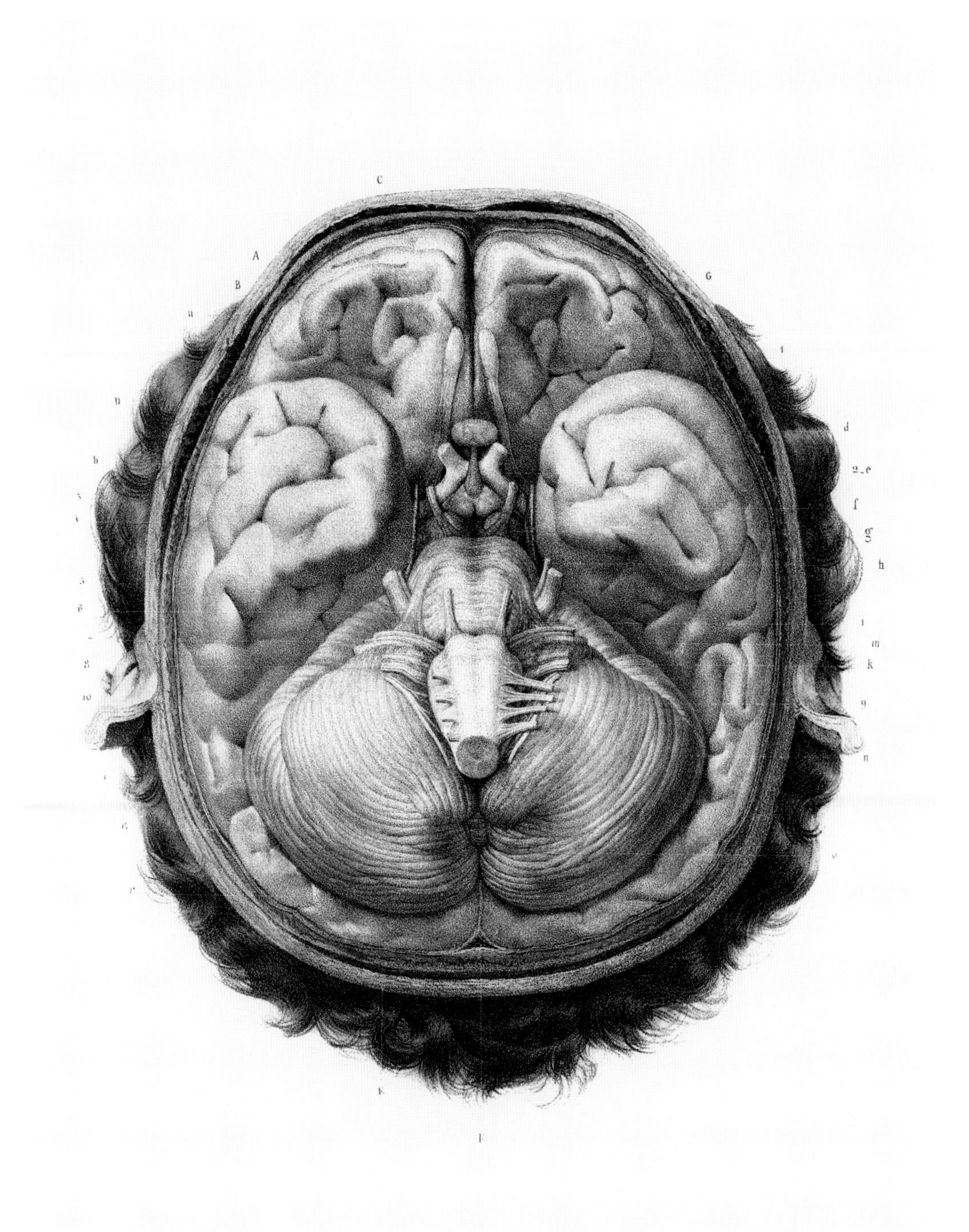

Encephalon / Encéphale / Encéfalo

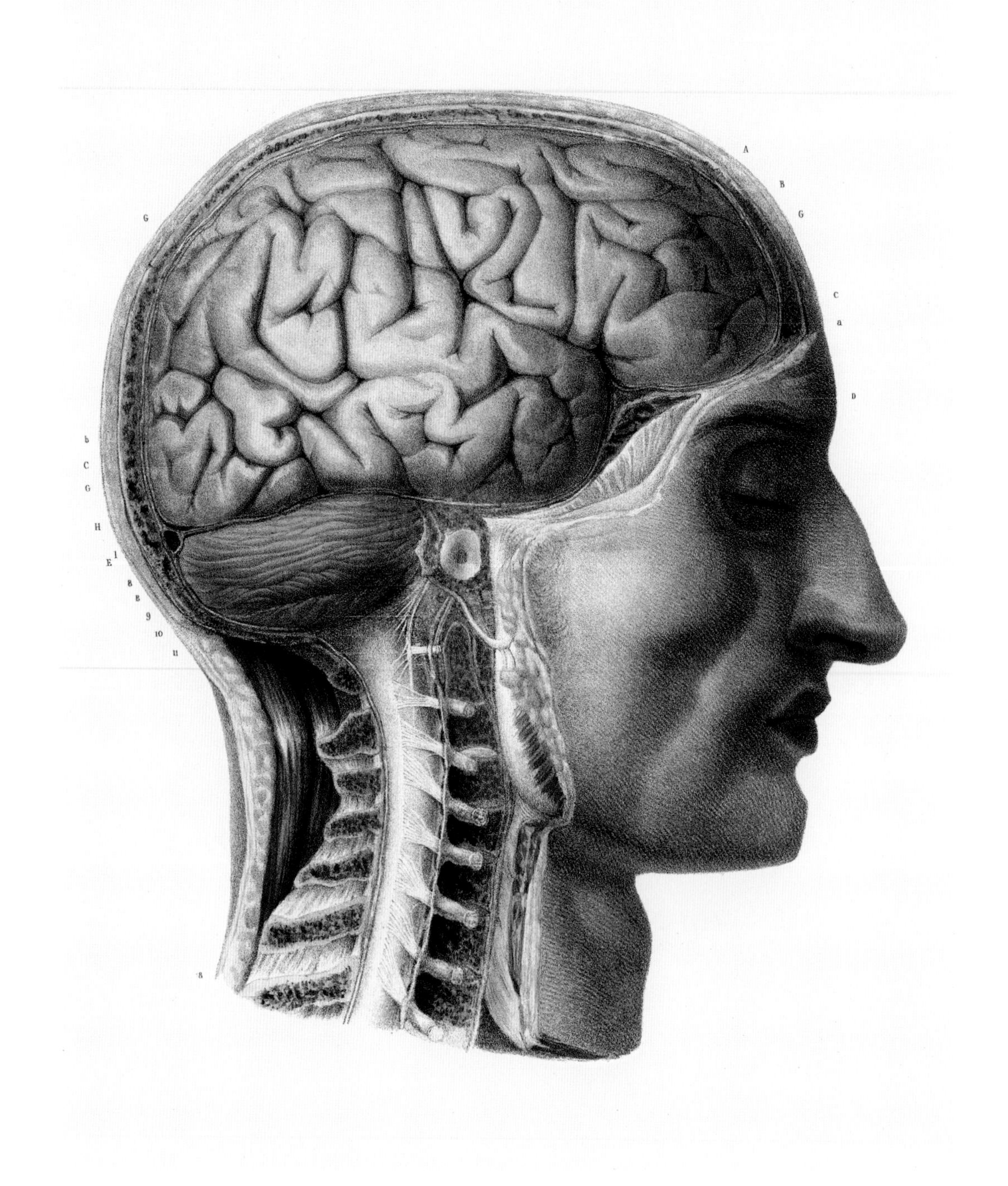

Encephalon / Encéphale / Encéfalo

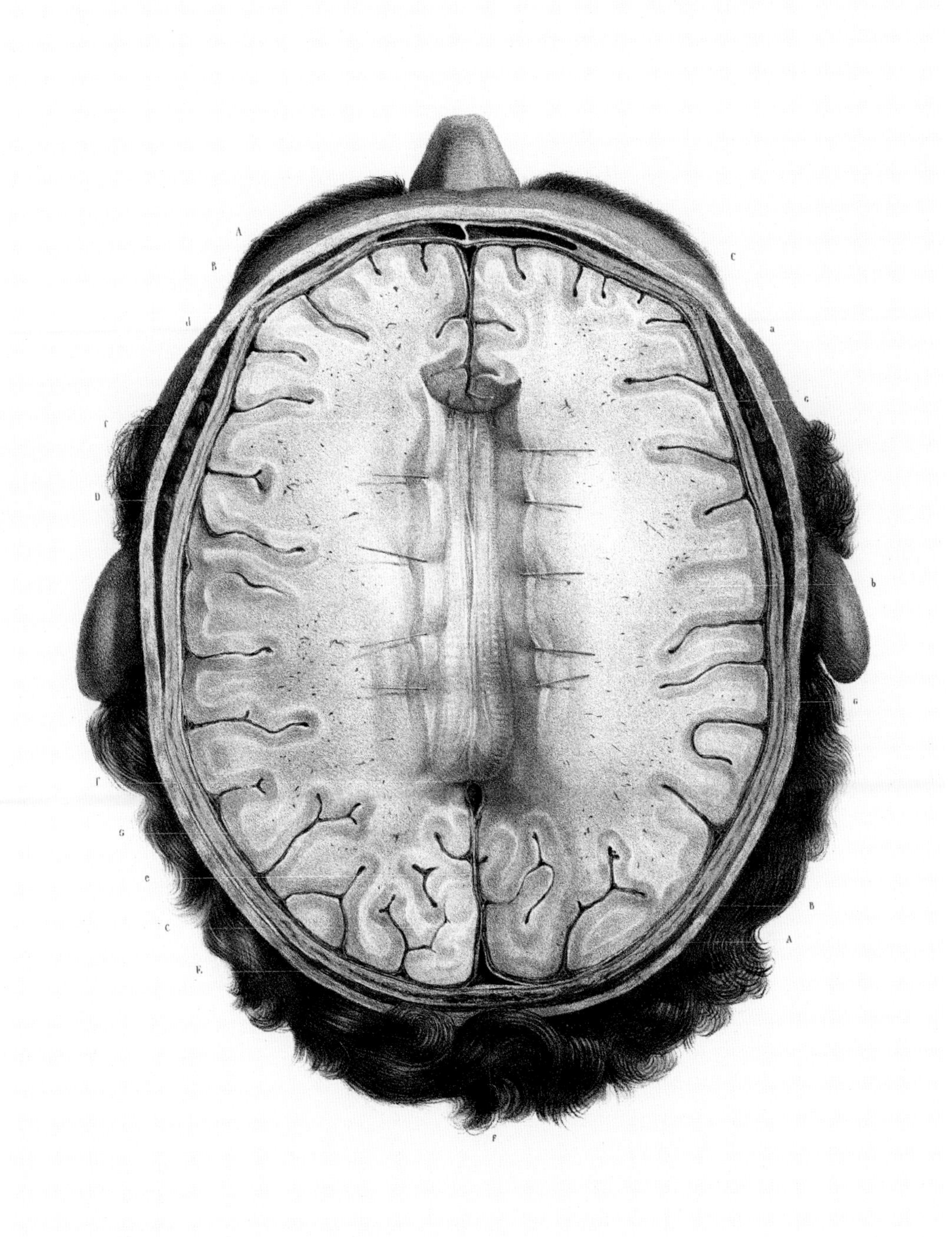

Brain / Cerveau / Cerebro

CANALIS VERTEBRALIS ET PLEXUS VENOSI VERTEBRALES. SYSTEMA NERVOSUM CENTRALE

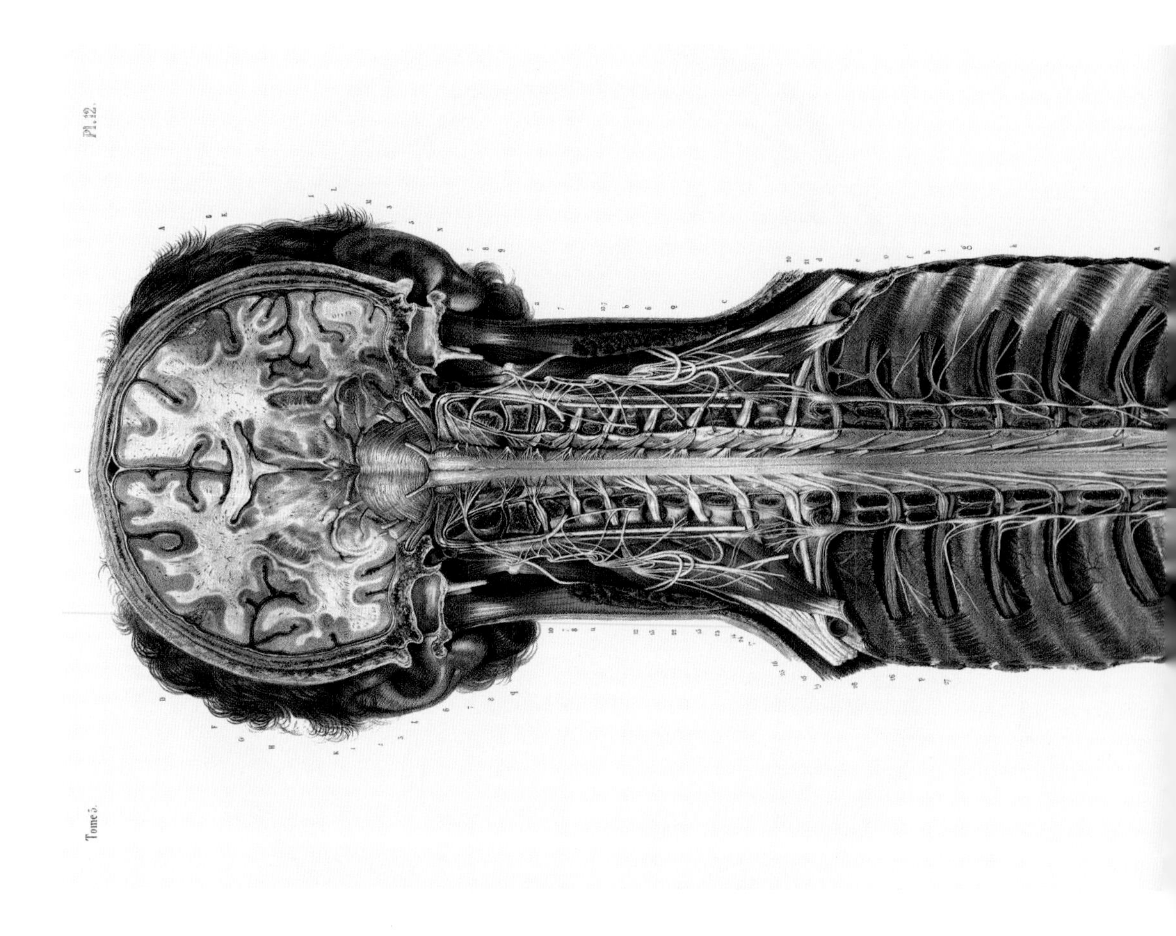

Central nervous system / Système nerveux central / Sistema nervioso central

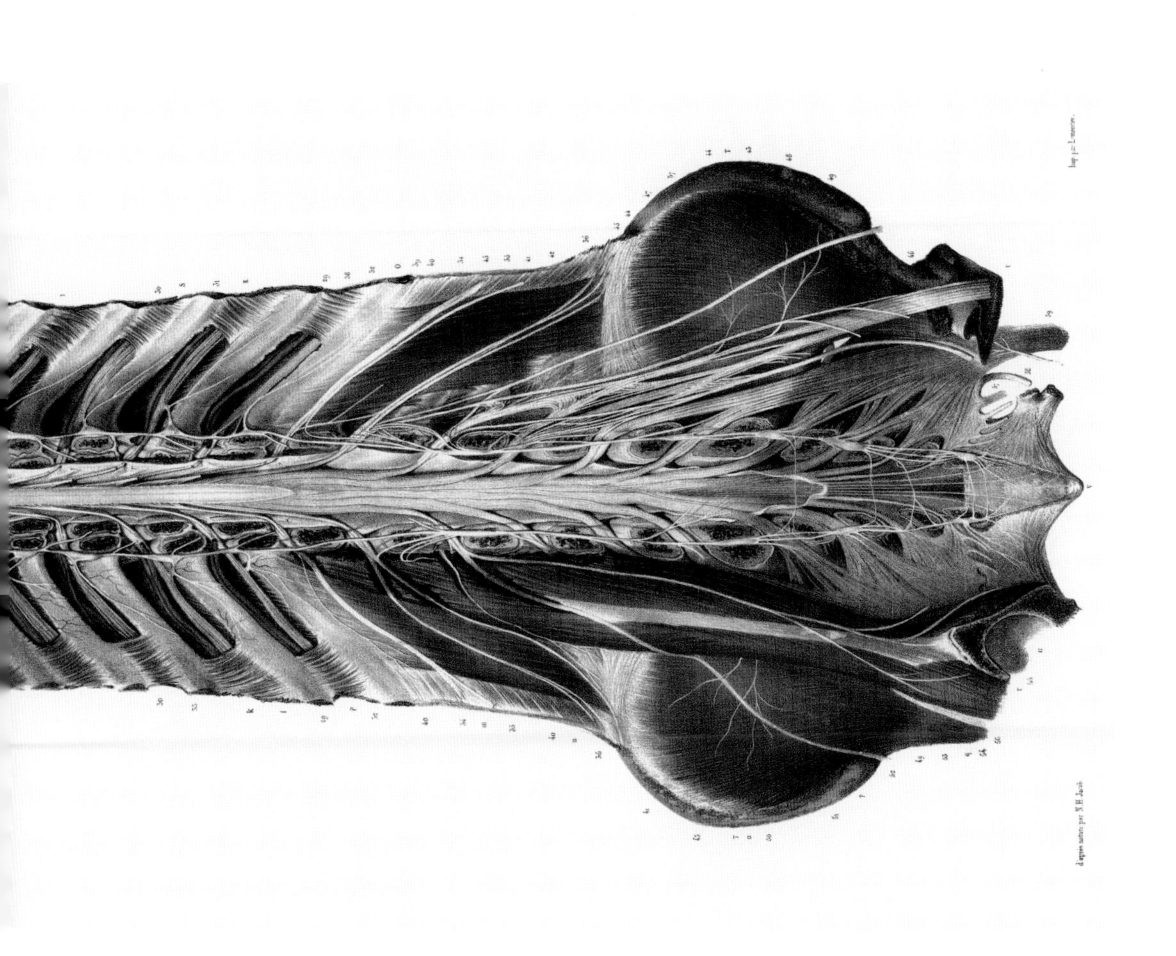

CANALIS VERTEBRALIS ET PLEXUS VENOSI VERTEBRALES. SYSTEMA NERVOSUM CENTRALE

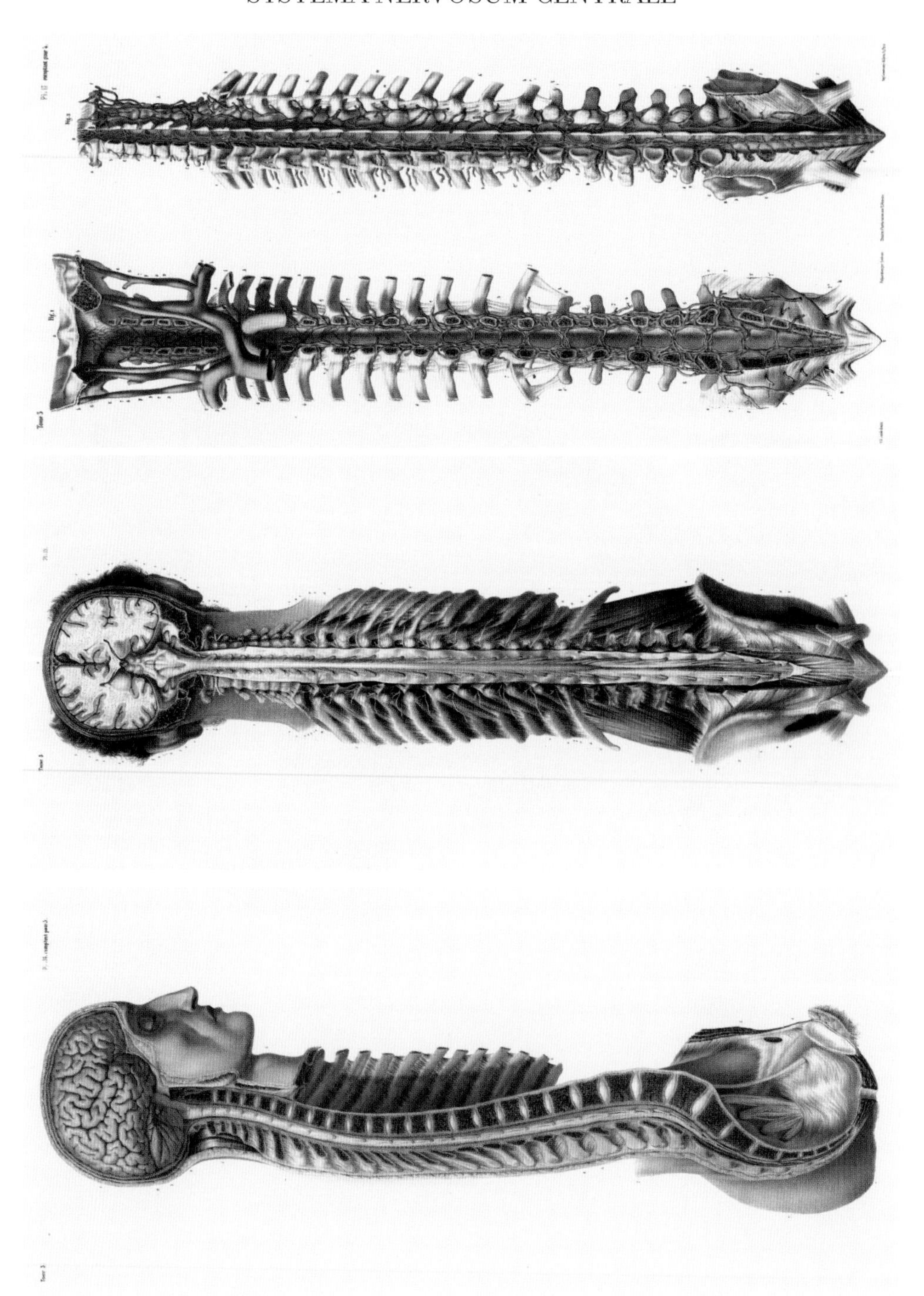

Vertebral canal and vertebral veinous plexuses / Central nervous system
Canal vertébral et plexus veineux vertébraux / Système nerveux central
Conducto raquídeo y plexos venosos vertebrales / Sistema nervioso central

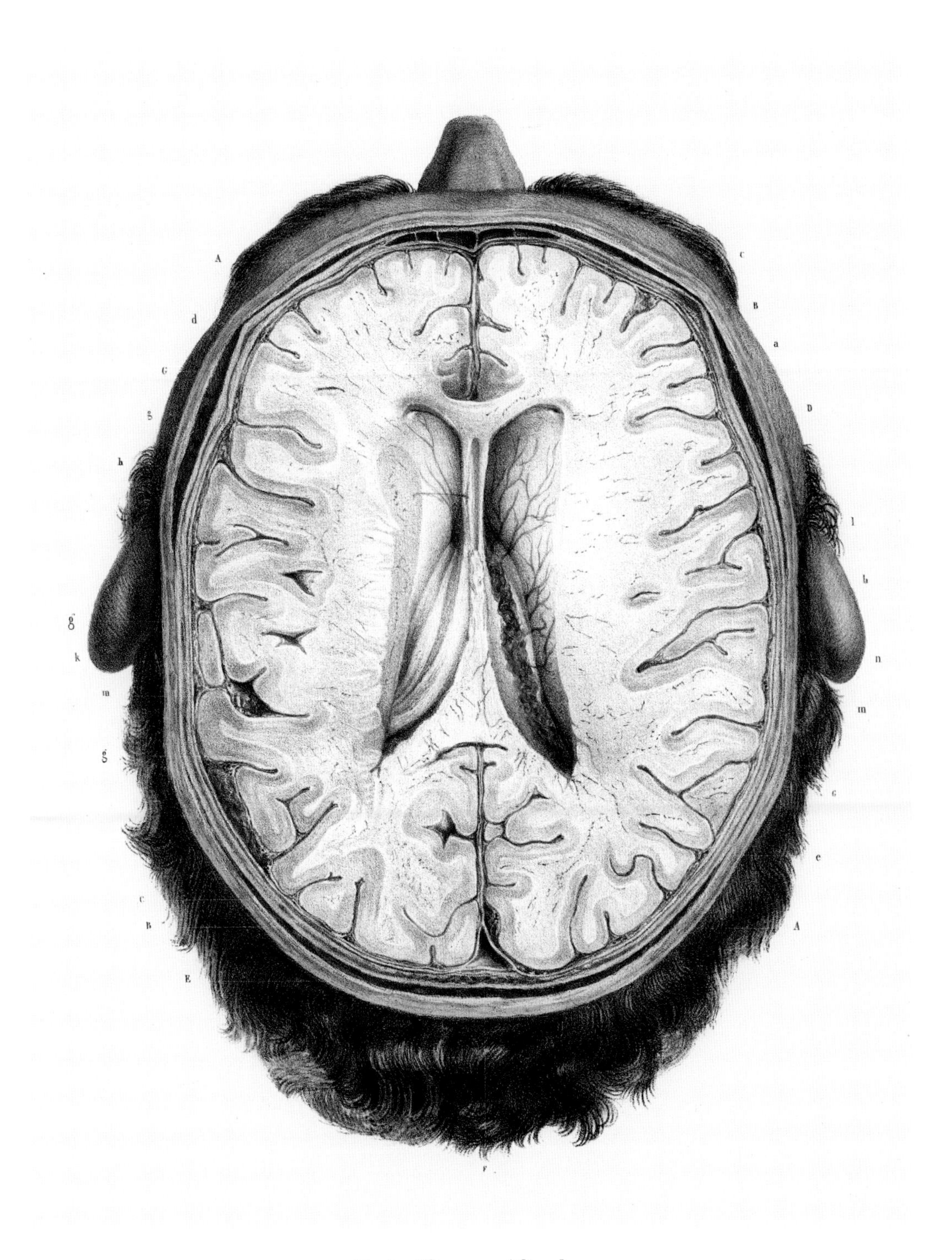

Brain / Cerveau / Cerebro

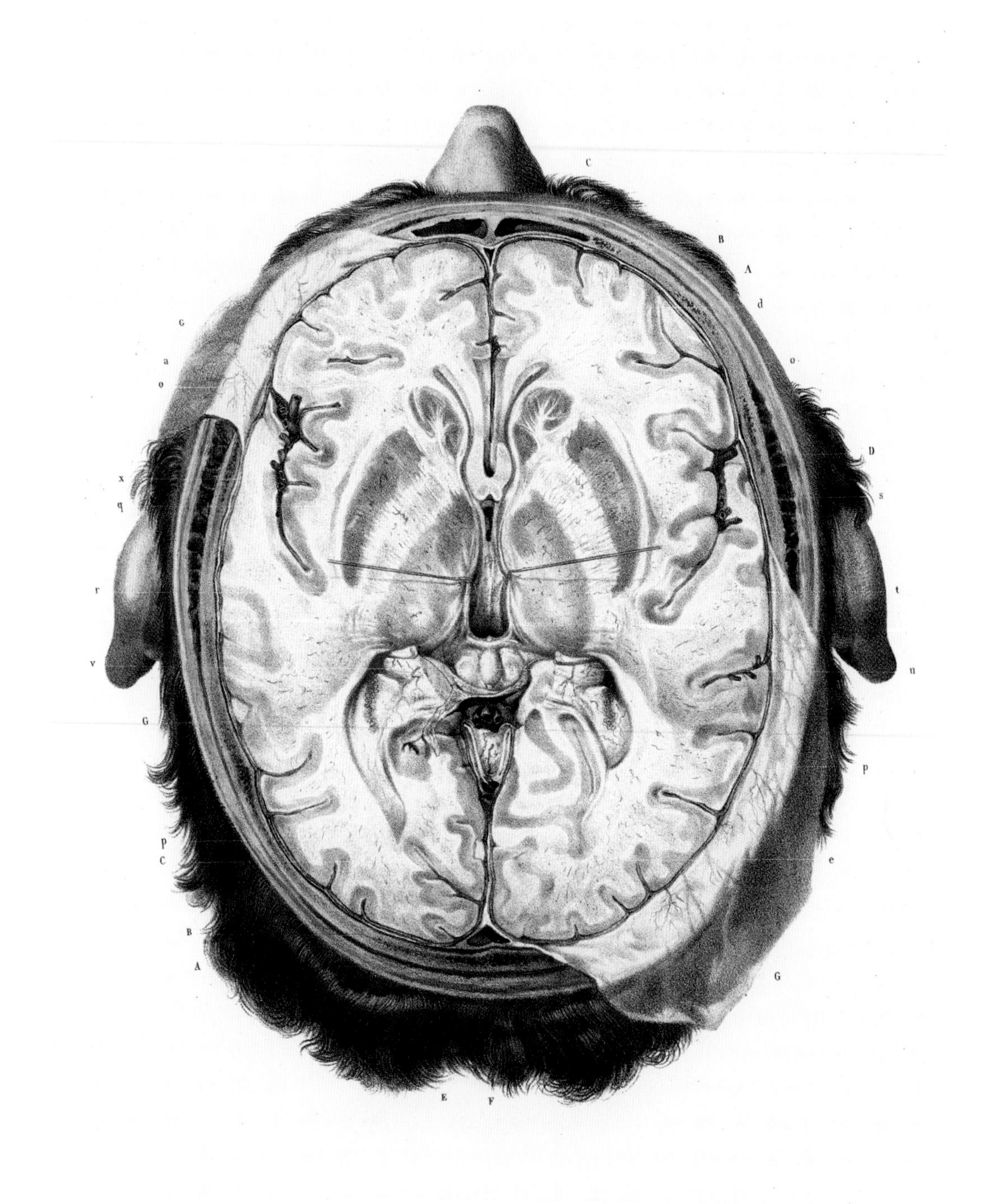

Brain / Cerveau / Cerebro

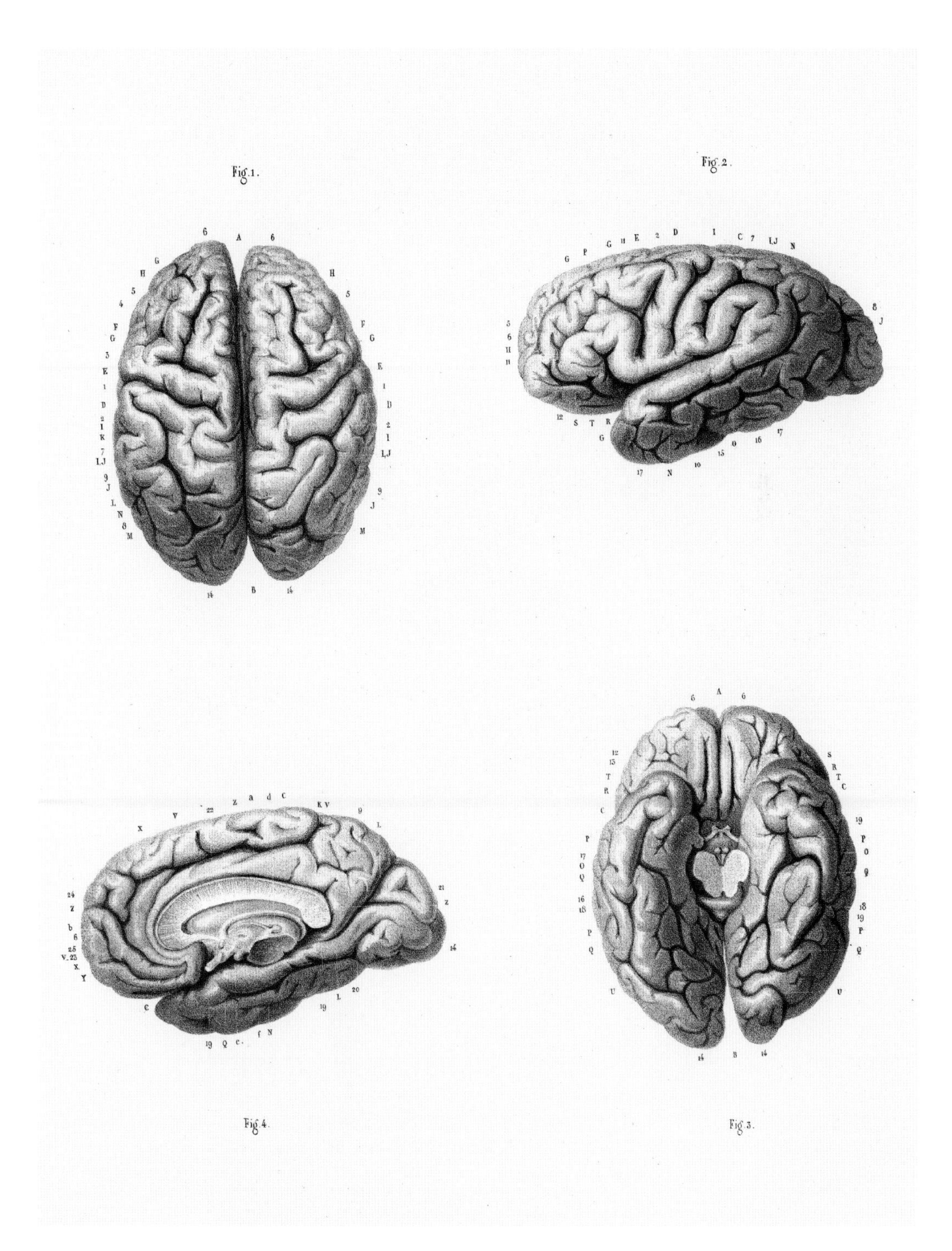

Brain / Cerveau / Cerebro

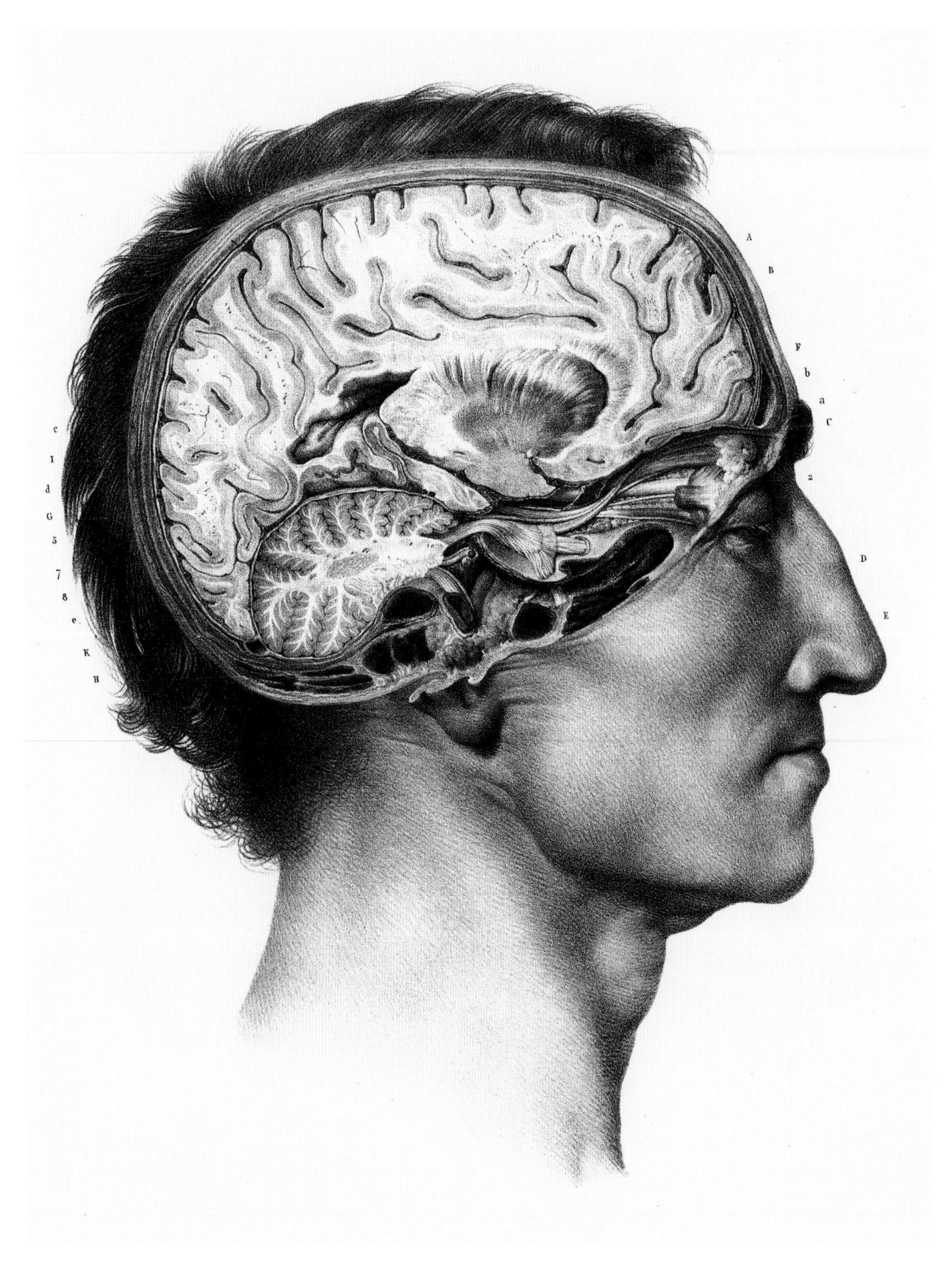

Brain / Cerveau / Cerebro

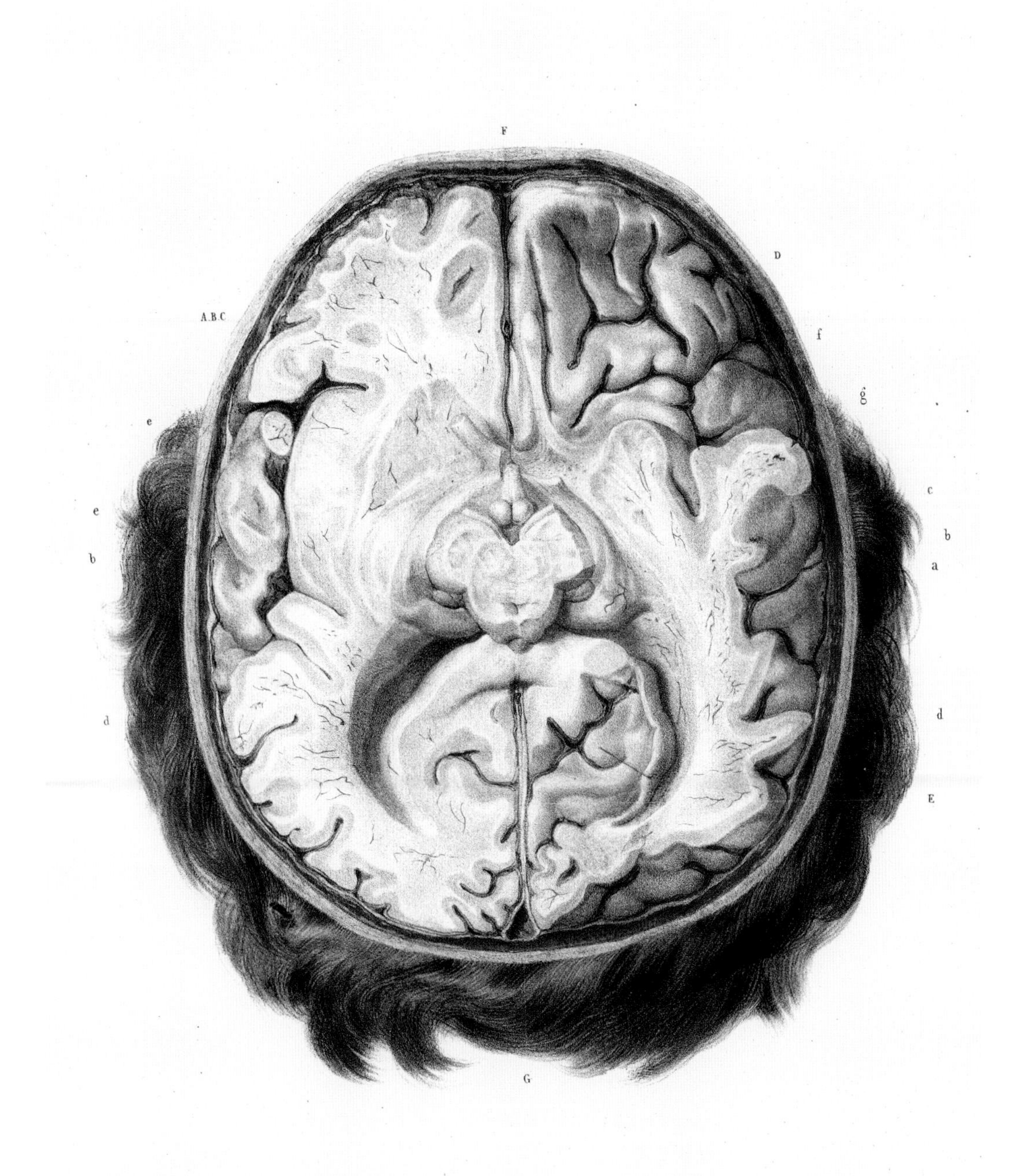

Brain / Cerveau / Cerebro

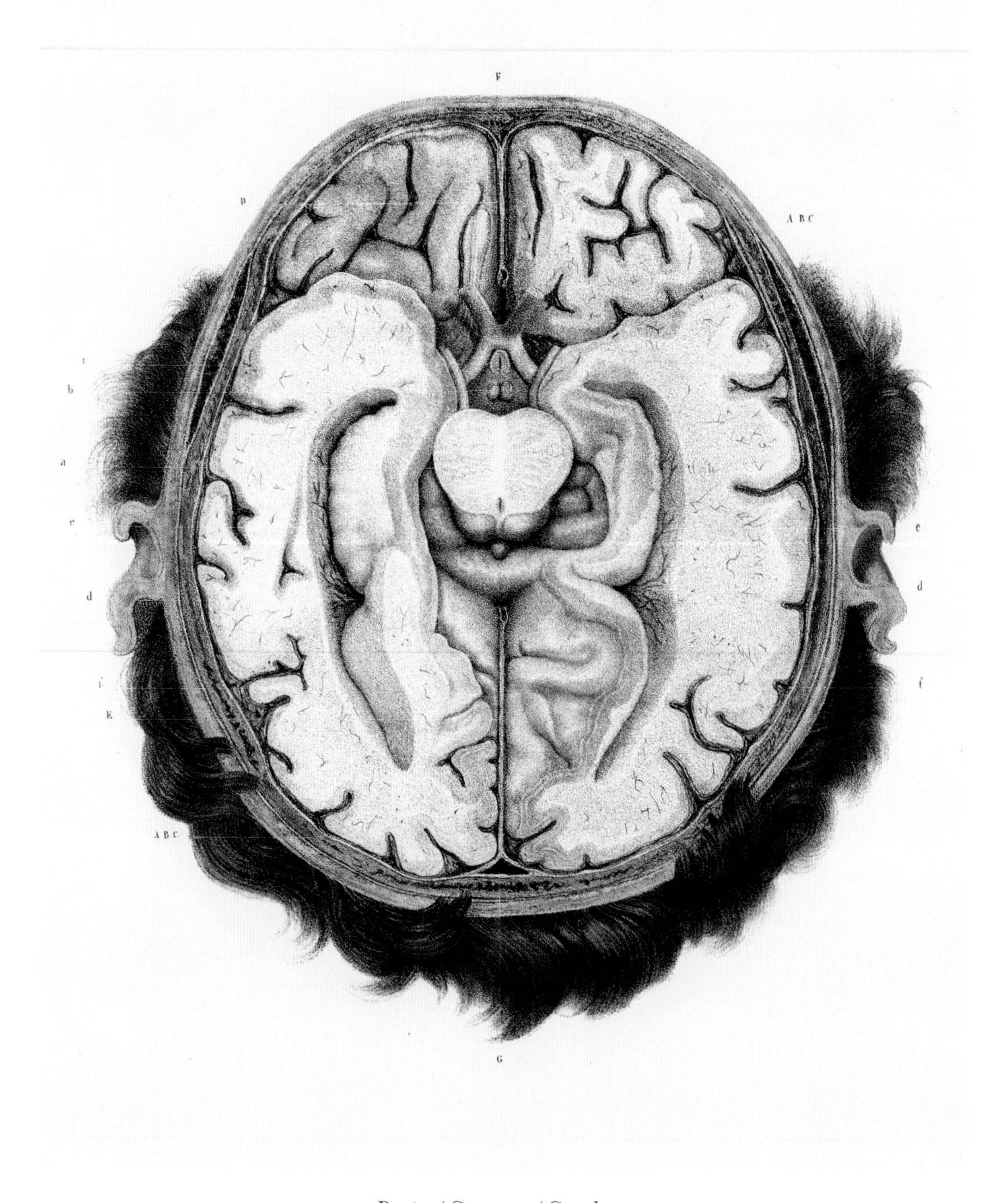

Brain / Cerveau / Cerebro

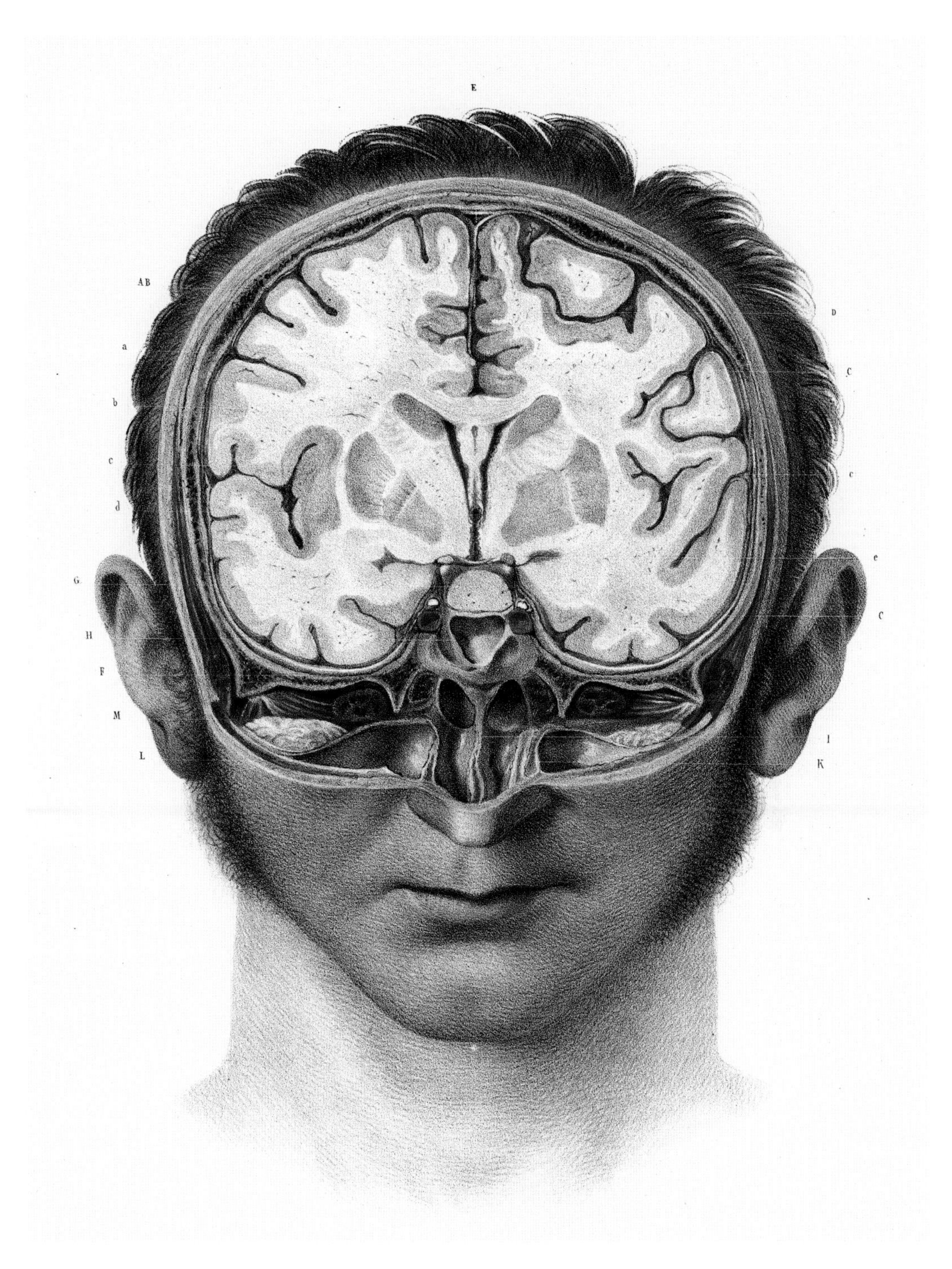

Brain / Cerveau / Cerebro

Brain / Cerveau / Cerebro

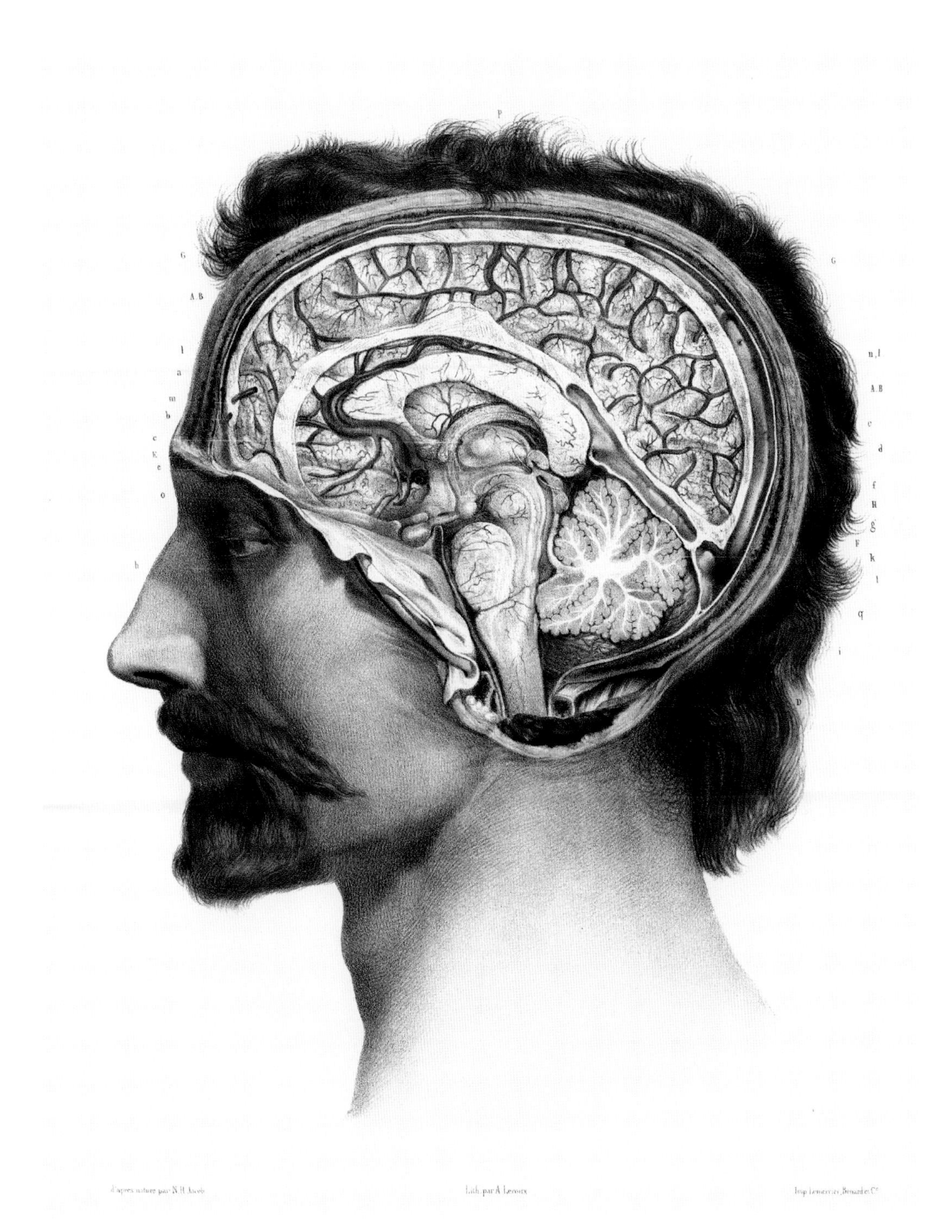

Encephalon / Encéphale / Encéfalo

Brain: Cerebral ventricles / Cerveau : Ventricules cérébraux
Cerebro: ventrículos cerebrales

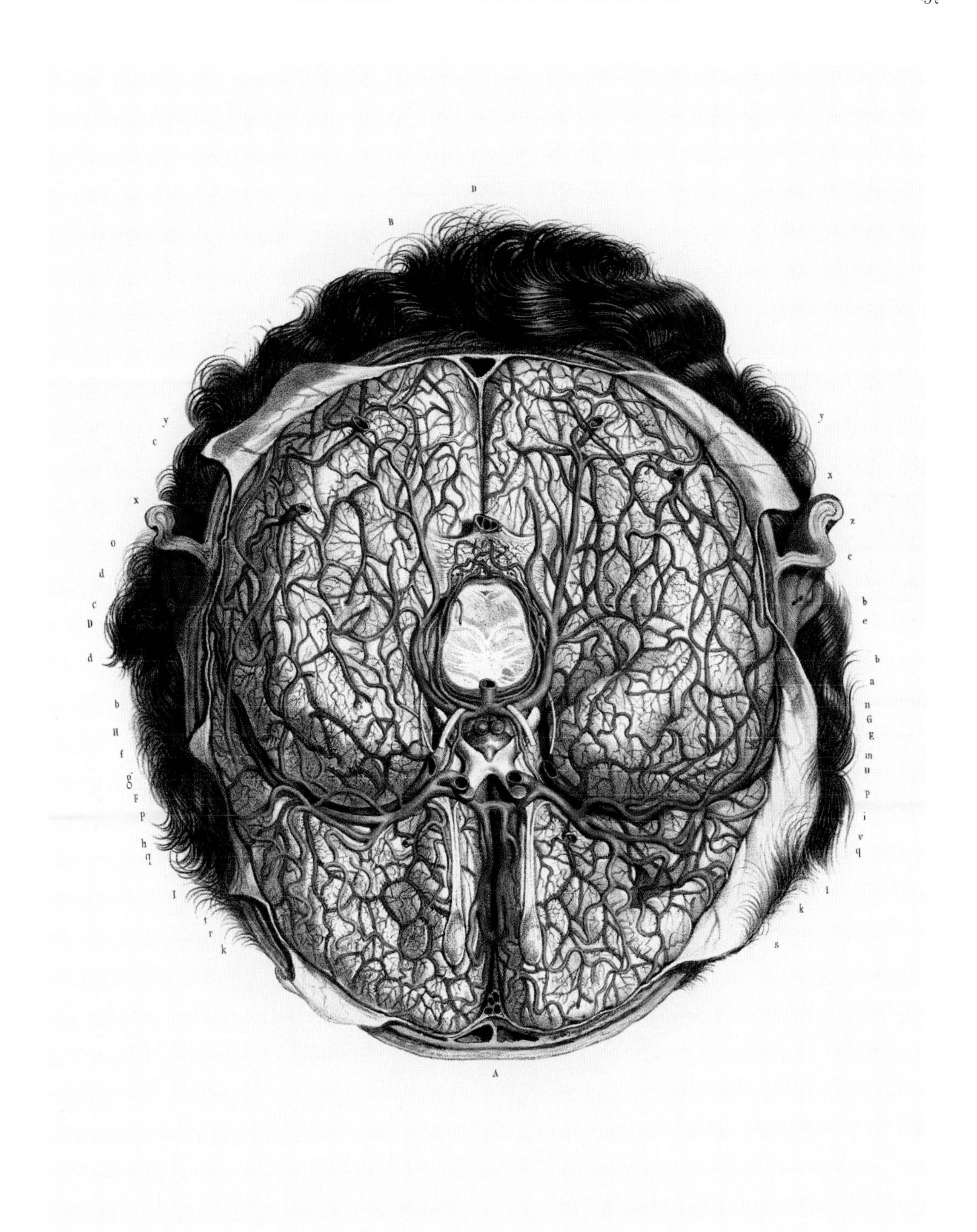

Brain: Cerebral arteries / Cerveau : Artères cérébrales
Cerebro: arterias cerebrales

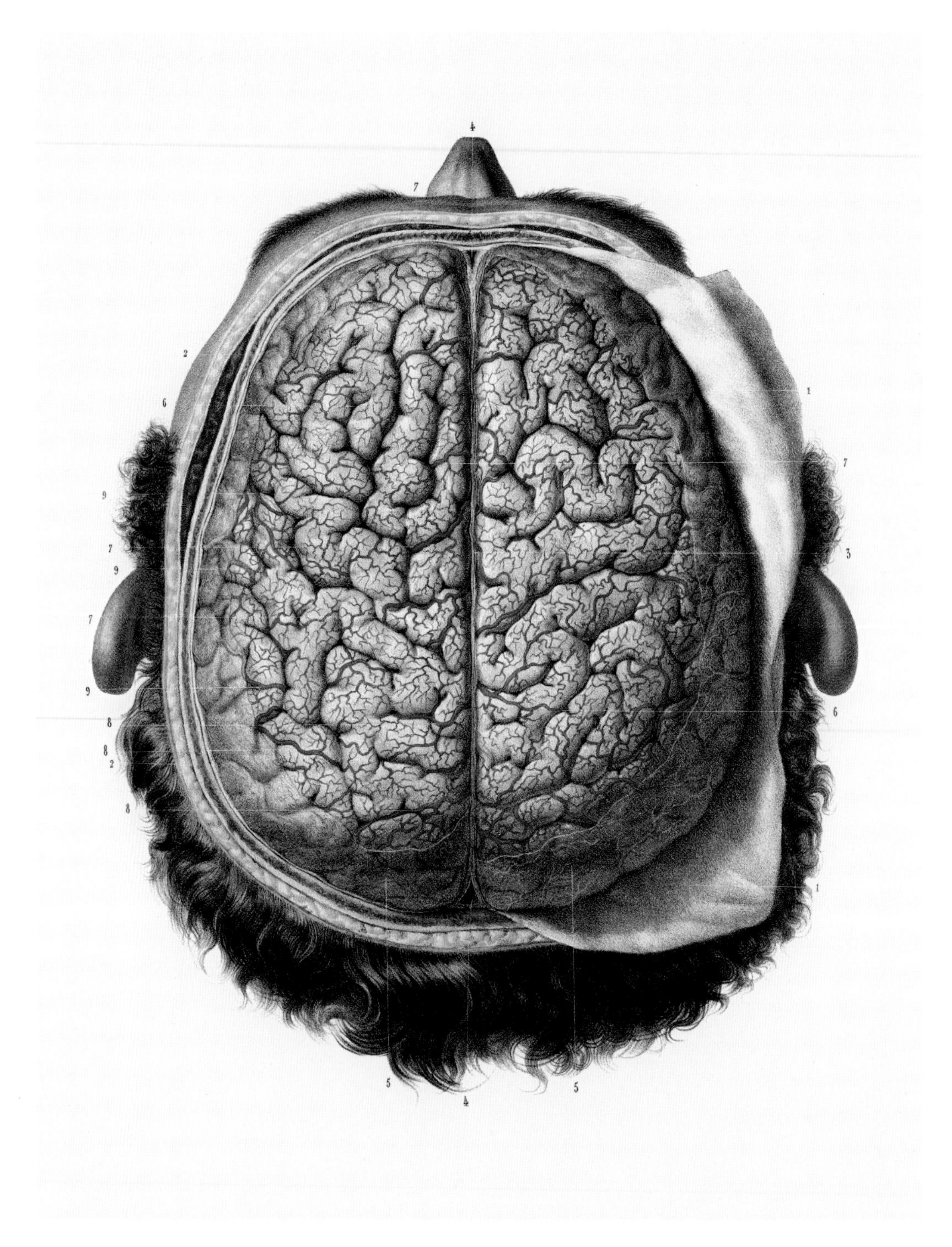

Brain: Cerebral arteries / Cerveau : Artères cérébrales
Cerebro: arterias cerebrales

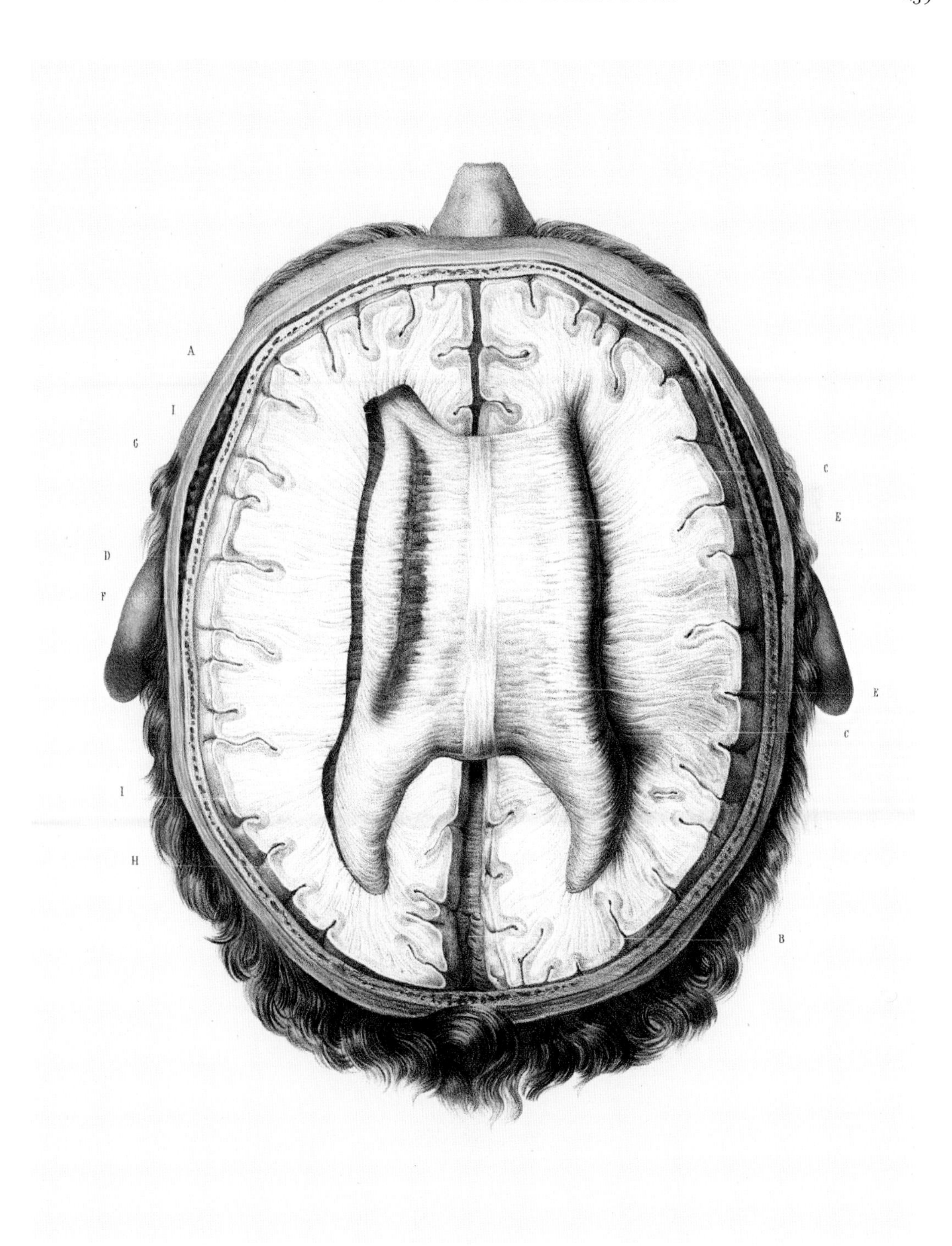

Brain: Corpus callosum / Cerveau : Corps calleux
Cerebro: cuerpo calloso

APLASIA TRACTUS OLFACTORII

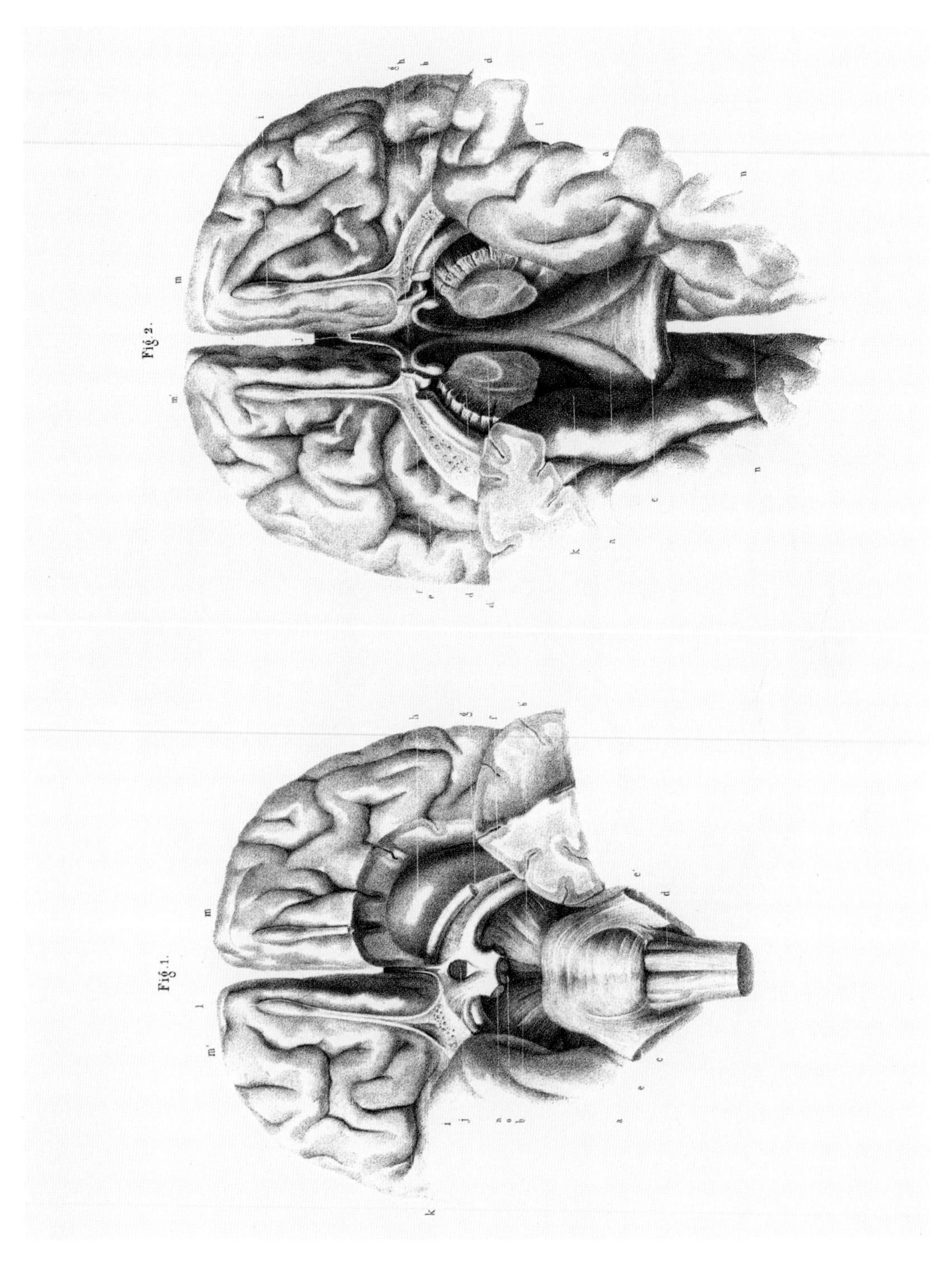

Brain: Commissures and fornix / Cerveau : Commissures et fornix
Cerebro: comisuras y fórnix

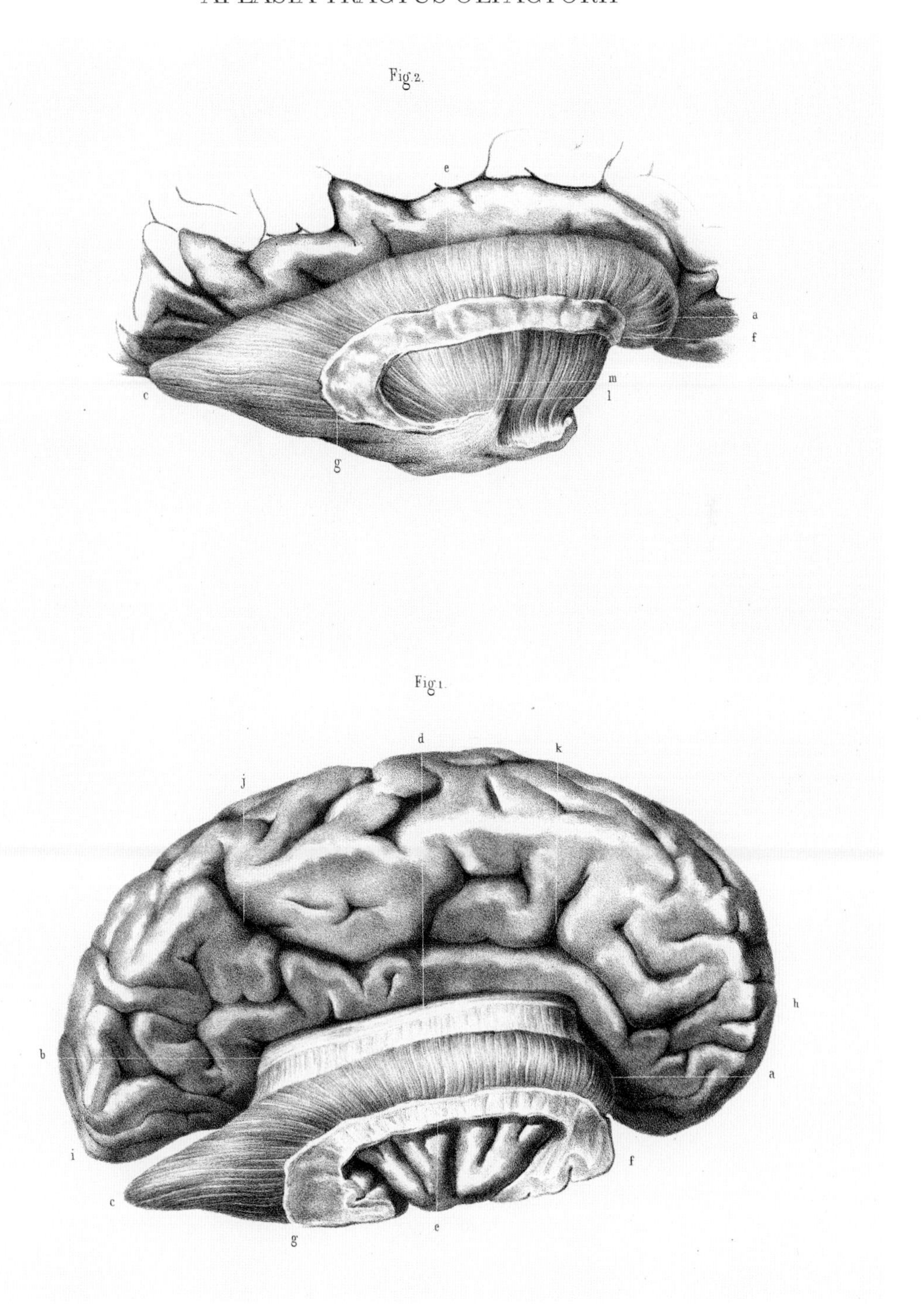

Brain: Tractus and fascicles / Cerveau : Tractus et faisceaux
Cerebro: tracto y haces

CEREBRUM: COMMISSURAE ET FORNIX, TRACTUS ET FASCICULI. APLASIA TRACTUS OLFACTORII

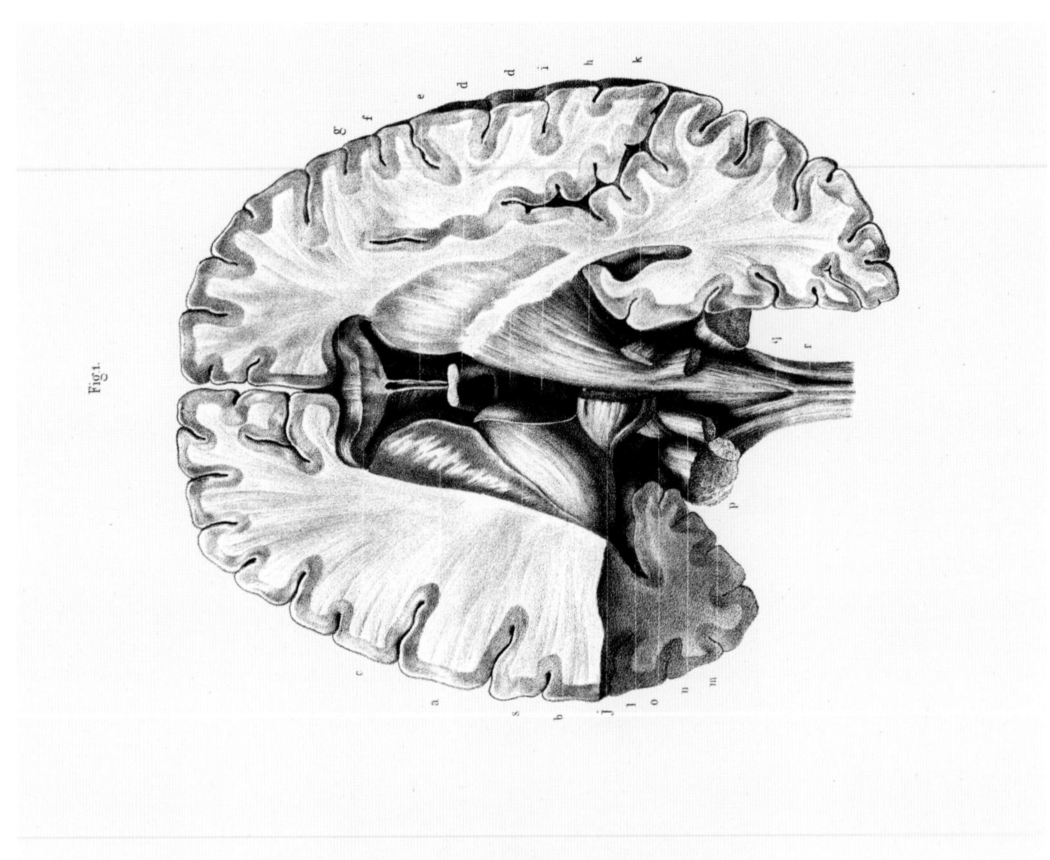

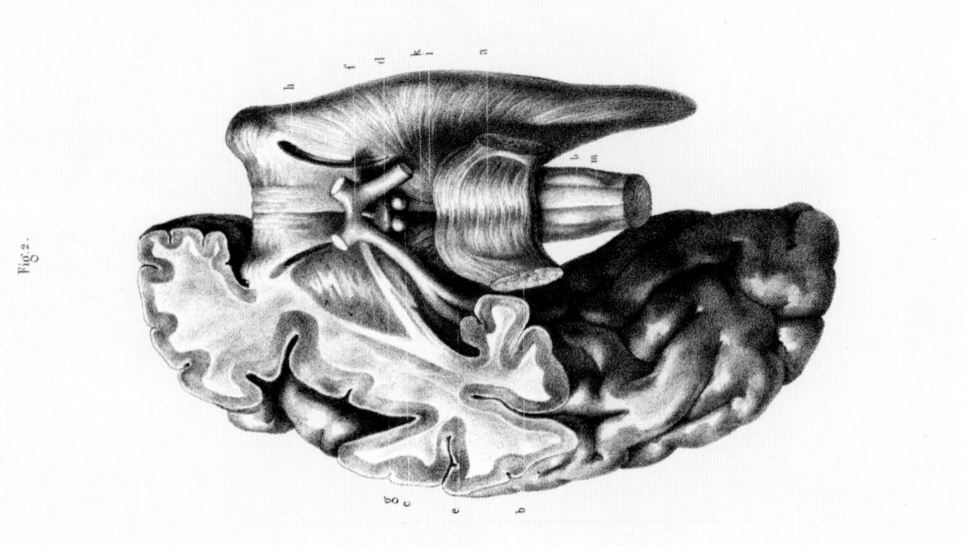

Brain: Tractus and fascicles / Cerveau : Tractus et faisceaux
Cerebro: tracto y haces

CEREBRUM: COMMISSURAE ET FORNIX, TRACTUS ET FASCICULI. APLASIA TRACTUS OLFACTORII

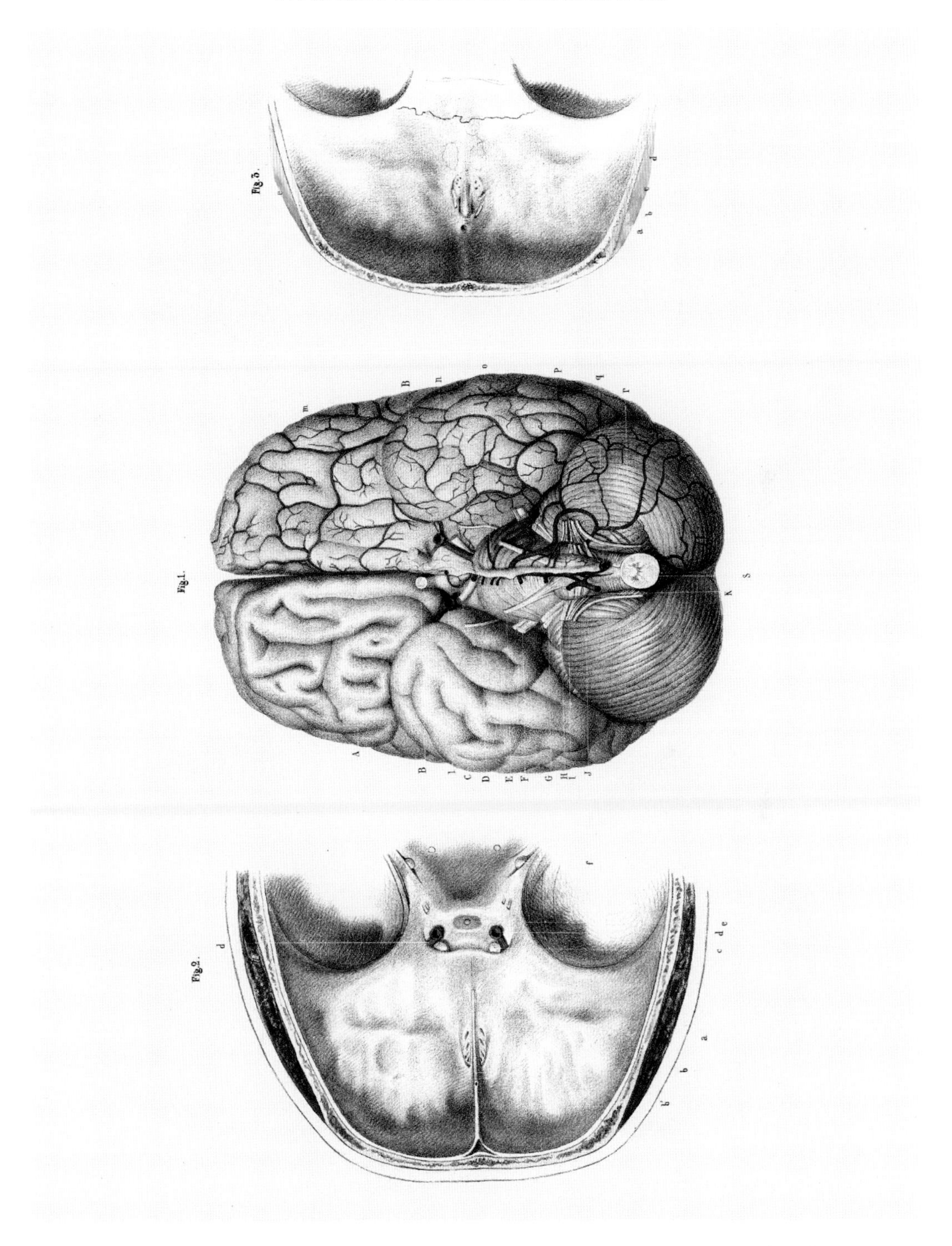

Brain: Aplasia of the olfactory tract / Cerveau : Aplasie du tractus olfactif
Cerebro: aplasia del tracto olfatorio

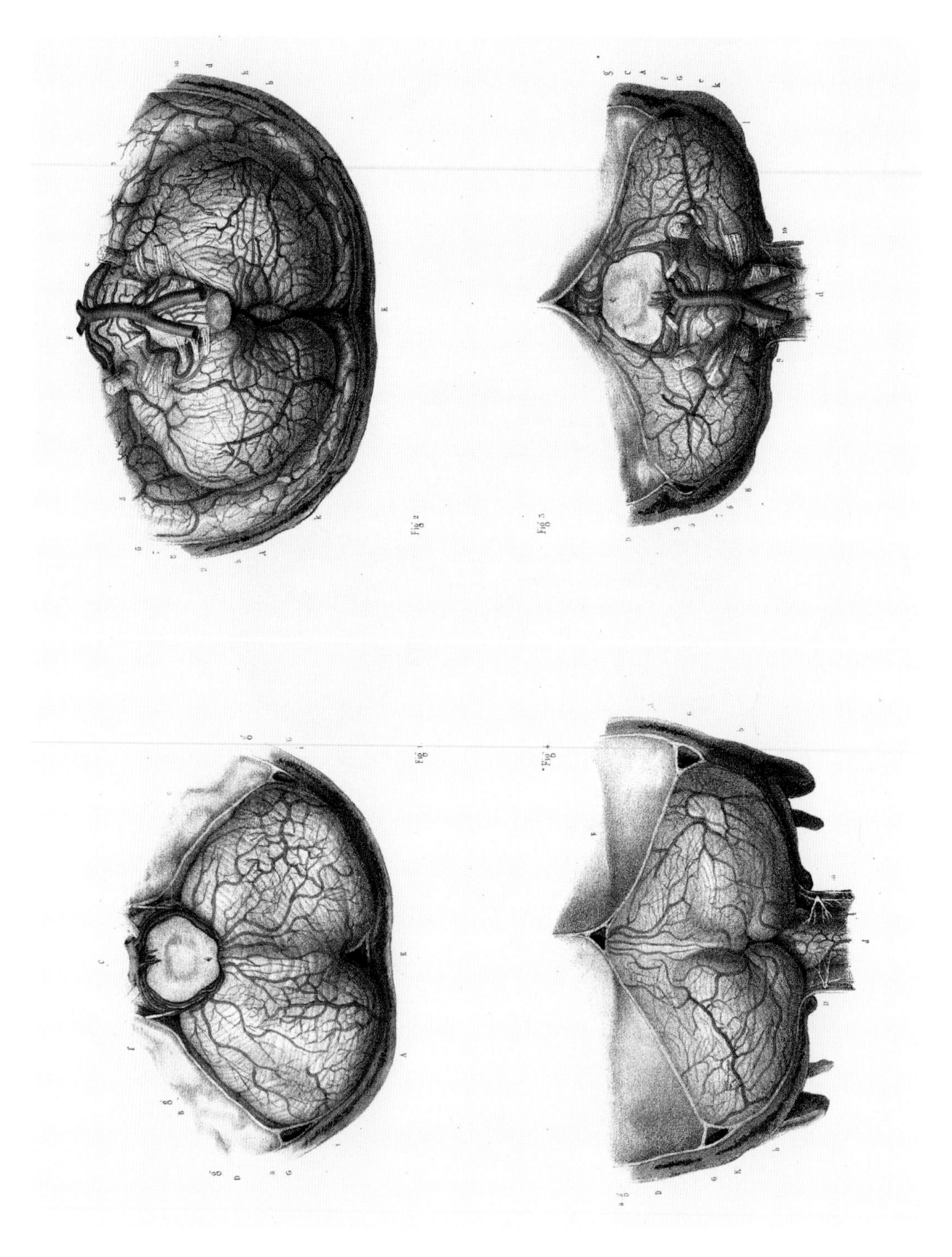

Cerebellum: Arteries and veins / Cervelet : Artères et veines
Cerebelo: arterias y venas

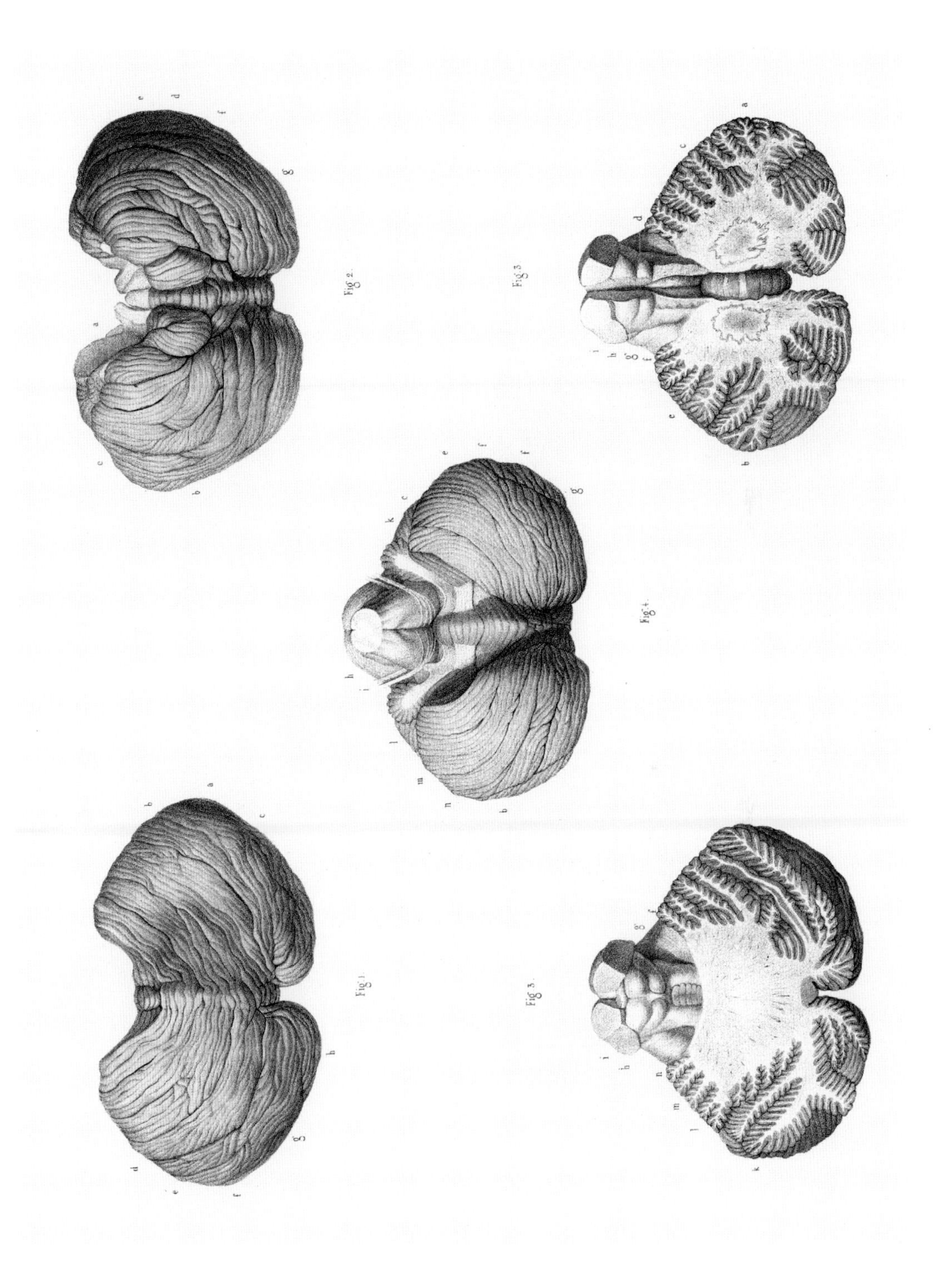

Cerebellum / Cervelet / Cerebelo

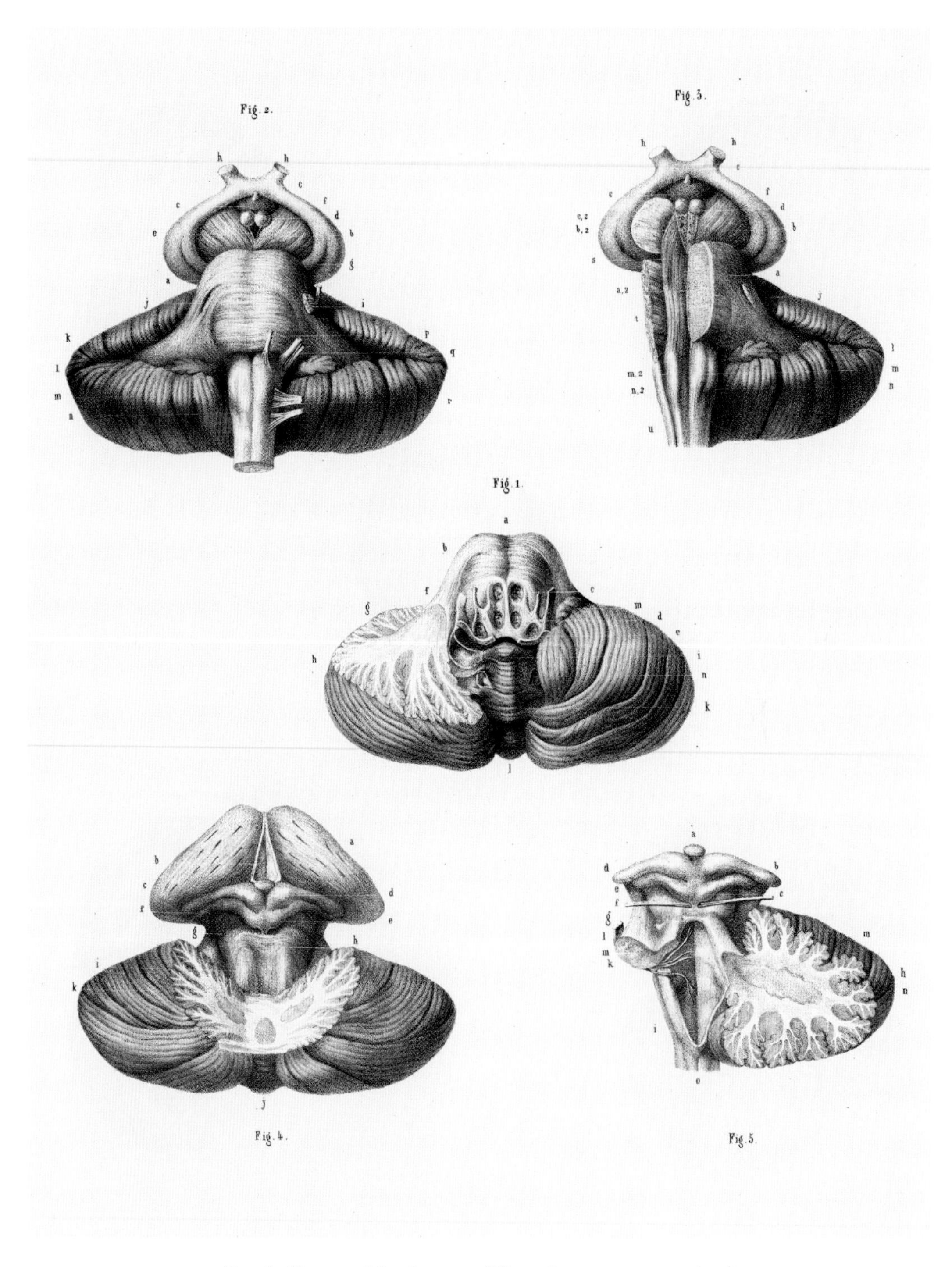

Cerebellum and brainstem / Cervelet et tronc cérébral
Cerebelo y tronco cerebral

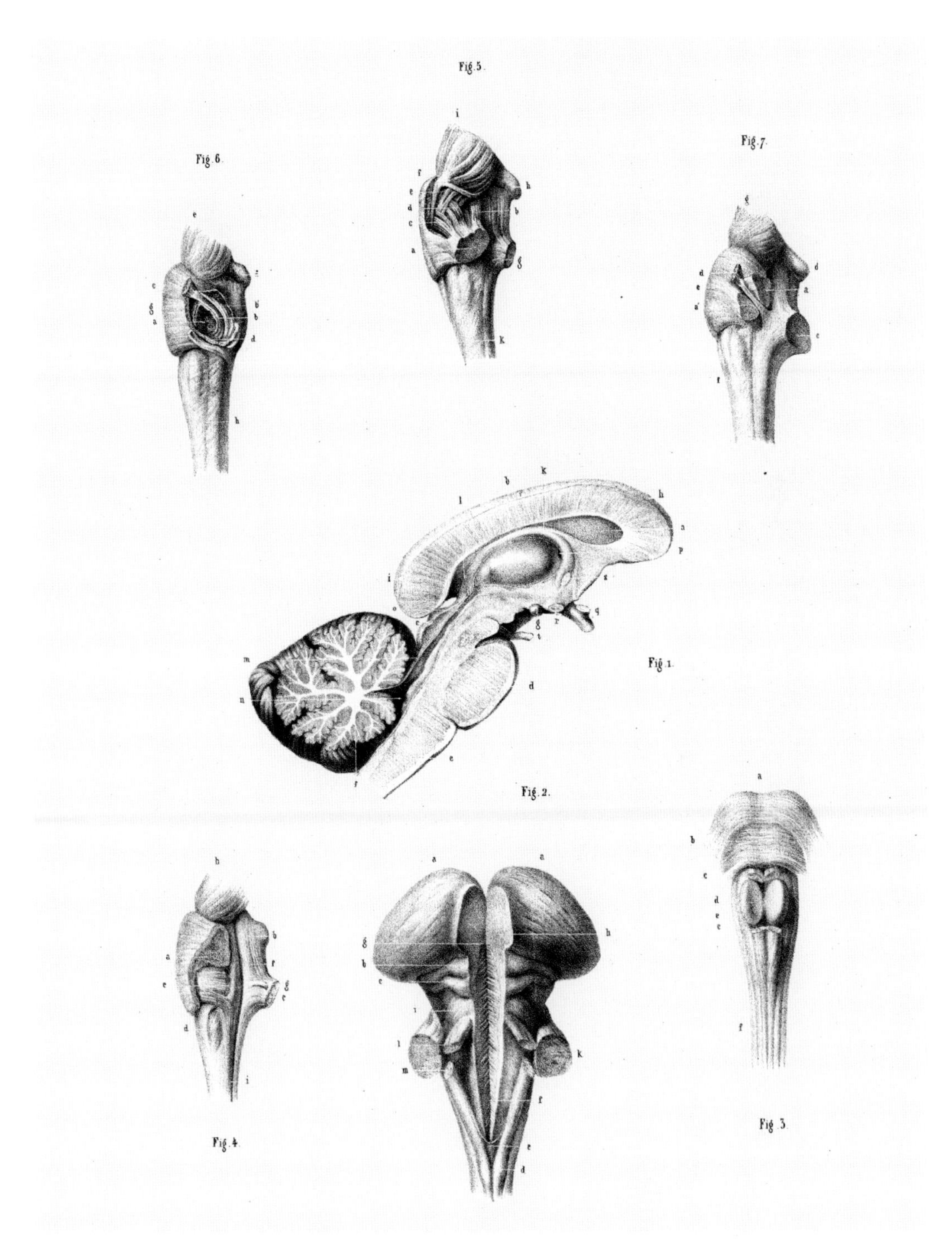

Brainstem / Tronc cérébral / Tronco cerebral

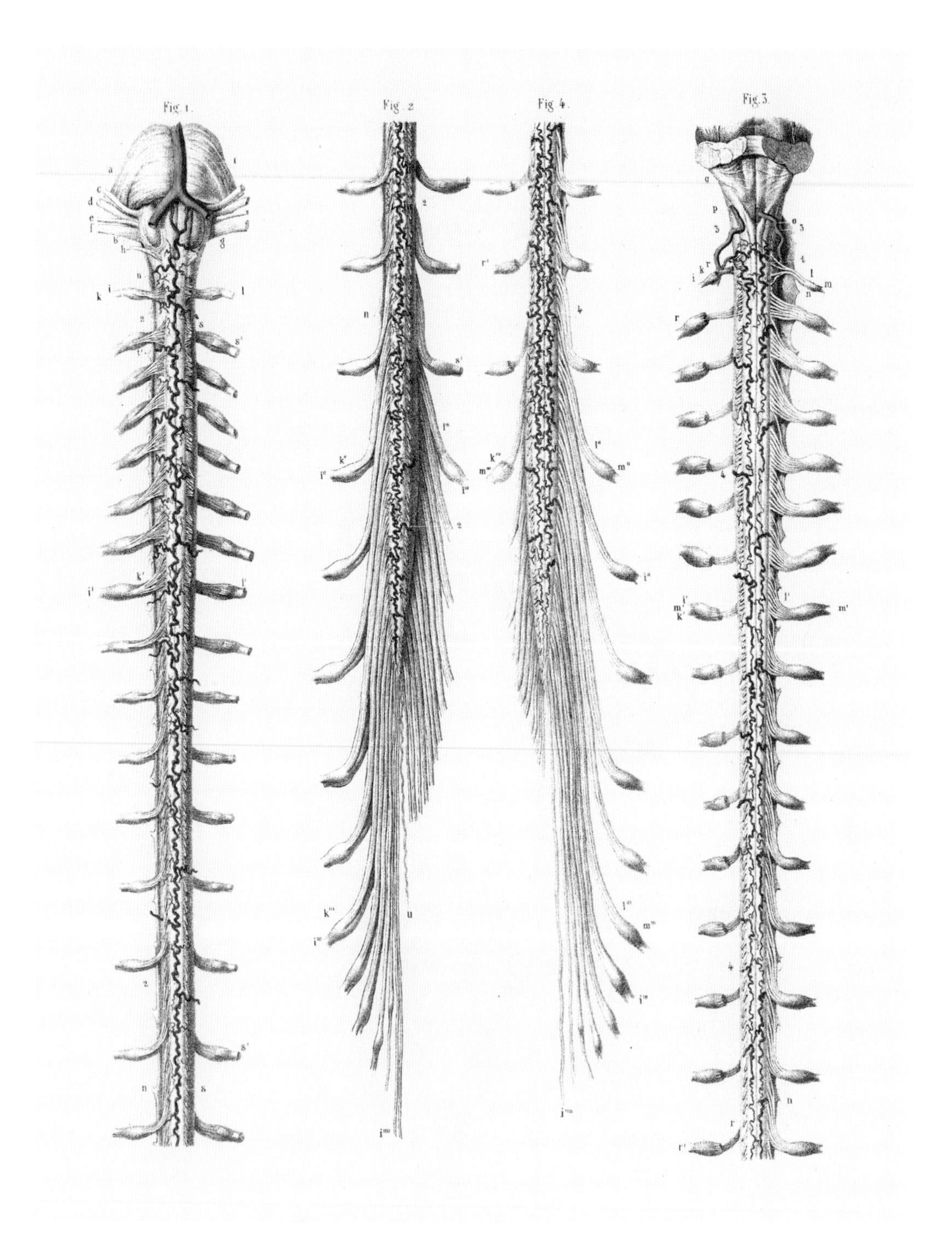

Spinal cord: Arteries / Moelle spinale : Artères / Médula espinal: arterias

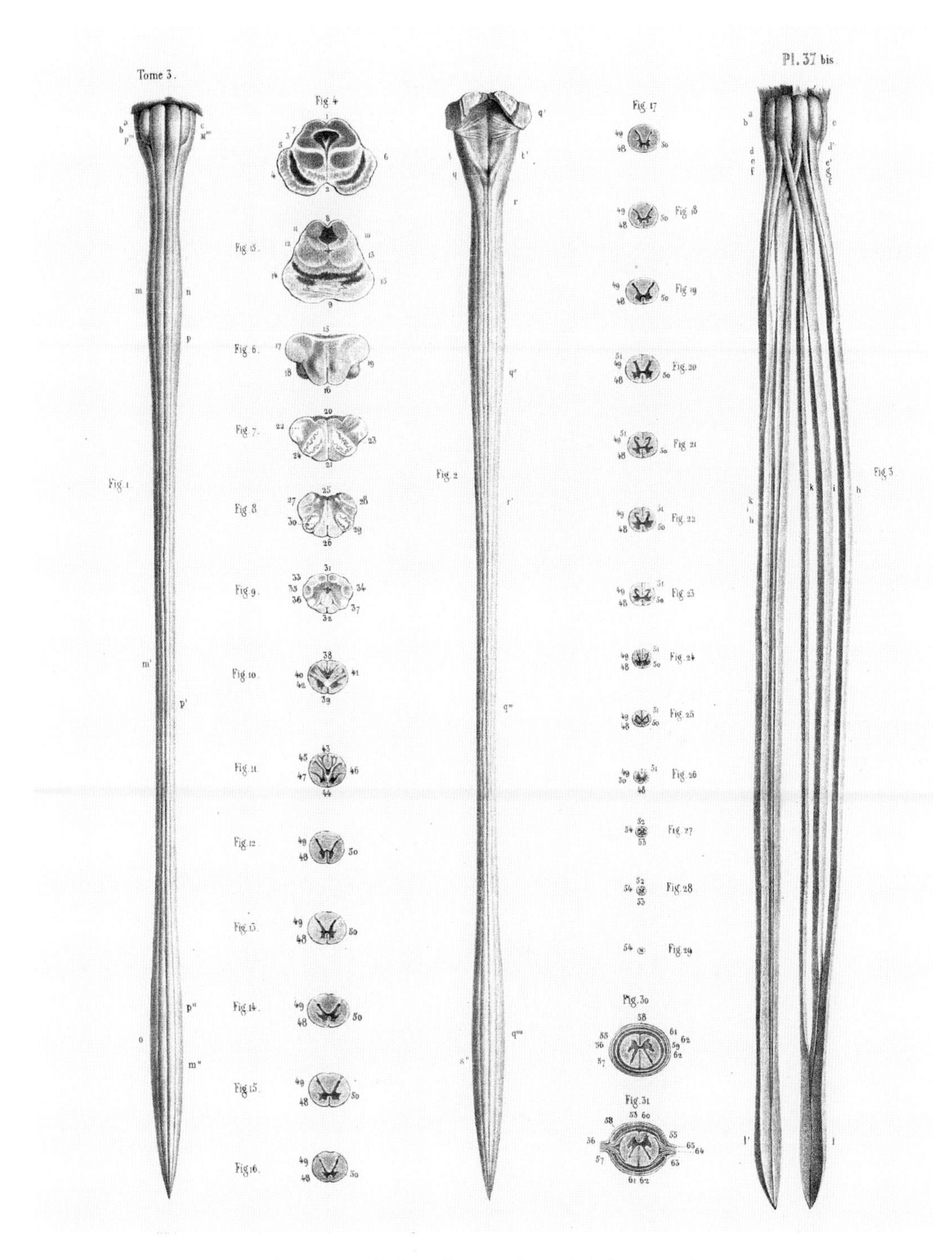

Spinal cord / Moelle spinale / Médula espinal

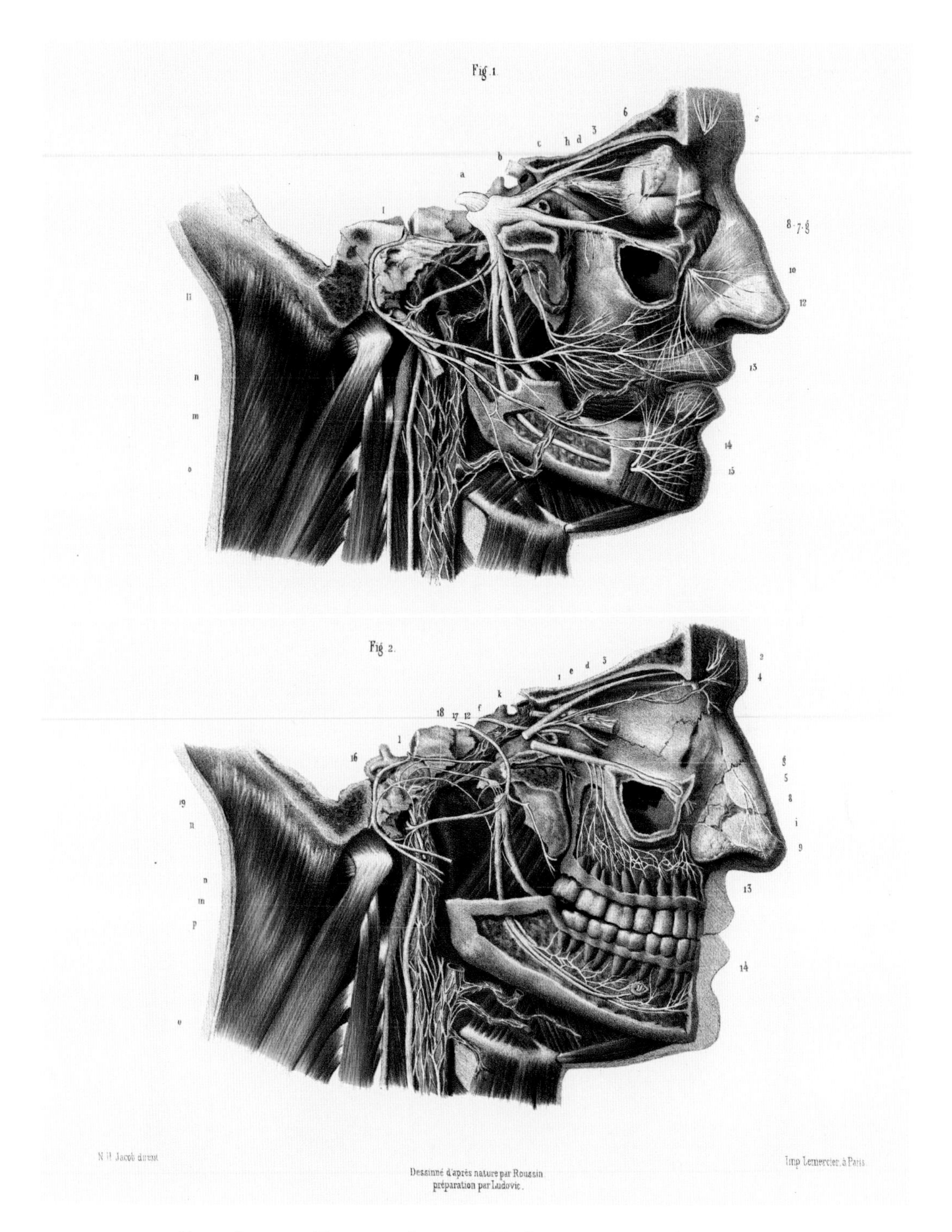

Cranial nerves: Trigeminal nerve / Nerfs crâniens : Nerf trijumeau
Nervios craneales: trigémino

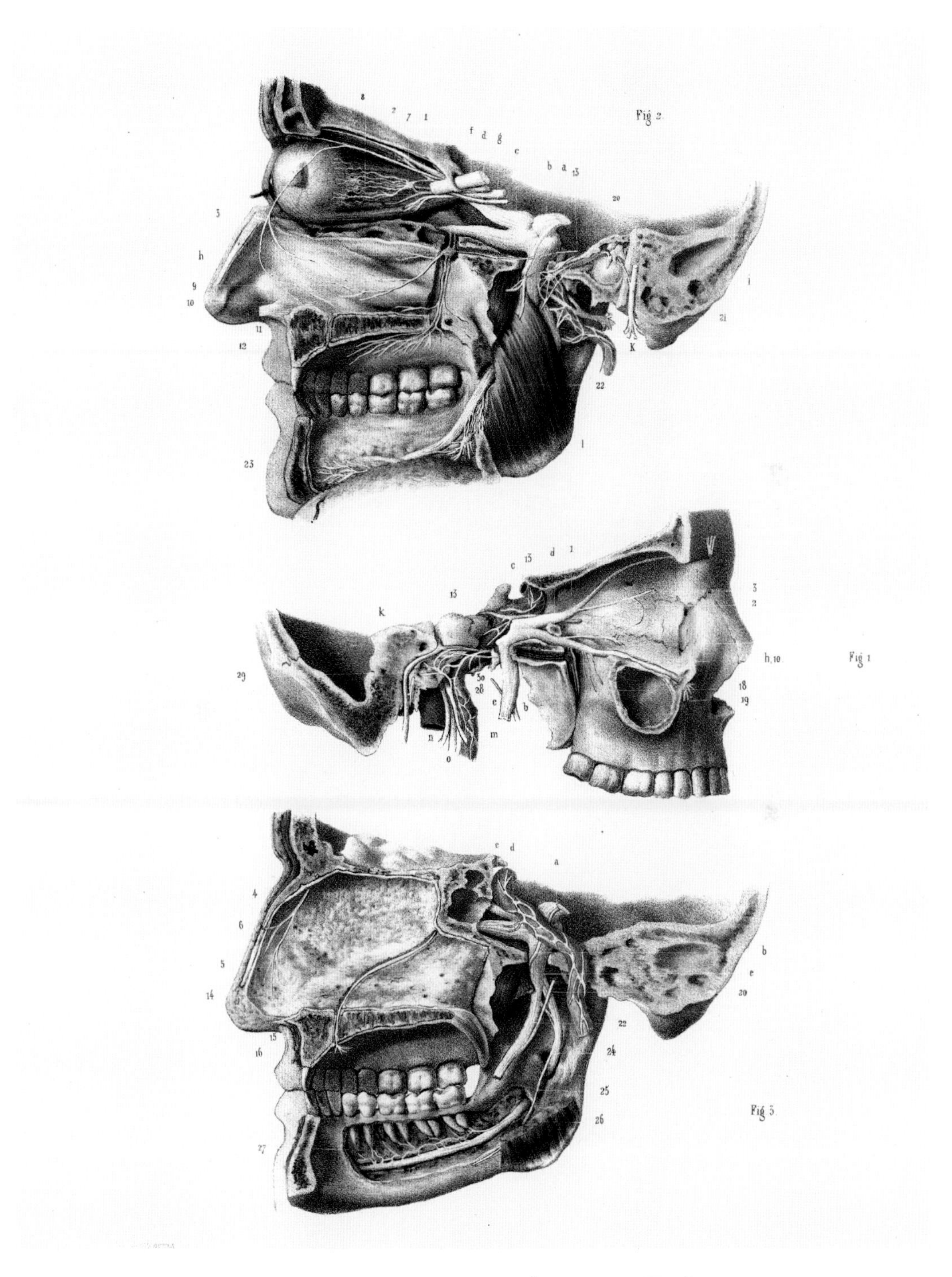

Cranial nerves: Trigeminal nerve / Nerfs crâniens : Nerf trijumeau
Nervios craneales: trigémino

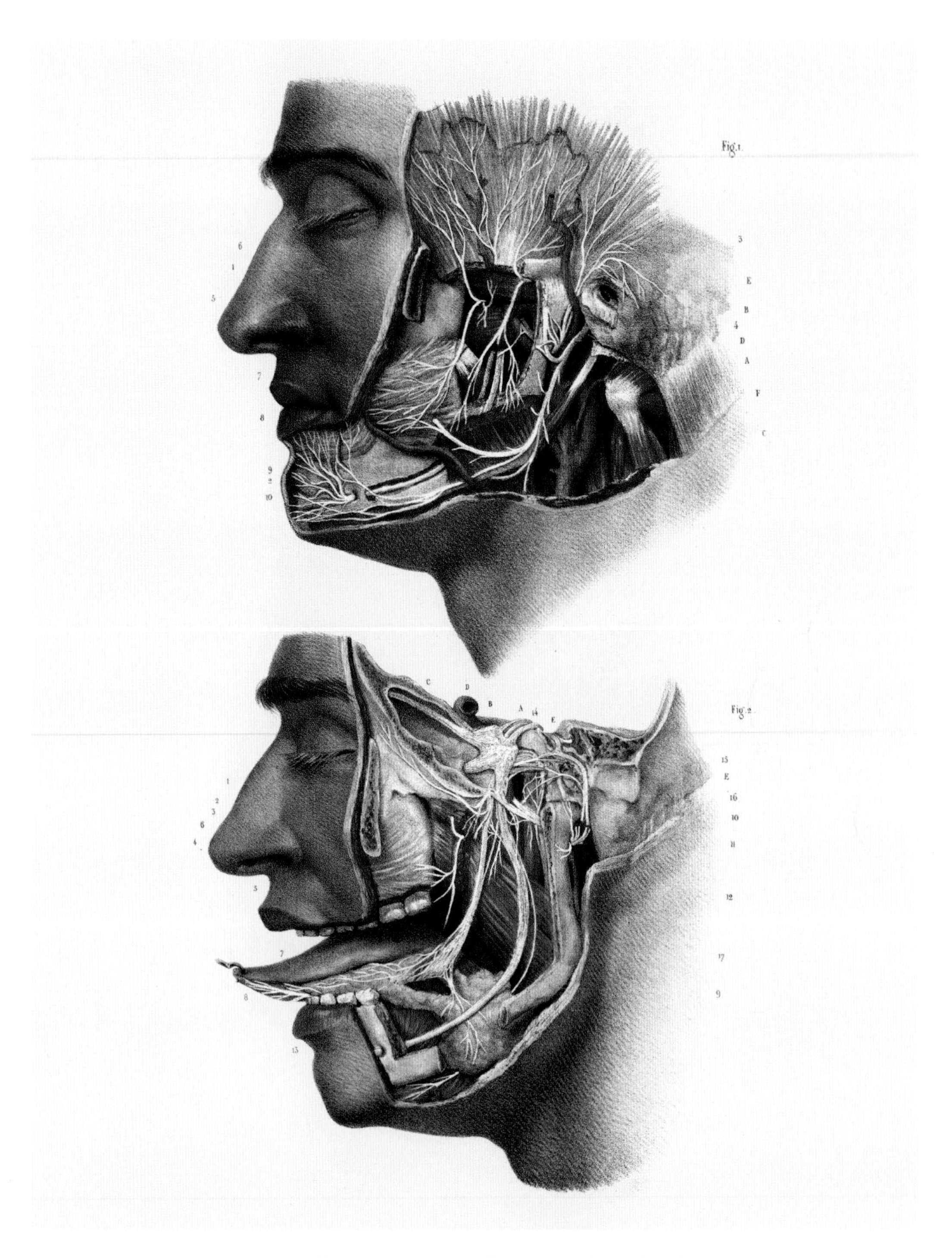

Cranial nerves: Trigeminal nerve / Nerfs crâniens : Nerf trijumeau
Nervios craneales: trigémino

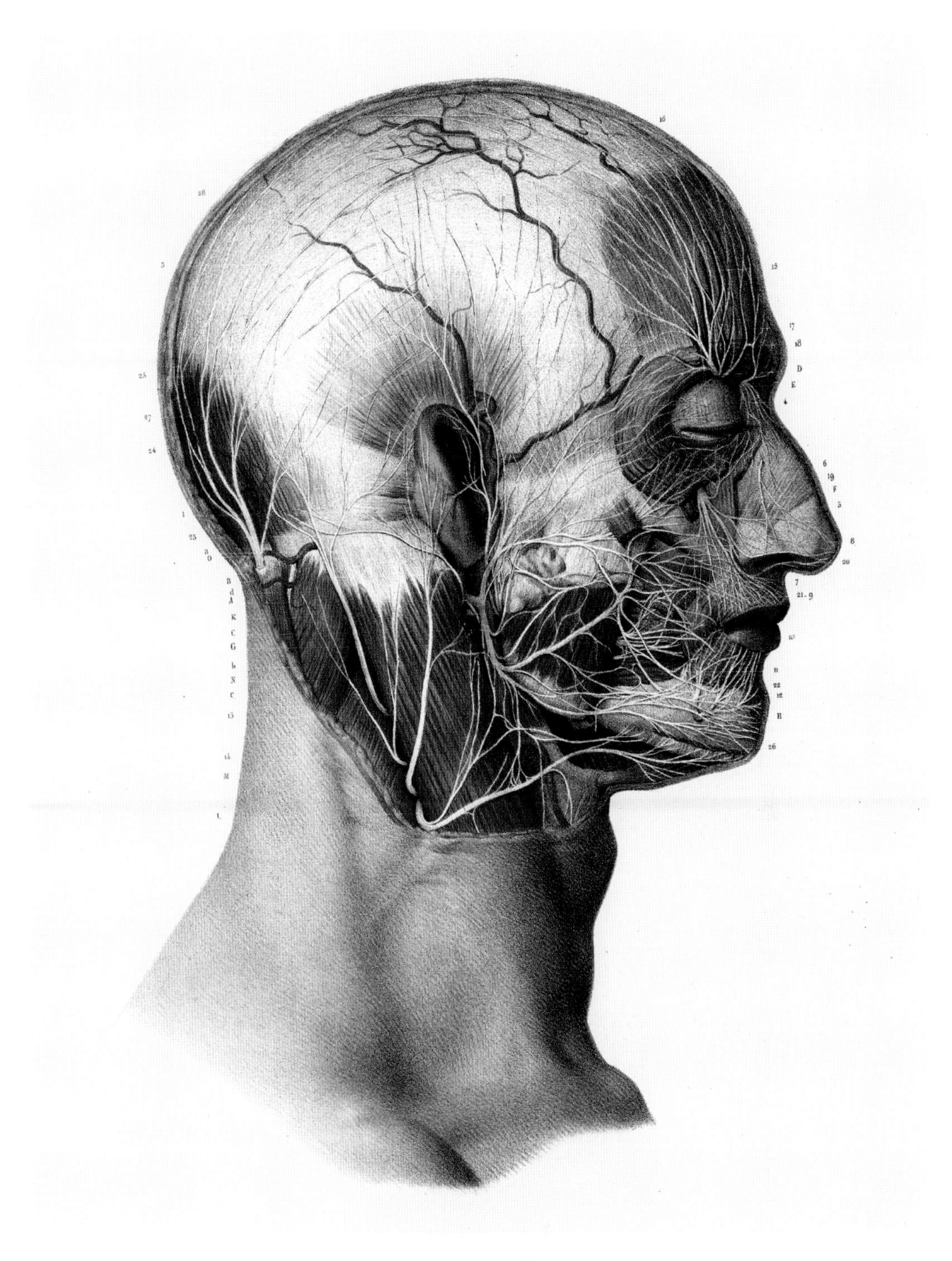

Cranial and cervical nerves / Nerfs crâniens et cervicaux
Nervios craneales y cervicales

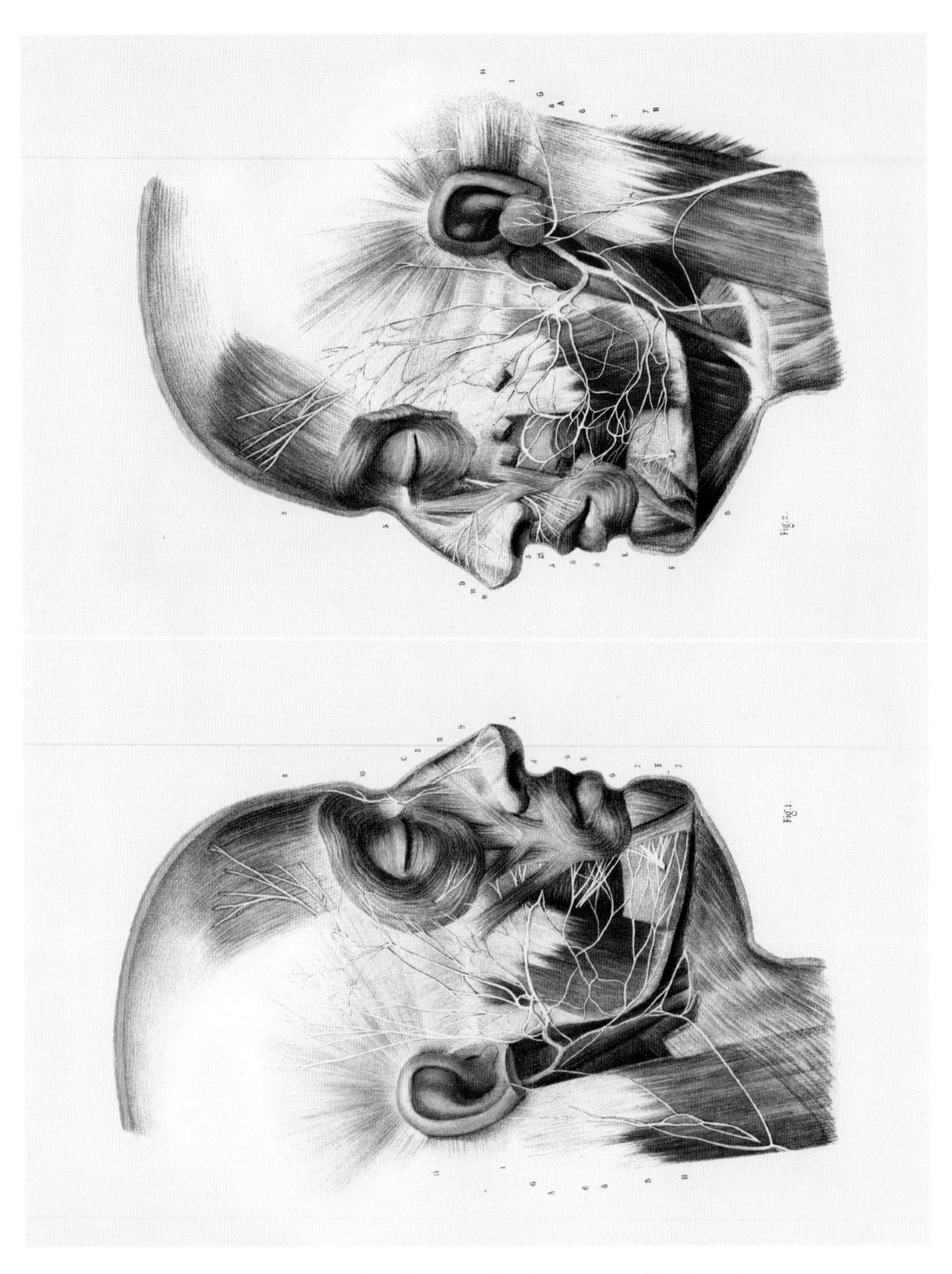

Cranial nerves: Facial nerve / Nerfs crâniens : Nerf facial
Nervios craneales: nervio facial

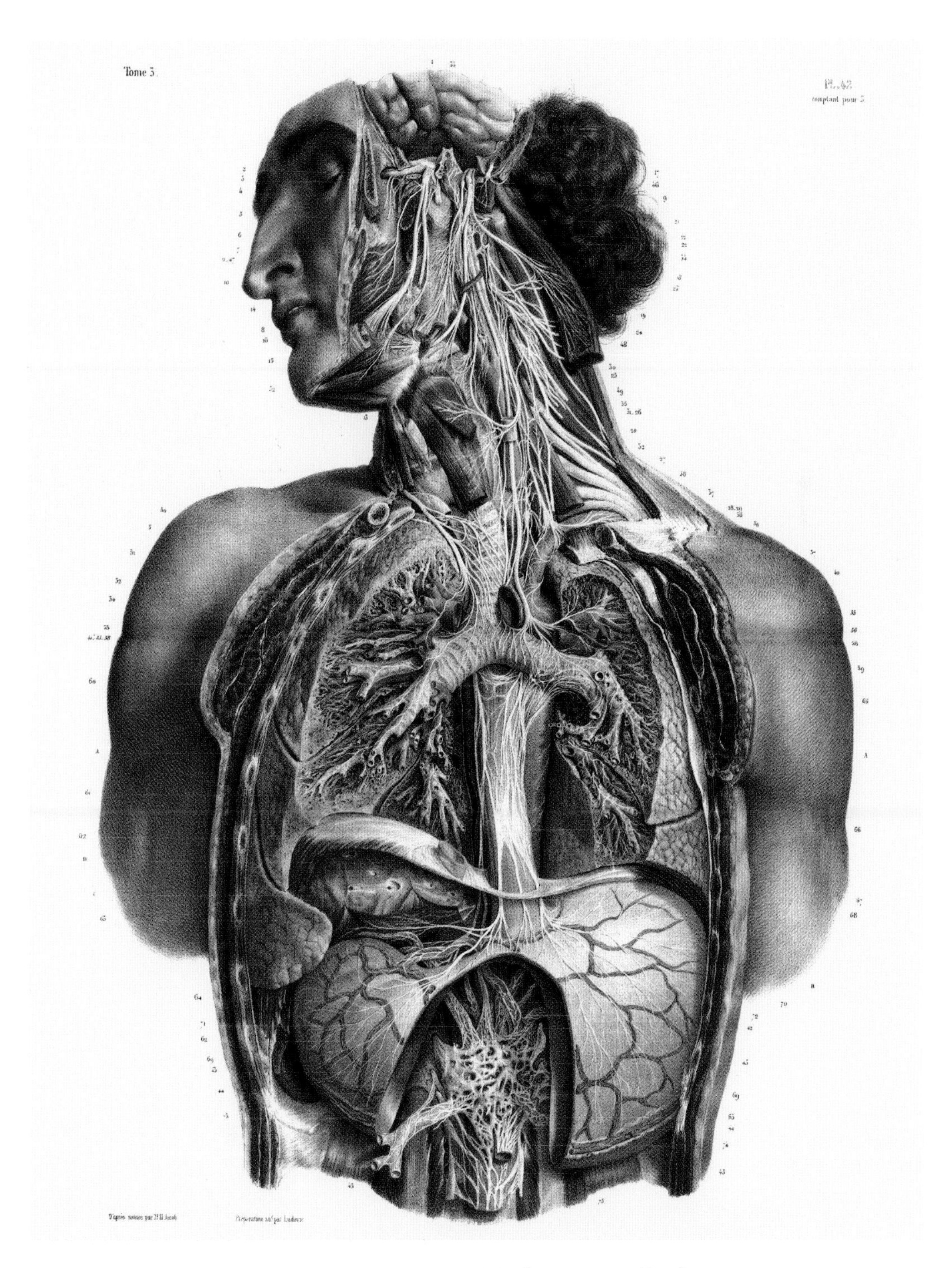

Cranial nerves: Vagus nerve / Nerfs crâniens : Nerf vague
Nervios craneales: nervio vago

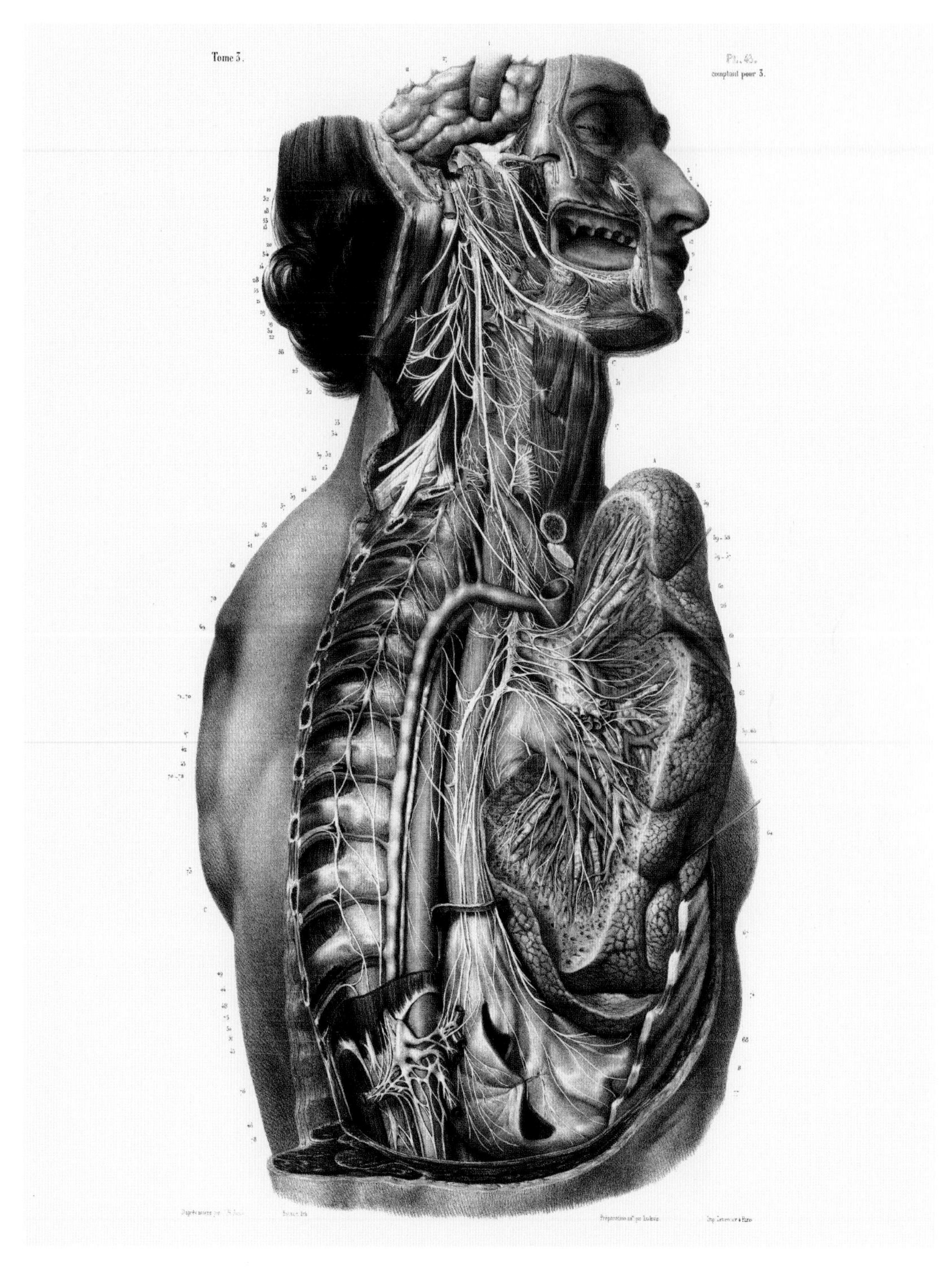

Cranial nerves: Vagus nerve / Nerfs crâniens : Nerf vague
Nervios craneales: nervio vago

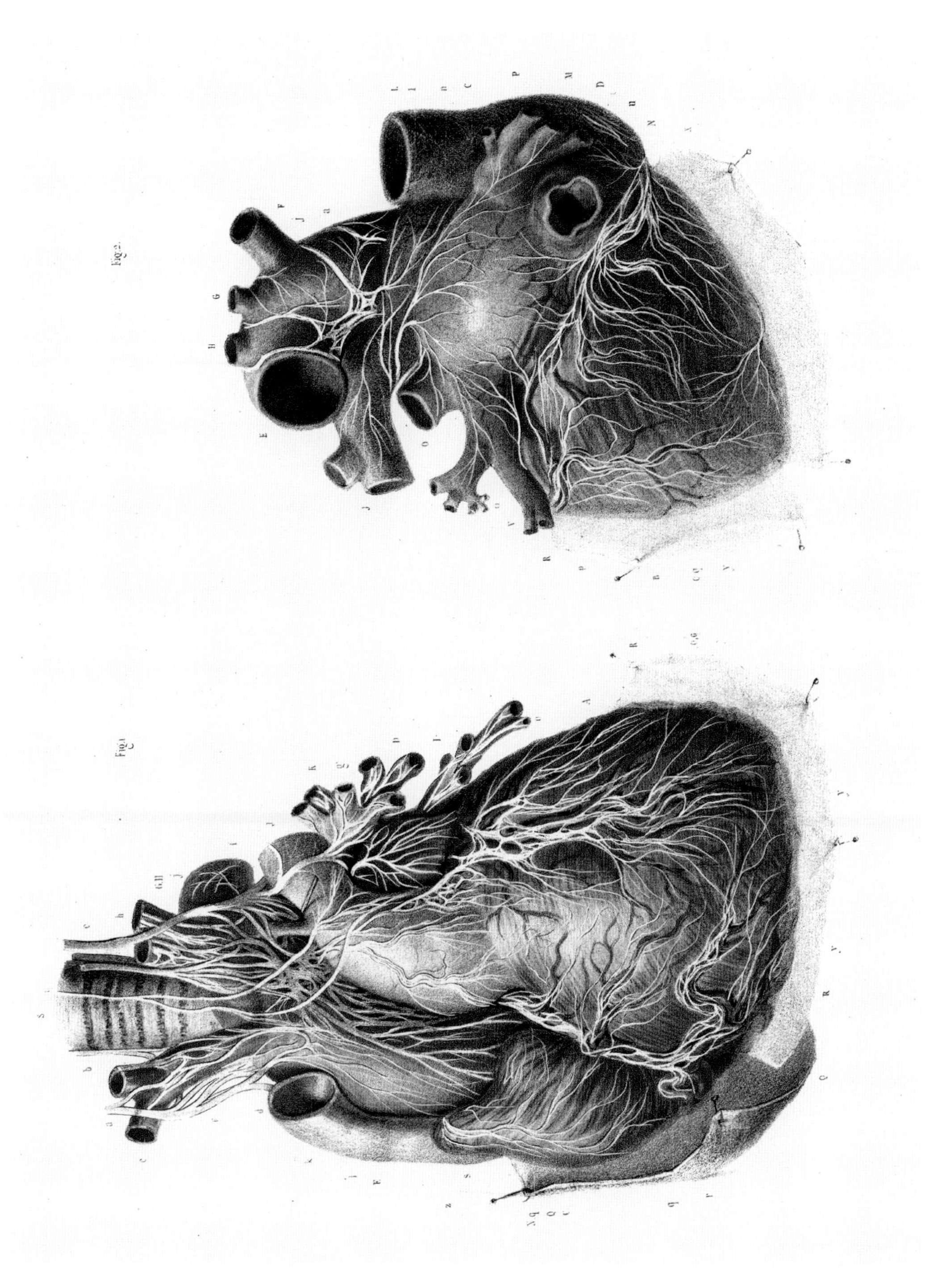

Cranial nerves: Vagus nerve – Cardiac plexus
Nerfs crâniens : Nerf vague – Plexus cardiaque
Nervios craneales: nervio vago – Plexo cardíaco

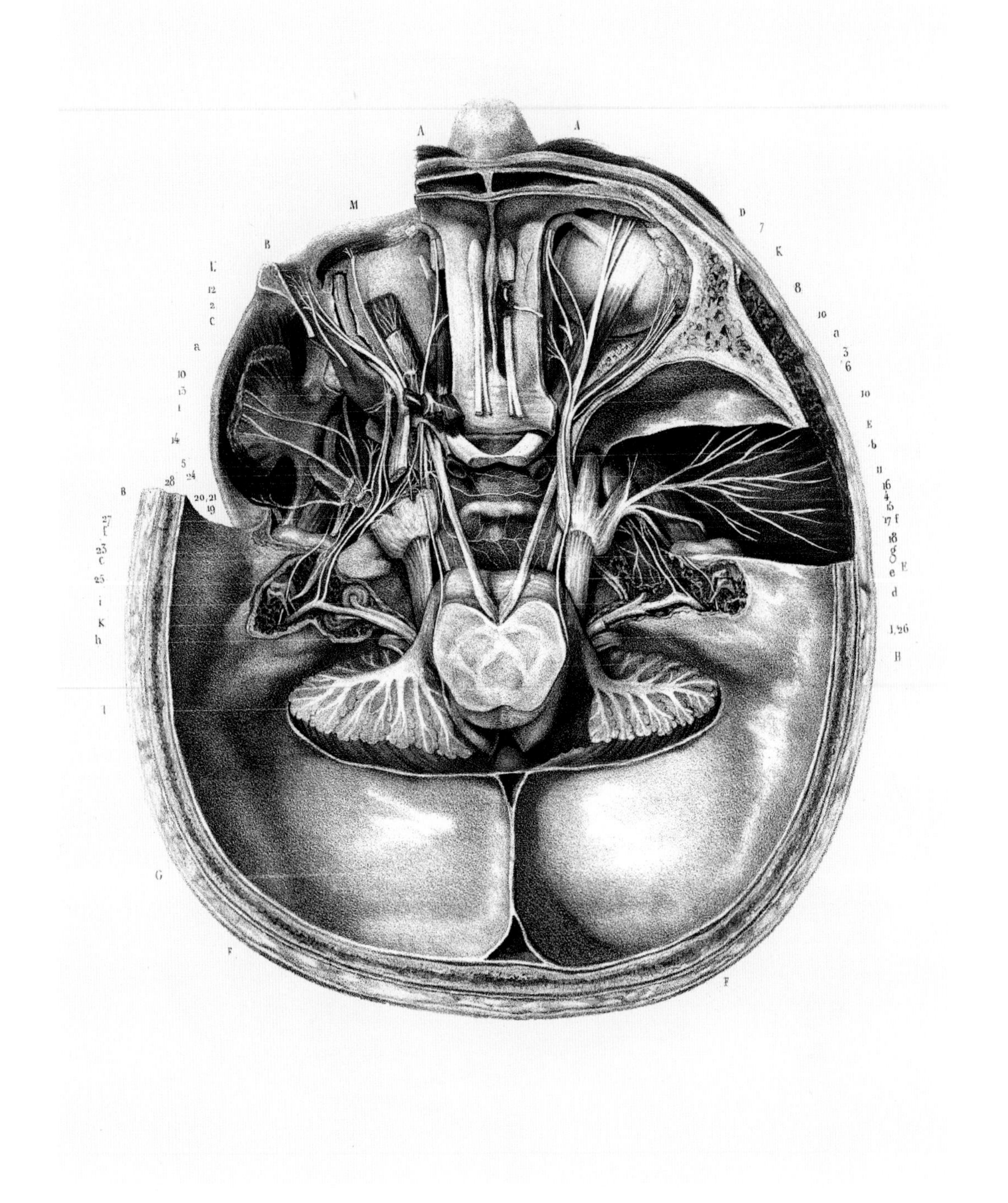

Cranial nerves / Nerfs crâniens / Nervios craneales

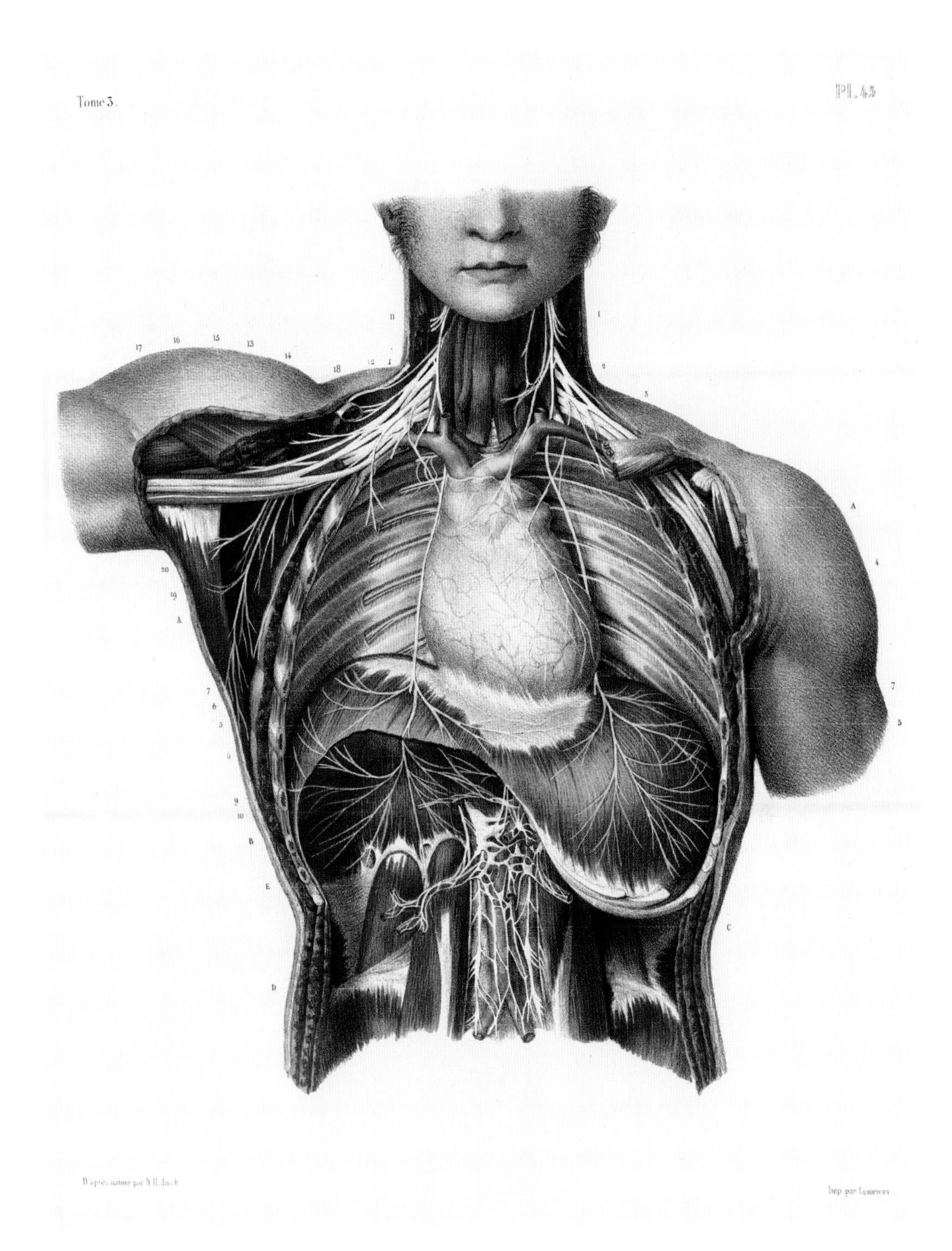

Phrenic nerve / Nerf phrénique / Nervio frénico

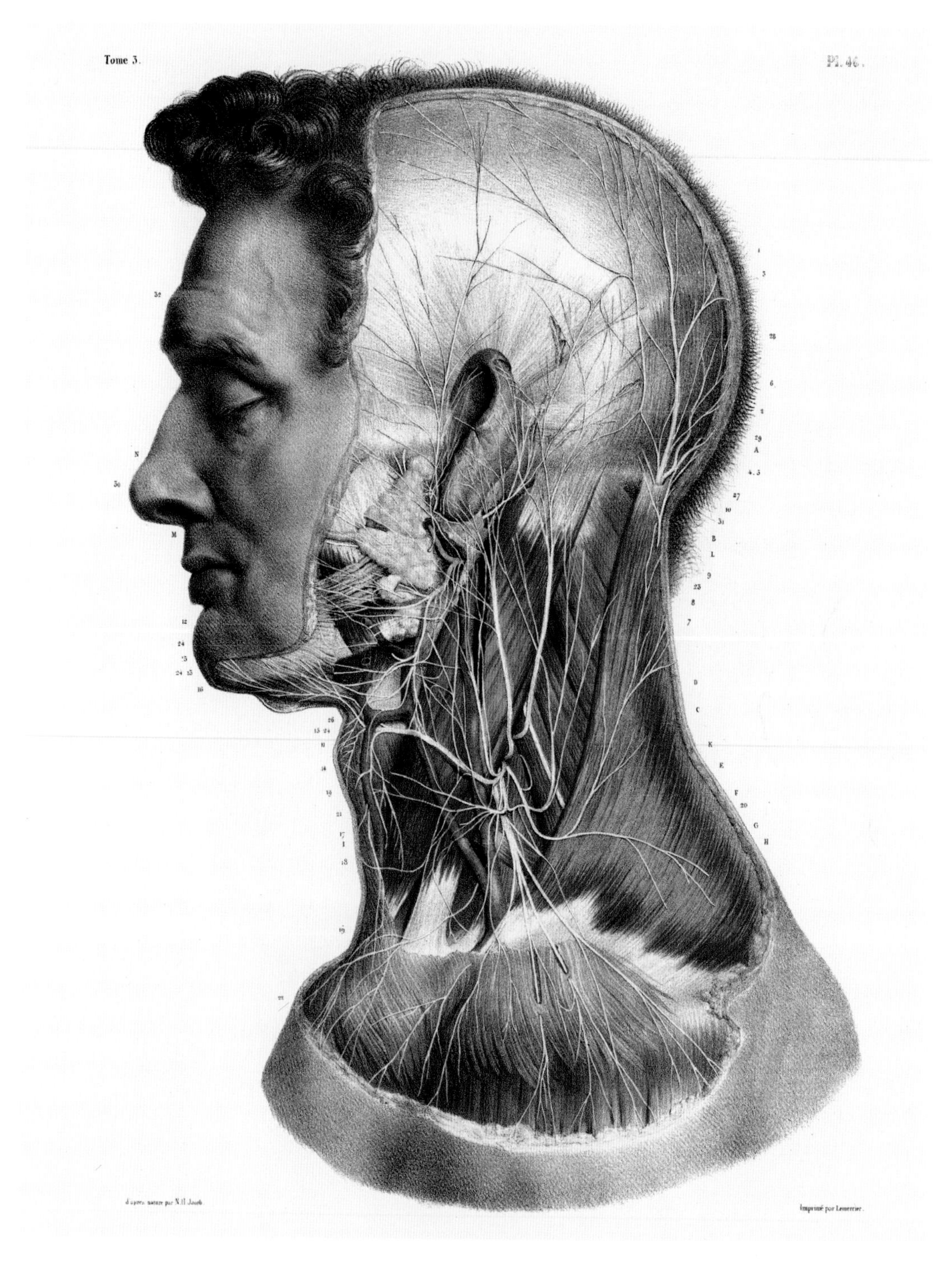

Nerves of the neck – Cervical plexus / Nerfs du cou – Plexus cervical
Nervios del cuello – Plexo cervical

NERVI COLLI – PLEXUS CERVICALIS. ANATOMIA MICROSCOPICA NERVI CRANII, PLEXUS COELIACI, ET PLEXI OESOPHAGEI

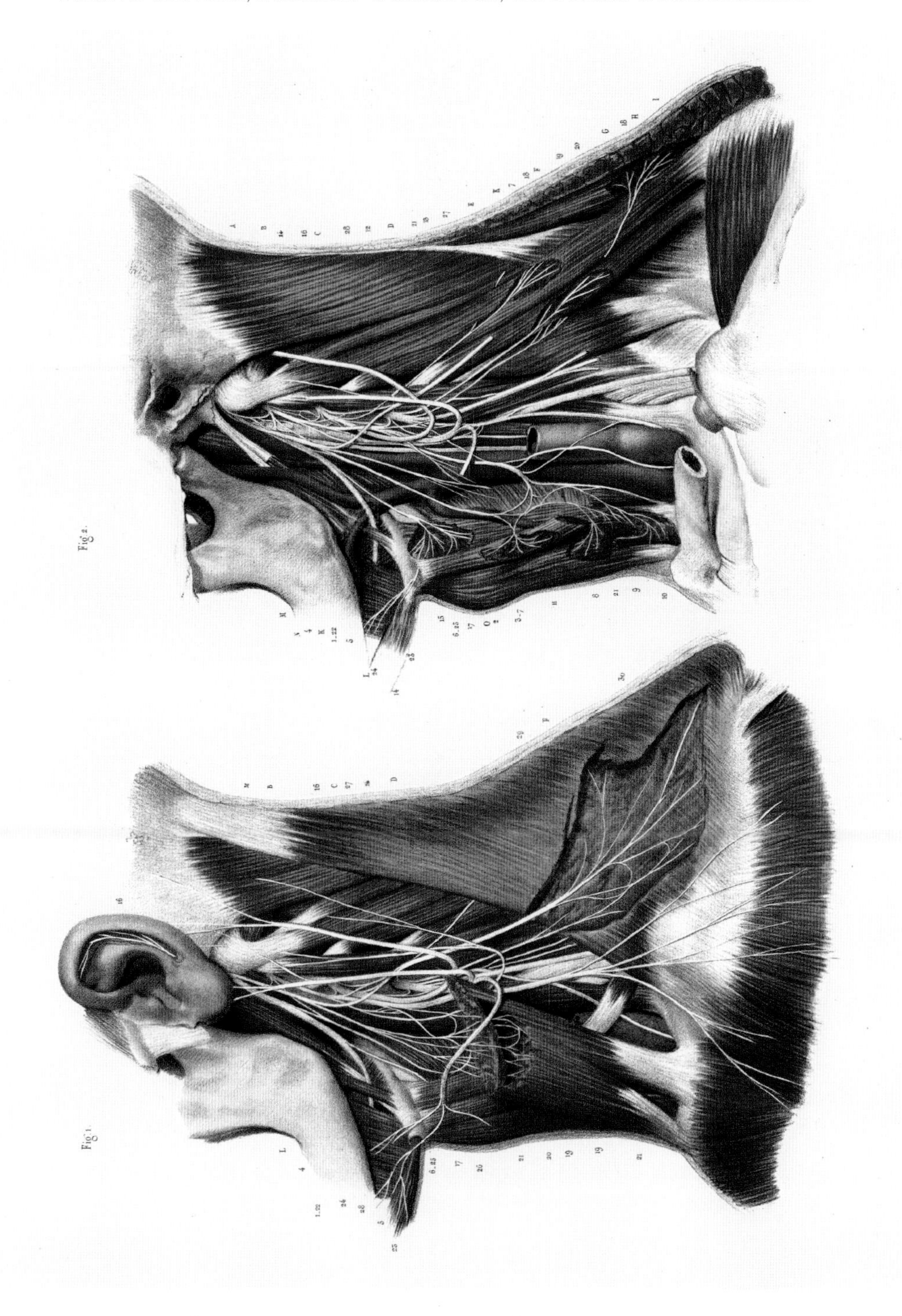

Nerves of the neck – Cervical plexus / Nerfs du cou – Plexus cervical
Nervios del cuello – Plexo cervical

NERVI COLLI – PLEXUS CERVICALIS. ANATOMIA MICROSCOPICA NERVI CRANII, PLEXUS COELIACI, ET PLEXI OESOPHAGEI

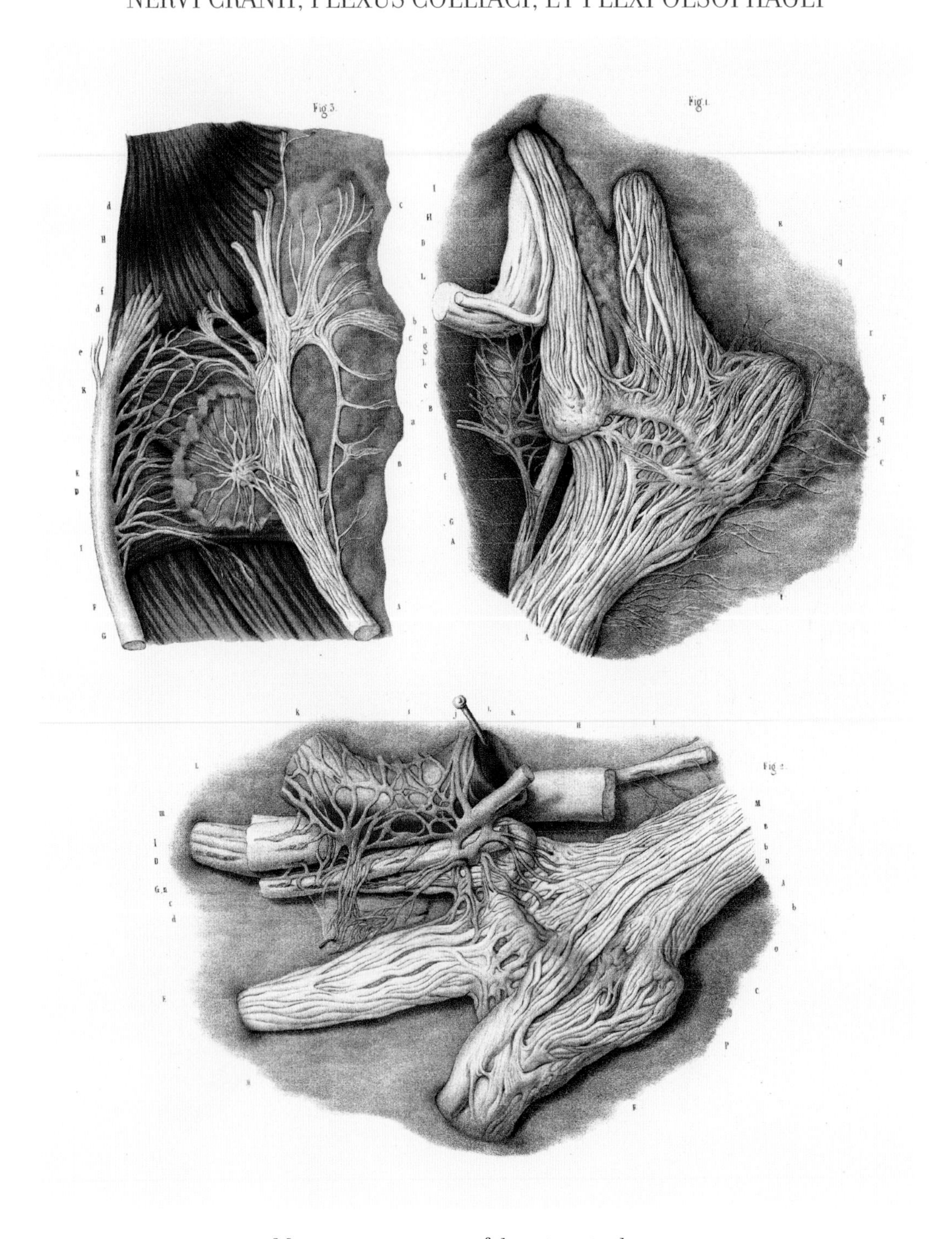

Microscopic anatomy of the trigeminal nerve
Anatomie microscopique du nerf trijumeau
Anatomía microscópica del nervio trigémino

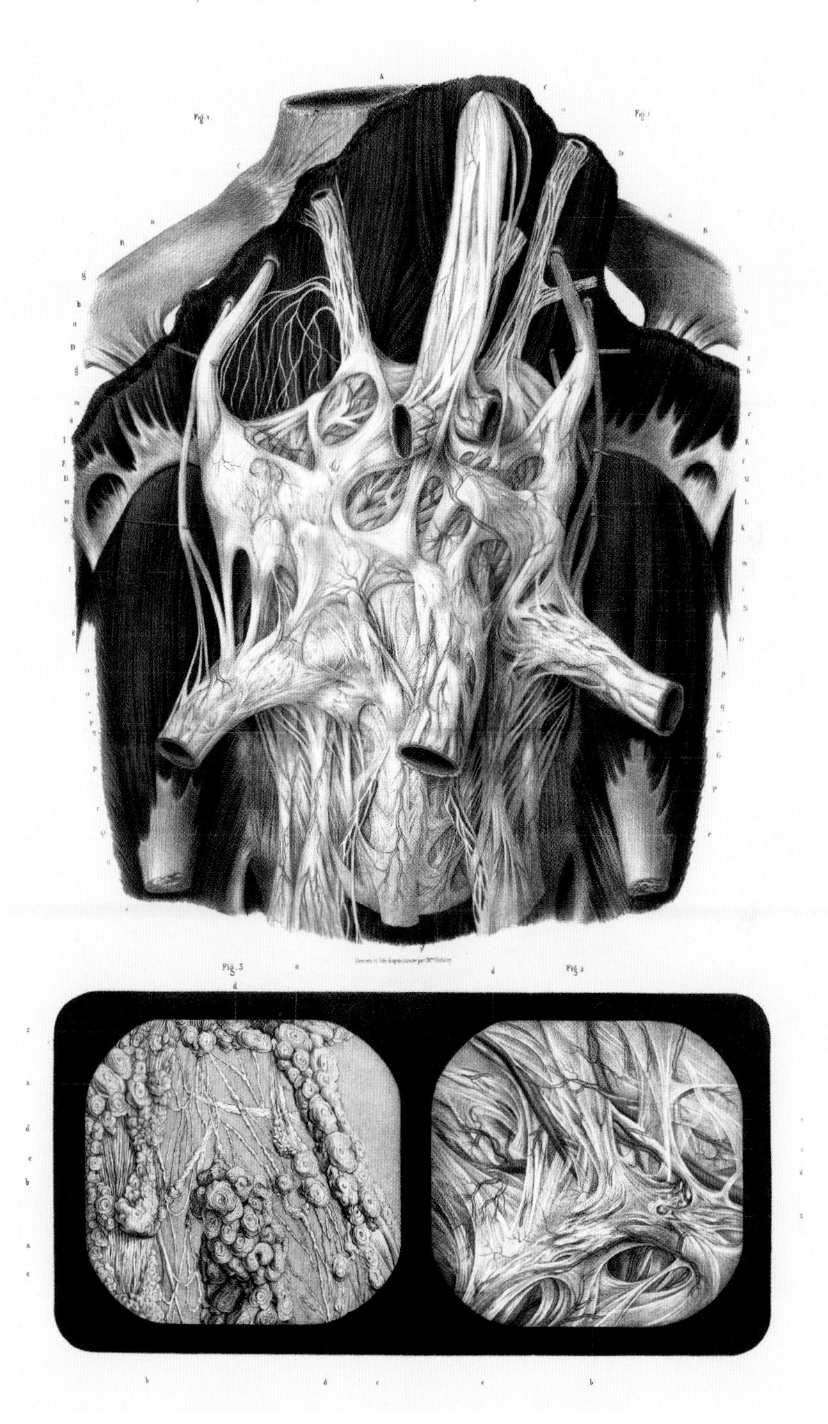

Microscopic anatomy of the cœliac plexus
Anatomie microscopique du plexus cœliaque
Anatomía microscópica del plexo celíaco

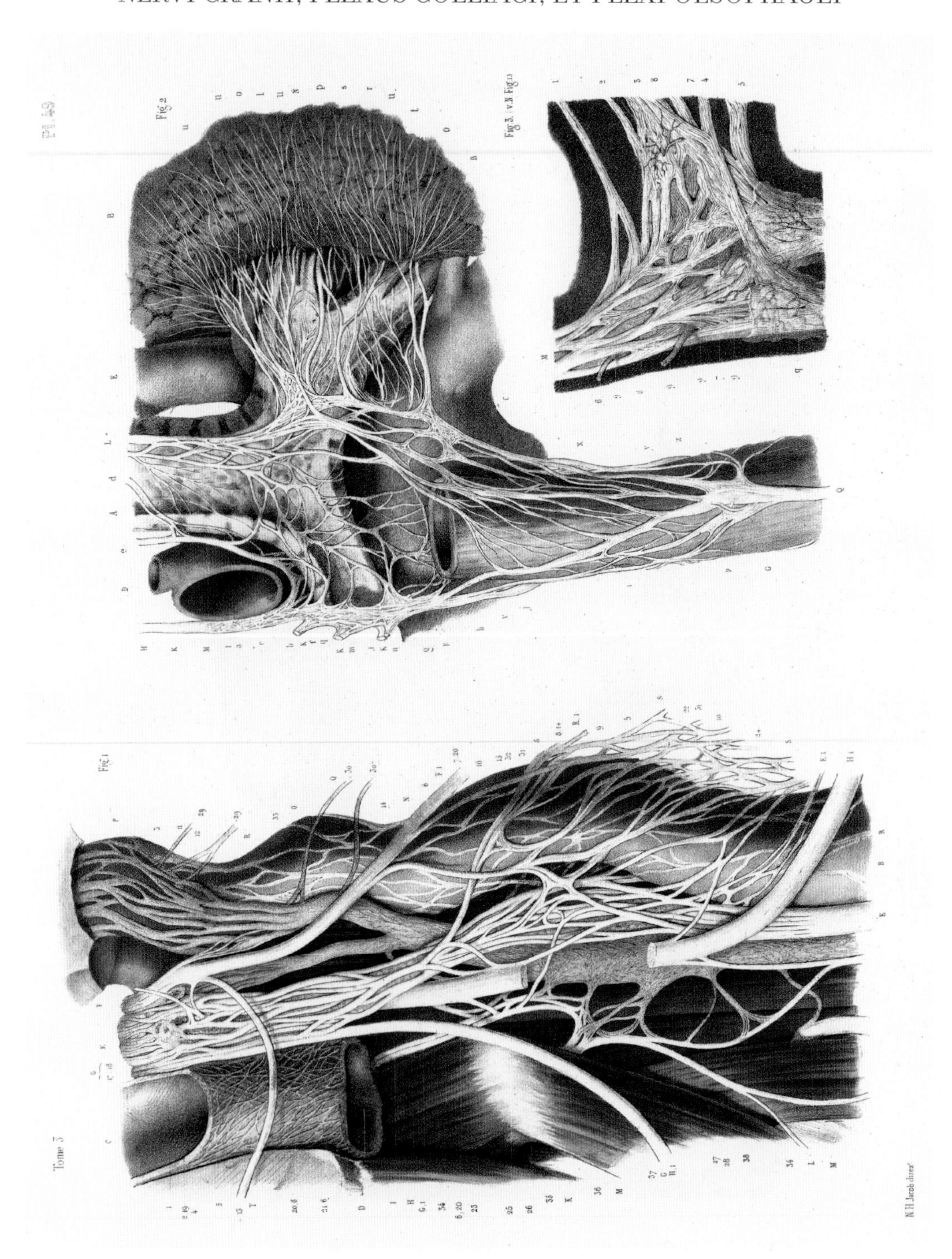

Microscopic anatomy of the vagus nerve and the œsophageal plexus
Anatomie microscopique du nerf vague et du plexus œsophagien
Anatomía microscópica del nervio vago y del plexo esofágico

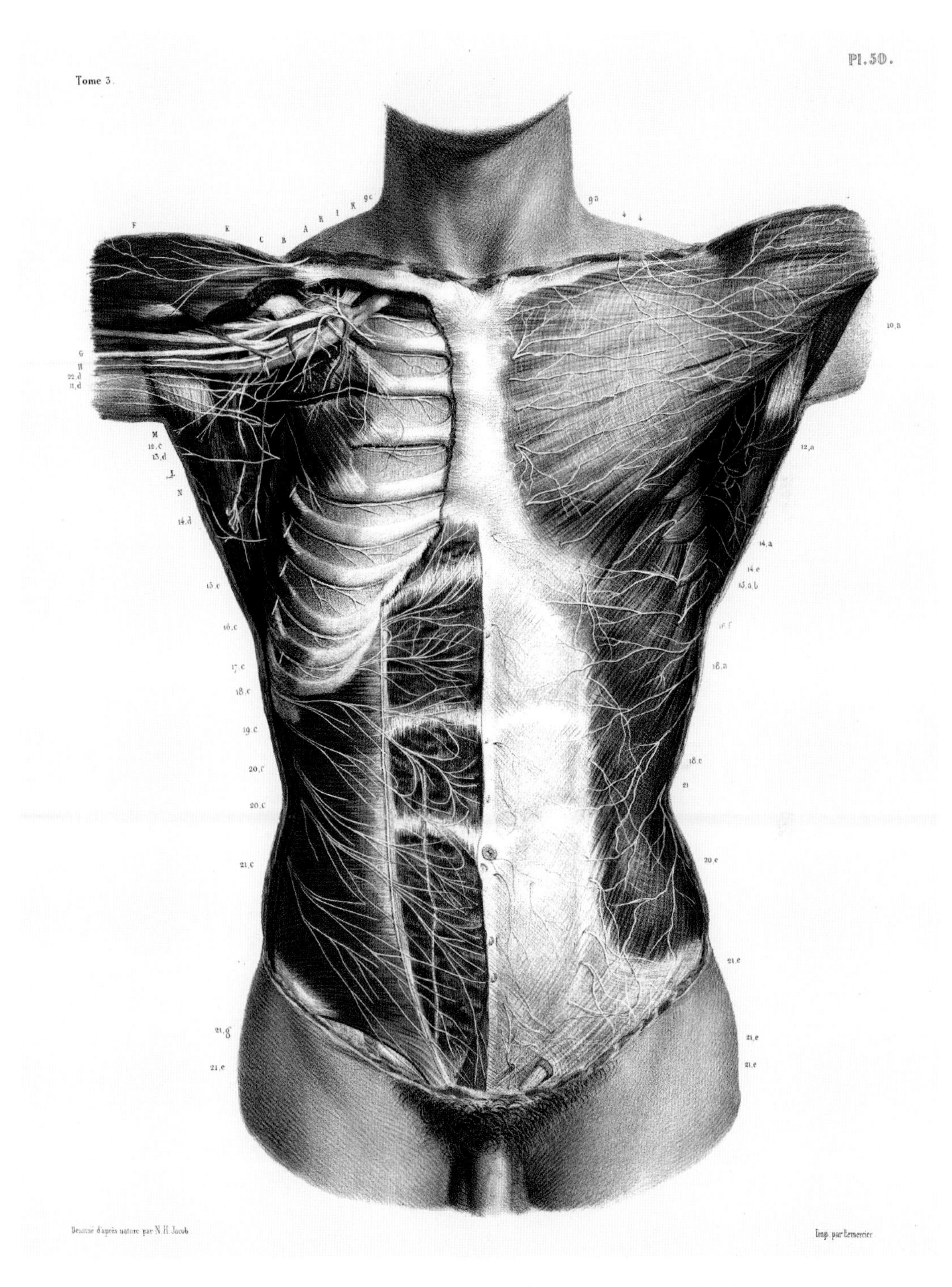

Thoracic and abdominal nerves / Nerfs du thorax et de l'abdomen
Nervios del tórax y del abdomen

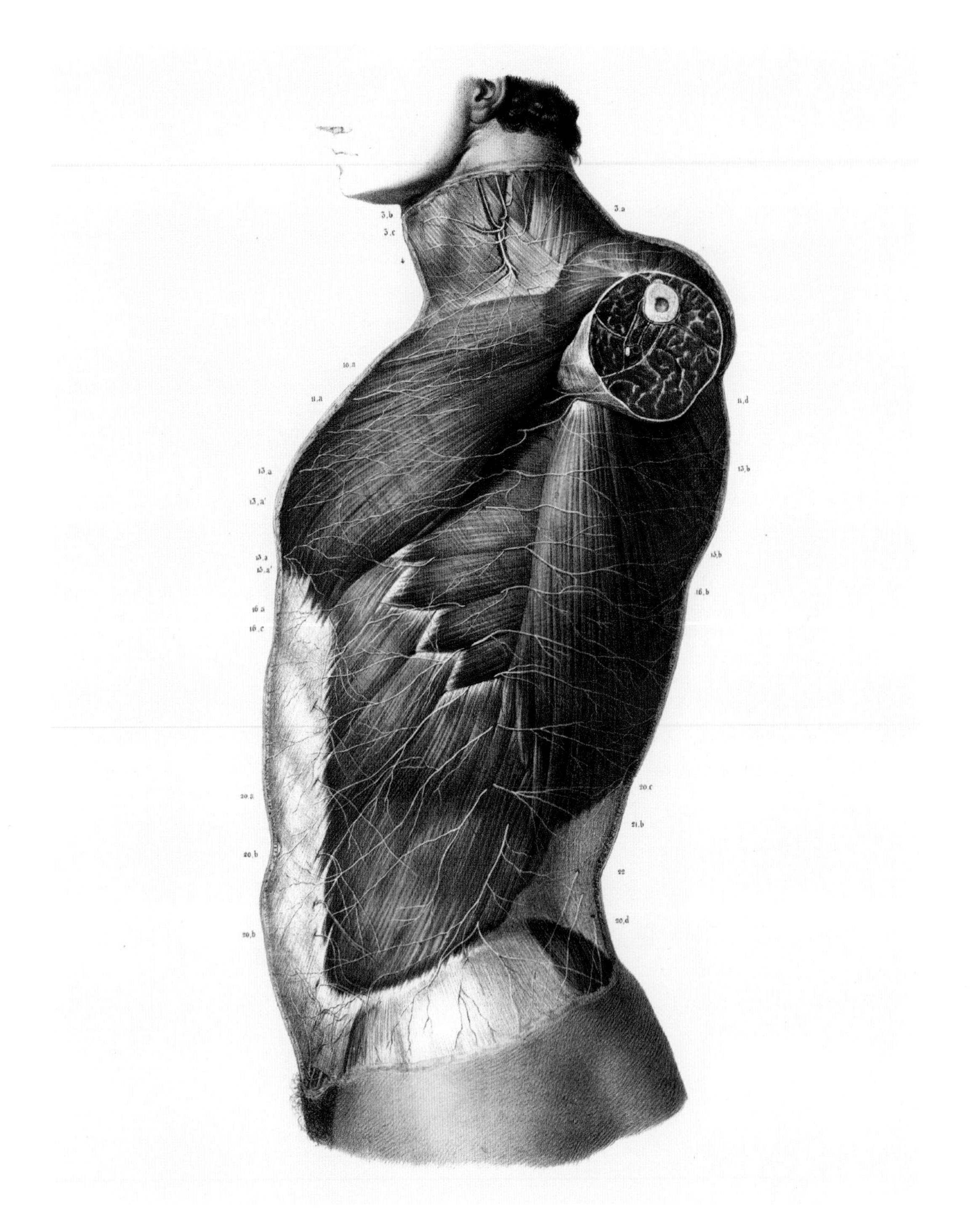

Thoracic and abdominal nerves / Nerfs du thorax et de l'abdomen
Nervios del tórax y del abdomen

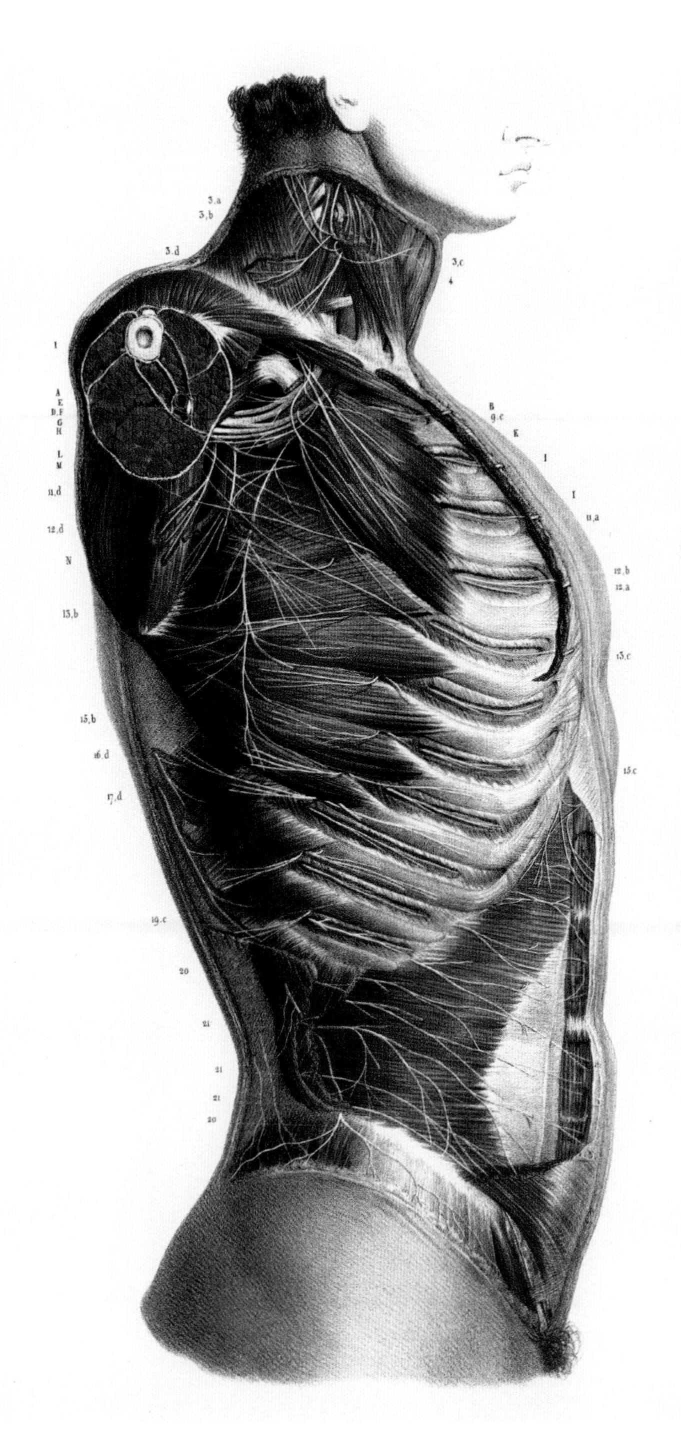

Thoracic and abdominal nerves / Nerfs du thorax et de l'abdomen
Nervios del tórax y del abdomen

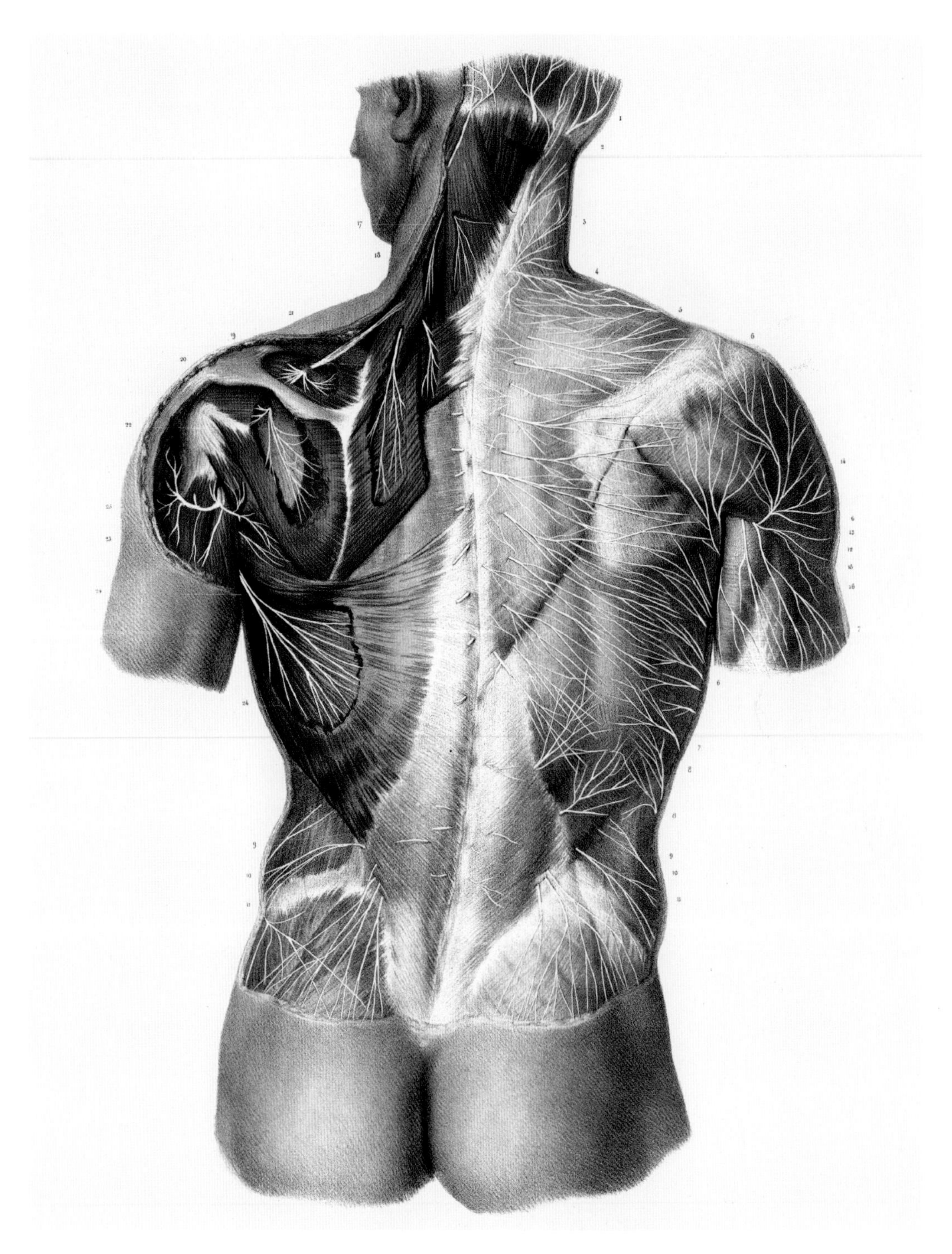

Thoracic and abdominal nerves / Nerfs du thorax et de l'abdomen
Nervios del tórax y del abdomen

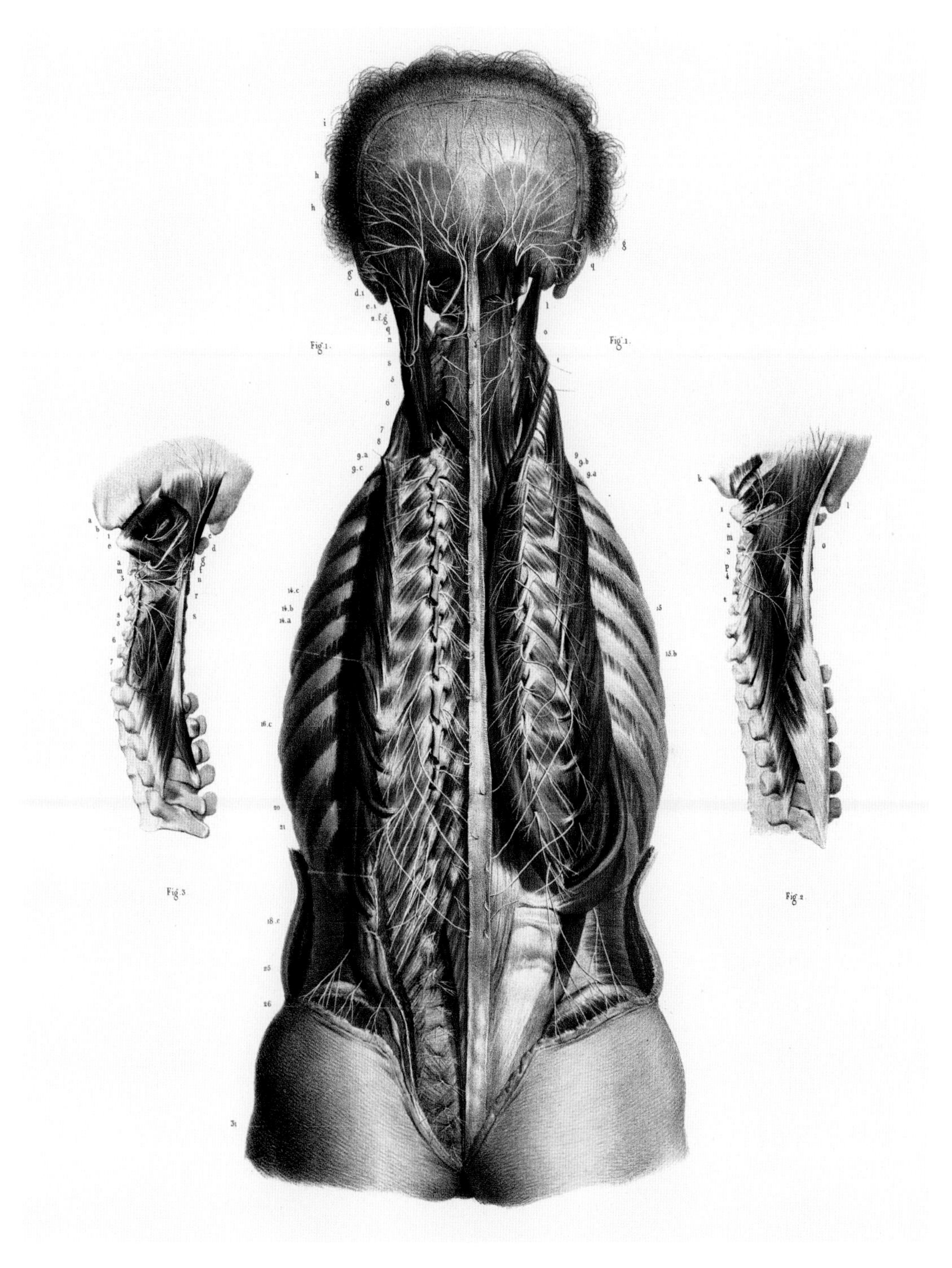

Thoracic and abdominal nerves / Nerfs du thorax et de l'abdomen
Nervios del tórax y del abdomen

PLEXUS LUMBOSACRALIS. PLEXUS BRACHIALIS. NERVI PERINEI

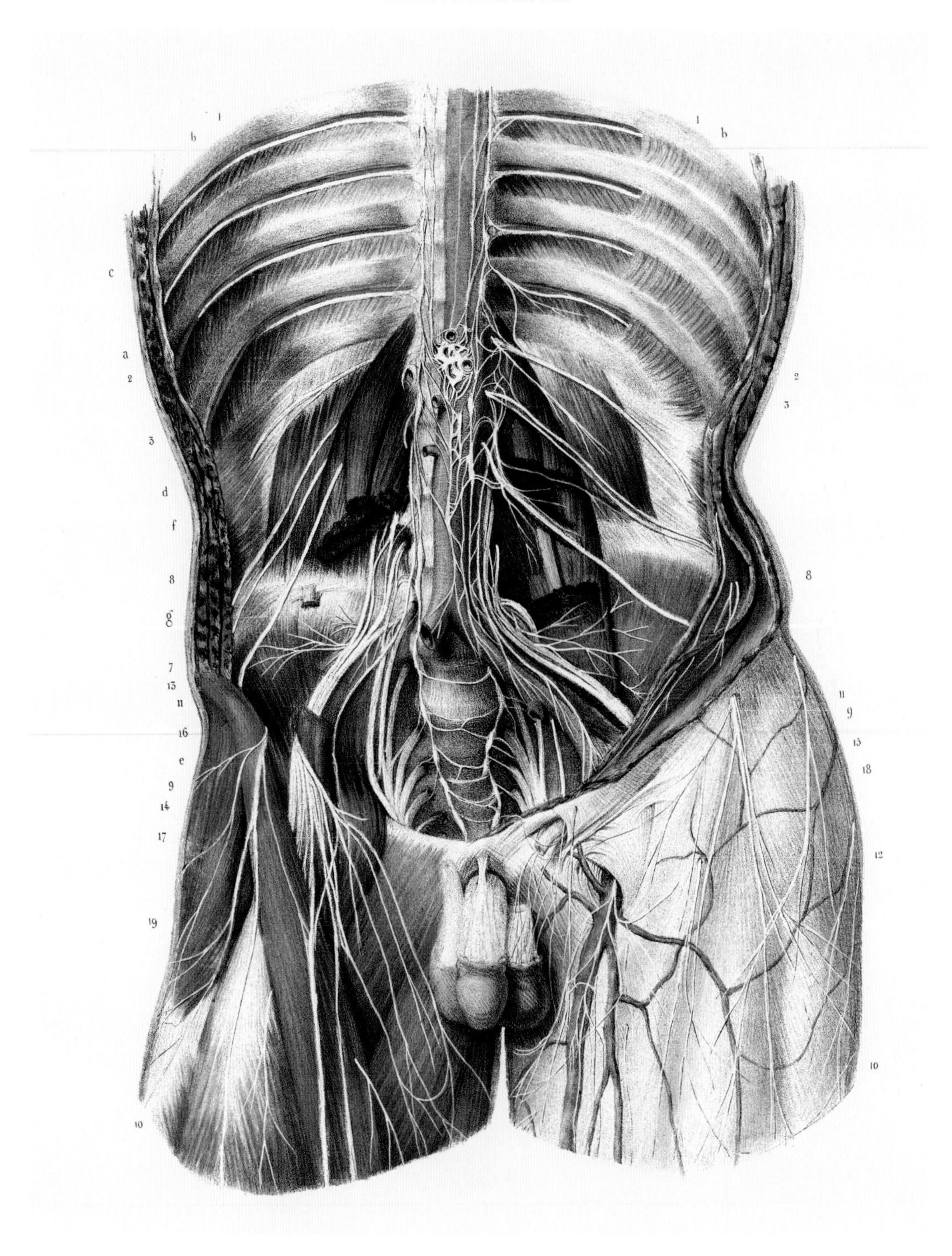

Lumbo-sacral plexus / Plexus lombo-sacré / Plexo lumbosacro

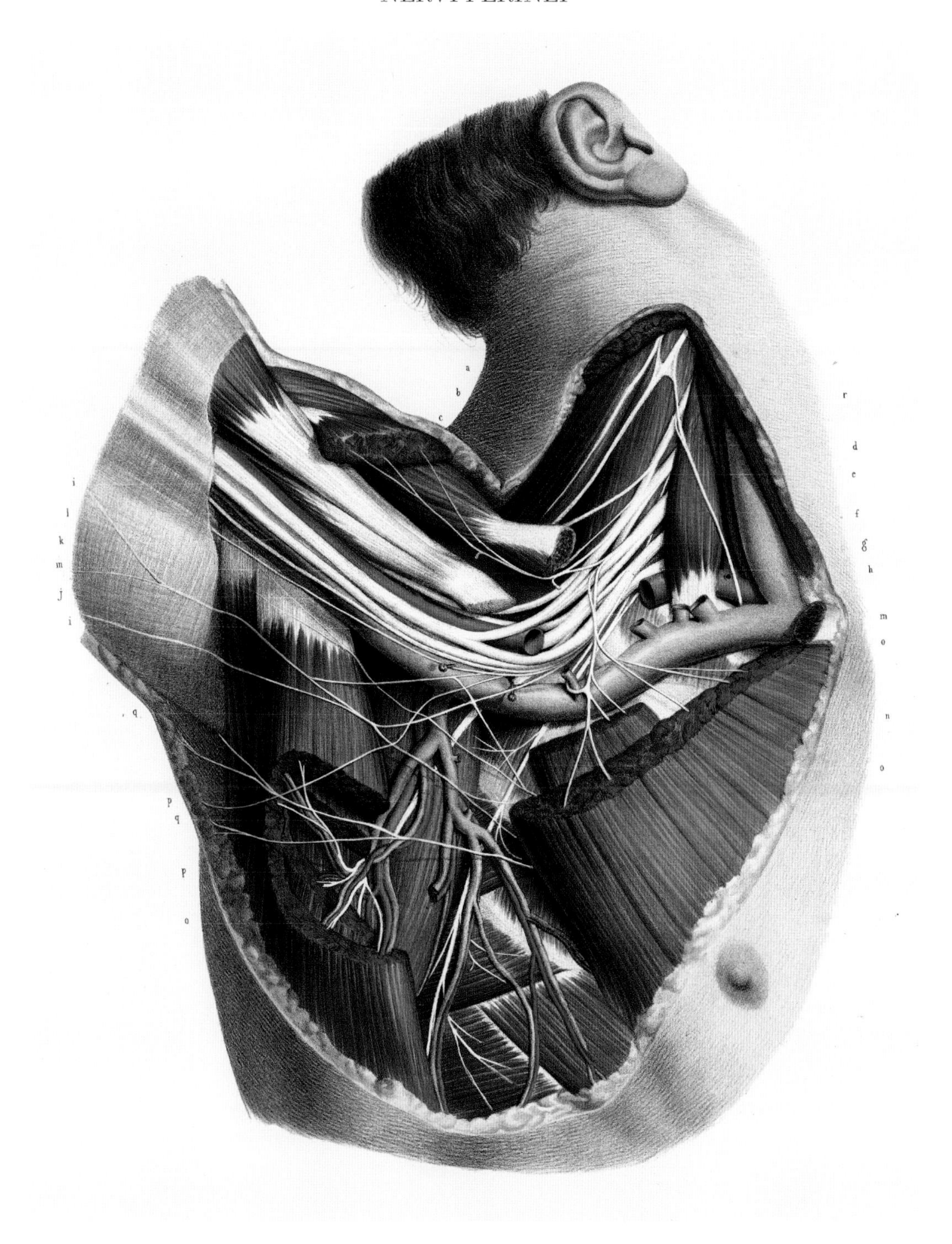

Brachial plexus / Plexus brachial / Plexo braquial

PLEXUS LUMBOSACRALIS. PLEXUS BRACHIALIS. NERVI PERINEI

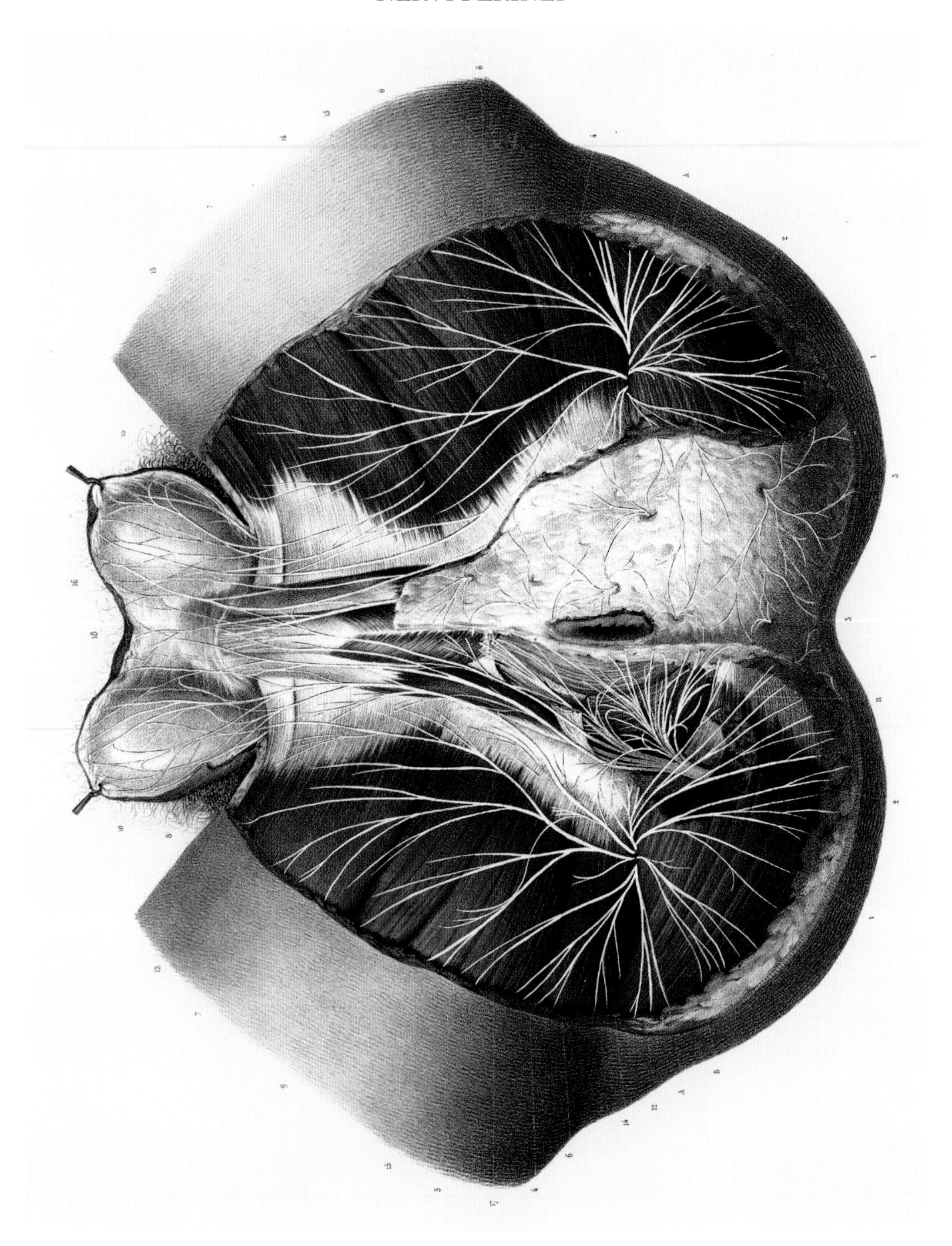

Perineal nerves / Nerfs du périnée / Nervios del periné

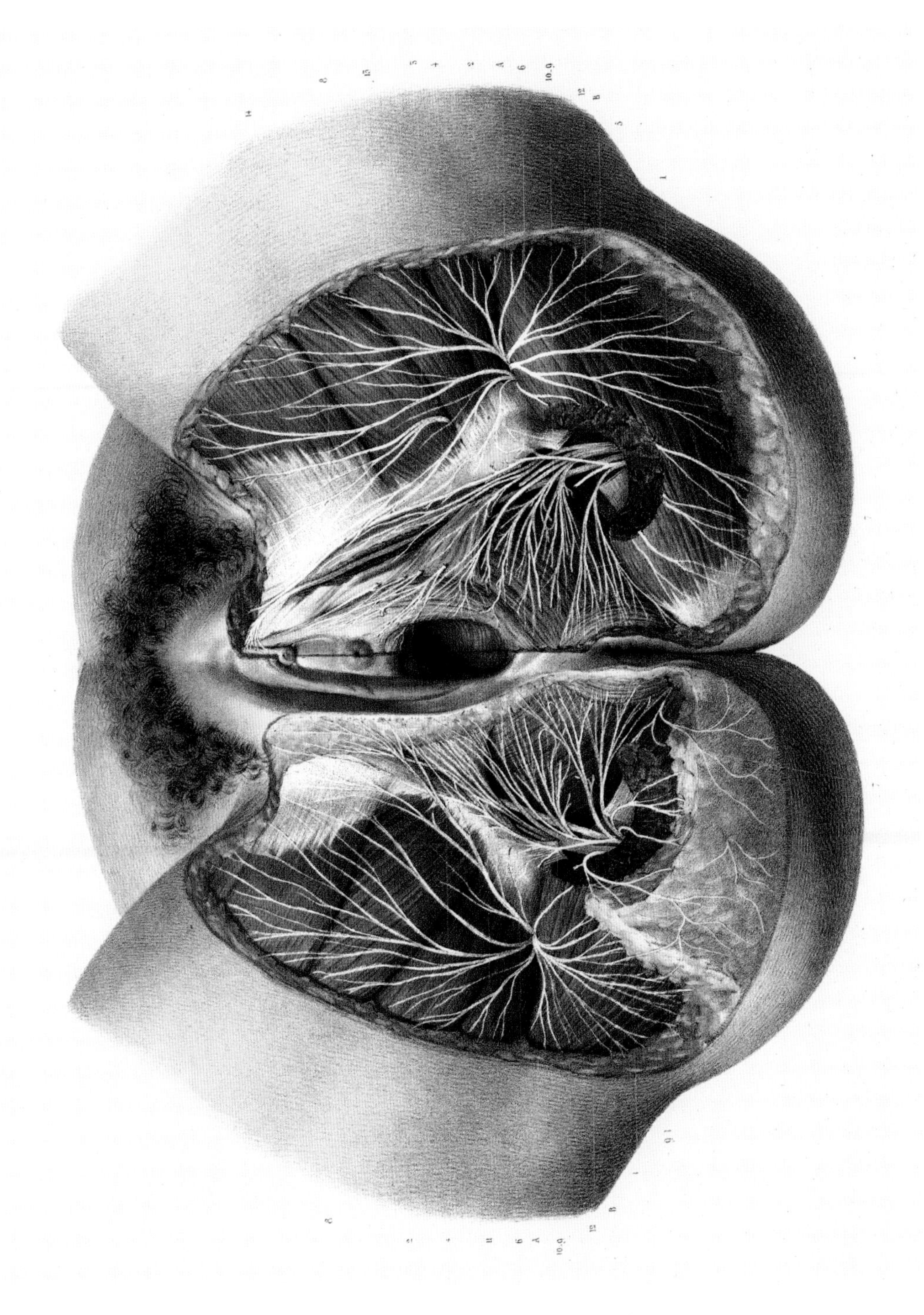

Perineal nerves / Nerfs du périnée / Nervios del periné

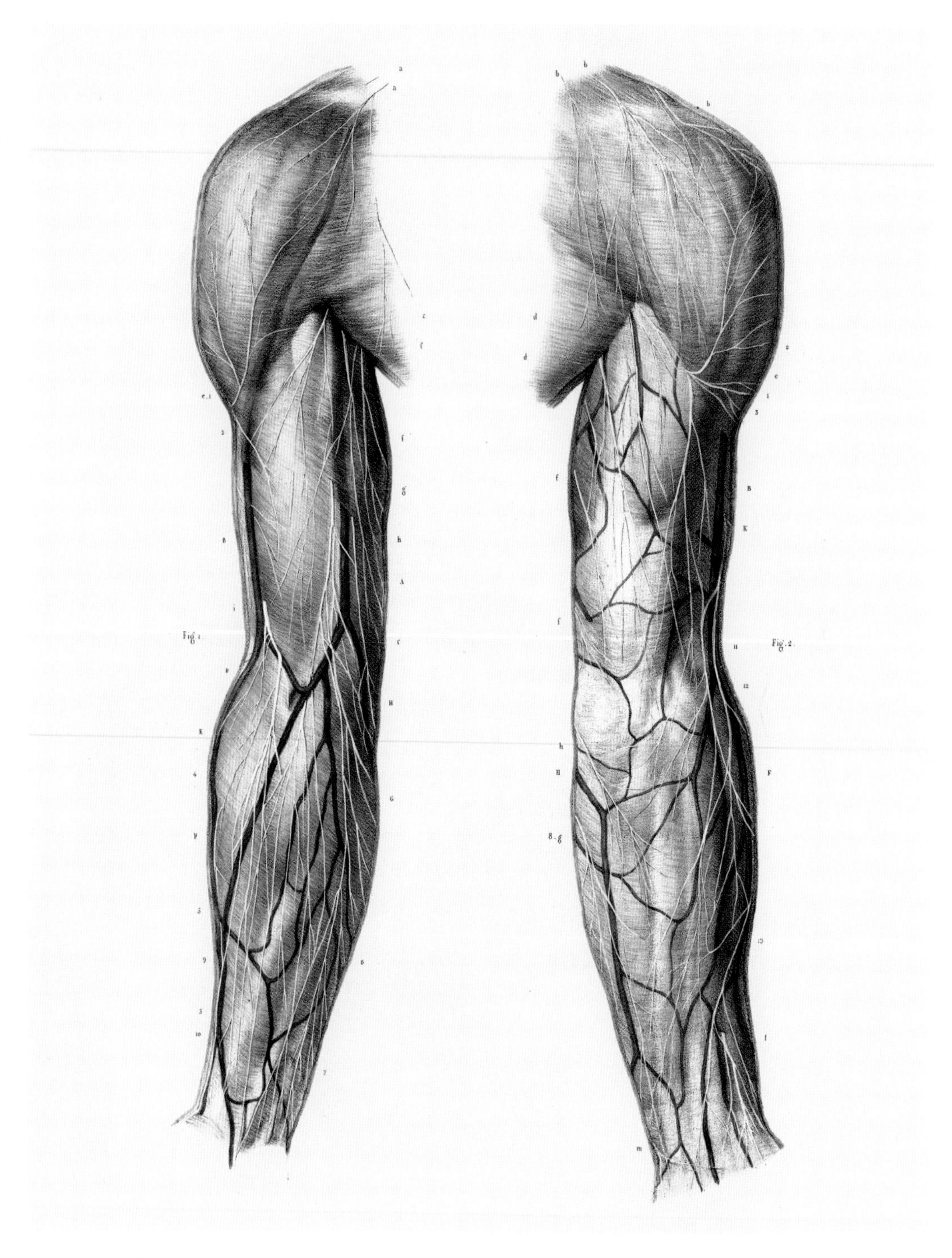

Cutaneous nerves of the upper limb / Nerfs cutanés du membre supérieur
Nervios cutáneos del miembro superior

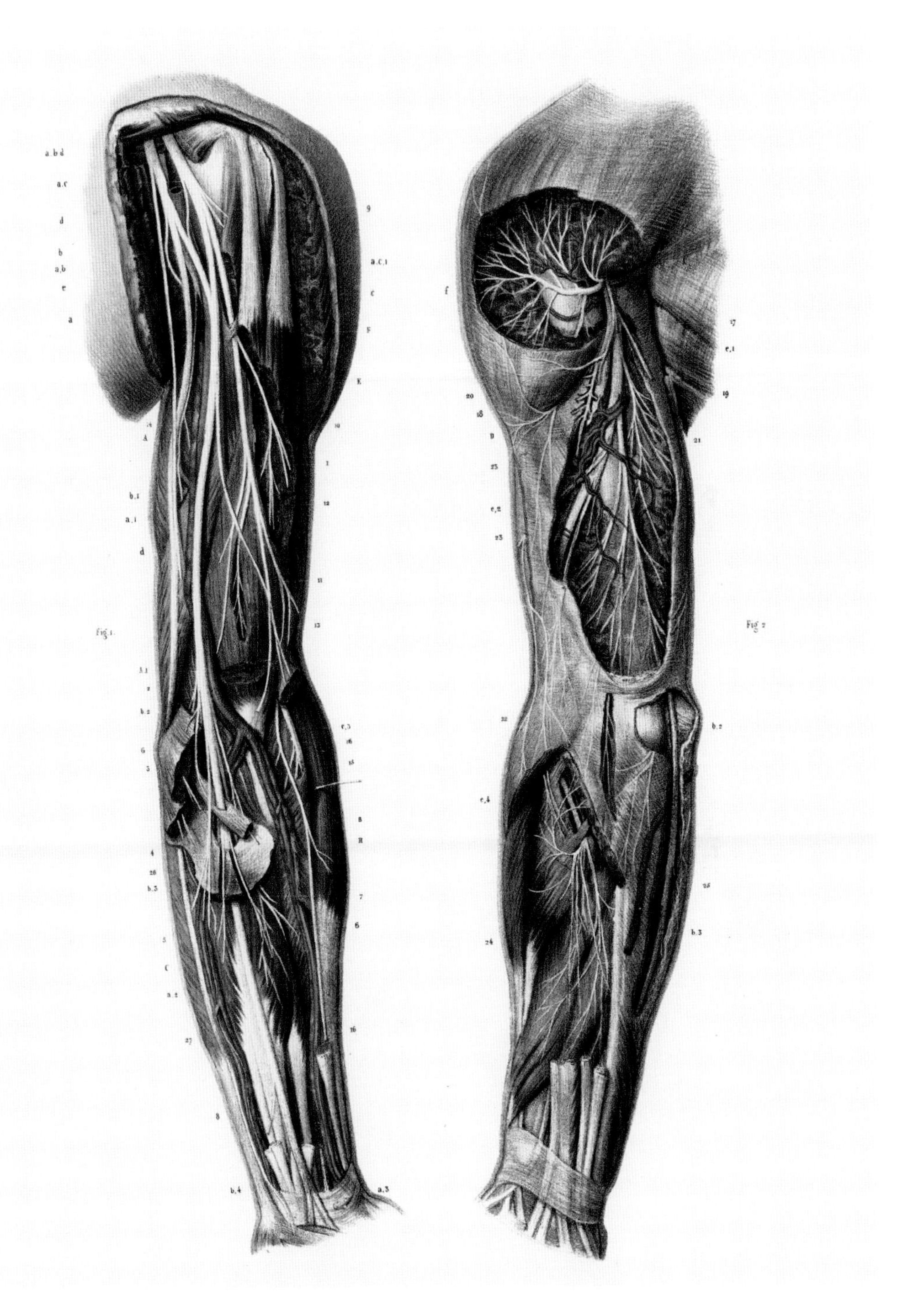

Nerves of the upper limb / Nerfs du membre supérieur
Nervios del miembro superior

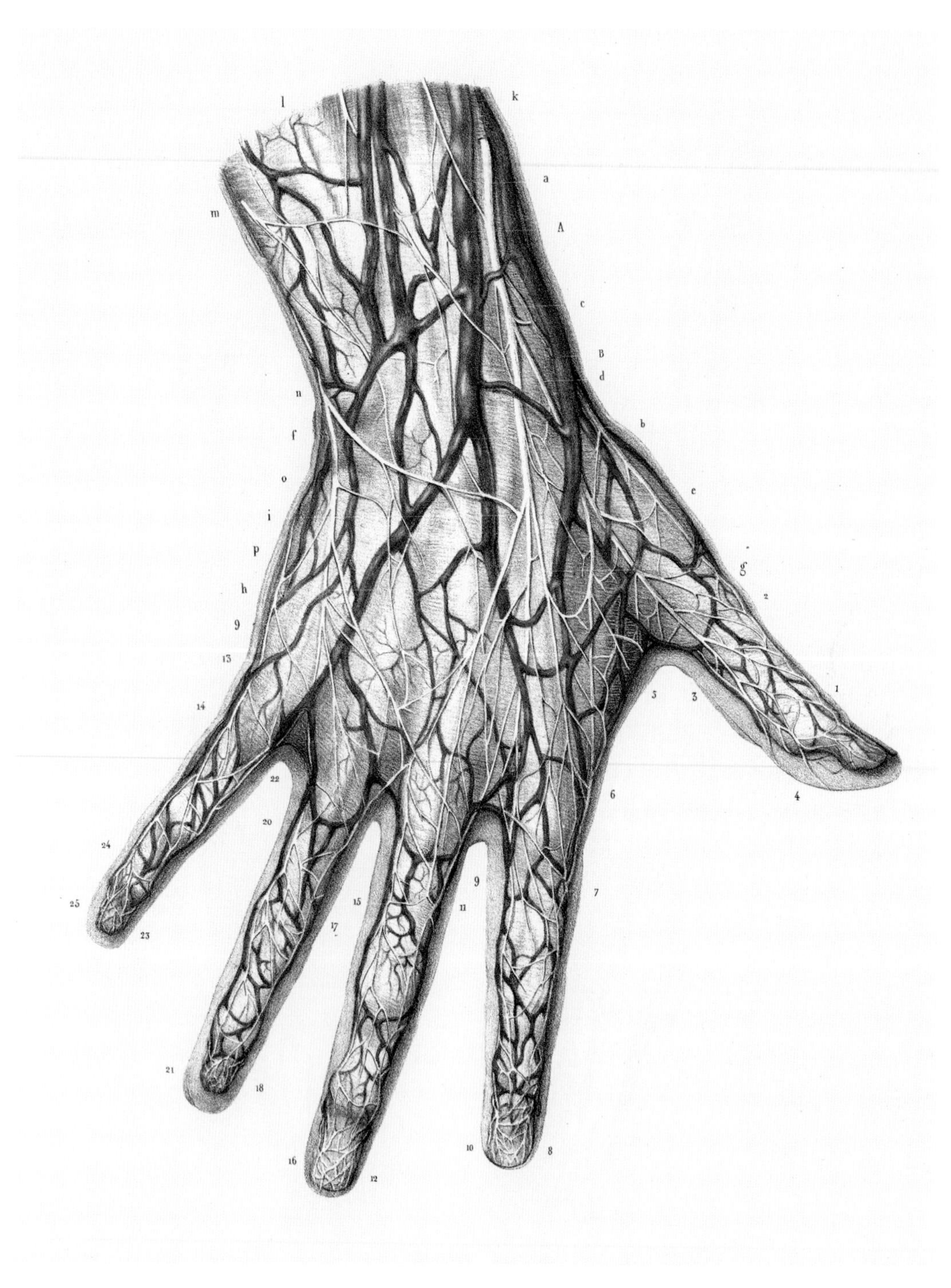

Nerves of the hand / Nerfs de la main / Nervios de la mano

Nerves of the hand / Nerfs de la main / Nervios de la mano

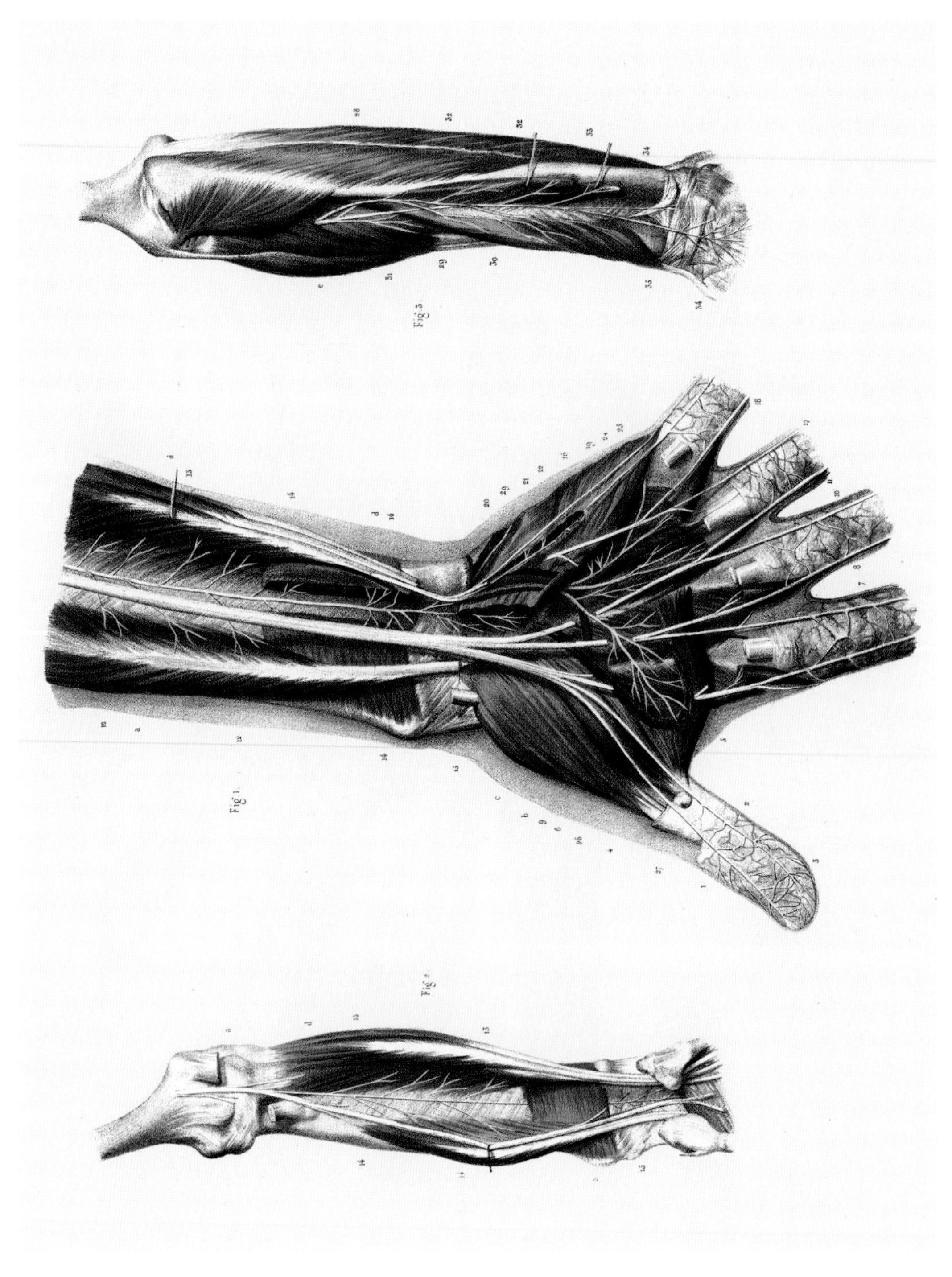

Nerves of the forearm and the hand / Nerfs de l’avant-bras et de la main
Nervios del antebrazo y de la mano

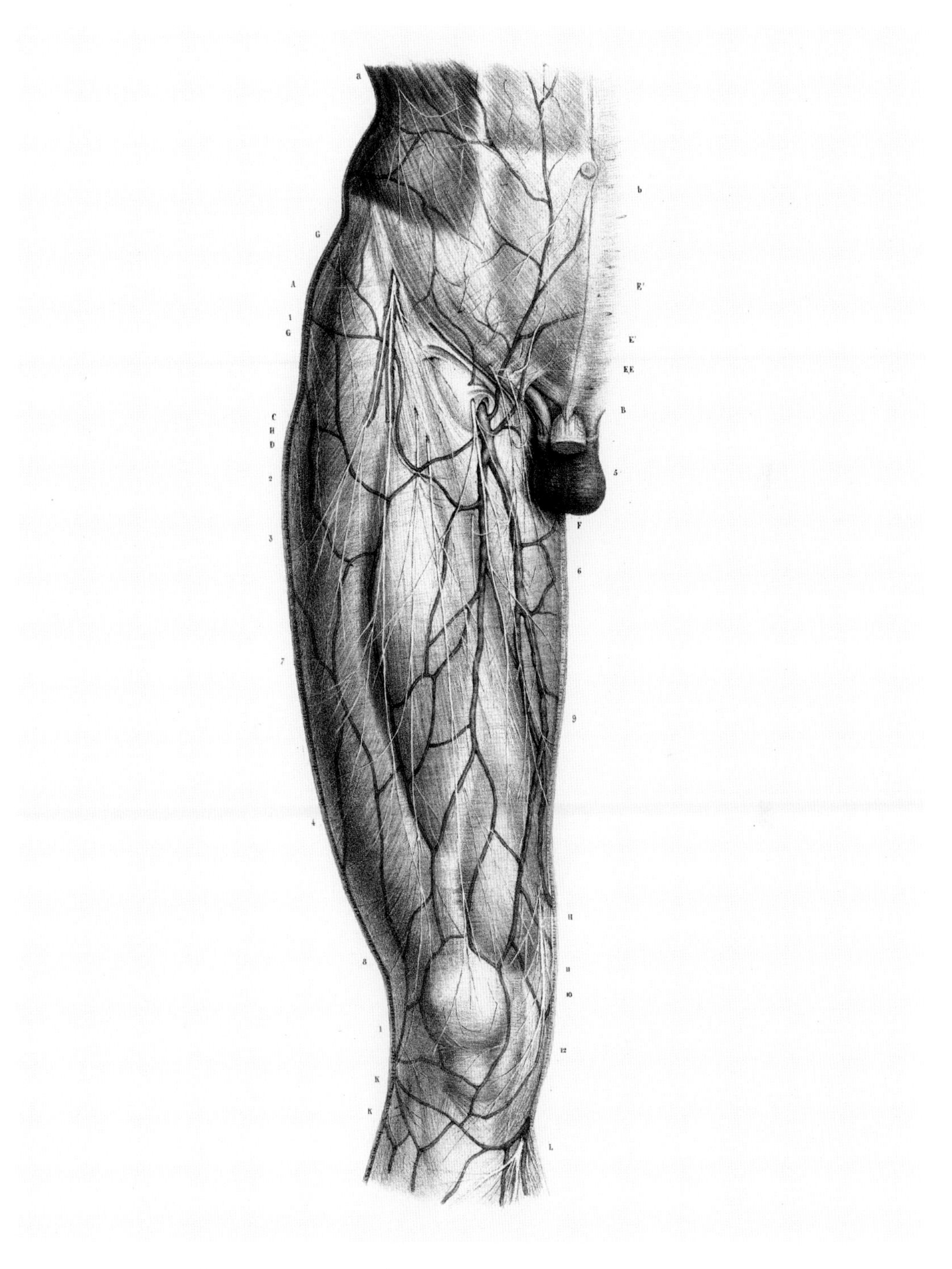

Cutaneous nerves of the thigh / Nerfs cutanés de la cuisse
Nervios cutáneos femorales

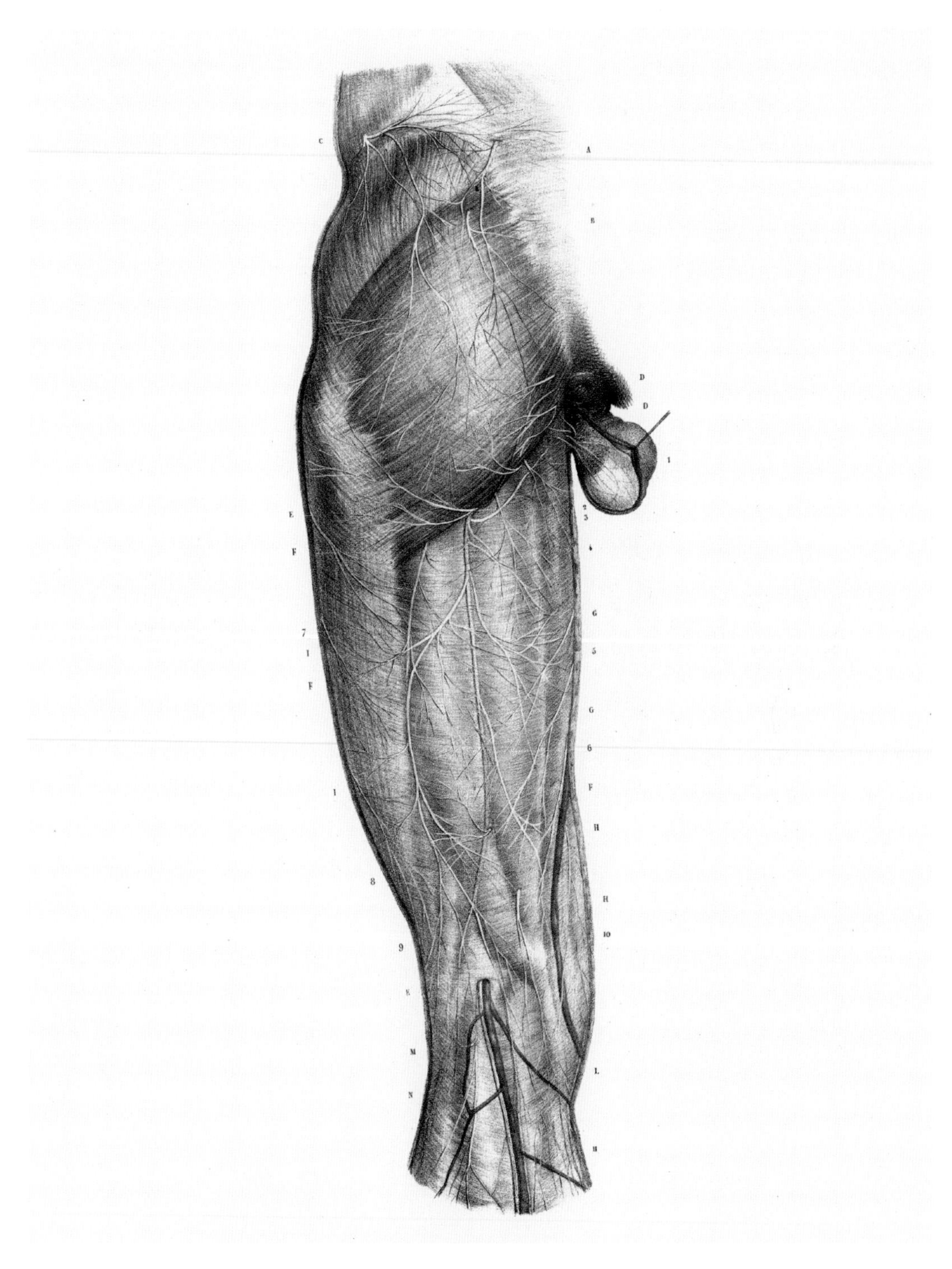

Cutaneous nerves of the thigh / Nerfs cutanés de la cuisse
Nervios cutáneos femorales

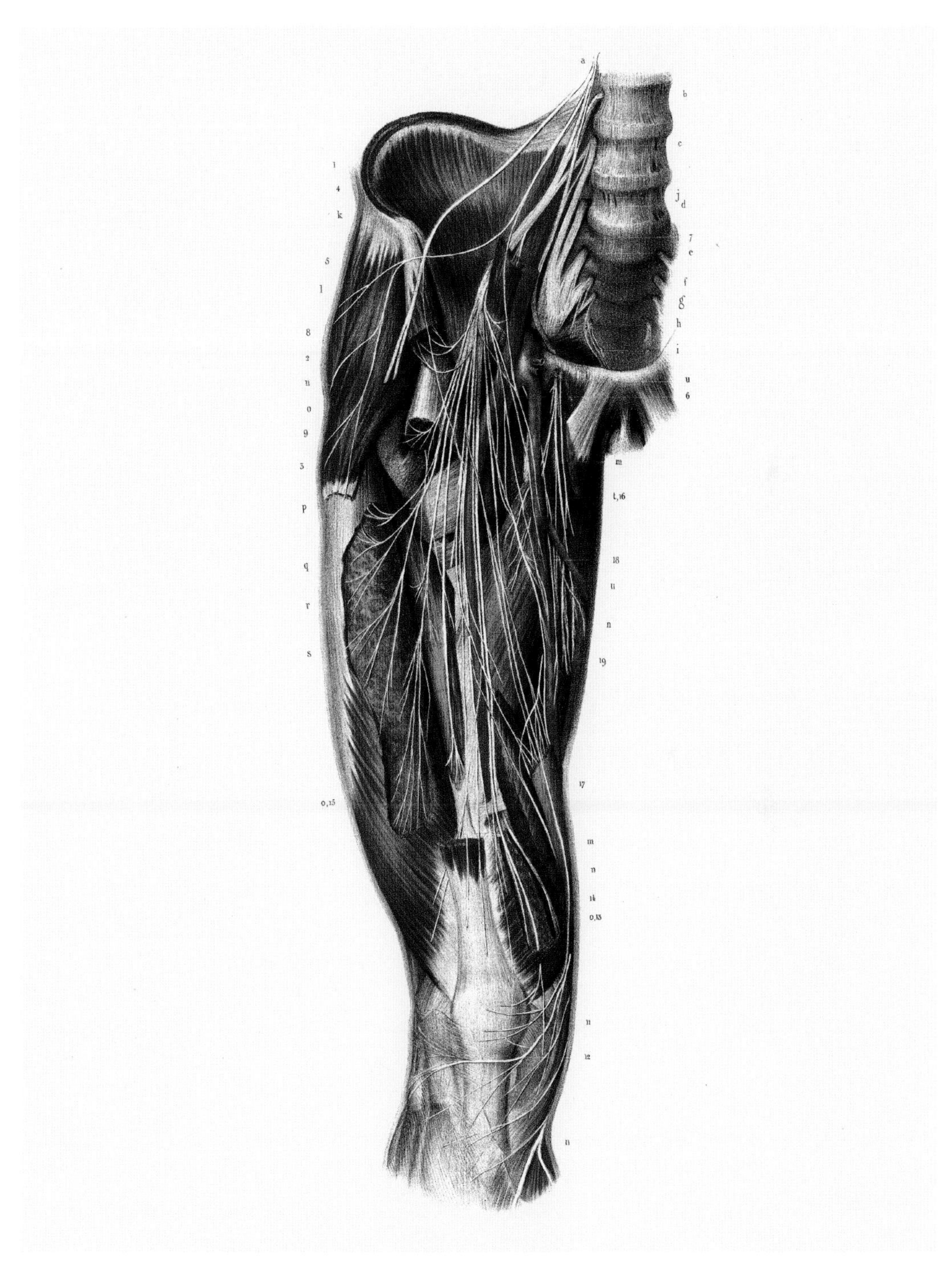

Nerves of the thigh / Nerfs de la cuisse
Nervios del muslo

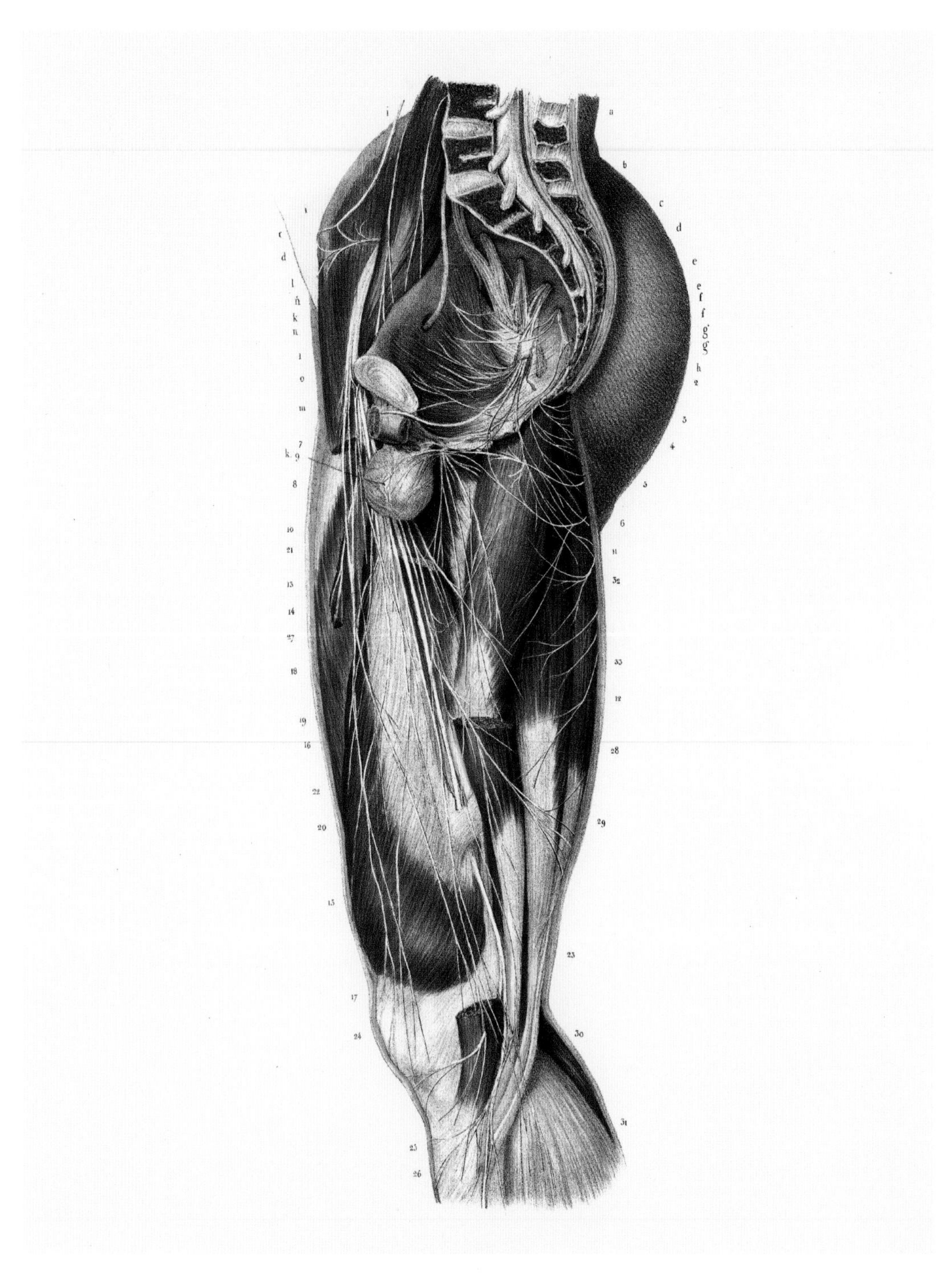

Nerves of the thigh / Nerfs de la cuisse / Nervios del muslo

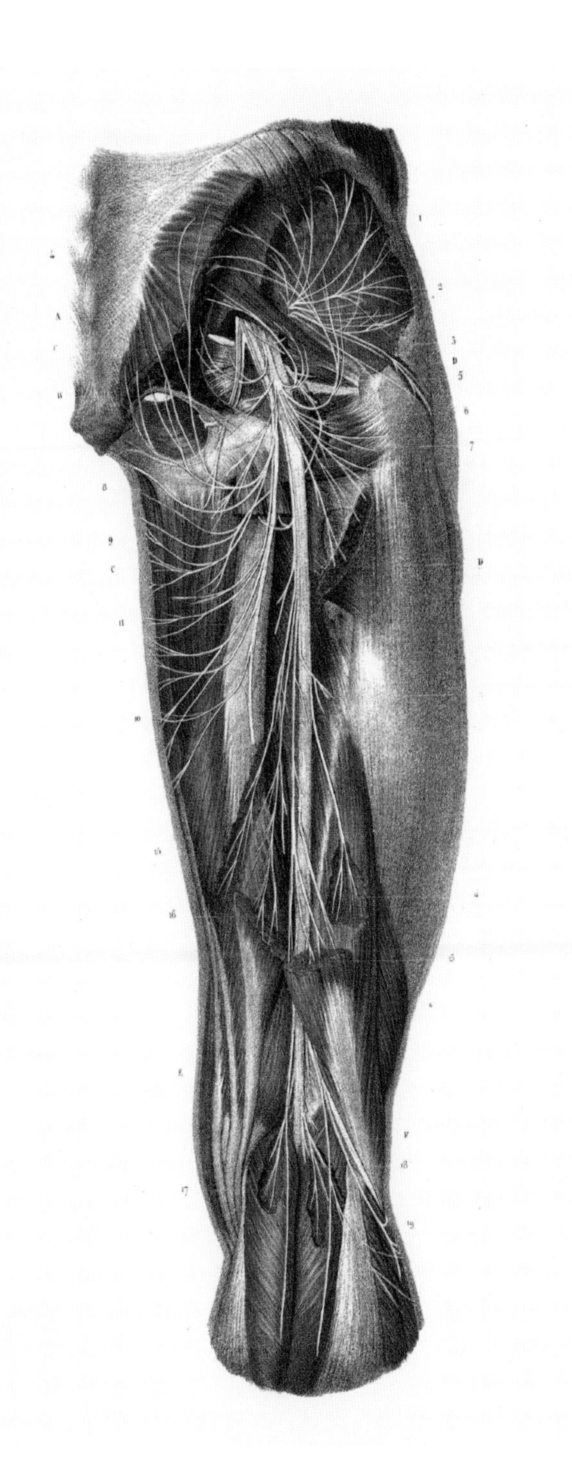

Nerves of the thigh / Nerfs de la cuisse / Nervios del muslo

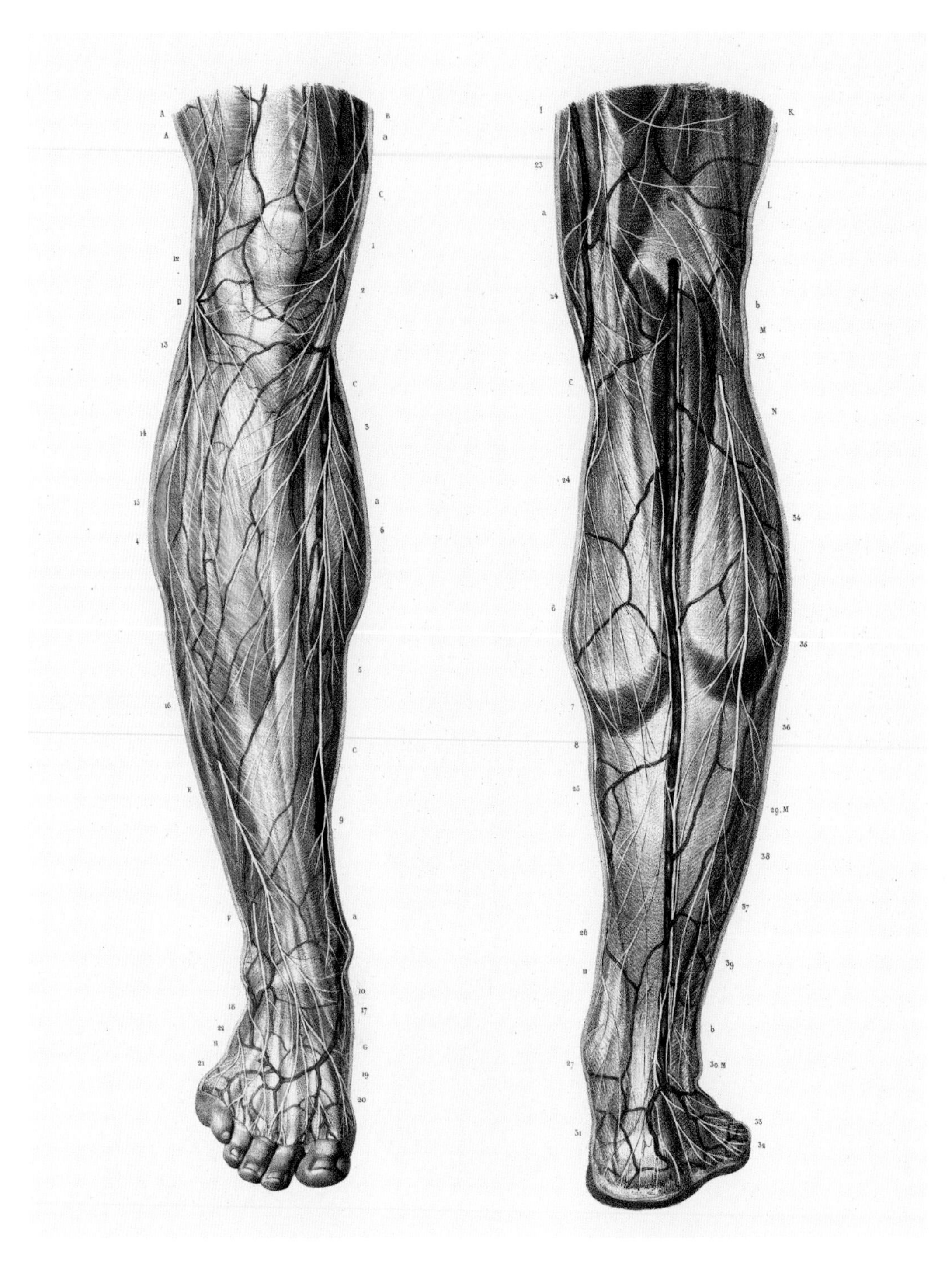

Cutaneous nerves of the leg and the foot / Nerfs cutanés de la jambe et du pied
Nervios cutáneos de la pierna y del pie

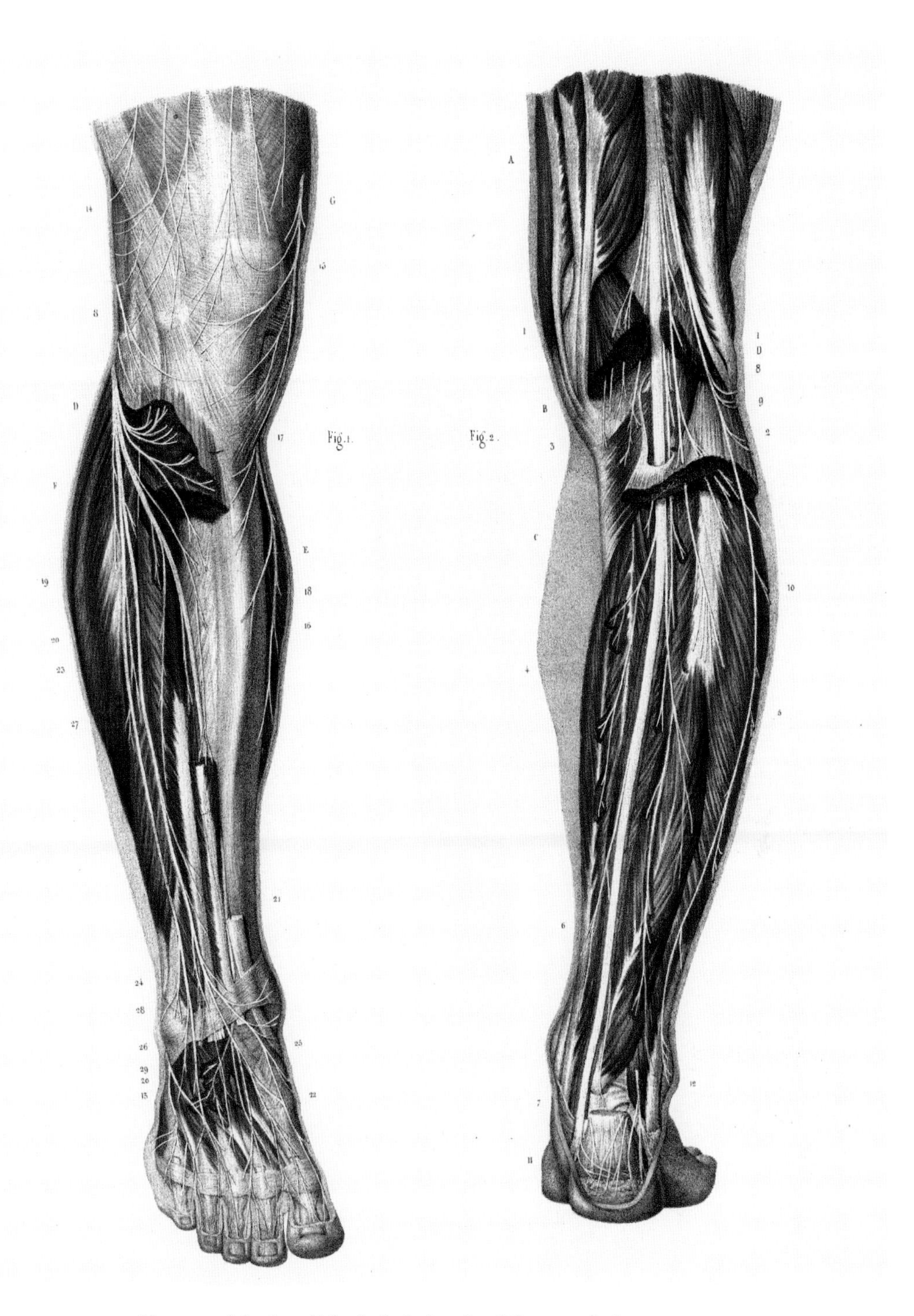

Nerves of the leg / Nerfs de la jambe / Nervios de la pierna

NERVI CRURIS ET PEDIS. NERVI ARTICULARES ET MUSCULARES PROFUNDI

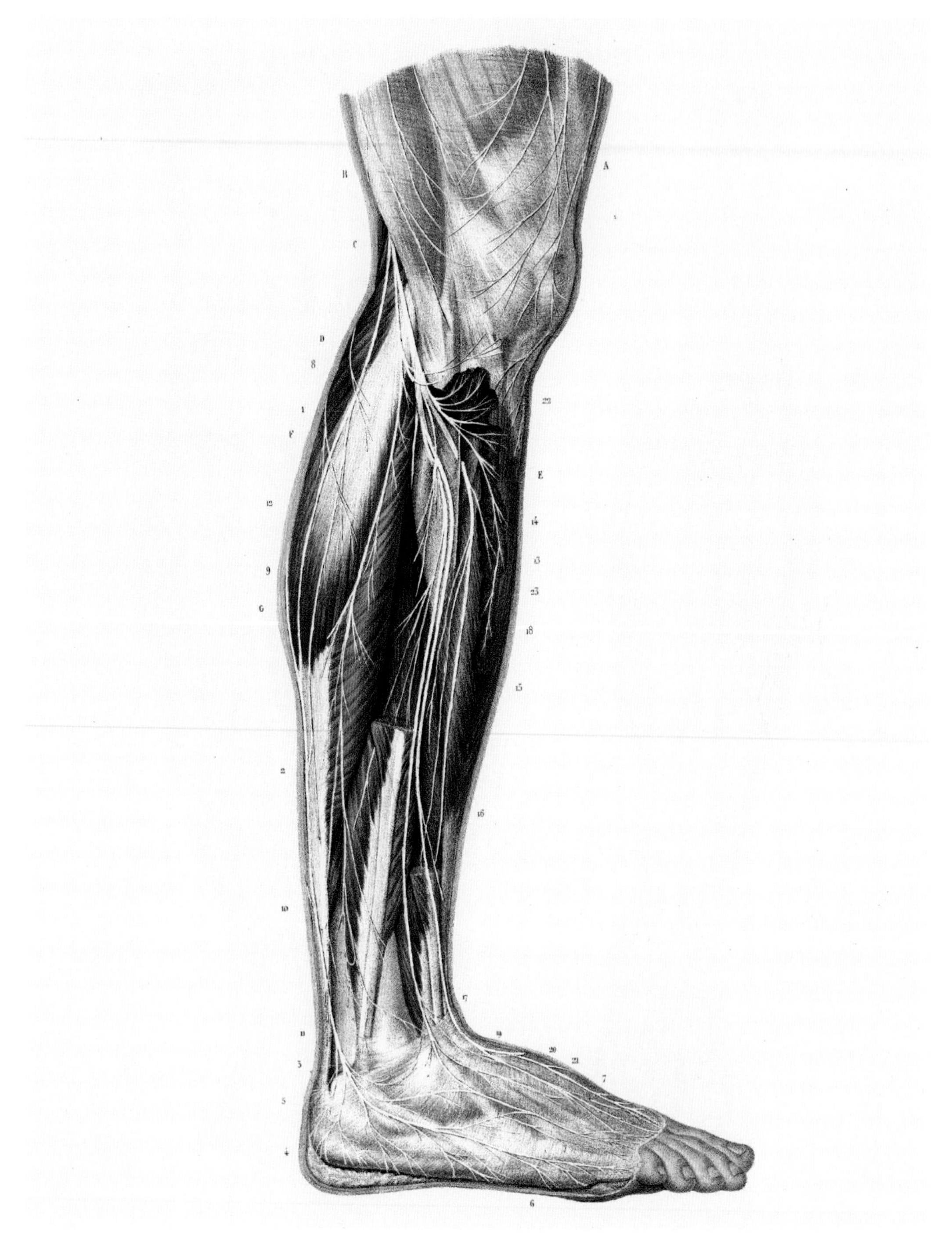

Nerves of the leg / Nerfs de la jambe / Nervios de la pierna

NERVI CRURIS ET PEDIS. NERVI ARTICULARES ET MUSCULARES PROFUNDI

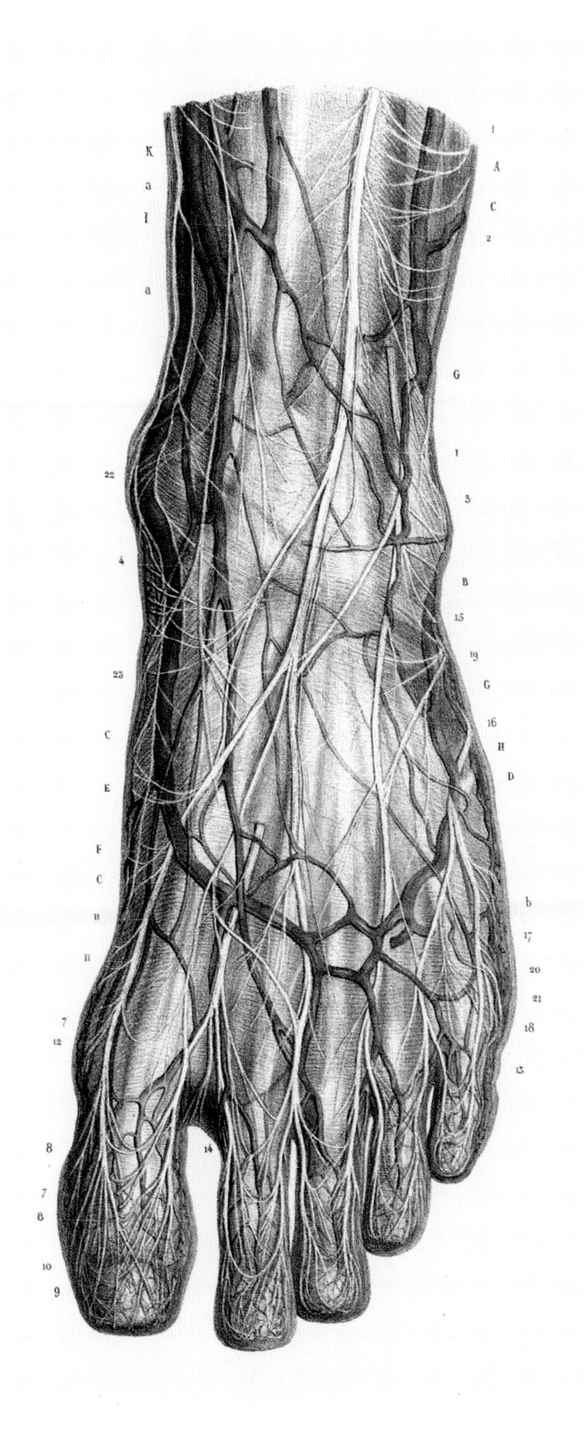

Cutaneous nerves of the foot / Nerfs cutanés du pied
Nervios cutáneos del pie

NERVI CRURIS ET PEDIS. NERVI ARTICULARES ET MUSCULARES PROFUNDI

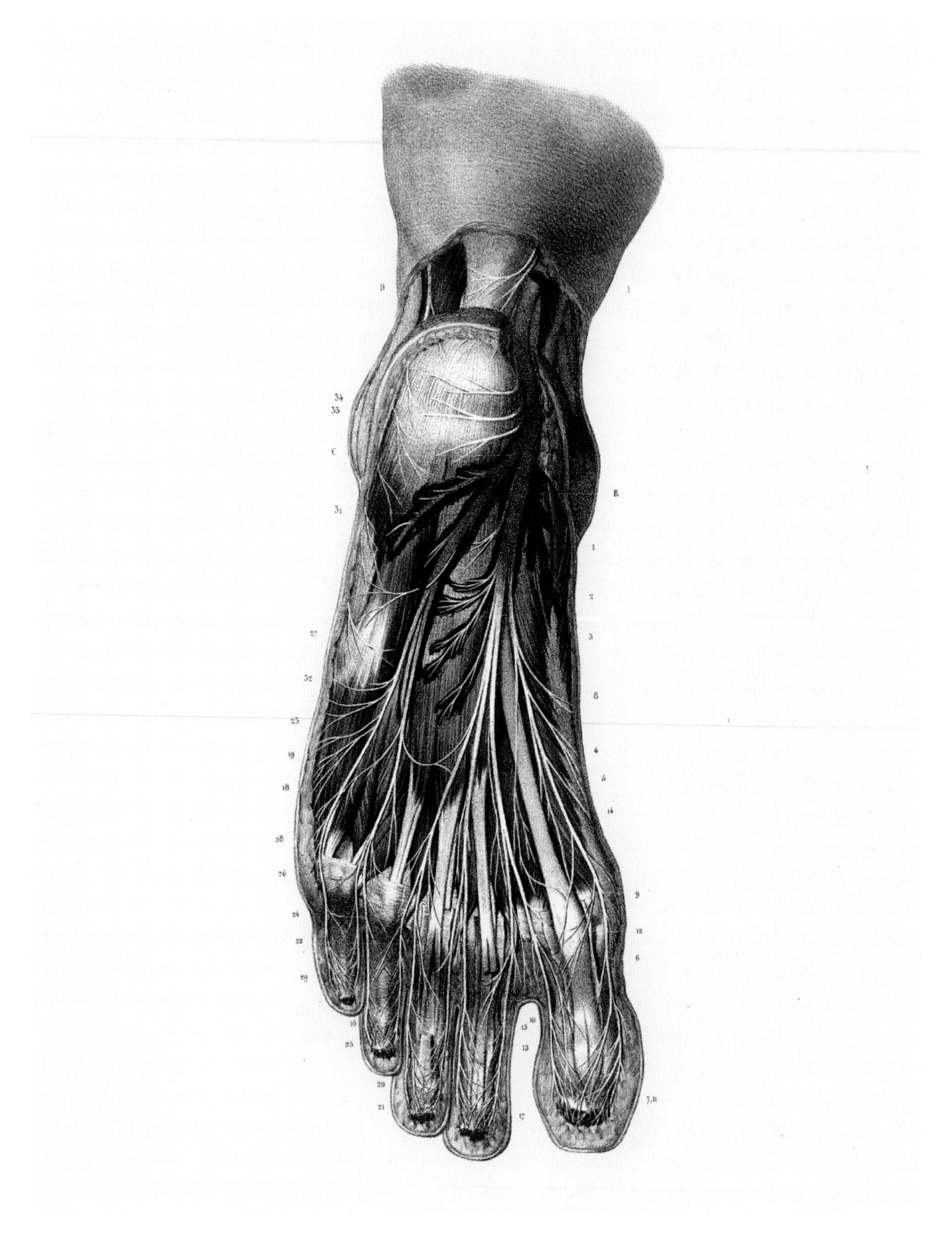

Nerves of the foot / Nerfs du pied / Nervios del pie

NERVI CRURIS ET PEDIS. NERVI ARTICULARES ET MUSCULARES PROFUNDI

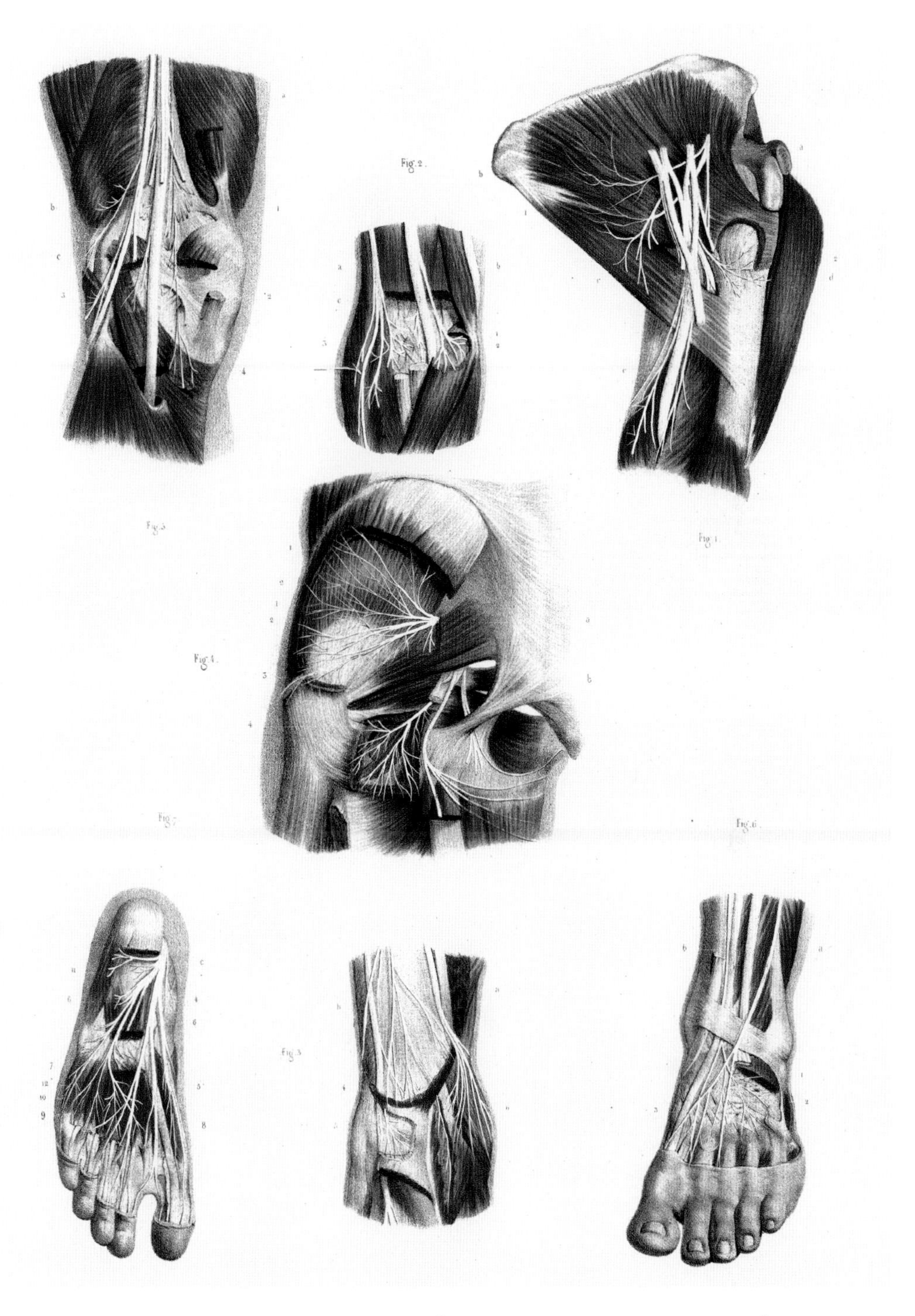

Articular and deep muscular nerves / Nerfs articulaires et musculaires profonds
Nervios articulares y musculares profundos

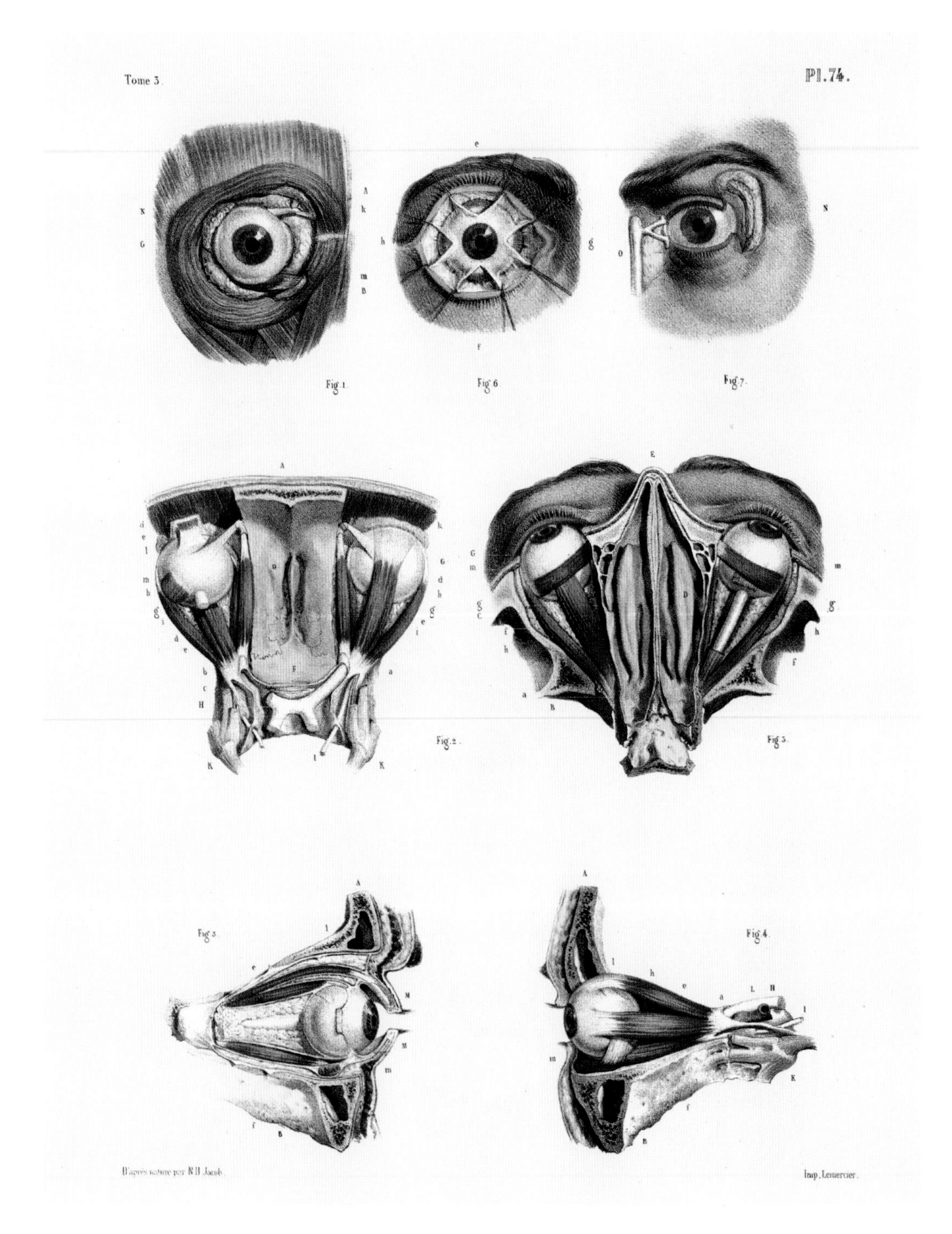

Organ of vision and orbital region: Muscles
Organe de la vision et région orbitaire : Muscles
Órgano de la vista y región orbitaria: músculos

ORGANUM VISUS: APPARATUS LACRIMALIS ET VASA BULBI OCULI

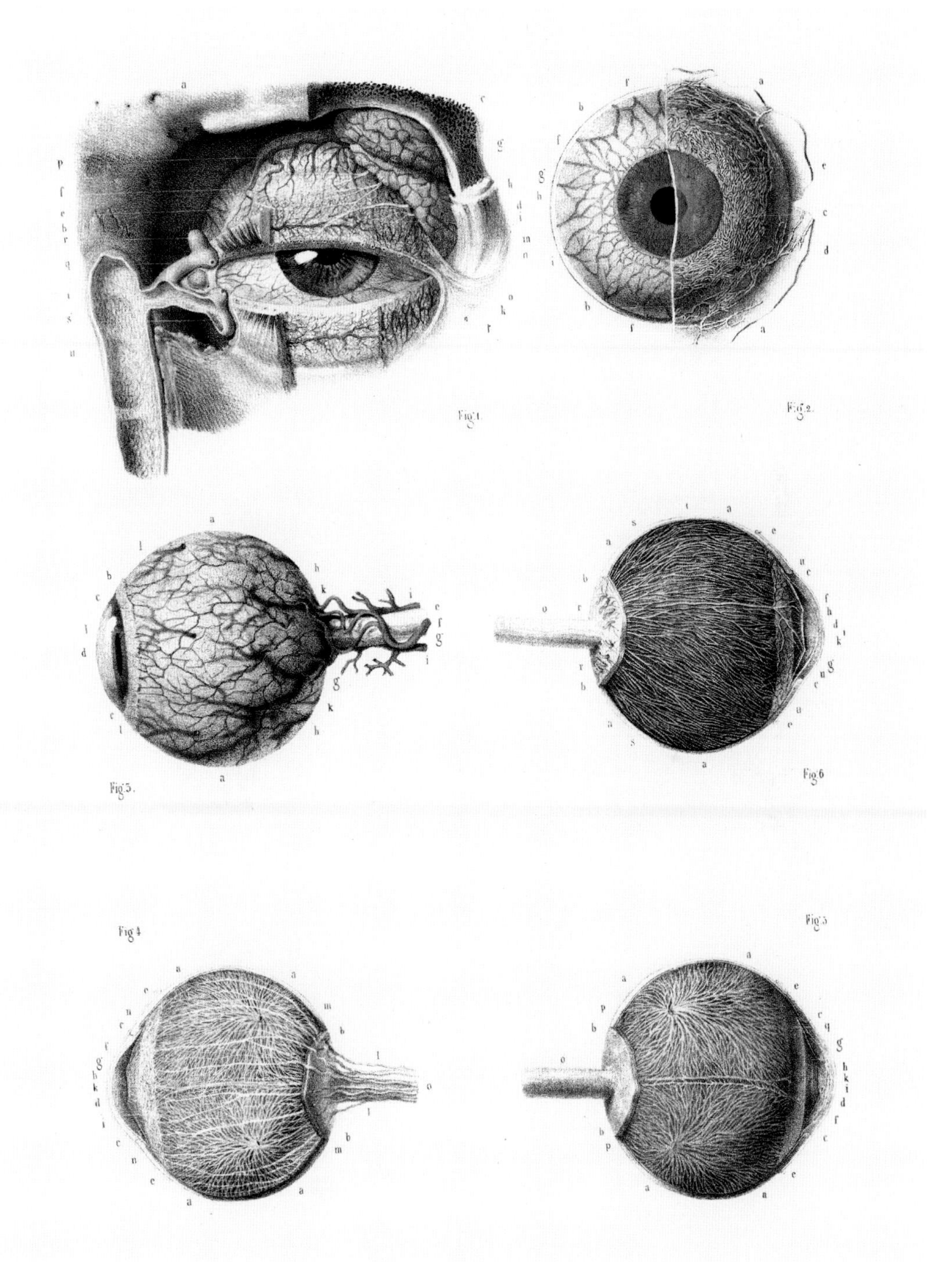

Organ of vision: Lacrimal apparatus and vessels of the ocular globe
Organe de la vision : Appareil lacrymal et vaisseaux du globe oculaire
Órgano de la vista: aparato lagrimal y vasos del globo ocular

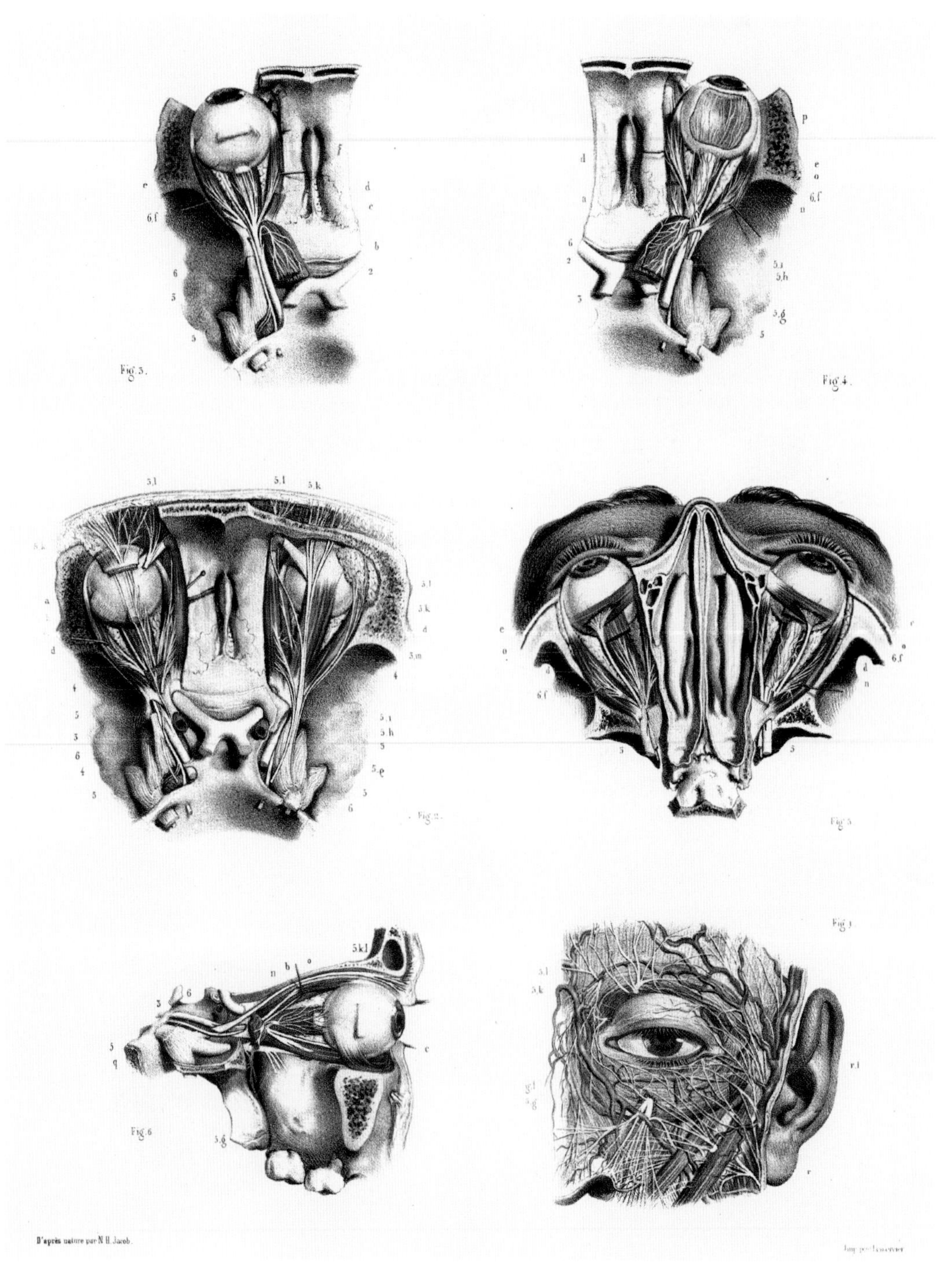

Organ of vision and orbital region: Nerves
Organe de la vision et région orbitaire : Nerfs
Órgano de la vista y región orbitaria: nervios

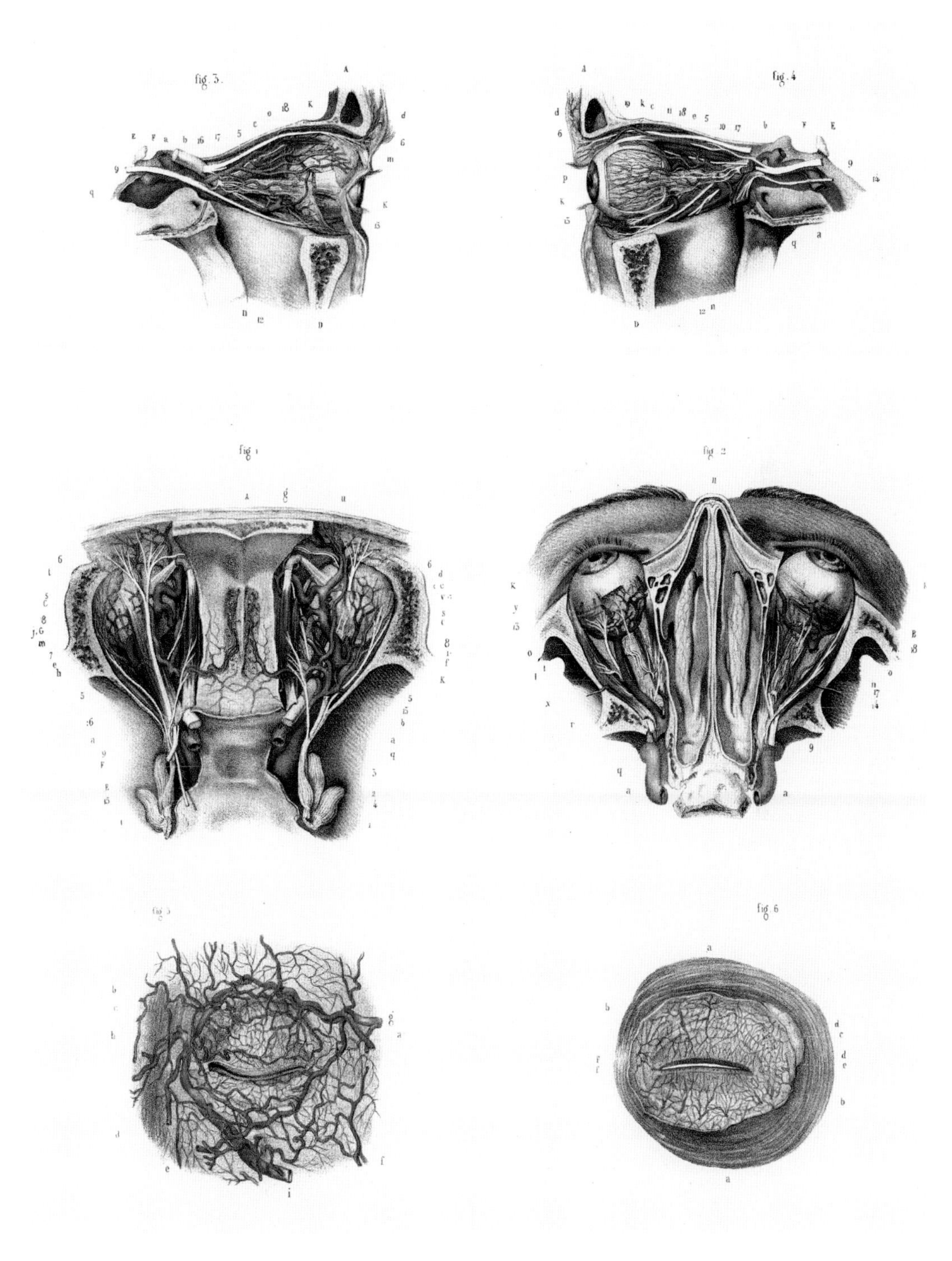

Organ of vision and orbital region: Arteries and veins
Organe de la vision et région orbitaire : Artères et veines
Órgano de la vista y región orbitaria: arterias y venas

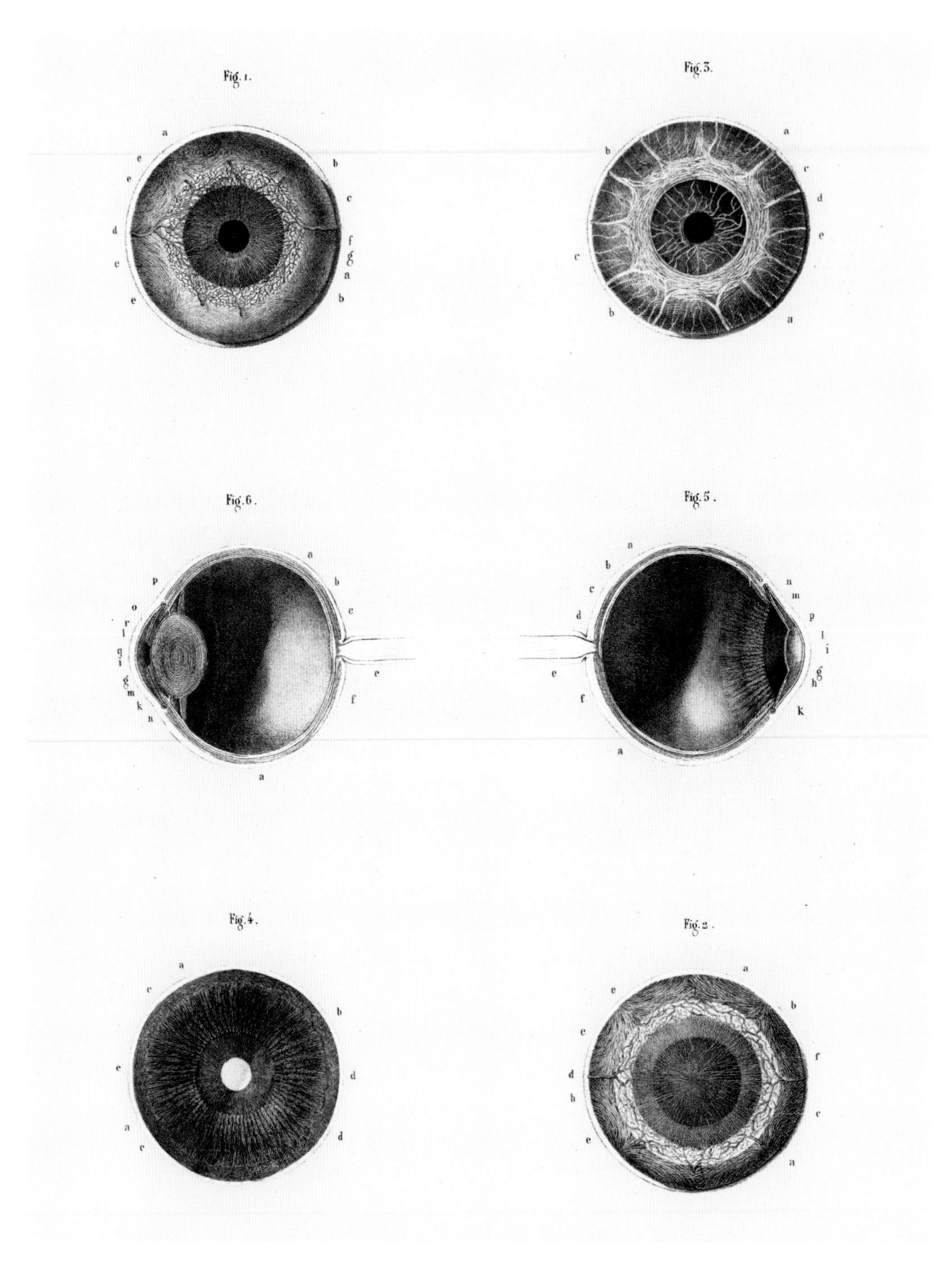

Organ of vision: Structure of the ocular globe
Organe de la vision : Structure du globe oculaire
Órgano de la vista: estructura del globo ocular

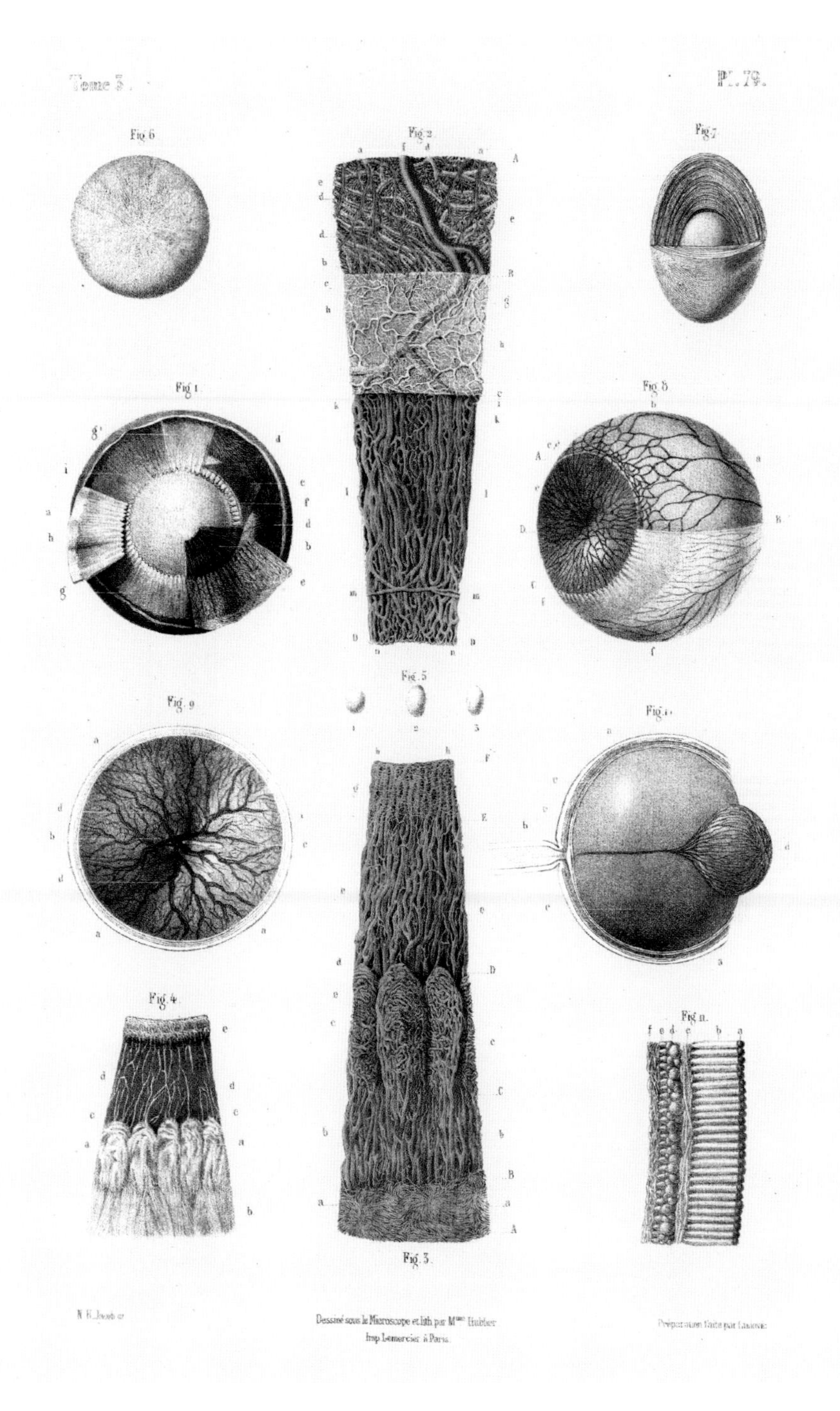

Organ of vision: Microscopic structure
Organe de la vision : Anatomie microscopique
Órgano de la vista: anatomía microscópica

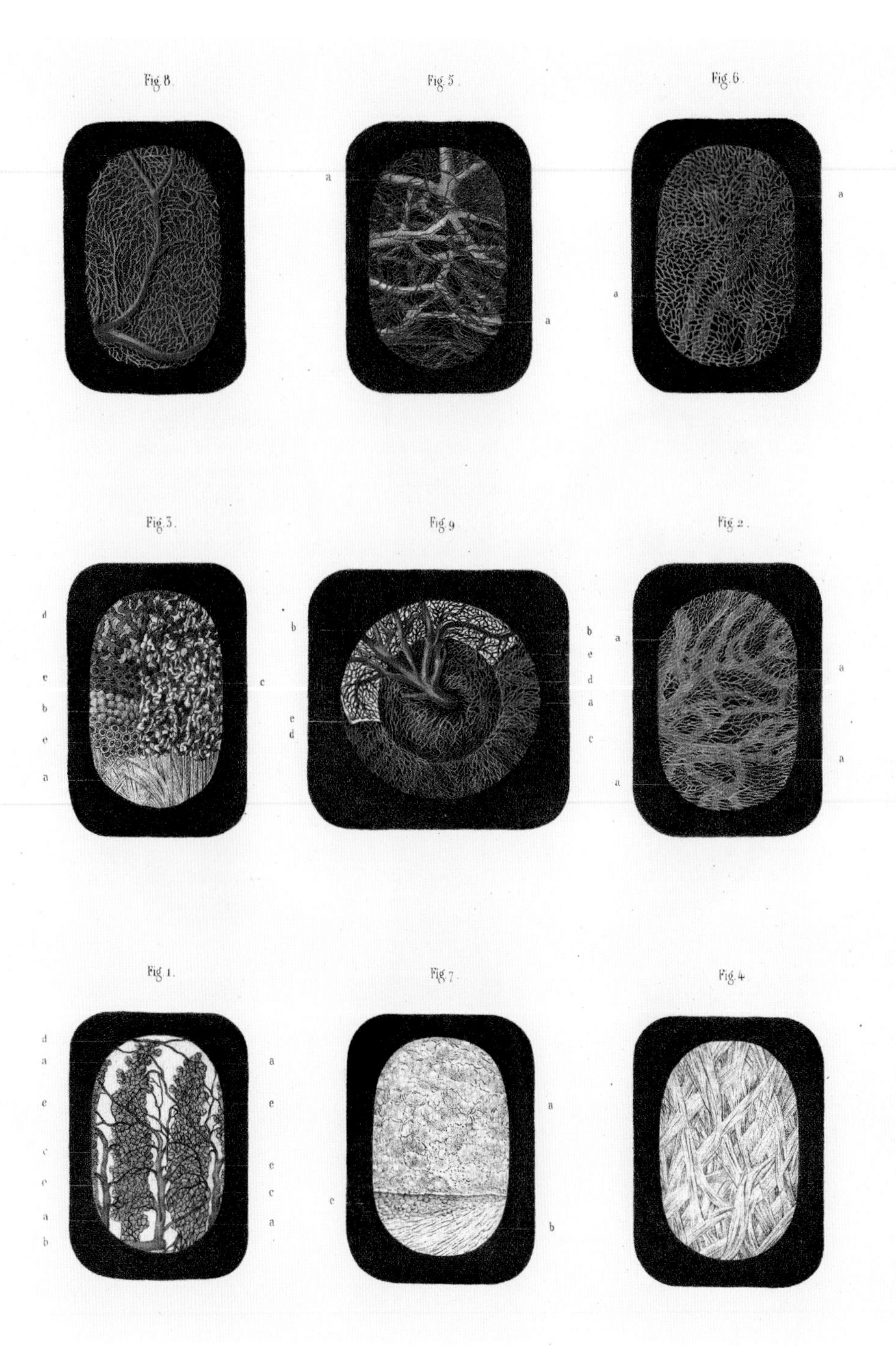

Organ of vision: Microscopic structure
Organe de la vision : Anatomie microscopique
Órgano de la vista: anatomía microscópica

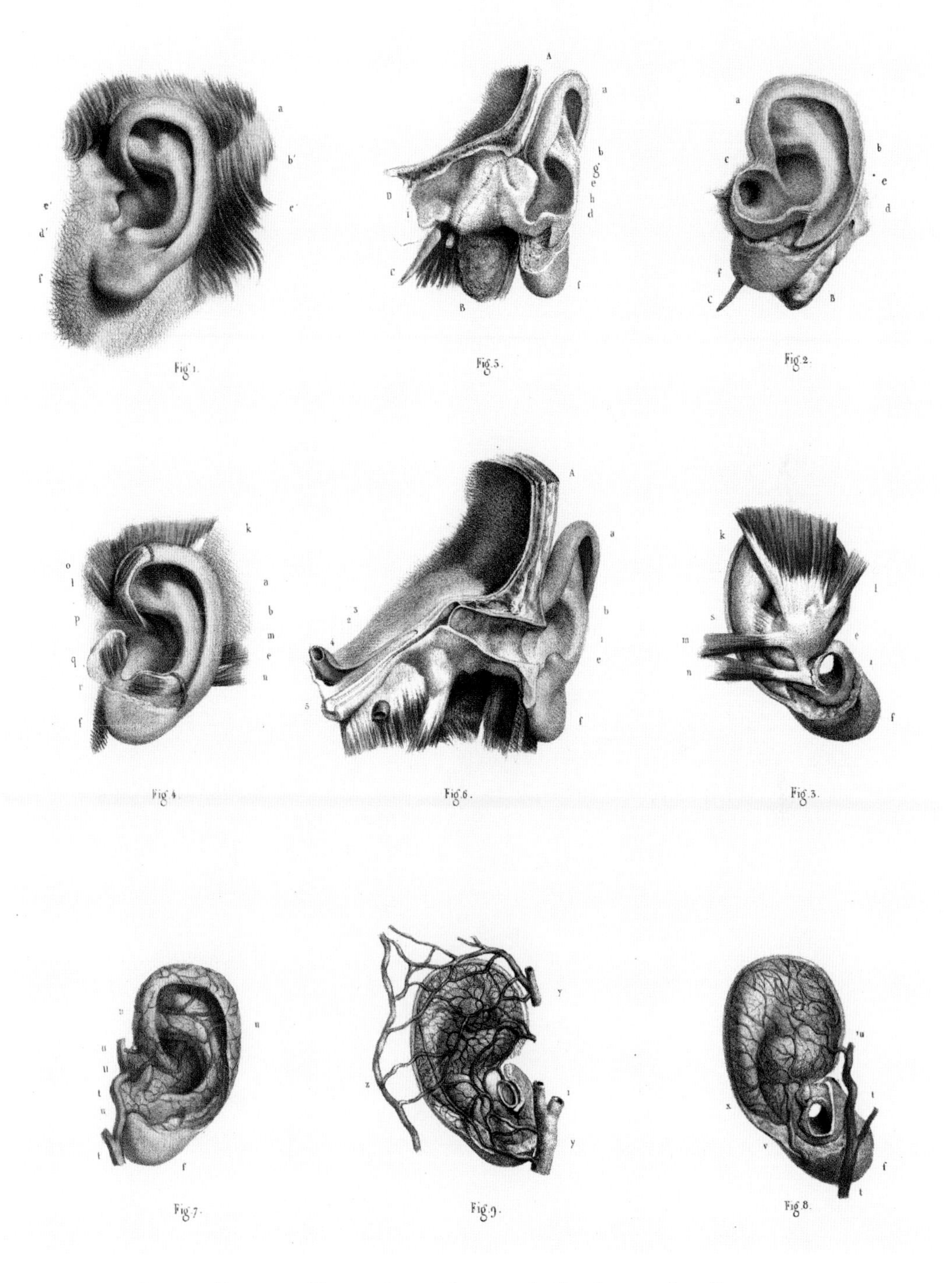

Organ of hearing: External ear / Organe de l'audition : Oreille externe
Órgano de la audición: oído externo

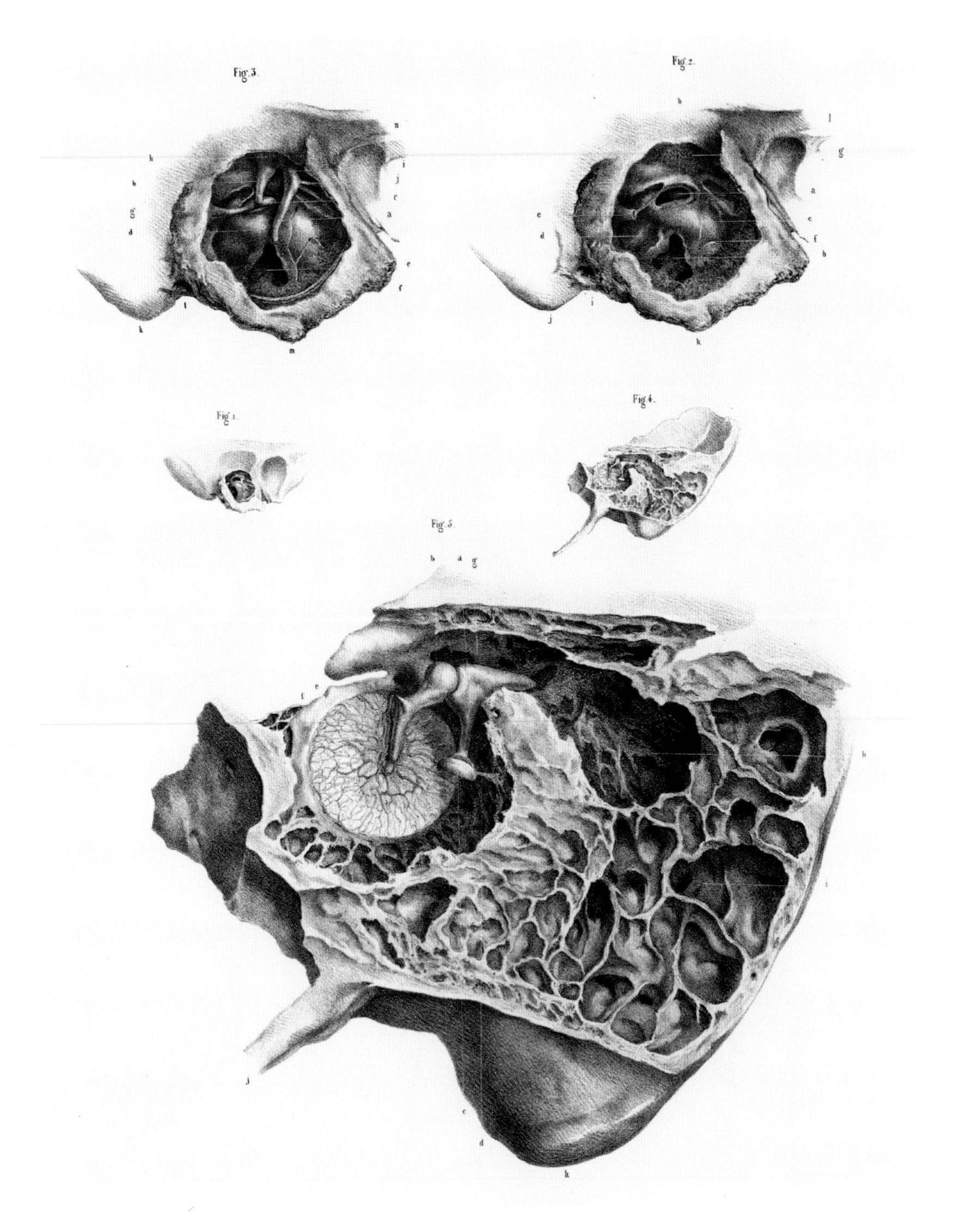

Organ of hearing: Middle ear / Organe de l'audition : Oreille moyenne
Órgano de la audición: oído medio

ORGANUM AUDITUS: AURIS MEDIA ET OSSICULA AUDITUS

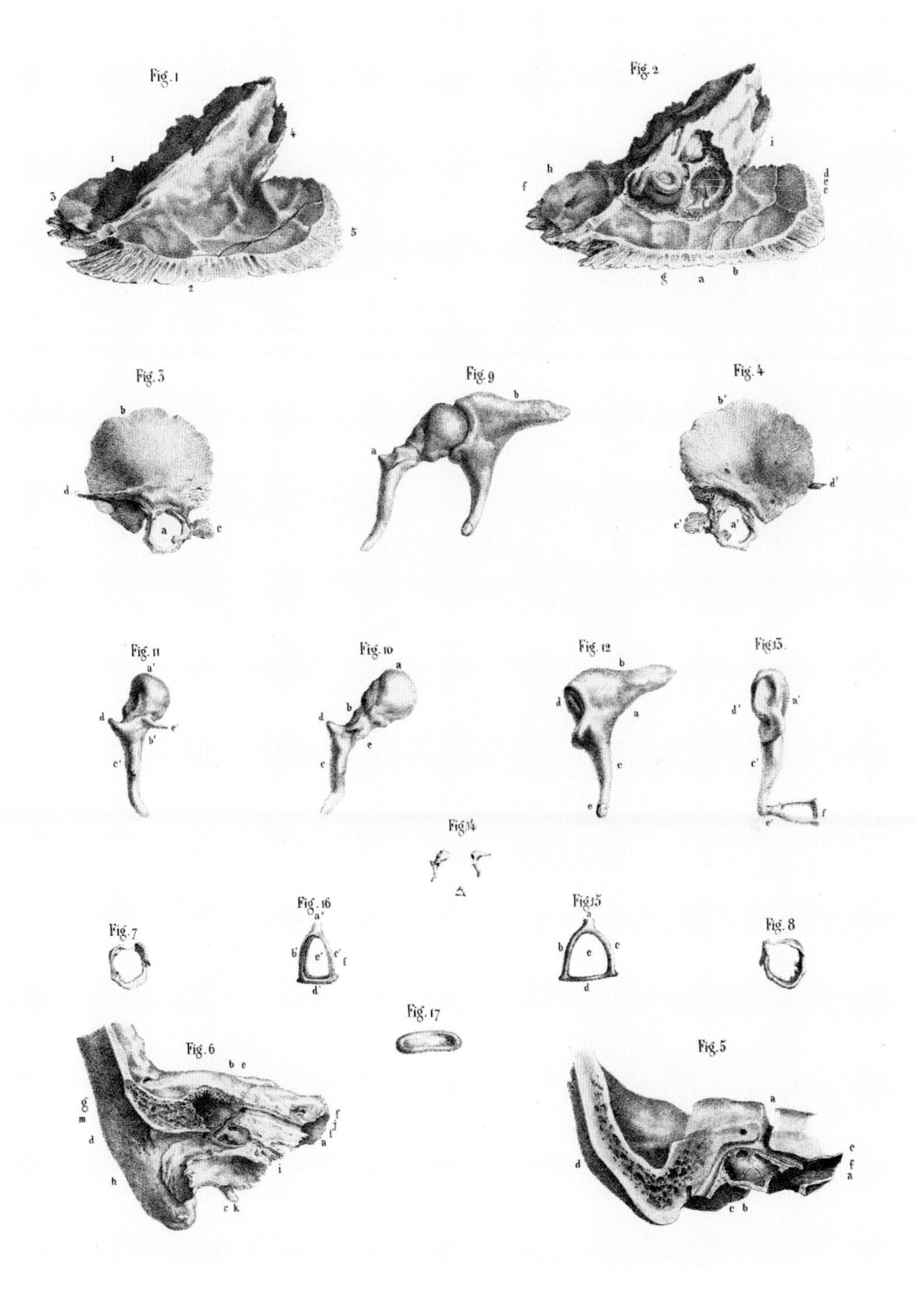

Organ of hearing: Middle ear and ossicles of the ear
Organe de l'audition : Oreille moyenne et osselets de l'ouïe
Órgano de la audición: oído medio y huesecillos del oído

ORGANUM AUDITUS: AURIS INTERNA. ORGANUM VESTIBULOCOCHLEARE

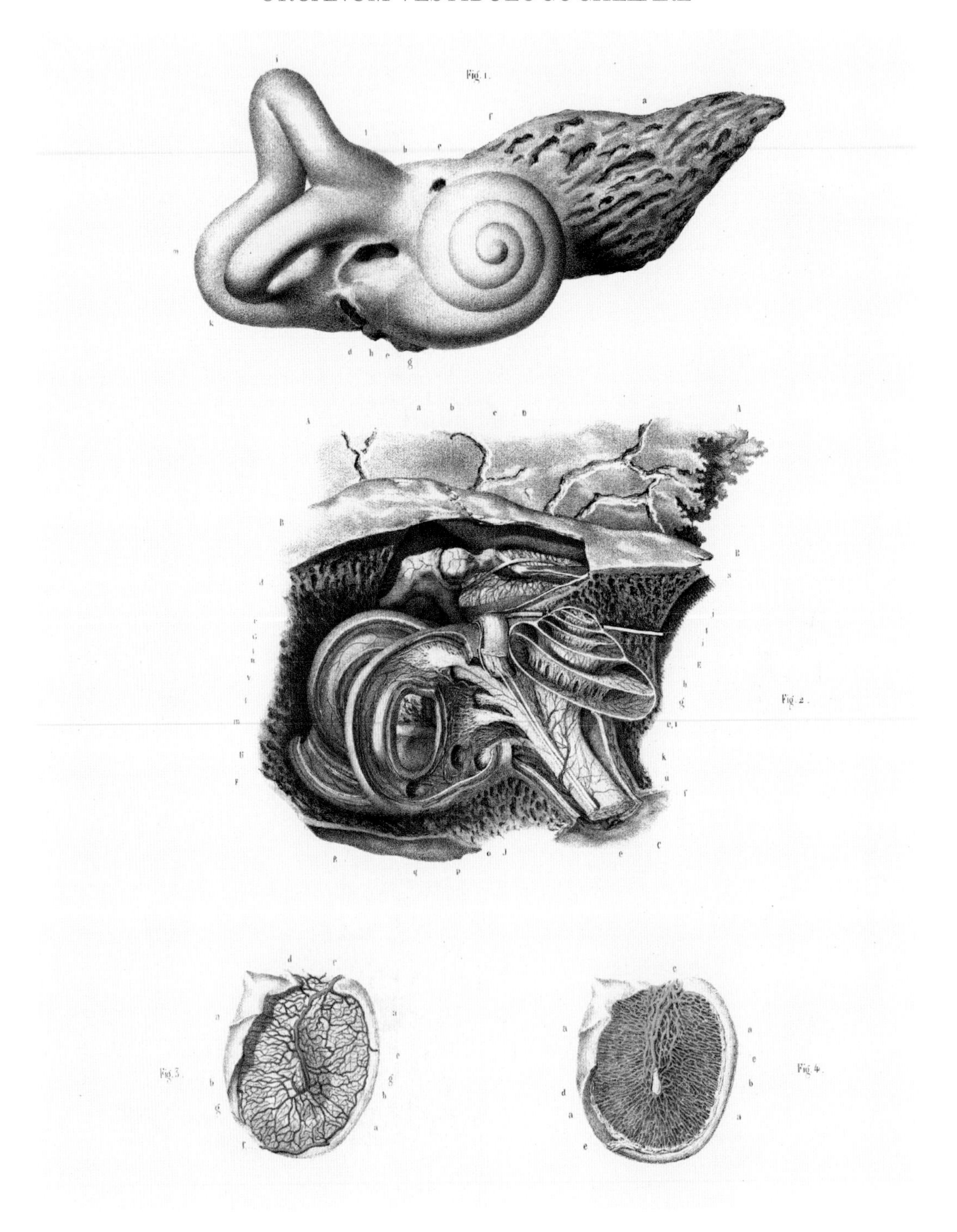

Organ of hearing: Inner ear. Vestibulocochlear organ
Organe de l'audition : Oreille interne. Organe vestibulo-cochléaire
Órgano de la audición: oído interno. Órgano vestibulococlear

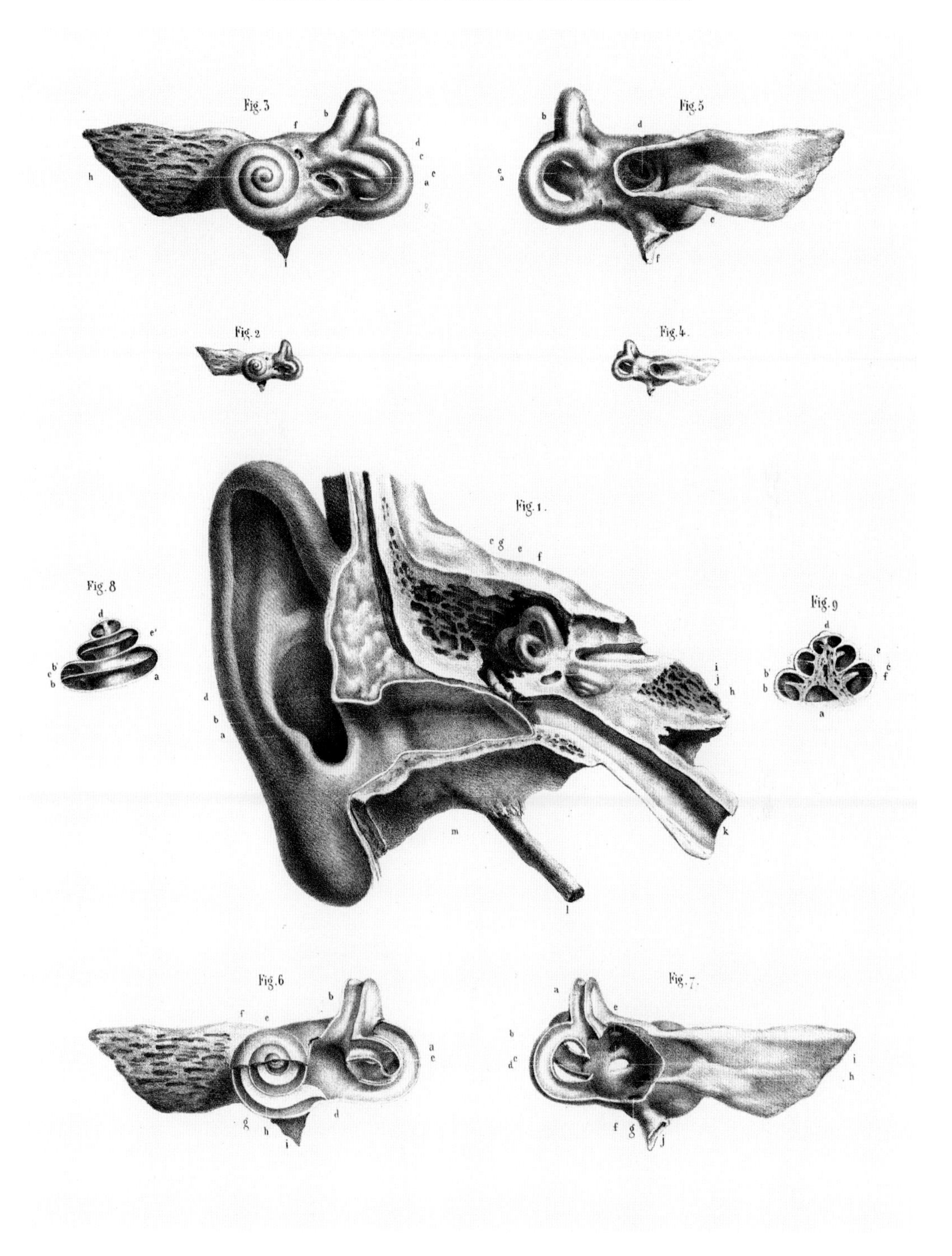

Organ of hearing: Inner ear. Vestibulocochlear organ
Organe de l'audition : Oreille interne. Organe vestibulo-cochléaire
Órgano de la audición: oído interno. Órgano vestibulococlear

ORGANUM OLFACTUS: NASUS EXTERNUS ET CAVITAS NASI

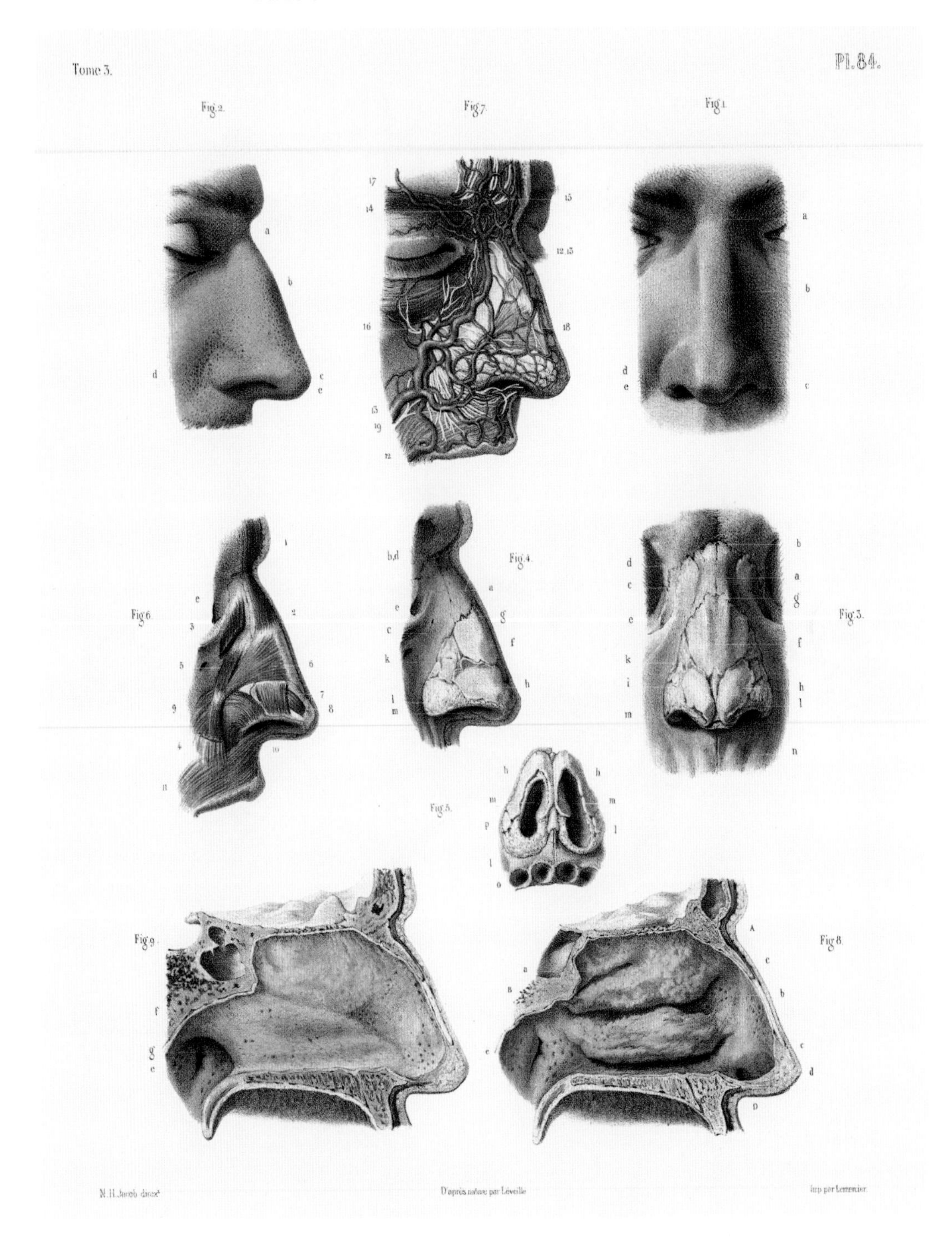

Organ of smell: Nose and nasal cavity
Organe de l'olfaction : Nez et cavité nasale
Órgano del olfato: nariz y cavidad nasal

ORGANUM OLFACTUS: CAVITAS NASI ET VASA

Tome 3. Pl. 85.

Fig. 2. Fig. 1. Fig. 3.

Fig. 5. Fig. 4.

Fig. 7. Fig. 6.

Organ of smell: Nasal cavity and vessels
Organe de l'olfaction : Cavité nasale et vaisseaux
Órgano del olfato: cavidad nasal y vasos

ORGANUM OLFACTUS: NERVI ET STRUCTURA

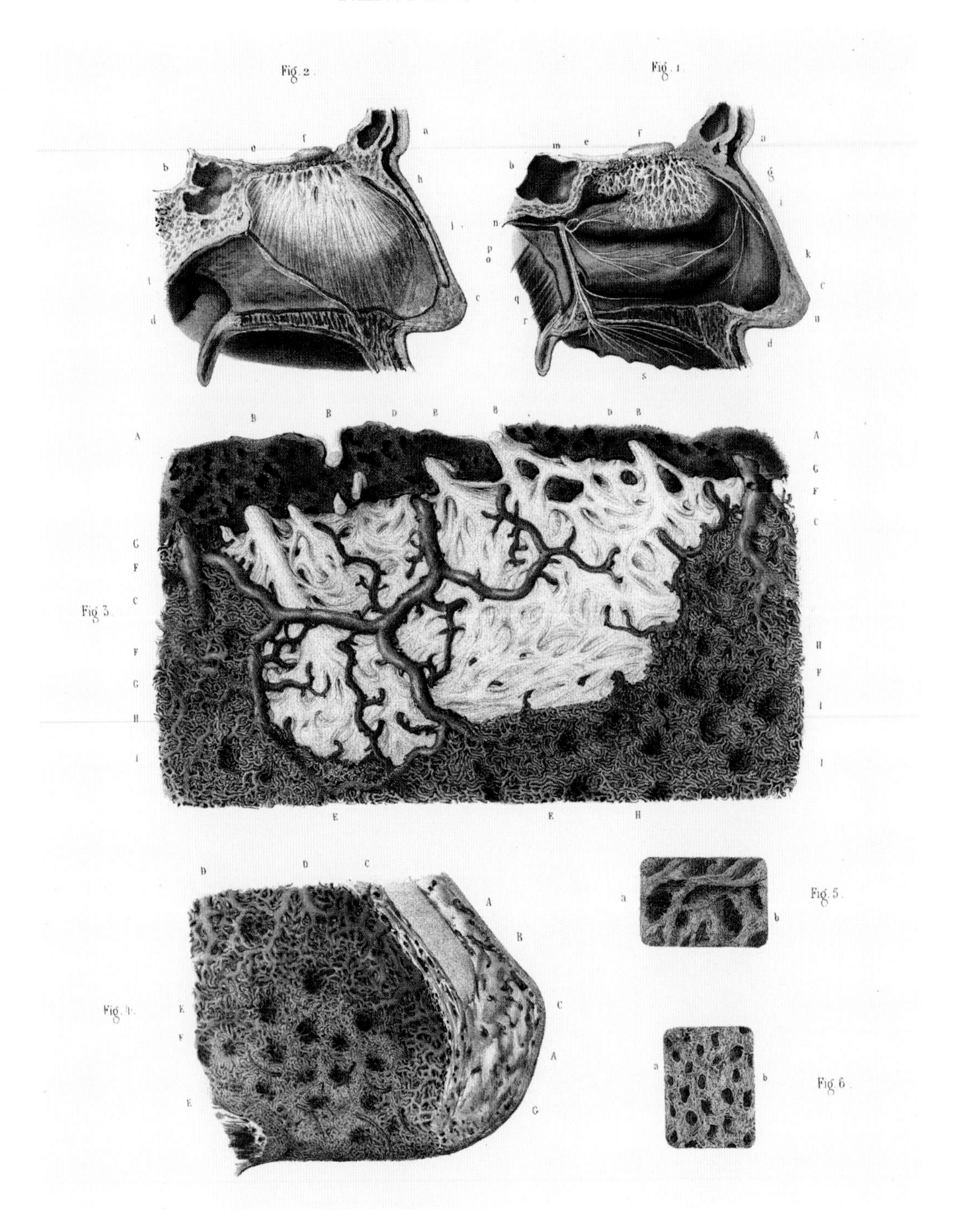

Organ of smell: Nerves and structure
Organe de l'olfaction : Nerfs et structure
Órgano del olfato: nervios y estructura

ORGANUM GUSTUS: NERVI CAVITATIS ORIS ET LINGUAE

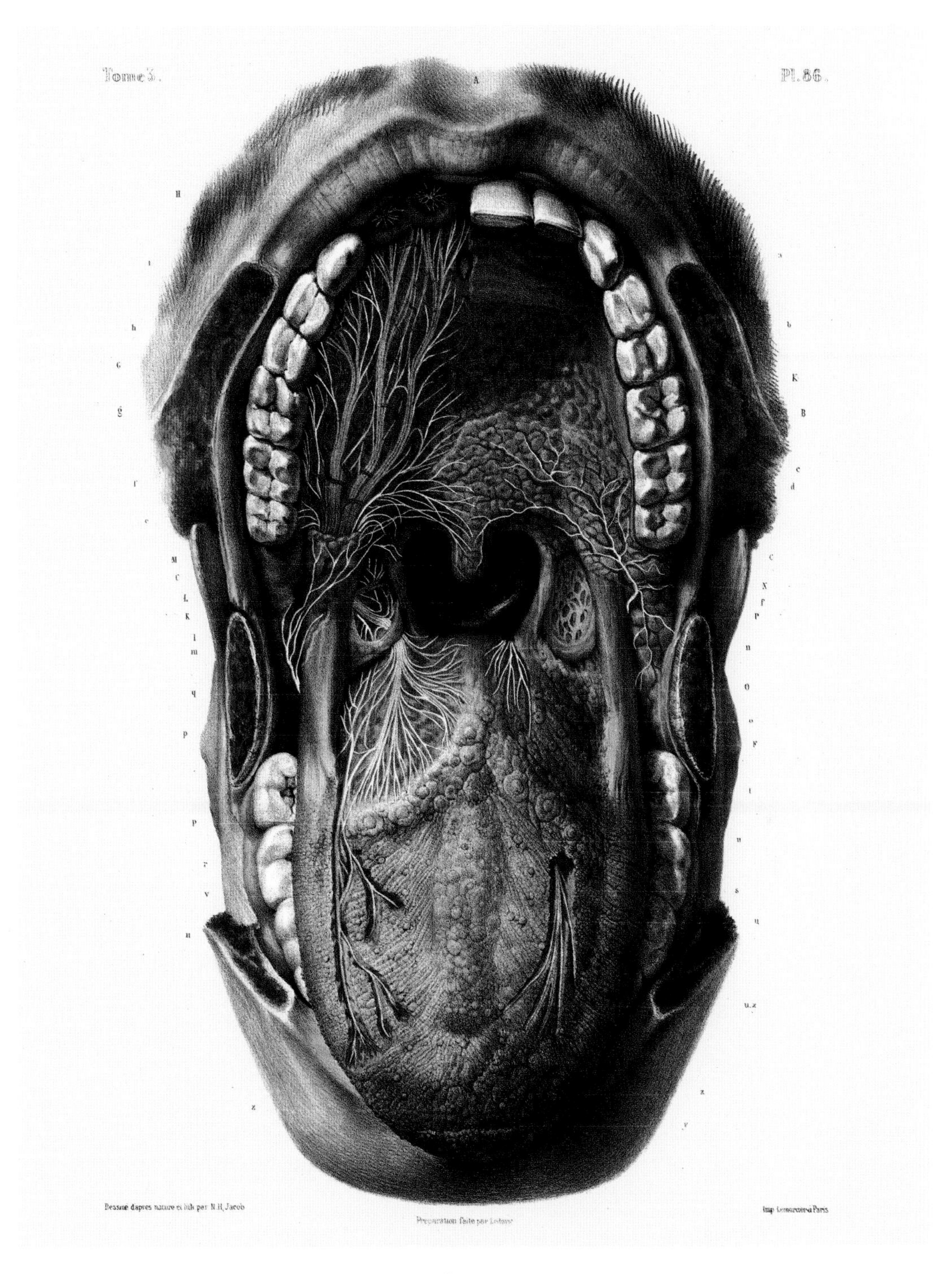

Organ of taste: Nerves of the oral cavity and the tongue
Organe du goût : Nerfs de la cavité orale et de la langue
Órgano del gusto: nervios de la cavidad bucal y de la lengua

ORGANUM GUSTUS: ANATOMIA MICROSCOPICA PAPILLARUM LINGUALIUM. ORGANUM TACTUS: ANATOMIA MICROSCOPICA CUTIS ET PILORUM

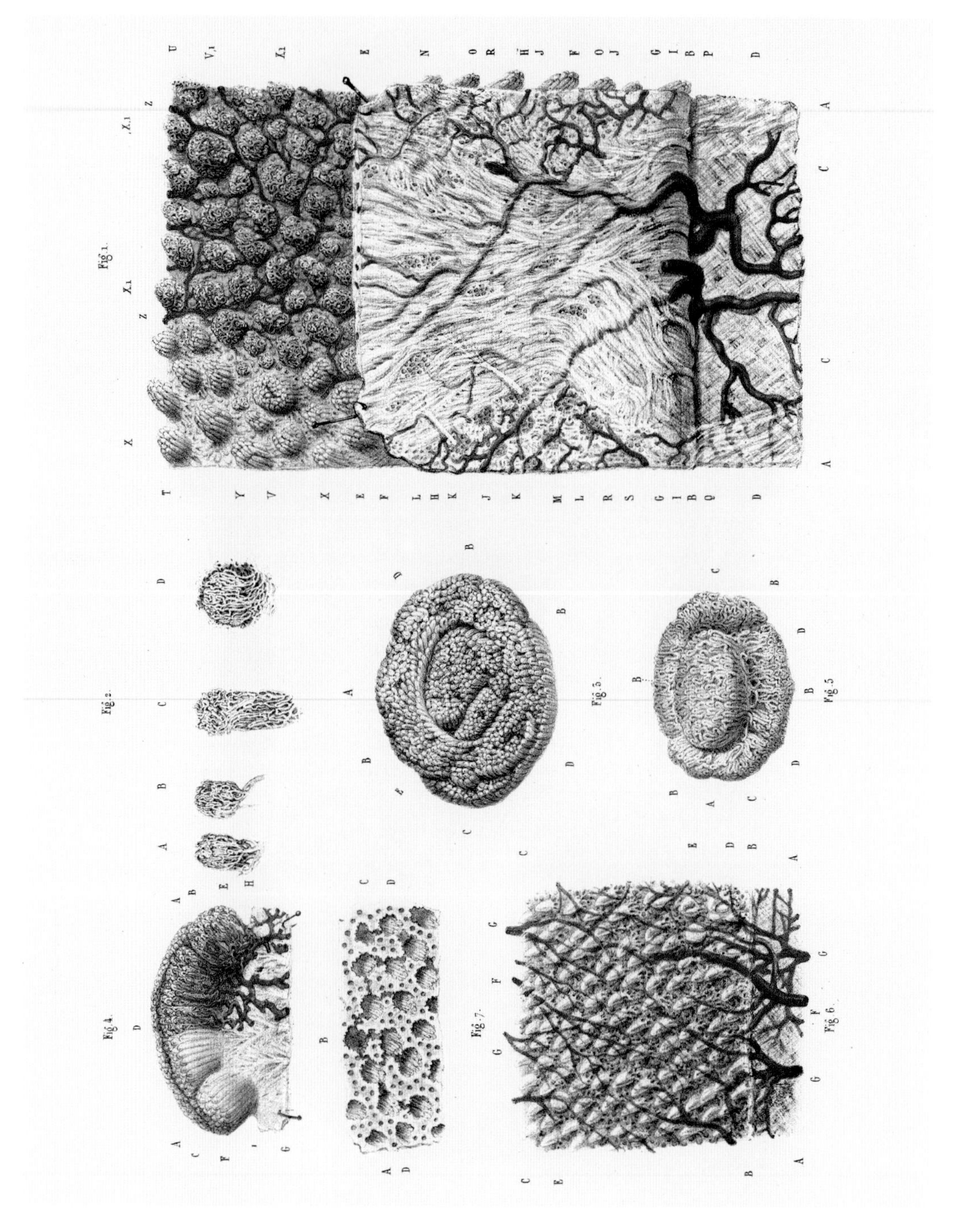

Organ of taste: Microscopic anatomy of the papillae of the tongue
Organe du goût : Anatomie microscopique des papilles linguales
Órgano del gusto: anatomía microscópica de las papilas linguales

ORGANUM GUSTUS: ANATOMIA MICROSCOPICA PAPILLARUM LINGUALIUM. ORGANUM TACTUS: ANATOMIA MICROSCOPICA CUTIS ET PILORUM

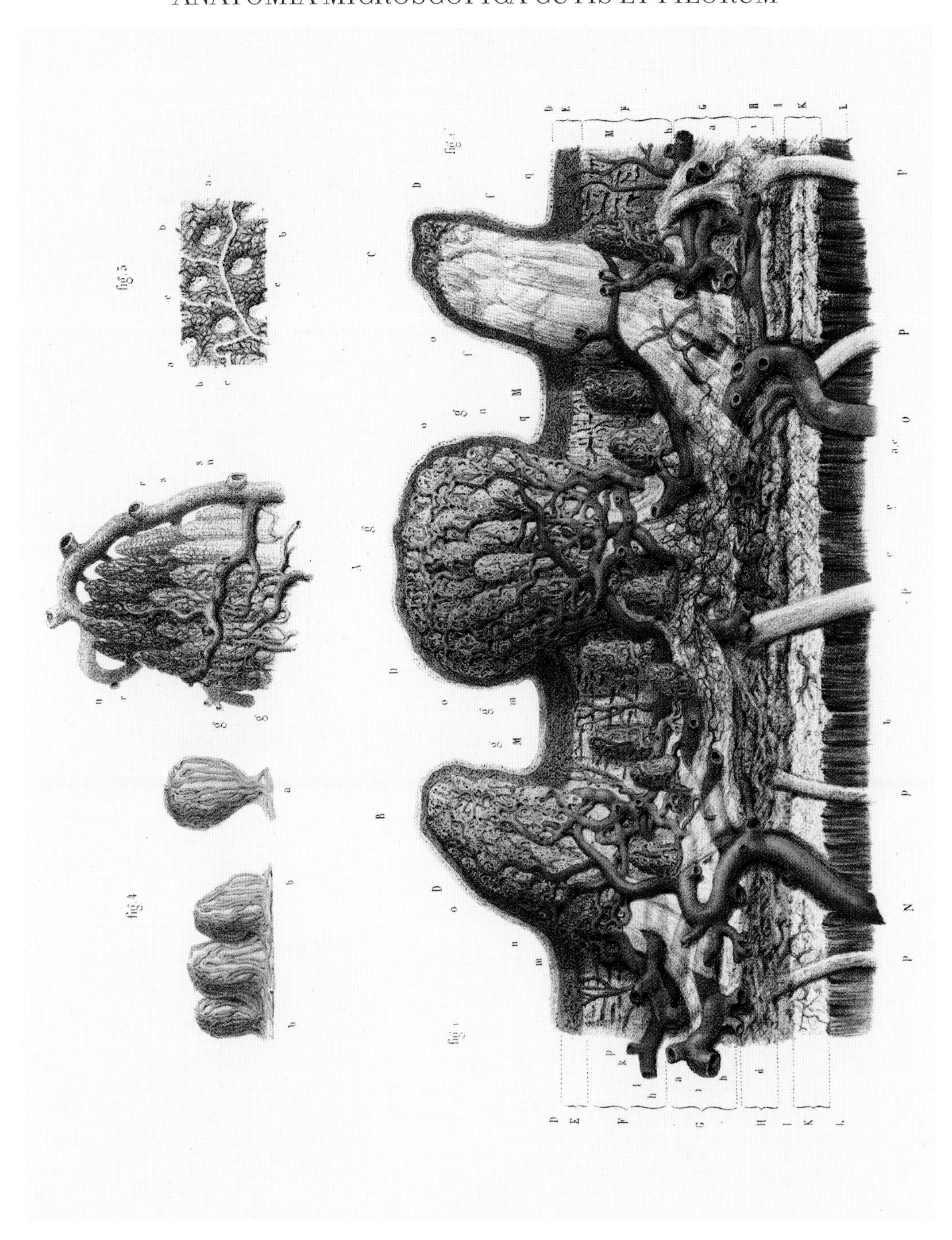

Organ of taste: Microscopic anatomy of the papillae of the tongue
Organe du goût : Anatomie microscopique des papilles linguales
Órgano del gusto: anatomía microscópica de las papilas linguales

ORGANUM GUSTUS: ANATOMIA MICROSCOPICA PAPILLARUM LINGUALIUM. ORGANUM TACTUS: ANATOMIA MICROSCOPICA CUTIS ET PILORUM

Organ of feeling: Microscopic anatomy of the skin
Organe du tact : Anatomie microscopique de la peau
Órgano del tacto: anatomía microscópica de la piel

ORGANUM GUSTUS: ANATOMIA MICROSCOPICA PAPILLARUM LINGUALIUM. ORGANUM TACTUS: ANATOMIA MICROSCOPICA CUTIS ET PILORUM

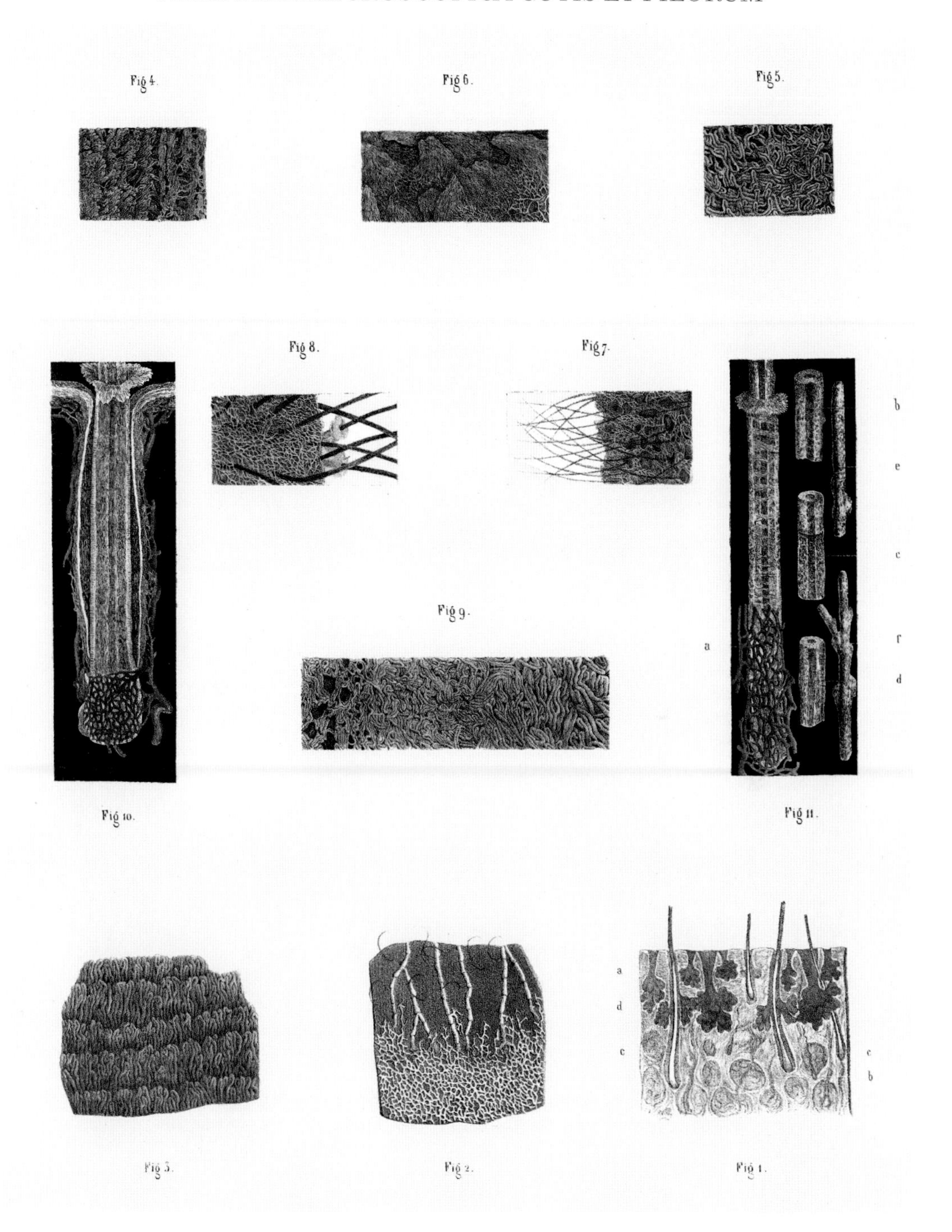

Organ of feeling: Microscopic anatomy of the skin and hair
Organe du tact : Anatomie microscopique de la peau et des poils
Órgano del tacto: anatomía microscópica de la piel y de los pelos

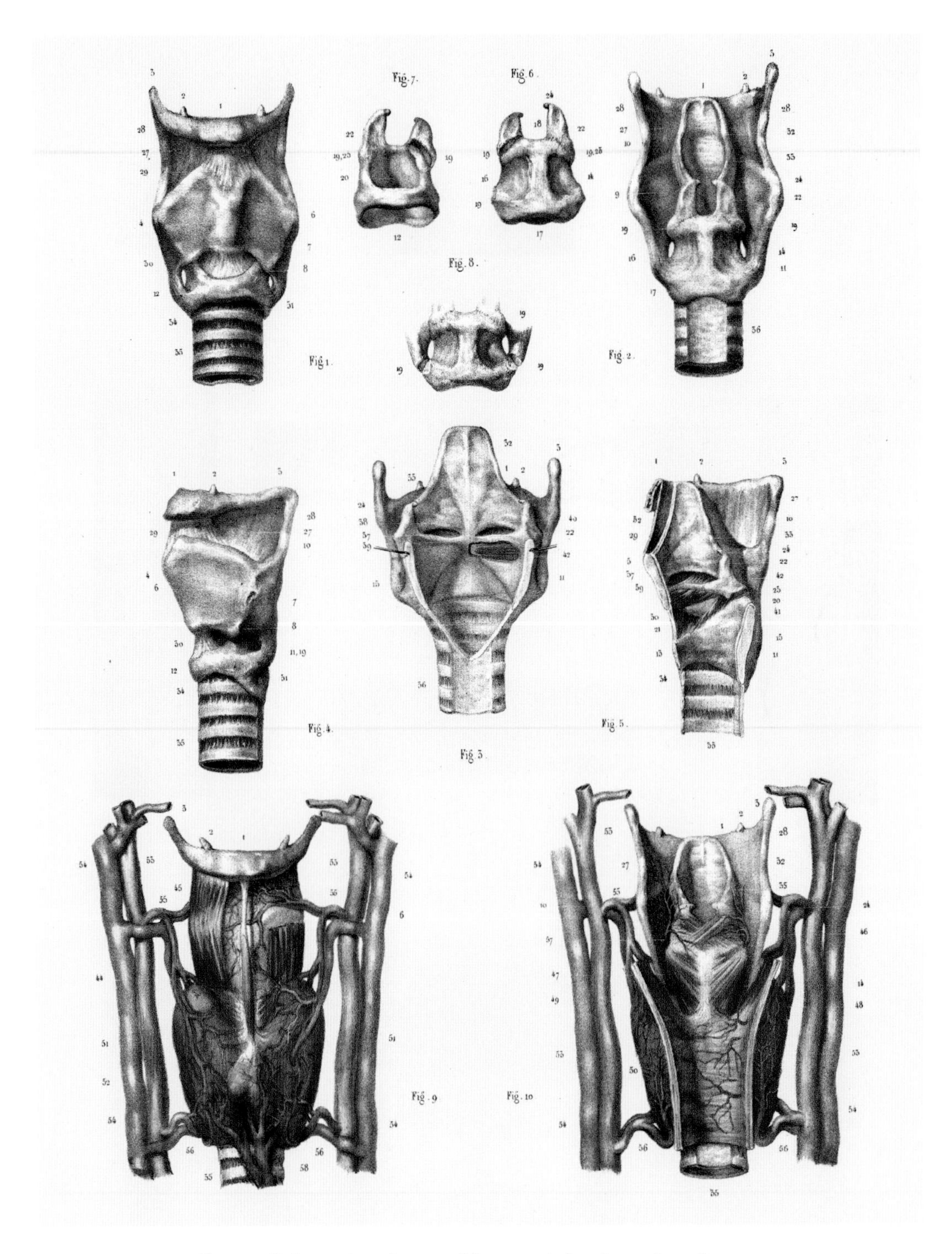

Organ of phonation: Larynx / Organe de la phonation : Larynx
Órgano de la fonación: laringe

ORGANUM VOCIS: LARYNX. SYSTEMA NERVOSUM AUTONOMICUM: PLEXUS CIRCULI ARTERIOSI CEREBRI ET PLEXUS CAROTICUS INTERNUS

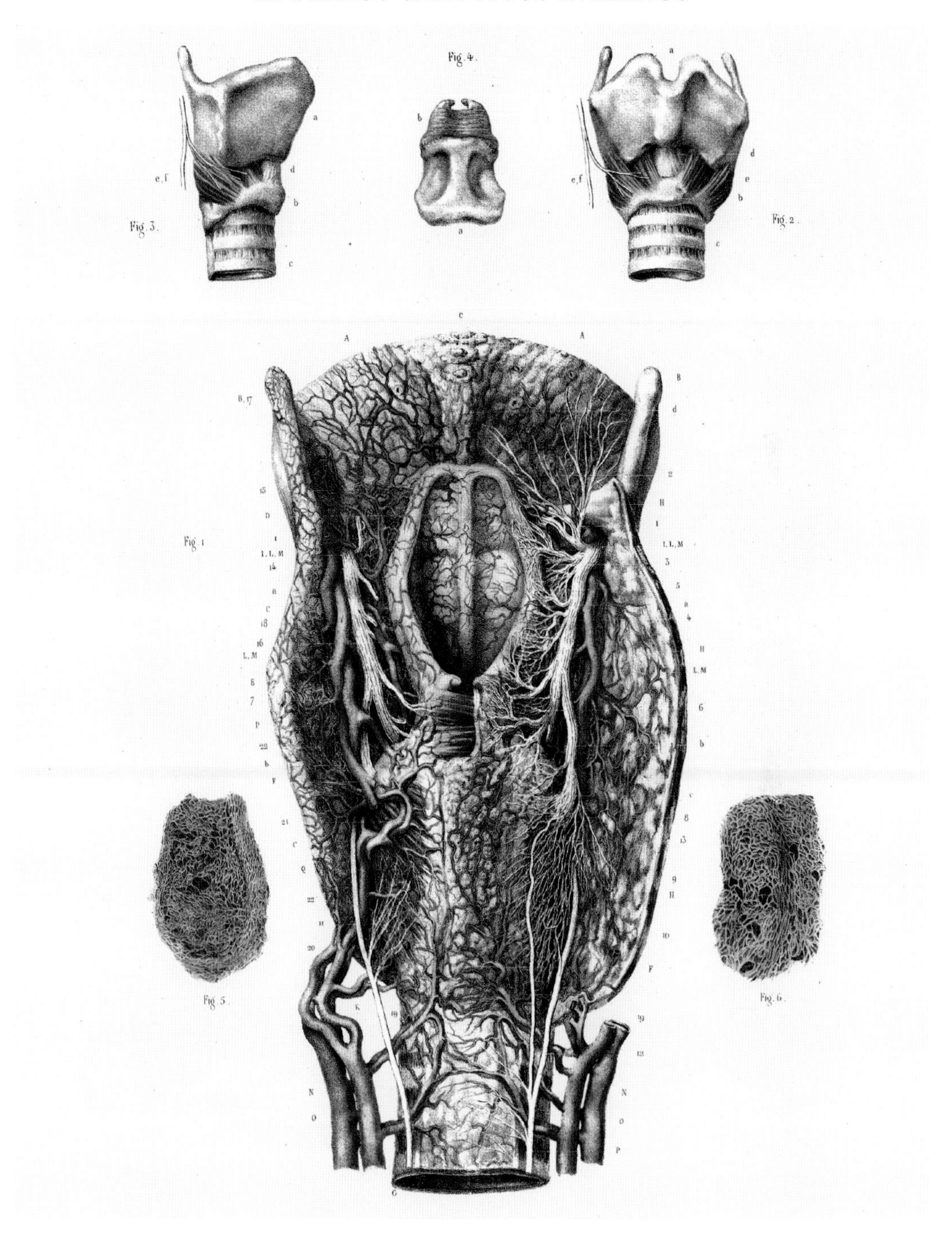

Organ of phonation: Larynx / Organe de la phonation : Larynx
Órgano de la fonación: laringe

ORGANUM VOCIS: LARYNX. SYSTEMA NERVOSUM AUTONOMICUM: PLEXUS CIRCULI ARTERIOSI CEREBRI ET PLEXUS CAROTICUS INTERNUS

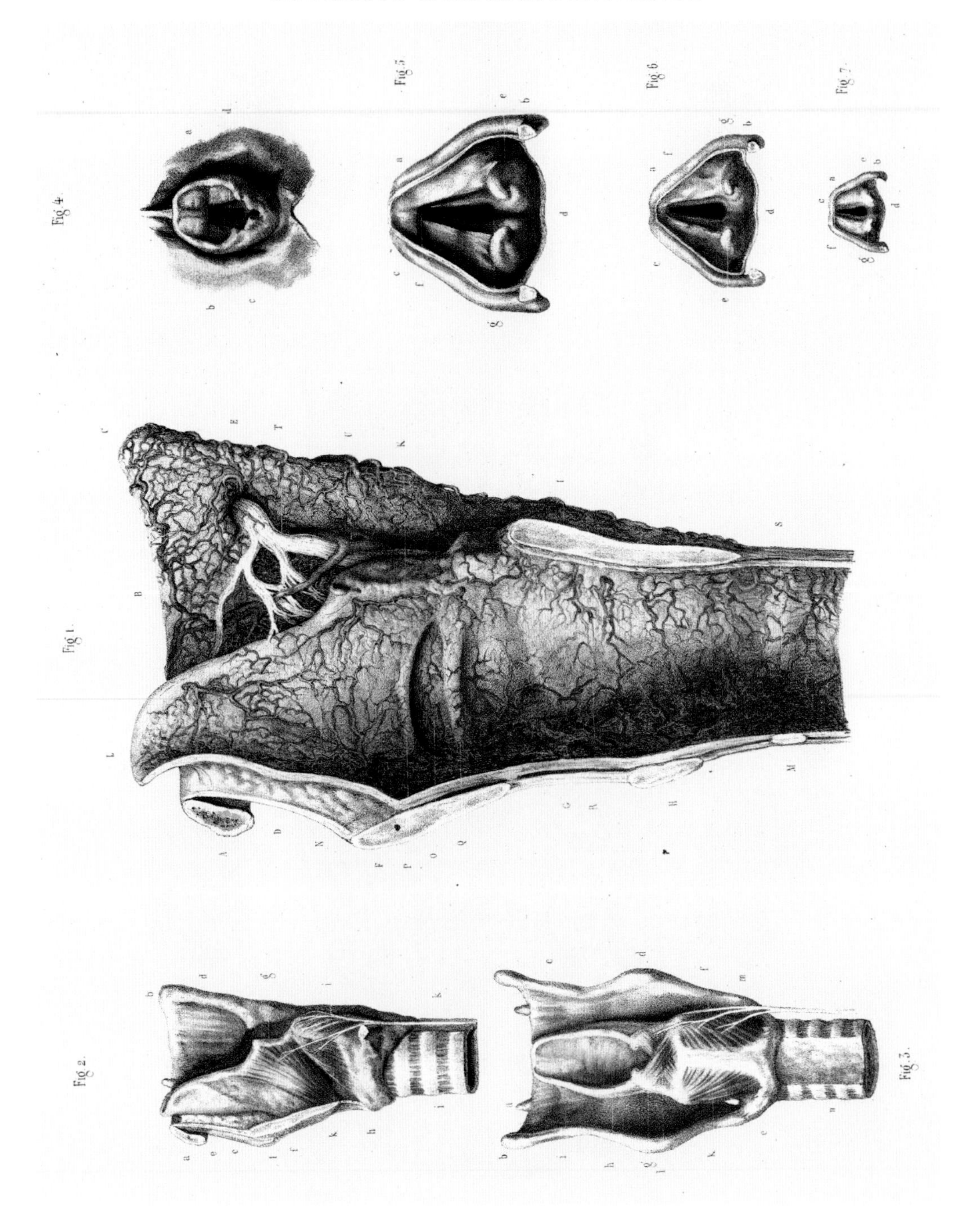

Organ of phonation: Larynx / Organe de la phonation : Larynx
Órgano de la fonación: laringe

ORGANUM VOCIS: LARYNX. SYSTEMA NERVOSUM AUTONOMICUM: PLEXUS CIRCULI ARTERIOSI CEREBRI ET PLEXUS CAROTICUS INTERNUS

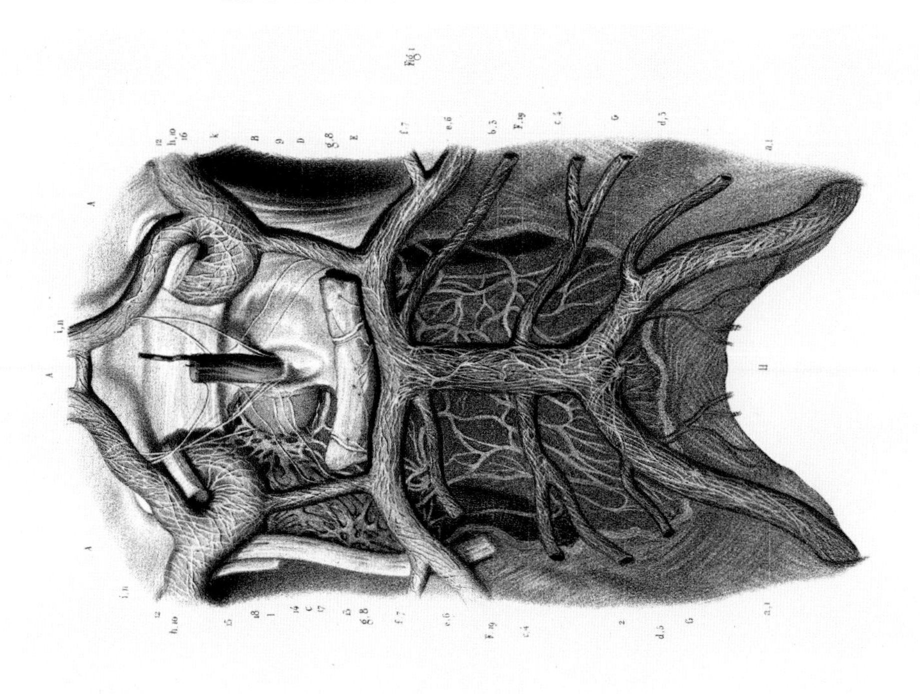

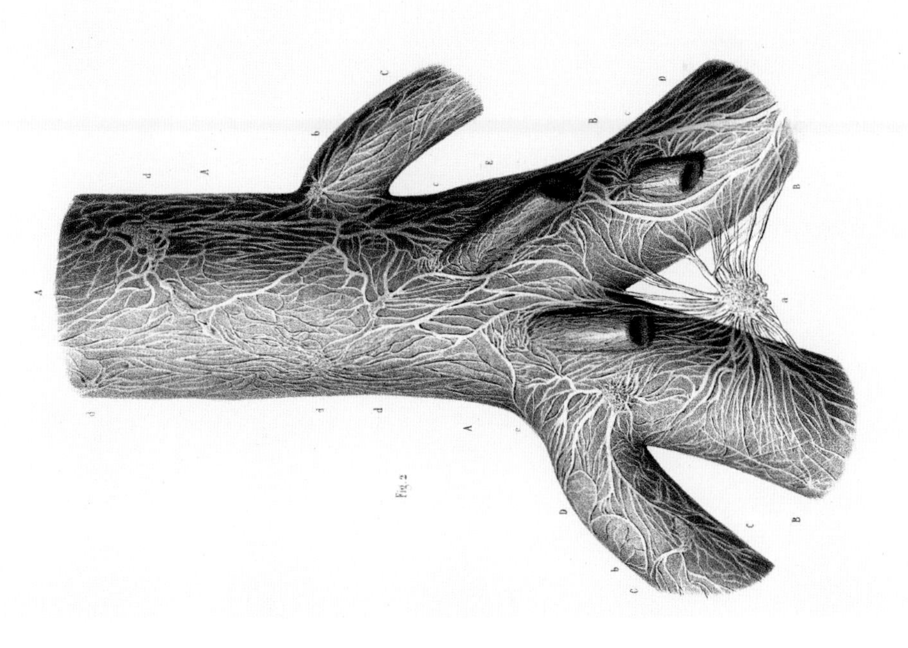

Autonomic nervous system: Plexus of the arterial circle of the brain
Système nerveux autonome : Plexus du cercle artériel du cerveau
Sistema nervioso autónomo: plexo del polígono arterial del cerebro

ORGANUM VOCIS: LARYNX. SYSTEMA NERVOSUM AUTONOMICUM: PLEXUS CIRCULI ARTERIOSI CEREBRI ET PLEXUS CAROTICUS INTERNUS

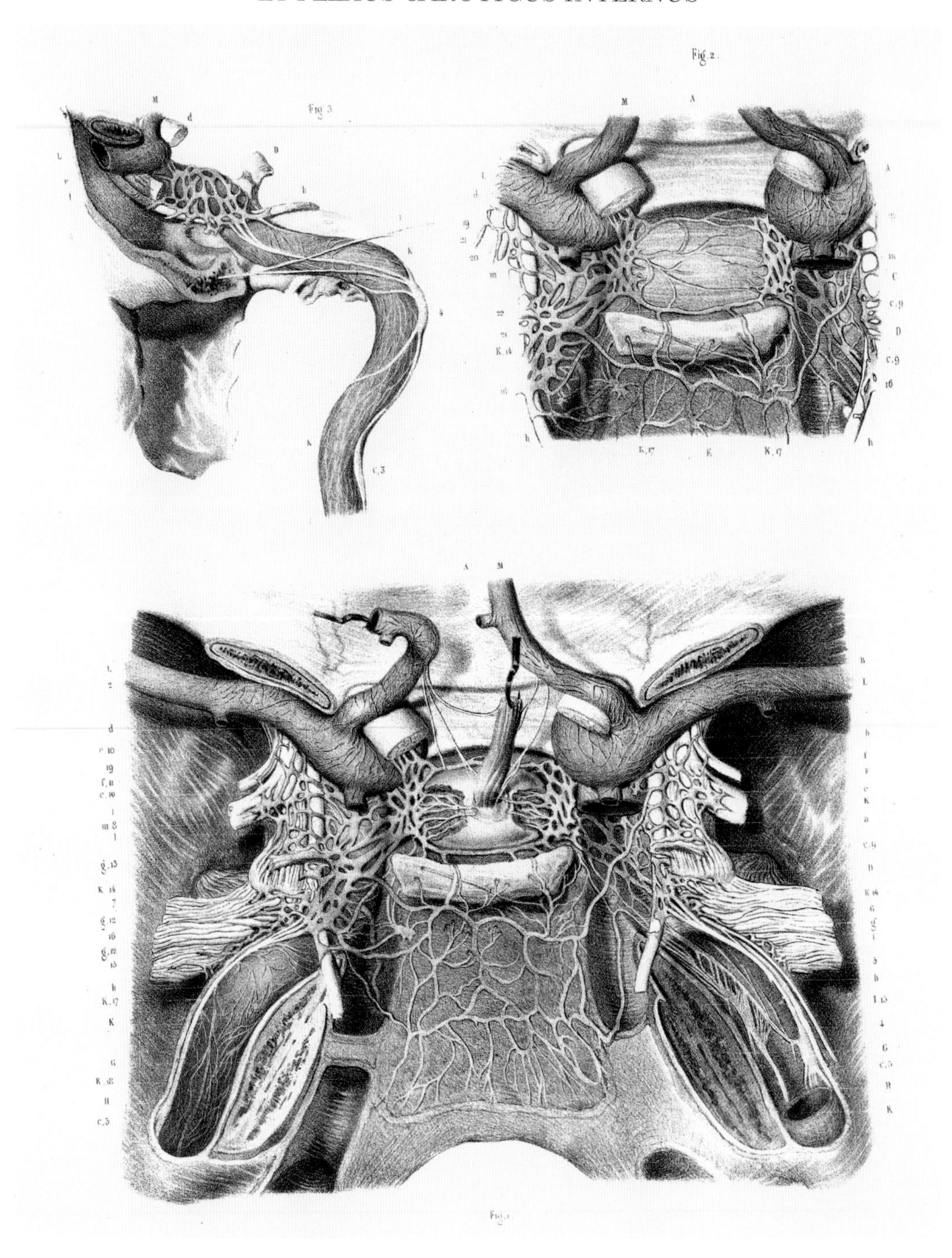

Autonomic nervous system: Plexus of the internal carotid artery
Système nerveux autonome : Plexus carotidien interne
Sistema nervioso autónomo: plexo carotídeo interno

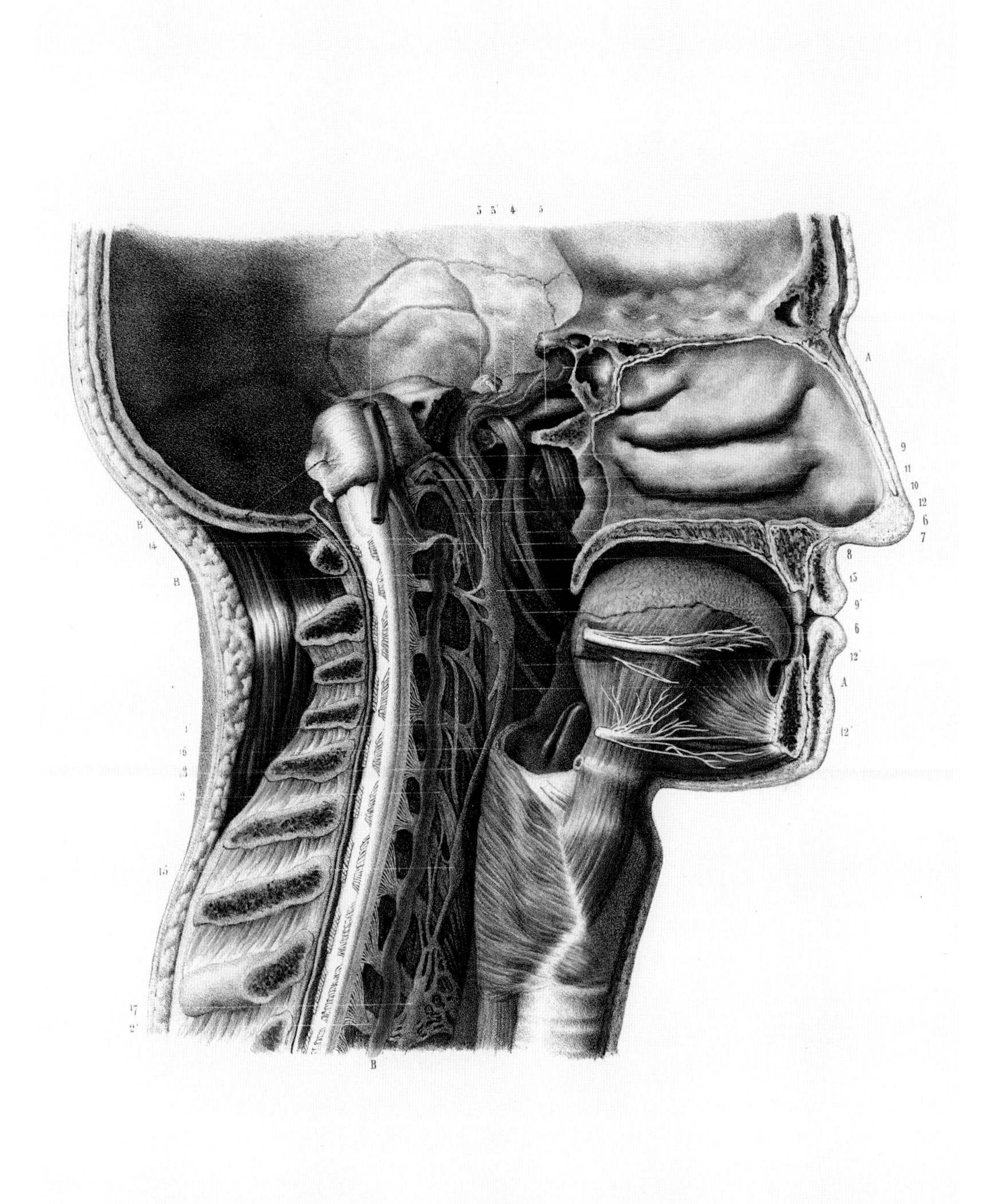

Autonomic nervous system: Cervical sympathetic trunk
Système nerveux autonome : Tronc sympathique cervical
Sistema nervioso autónomo: tronco simpático cervical

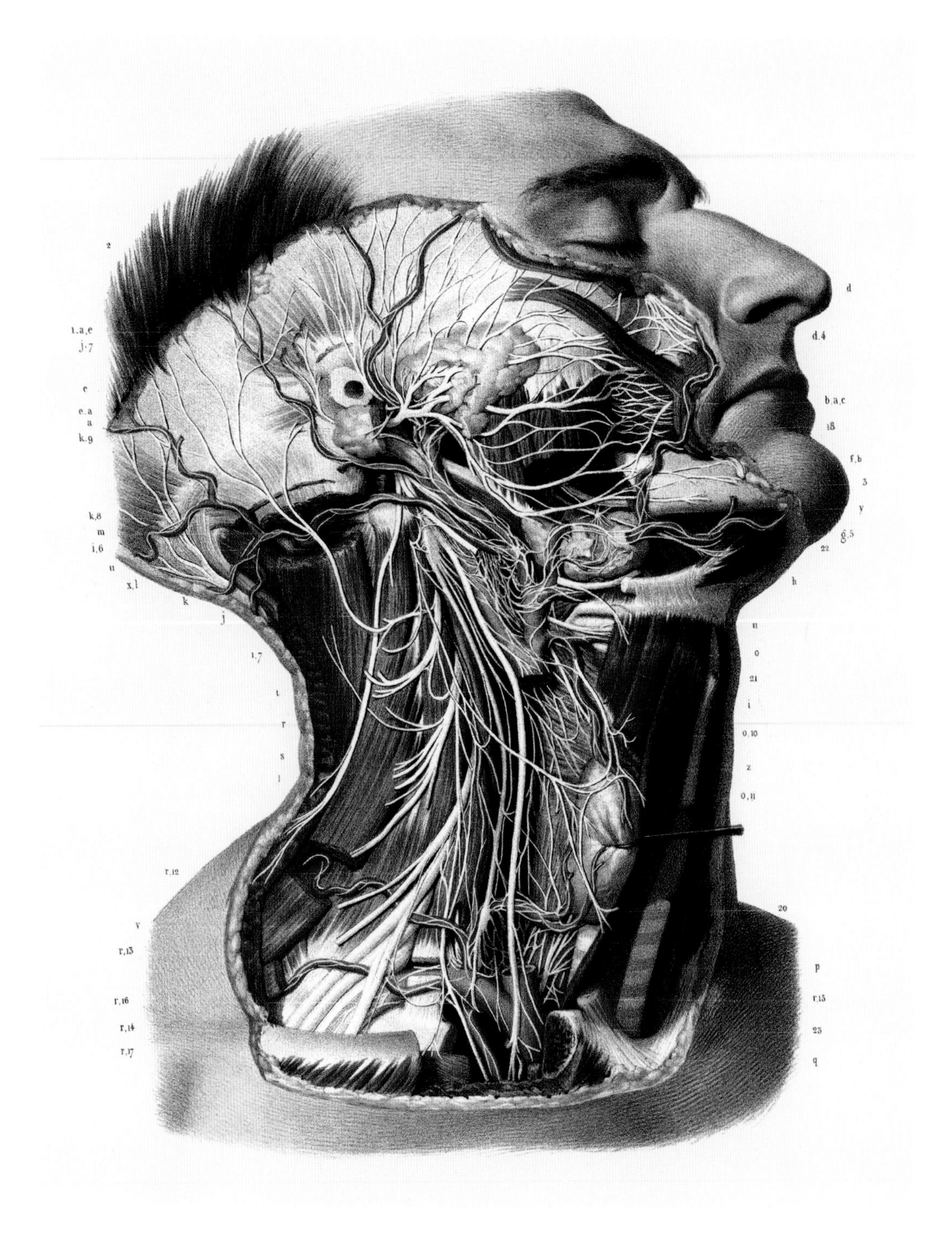

Autonomic nervous system of the head and neck
Système nerveux autonome de la tête et cou
Sistema nervioso autónomo de la cabeza y del cuello

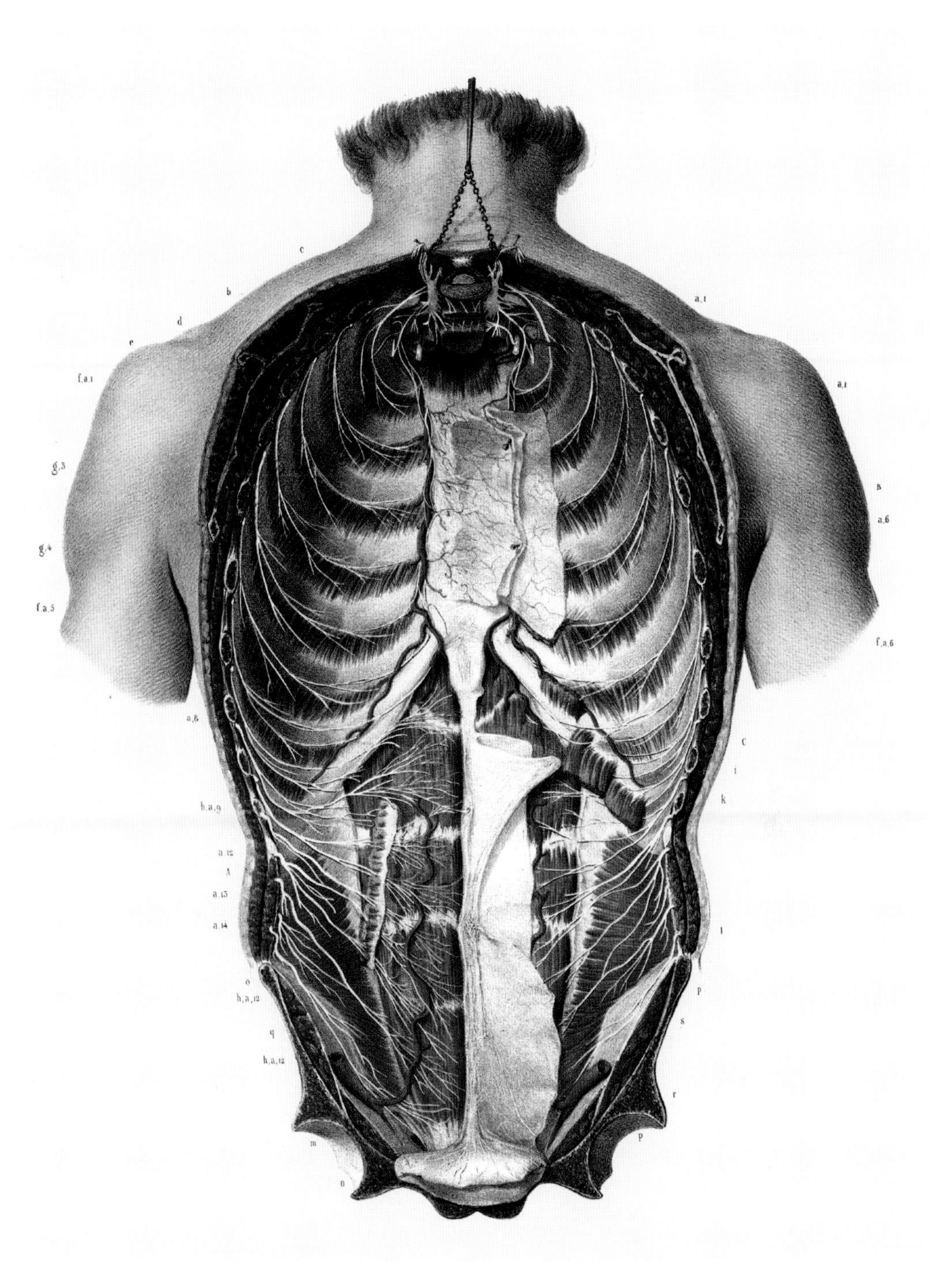

Autonomic nervous system of the thorax and abdomen
Système nerveux autonome du thorax et de l'abdomen
Sistema nervioso autónomo del tórax y del abdomen

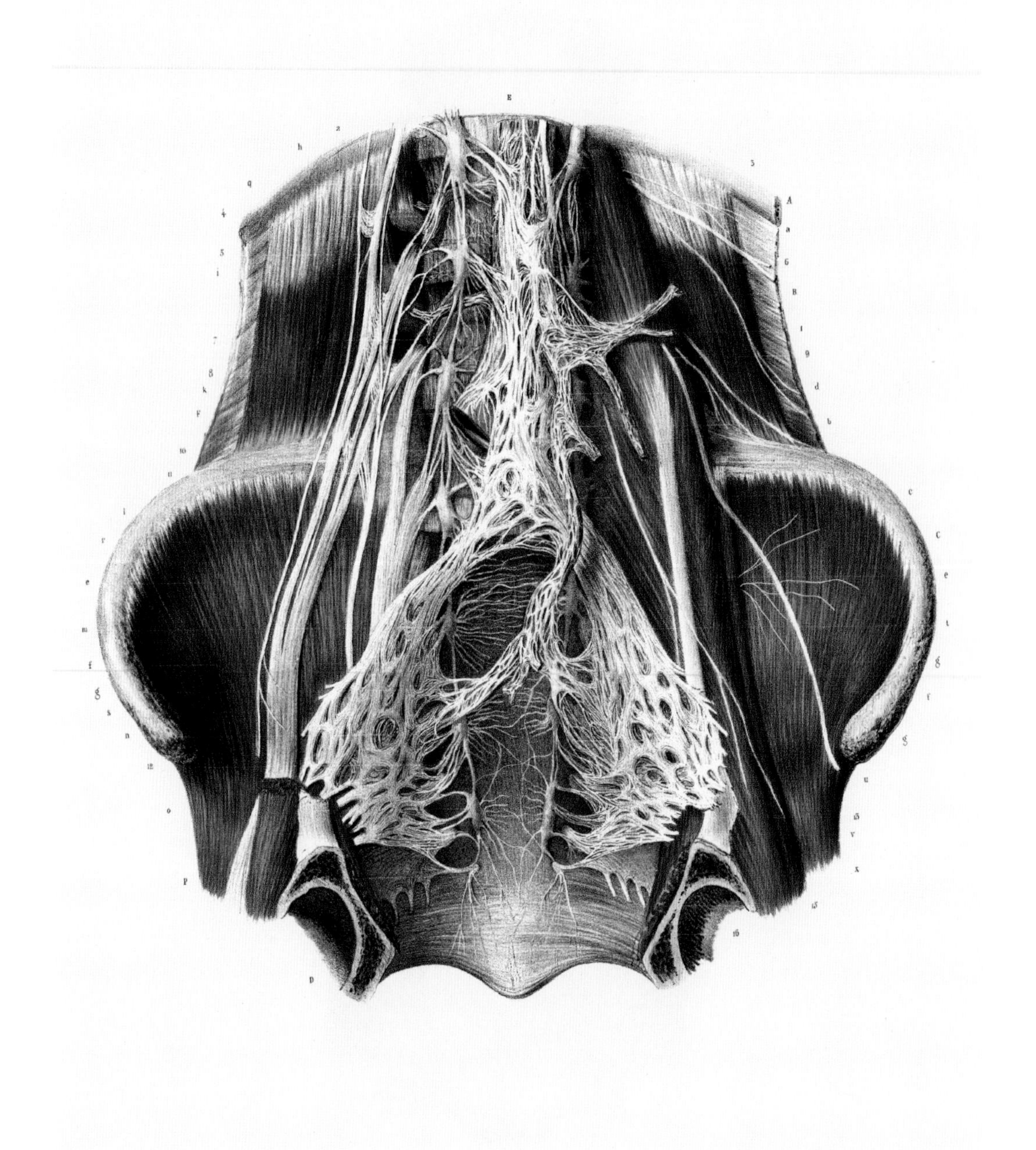

Autonomic nervous system of the abdomen and pelvis
Système nerveux autonome de l'abdomen et du pelvis
Sistema nervioso autónomo del abdomen y de la pelvis

SYSTEMA NERVOSUM AUTONOMICUM: NERVI VASORUM, PLEXUS CARDIACUS, TRUNCUS SYMPATHICUS THORACIS

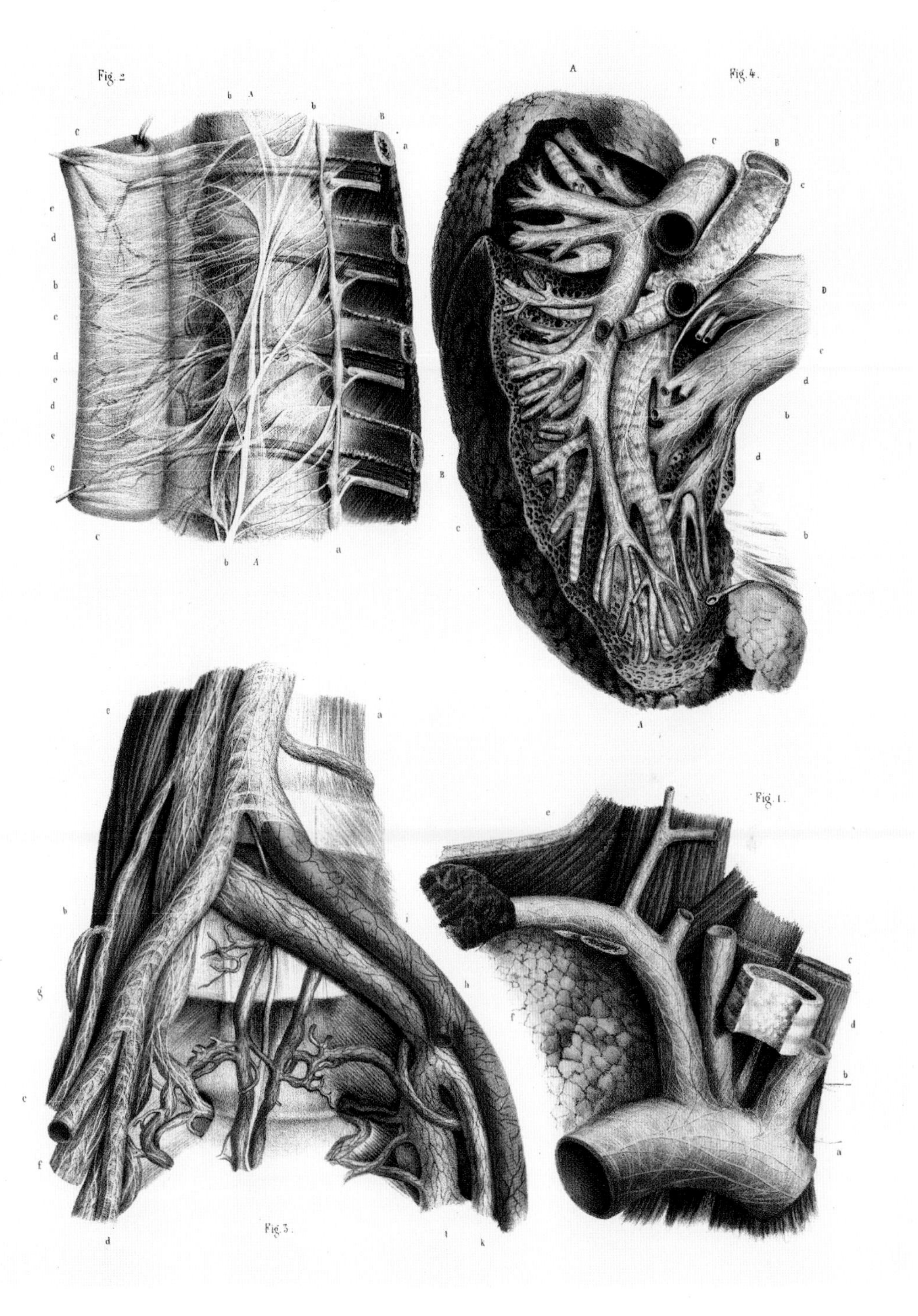

Autonomic nervous system: Nerves of the vessels
Système nerveux autonome : Nerfs des vaisseaux
Sistema nervioso autónomo: nervios de los vasos sanguíneos

Autonomic nervous system: Nerves of the vessels
Système nerveux autonome : Nerfs des vaisseaux
Sistema nervioso autónomo: nervios de los vasos sanguíneos

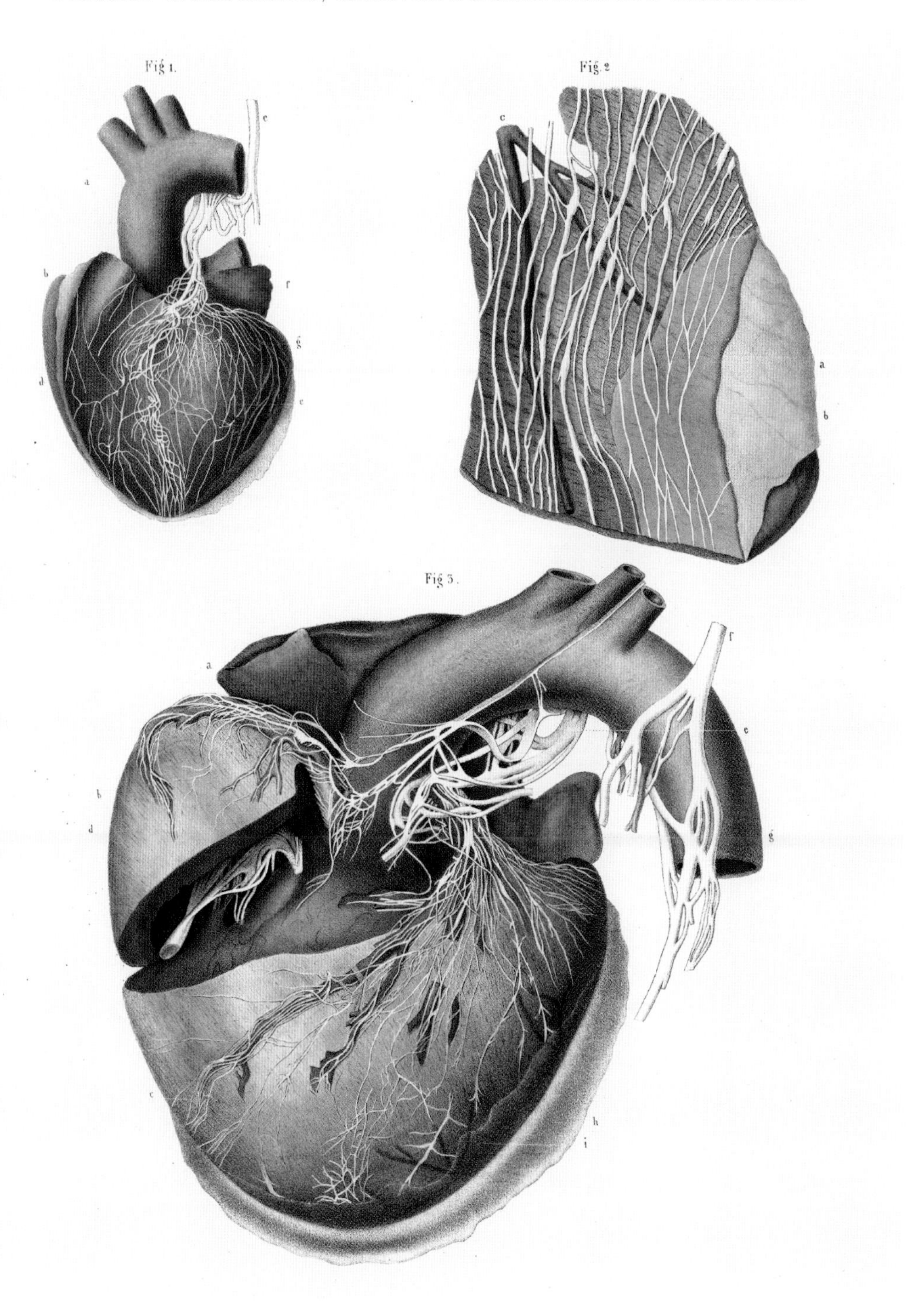

Autonomic nervous system: Cardiac plexus
Système nerveux autonome : Plexus cardiaque
Sistema nervioso autónomo: plexo cardíaco

SYSTEMA NERVOSUM AUTONOMICUM: NERVI VASORUM, PLEXUS CARDIACUS, TRUNCUS SYMPATHICUS THORACIS

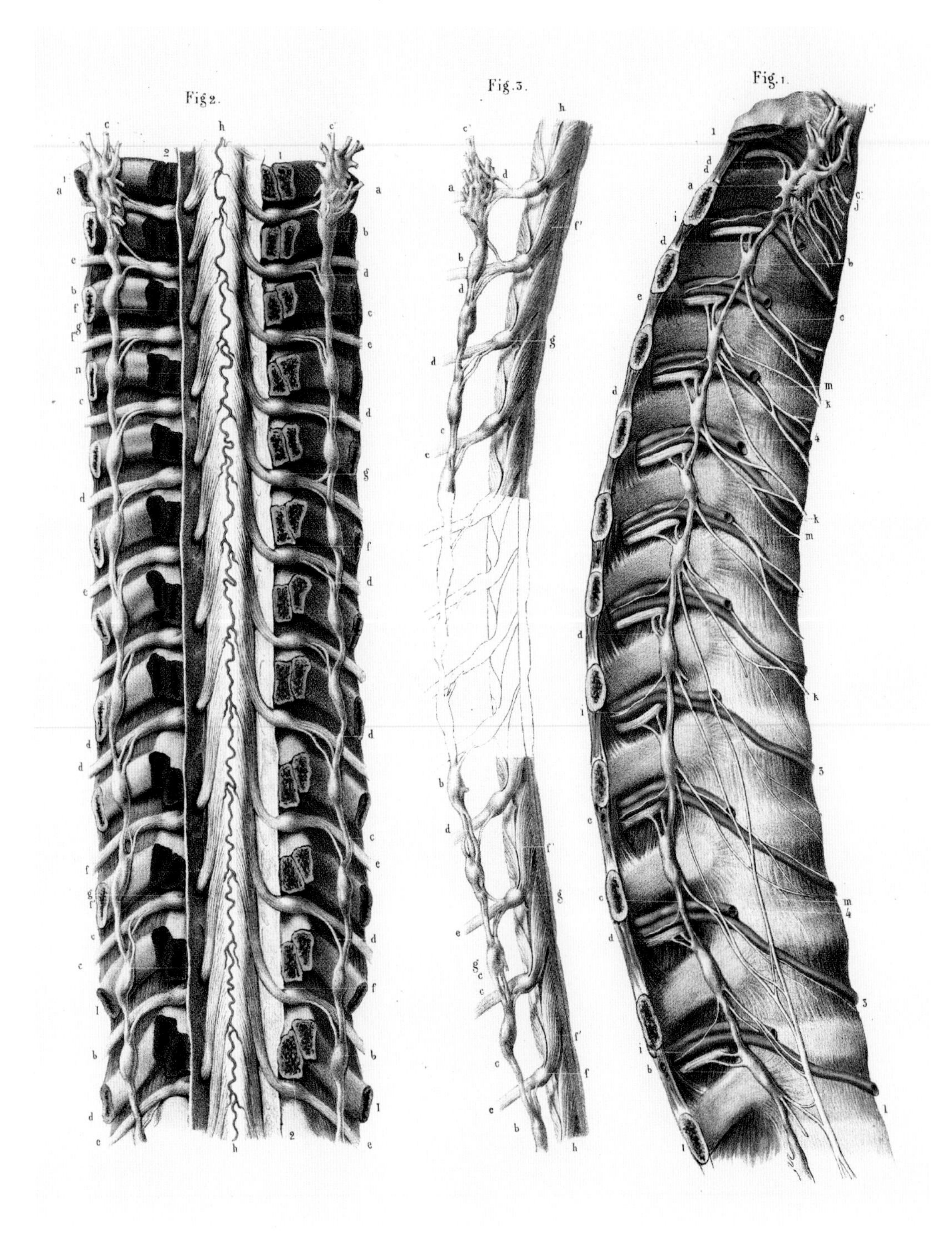

Autonomic nervous system: Thoracic sympathetic trunk
Système nerveux autonome : Tronc sympathique thoracique
Sistema nervioso autónomo: tronco simpático torácico

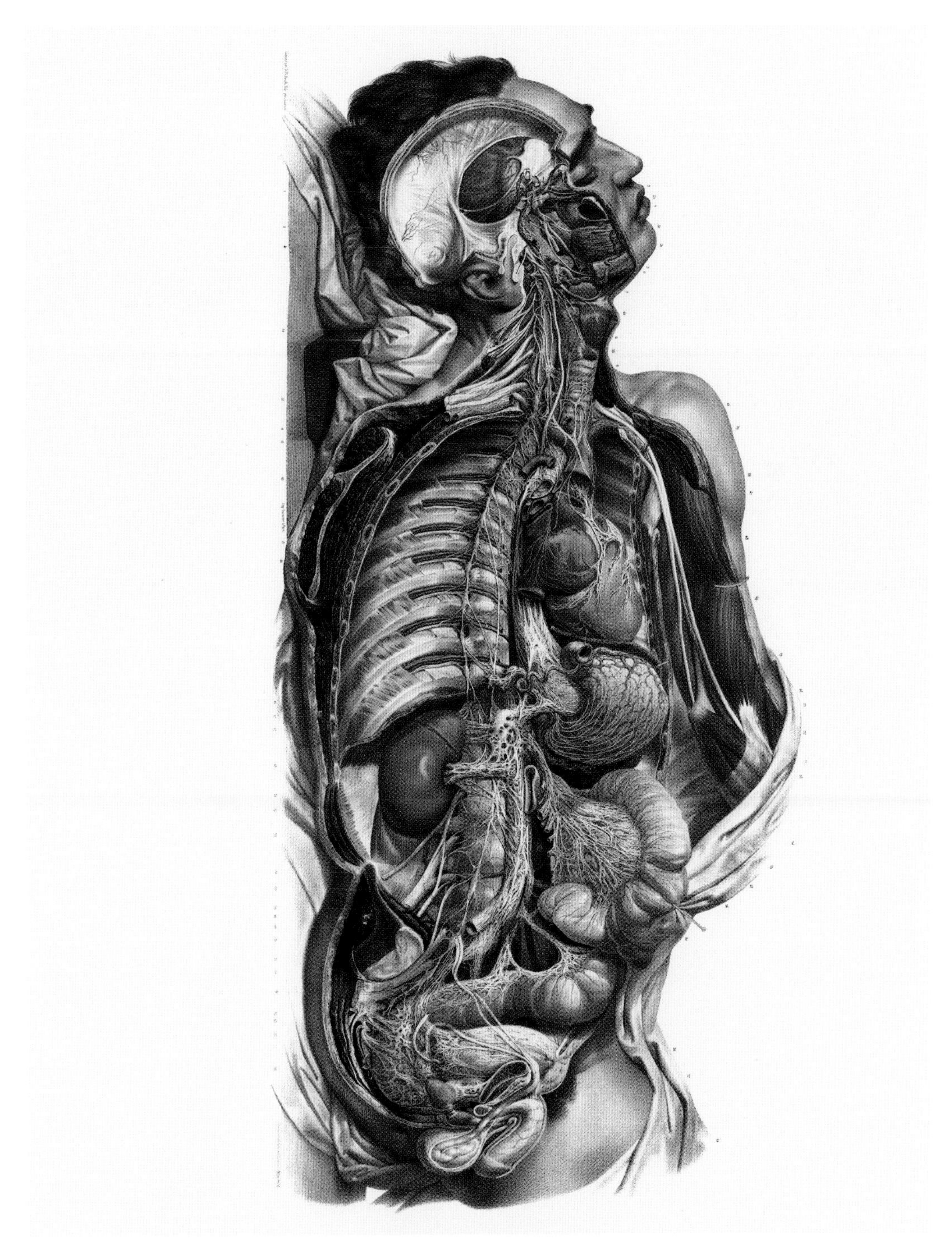

Autonomic nervous system / Système nerveux autonome
Sistema nervioso autónomo

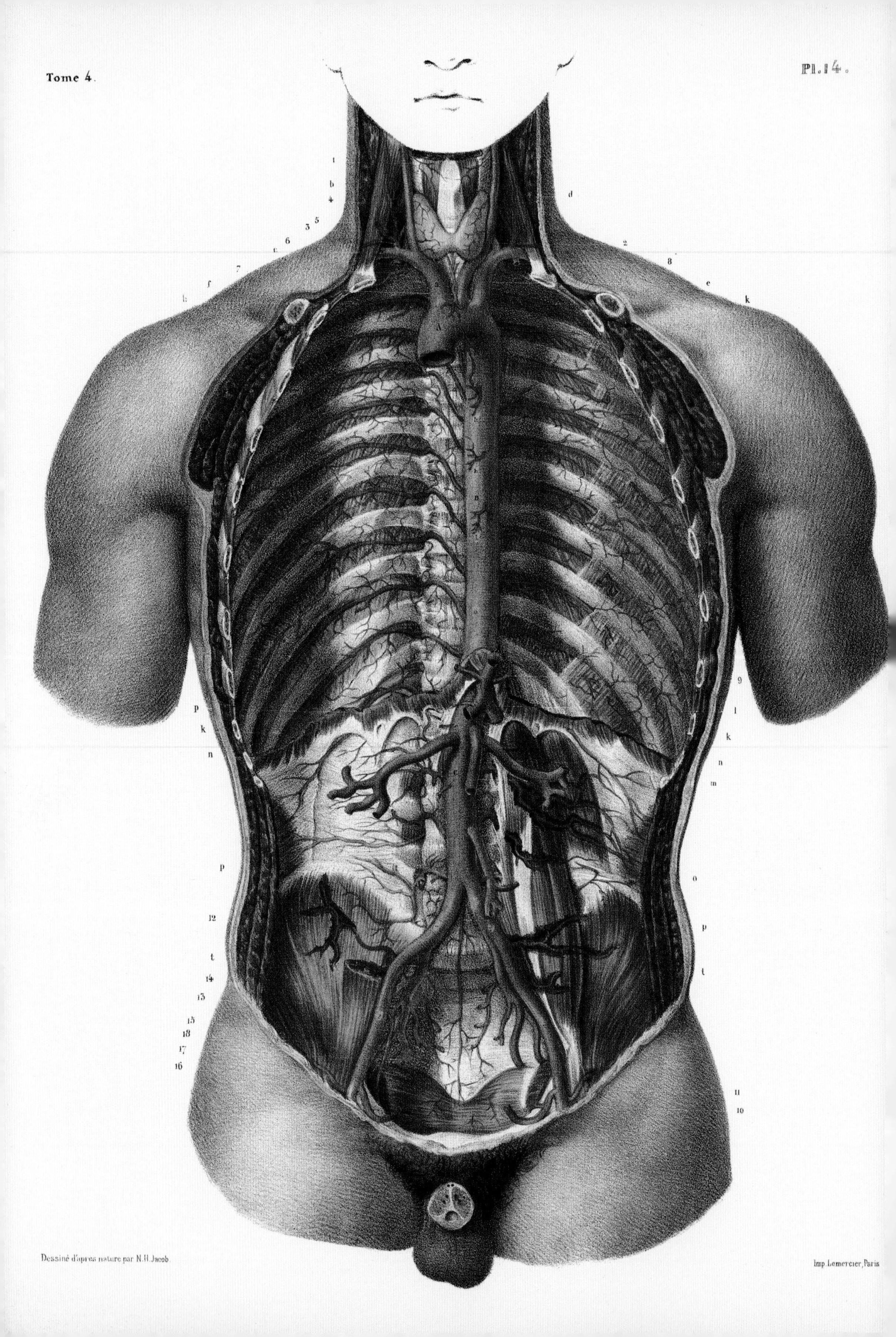

Dessiné d'après nature par N.H. Jacob.

Imp. Lemercier, Paris

VOL. 4

Angiologia: Cor, Arteriae, Venae, Systema Lymphaticum

Splanchnologia: Viscera Thoracis (Apparatus Respiratorius)

ANGIOLOGY:
HEART, ARTERIES, VEINS, LYMPHATIC SYSTEM

SPLANCHNOLOGY:
THORACIC ORGANS (RESPIRATORY TRACT)

ANGIOLOGIE :
CŒUR, ARTERES, VEINES, SYSTEME LYMPHATIQUE

SPLANCHNOLOGIE :
VISCERES THORACIQUES (APPAREIL RESPIRATOIRE)

ANGIOLOGÍA:
CORAZÓN, ARTERIAS, VENAS, SISTEMA LINFÁTICO

ESPLACNOLOGÍA:
VÍSCERAS TORÁCICAS (APARATO RESPIRATORIO)

Left page / Ci-contre / Página contigua:
Aorta / Aorte / Aorta

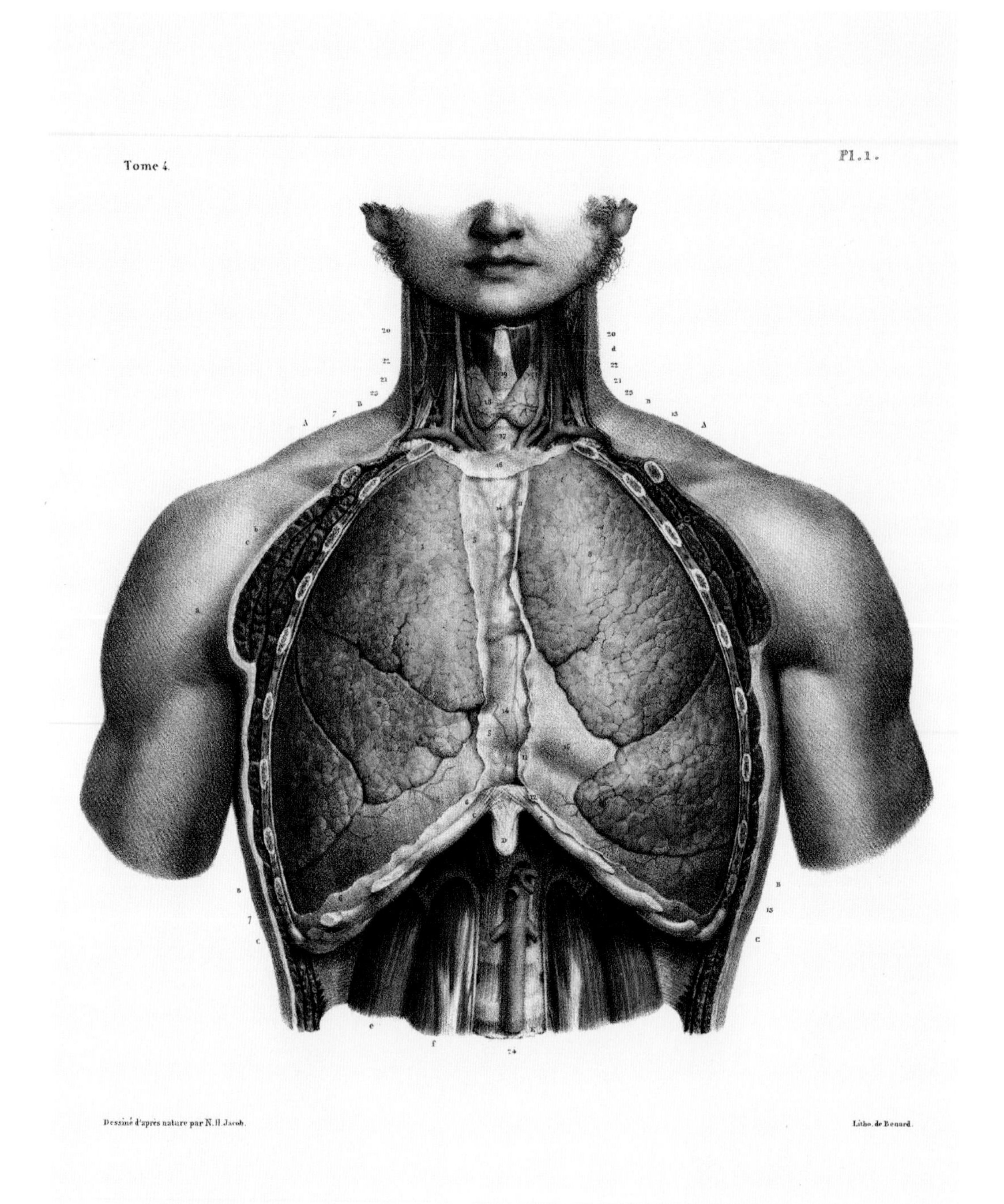

Thoracic organs / Viscères thoraciques / Vísceras torácicas

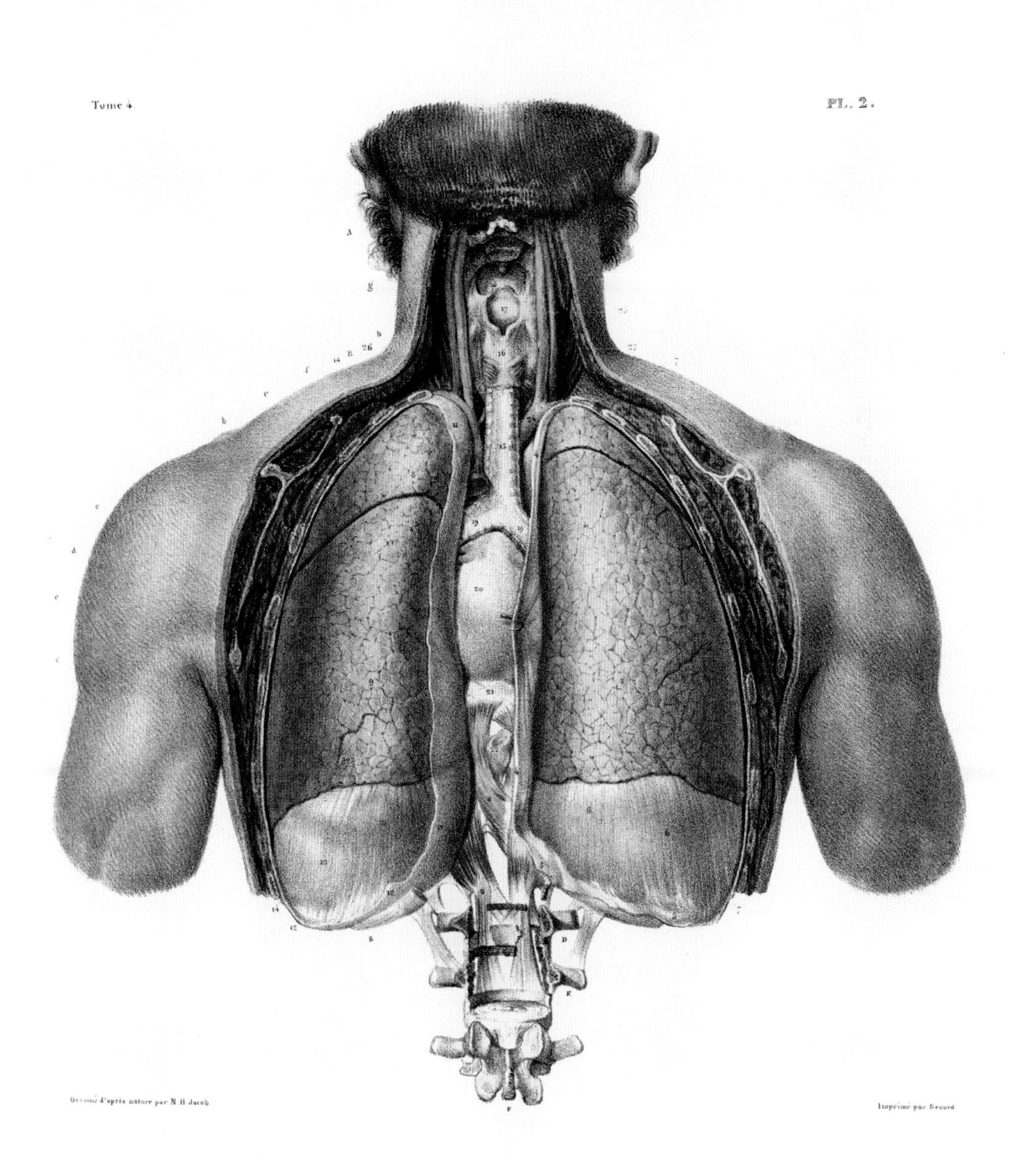

Thoracic organs / Viscères thoraciques / Vísceras torácicas

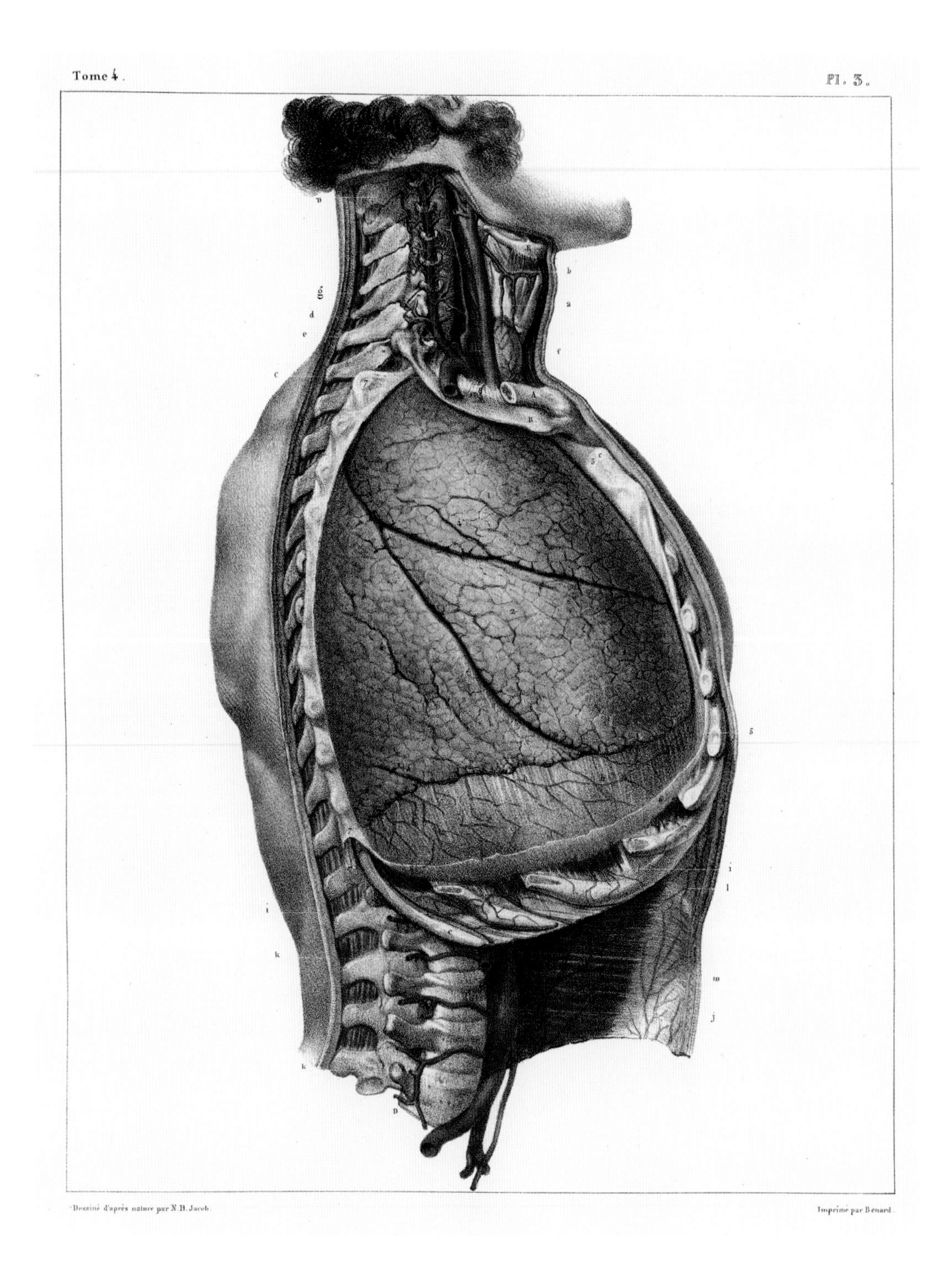

Thoracic organs / Viscères thoraciques / Vísceras torácicas

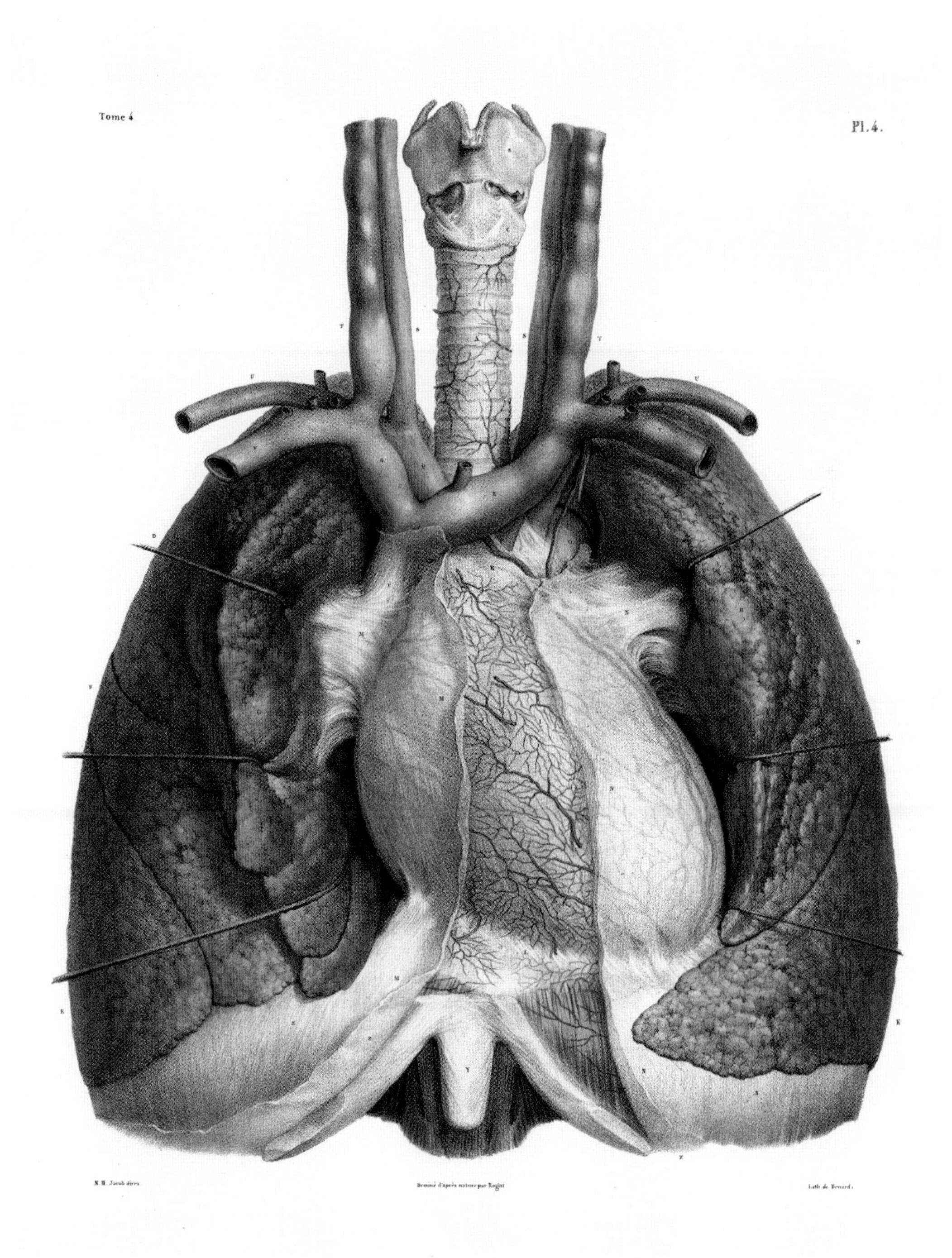

Lungs and heart / Poumons et cœur / Pulmones y corazón

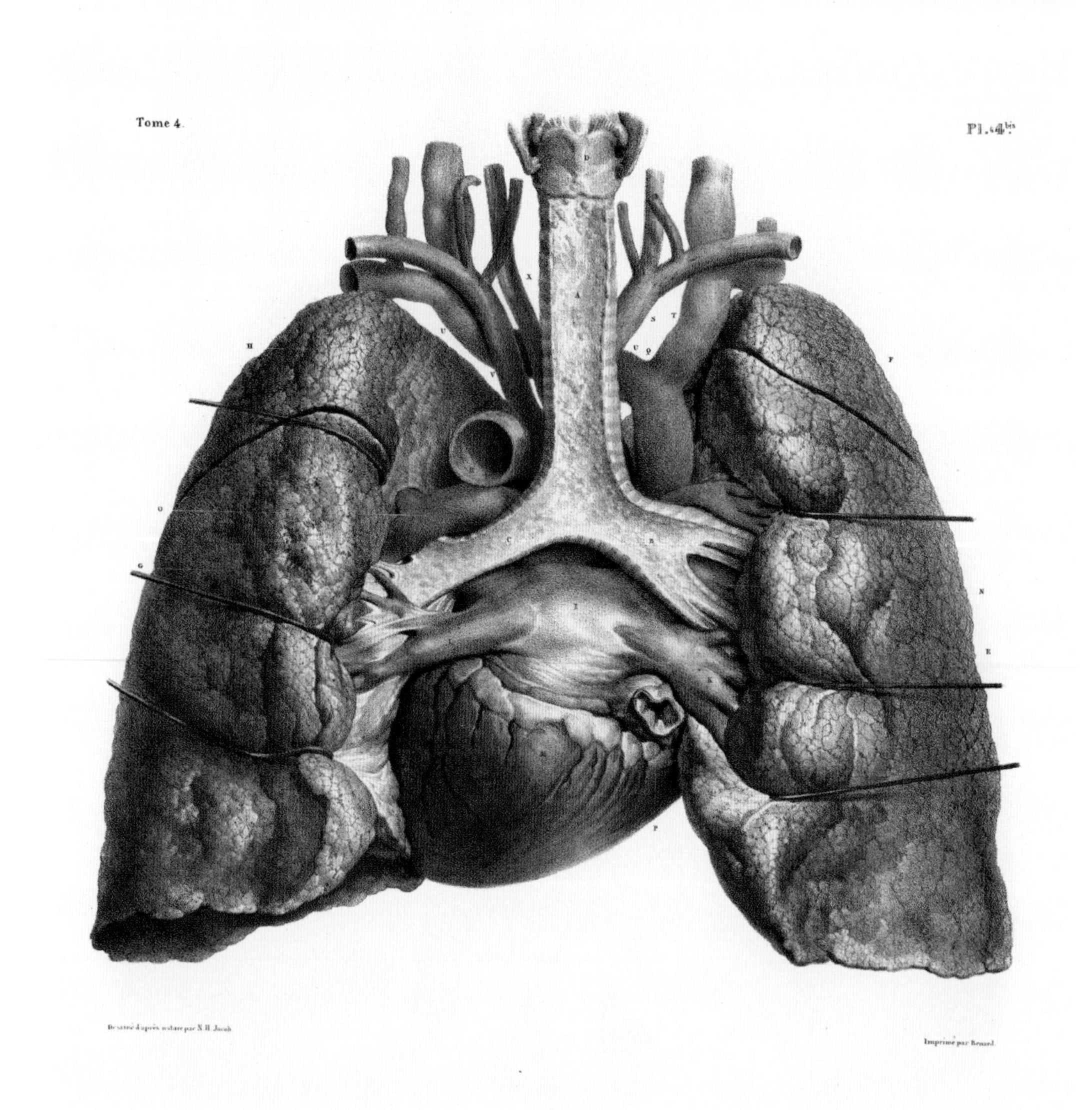

Lungs and heart / Poumons et cœur / Pulmones y corazón

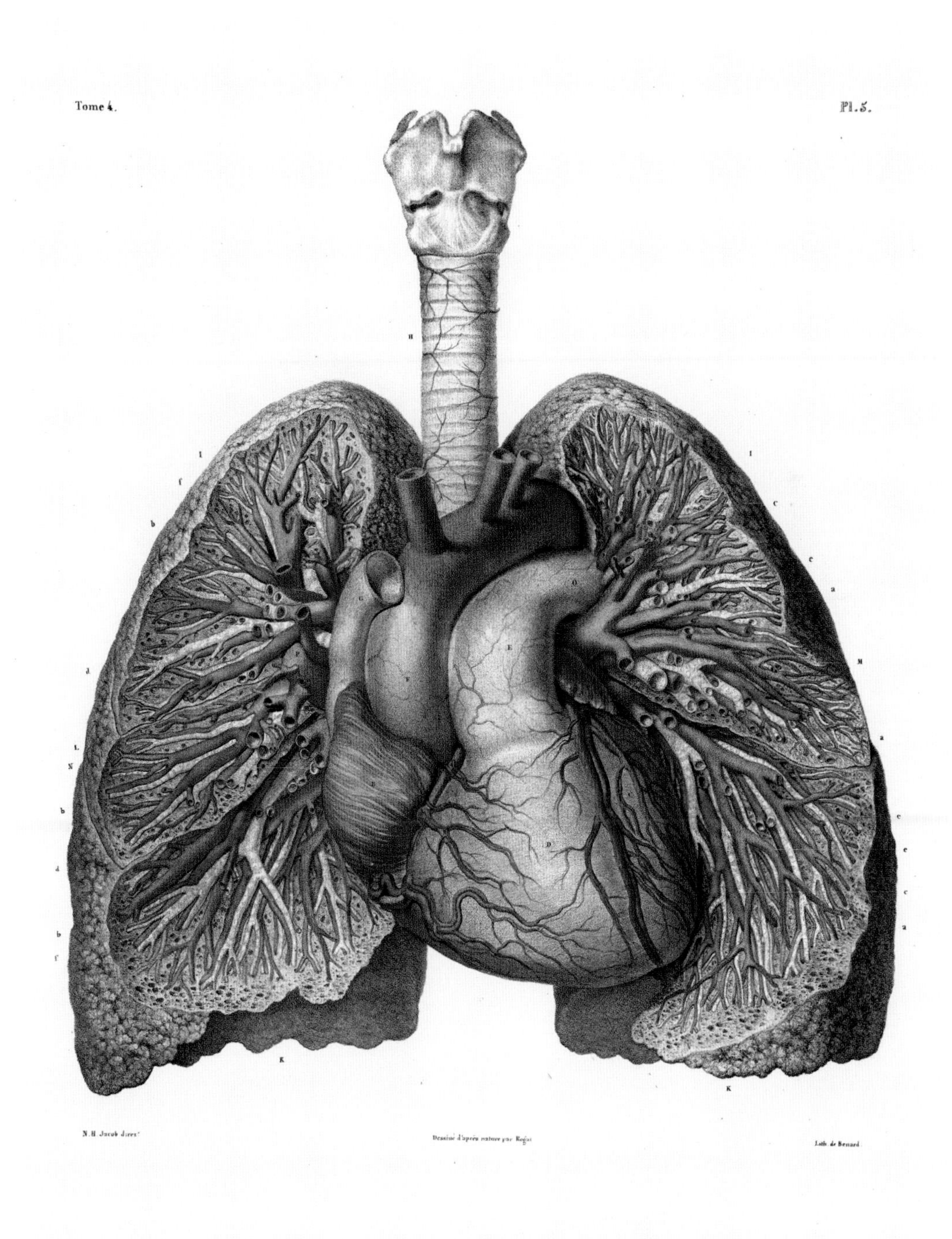

Lungs and heart: Pulmonary arteries and veins
Poumons et cœur : Artères et veines pulmonaires
Pulmones y corazón: arterias y venas pulmonares

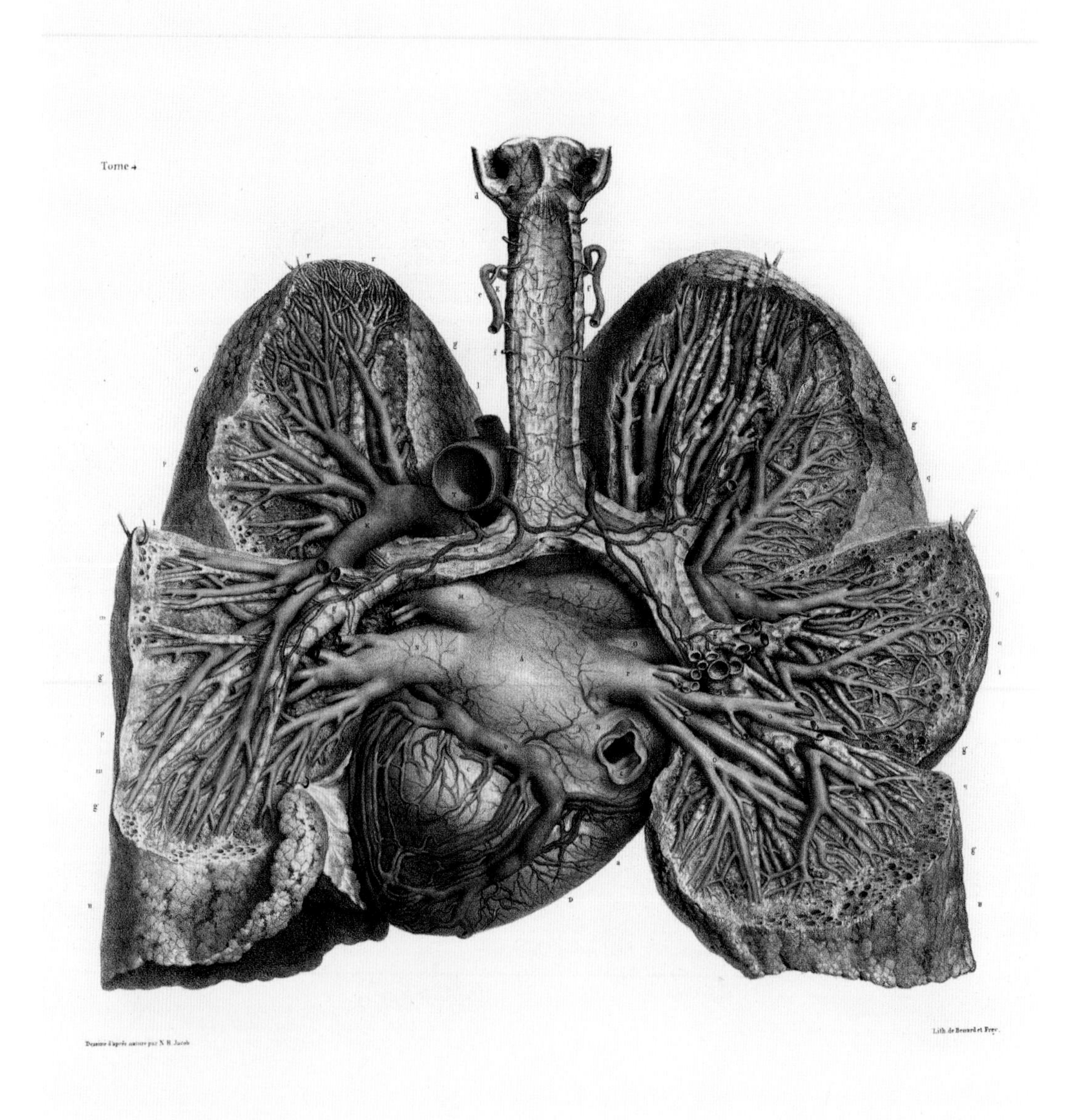

Lungs and heart: Pulmonary arteries and veins
Poumons et cœur : Artères et veines pulmonaires
Pulmones y corazón: arterias y venas pulmonares

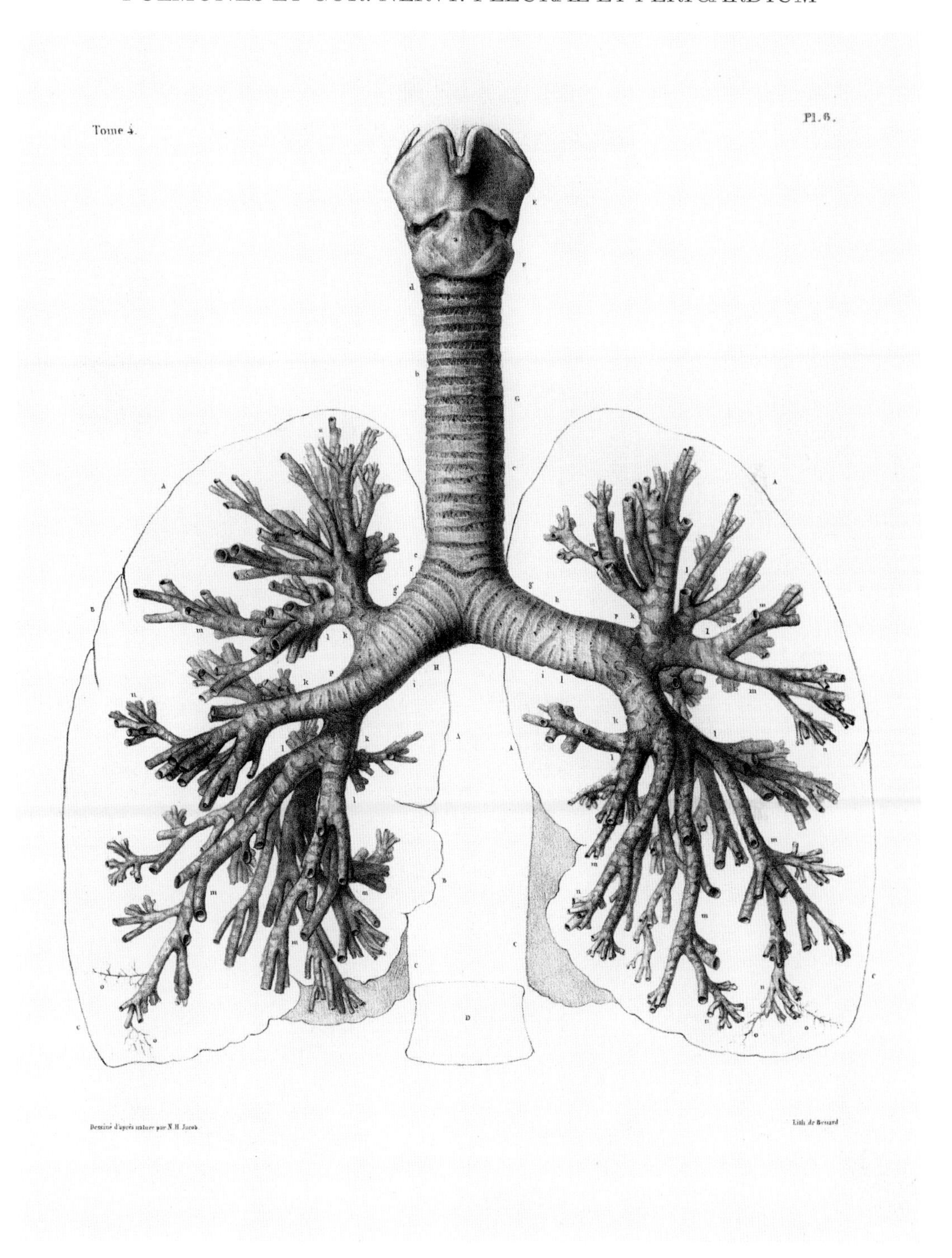

Trachea and bronchi / Trachée et bronches / Tráquea y bronquios

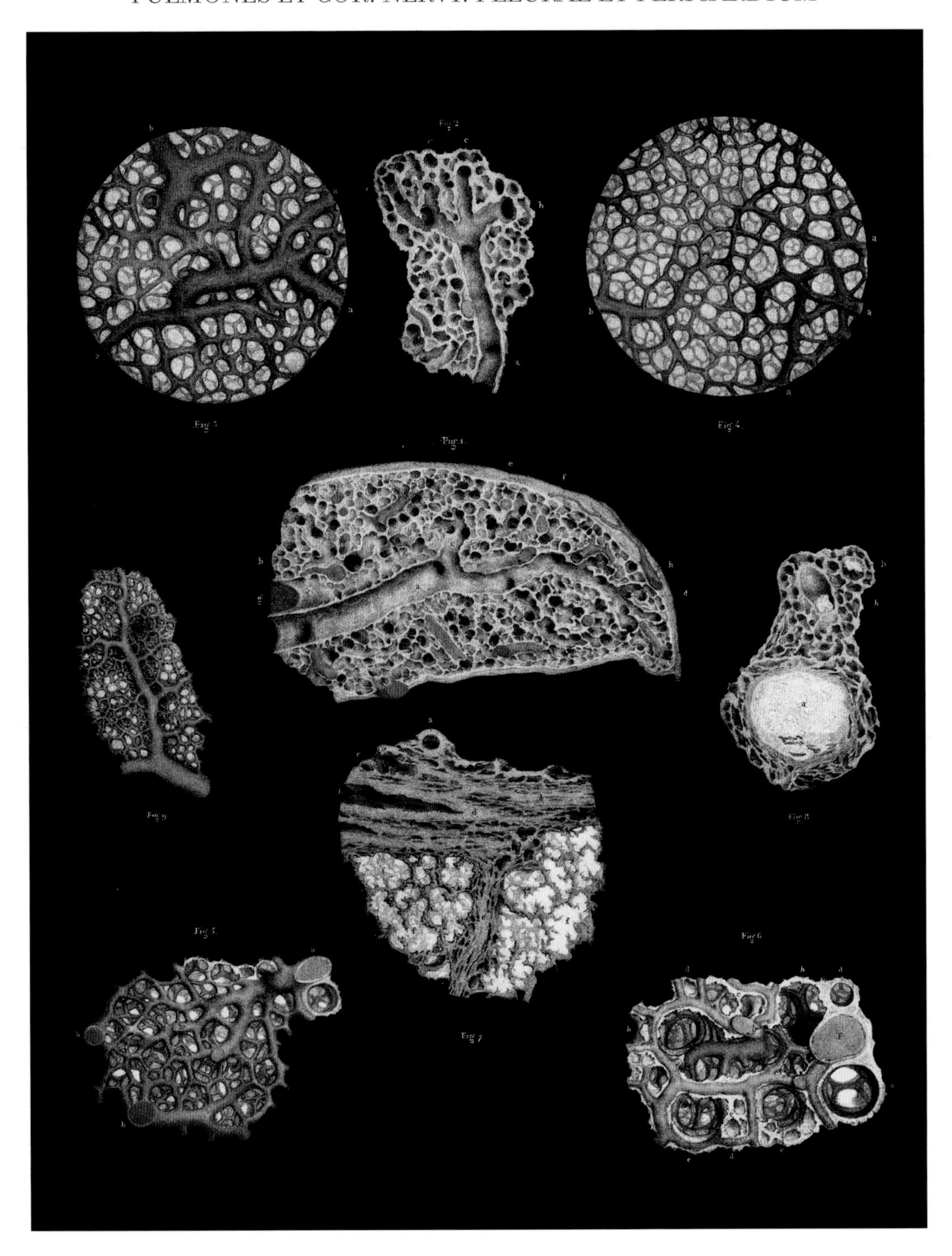

Lungs: Microscopic Anatomy / Poumons : Anatomie microscopique
Pulmones: anatomía microscópica

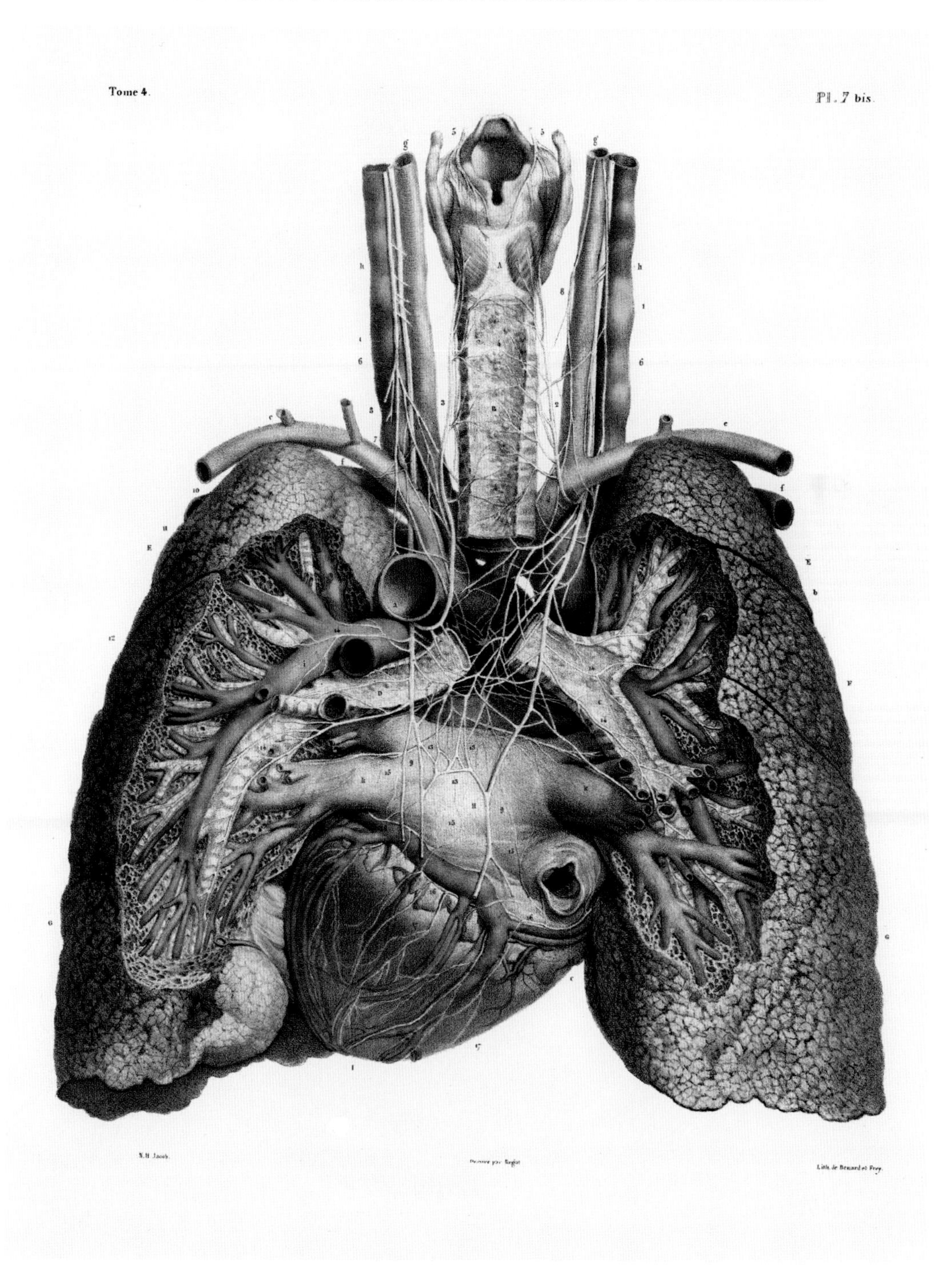

Lungs and heart: Nerves / Poumons et cœur : Nerfs
Pulmones y corazón: nervios

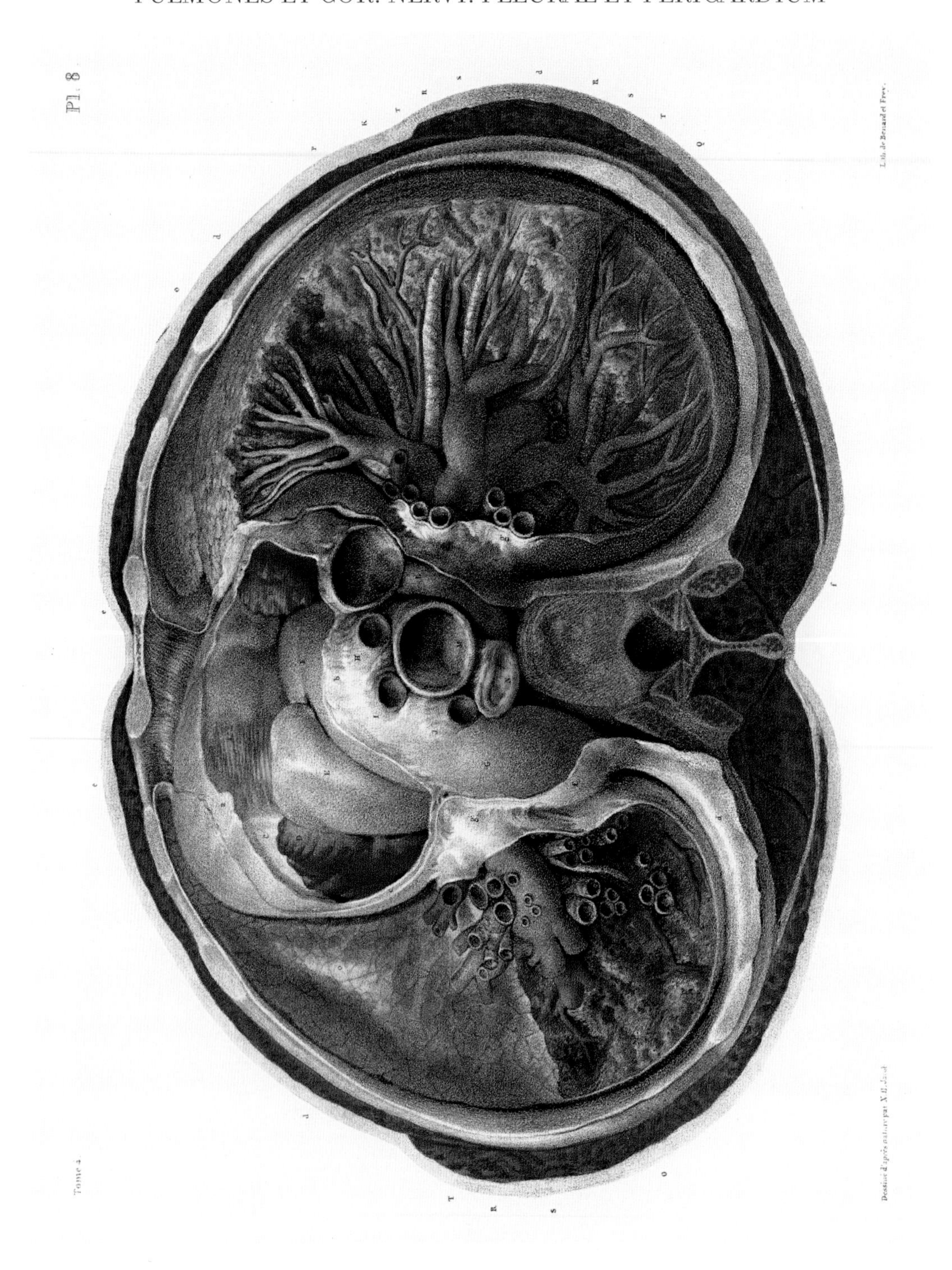

Lungs and heart: Pleuræ and pericardium / Poumons et cœur : Plèvres et péricarde
Pulmones y corazón: pleuras y pericardio

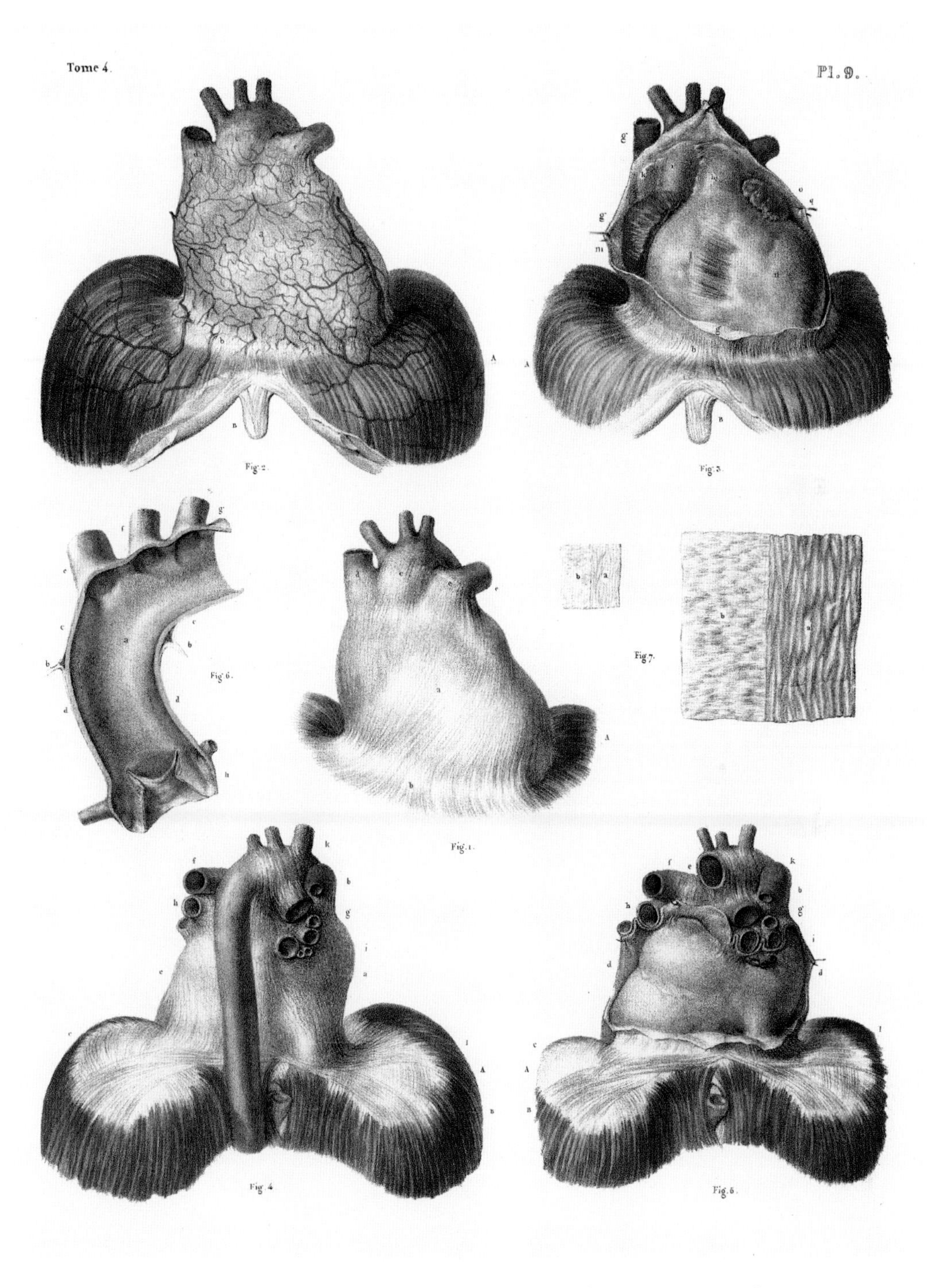

Heart and pericardium / Cœur et péricarde / Corazón y pericardio

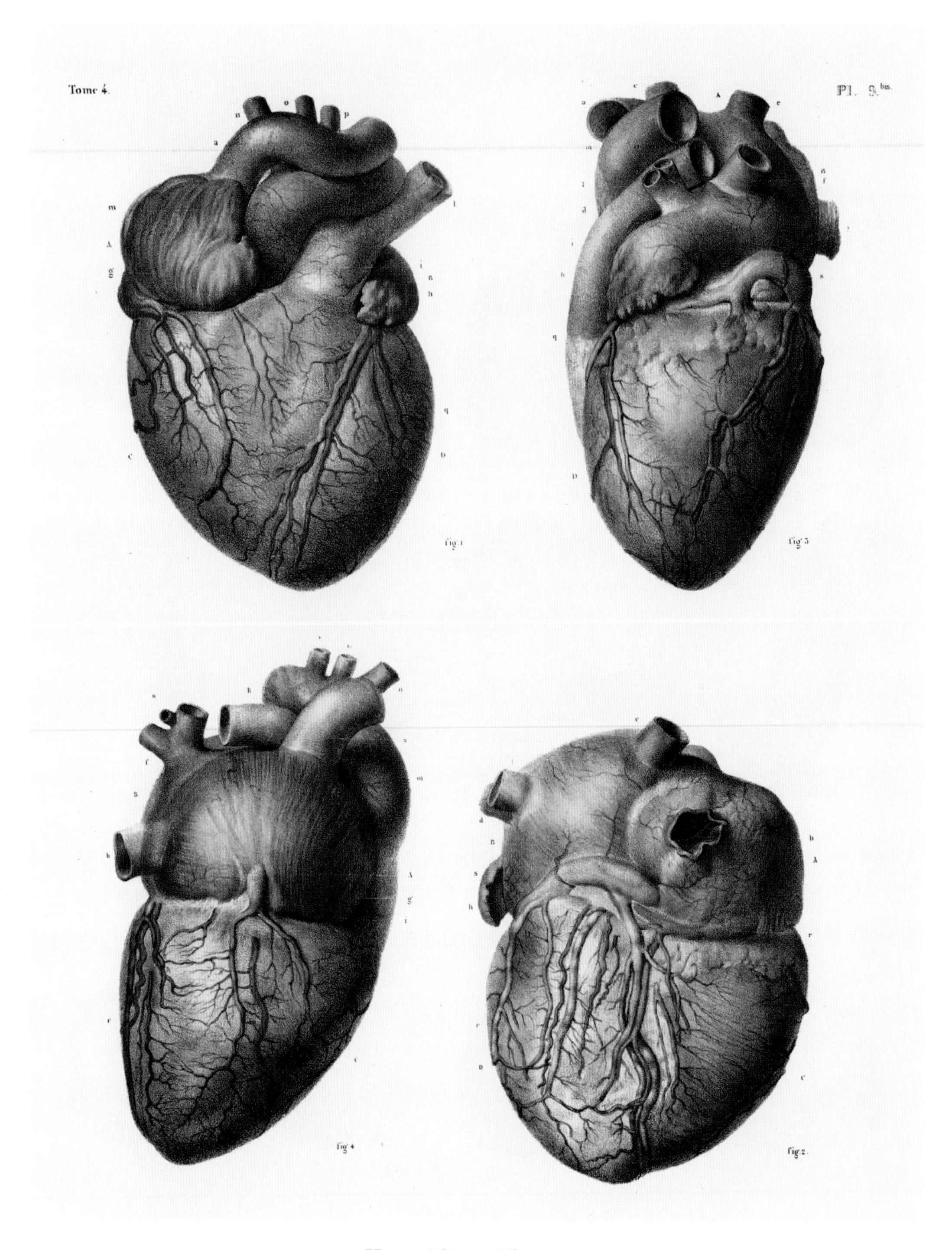

Heart / Cœur / Corazón

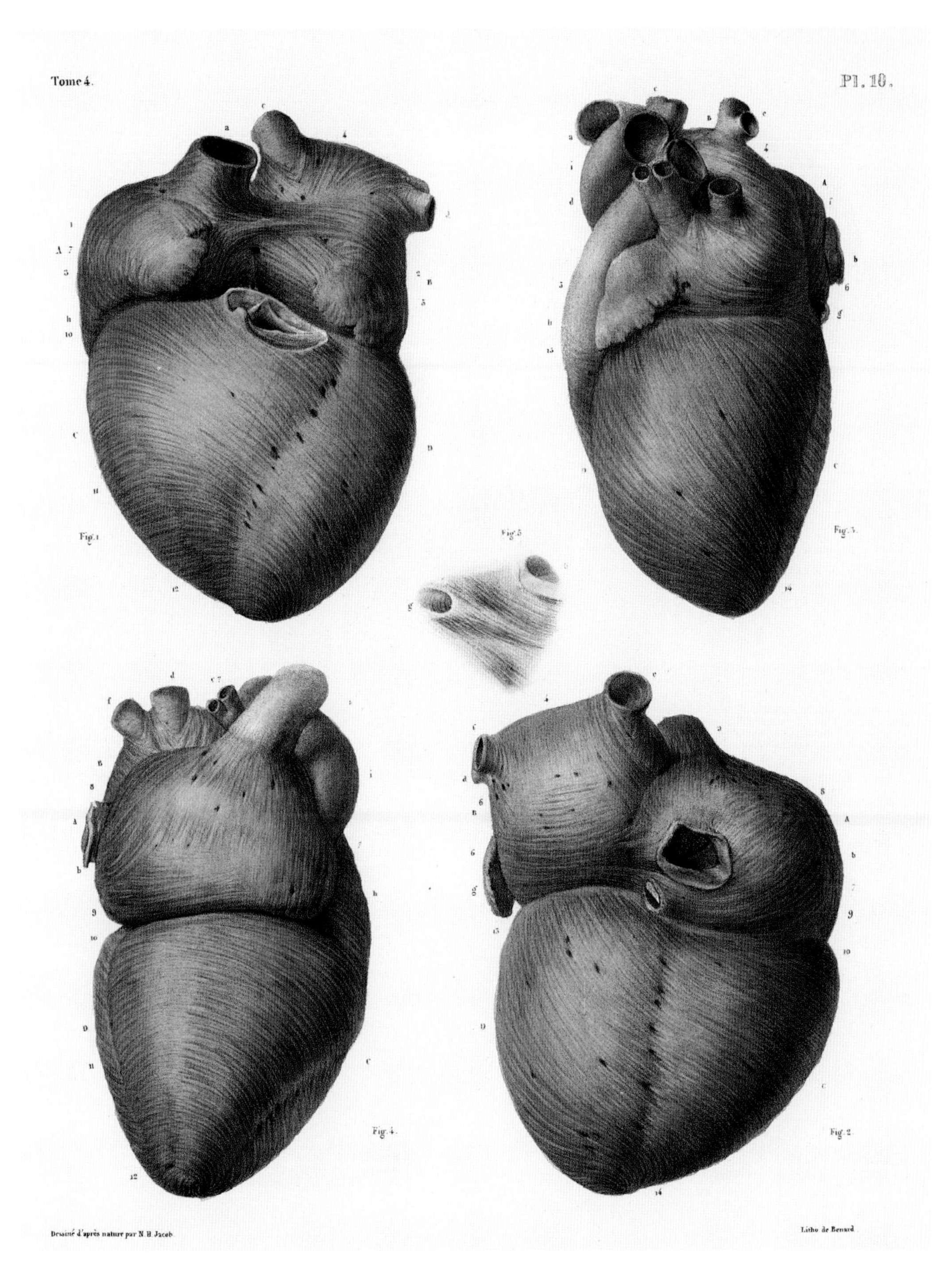

Heart: Myocardium / Cœur : Myocarde / Corazón: miocardio

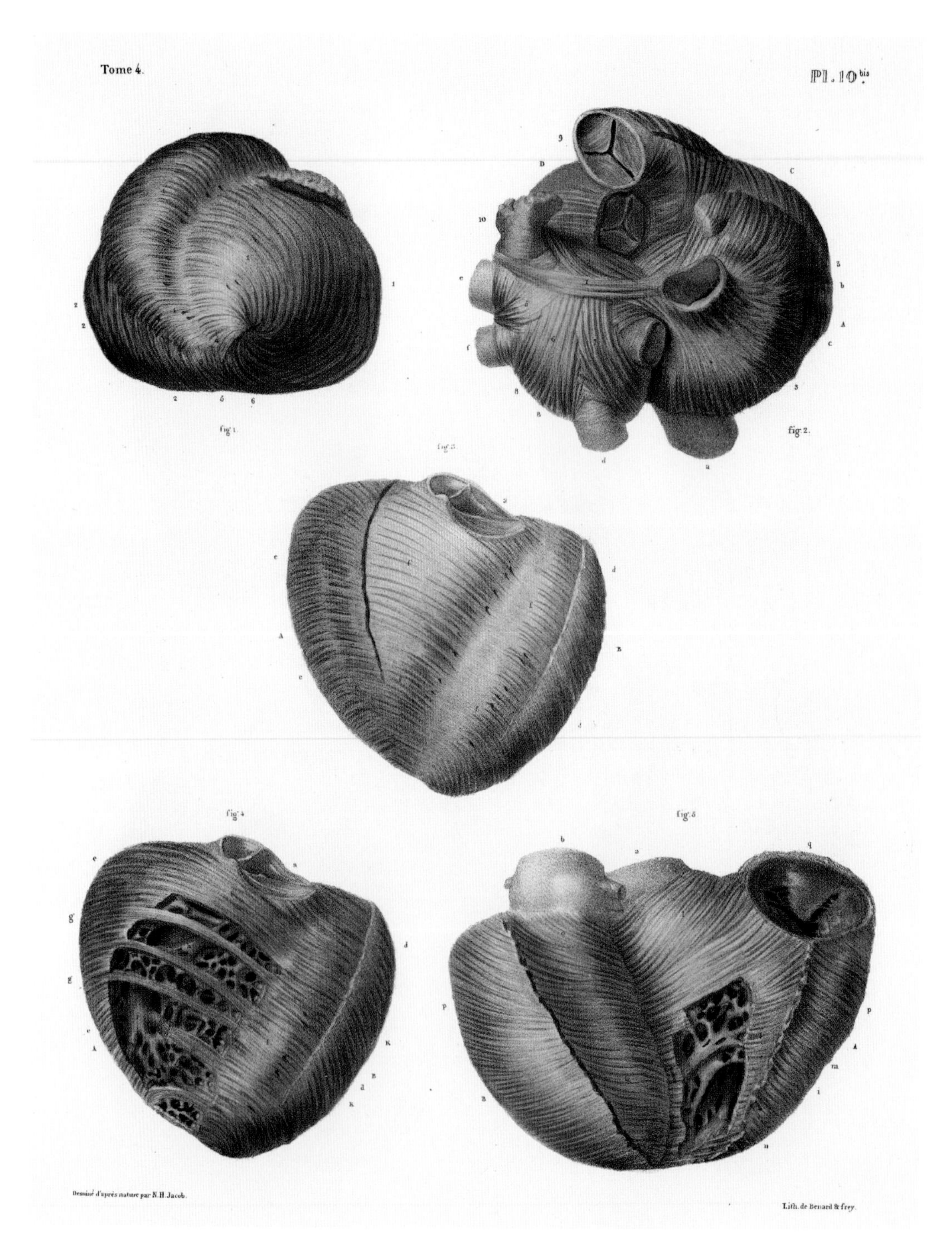

Heart: Structure of the myocardium / Cœur : Structure du myocarde
Corazón: estructura del miocardio

COR: STRUCTURA MYOCARDII, CAVITATES CORDIS, VASA ET NERVI

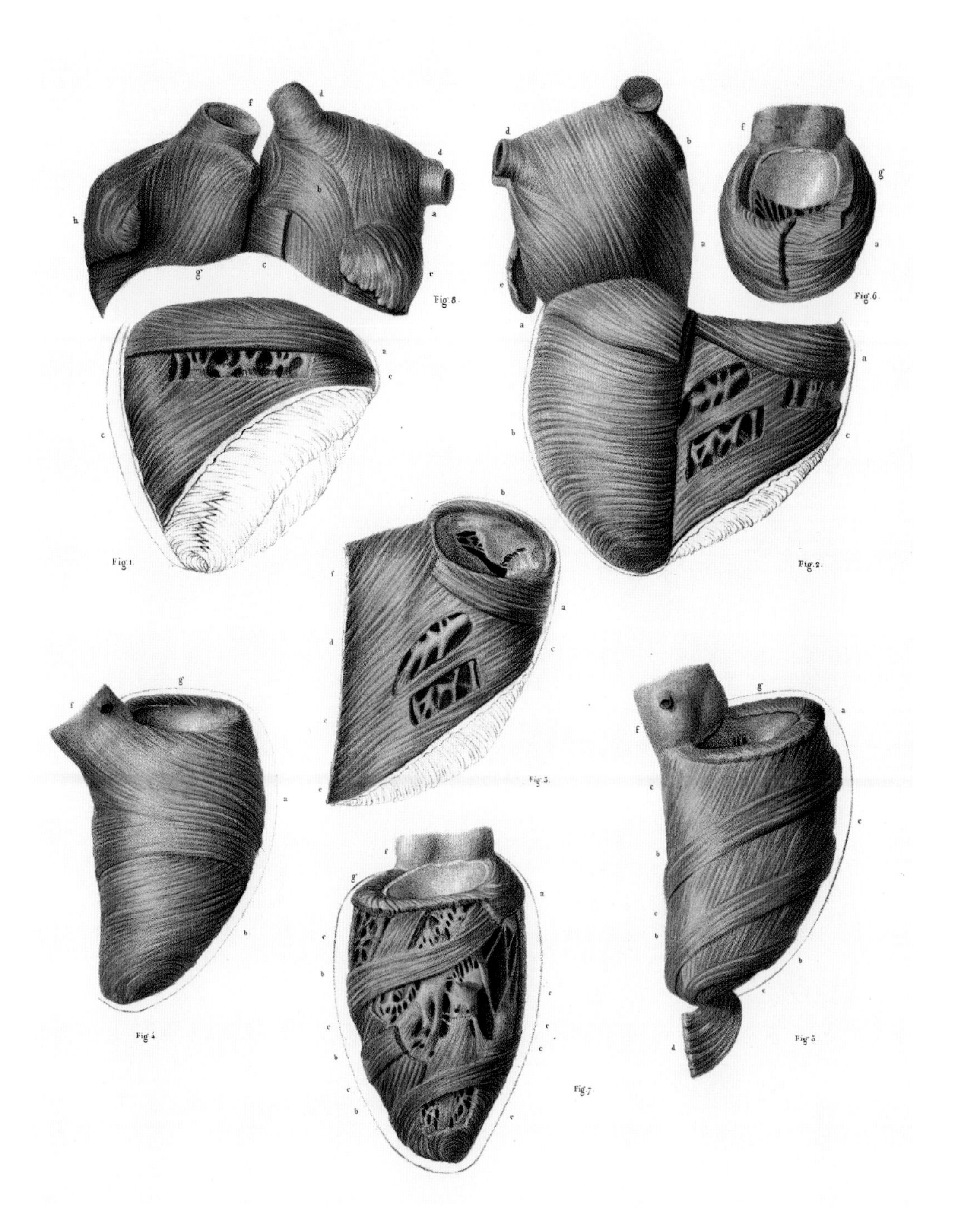

Heart: Structure of the myocardium / Cœur : Structure du myocarde
Corazón: estructura del miocardio

COR: STRUCTURA MYOCARDII, CAVITATES CORDIS, VASA ET NERVI

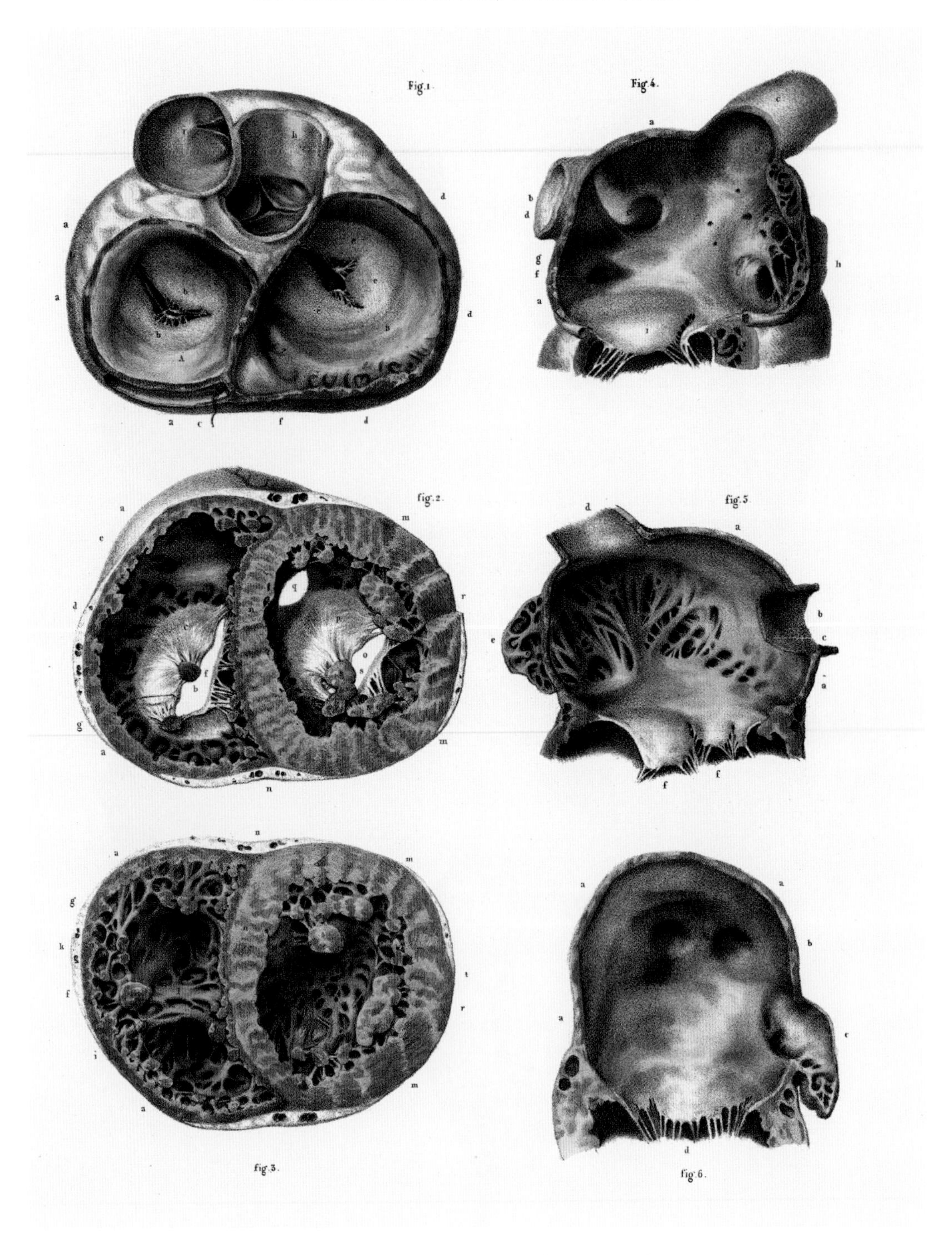

Heart: Cardiac cavities / Cœur : Cavités cardiaques
Corazón: cavidades cardíacas

COR: STRUCTURA MYOCARDII, CAVITATES CORDIS, VASA ET NERVI

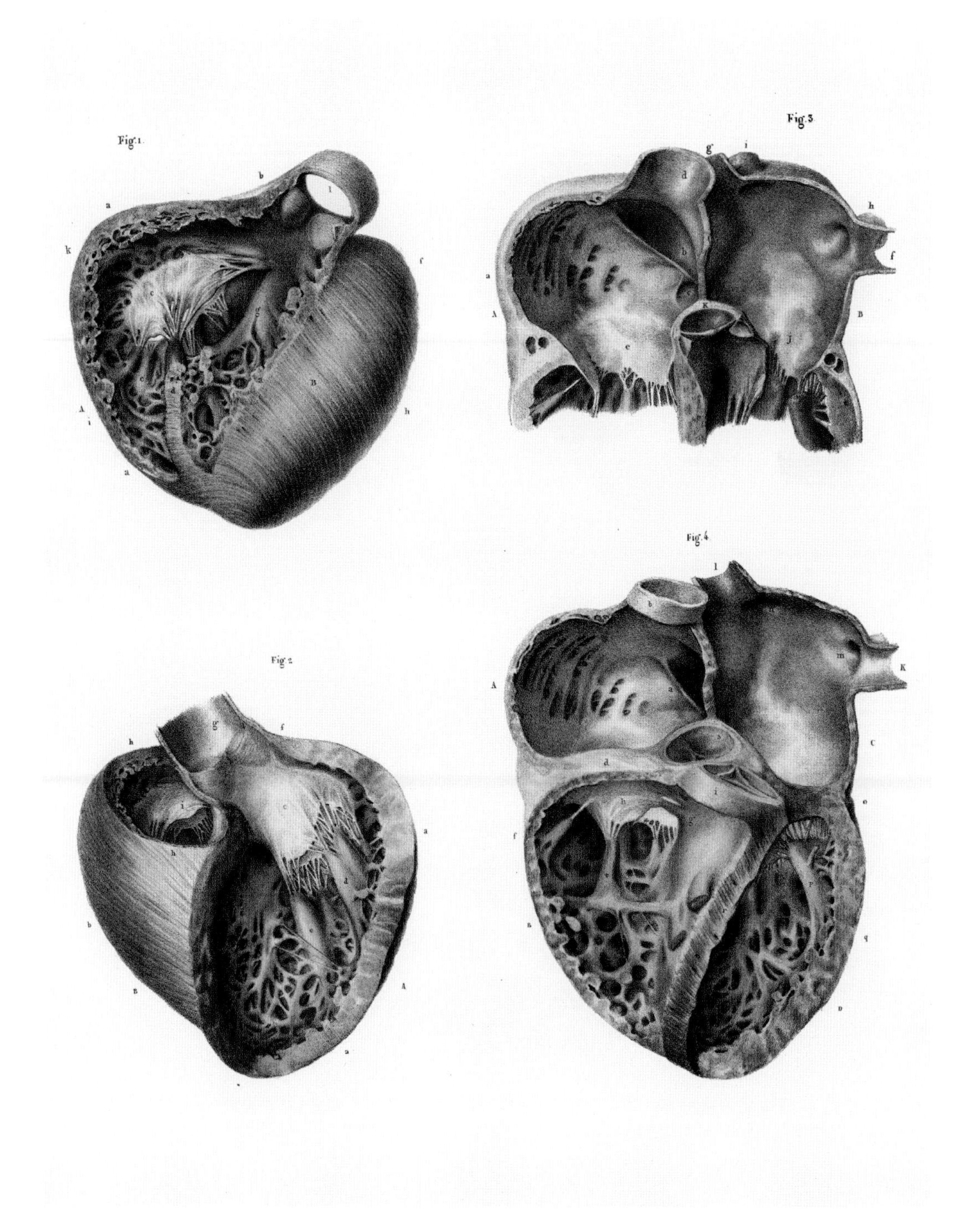

Heart: Cardiac cavities / Cœur : Cavités cardiaques
Corazón: cavidades cardíacas

COR: STRUCTURA MYOCARDII, CAVITATES CORDIS, VASA ET NERVI

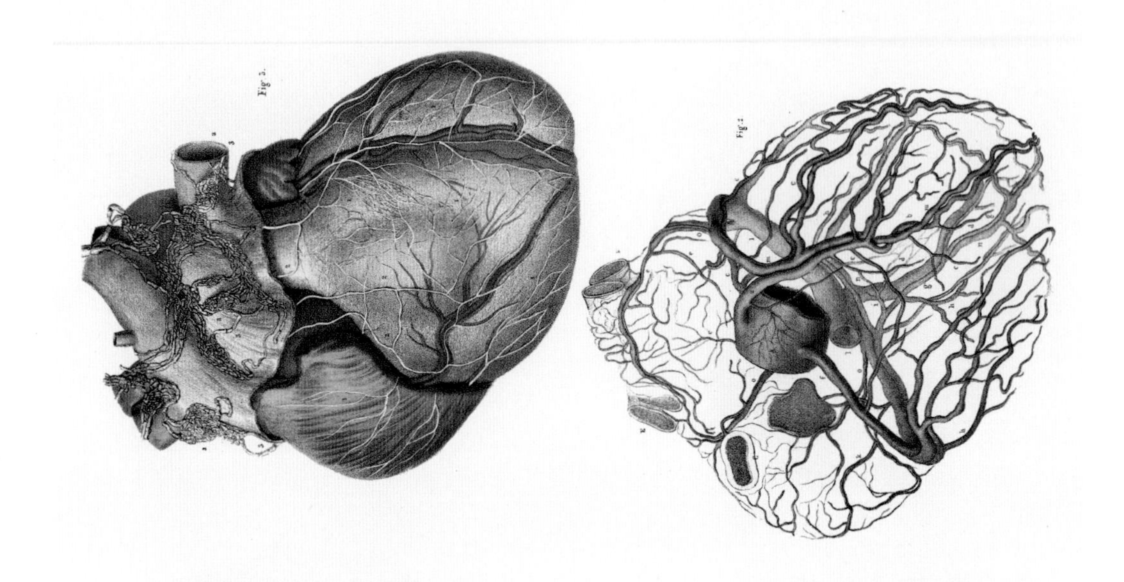

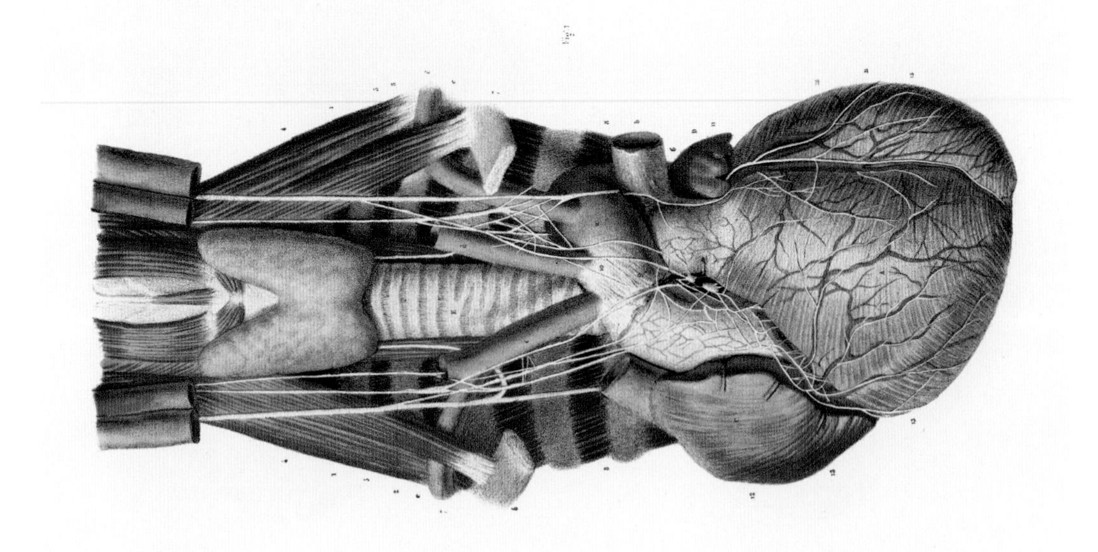

Heart: Vessels and nerves / Cœur : Vaisseaux et nerfs
Corazón: vasos y nervios

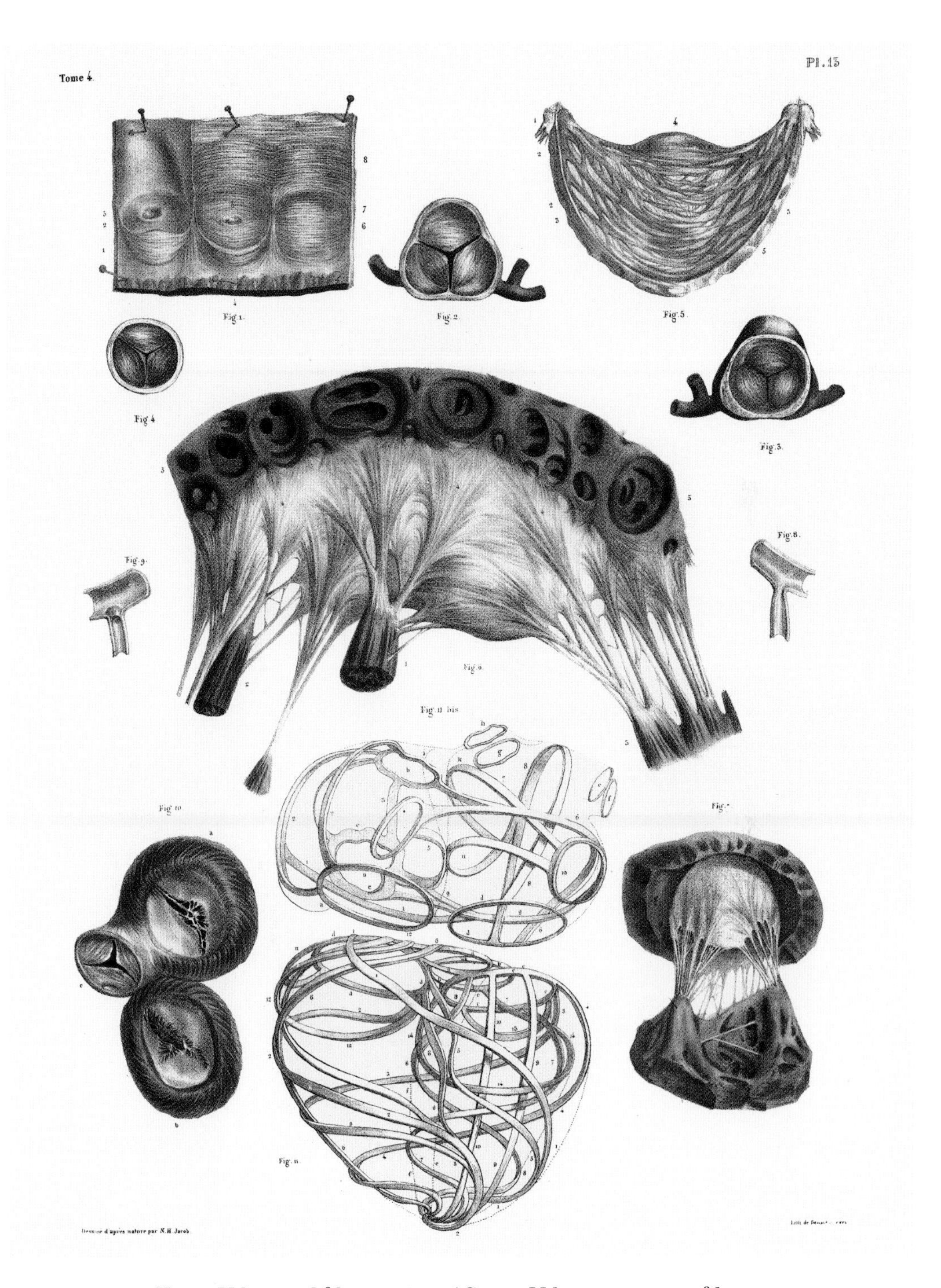

Heart: Valves and fibrous rings / Cœur : Valves et anneaux fibreux
Corazón: válvulas y anillos fibrosos

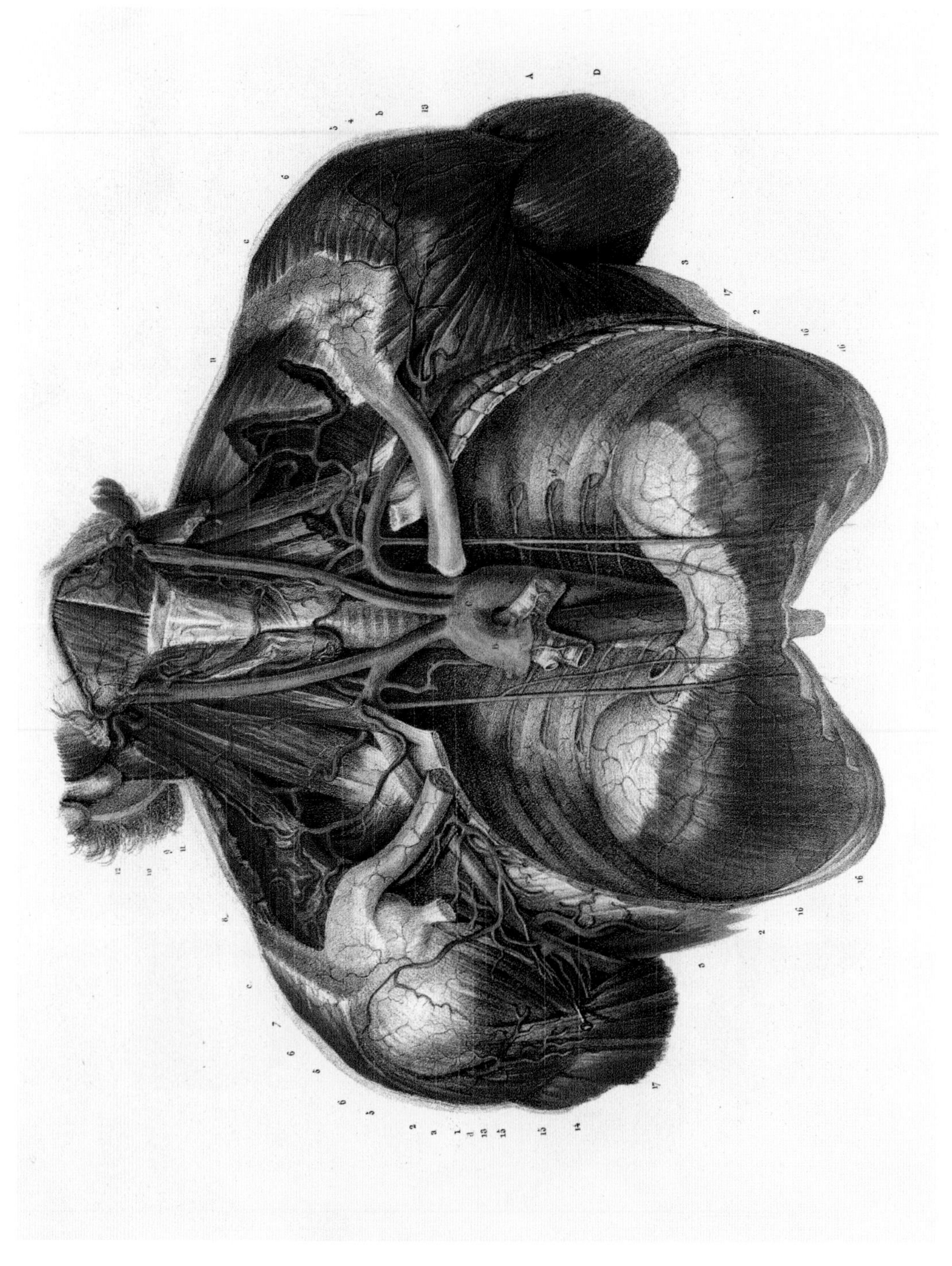

Aortic arch and thoracic aorta / Arc aortique et aorte thoracique
Arco aórtico y aorta torácica

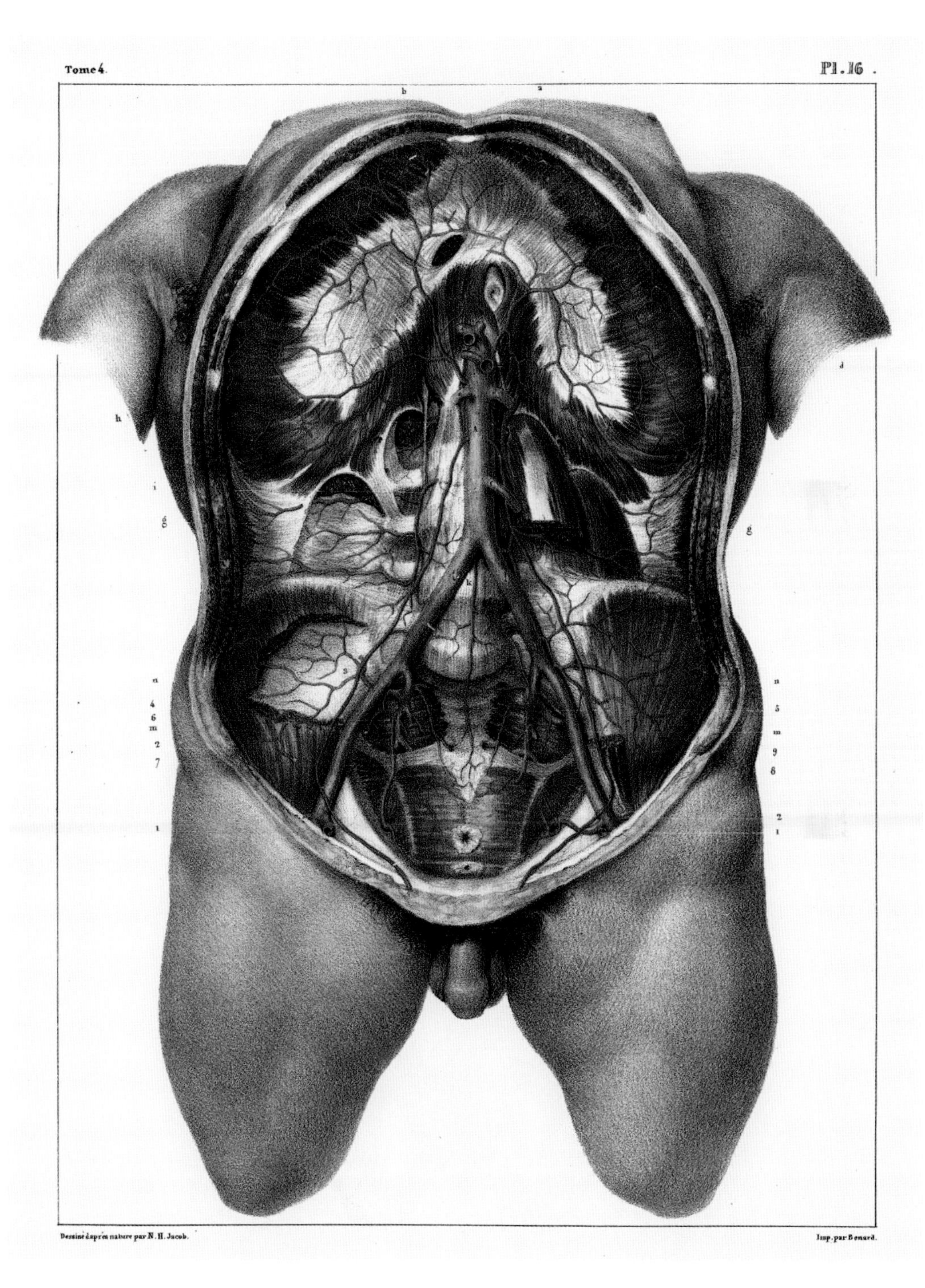

Abdominal aorta / Aorte abdominale
Aorta abdominal

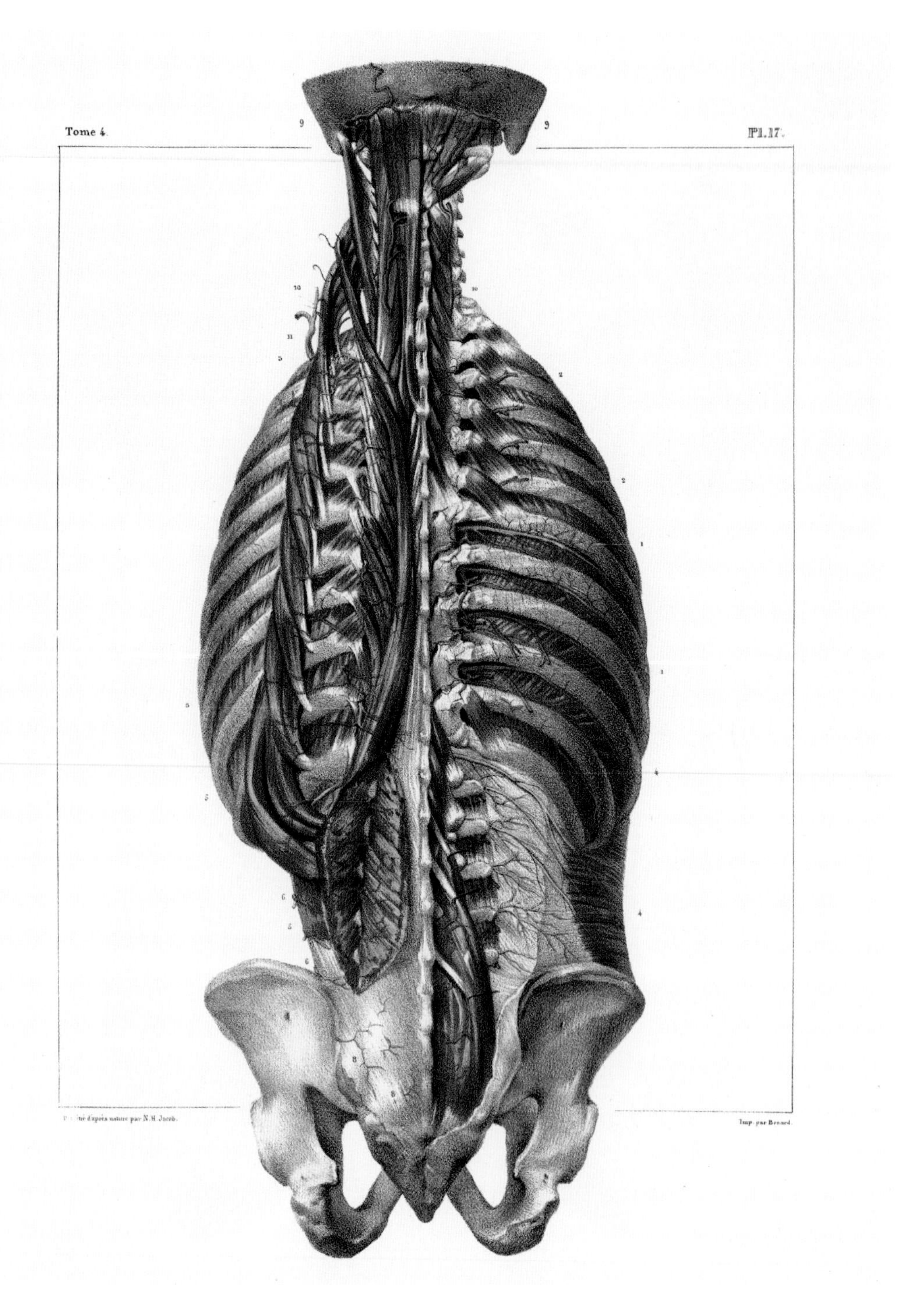

Arteries of the walls of thorax and abdomen
Artères des parois du thorax et de l'abdomen
Arterias de las paredes del tórax y del abdomen

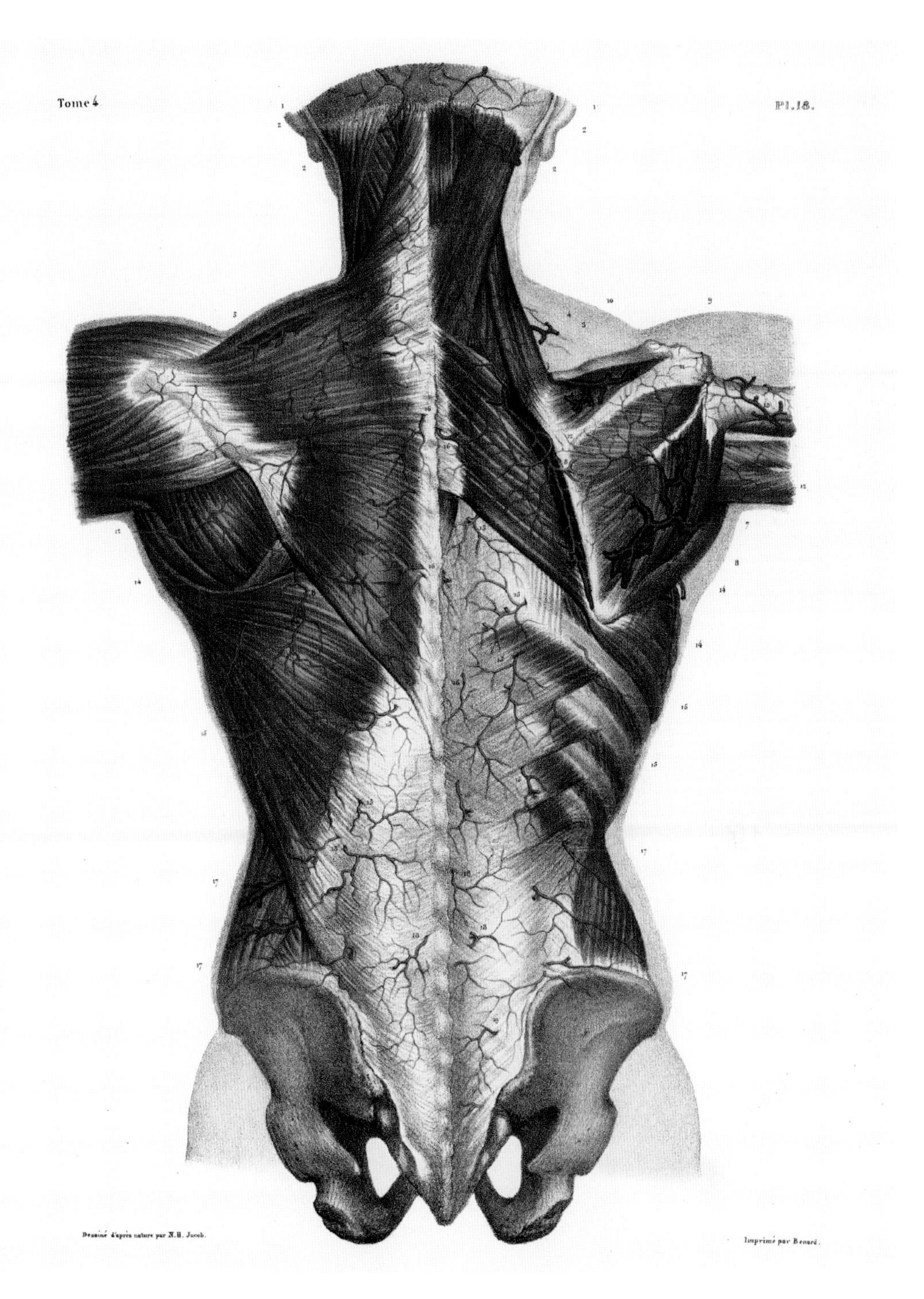

Arteries of the walls of thorax and abdomen
Artères des parois du thorax et de l'abdomen
Arterias de las paredes del tórax y del abdomen

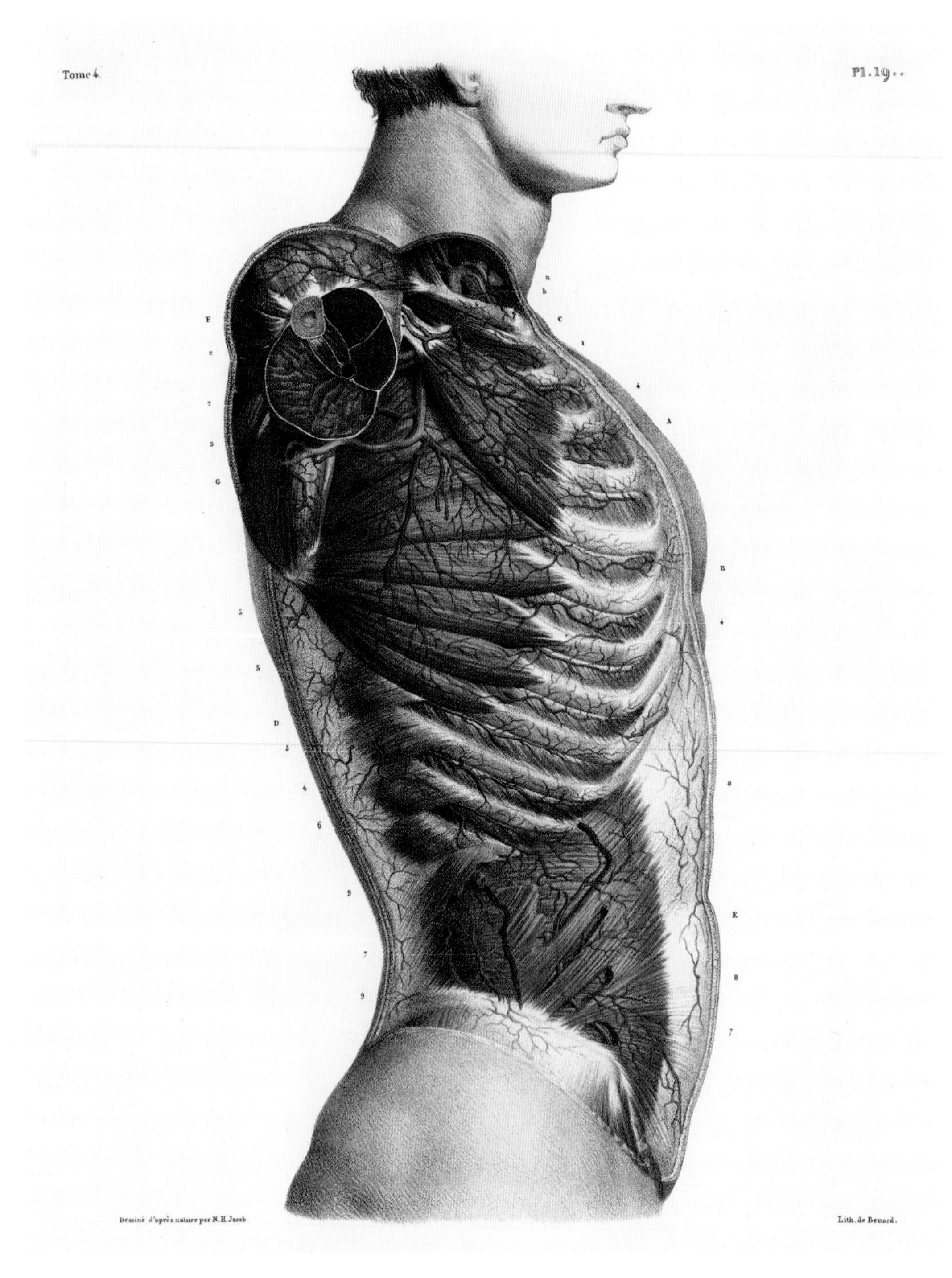

Arteries of the walls of thorax and abdomen
Artères des parois du thorax et de l'abdomen
Arterias de las paredes del tórax y del abdomen

Arteries of the walls of thorax and abdomen
Artères des parois du thorax et de l'abdomen
Arterias de las paredes del tórax y del abdomen

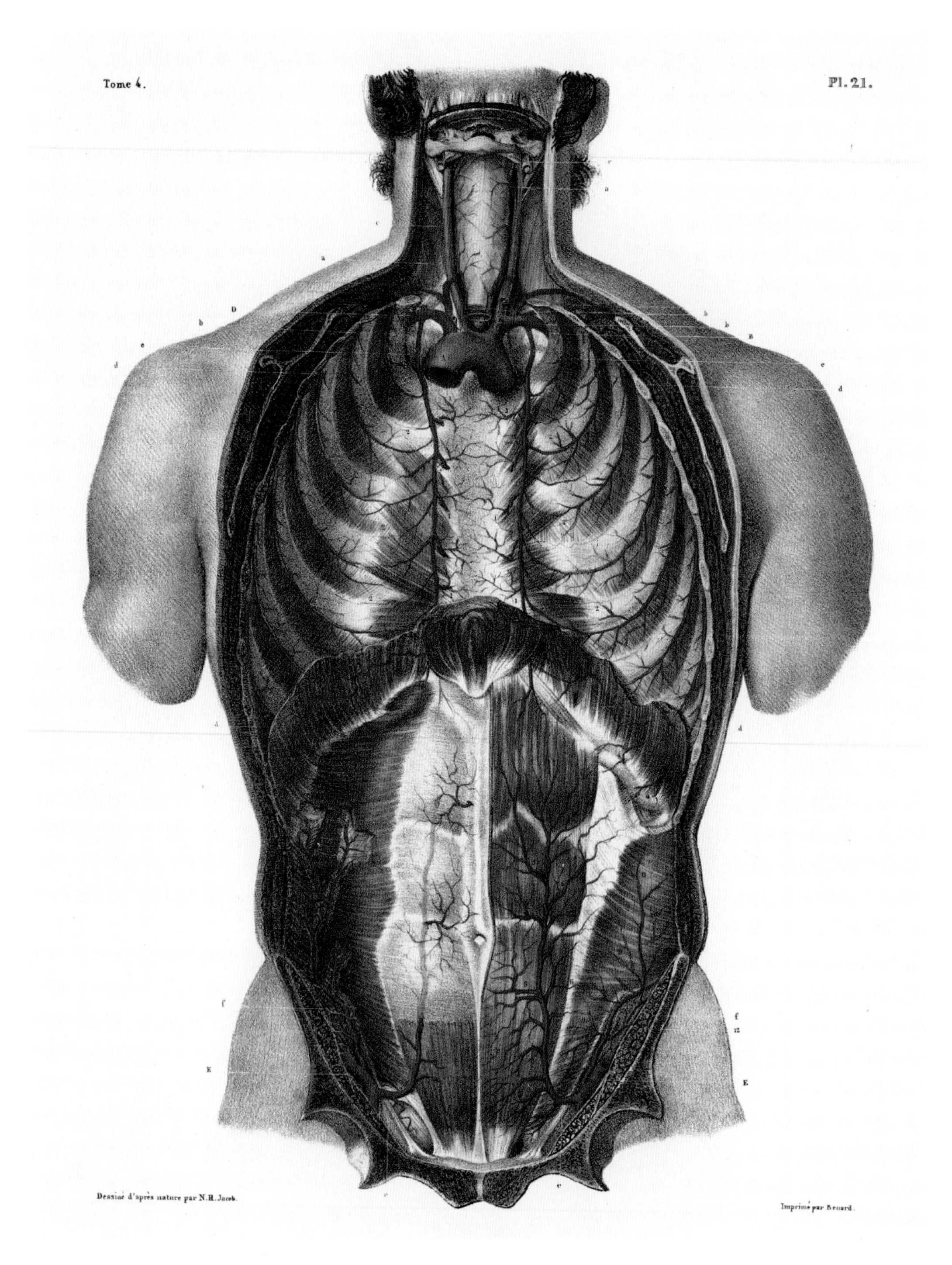

Arteries of the walls of thorax and abdomen
Artères des parois du thorax et de l'abdomen
Arterias de las paredes del tórax y del abdomen

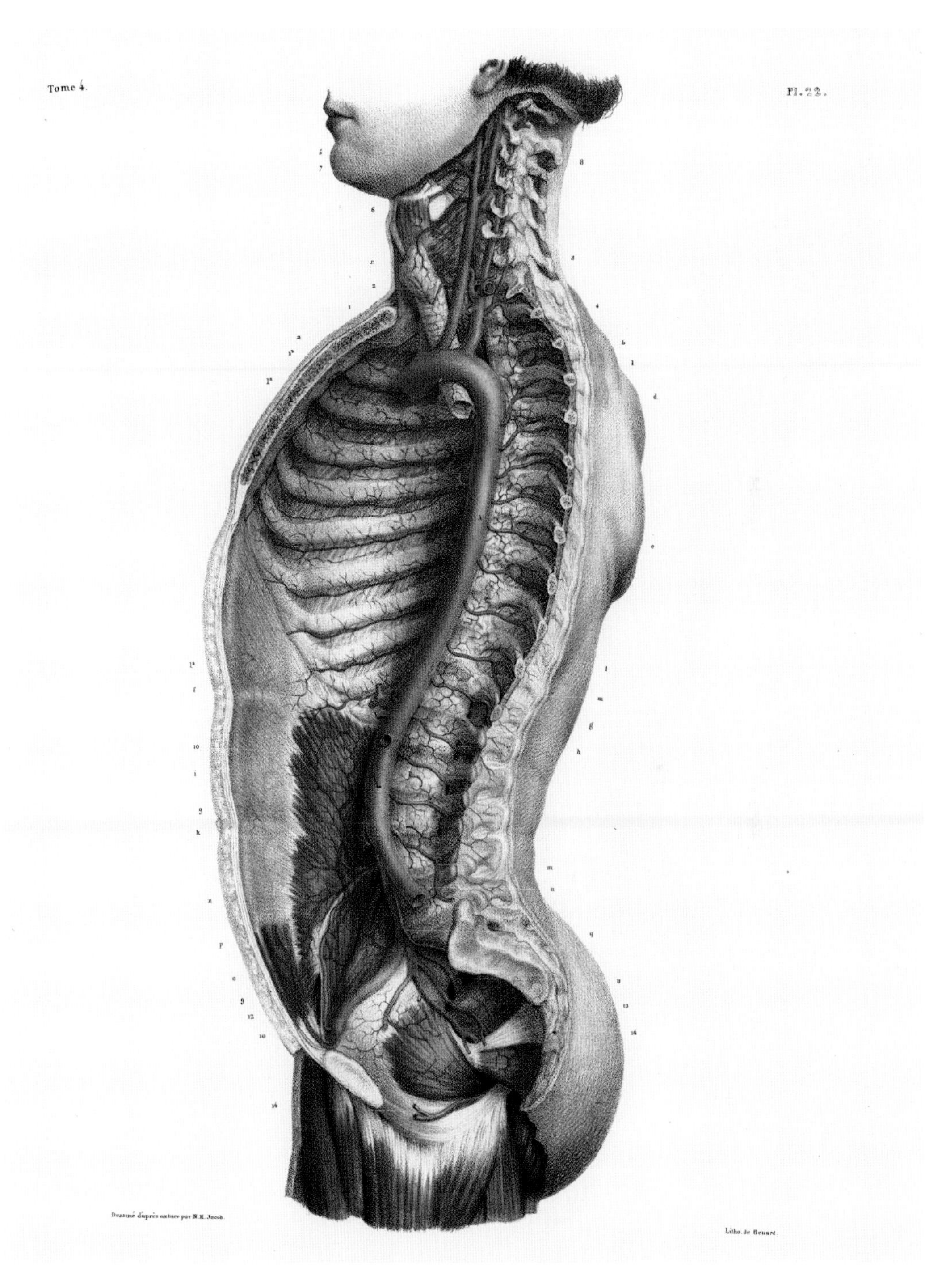

Arteries of the walls of thorax and abdomen
Artères des parois du thorax et de l'abdomen
Arterias de las paredes del tórax y del abdomen

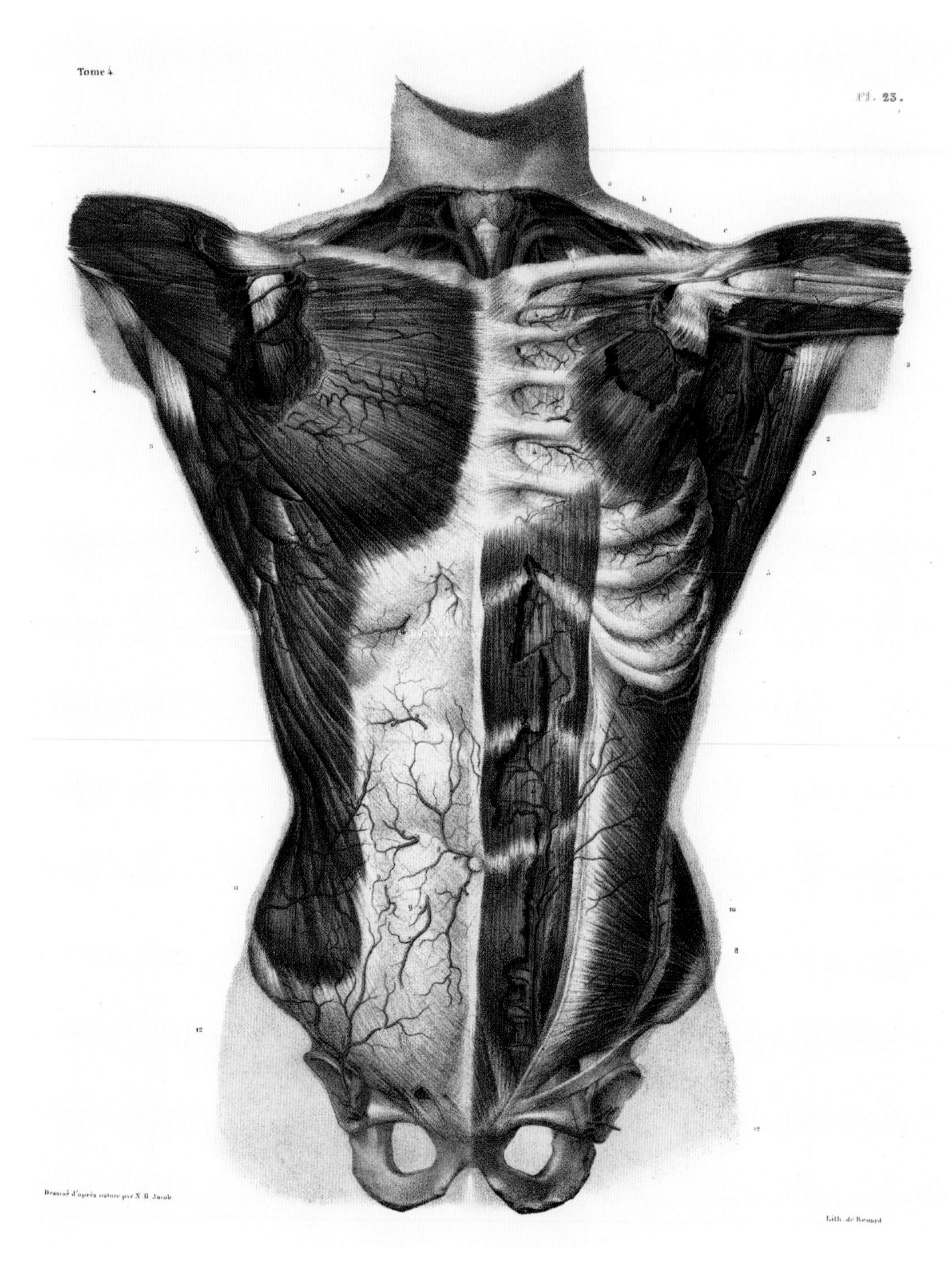

Arteries of the walls of thorax and abdomen
Artères des parois du thorax et de l'abdomen
Arterias de las paredes del tórax y del abdomen

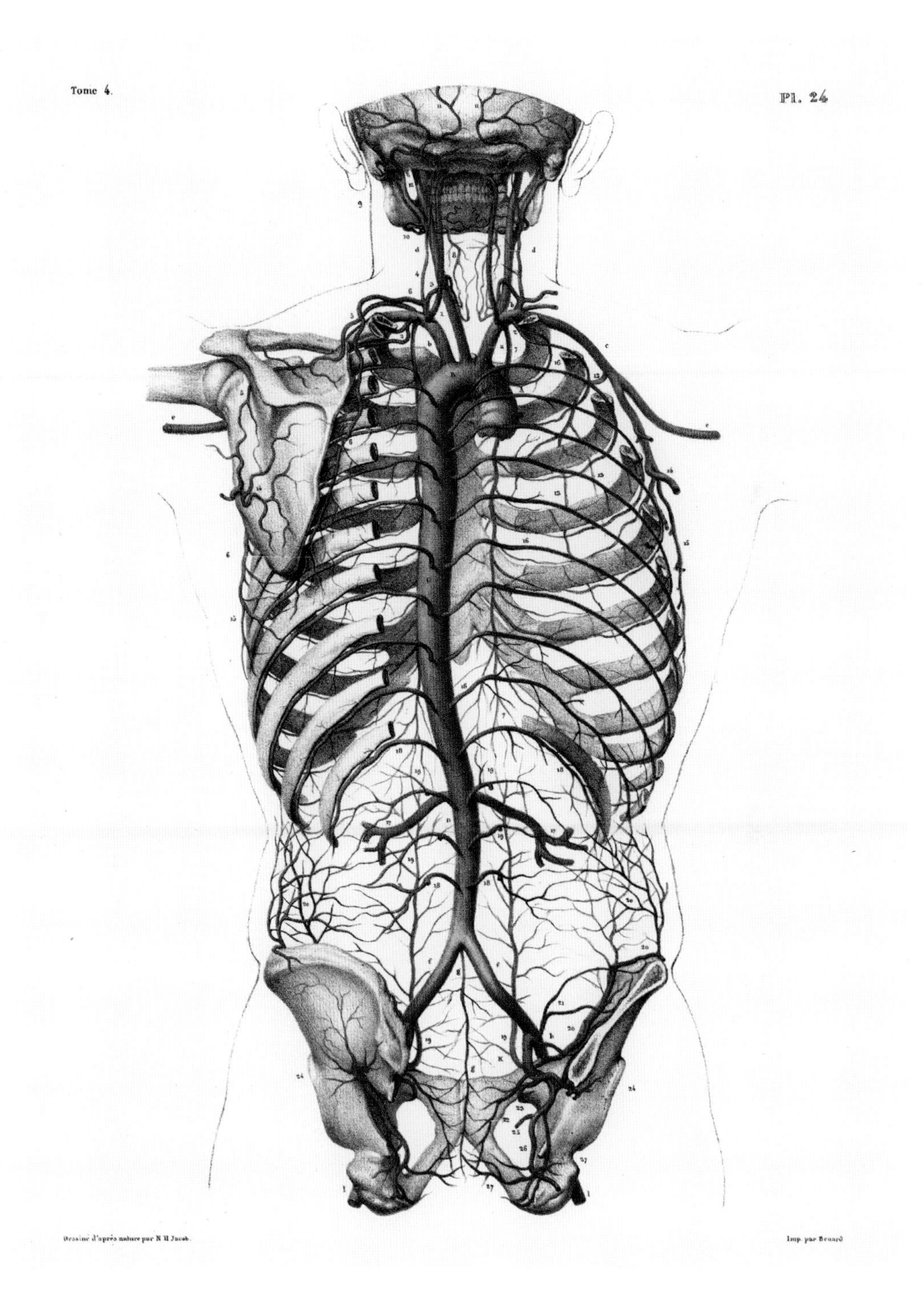

Aorta / Aorte / Aorta

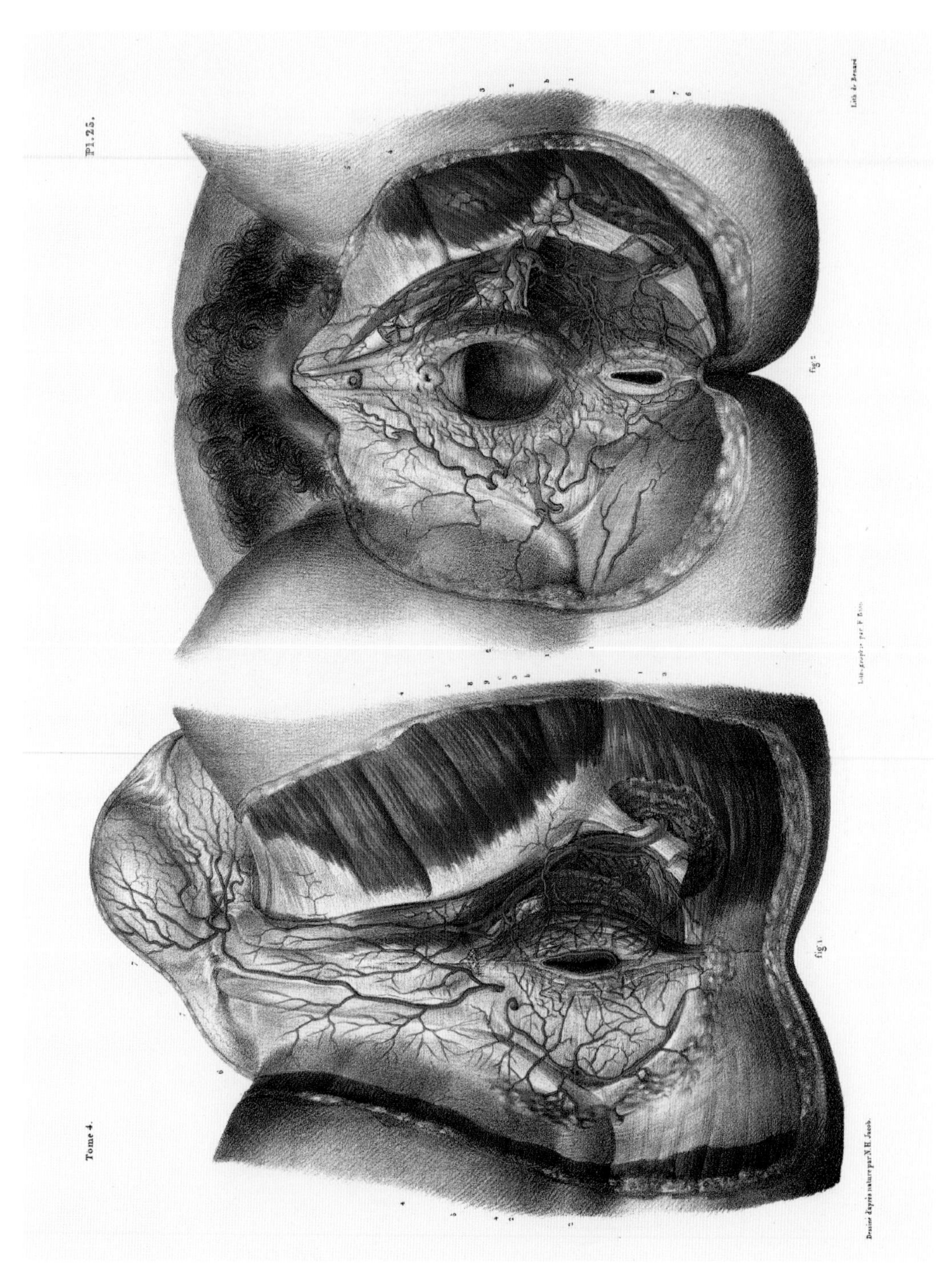

Arteries of the perineum / Artères du périnée
Arterias del periné

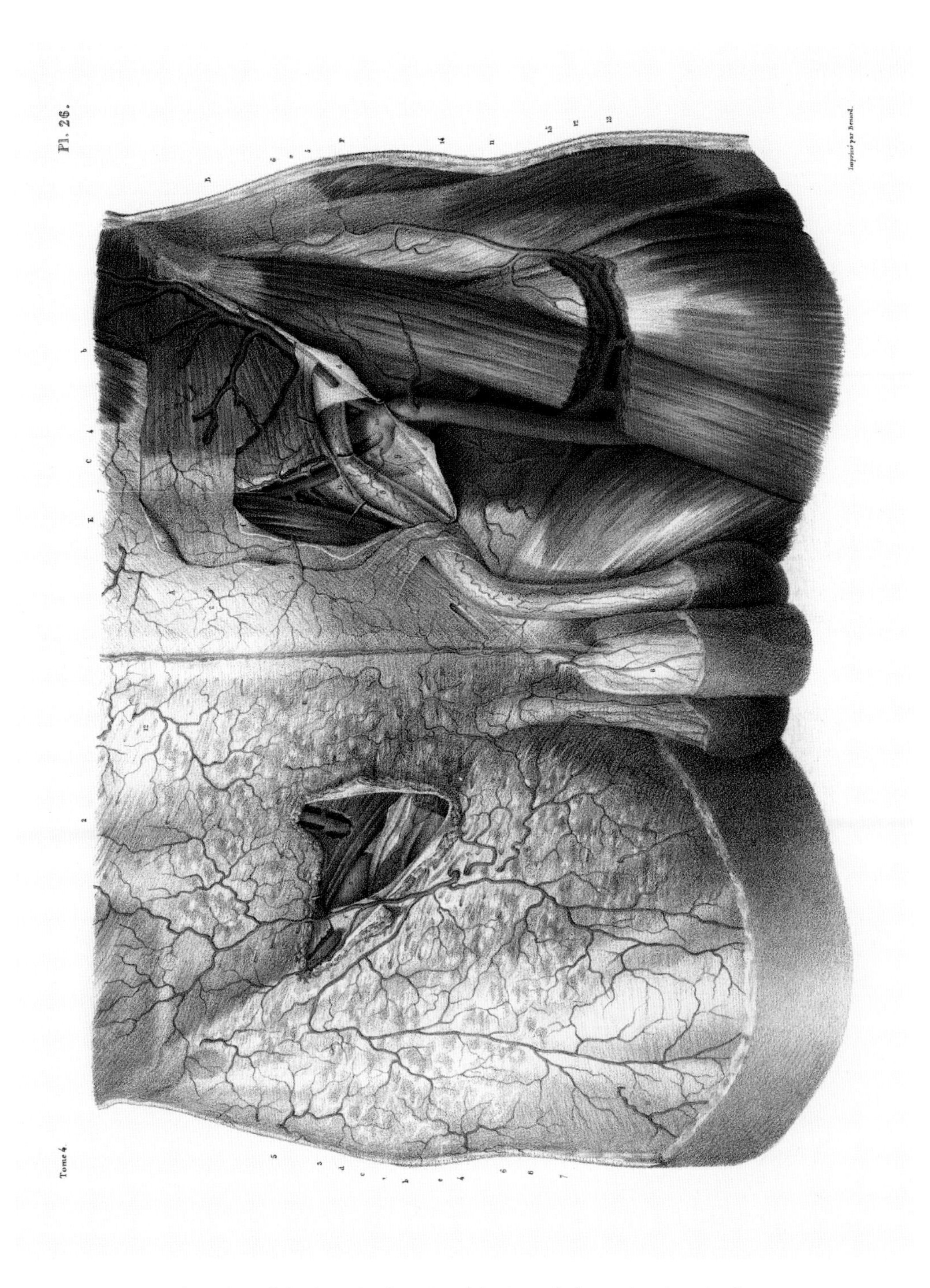

Arteries of the inguinal region / Artères de la région inguinale
Arterias de la región inguinal

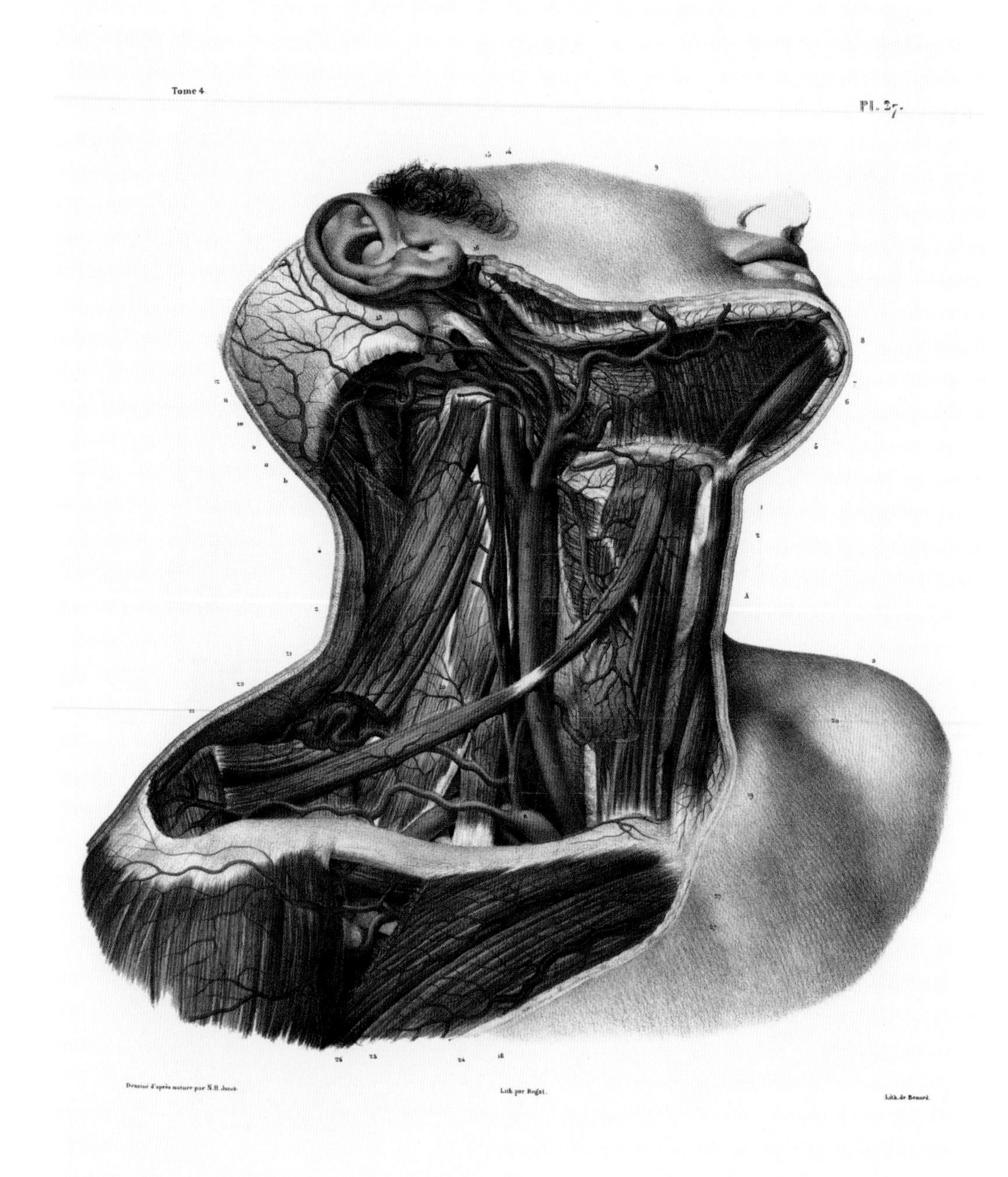

Arteries of the neck / Artères du cou / Arterias del cuello

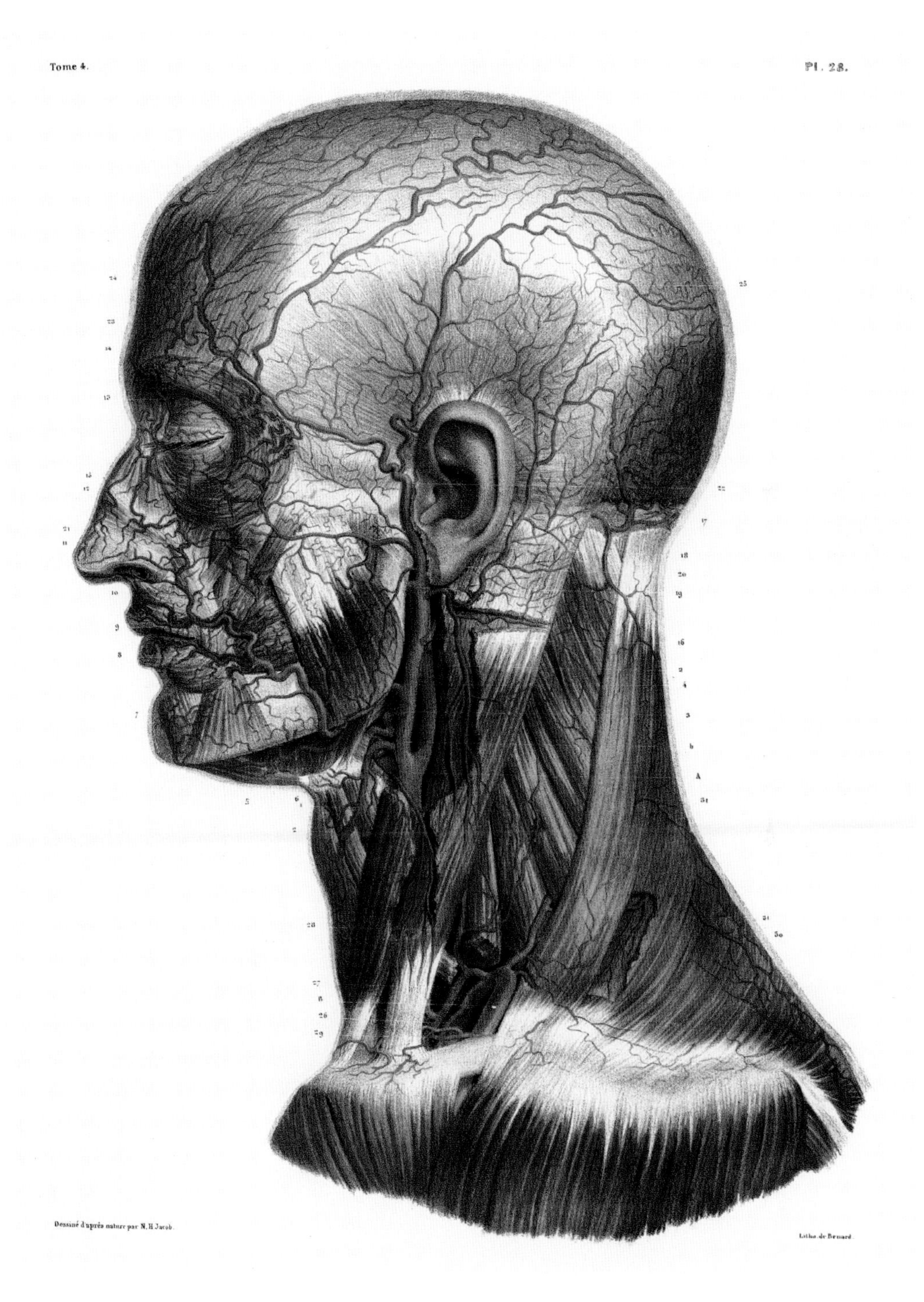

Arteries of the head and neck / Artères de la tête et du cou
Arterias de la cabeza y del cuello

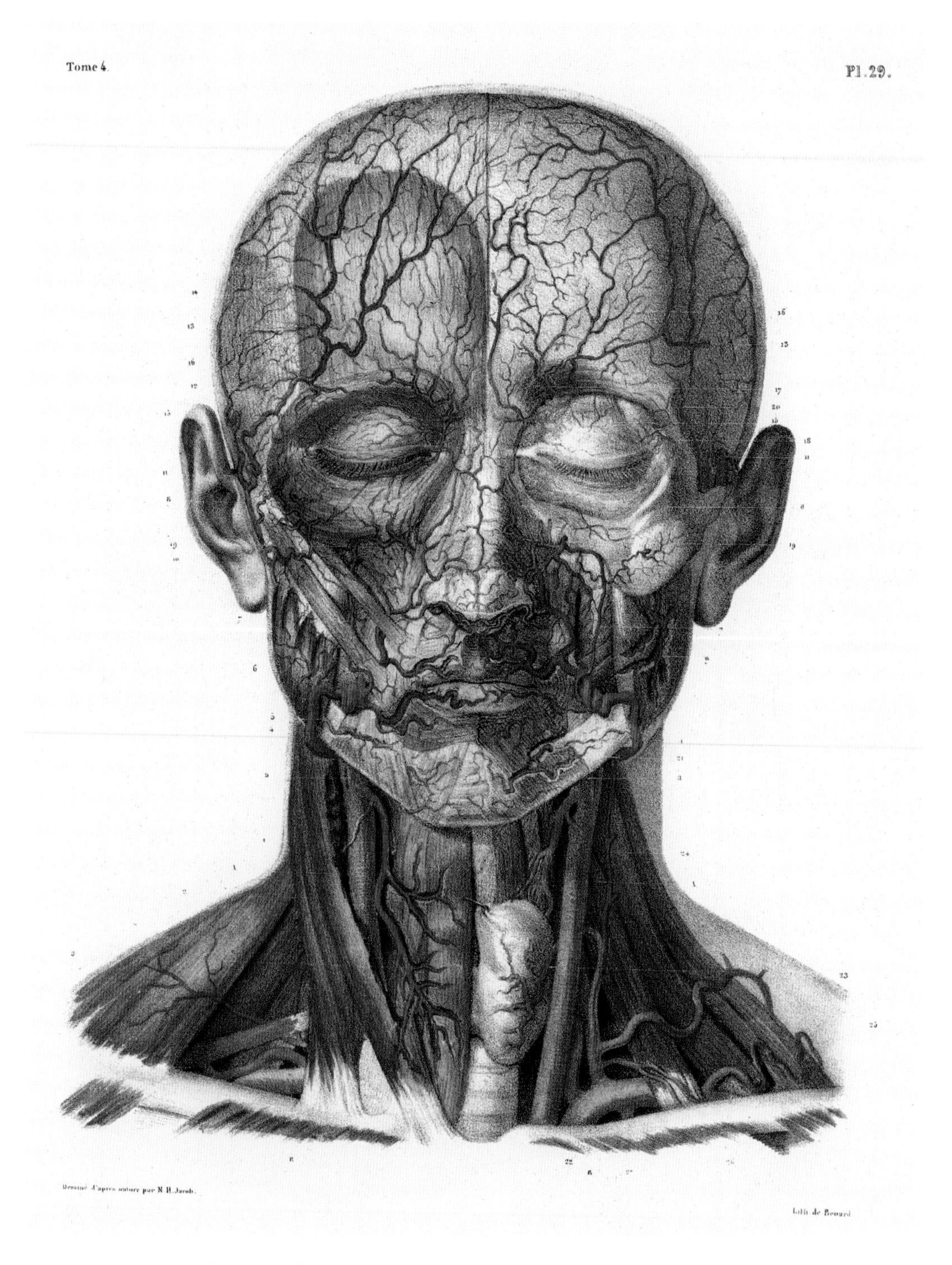

Arteries of the head and neck / Artères de la tête et du cou
Arterias de la cabeza y del cuello

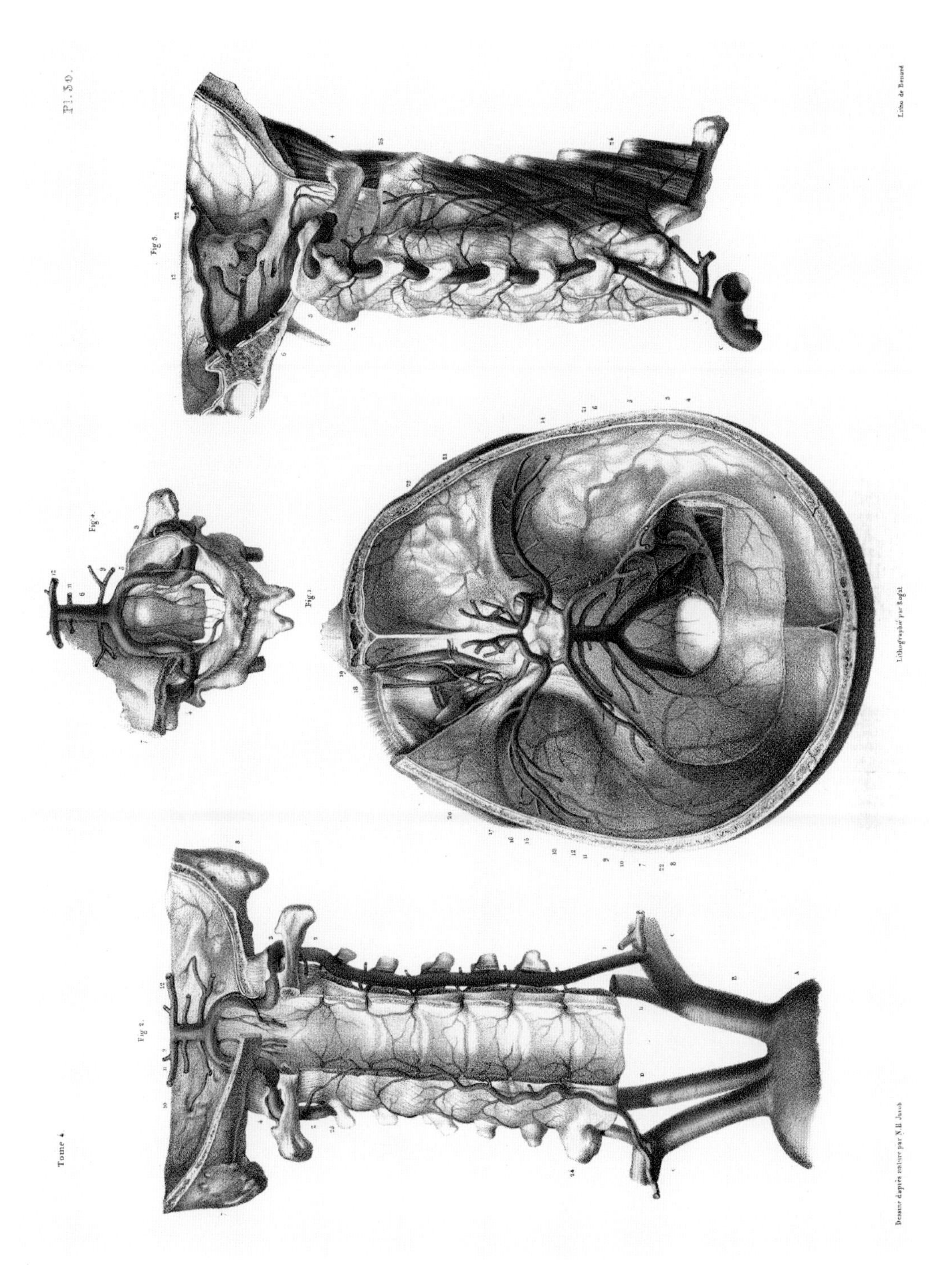

Arteries of the head and neck / Artères de la tête et du cou
Arterias de la cabeza y del cuello

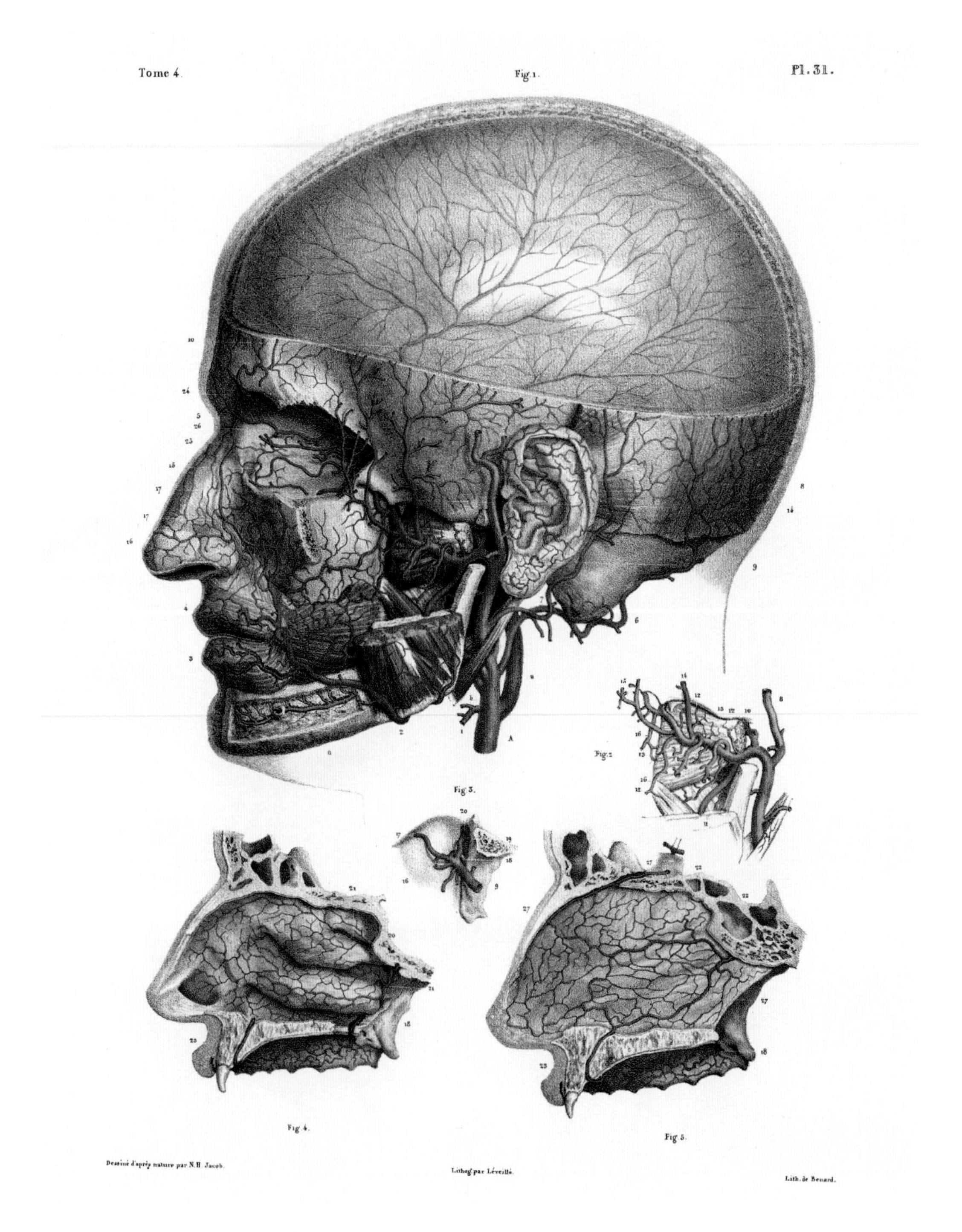

Arteries of the head / Artères de la tête / Arterias de la cabeza

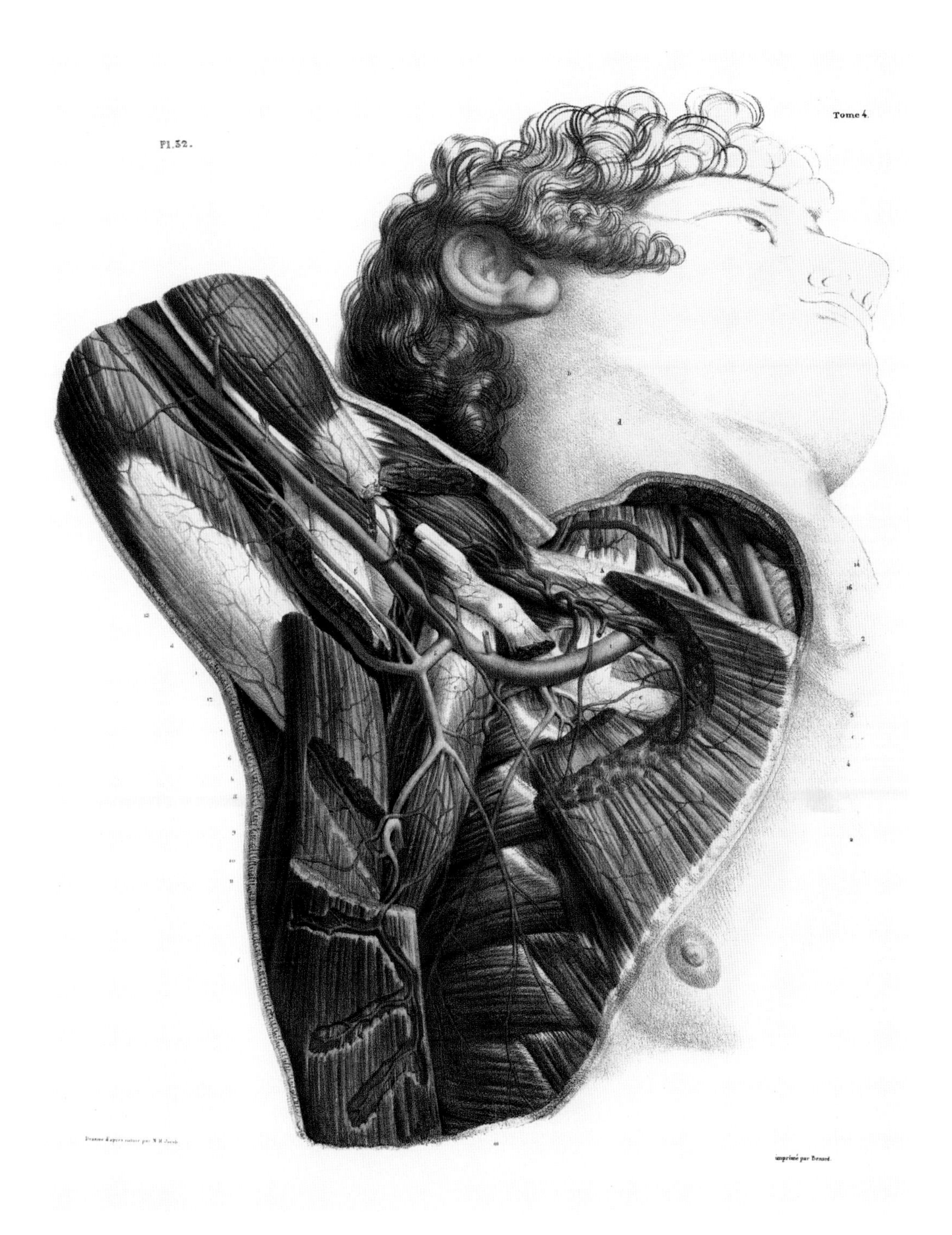

Arteries of the axillary region / Artères de la région axillaire
Arterias de la región axilar

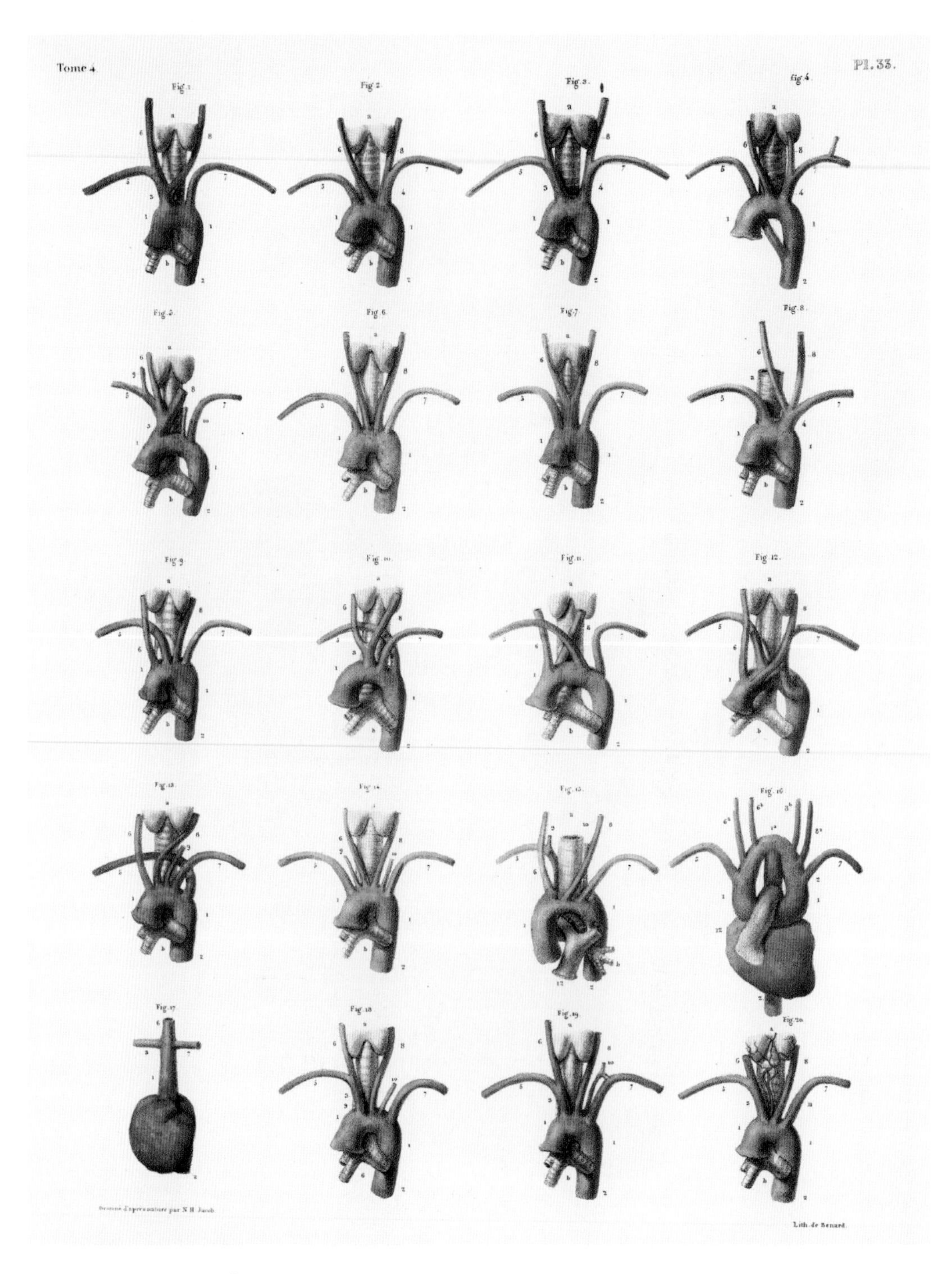

Branches of the aortic arch: Variants / Branches de l'arc aortique : Variantes
Ramas del arco aórtico: variantes

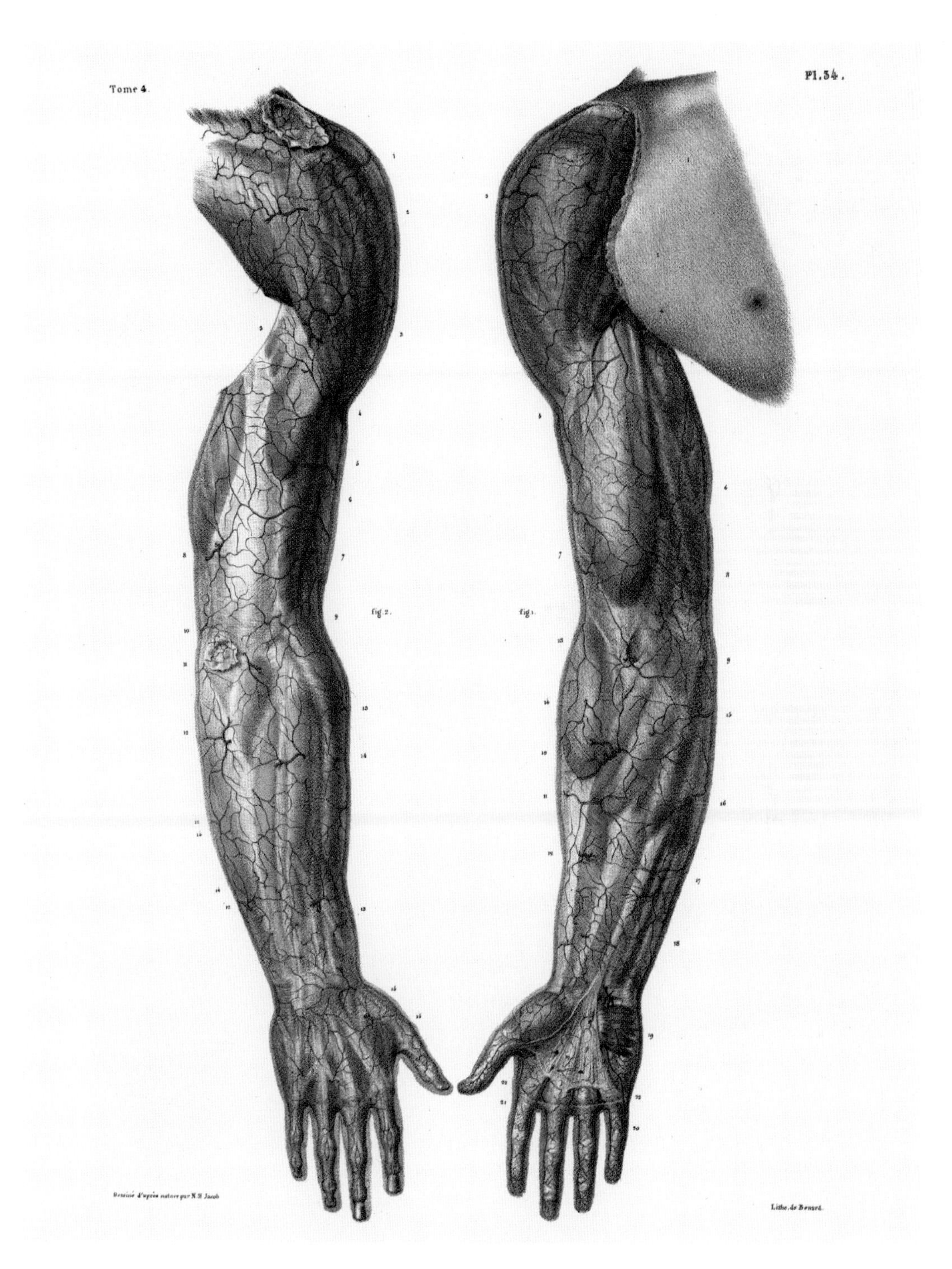

Cutaneous arteries of the upper limb / Artères cutanées du membre supérieur
Arterias cutáneas del miembro superior

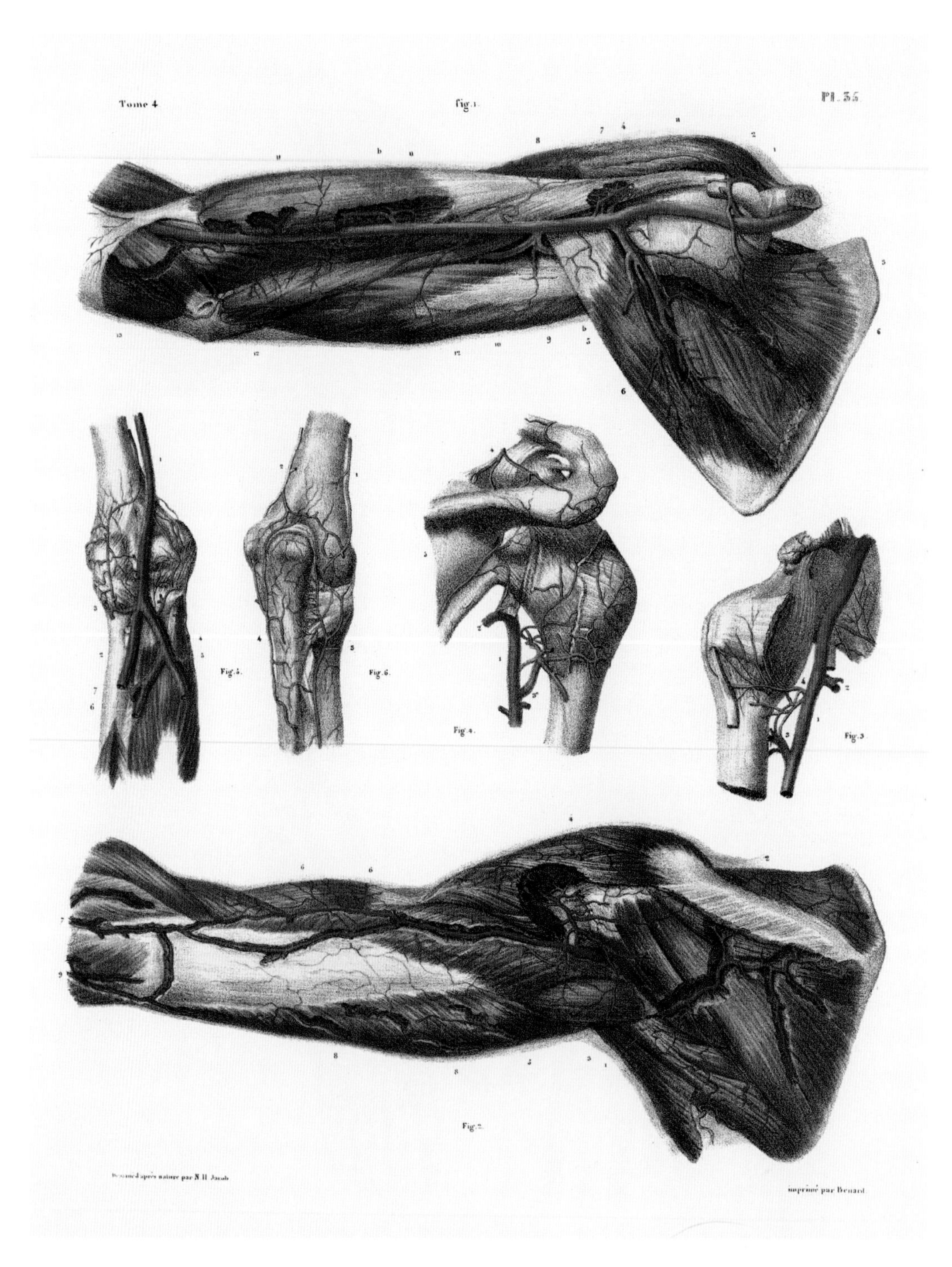

Arteries of the axillary region and arm / Artères de la région axillaire et du bras
Arterias de la región axilar y del brazo

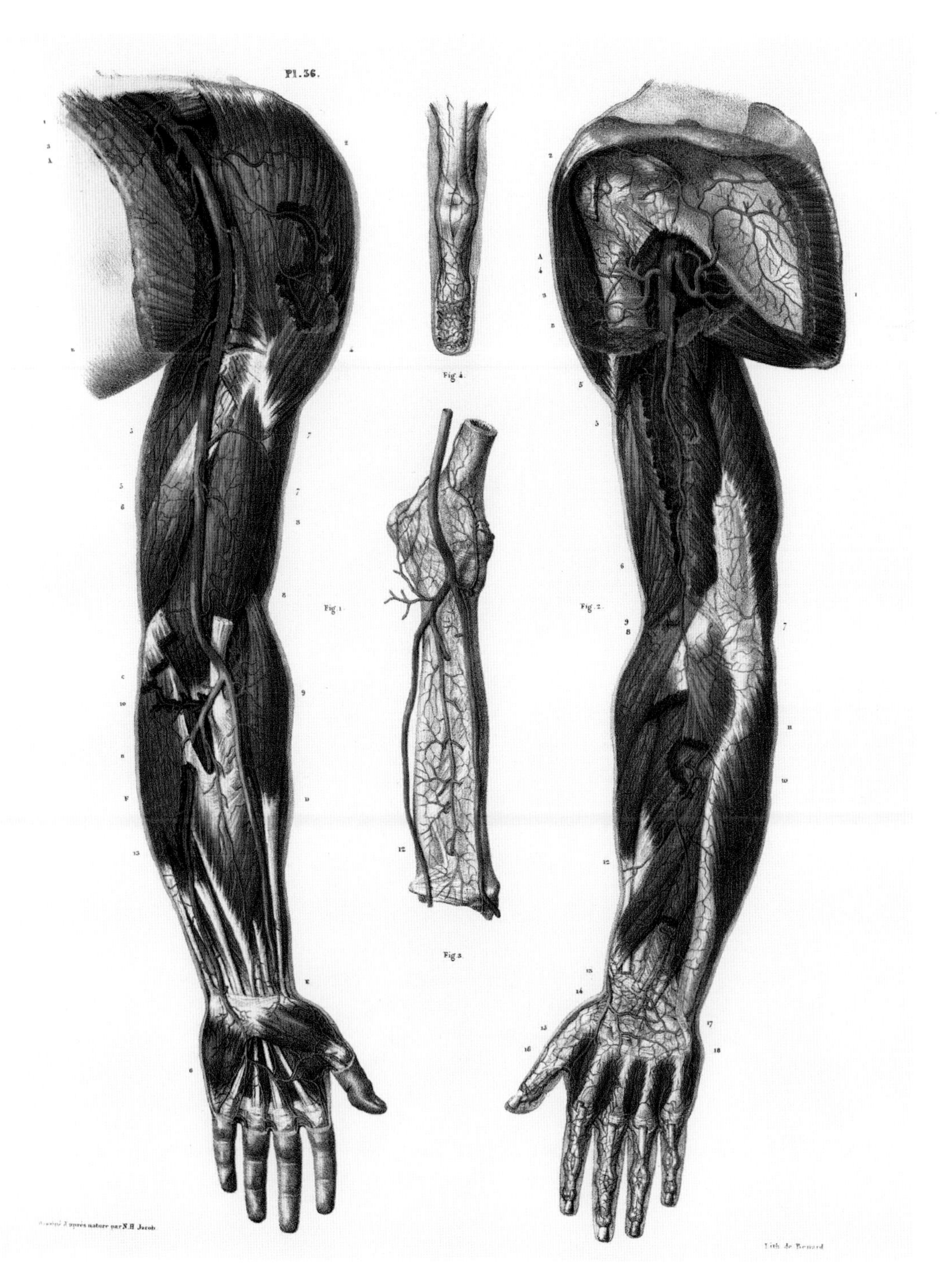

Arteries of the upper limb / Artères du membre supérieur
Arterias del miembro superior

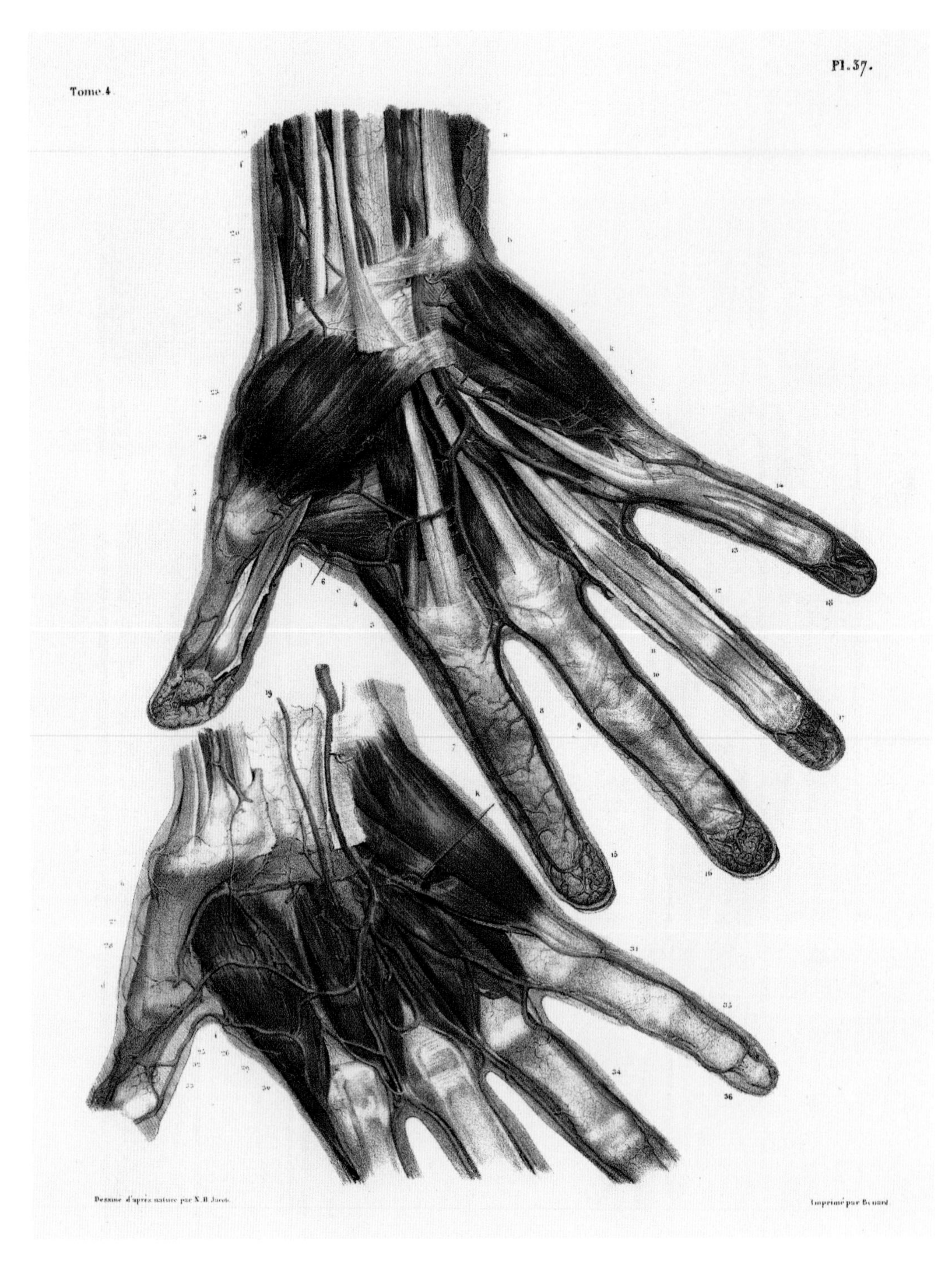

Arteries of the hand / Artères de la main / Arterias de la mano

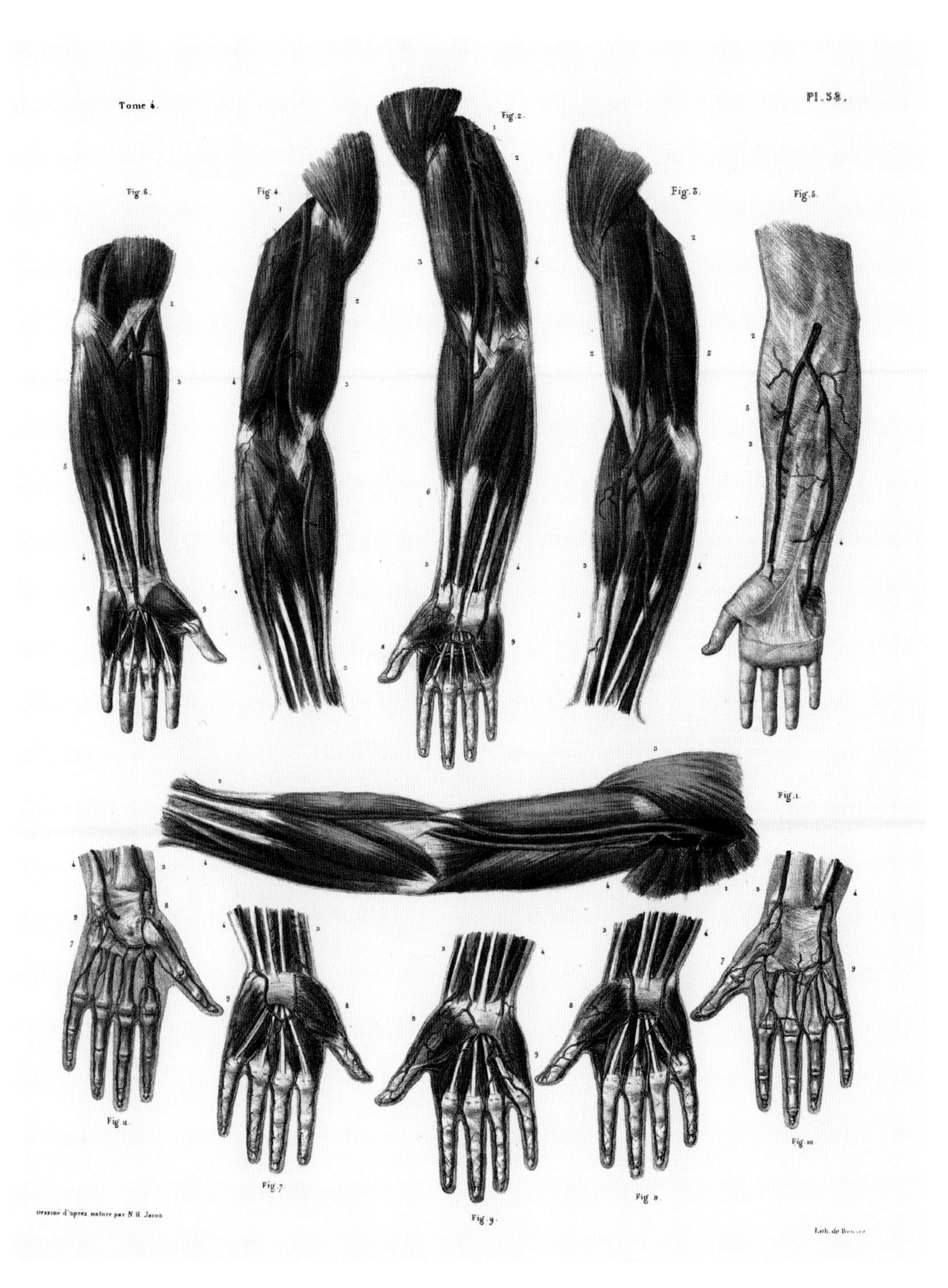

Arteries of the upper limb: Variants / Artères du membre supérieur : Variantes
Arterias del miembro superior: variantes

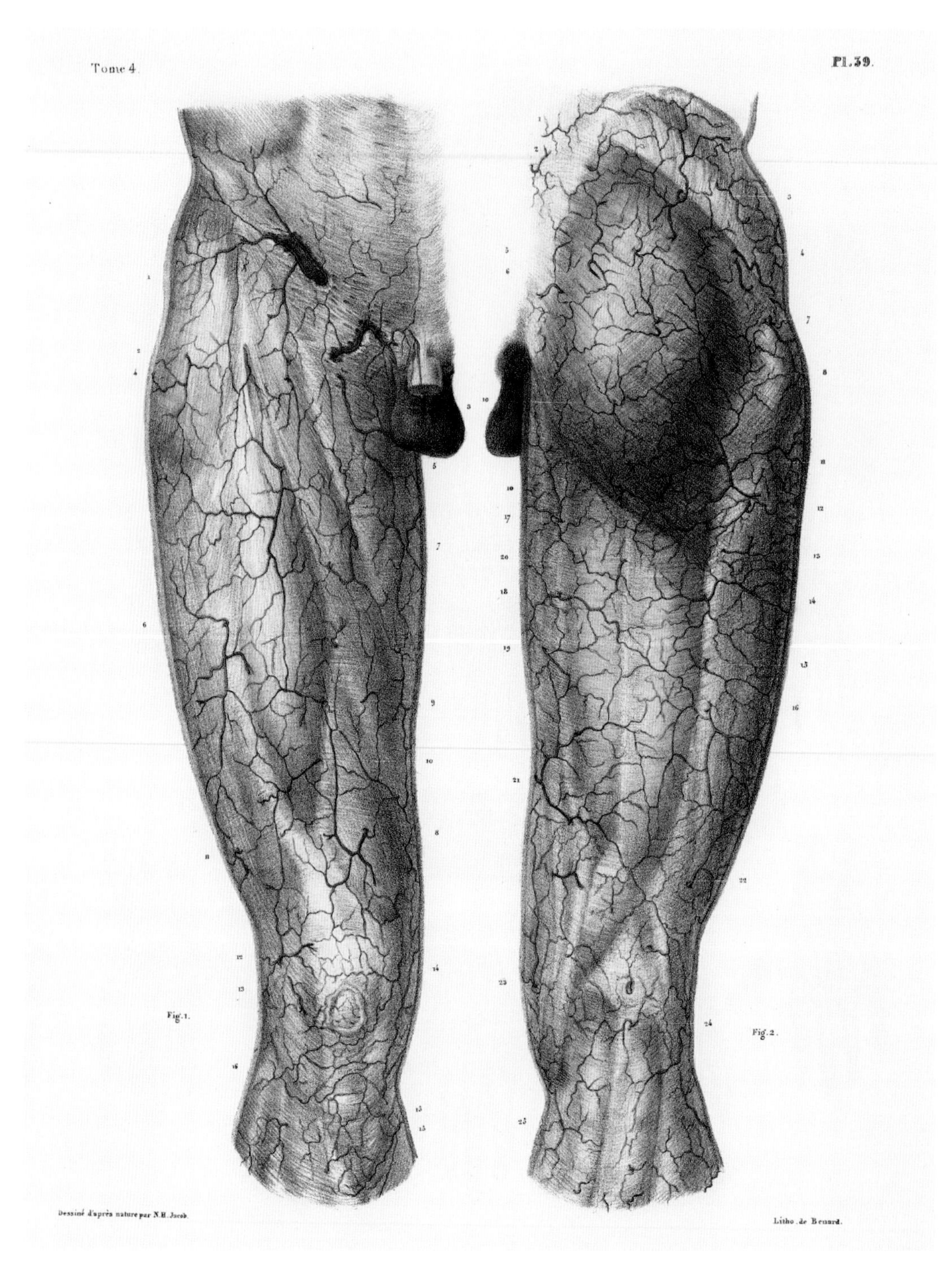

Cutaneous arteries of the gluteal region and thigh
Artères cutanées de la région glutéale et de la cuisse
Arterias cutáneas de la región glútea y femoral

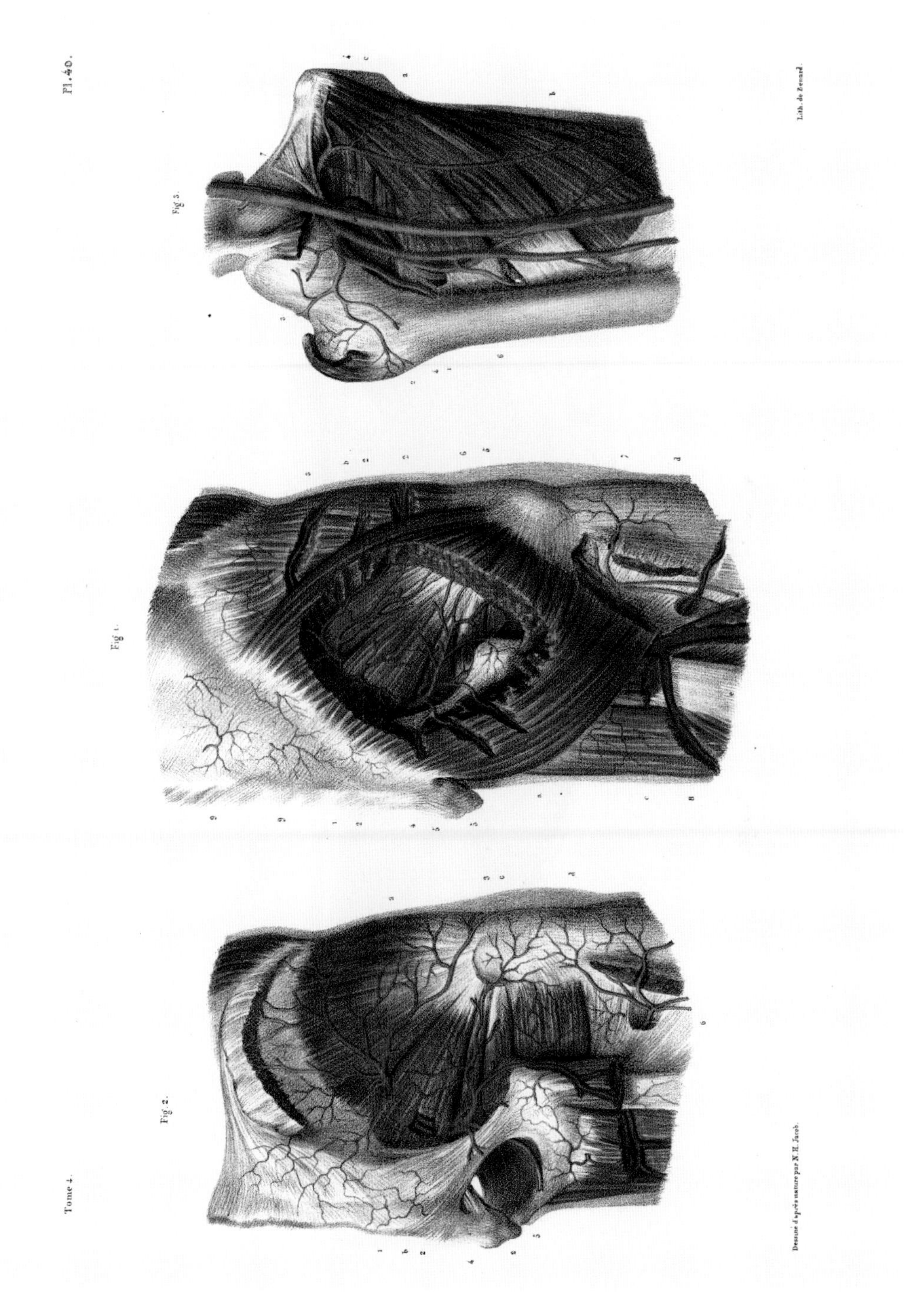

Arteries of the gluteal region and hip / Artères de la région glutéale et de la hanche
Arterias de la región glútea y de la cadera

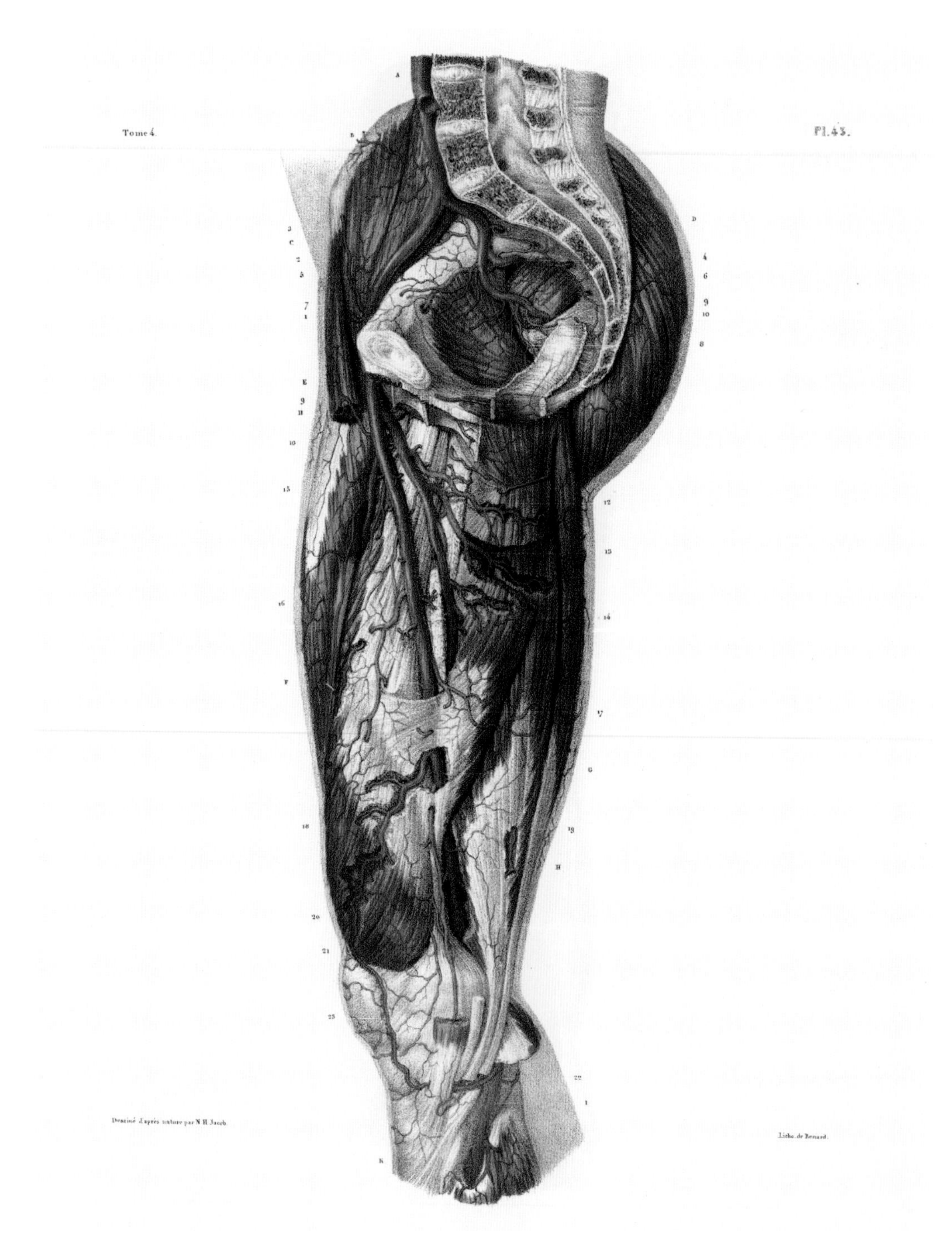

Arteries of the thigh / Artères de la cuisse / Arterias del muslo

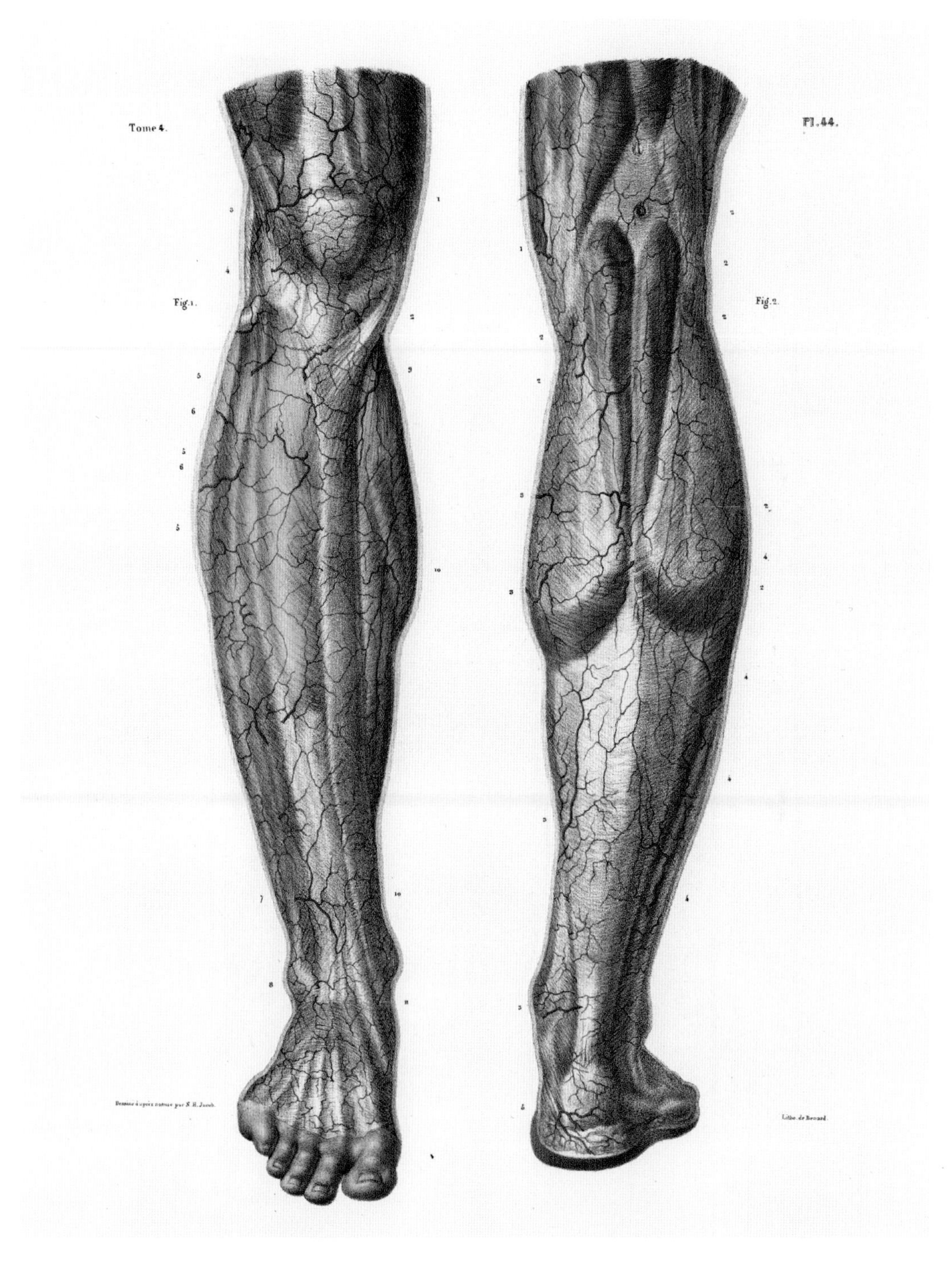

Cutaneous arteries of the lower leg and foot / Artères cutanées de la jambe et du pied
Arterias cutáneas de la pierna y del pie

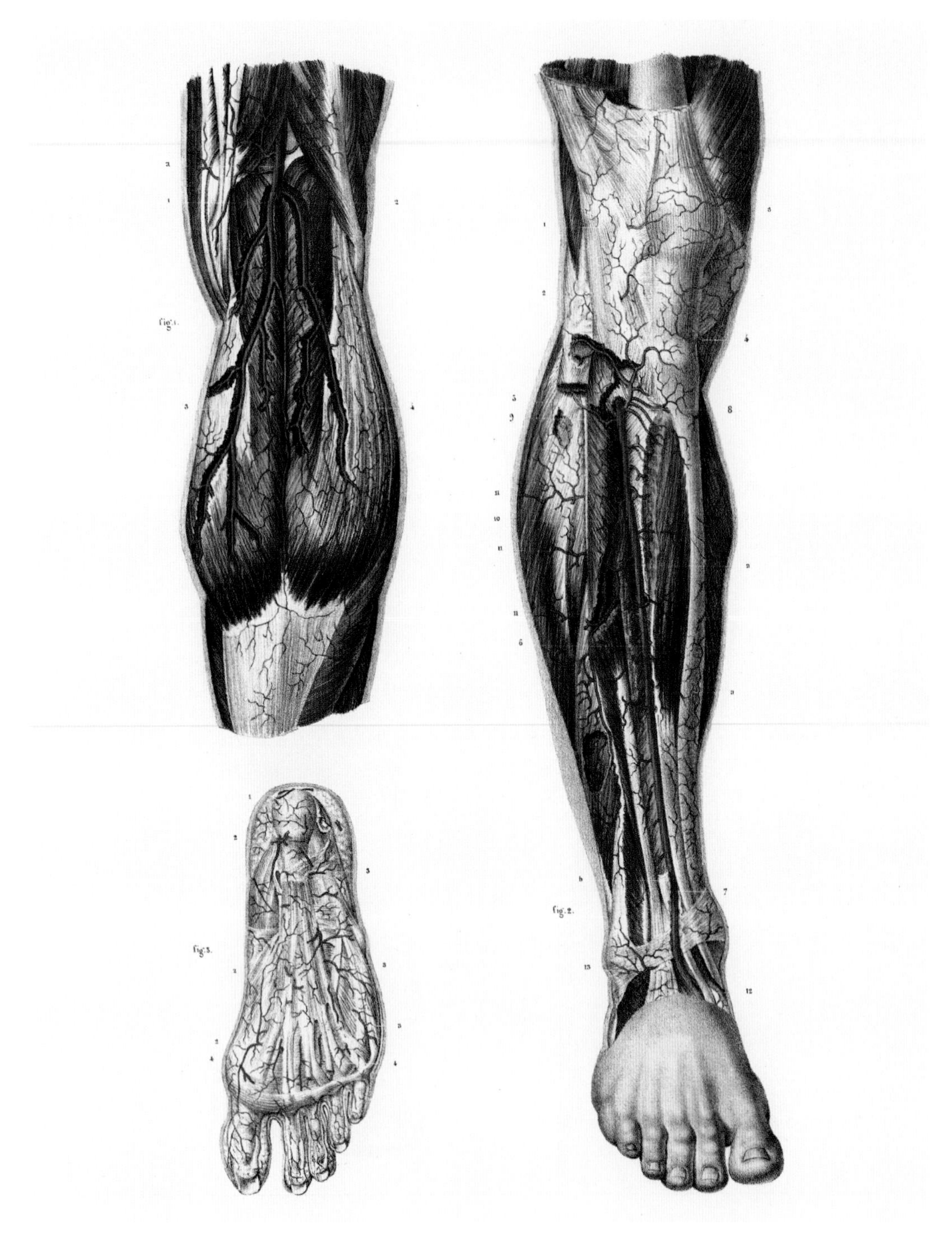

Arteries of the lower leg and foot / Artères de la jambe et du pied
Arterias de la pierna y del pie

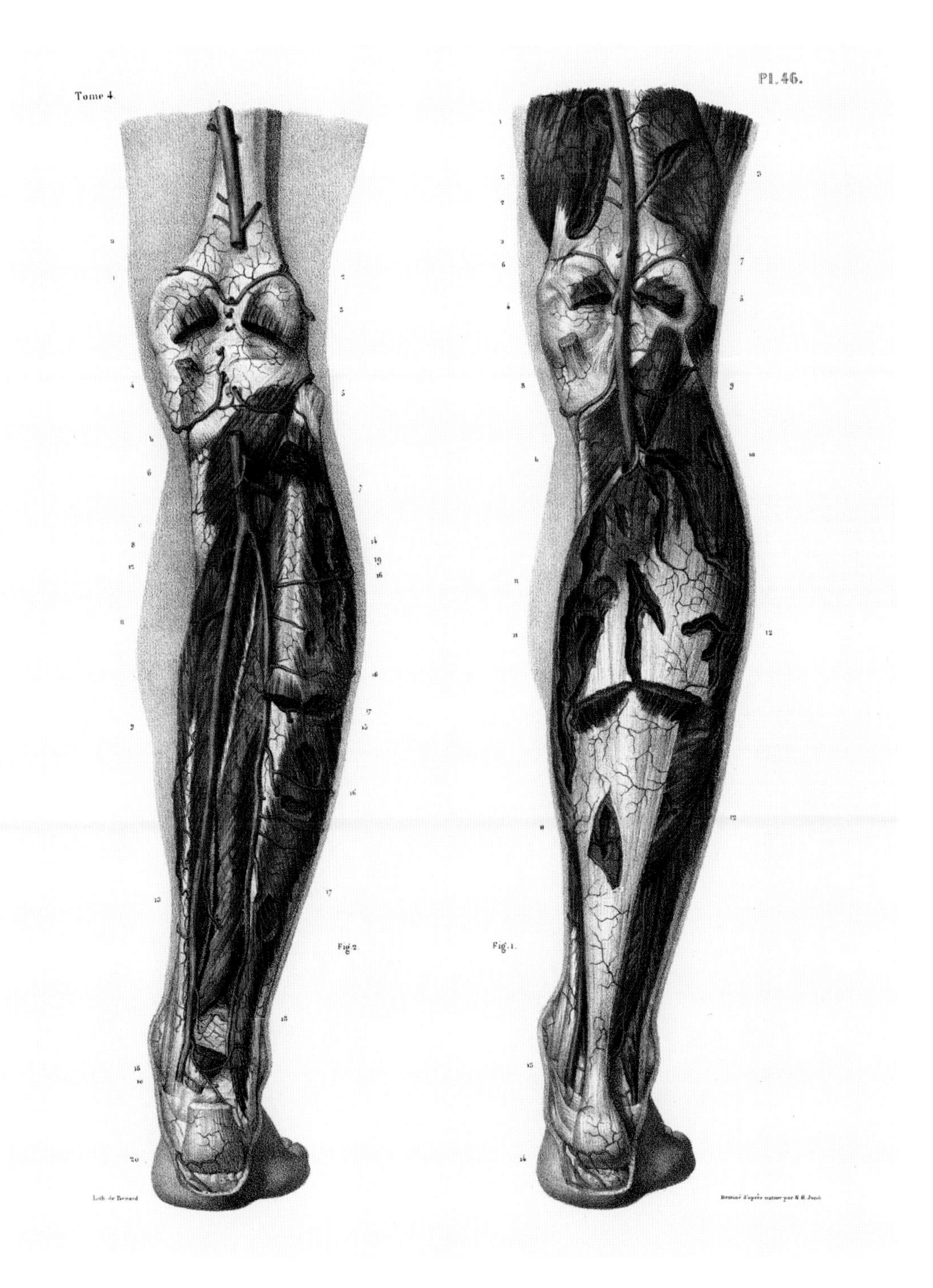

Arteries of the lower leg / Artères de la jambe
Arterias de la pierna

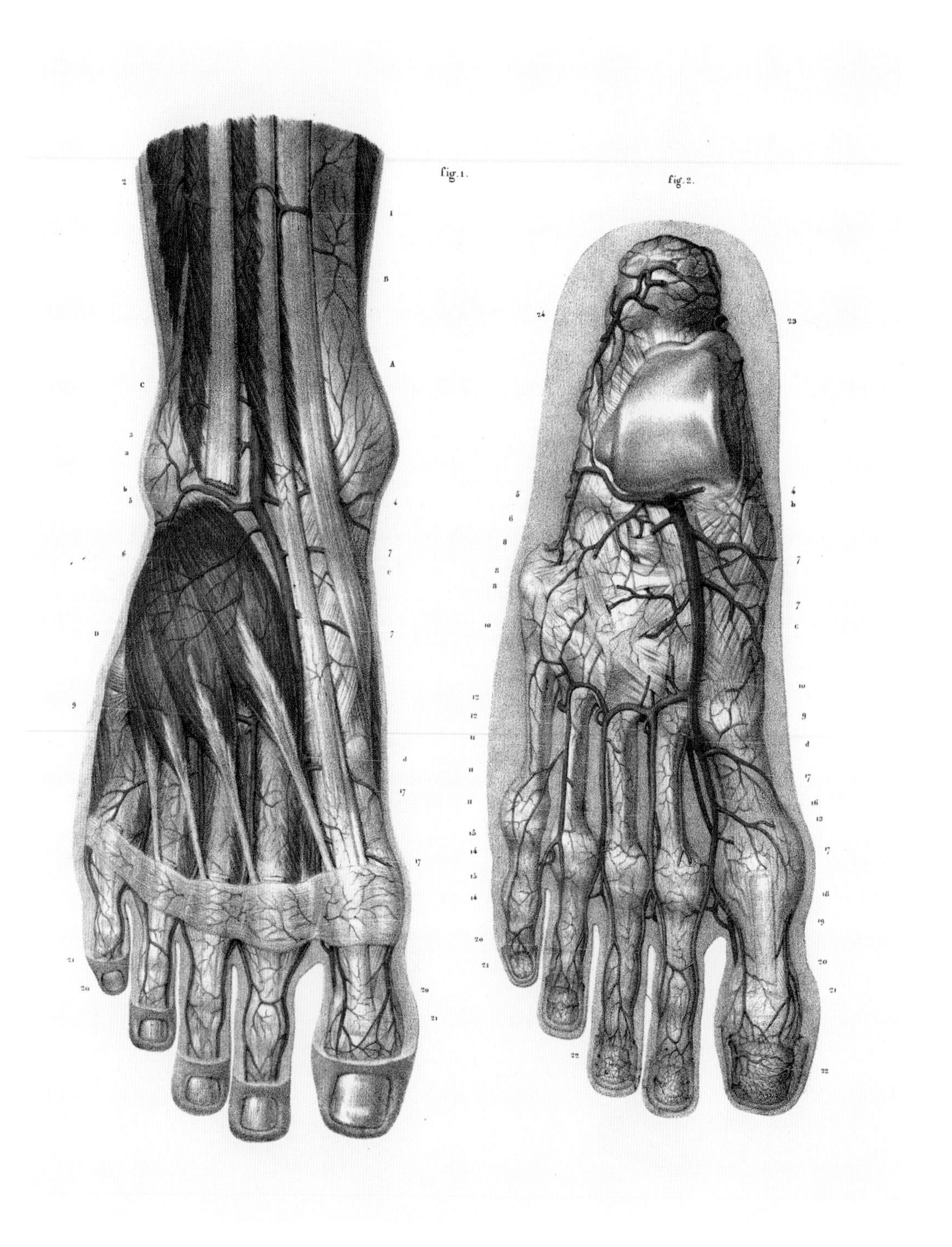

Arteries of the foot / Artères du pied / Arterias del pie

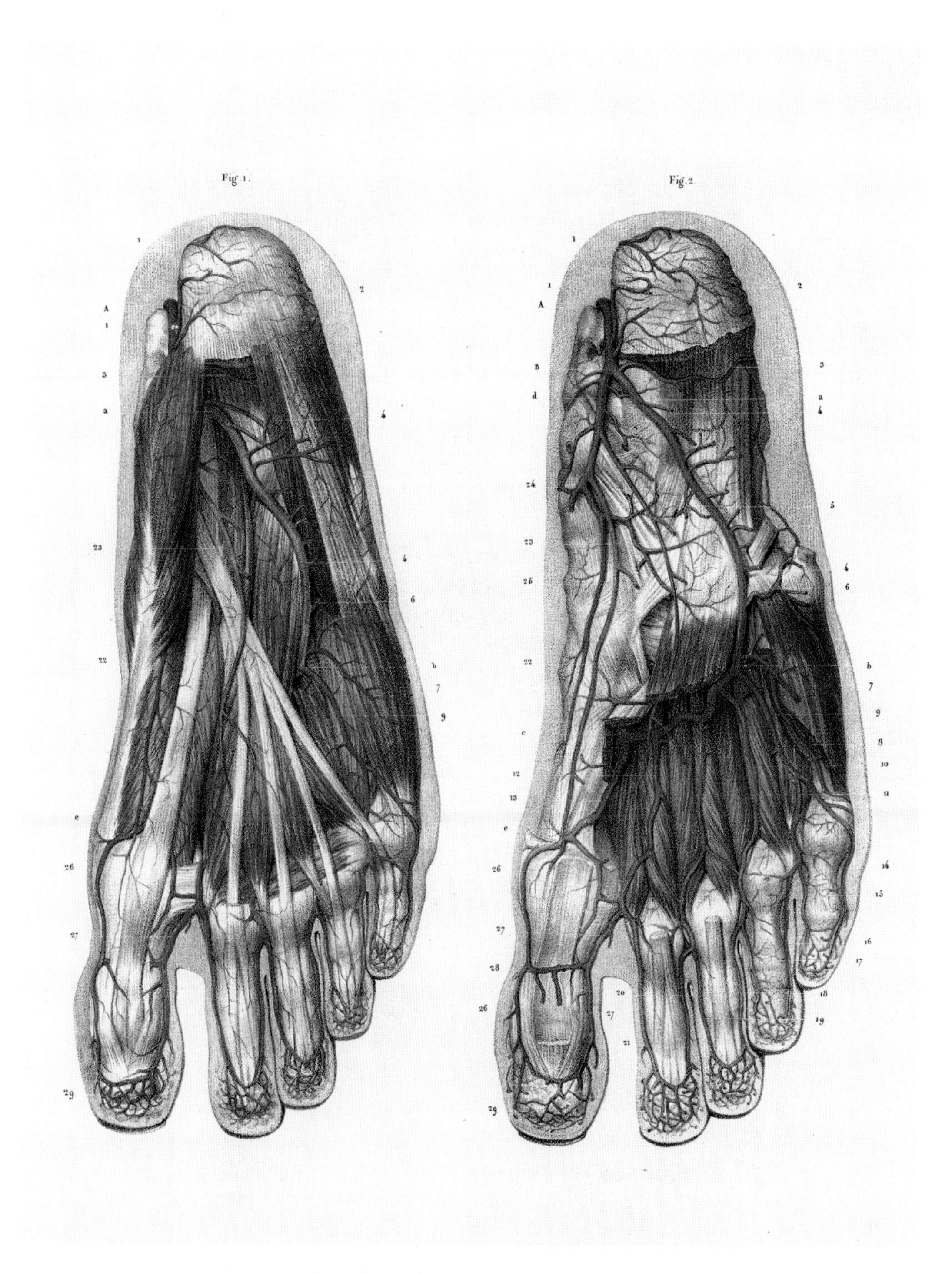

Arteries of the foot / Artères du pied / Arterias del pie

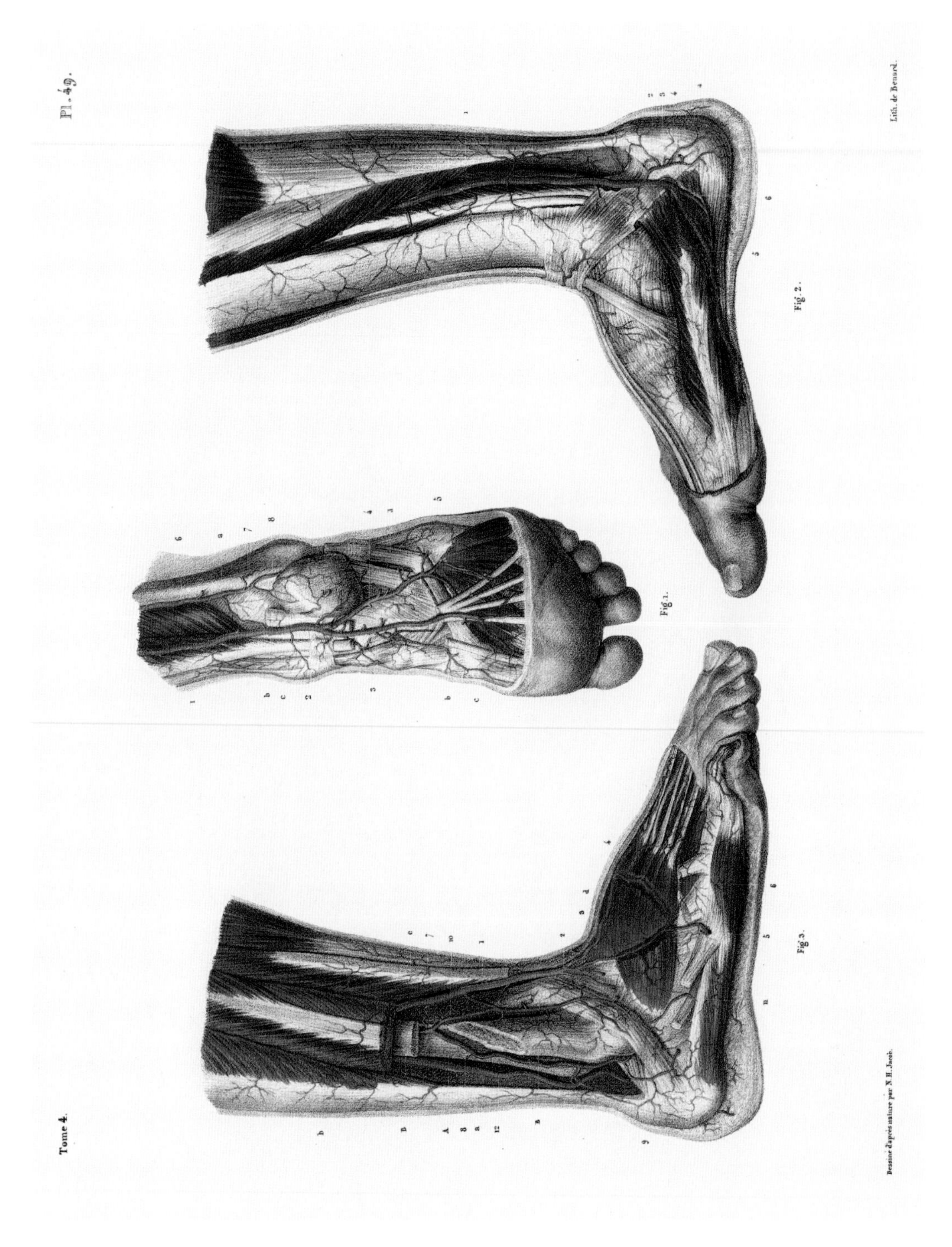

Arteries of the lower leg and foot / Artères de la jambe et du pied
Arterias de la pierna y del pie

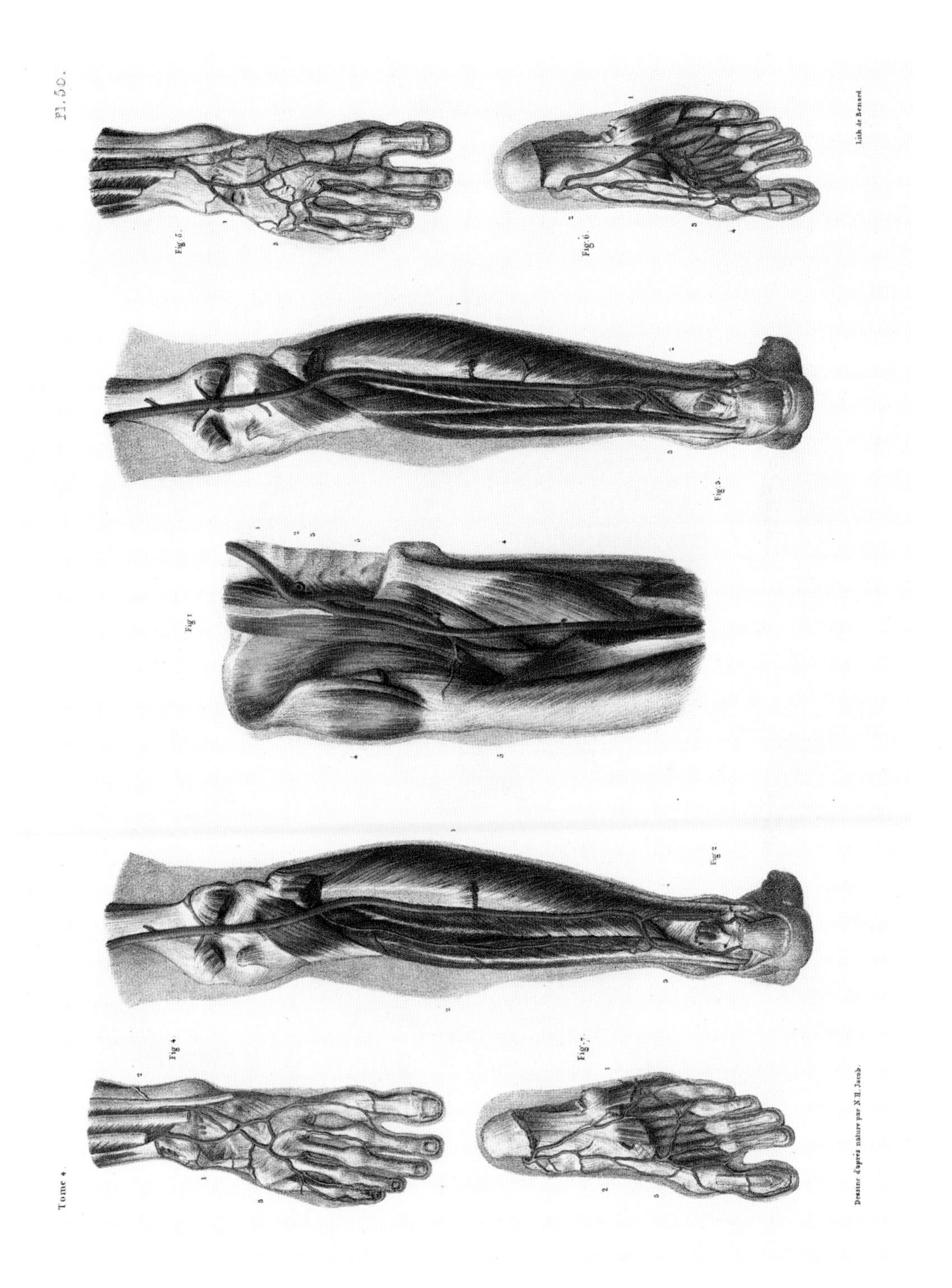

Arteries of the lower leg and foot: Variants / Artères de la jambe et du pied : Variantes
Arterias de la pierna y del pie: variantes

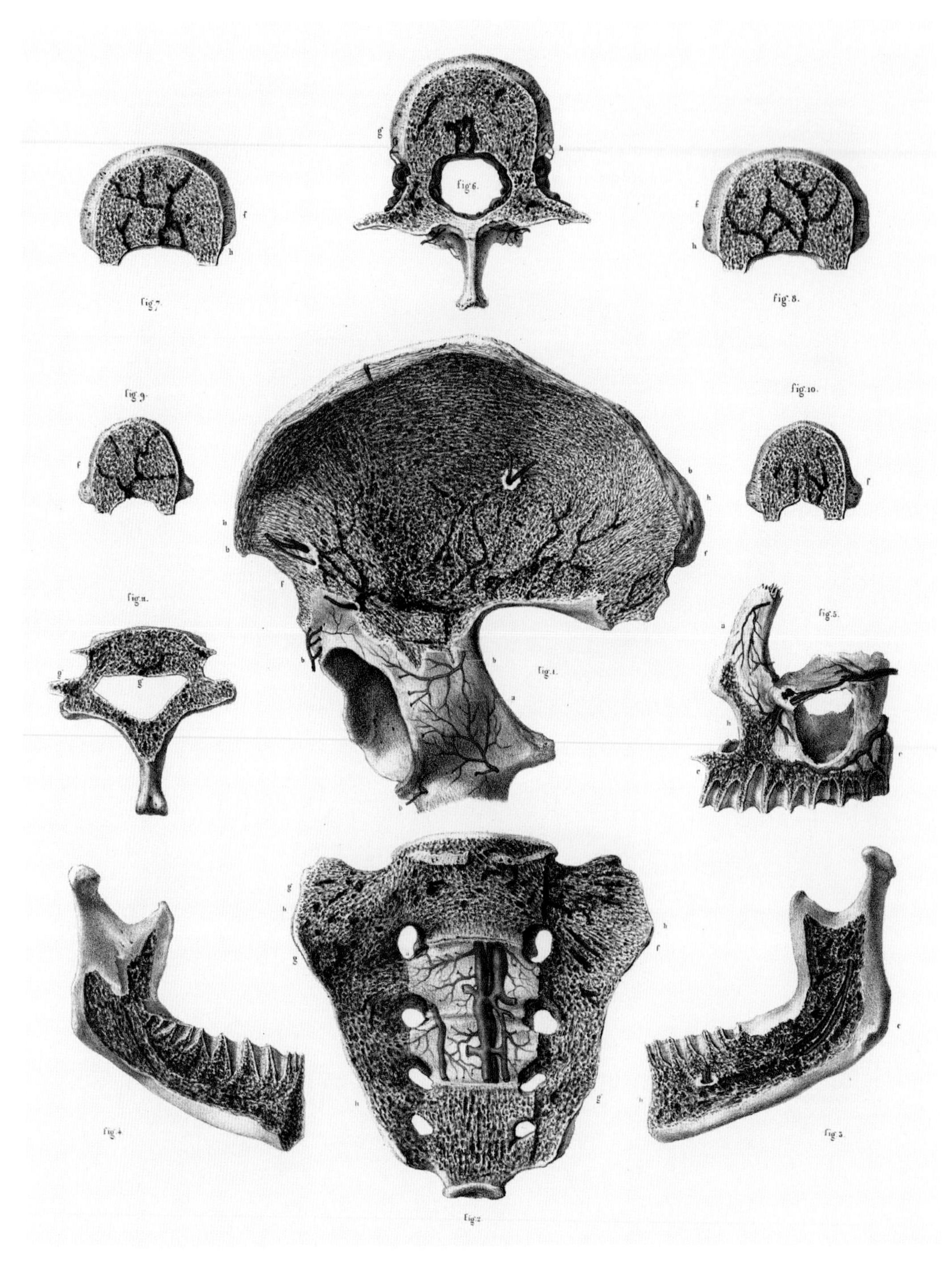

Arteries and veins of the bones / Artères et veines des os
Arterias y venas de los huesos

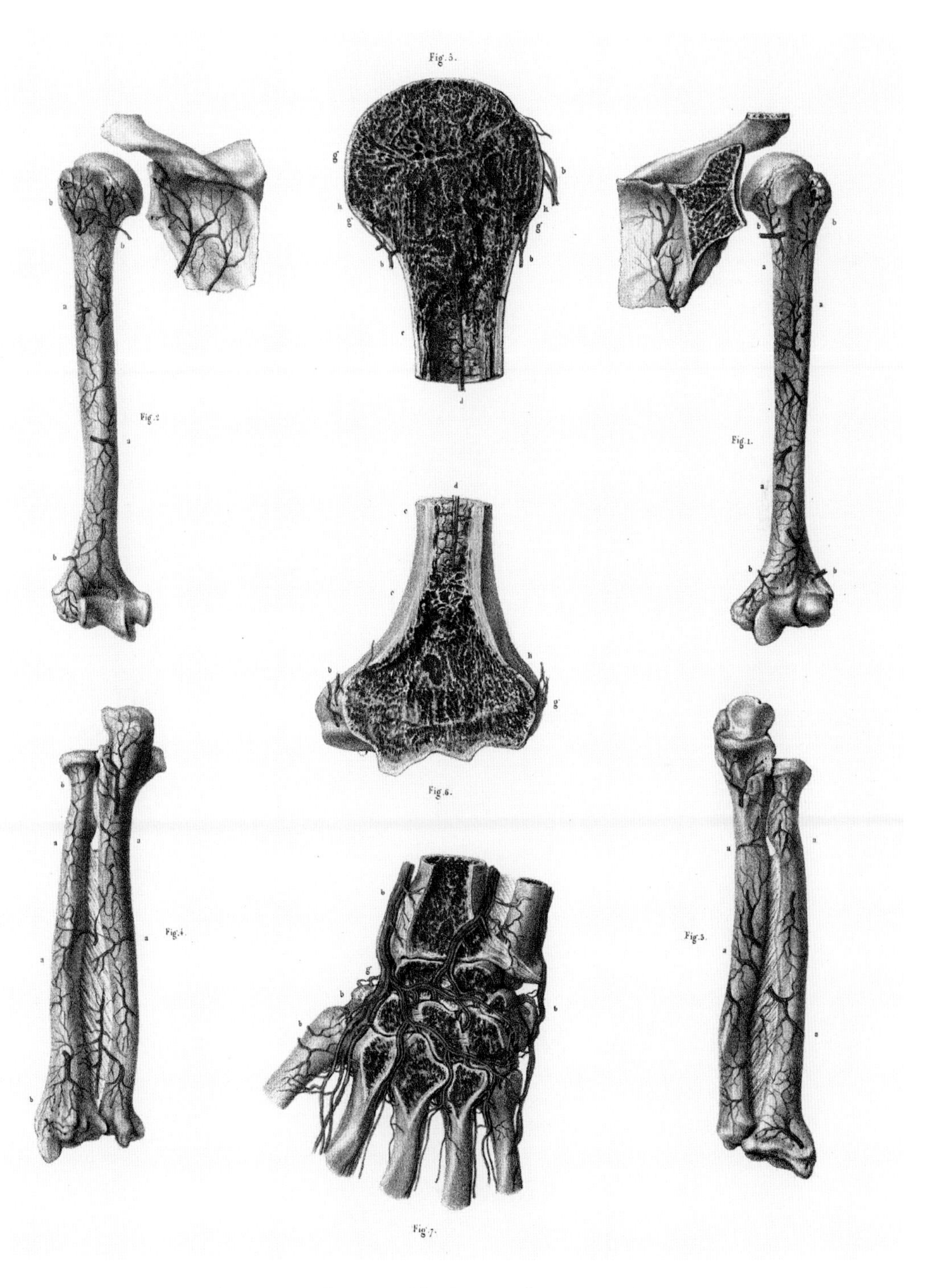

Arteries and veins of the bones of the upper limb
Artères et veines des os du membre supérieur
Arterias y venas de los huesos del miembro superior

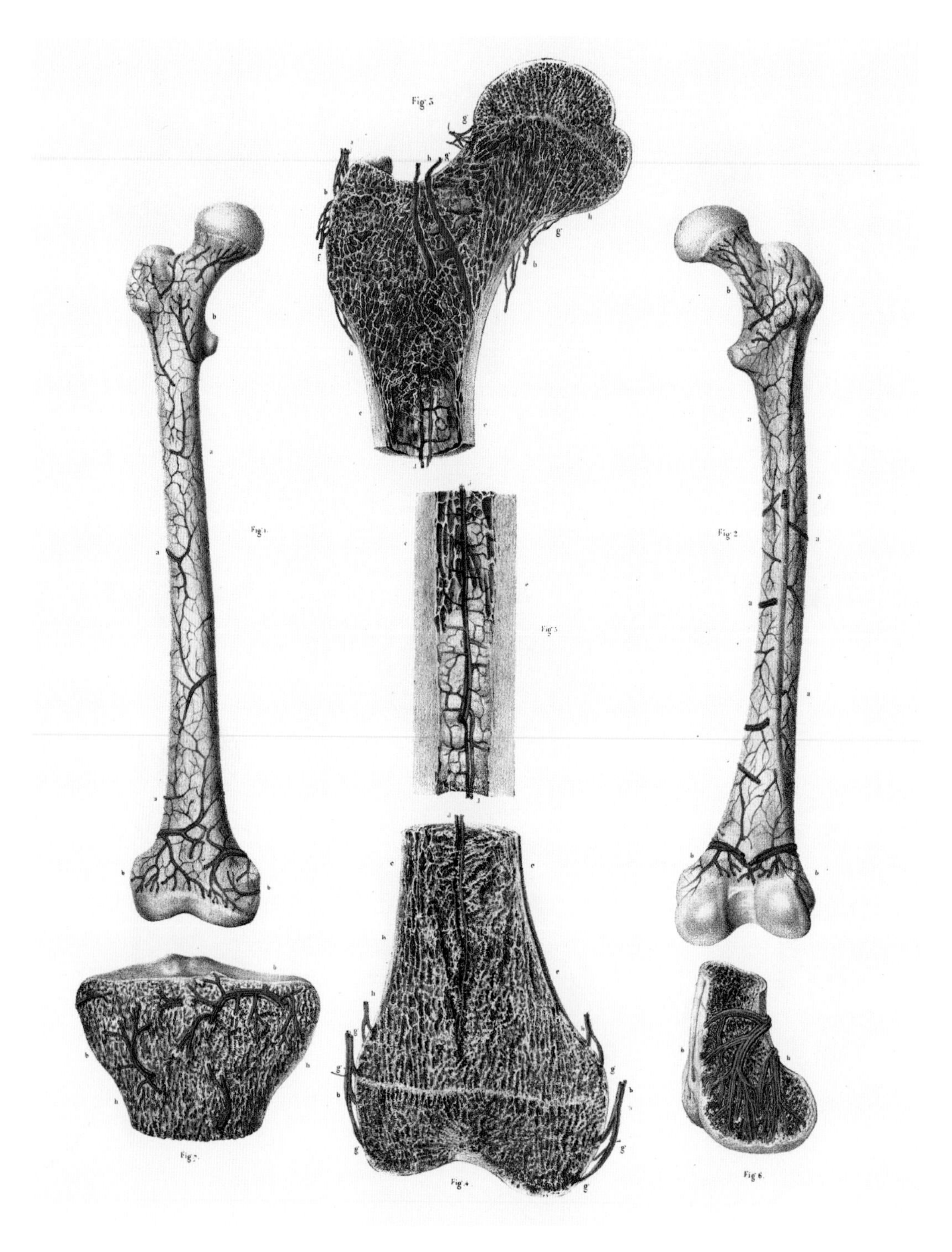

Arteries and veins of the bones of the lower limb
Artères et veines des os du membre inférieur
Arterias y venas de los huesos del miembro inferior

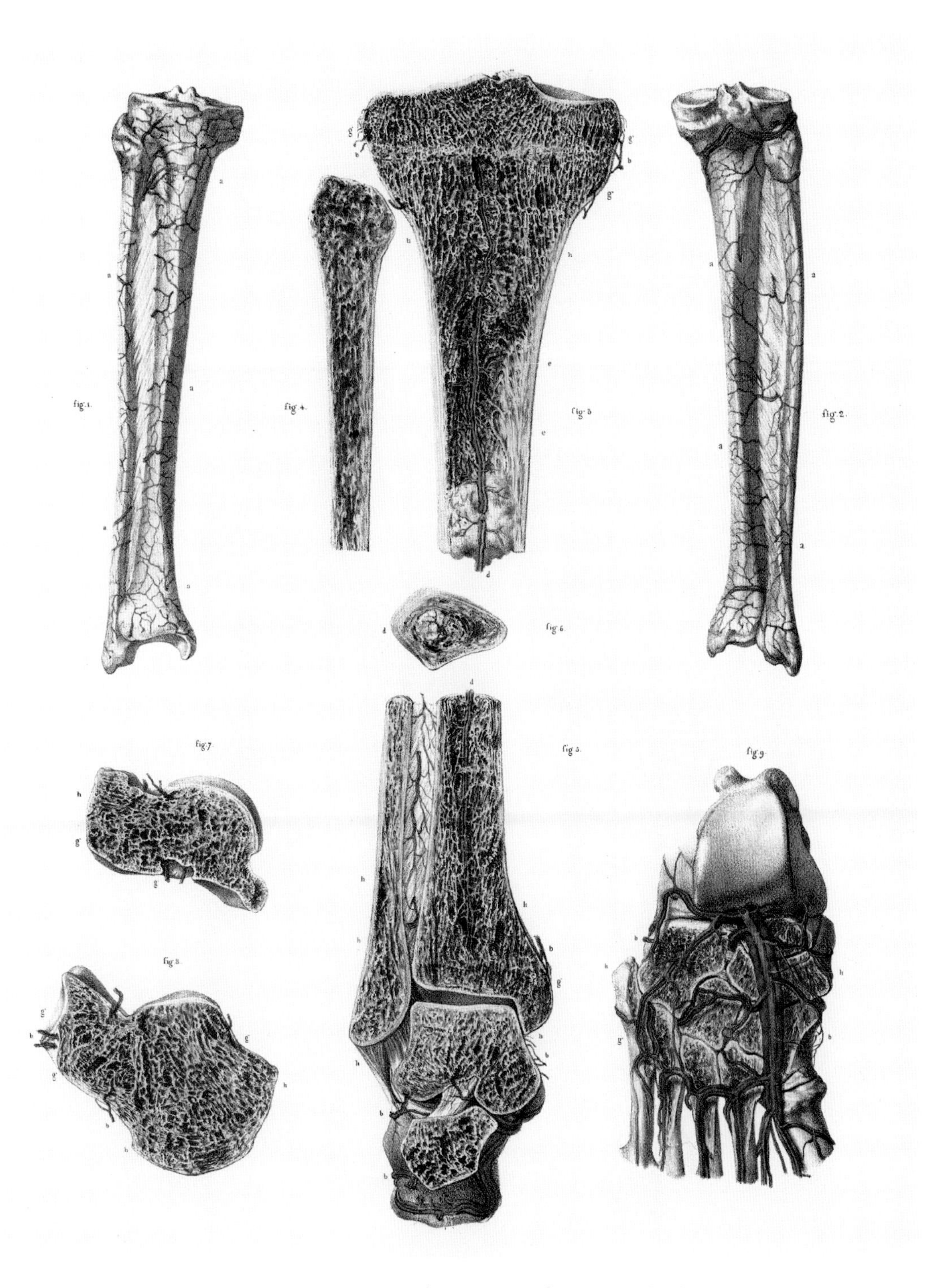

Arteries and veins of the bones of the lower limb
Artères et veines des os du membre inférieur
Arterias y venas de los huesos del miembro inferior

VENAE SUPERFICIALES MEMBRI INFERIORIS. VENAE PEDIS ET CRURIS

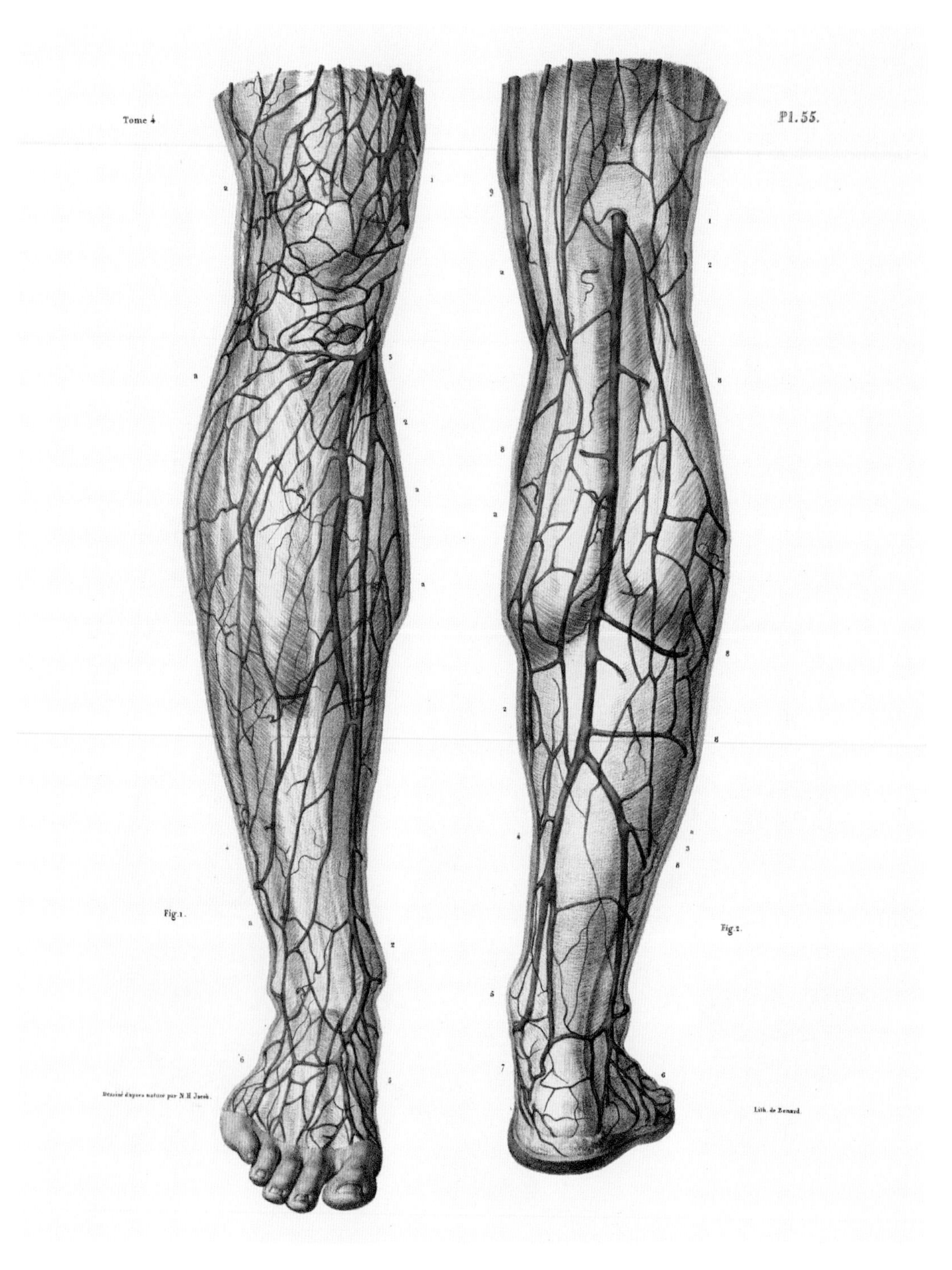

Superficial veins of the lower leg and foot
Veines superficielles de la jambe et du pied
Venas superficiales de la pierna y del pie

VENAE SUPERFICIALES MEMBRI INFERIORIS.
VENAE PEDIS ET CRURIS

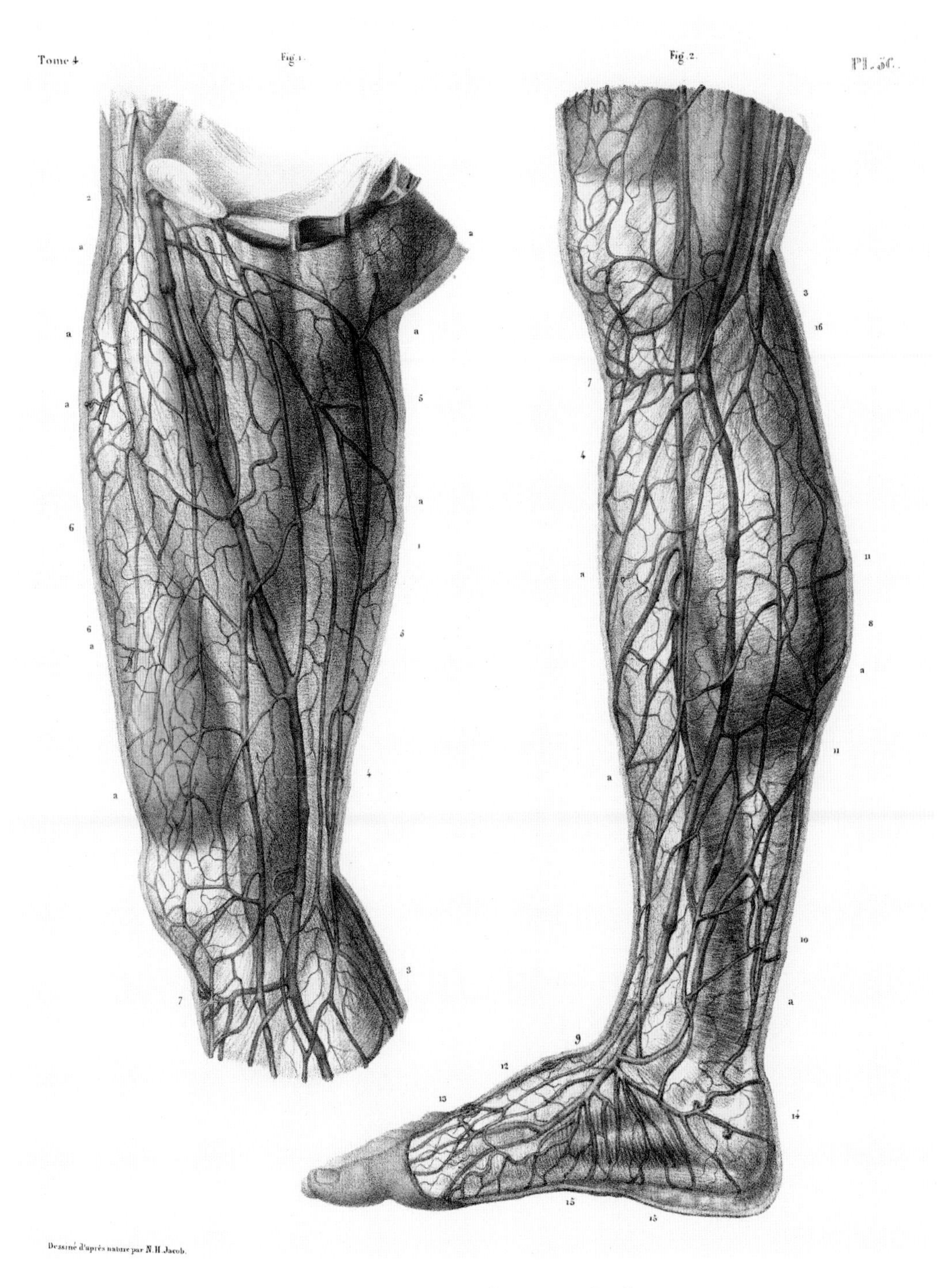

Superficial veins of the lower limb
Veines superficielles du membre inférieur
Venas superficiales del miembro inferior

VENAE SUPERFICIALES MEMBRI INFERIORIS. VENAE PEDIS ET CRURIS

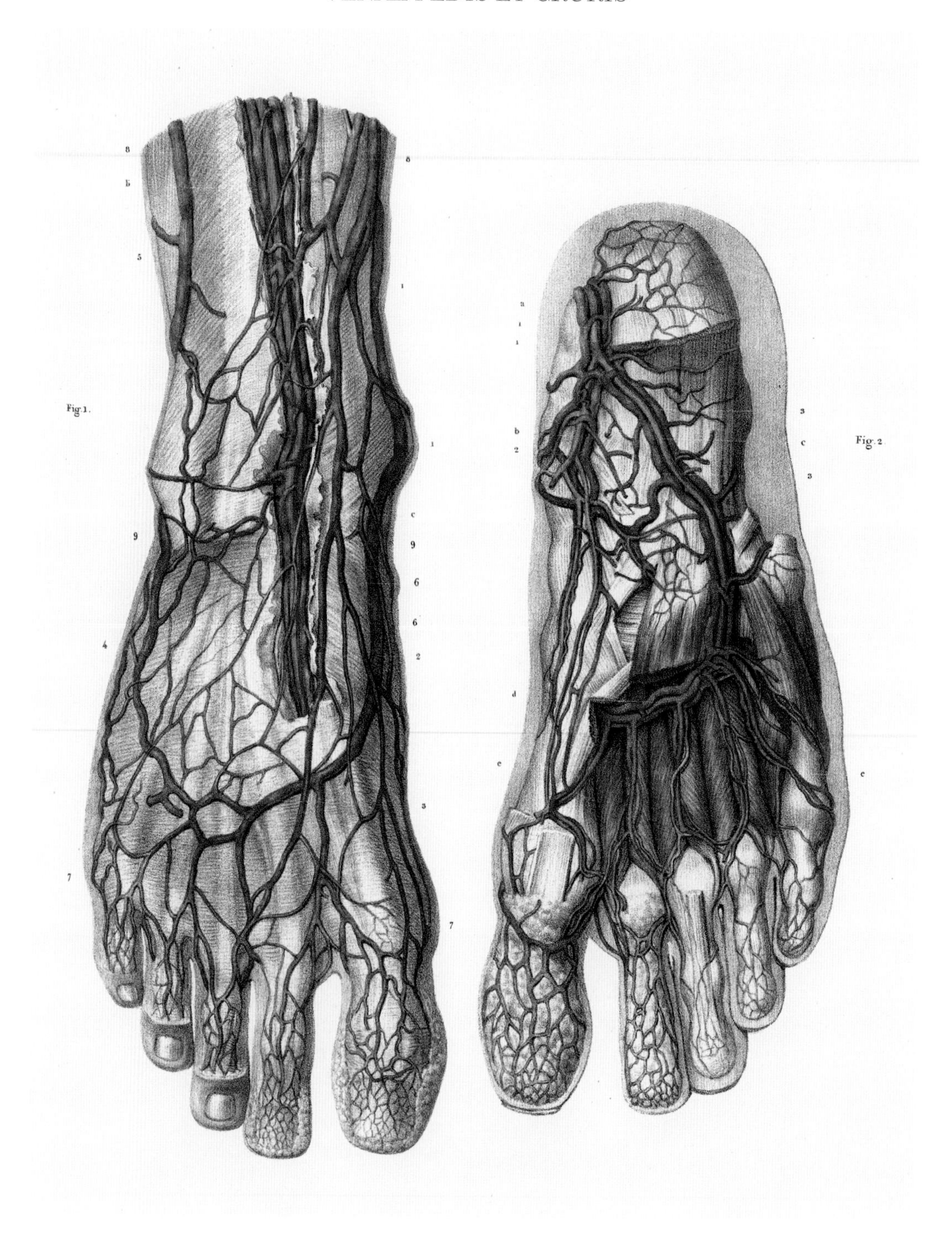

Veins of the foot / Veines du pied / Venas del pie

VENAE SUPERFICIALES MEMBRI INFERIORIS. VENAE PEDIS ET CRURIS

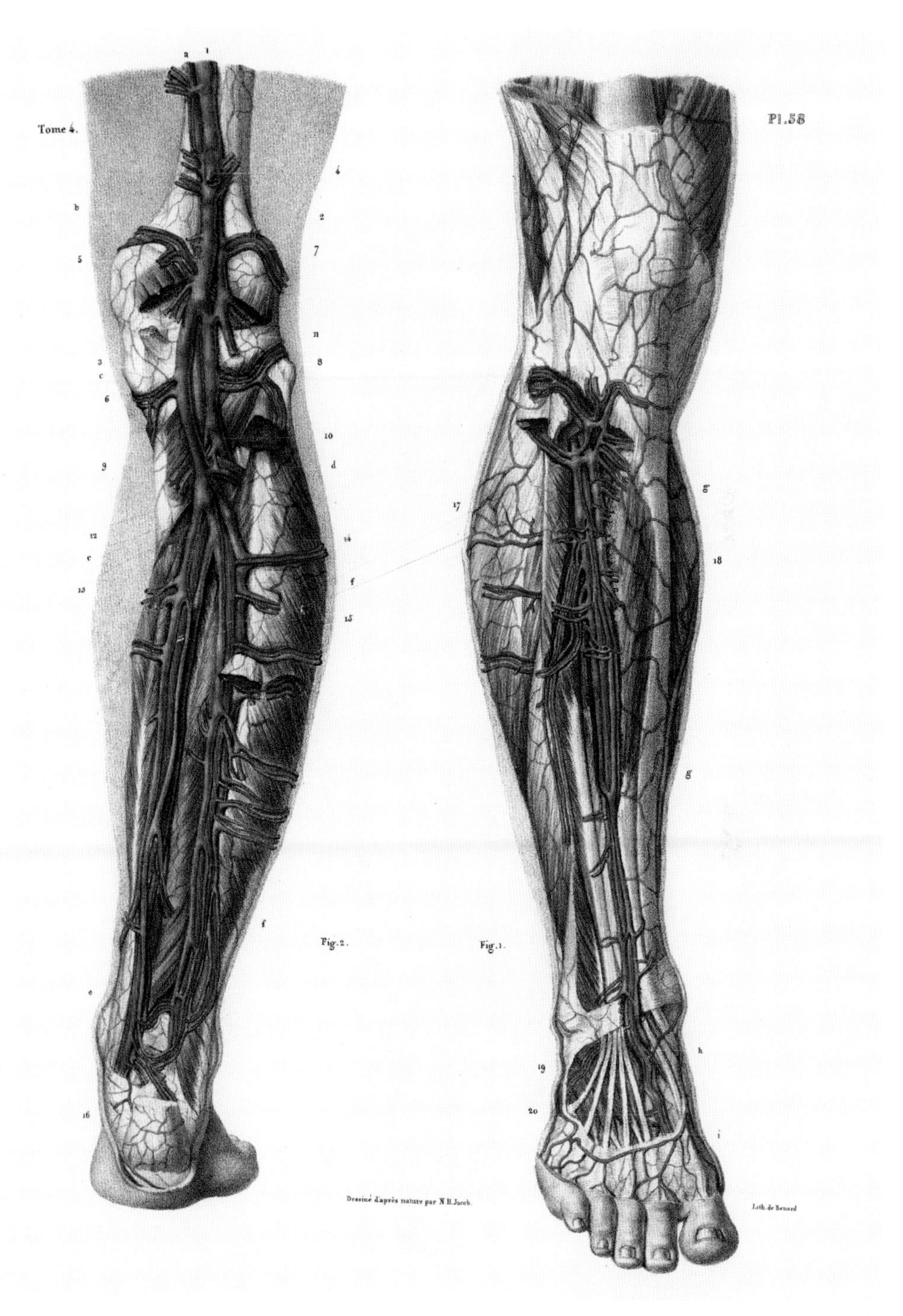

Veins of the lower leg / Veines de la jambe / Venas de la pierna

VENAE FEMORIS. VENAE SUPERFICIALES MEMBRI SUPERIORIS. VENAE MANUS

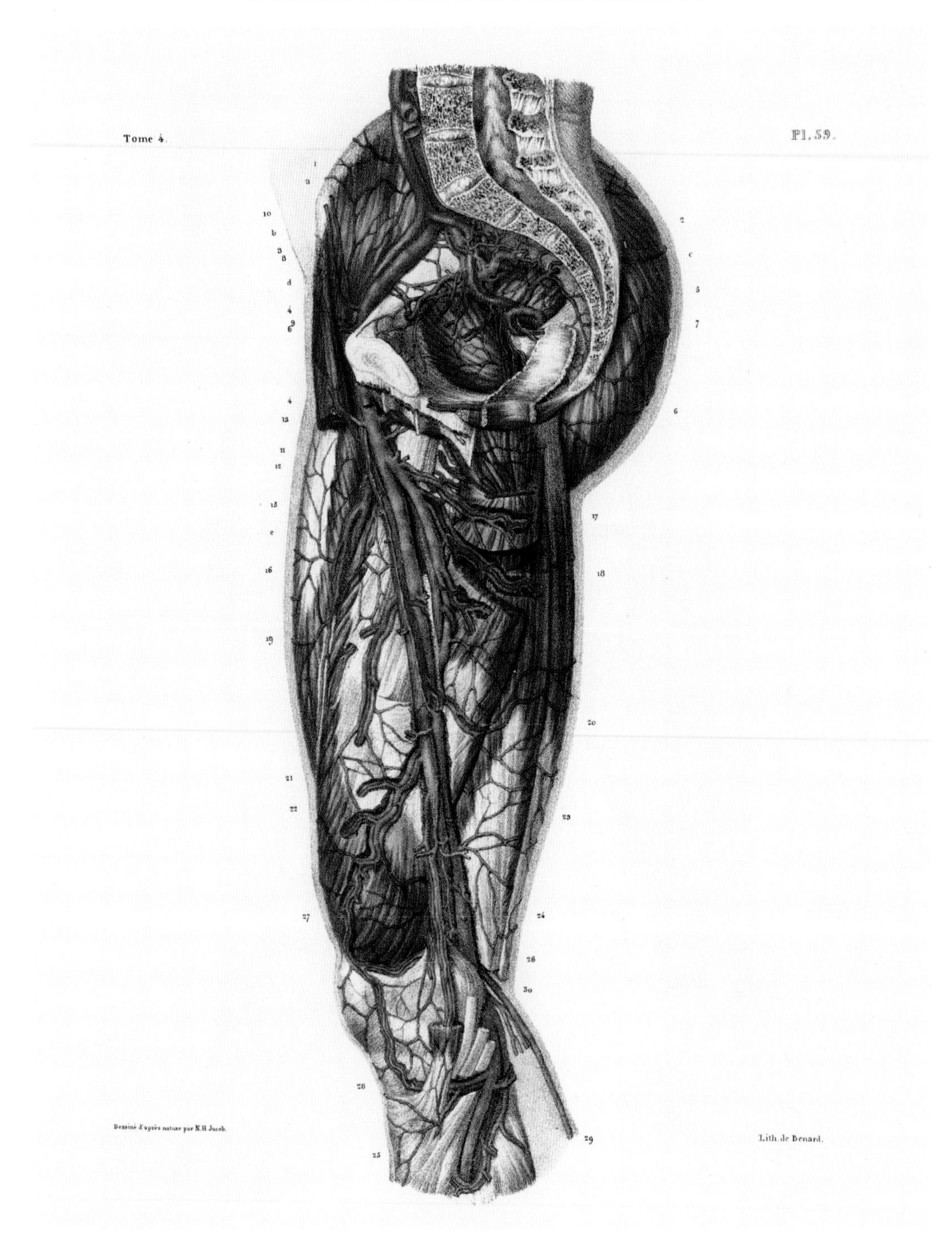

Veins of the thigh / Veines de la cuisse / Venas del muslo

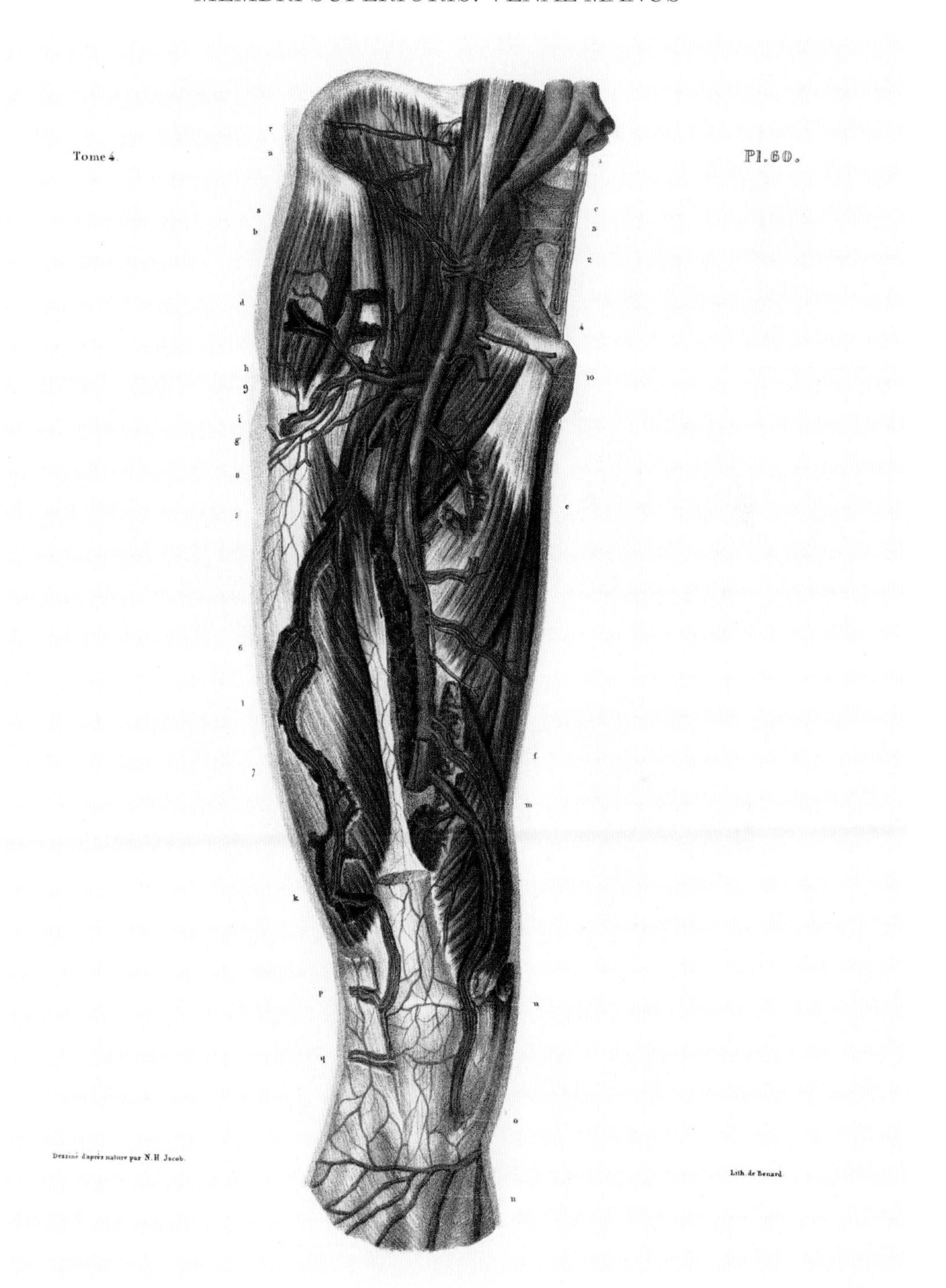

Veins of the thigh / Veines de la cuisse / Venas del muslo

VENAE FEMORIS. VENAE SUPERFICIALES MEMBRI SUPERIORIS. VENAE MANUS

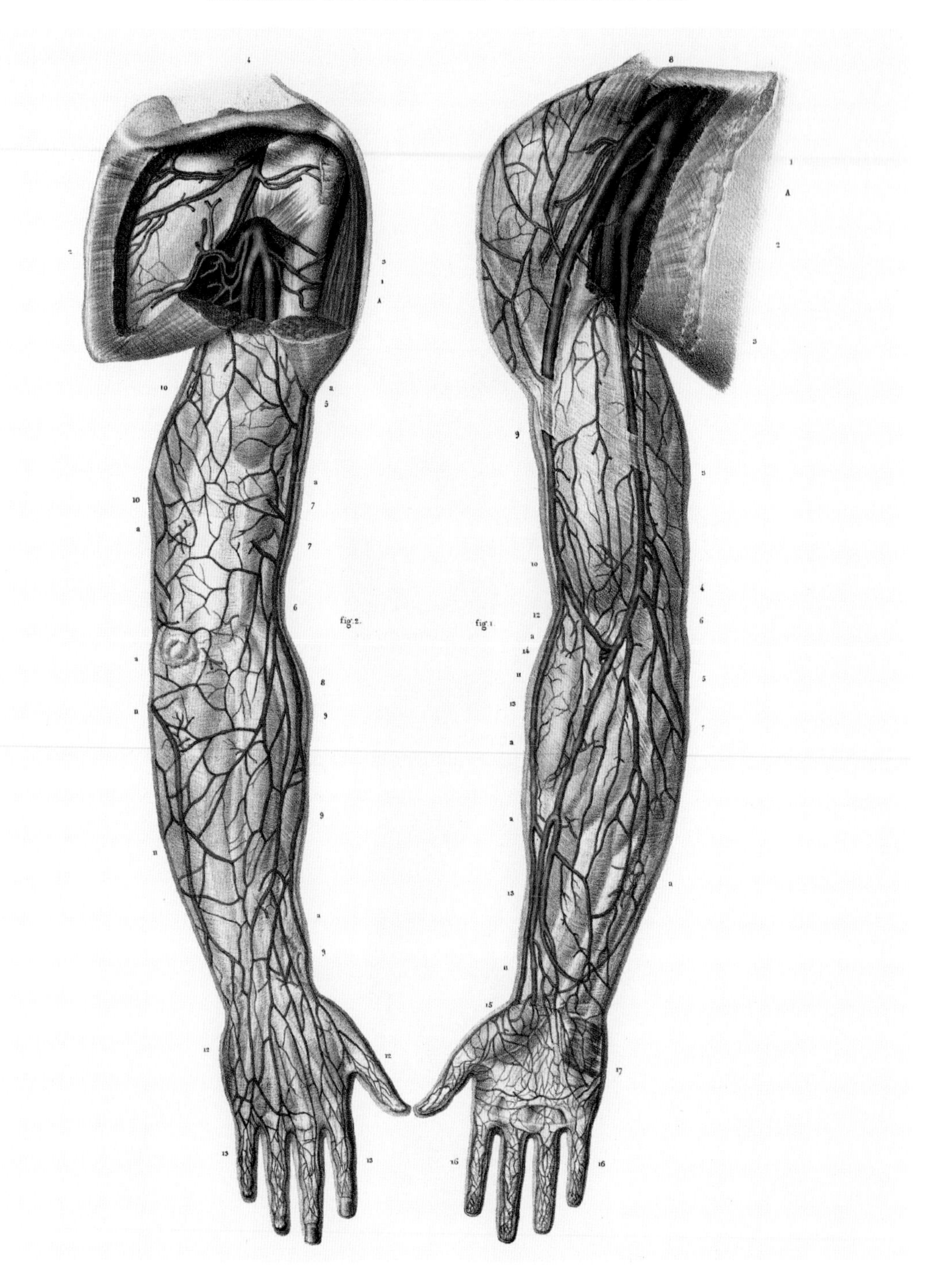

Superficial veins of the upper limb / Veines superficielles du membre supérieur
Venas superficiales del miembro superior

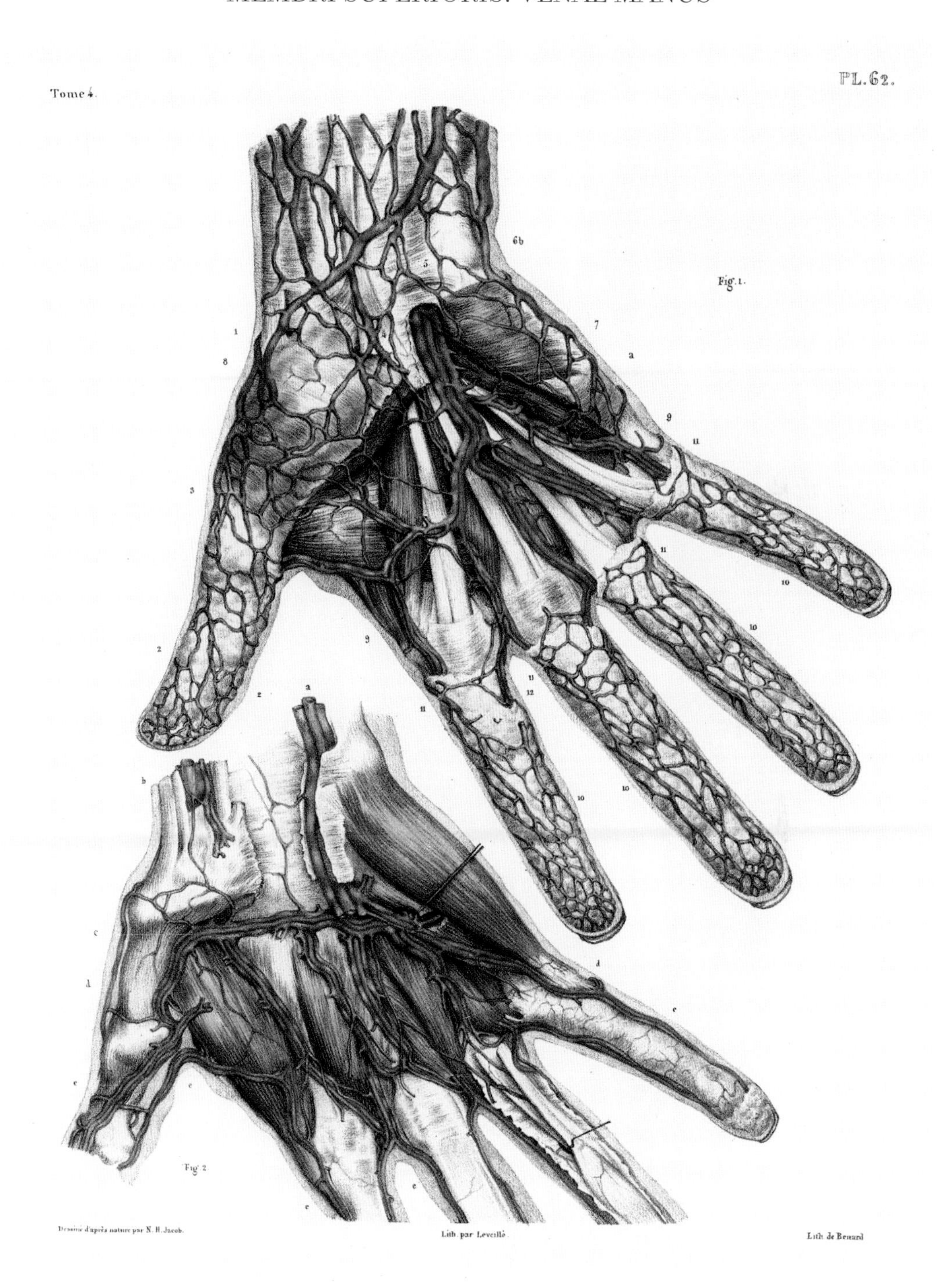

Veins of the hand / Veines de la main / Venas de la mano

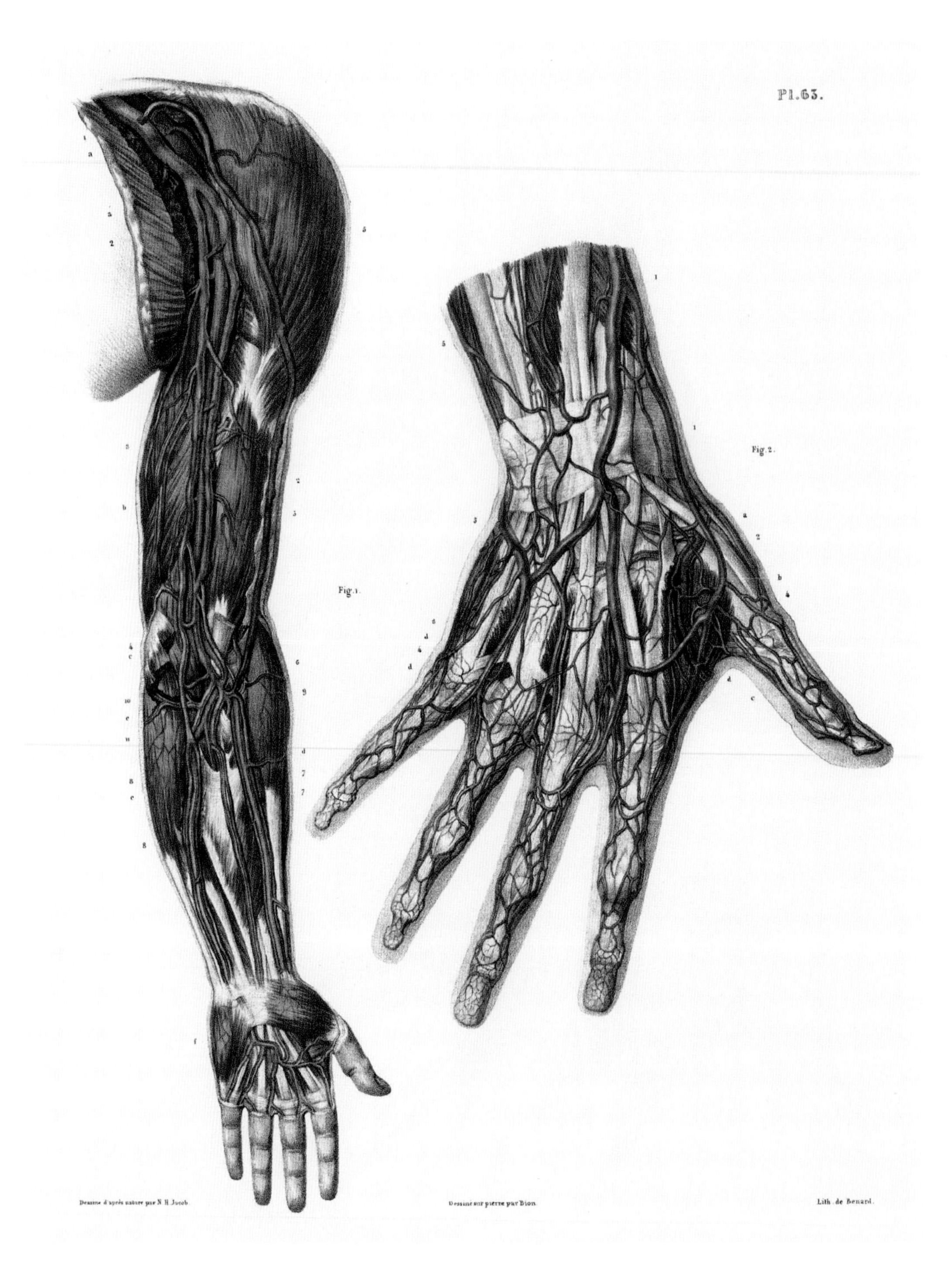

Veins of the upper limb / Veines du membre supérieur
Venas del miembro superior

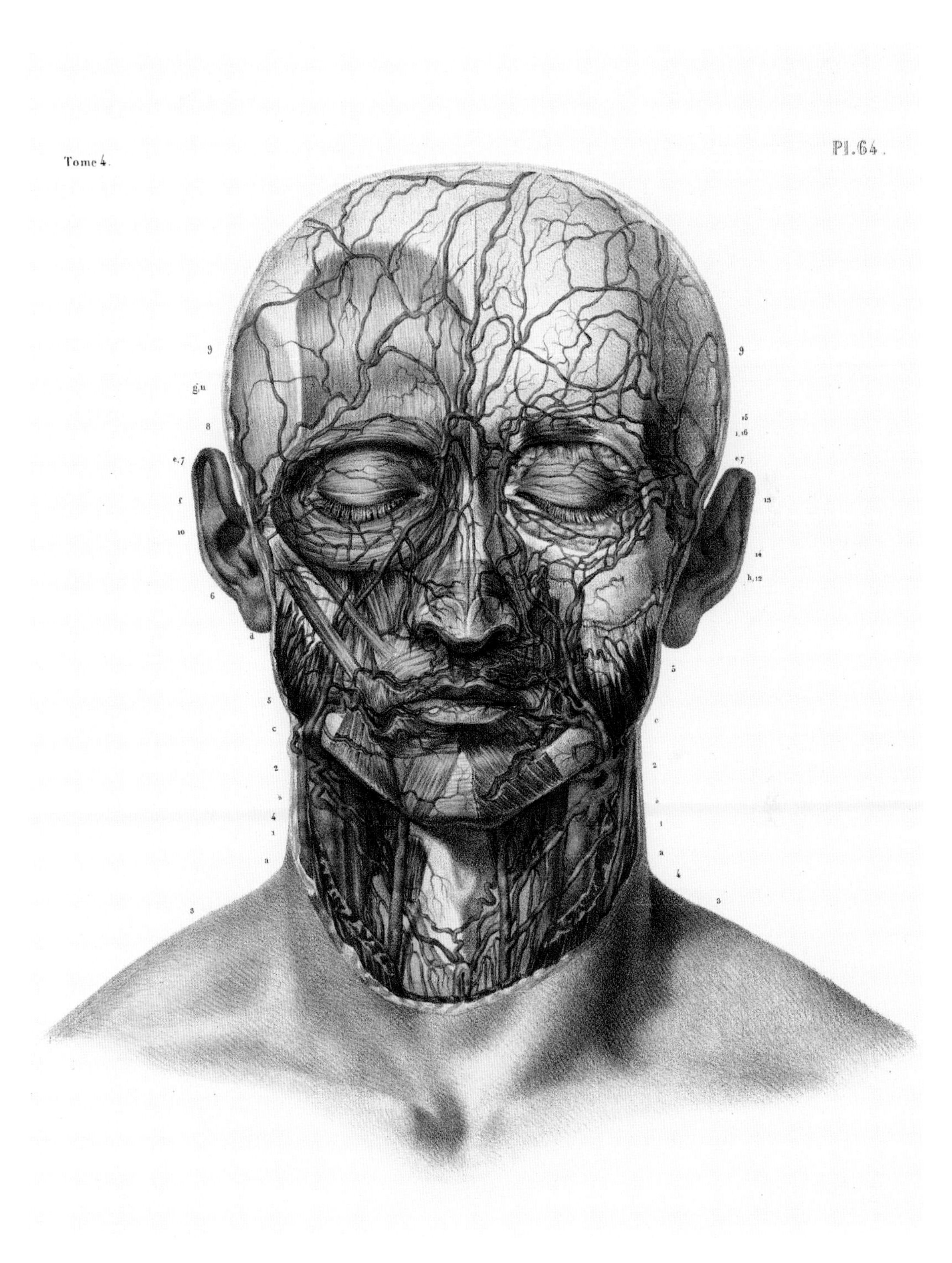

Veins of the head and neck / Veines de la tête et du cou
Venas de la cabeza y del cuello

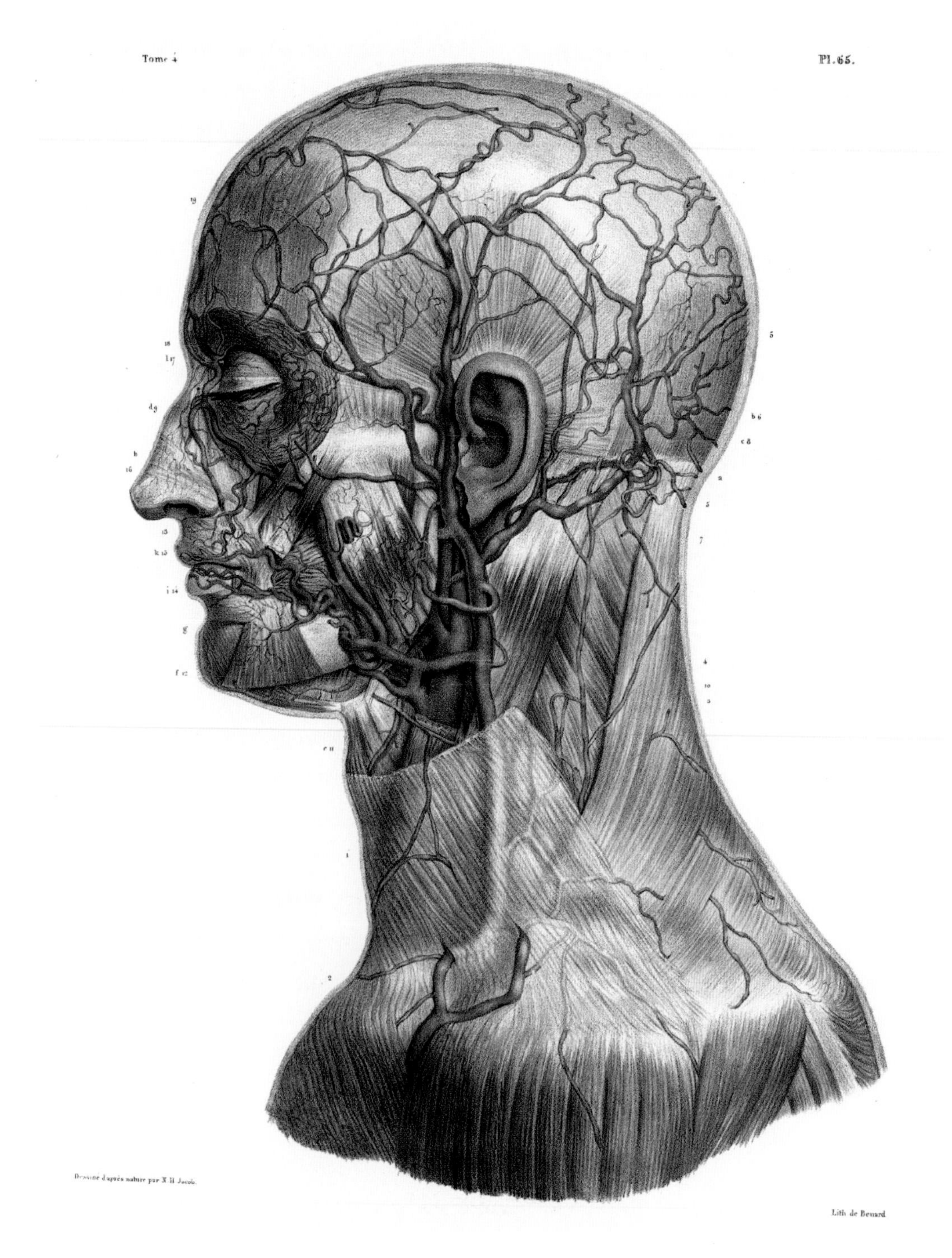

Veins of the head and neck / Veines de la tête et du cou
Venas de la cabeza y del cuello

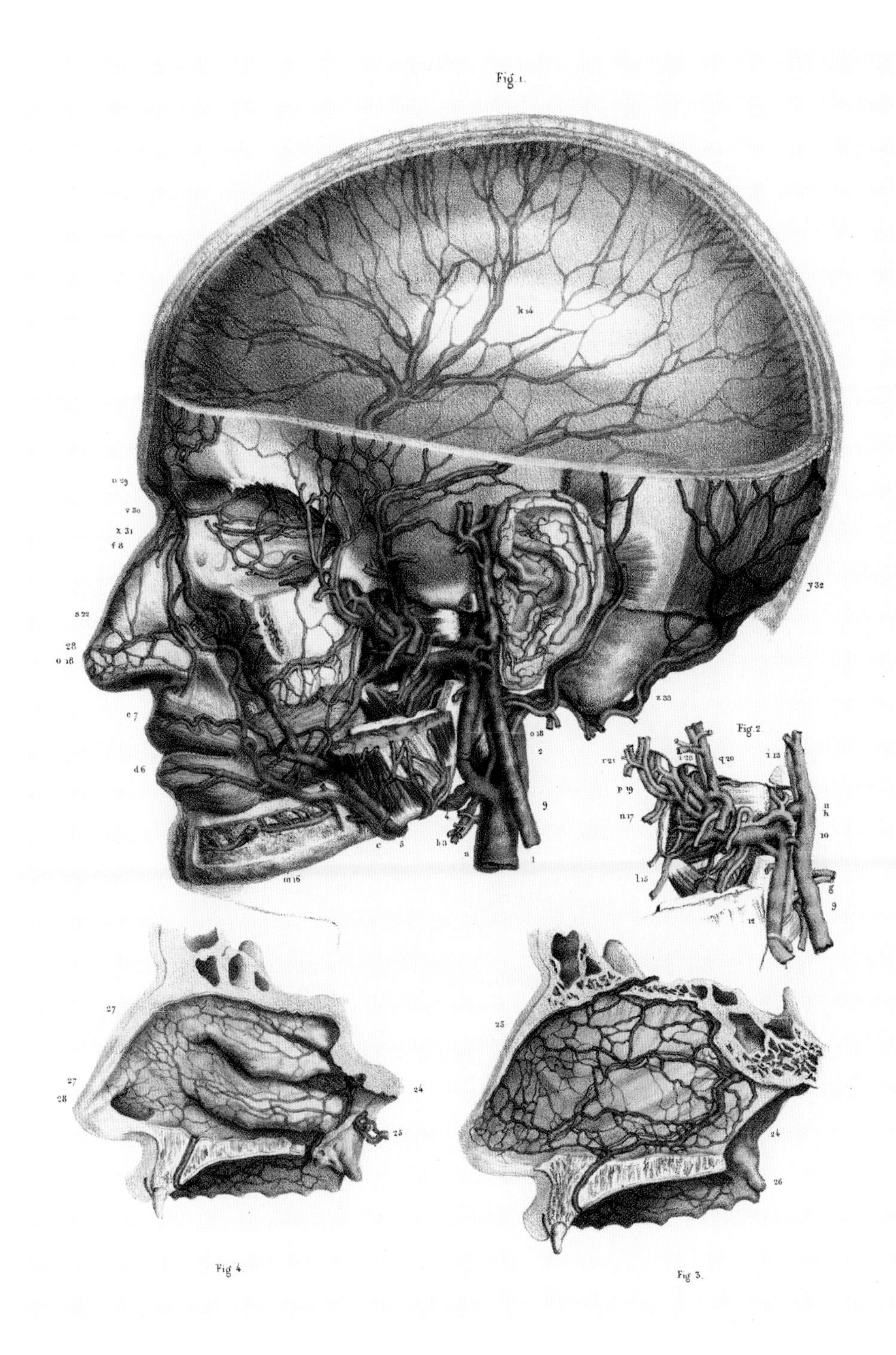

Veins of the head / Veines de la tête / Venas de la cabeza

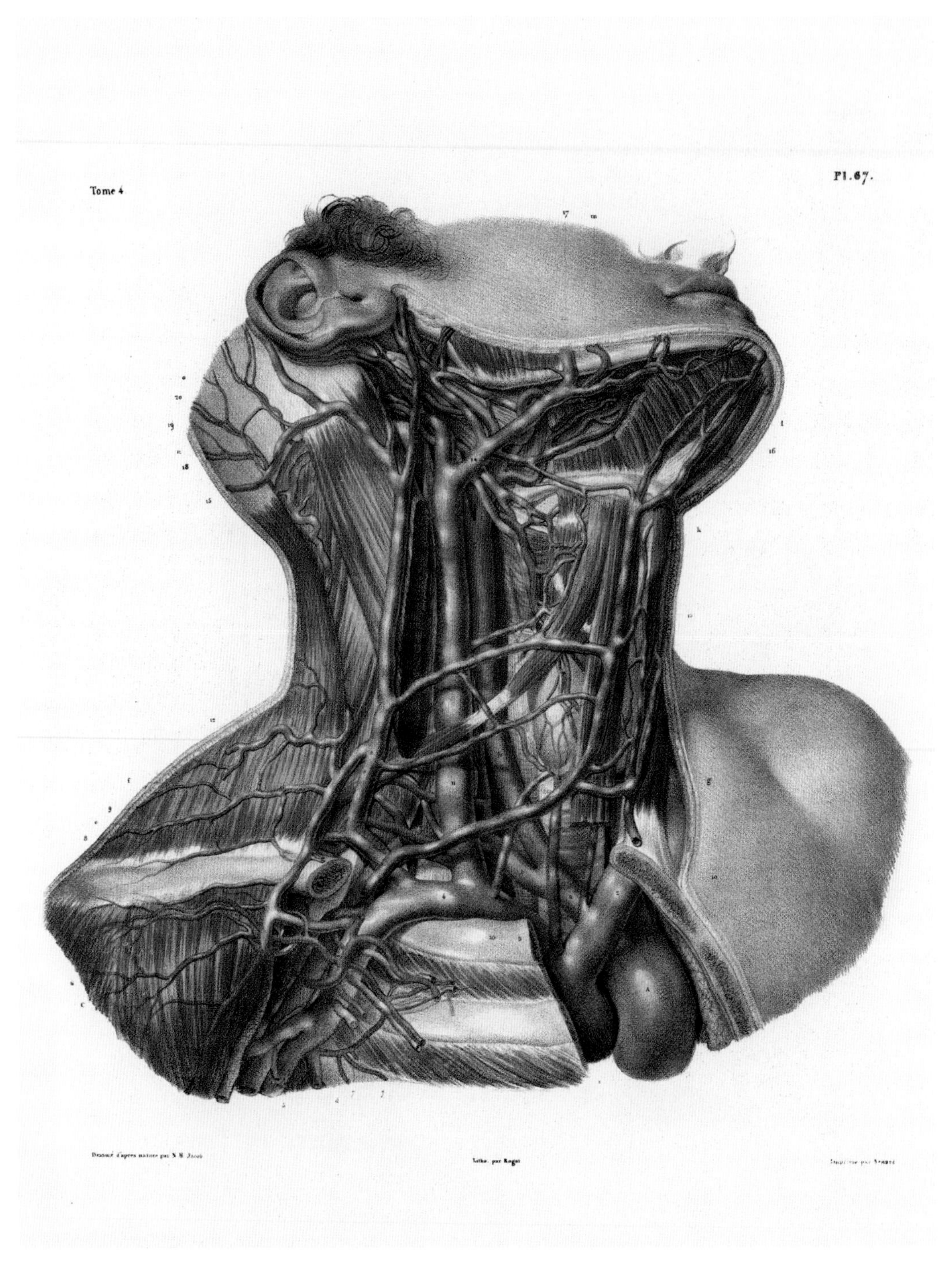

Veins of the neck / Veines du cou / Venas del cuello

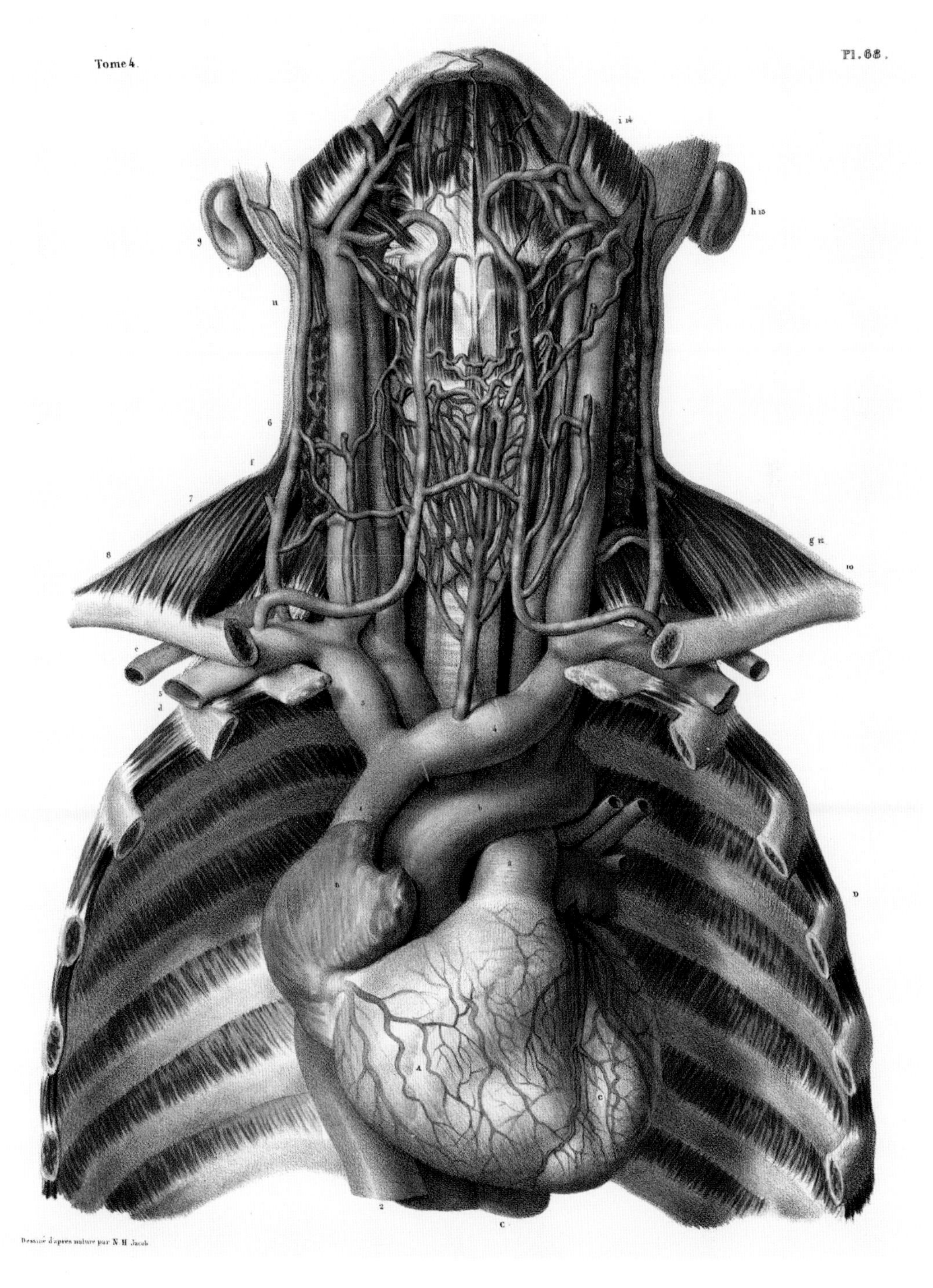

Veins of the neck / Veines du cou / Venas del cuello

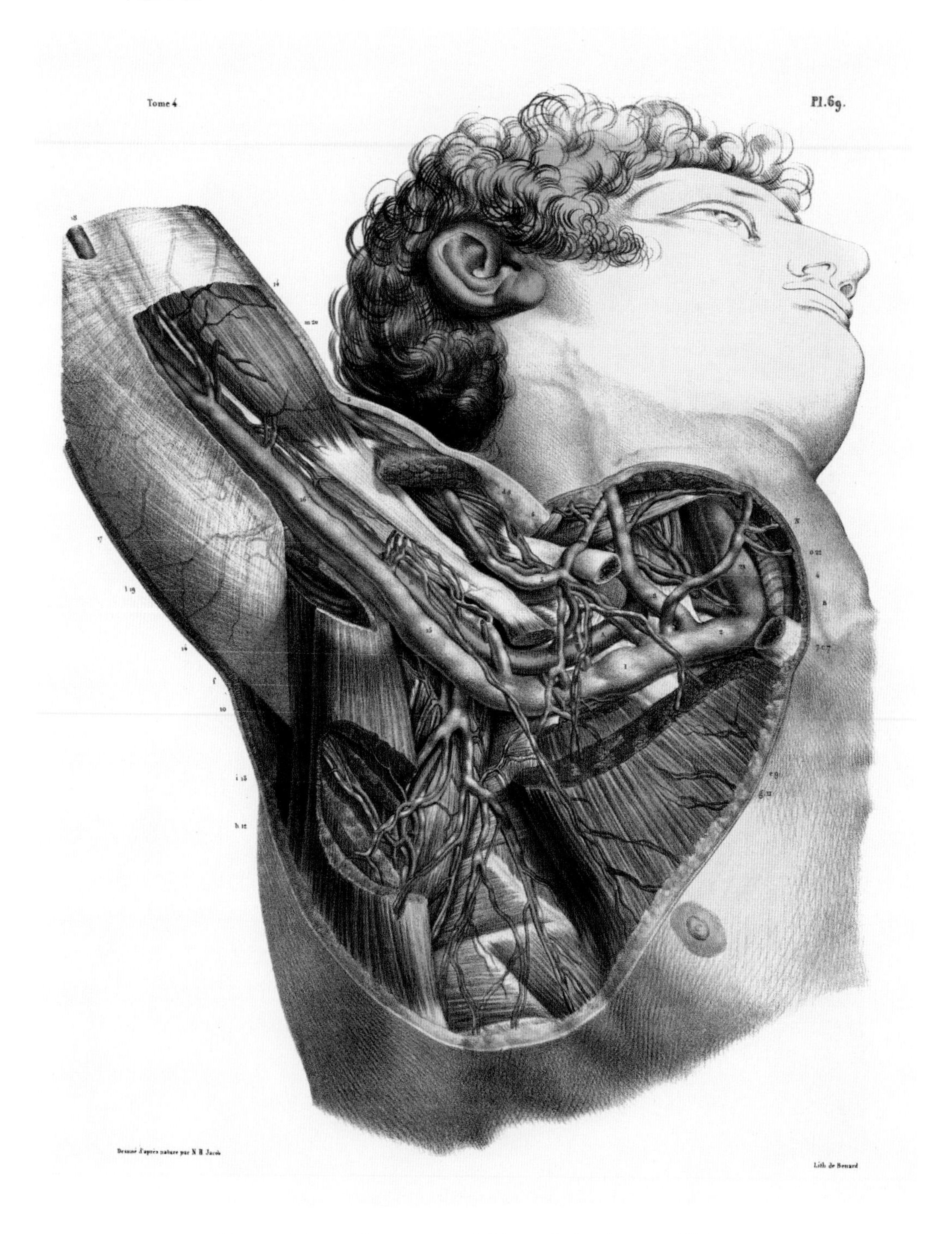

Veins of the axillary region / Veines de la région axillaire
Venas de la región axilar

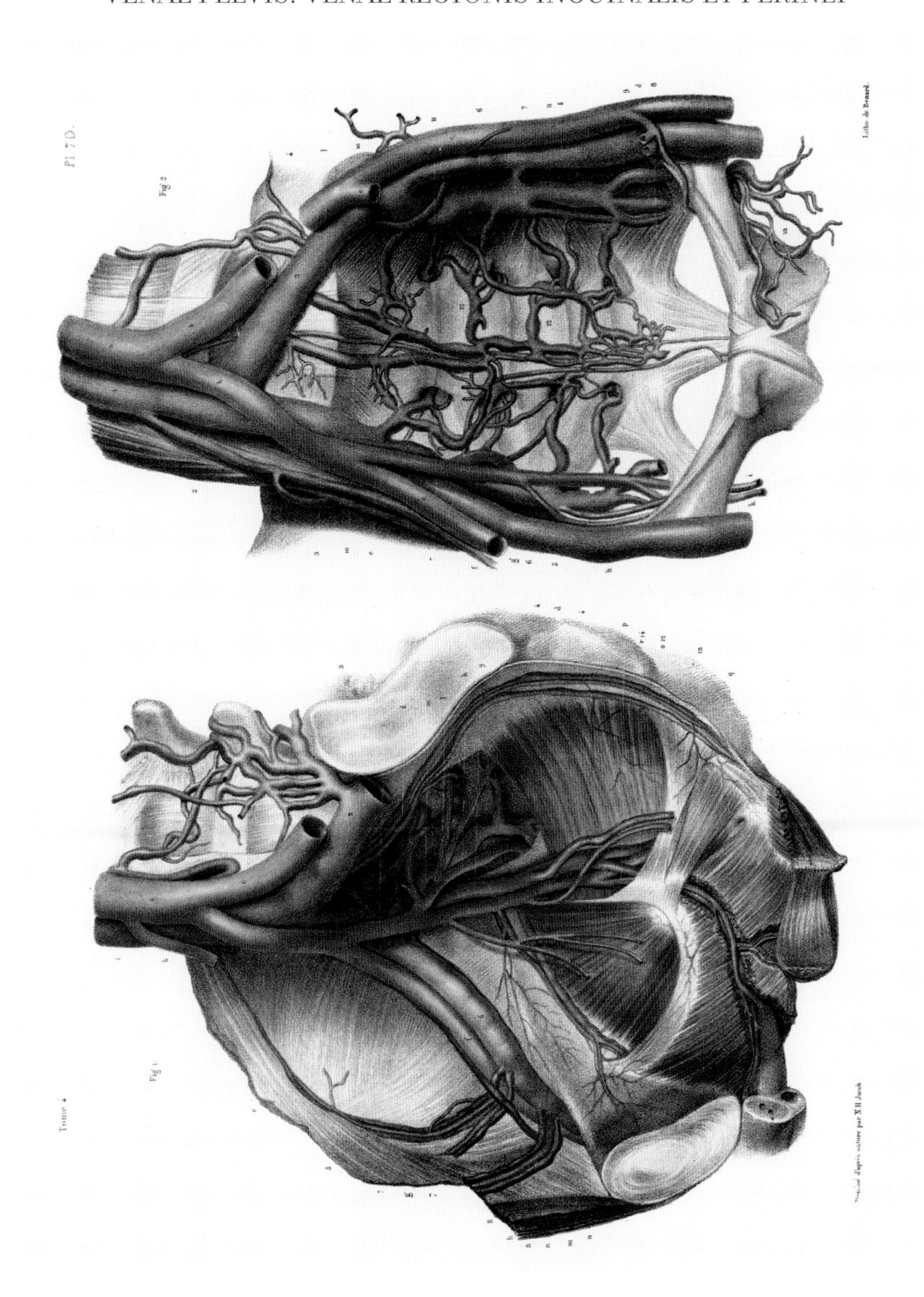

Veins of the pelvis / Veines du bassin / Venas de la pelvis

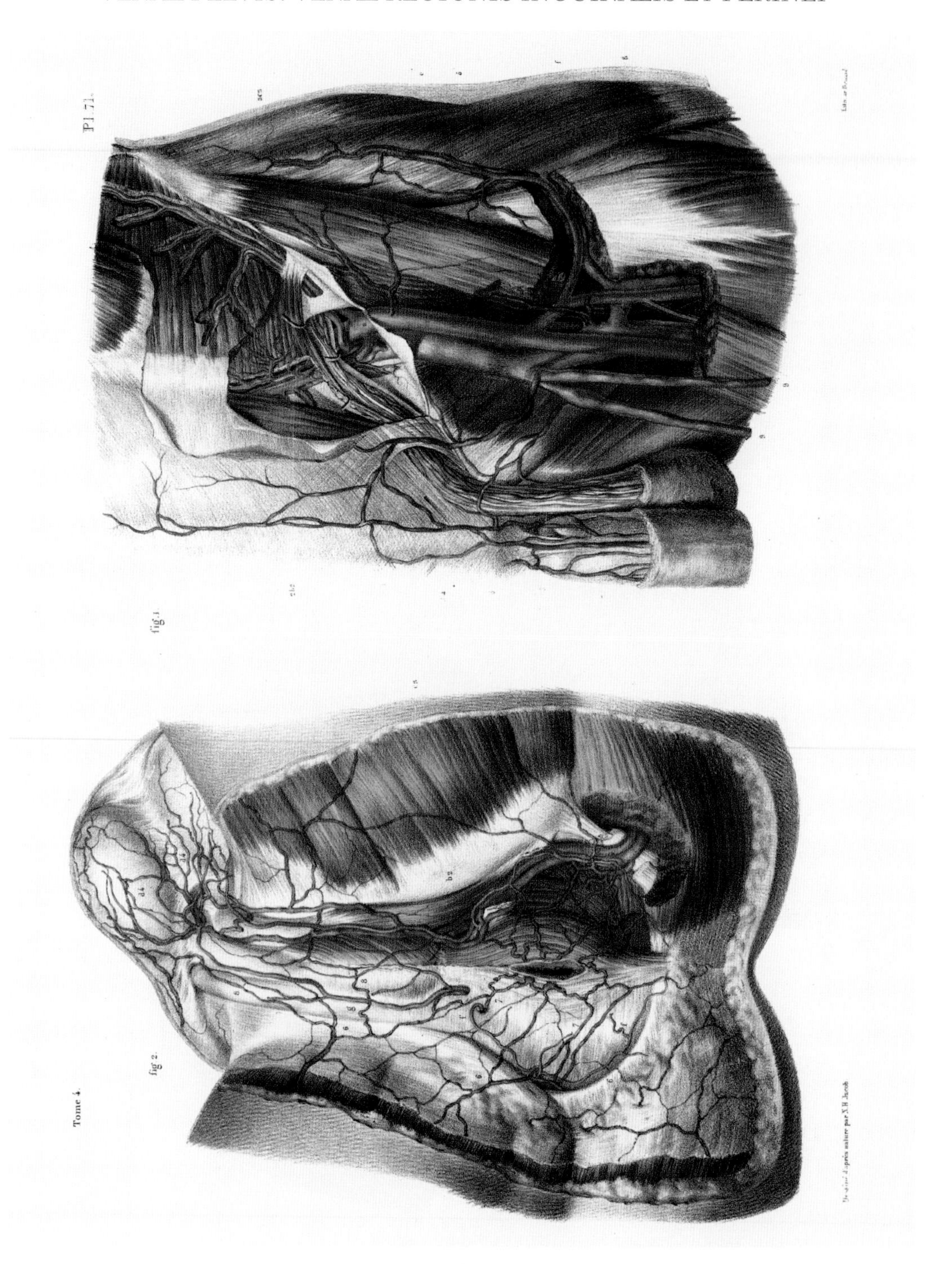

Veins of the inguinal region and the perineum
Veines de la région inguinale et du périnée
Venas de la región inguinal y del periné

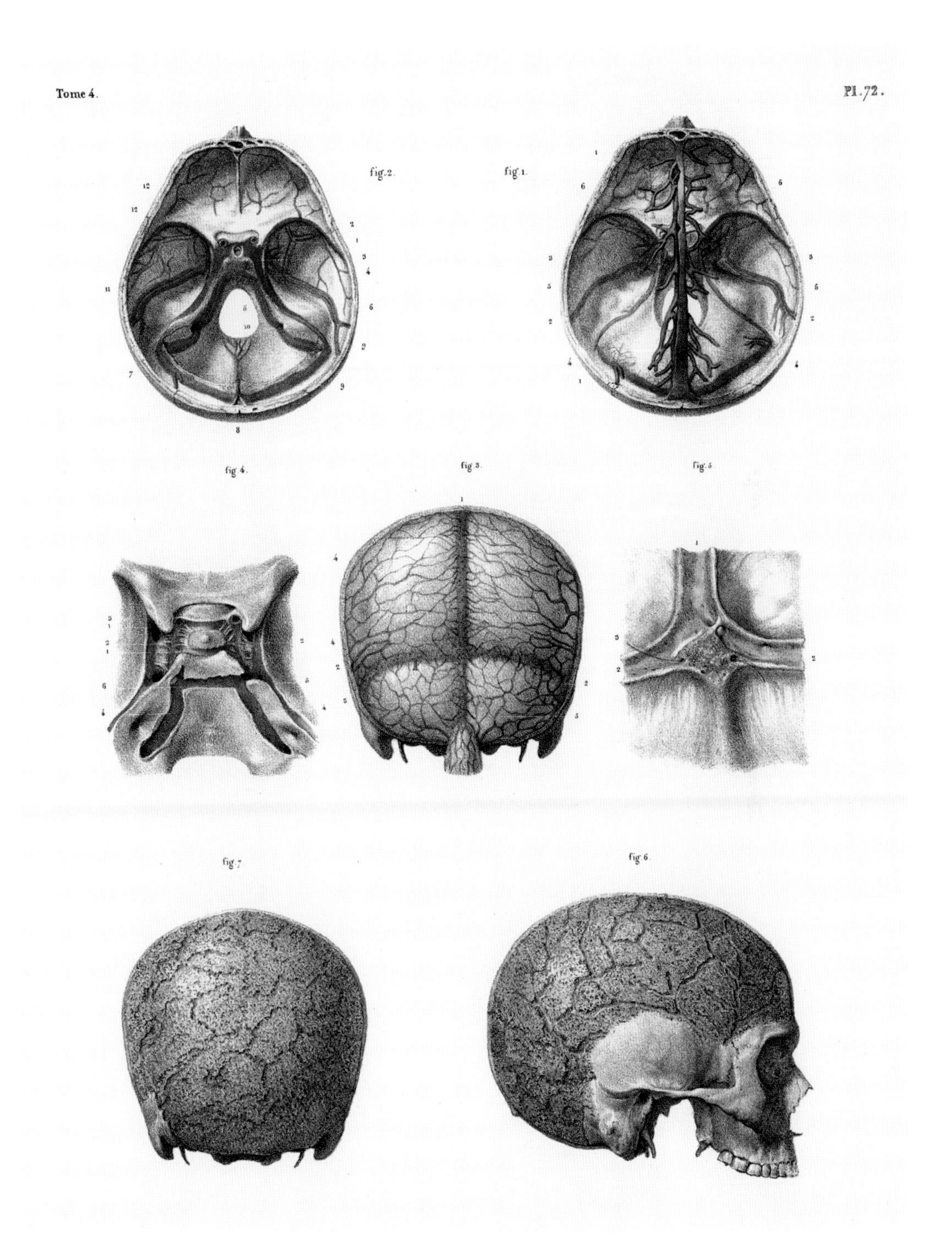

Veins of the skull and sinuses of the dura mater
Veines du crâne et sinus de la dure-mère
Venas del cráneo y senos de la duramadre

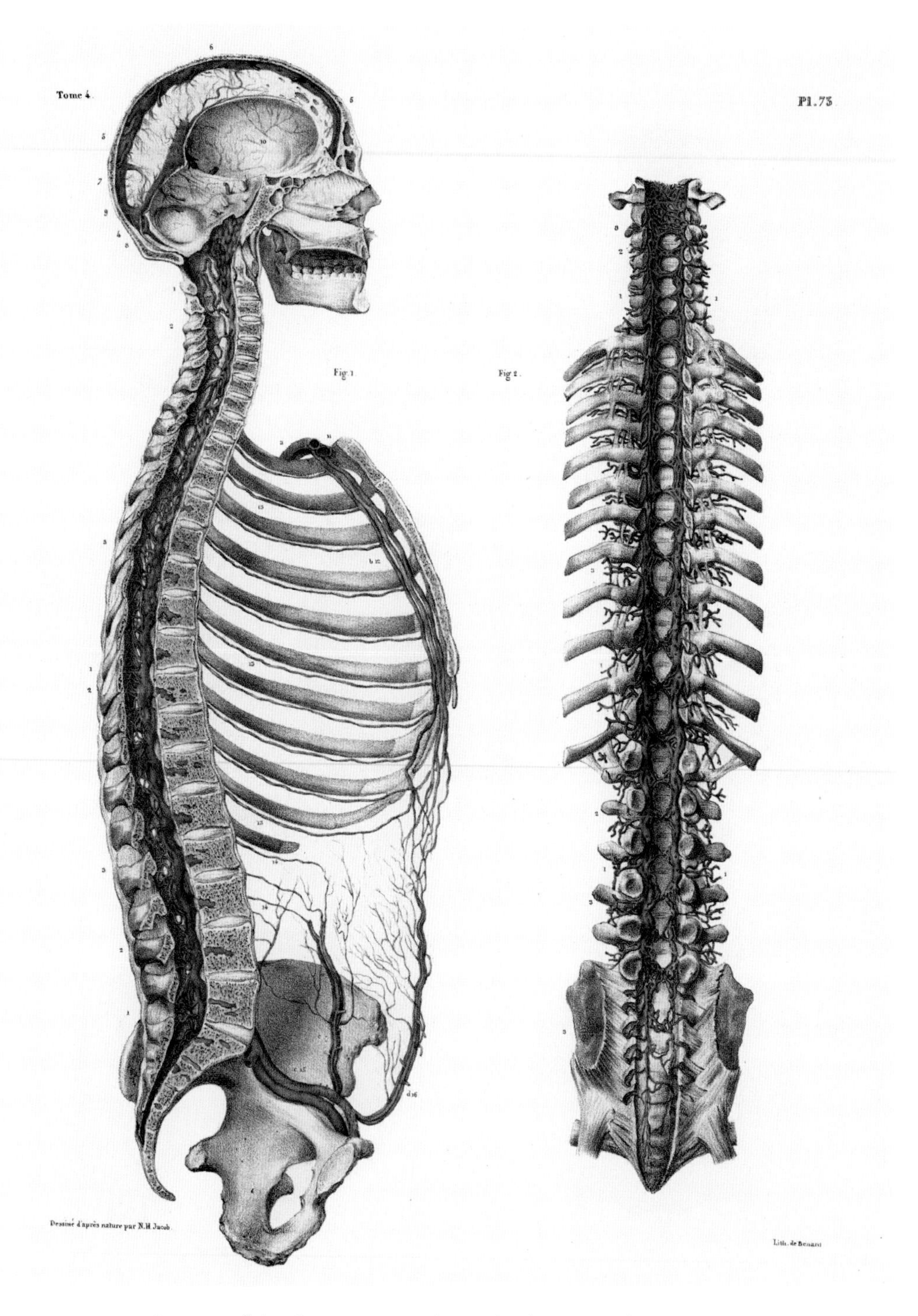

Sinuses of the dura mater and vertebral venous plexuses
Sinus de la dure-mère et plexus veineux vertébraux
Senos de la duramadre y plexos venosos vertebrales

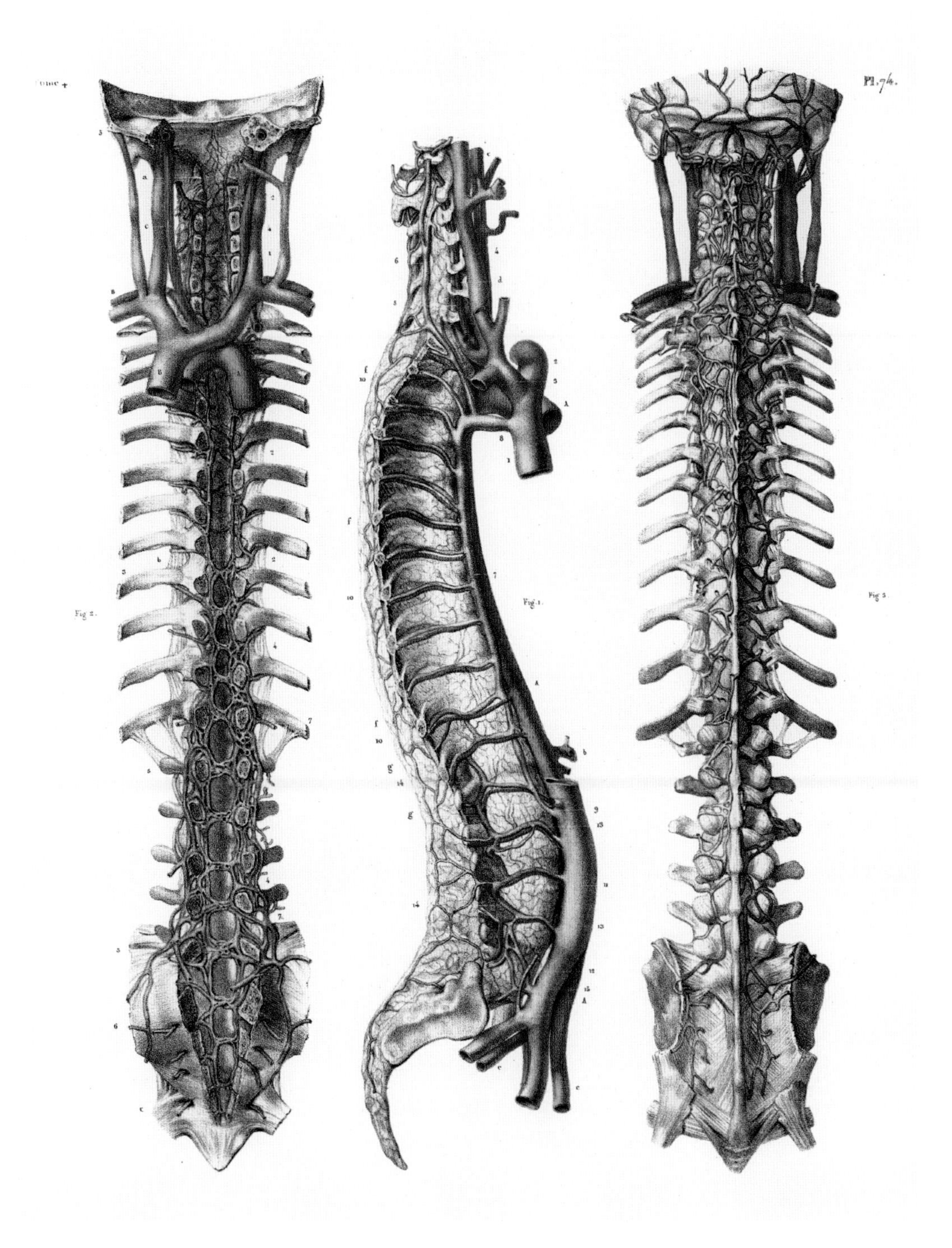

Vertebral venous plexuses / Plexus veineux vertébraux
Plexos venosos vertebrales

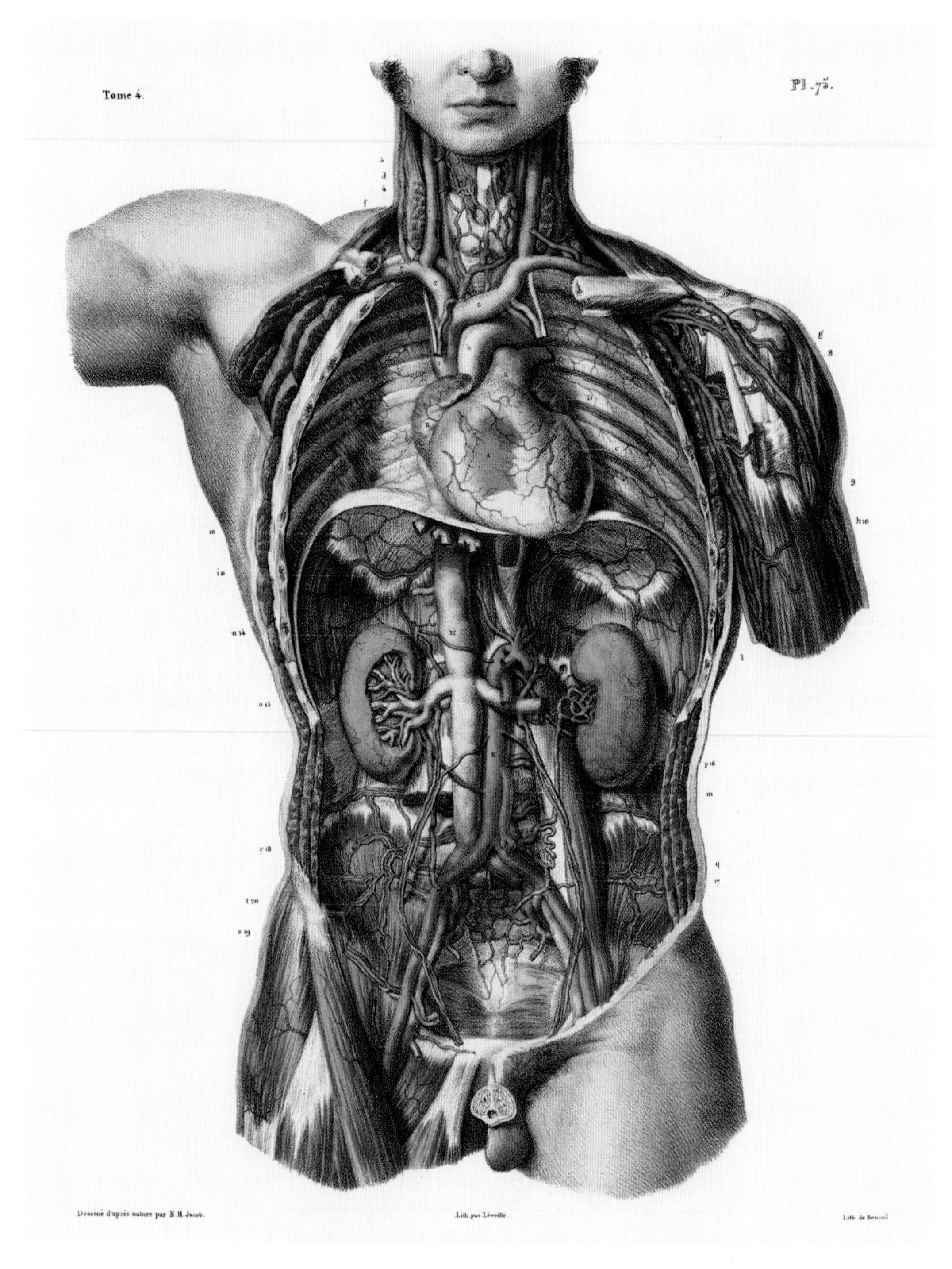

Veins of thorax and abdomen / Veines du thorax et de l'abdomen
Venas del tórax y del abdomen

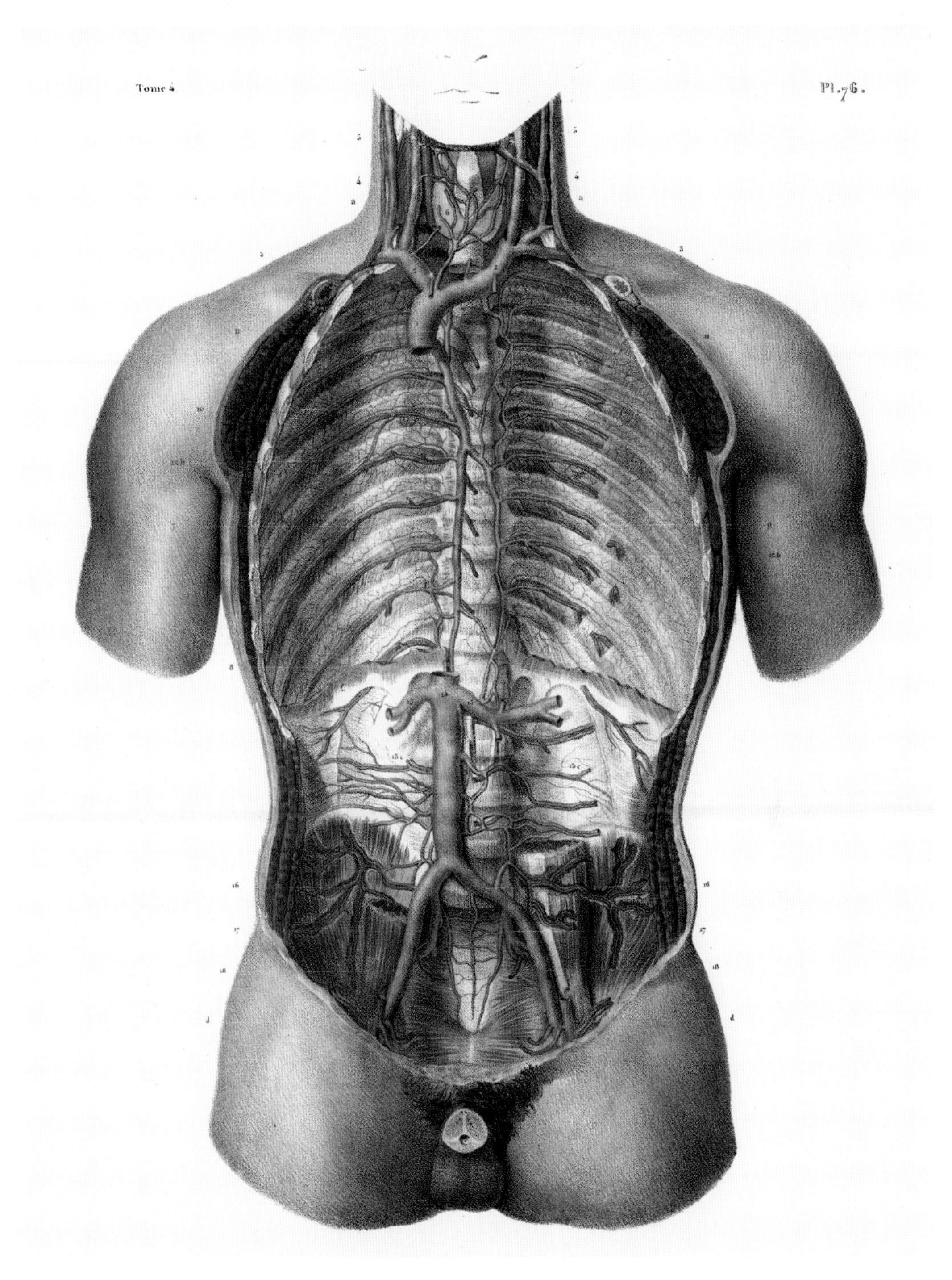

Veins of the walls of thorax and abdomen
Veines des parois du thorax et de l'abdomen
Venas de las paredes del tórax y del abdomen

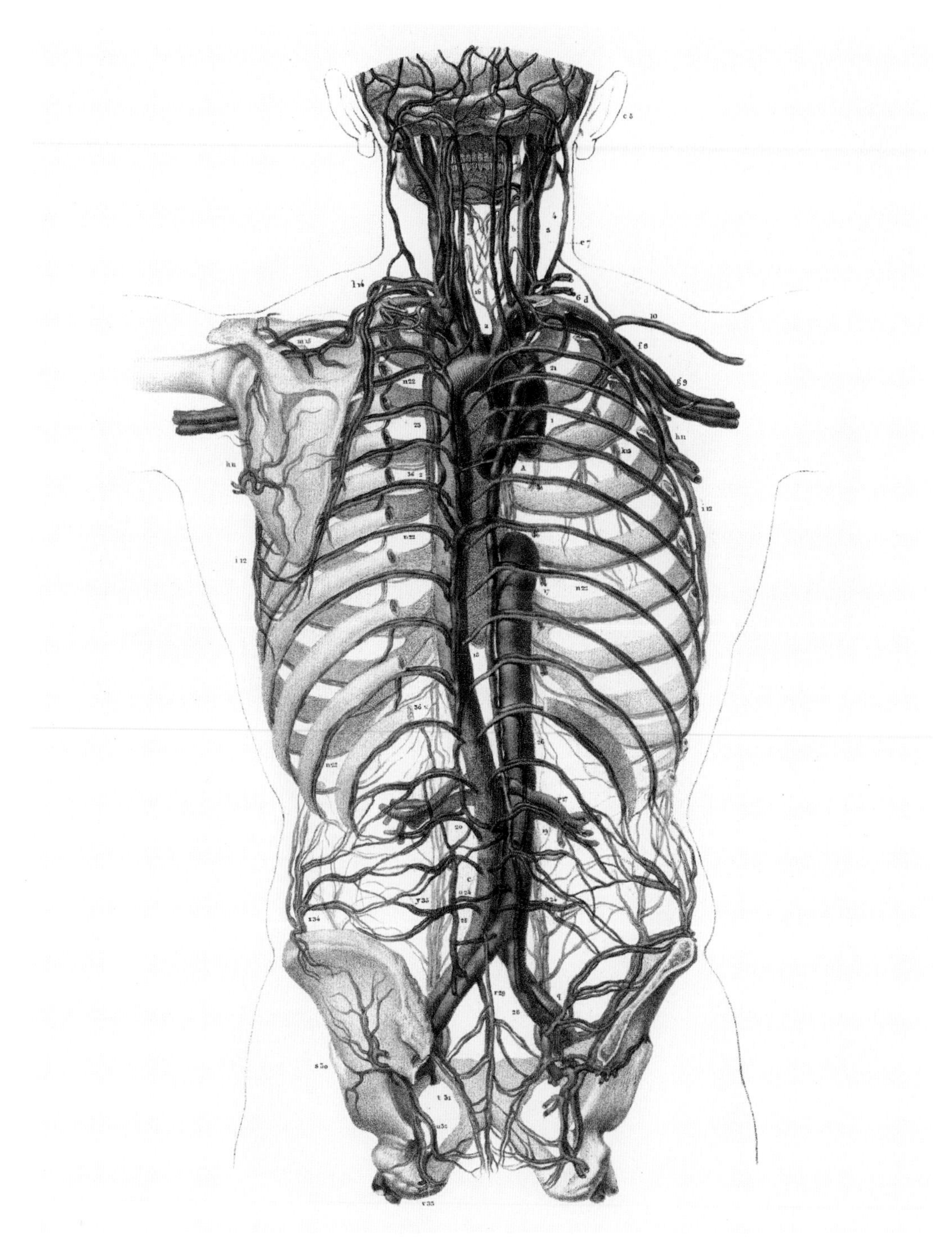

Veins of the walls of thorax and abdomen
Veines des parois du thorax et de l'abdomen
Venas de las paredes del tórax y del abdomen

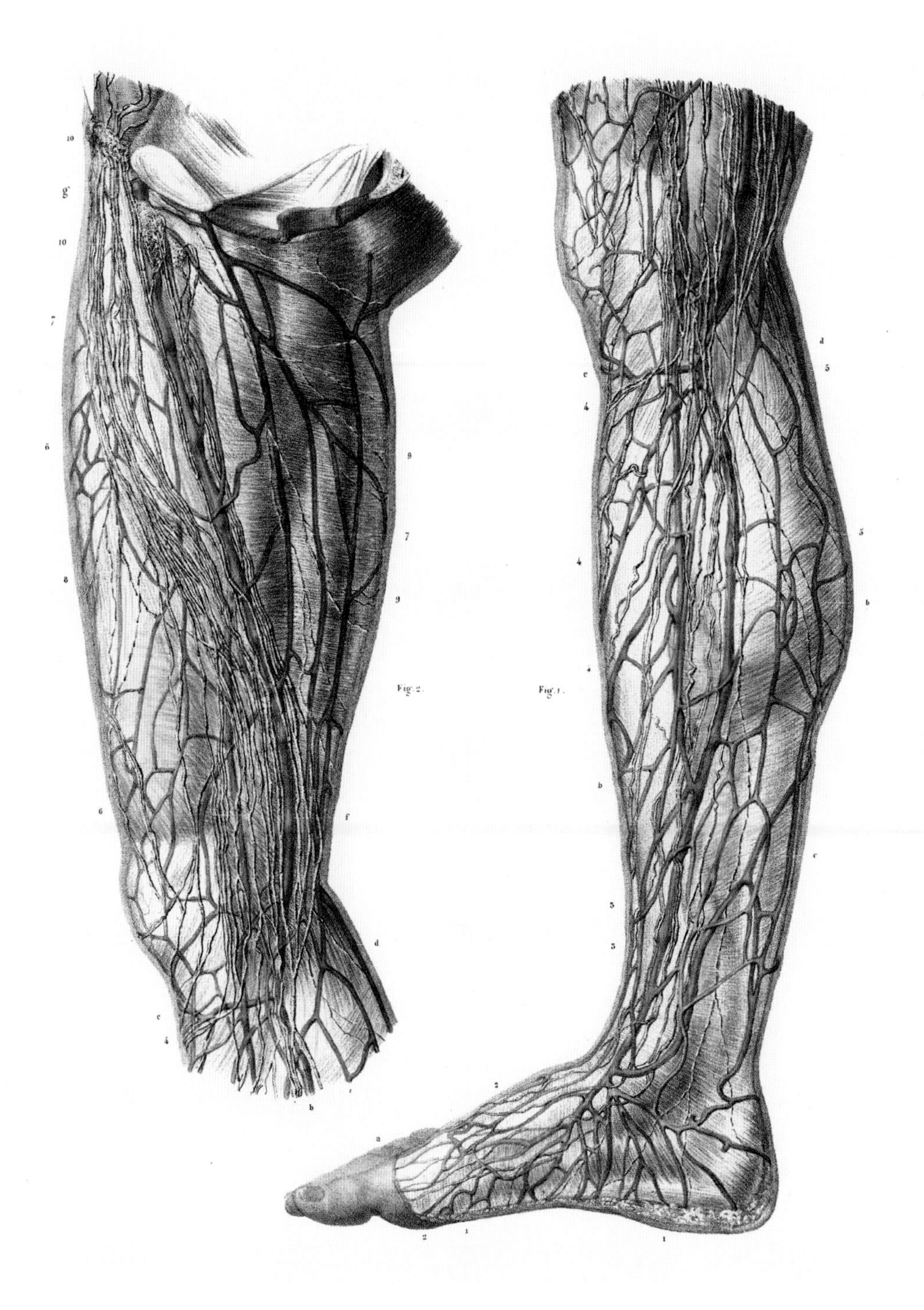

Lymph vessels and nodes of the lower limb
Vaisseaux et nœuds lymphatiques du membre inférieur
Vasos y ganglios linfáticos del miembro inferior

VASA LYMPHATICA ET LYMPHONODI MEMBRI INFERIORIS ET REGIONIS INGUINALIS

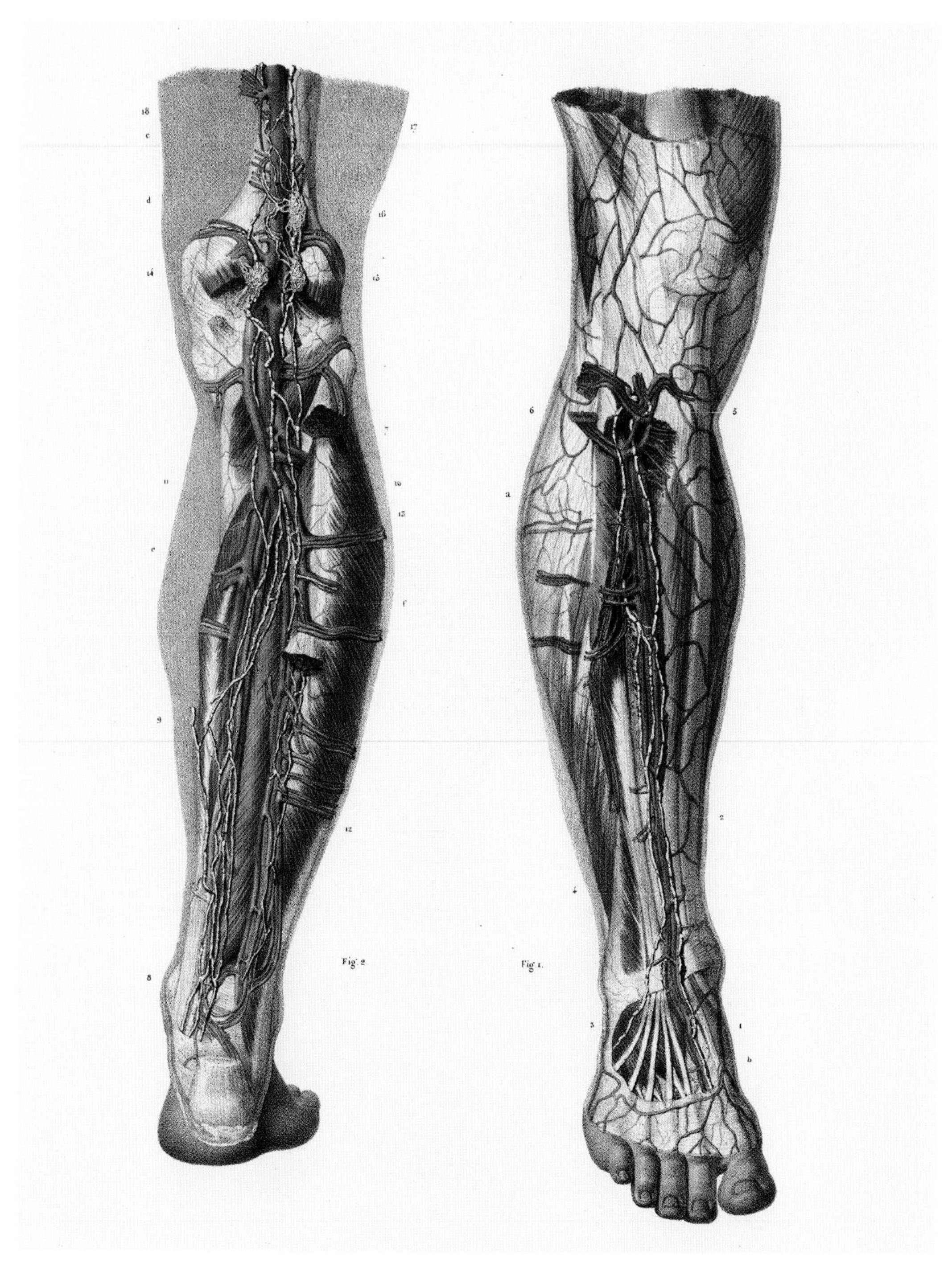

Lymph vessels and nodes of the lower leg
Vaisseaux et nœuds lymphatiques de la jambe
Vasos y ganglios linfáticos de la pierna

VASA LYMPHATICA ET LYMPHONODI MEMBRI INFERIORIS ET REGIONIS INGUINALIS

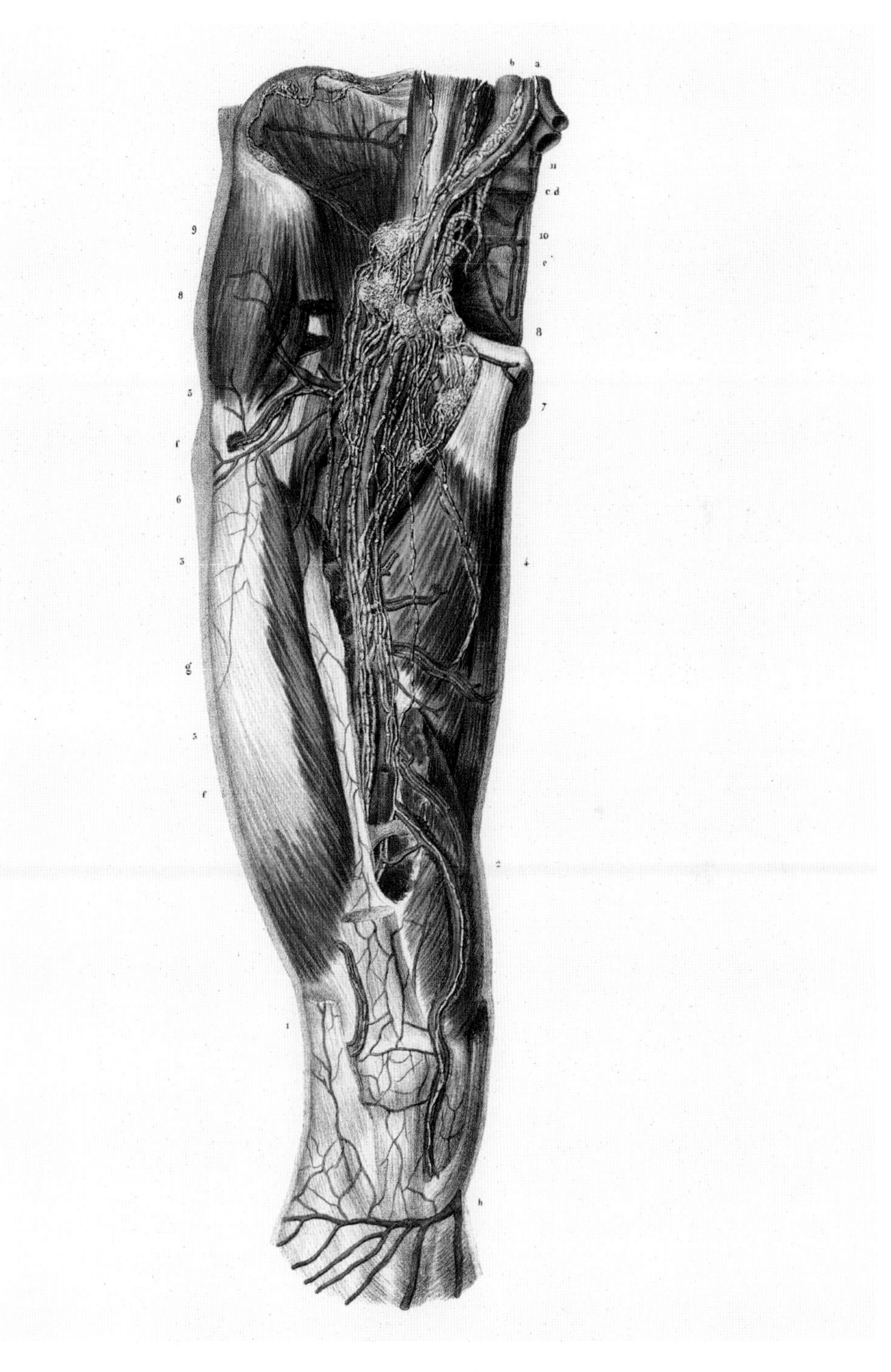

Lymph vessels and nodes of the thigh
Vaisseaux et nœuds lymphatiques de la cuisse
Vasos y ganglios linfáticos del muslo

VASA LYMPHATICA ET LYMPHONODI MEMBRI INFERIORIS ET REGIONIS INGUINALIS

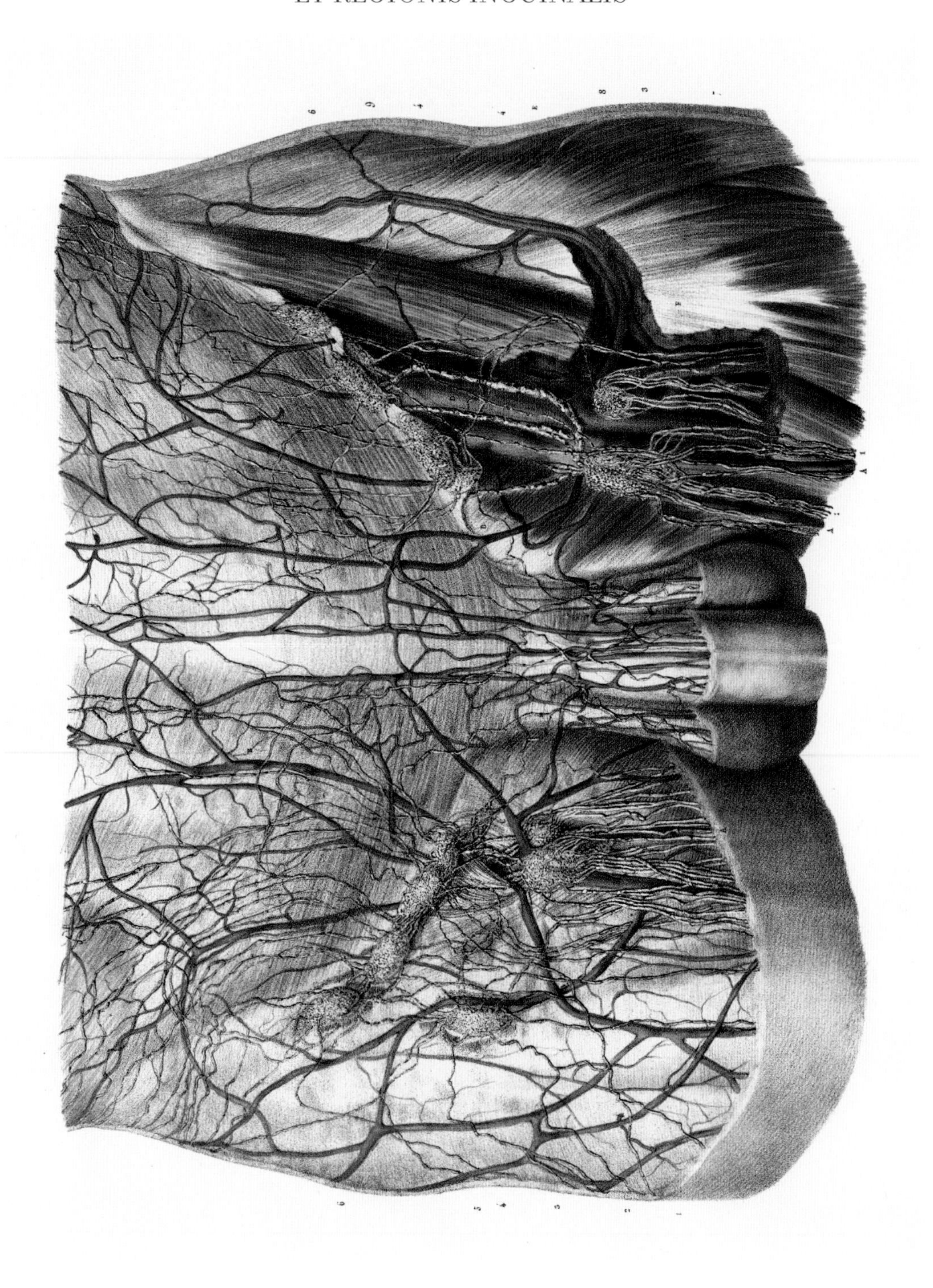

Lymph vessels and nodes of the inguinal region
Vaisseaux et nœuds lymphatiques de la région inguinale
Vasos y ganglios linfáticos de la región inguinal

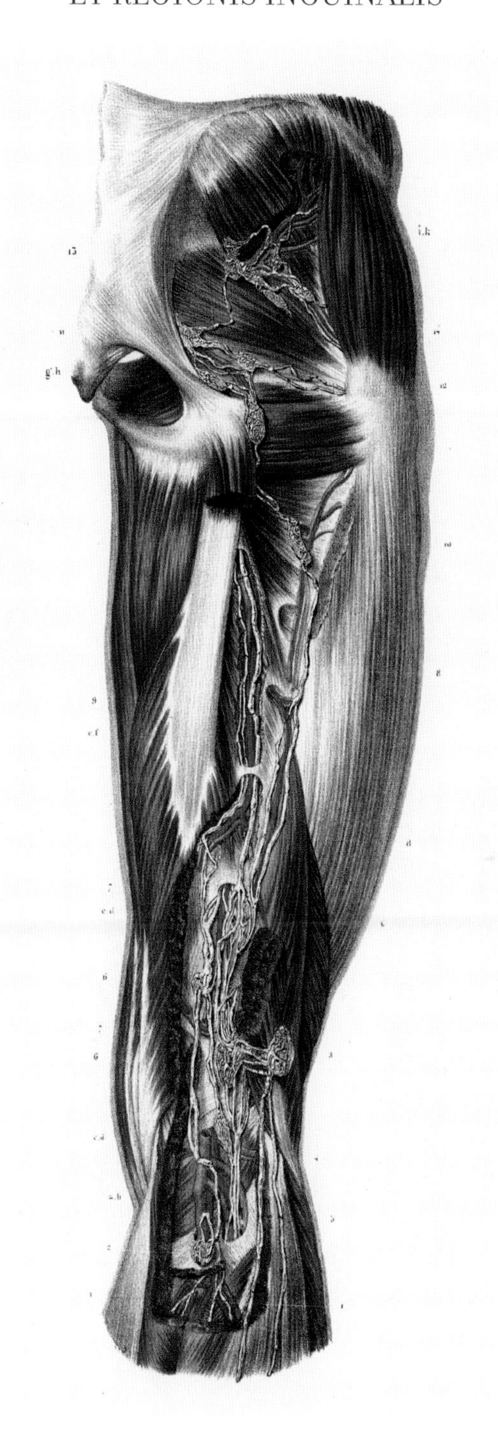

Lymph vessels and nodes of the thigh
Vaisseaux et nœuds lymphatiques de la cuisse
Vasos y ganglios linfáticos del muslo

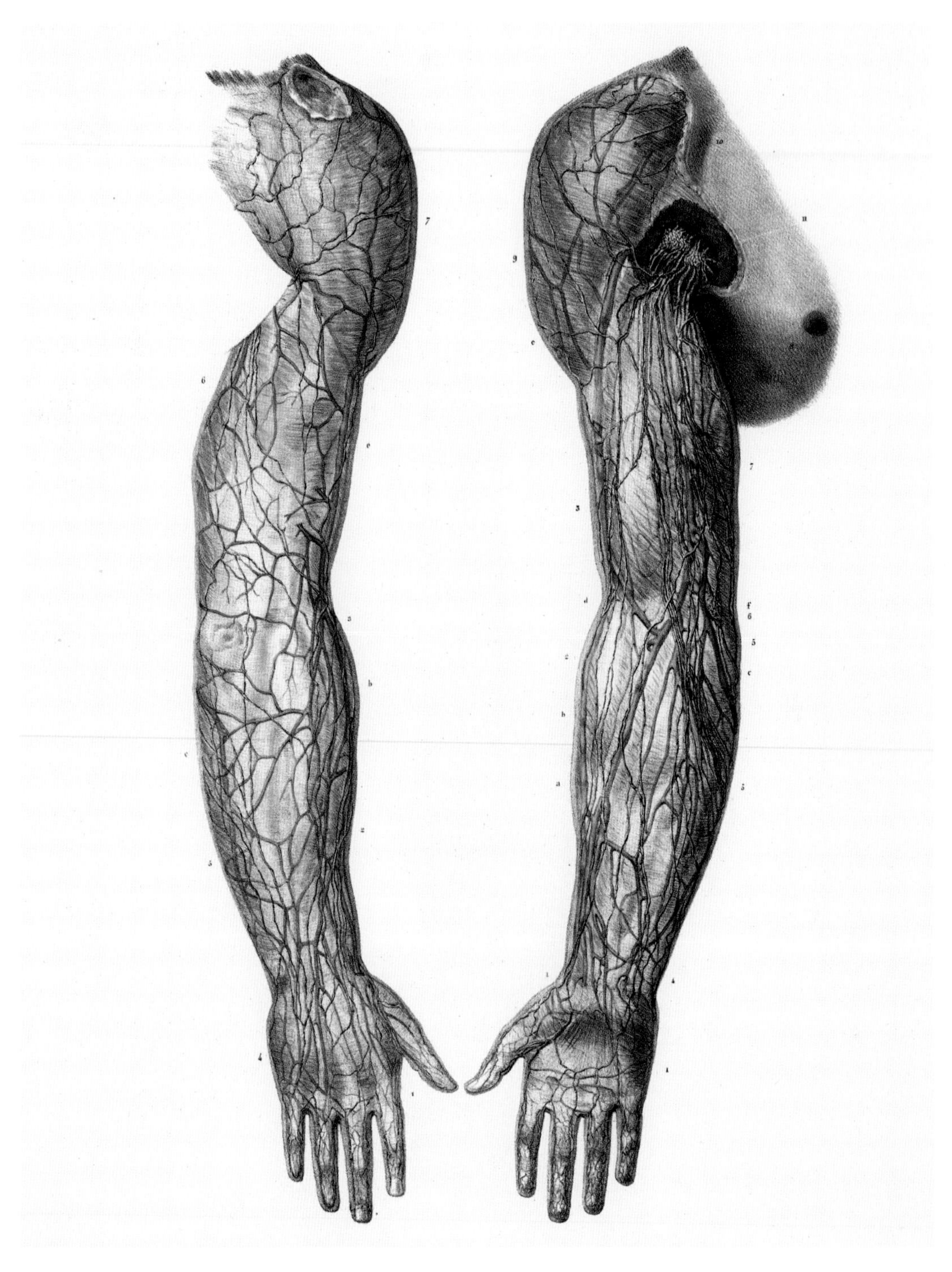

Lymph vessels and nodes of the upper limb
Vaisseaux et nœuds lymphatiques du membre supérieur
Vasos y ganglios linfáticos del miembro superior

VASA LYMPHATICA ET LYMPHONODI MEMBRI SUPERIORIS, THORACIS ET ABDOMINIS, CAPITIS ET COLLI

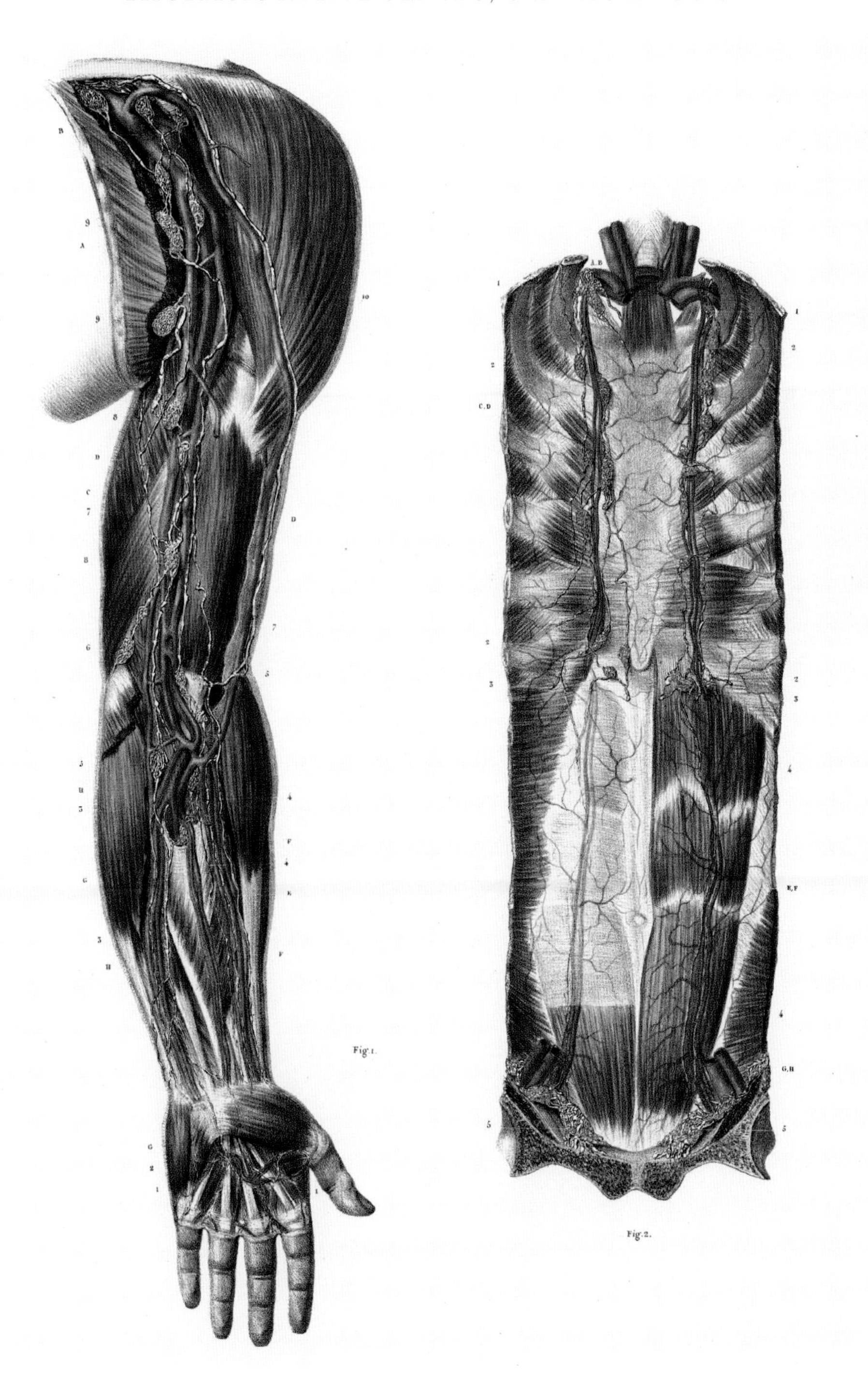

Lymph vessels and nodes of upper limb, thorax, and abdomen
Vaisseaux et nœuds lymphatiques du membre supérieur, du thorax et de l'abdomen
Vasos y ganglios linfáticos del miembro superior, del tórax y del abdomen

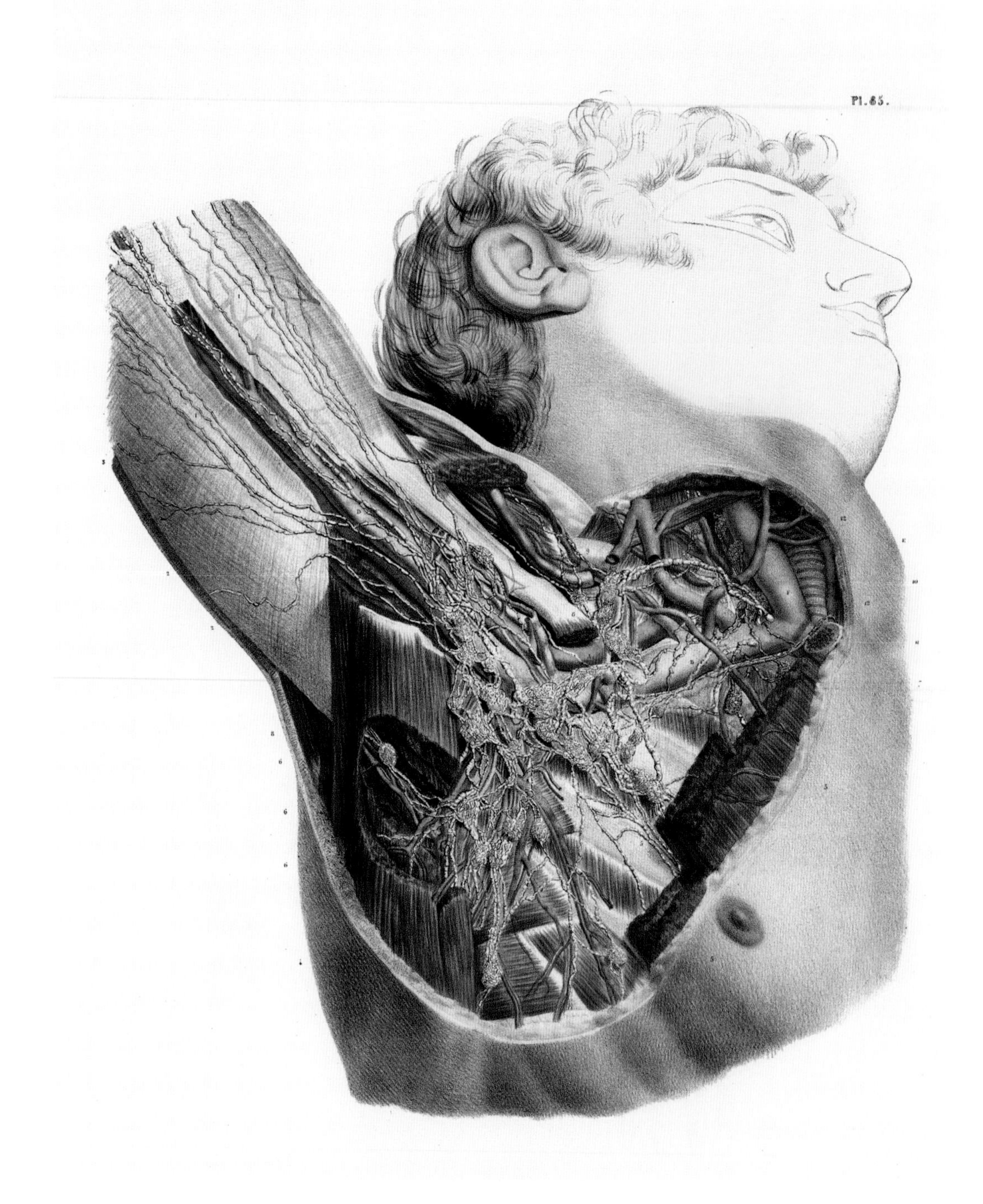

Lymph vessels and nodes of the axillary region
Vaisseaux et nœuds lymphatiques de la région axillaire
Vasos y ganglios linfáticos de la región axilar

VASA LYMPHATICA ET LYMPHONODI MEMBRI SUPERIORIS, THORACIS ET ABDOMINIS, CAPITIS ET COLLI

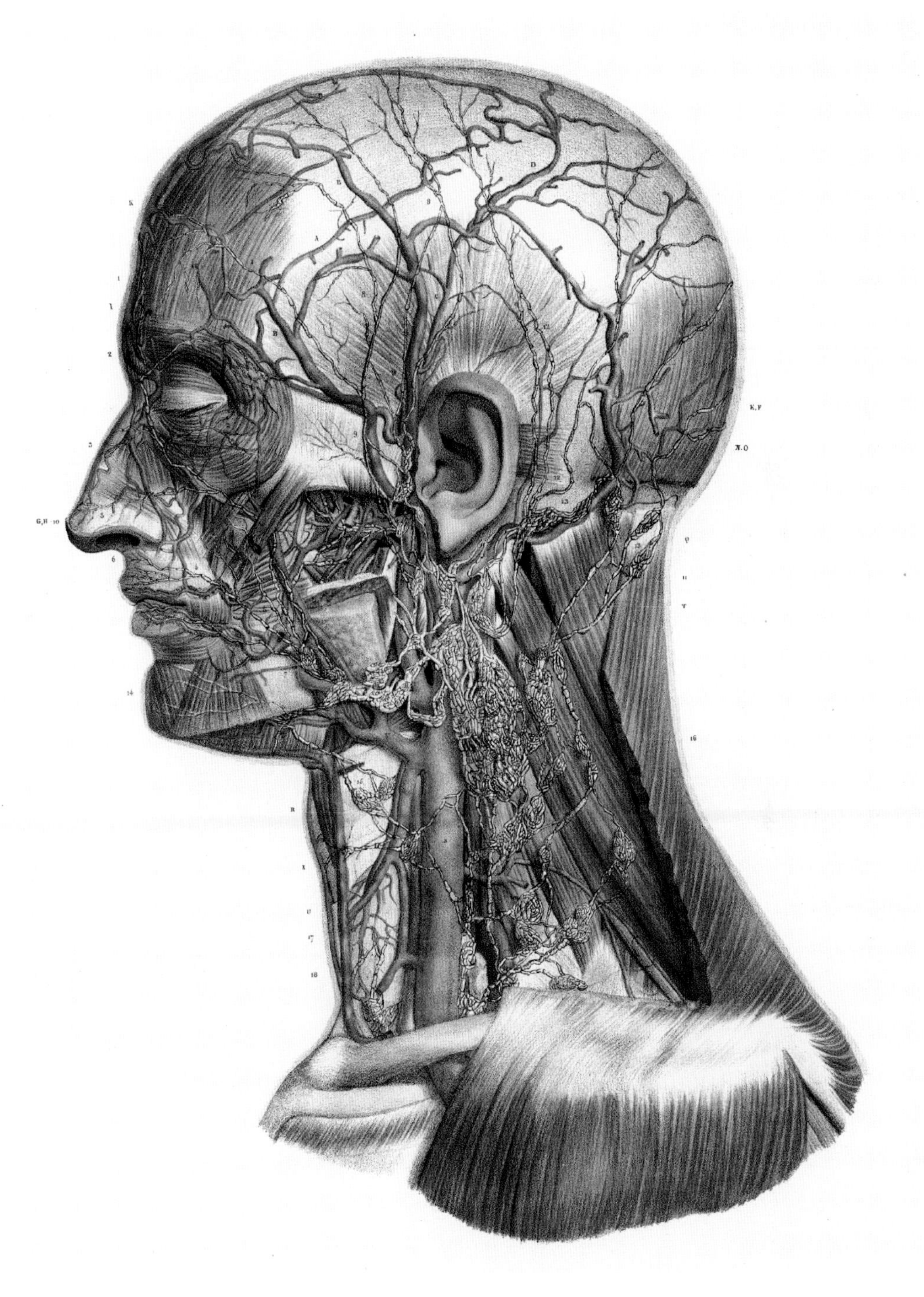

Lymph vessels and nodes of the head and neck
Vaisseaux et nœuds lymphatiques de la tête et du cou
Vasos y ganglios linfáticos de la cabeza y del cuello

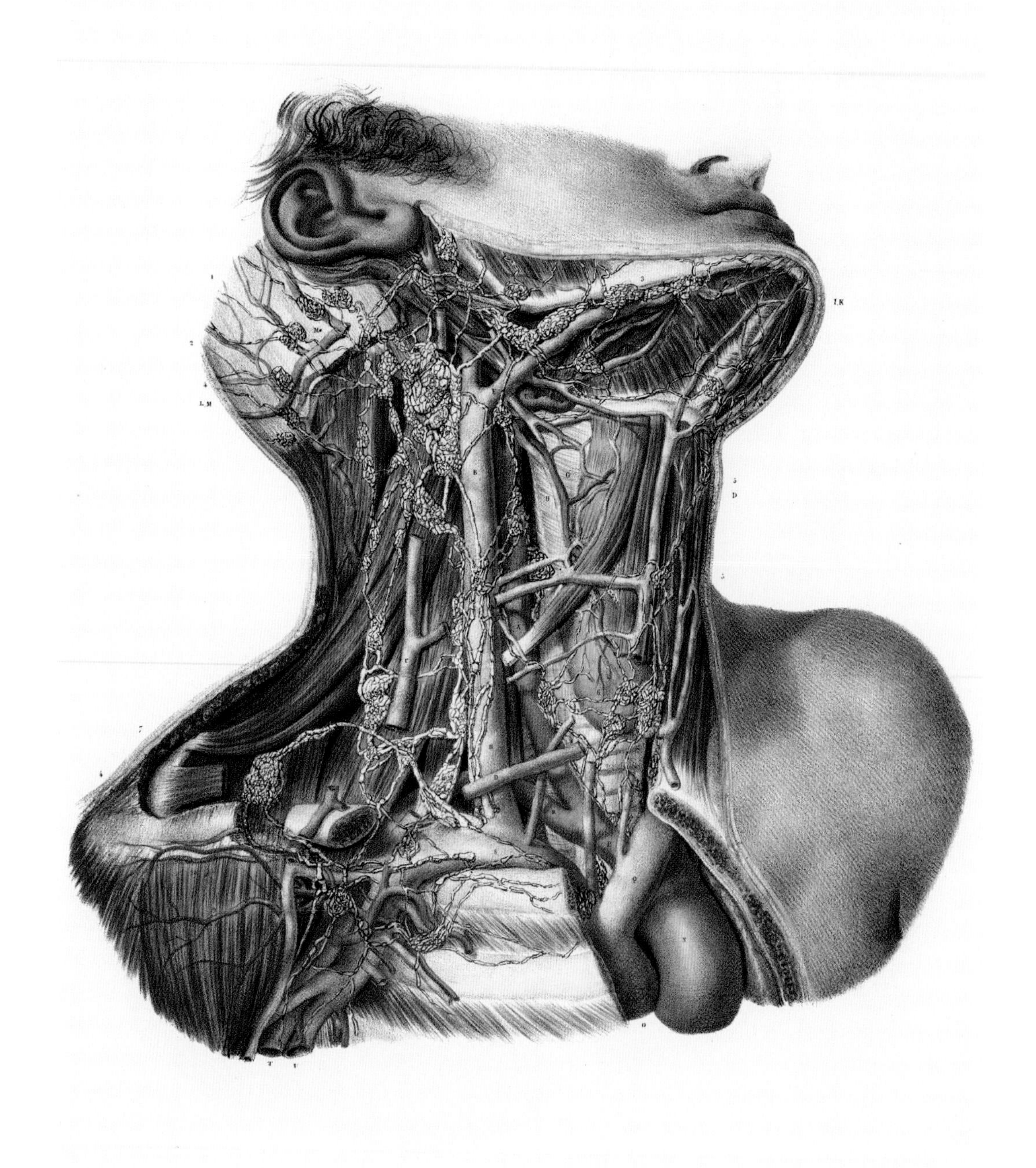

Lymph vessels and nodes of the neck
Vaisseaux et nœuds lymphatiques du cou
Vasos y ganglios linfáticos del cuello

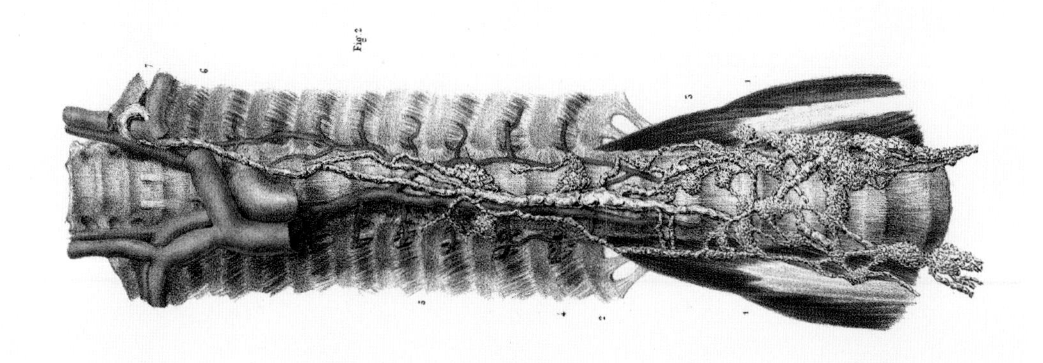

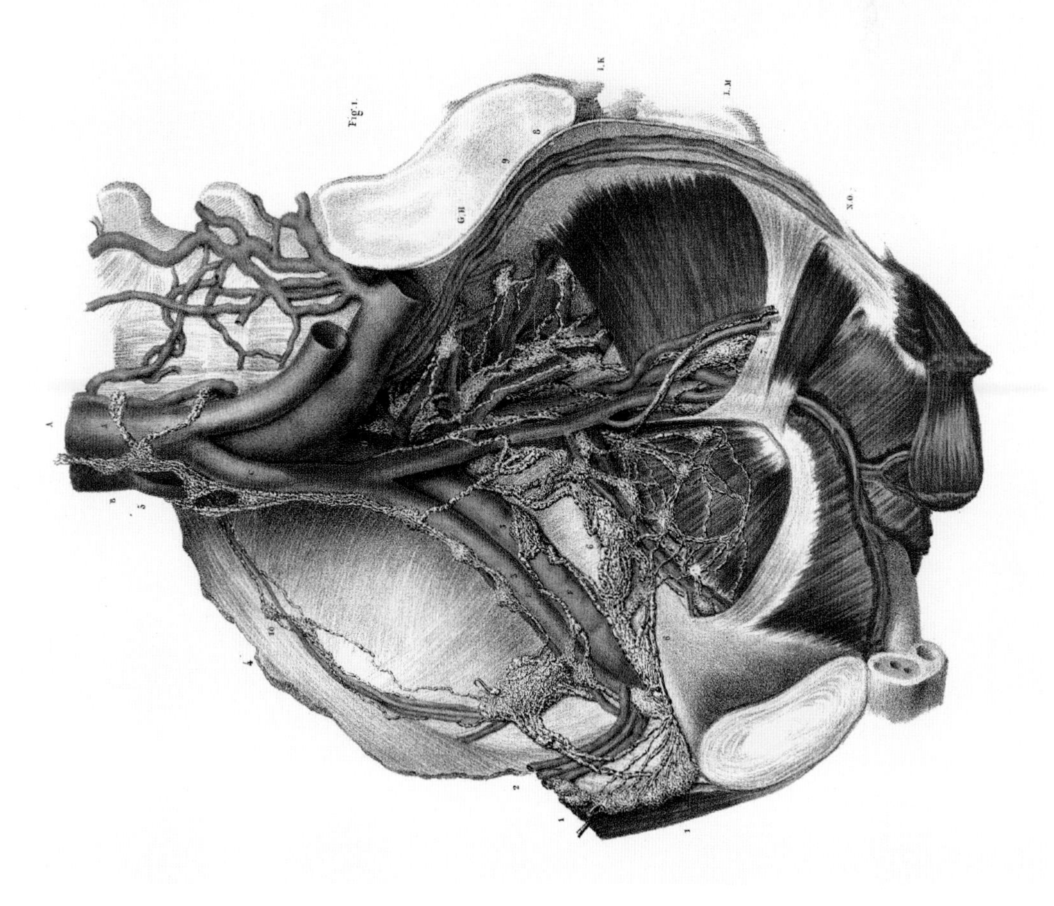

Lymph vessels and nodes of the pelvis. Thoracic duct
Vaisseaux et nœuds lymphatiques du bassin. Conduit thoracique
Vasos y ganglios linfáticos de la pelvis. Conducto torácico

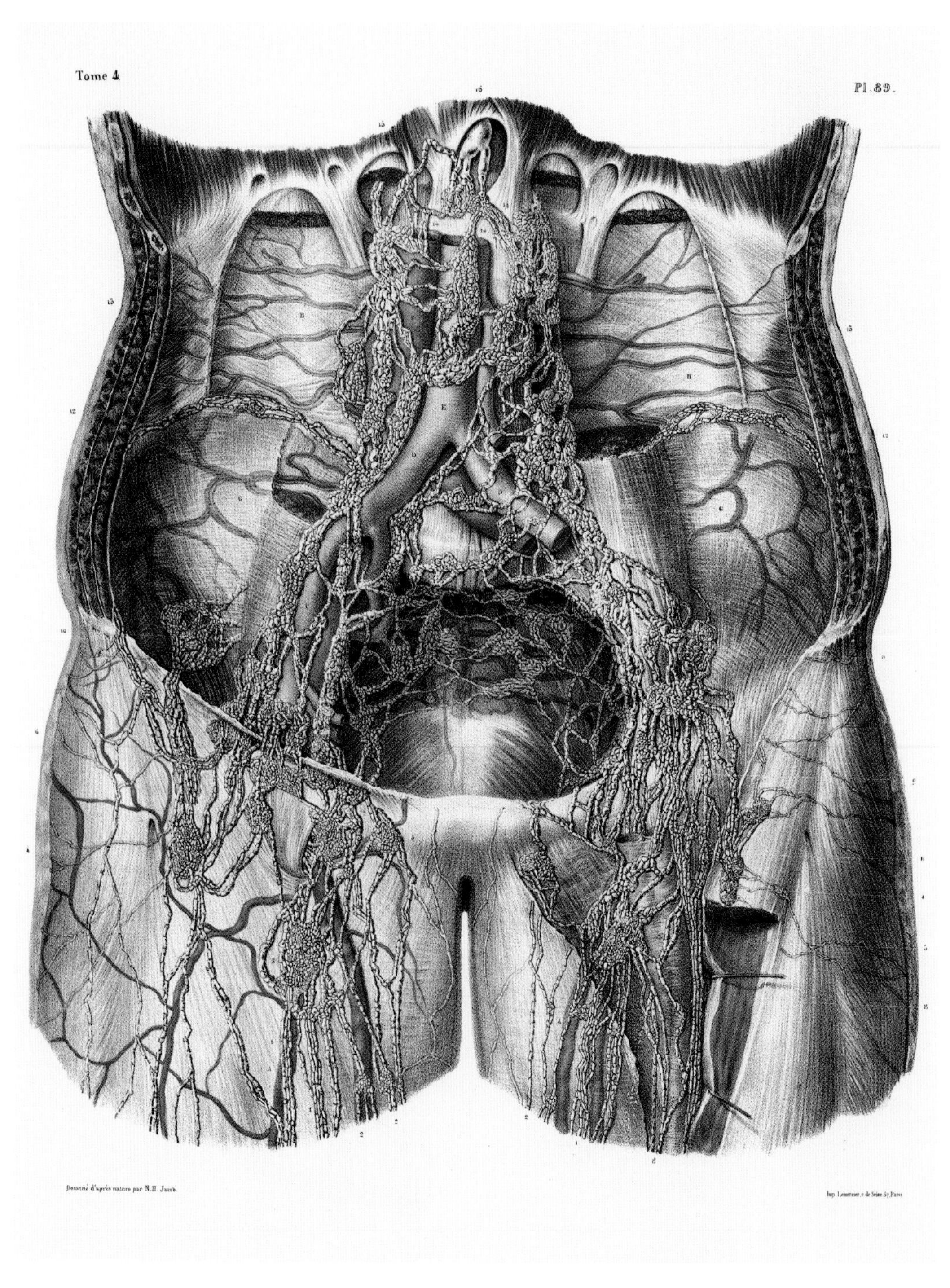

Lymph vessels and nodes of the pelvis and abdomen
Vaisseaux et nœuds lymphatiques du pelvis et de l'abdomen
Vasos y ganglios linfáticos de la pelvis y del abdomen

VASA LYMPHATICA ET LYMPHONODI ABDOMINIS ET THORACIS. DUCTUS THORACICUS

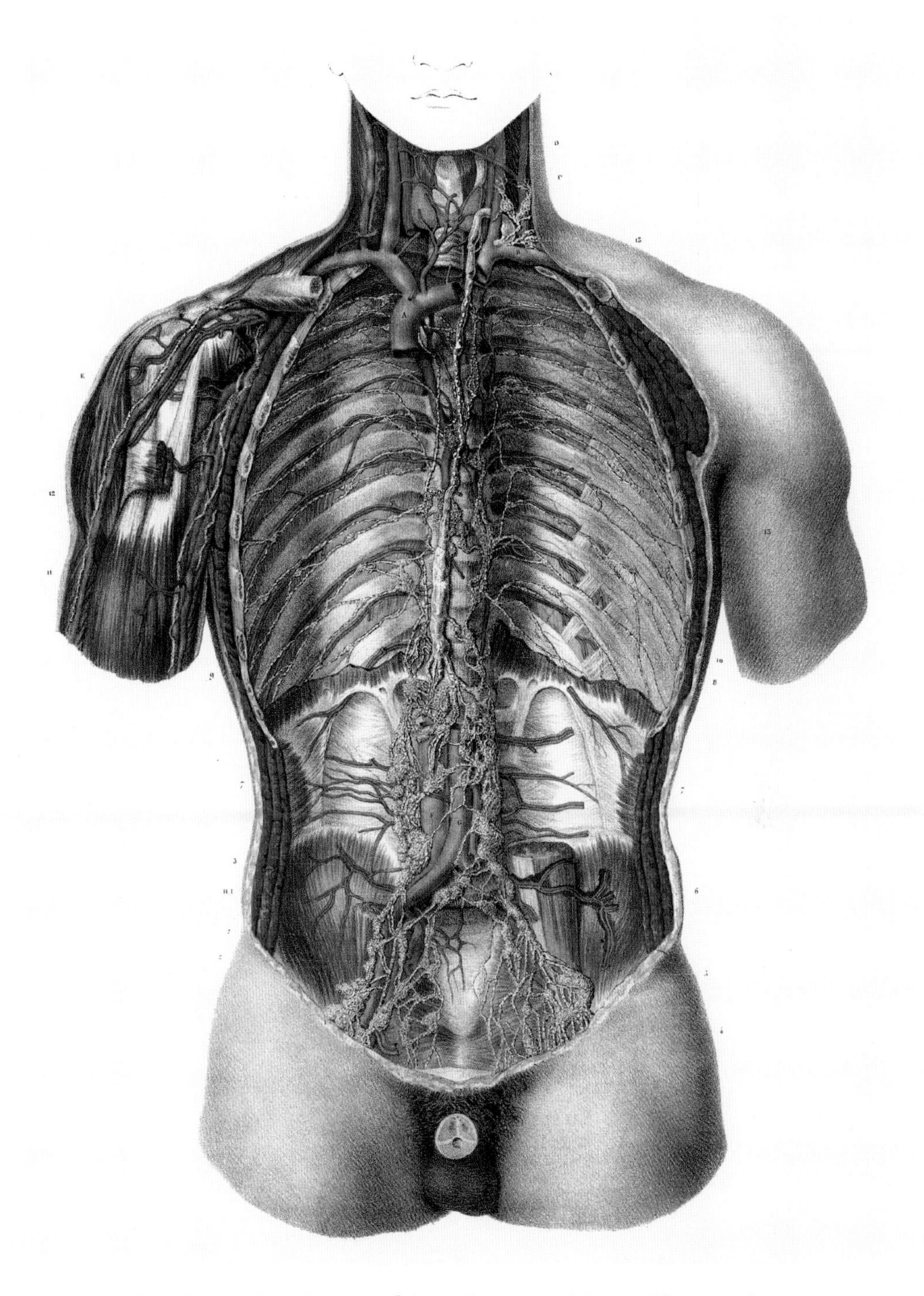

Lymph vessels and nodes of the abdomen and thorax. Thoracic duct
Vaisseaux et nœuds lymphatiques de l'abdomen et du thorax. Conduit thoracique
Vasos y ganglios linfáticos del abdomen y del tórax. Conducto torácico

VASA LYMPHATICA ET LYMPHONODI THORACIS ET COLLI. DUCTUS THORACICUS

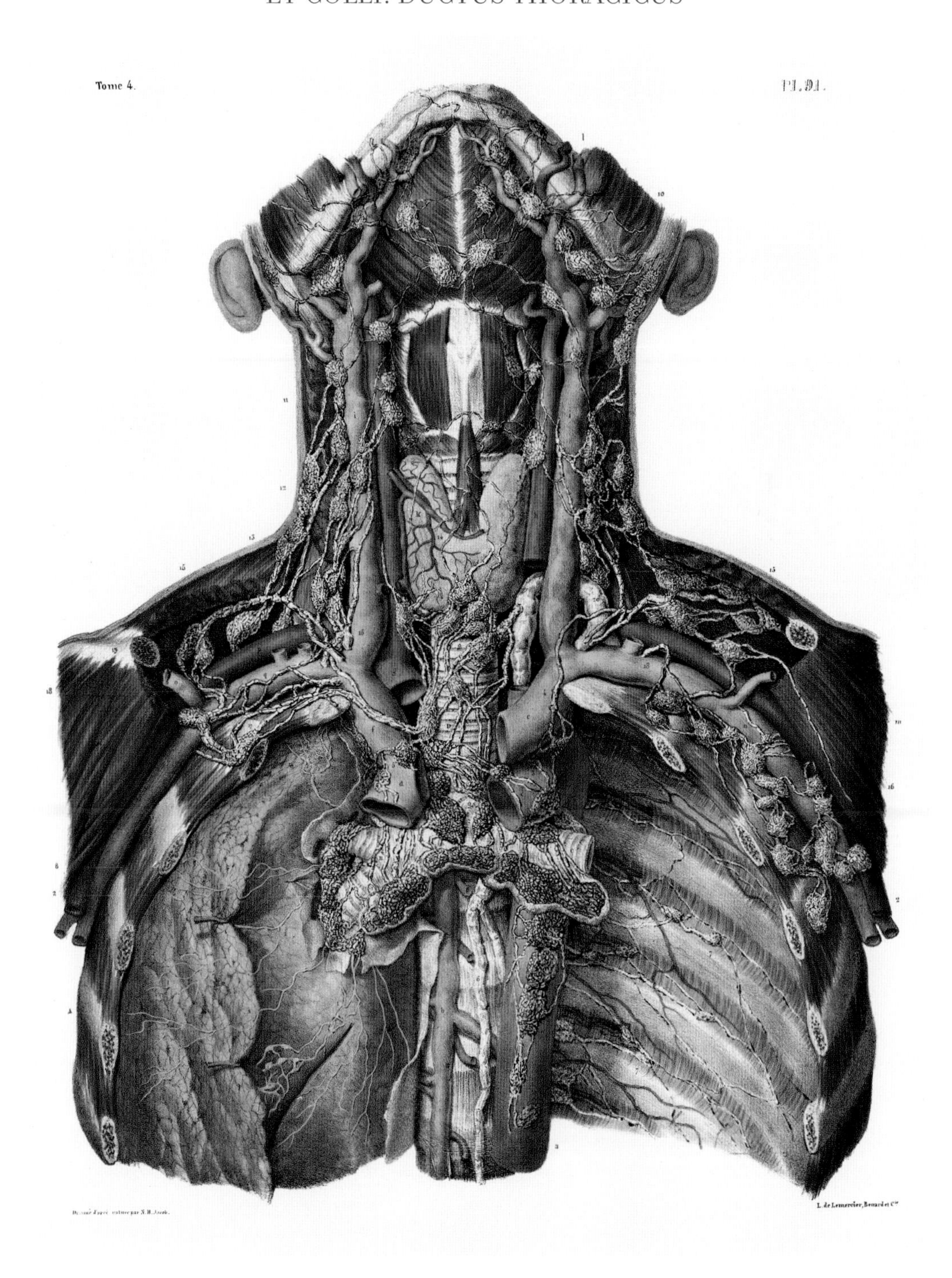

Lymph vessels and nodes of the thorax and neck. Thoracic duct
Vaisseaux et nœuds lymphatiques du thorax et du cou. Conduit thoracique
Vasos y ganglios linfáticos del tórax y del cuello. Conducto torácico

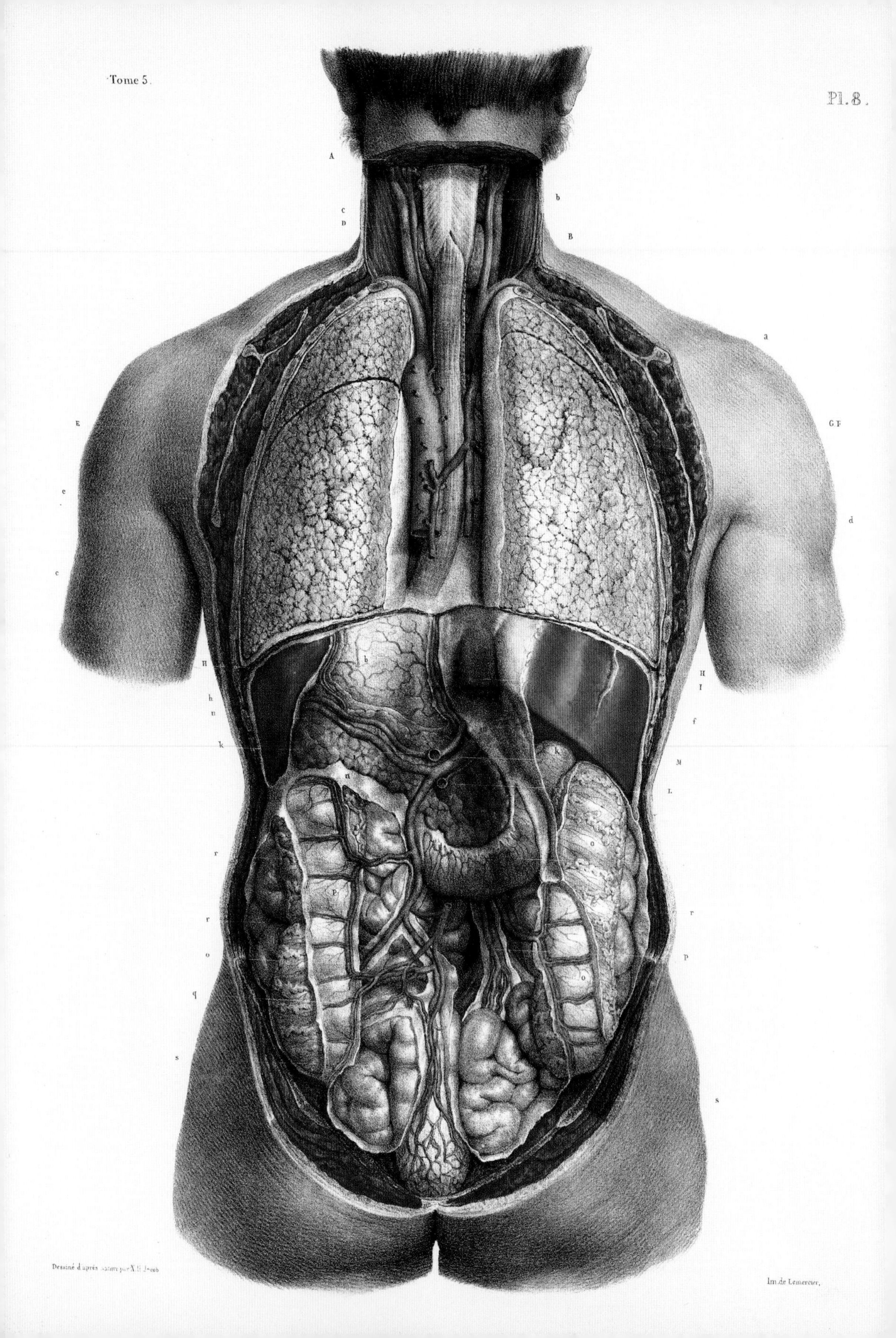
Tome 5.
Pl. 8.
Dessiné d'après nature par N.H. Jacob
Im. de Lemercier.

VOL. 5

Splanchnologia: Viscera Abdominis (Apparatus Digestorius et Apparatus Urogenitalis)

SPLANCHNOLOGY: ABDOMINAL ORGANS (GASTROINTESTINAL AND UROGENITAL TRACTS)

SPLANCHNOLOGIE : VISCERES DE L'ABDOMEN (APPAREIL DIGESTIF ET APPAREIL UROGENITAL)

ESPLACNOLOGÍA: VÍSCERAS ABDOMINALES (APARATOS DIGESTIVO Y GENITOURINARIO)

Left page / Ci-contre / Página contigua:
Thoracic and abdominal organs / Viscères thoraciques et abdominaux
Vísceras torácicas y abdominales

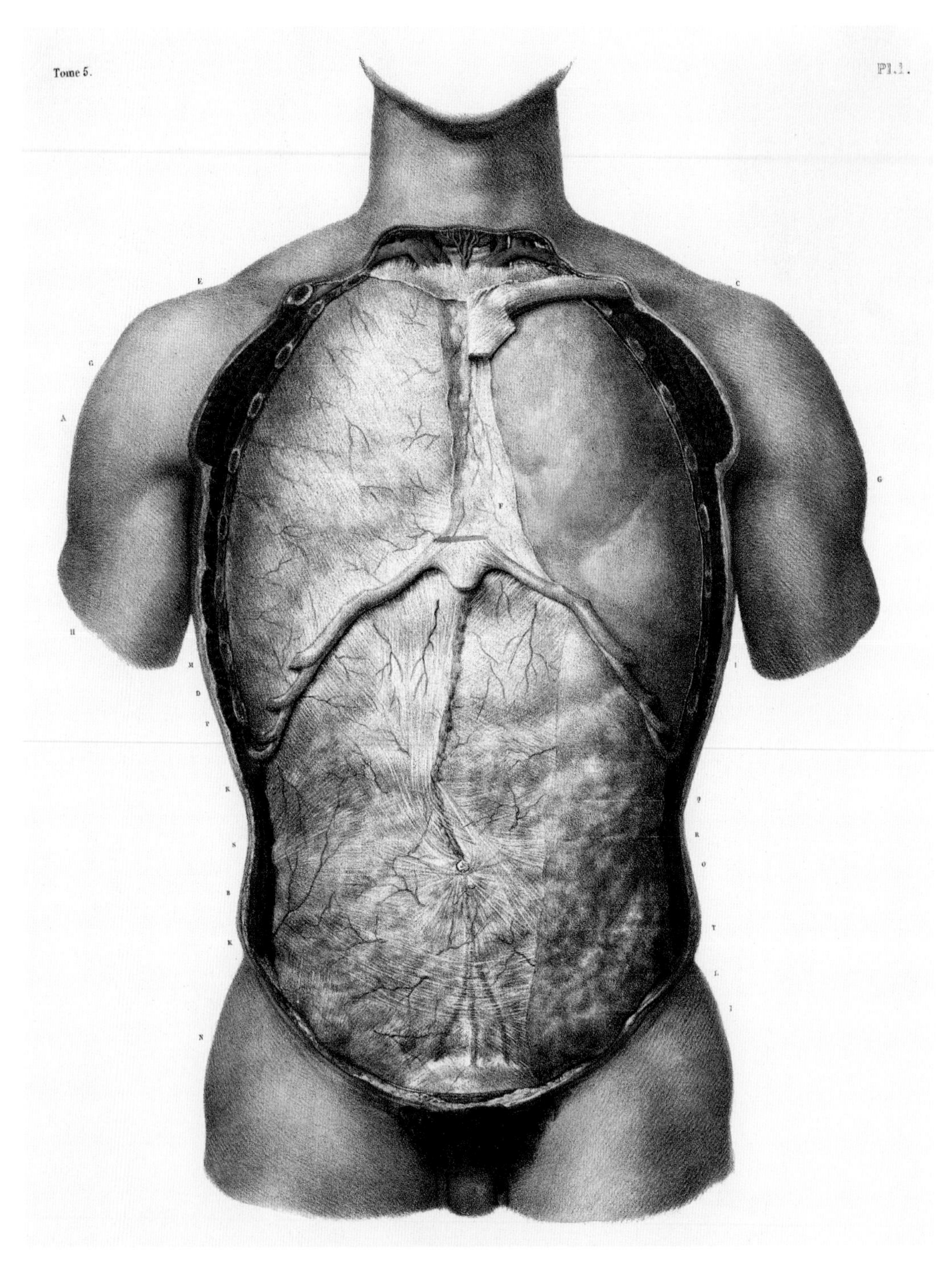

Thoracic and abdominal organs / Viscères thoraciques et abdominaux
Vísceras torácicas y abdominales

Tome 5. Pl. 2.

Dessiné d'après nature par N. H. Jacob. Imp. de Lemercier, Benard et Cie

Abdominal organs / Viscères abdominaux / Vísceras abdominales

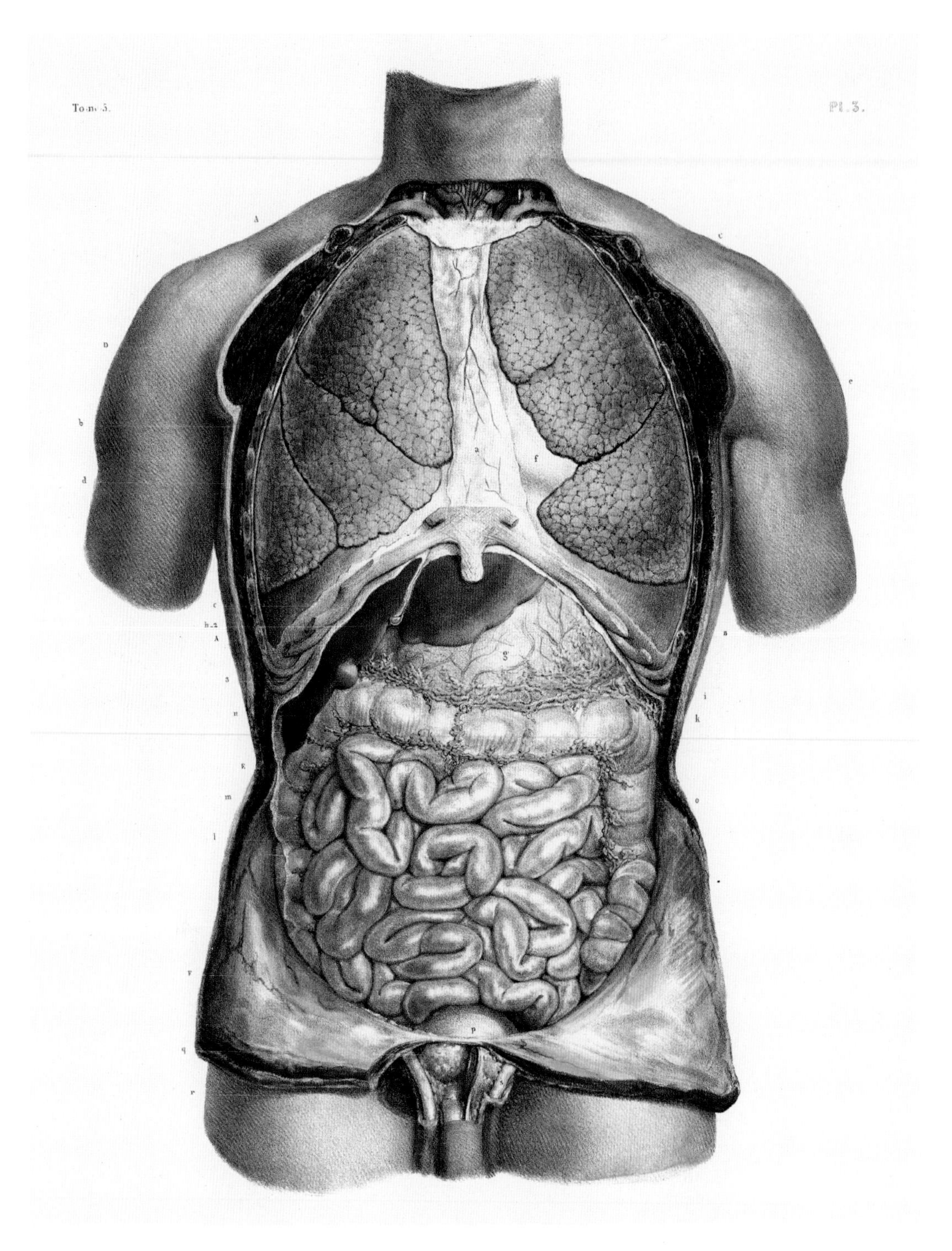

Thoracic and abdominal organs / Viscères thoraciques et abdominaux
Vísceras torácicas y abdominales

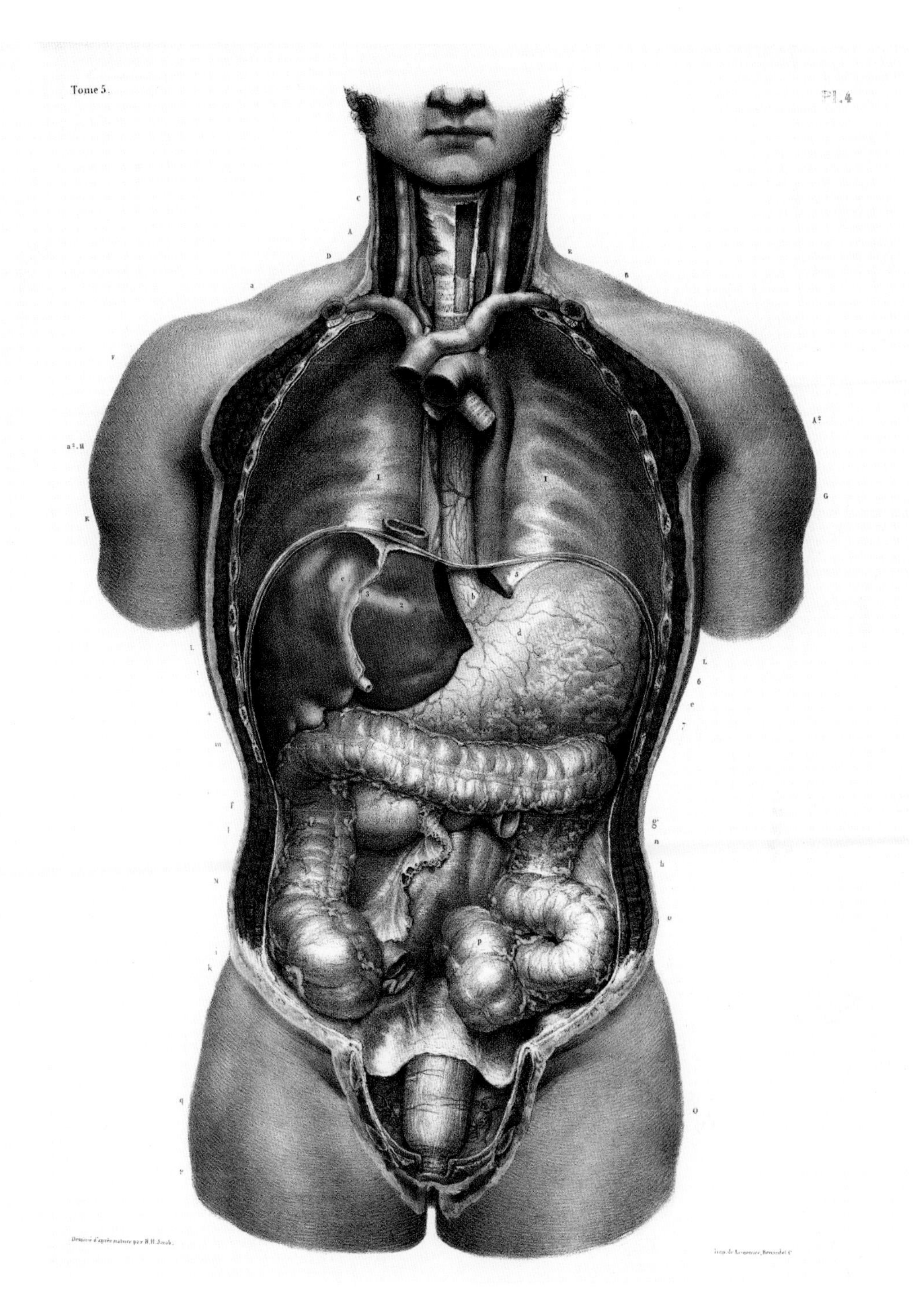

Abdominal organs / Viscères abdominaux / Vísceras abdominales

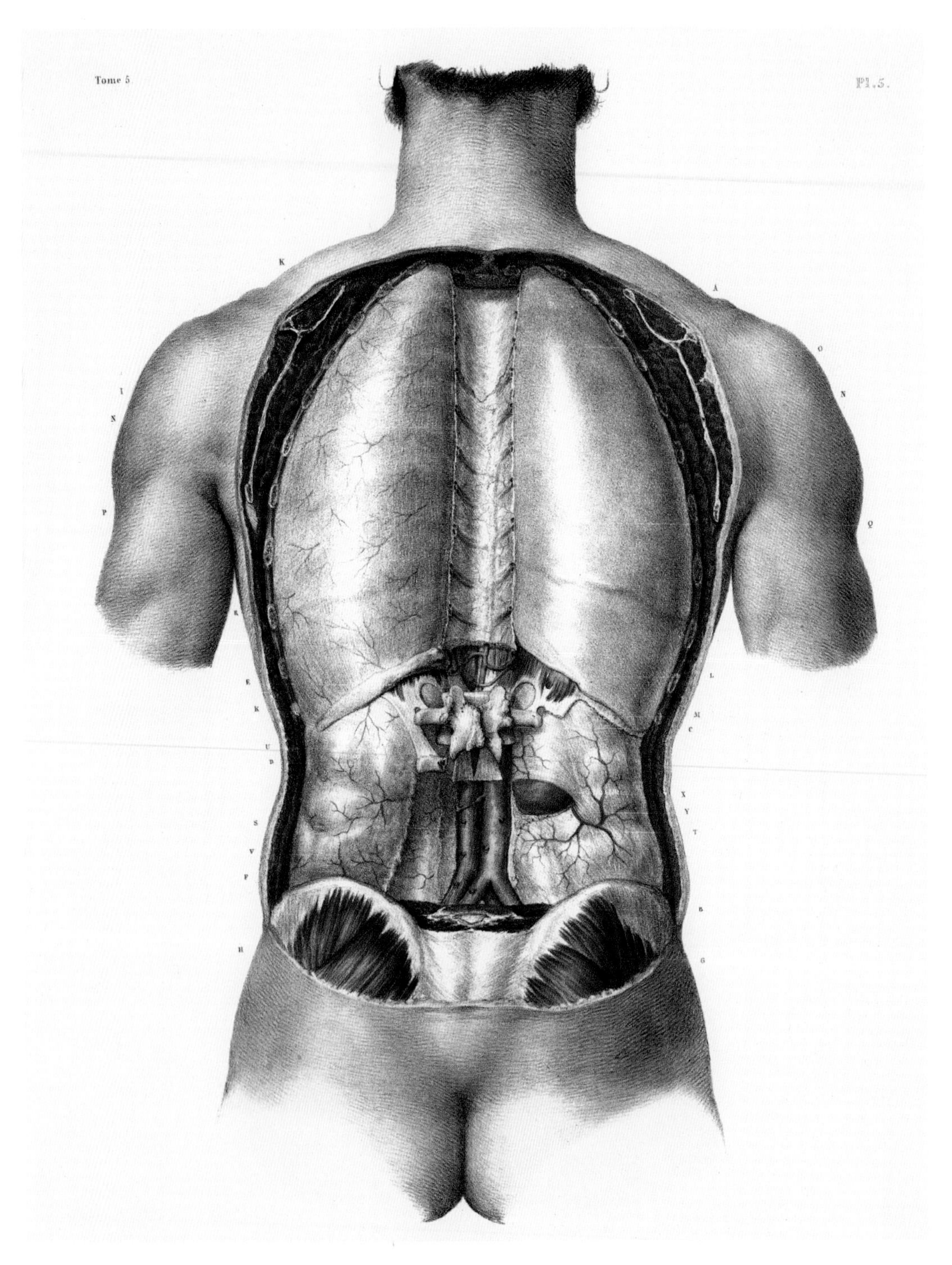

Thoracic and abdominal organs / Viscères thoraciques et abdominaux
Vísceras torácicas y abdominales

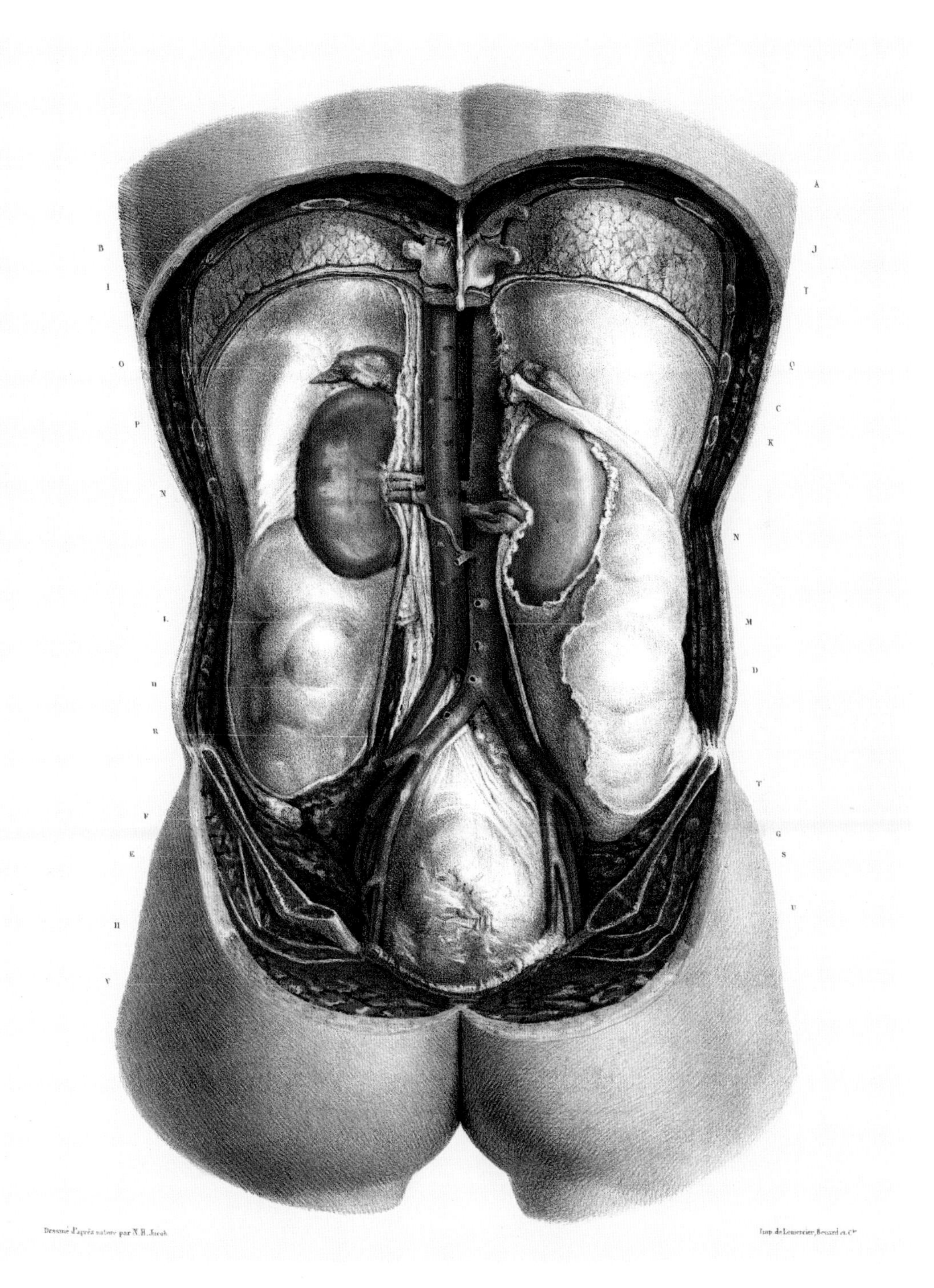

Abdominal organs / Viscères abdominaux
Vísceras abdominales

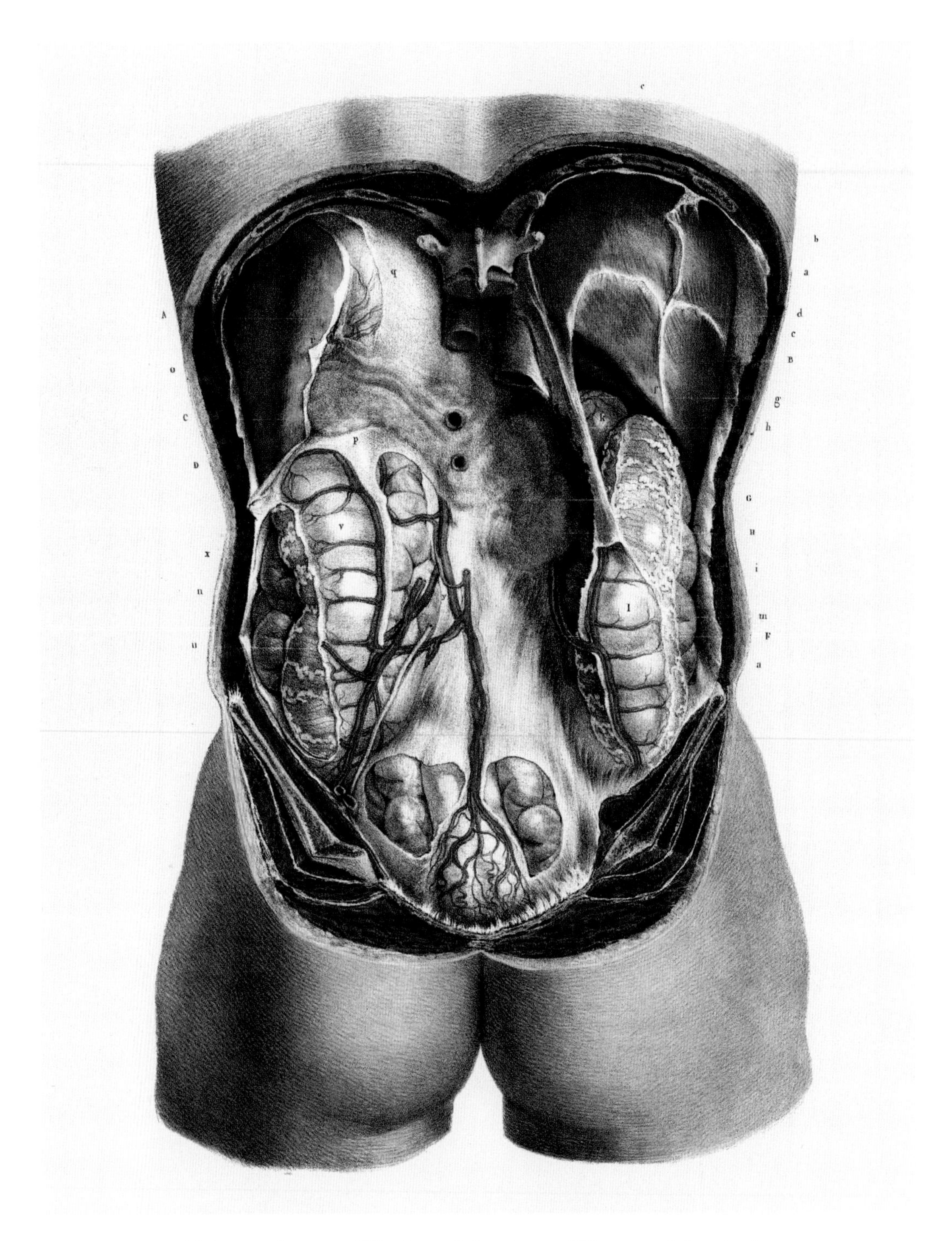

Abdominal organs / Viscères abdominaux / Vísceras abdominales

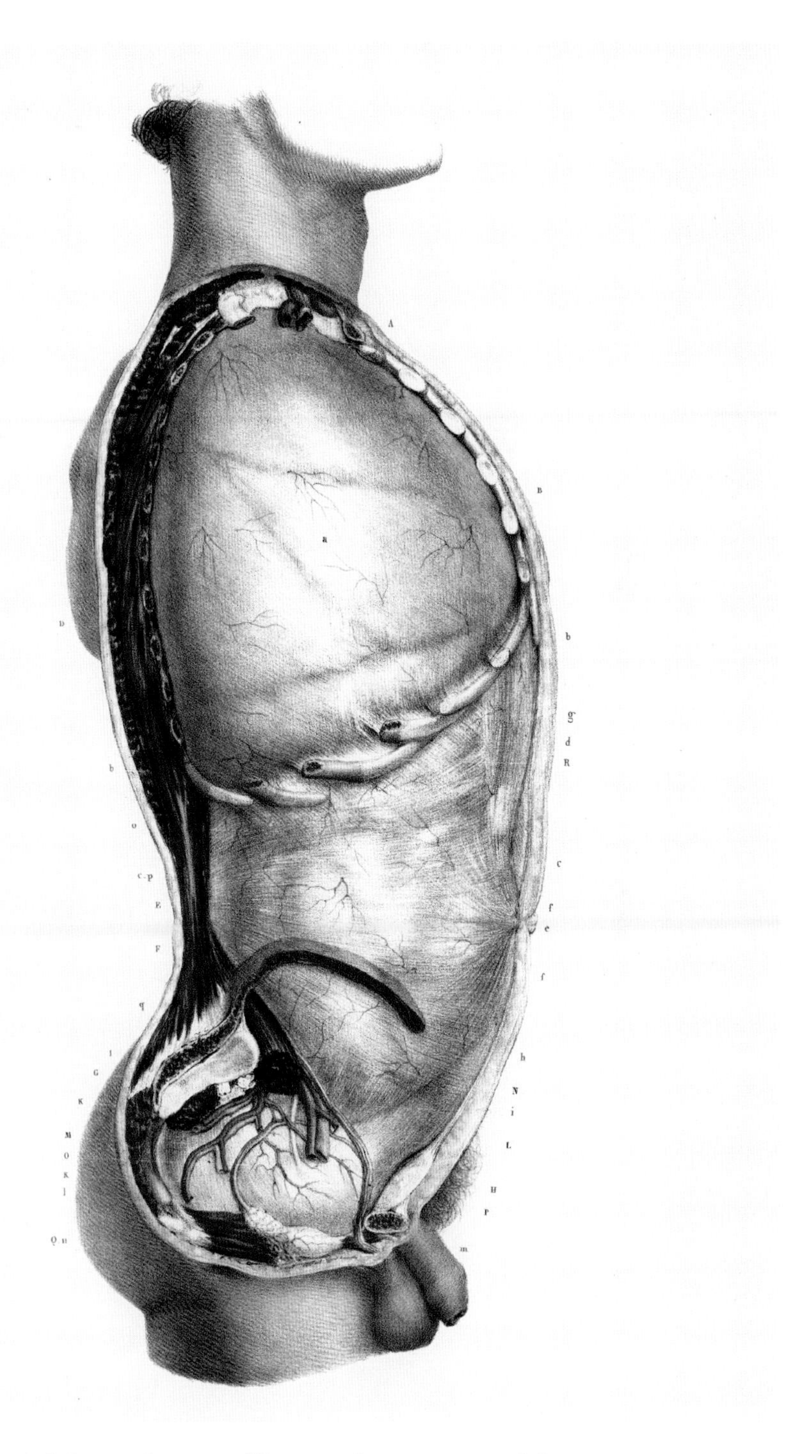

Thoracic and abdominal organs / Viscères thoraciques et abdominaux
Vísceras torácicas y abdominales

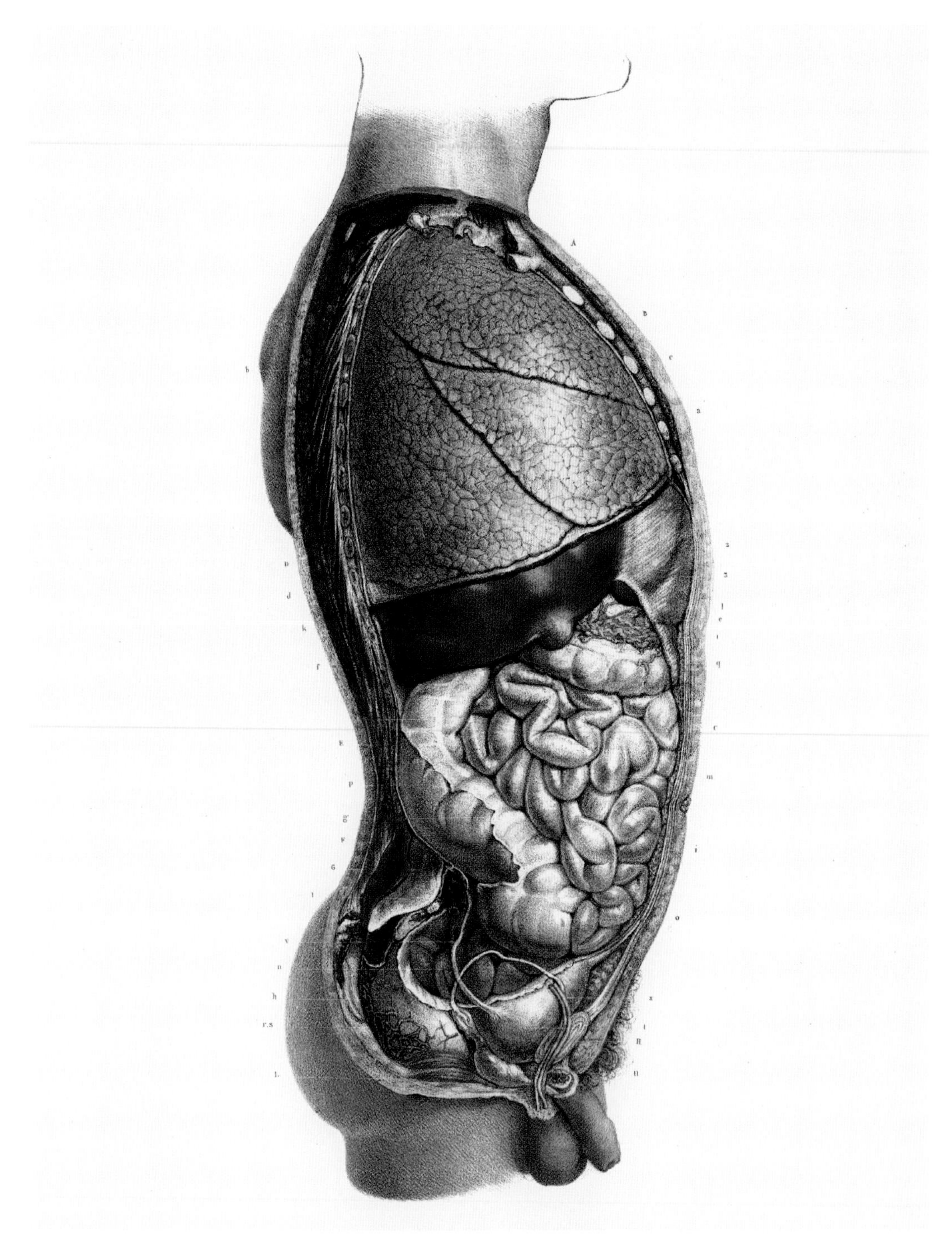

Thoracic and abdominal organs / Viscères thoraciques et abdominaux
Vísceras torácicas y abdominales

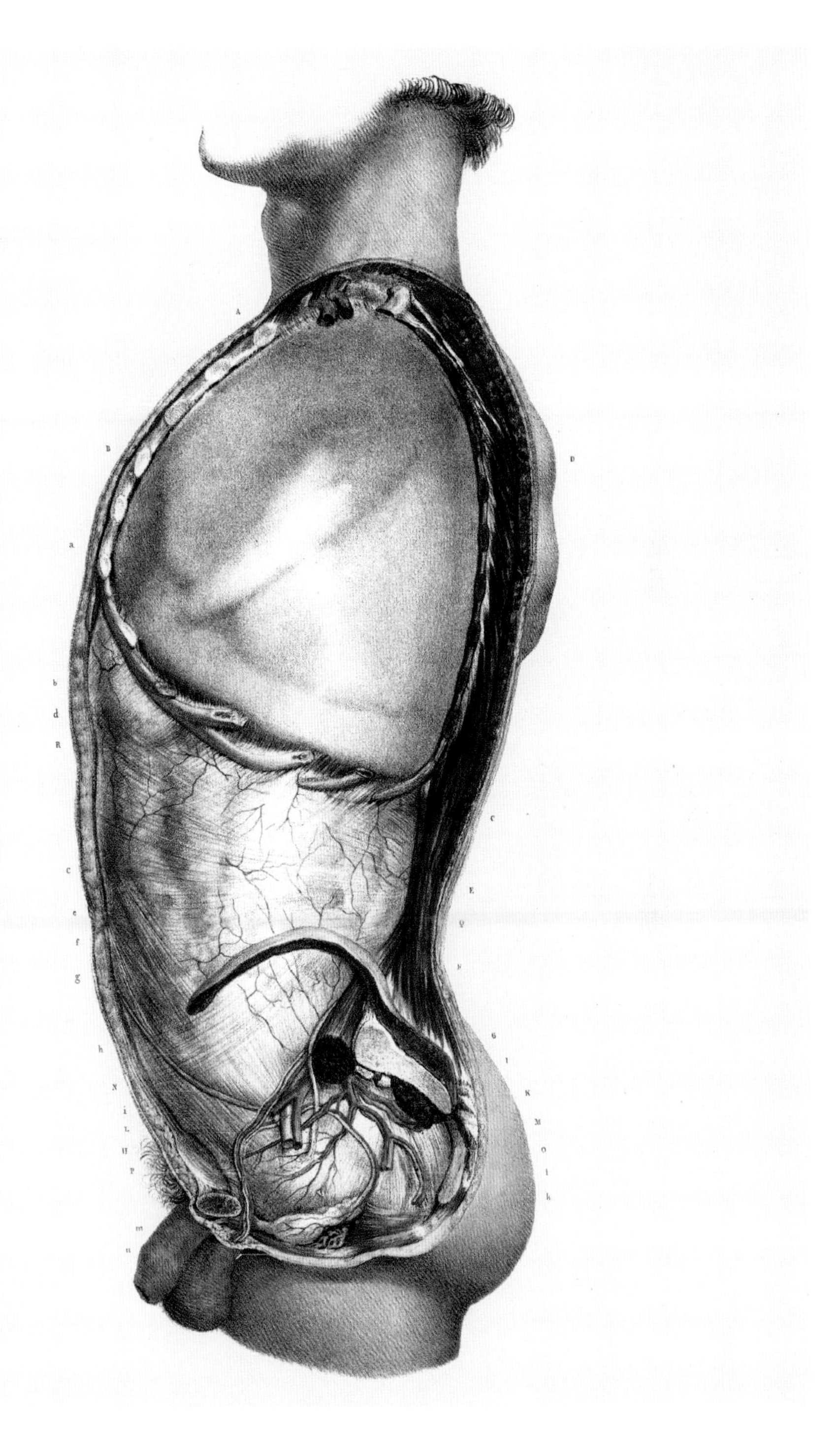

Thoracic and abdominal organs / Viscères thoraciques et abdominaux
Vísceras torácicas y abdominales

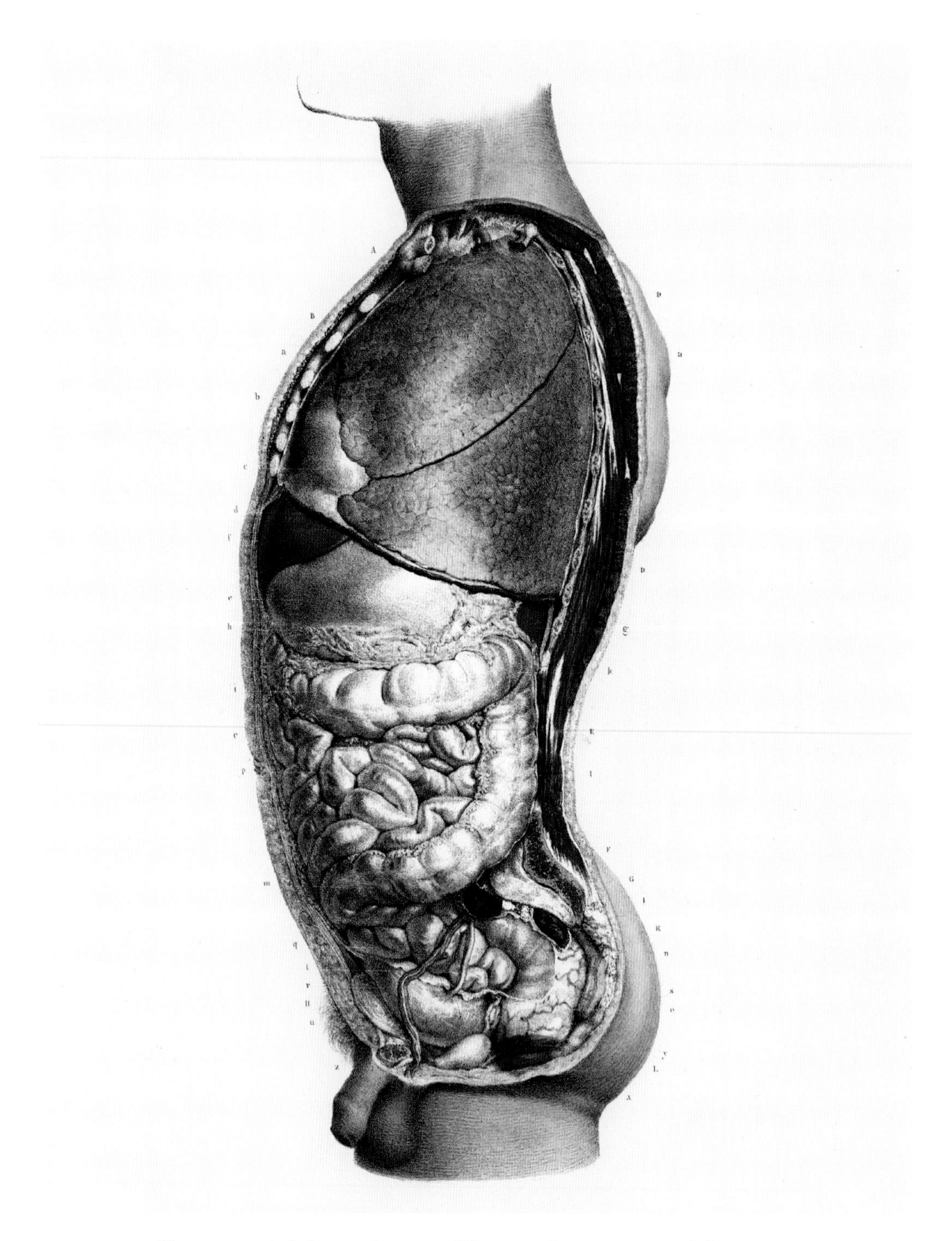

Thoracic and abdominal organs / Viscères thoraciques et abdominaux
Vísceras torácicas y abdominales

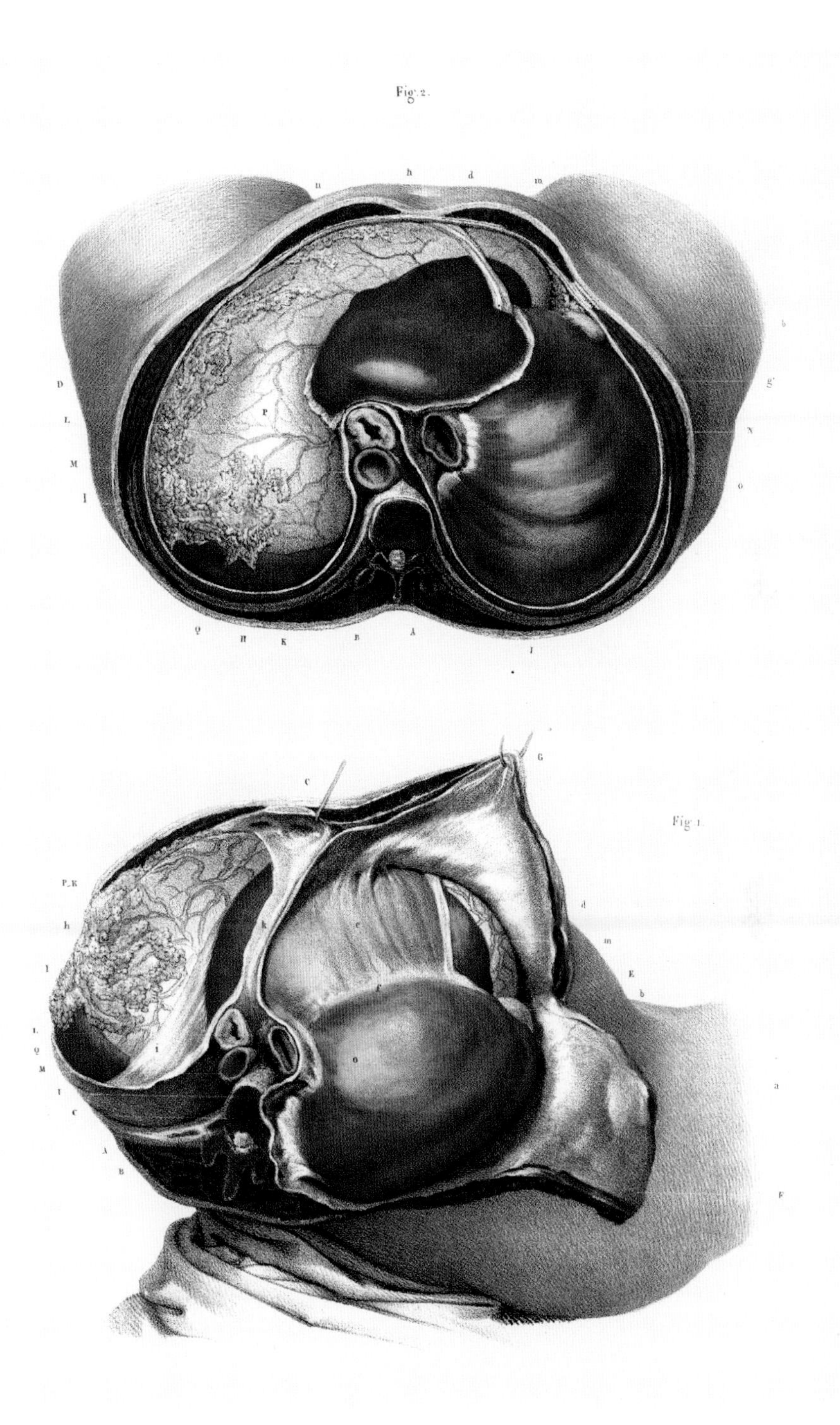

Abdominal organs / Viscères abdominaux / Vísceras abdominales

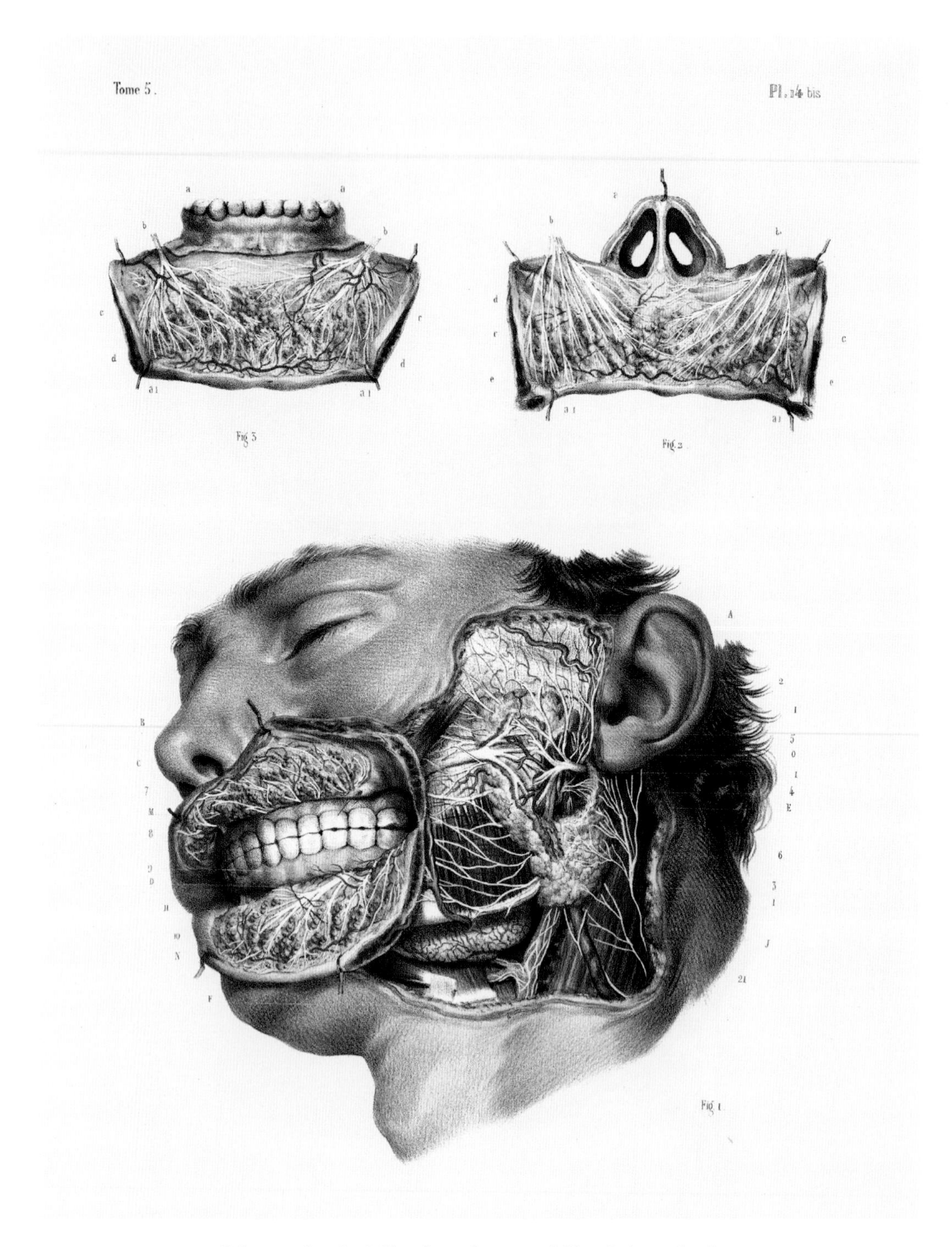

Salivary glands / Glandes salivaires / Glándulas salivales

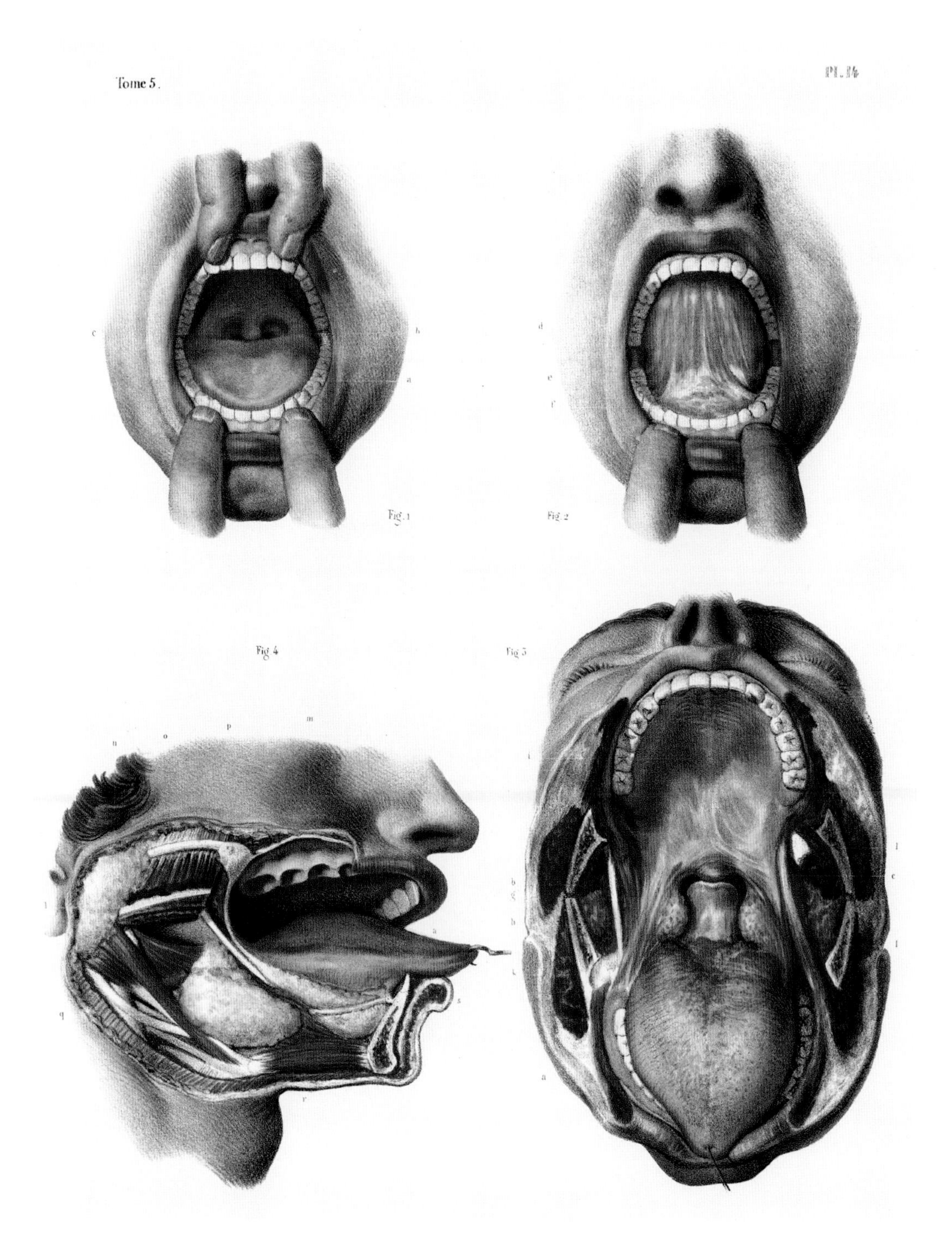

Oral cavity / Cavité orale / Cavidad bucal

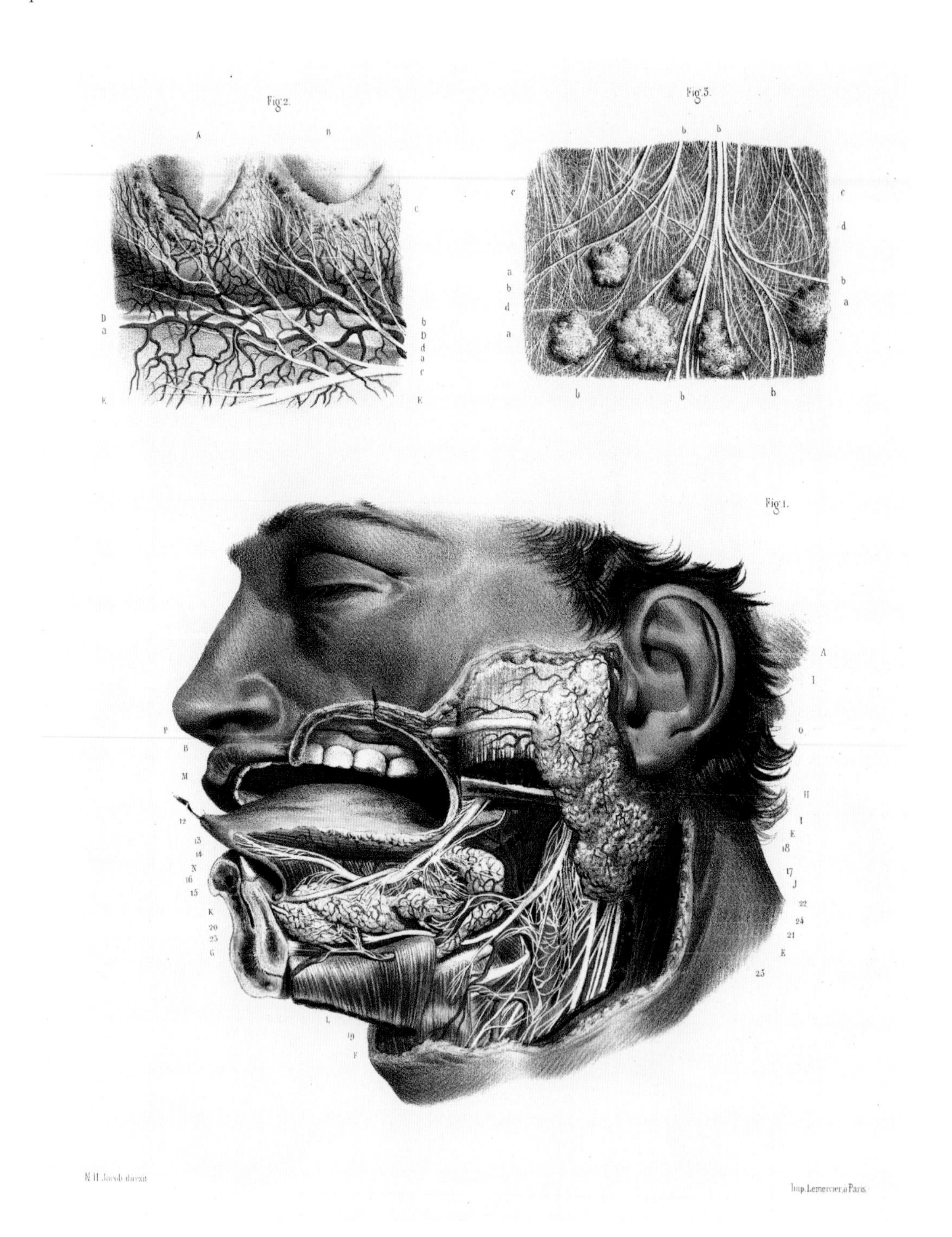

Salivary glands / Glandes salivaires / Glándulas salivales

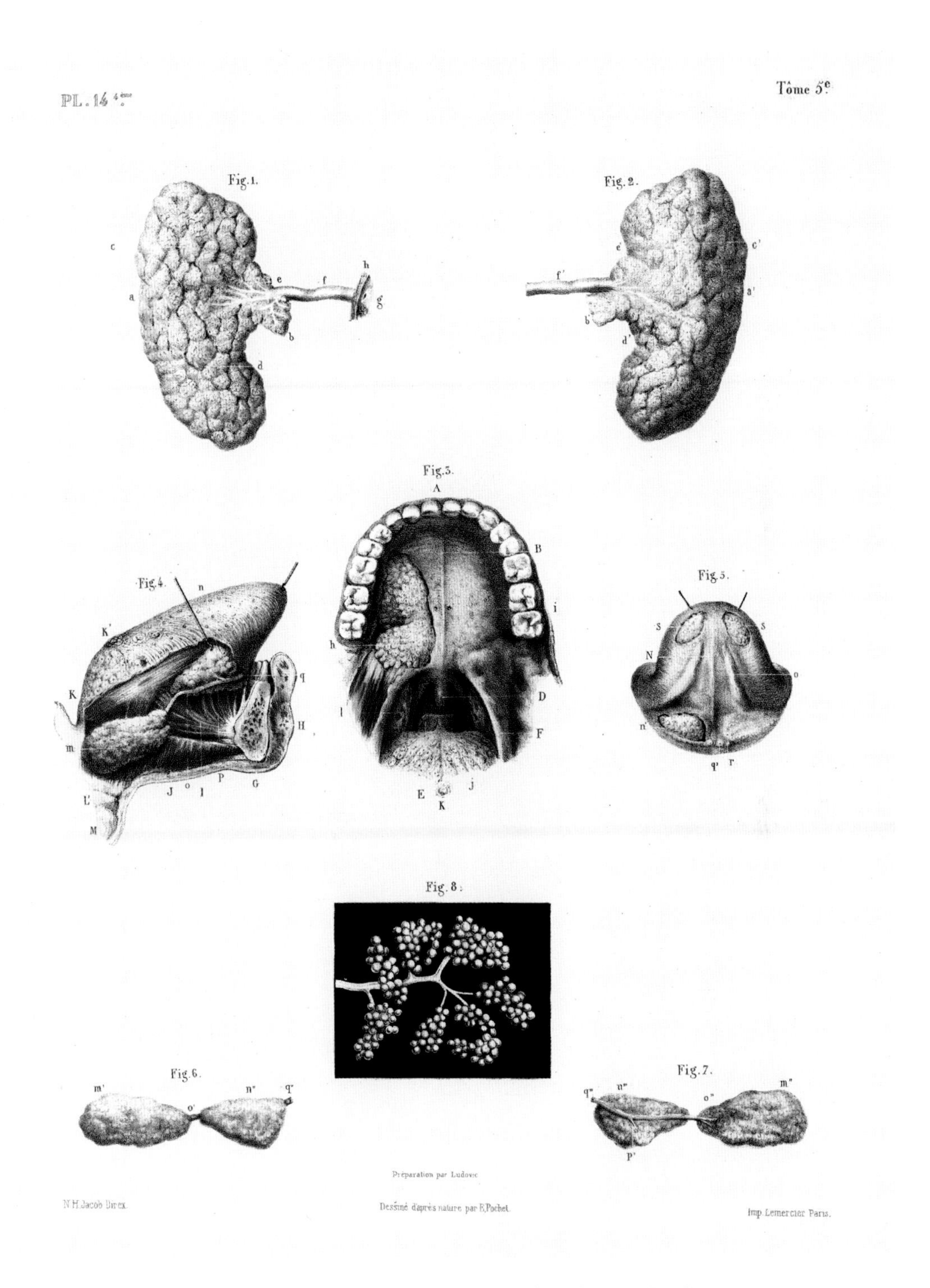

Salivary glands / Glandes salivaires / Glándulas salivales

LINGUA: MUSCULI, VASA ET NERVI, ET ANATOMIA MICROSCOPICA. PHARYNX ET OESOPHAGUS

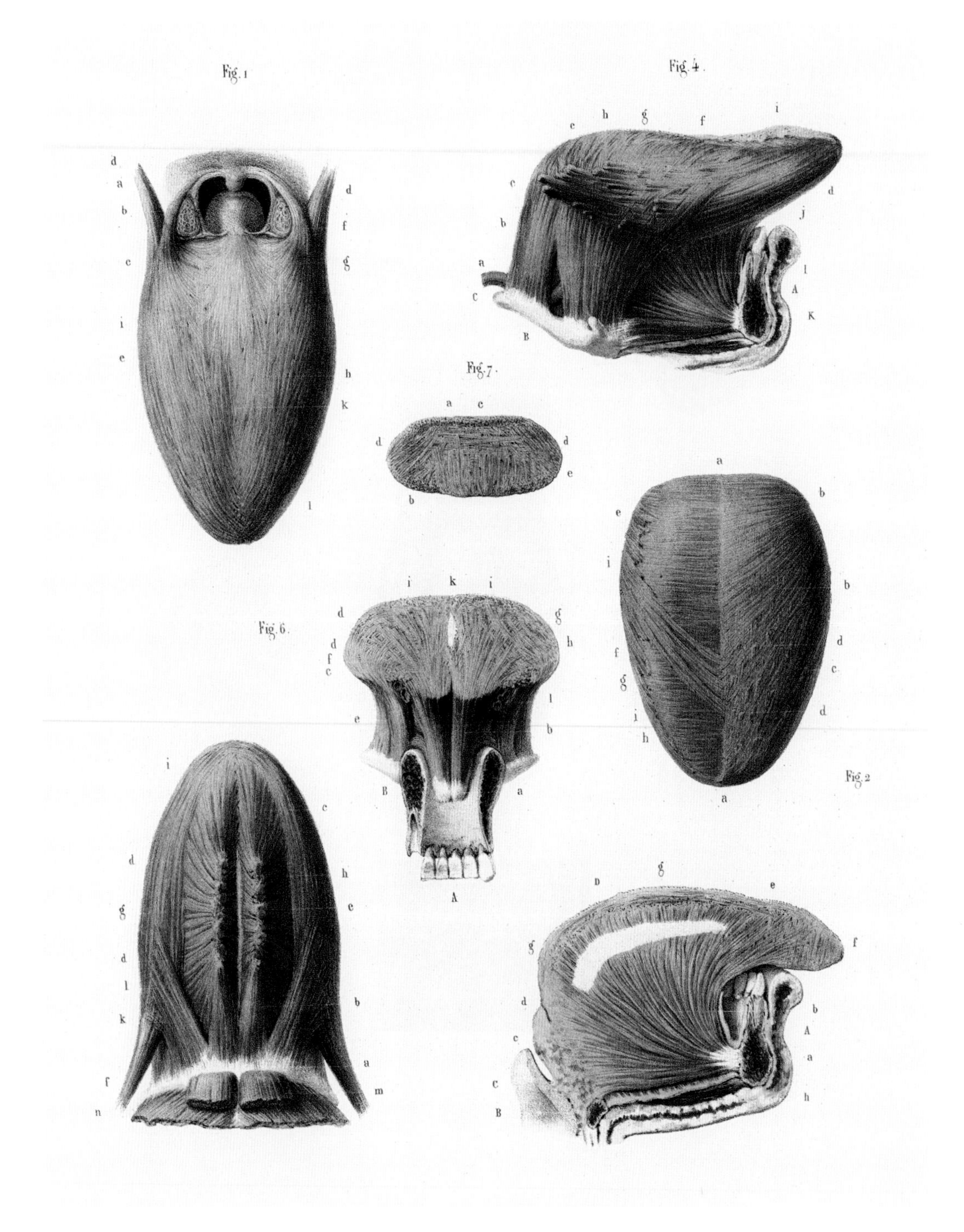

Tongue: Muscles / Langue : Muscles / Lengua: músculos

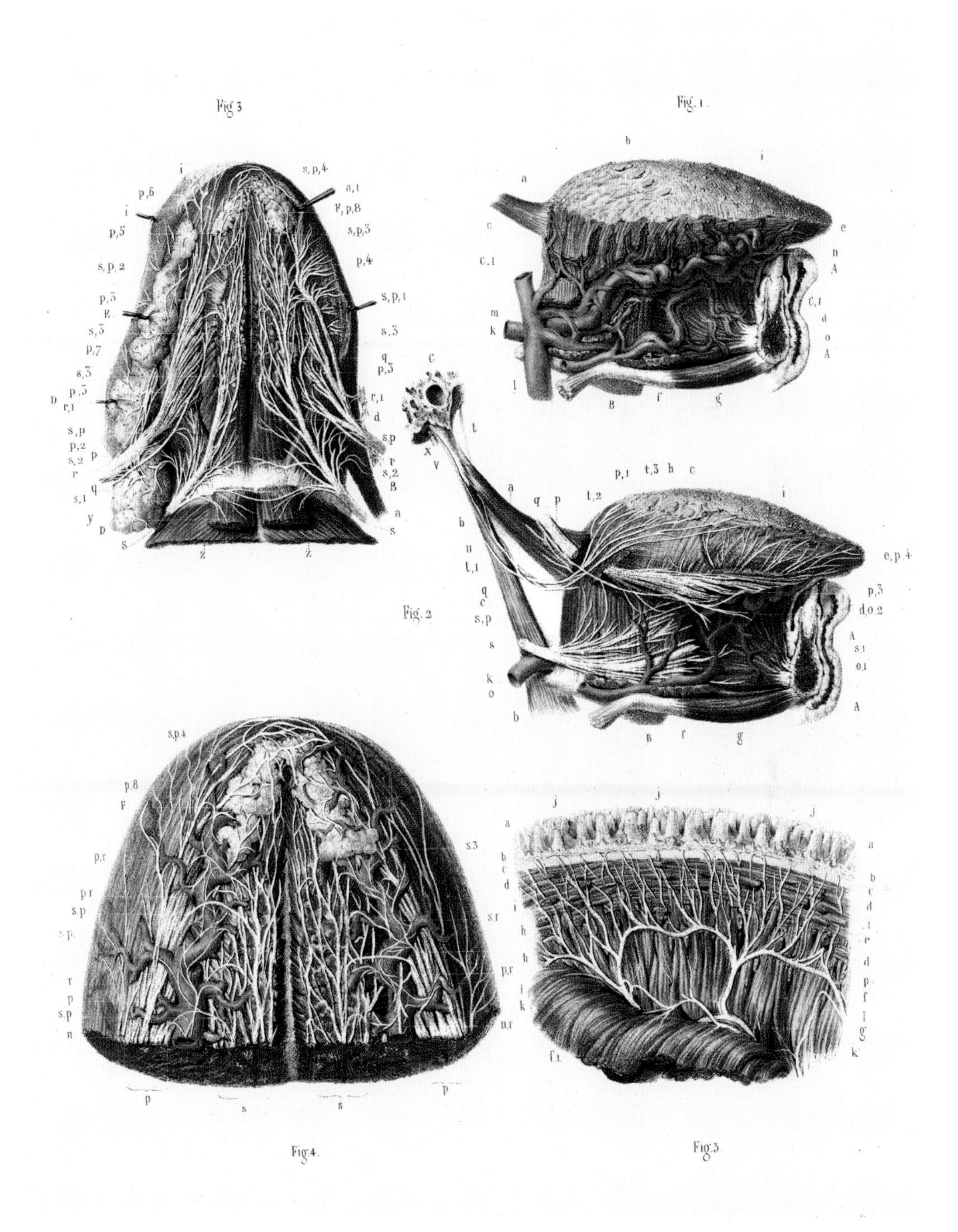

Tongue: Vessels and nerves / Langue : Vaisseaux et nerfs
Lengua: vasos y nervios

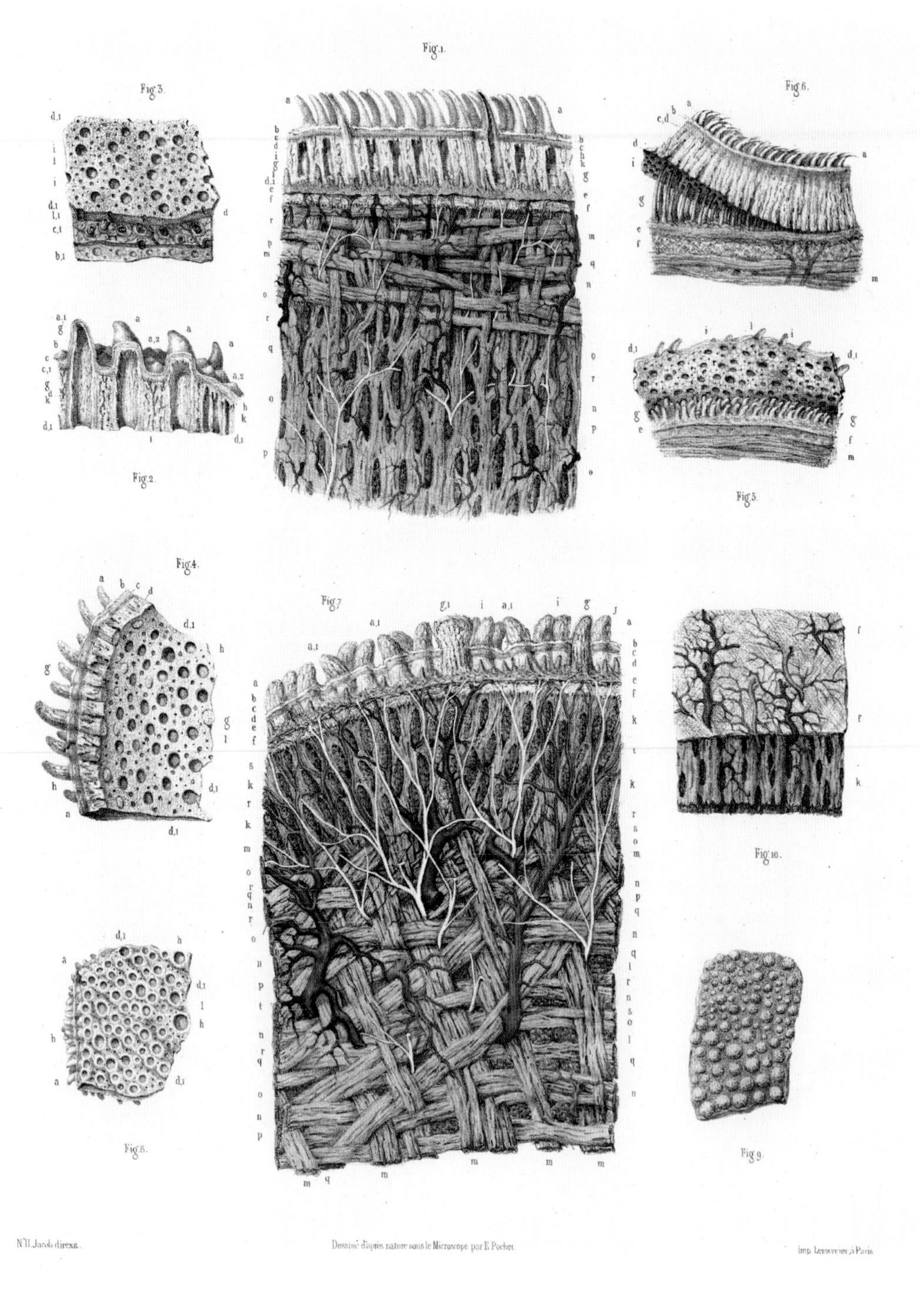

Tongue: Microscopic anatomy / Langue : Anatomie microscopique
Lengua: anatomía microscópica

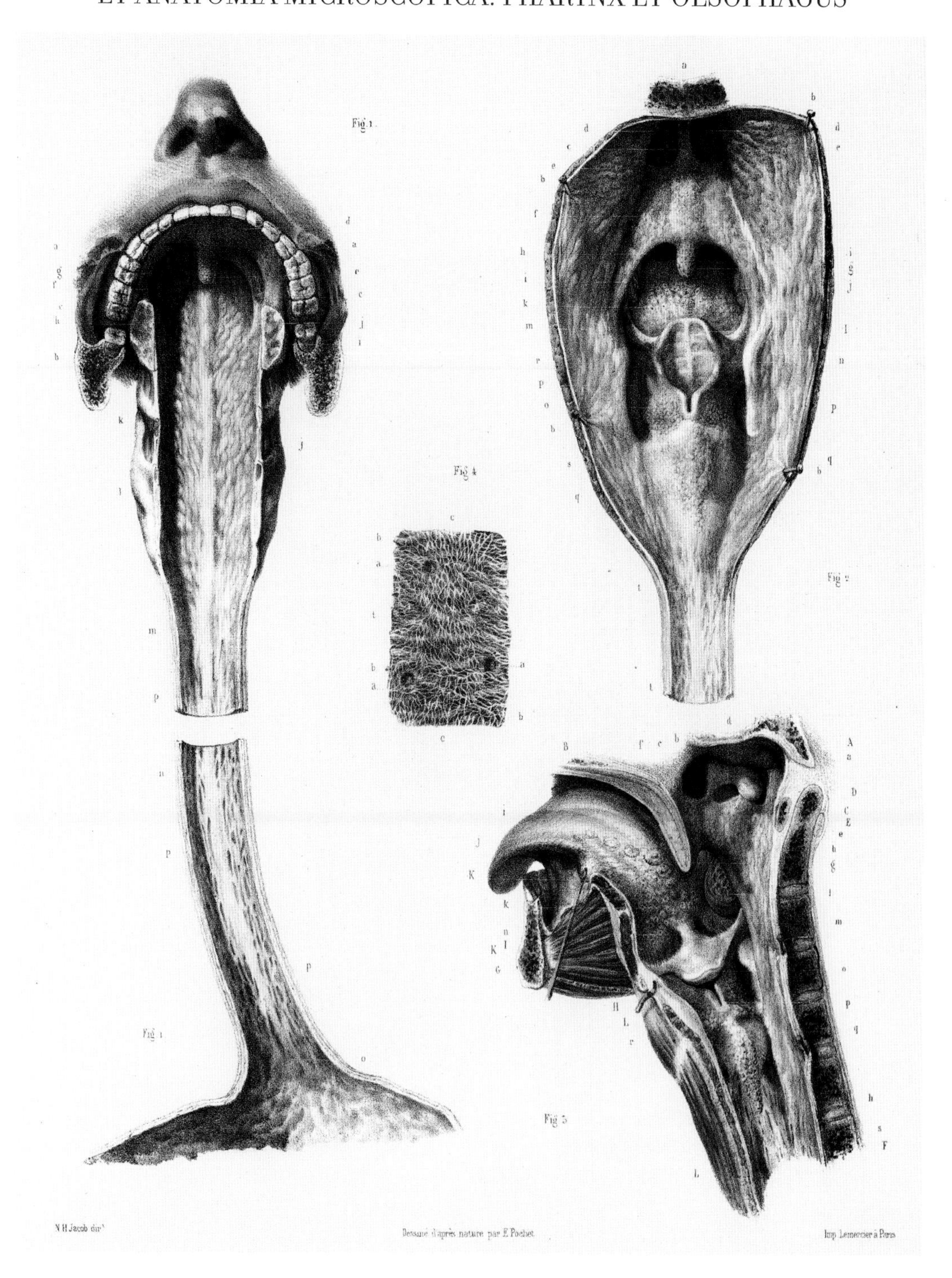

Pharynx and oesophagus / Pharynx et œsophage
Faringe y esófago

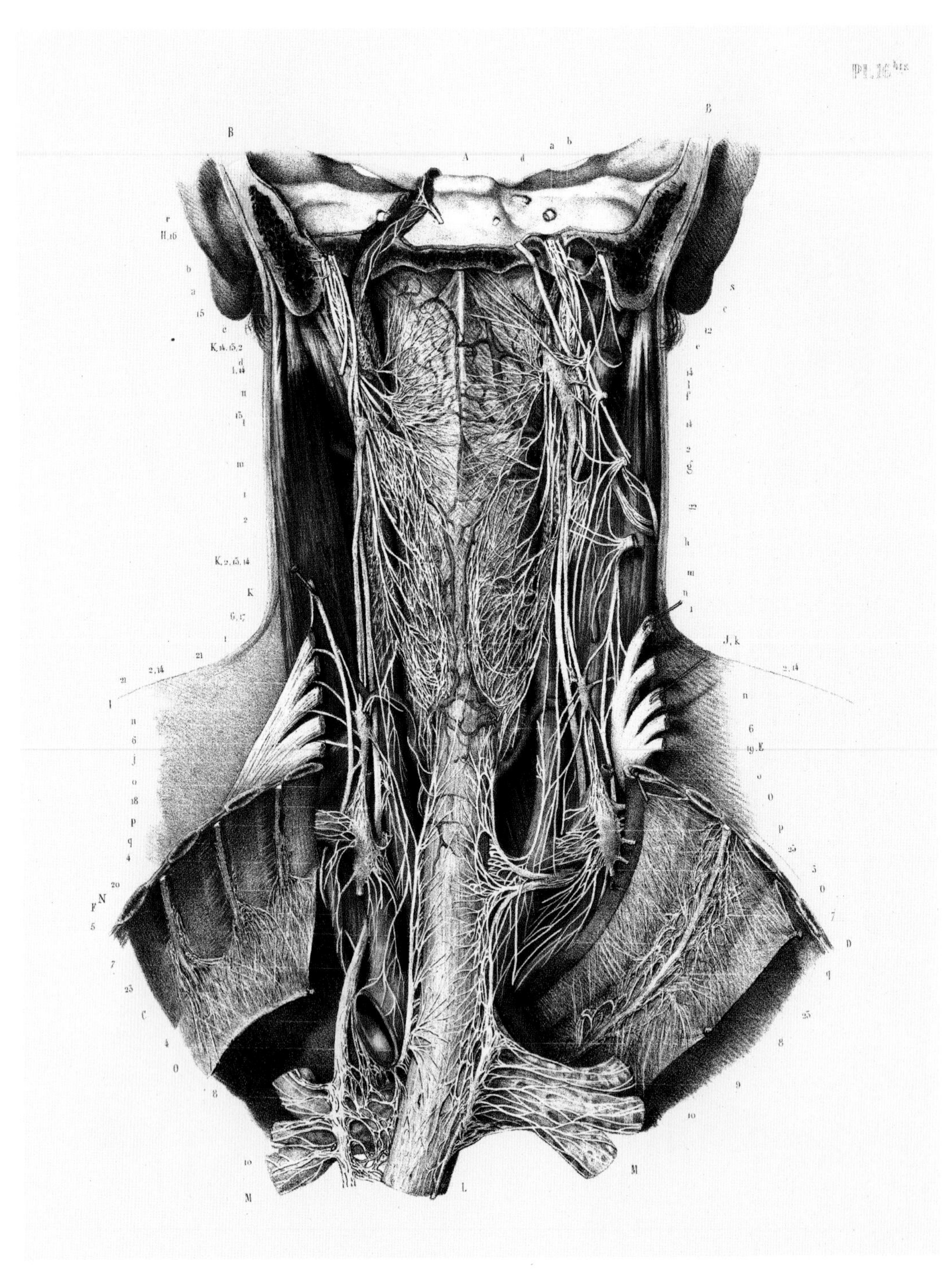

Pharynx and oesophagus: Nerves / Pharynx et œsophage : Nerfs
Faringe y esófago: nervios

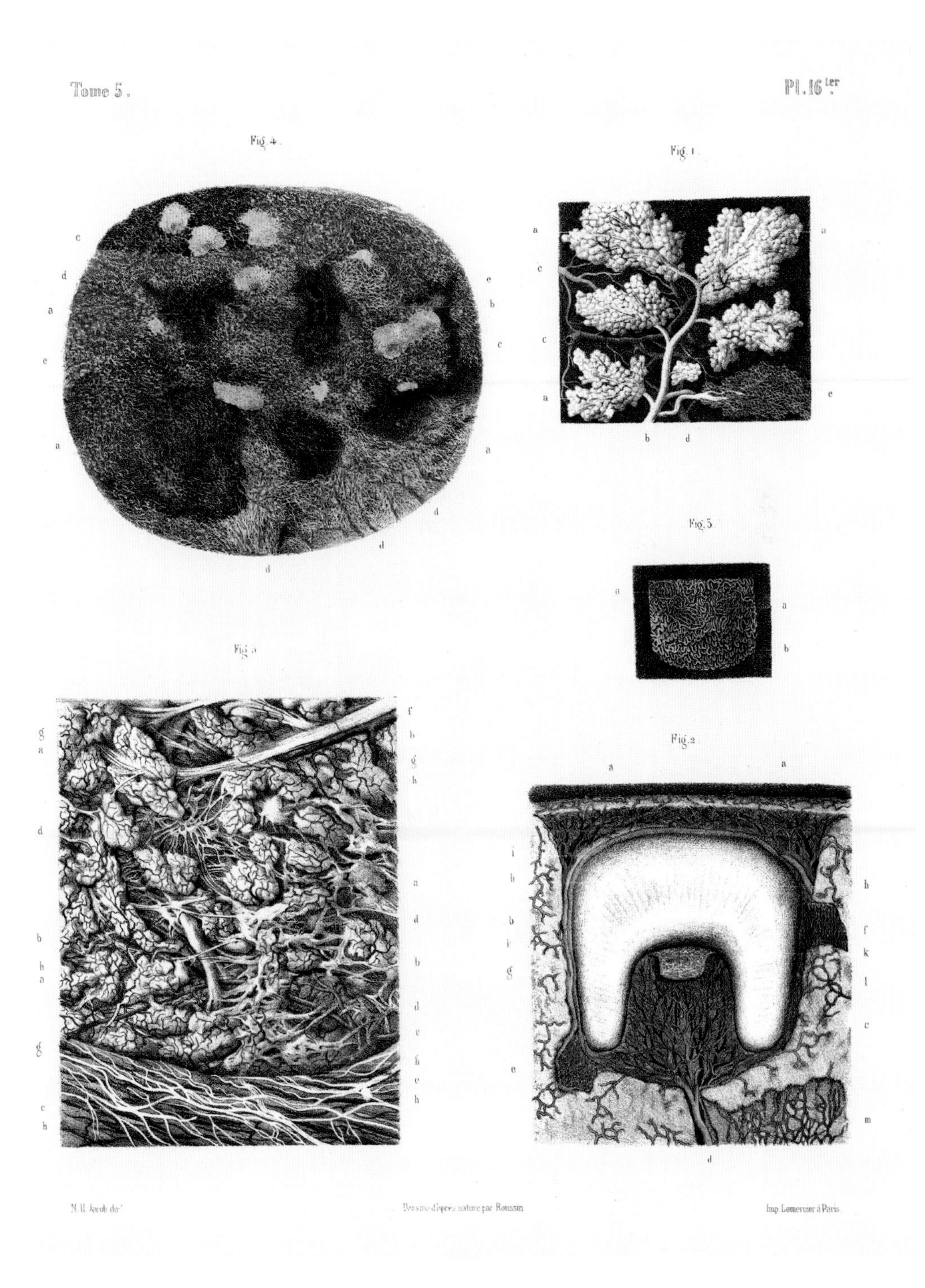

Oral cavity and pharynx: Microscopic anatomy
Cavité orale et pharynx : Aanatomie microscopique
Cavidad bucal y faringe: anatomía microscópica

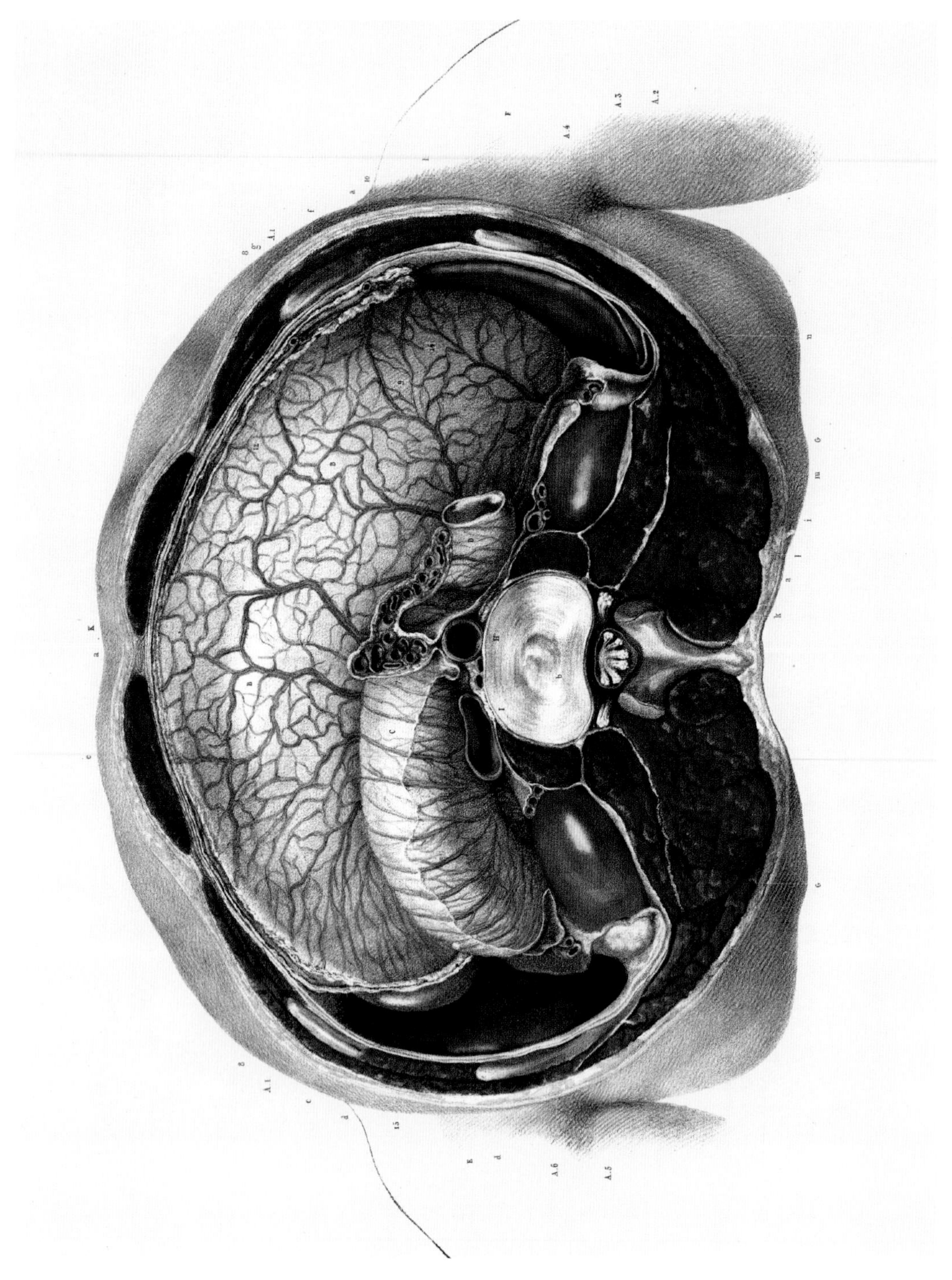

Stomach / Estomac / Estómago

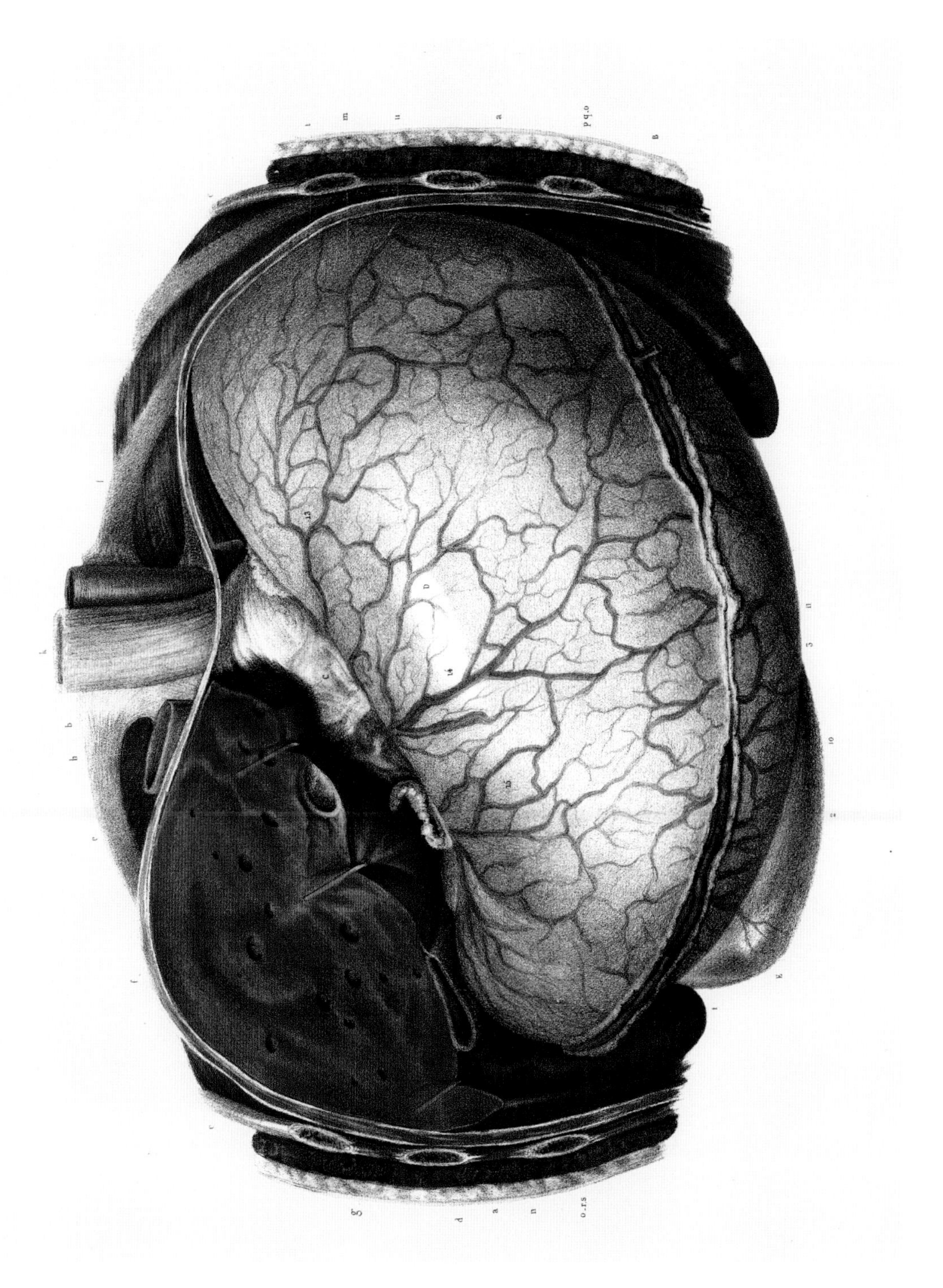

Stomach / Estomac / Estómago

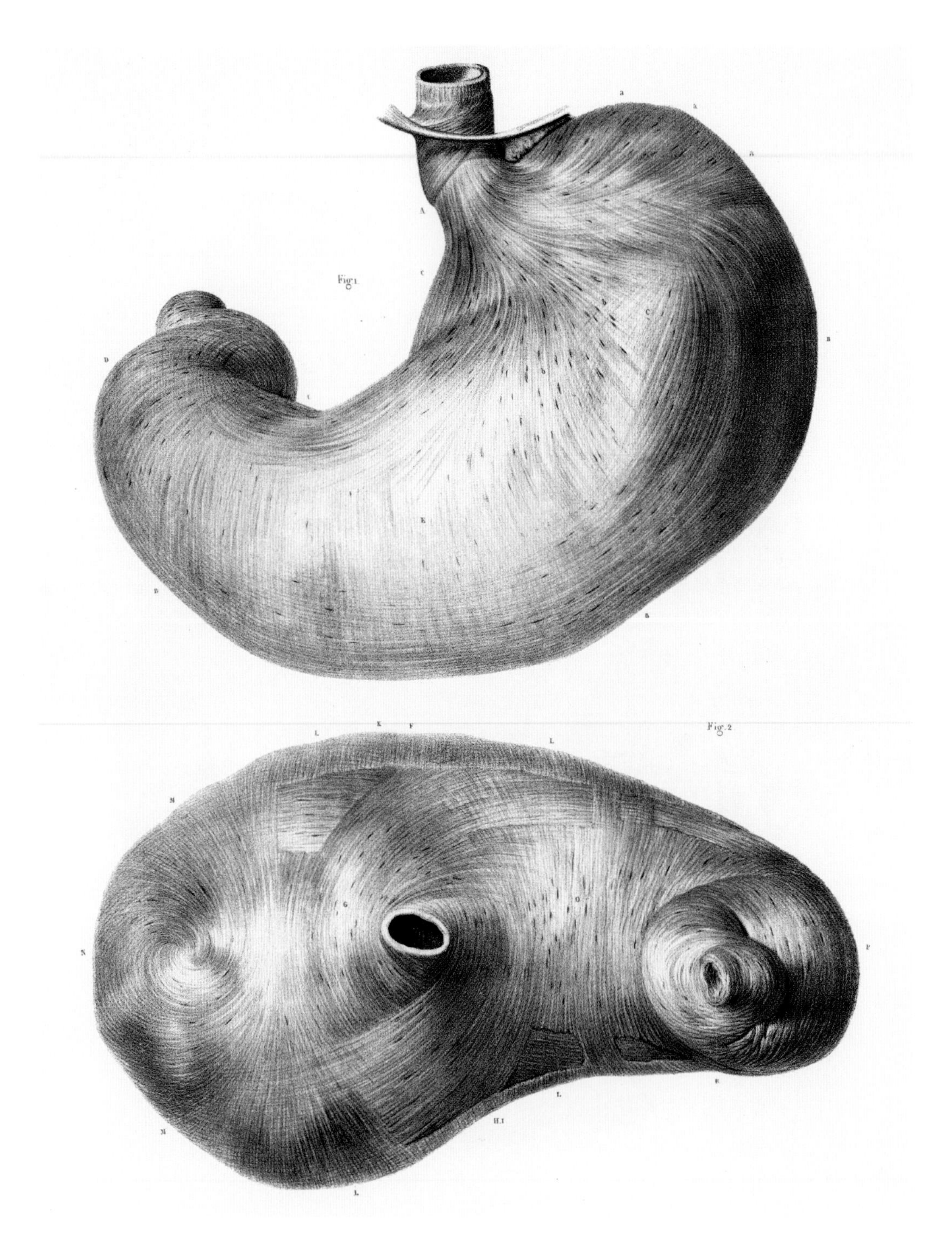

Stomach: Muscle layer / Estomac : Musculeuse / Estómago: capa muscular

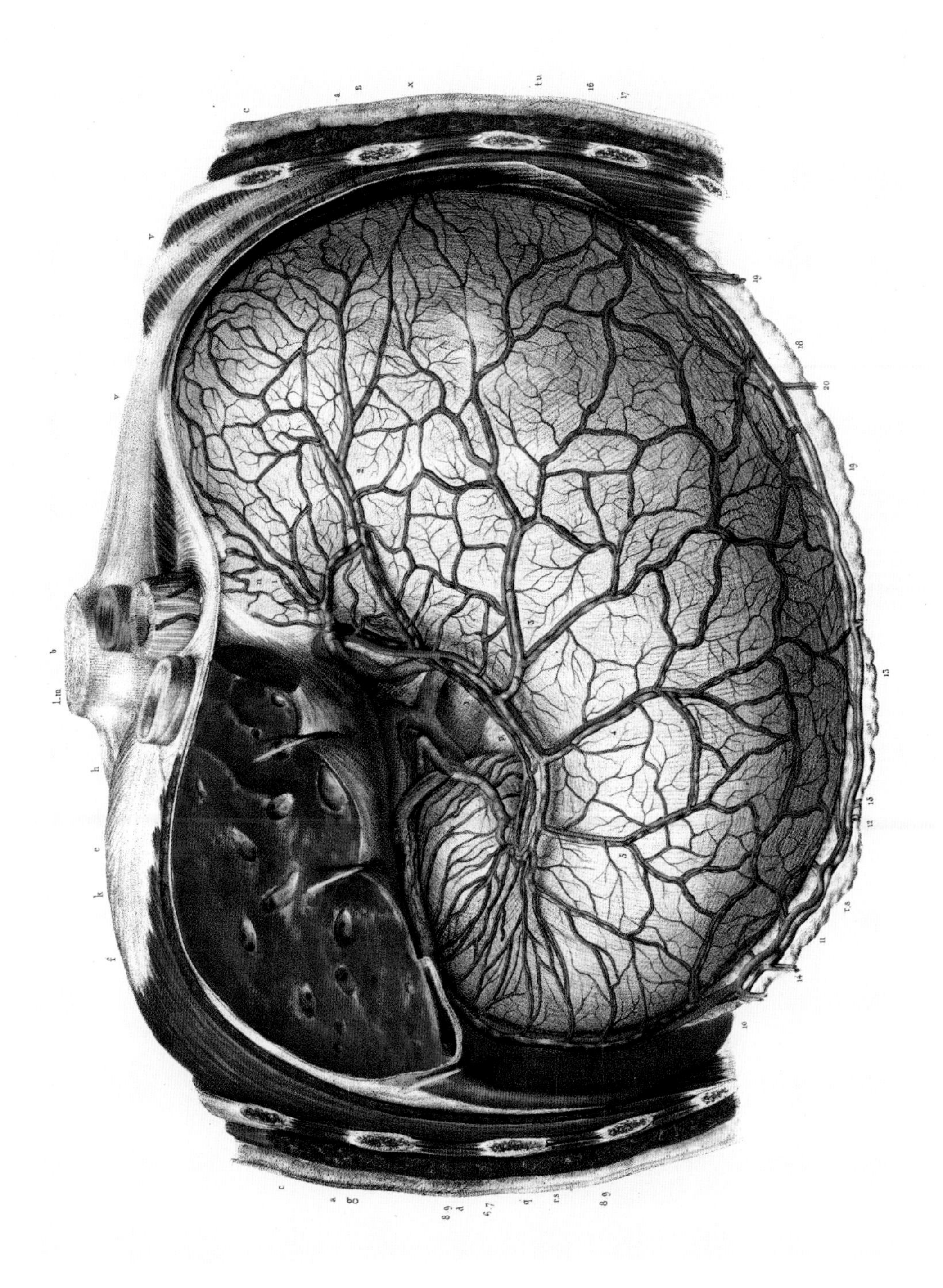

Stomach: Arteries and veins / Estomac : Artères et veines / Estómago: arterias y venas

VENTRICULUS (GASTER): ARTERIAE ET VENAE, VASA LYMPHATICA, ANATOMIA MICROSCOPICA, ET NERVI

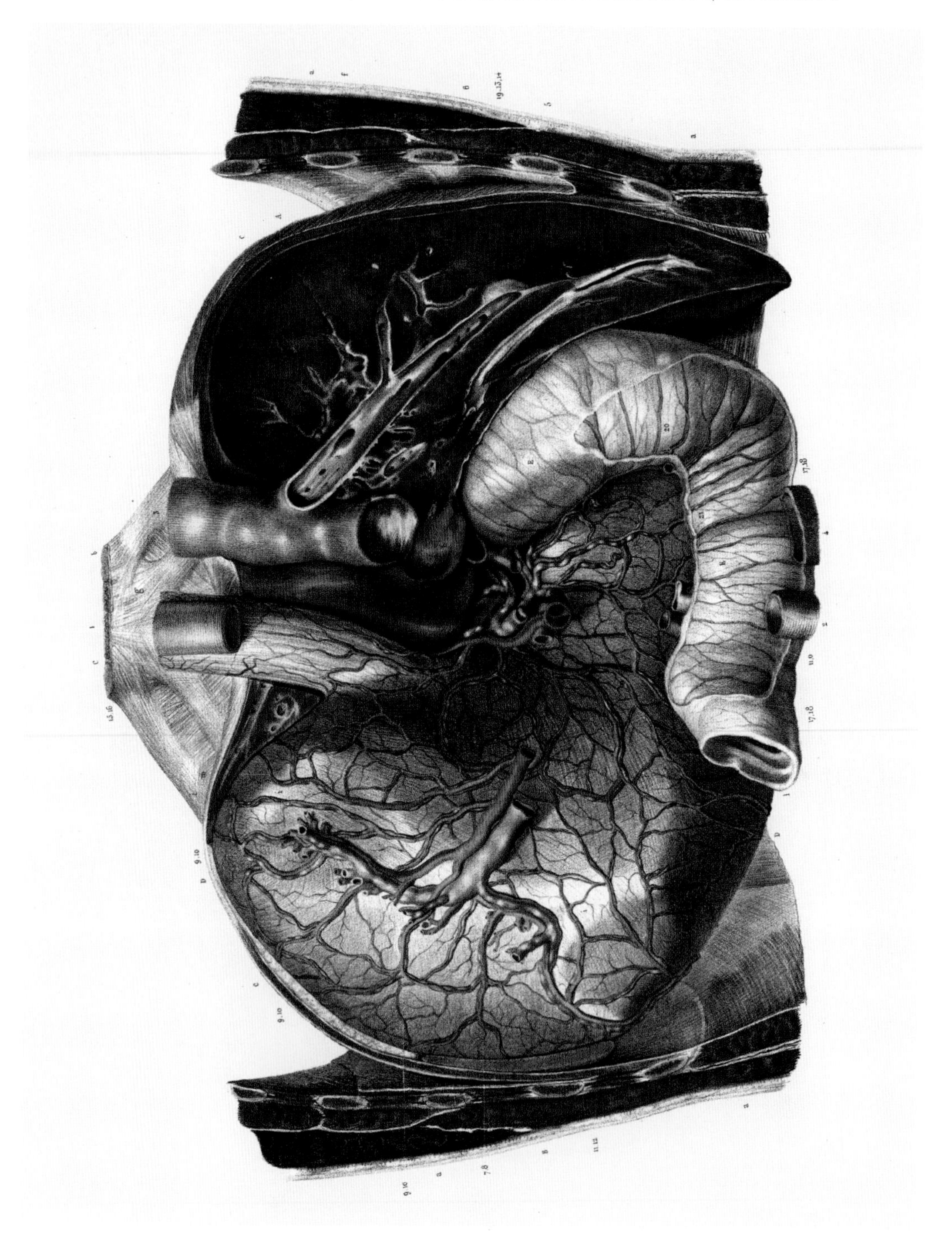

Stomach: Arteries and veins / Estomac : Artères et veines
Estómago: arterias y venas

VENTRICULUS (GASTER): ARTERIAE ET VENAE, VASA LYMPHATICA, ANATOMIA MICROSCOPICA, ET NERVI

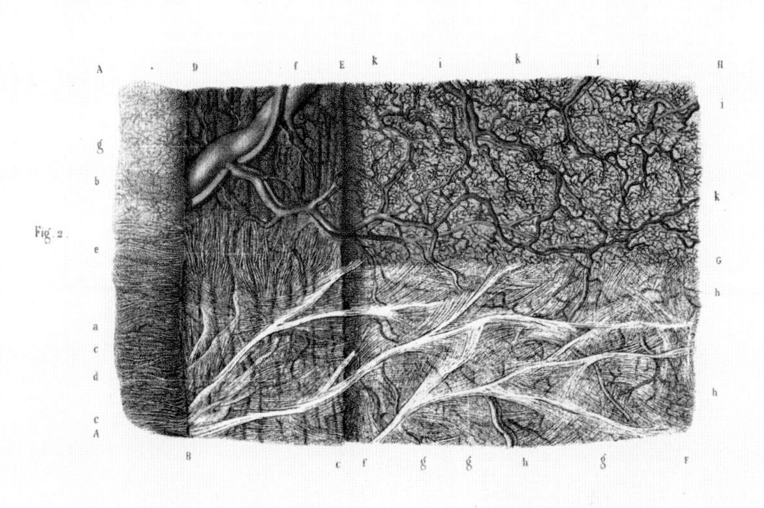

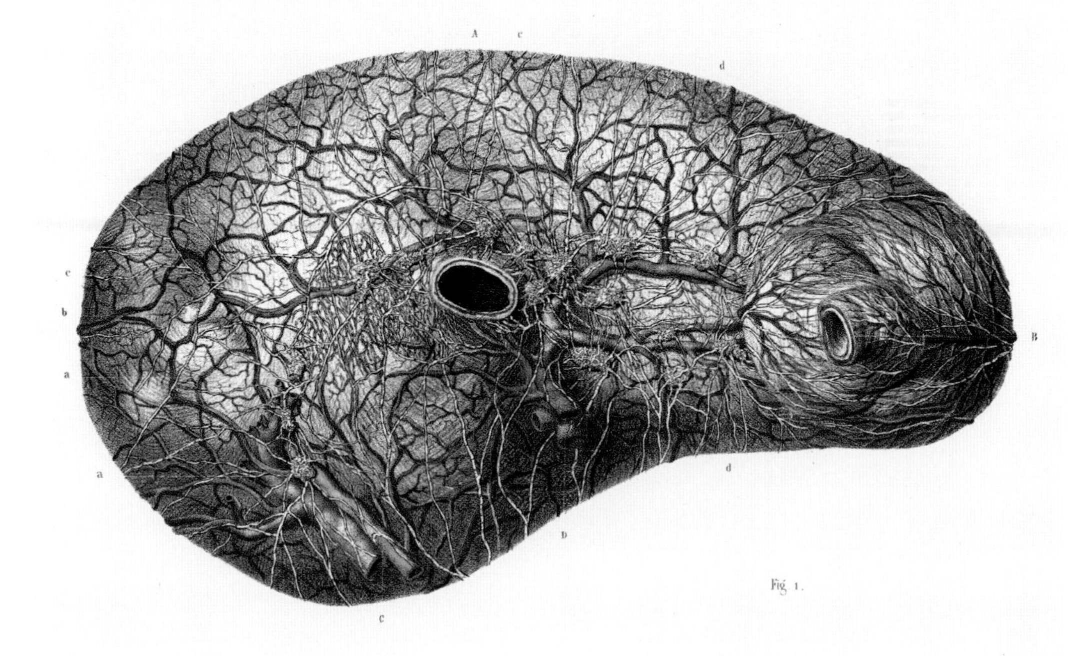

Stomach: Lymph vessels and microscopic anatomy
Estomac : Vaisseaux lymphatiques et anatomie microscopique
Estómago: vasos linfáticos y anatomía microscópica

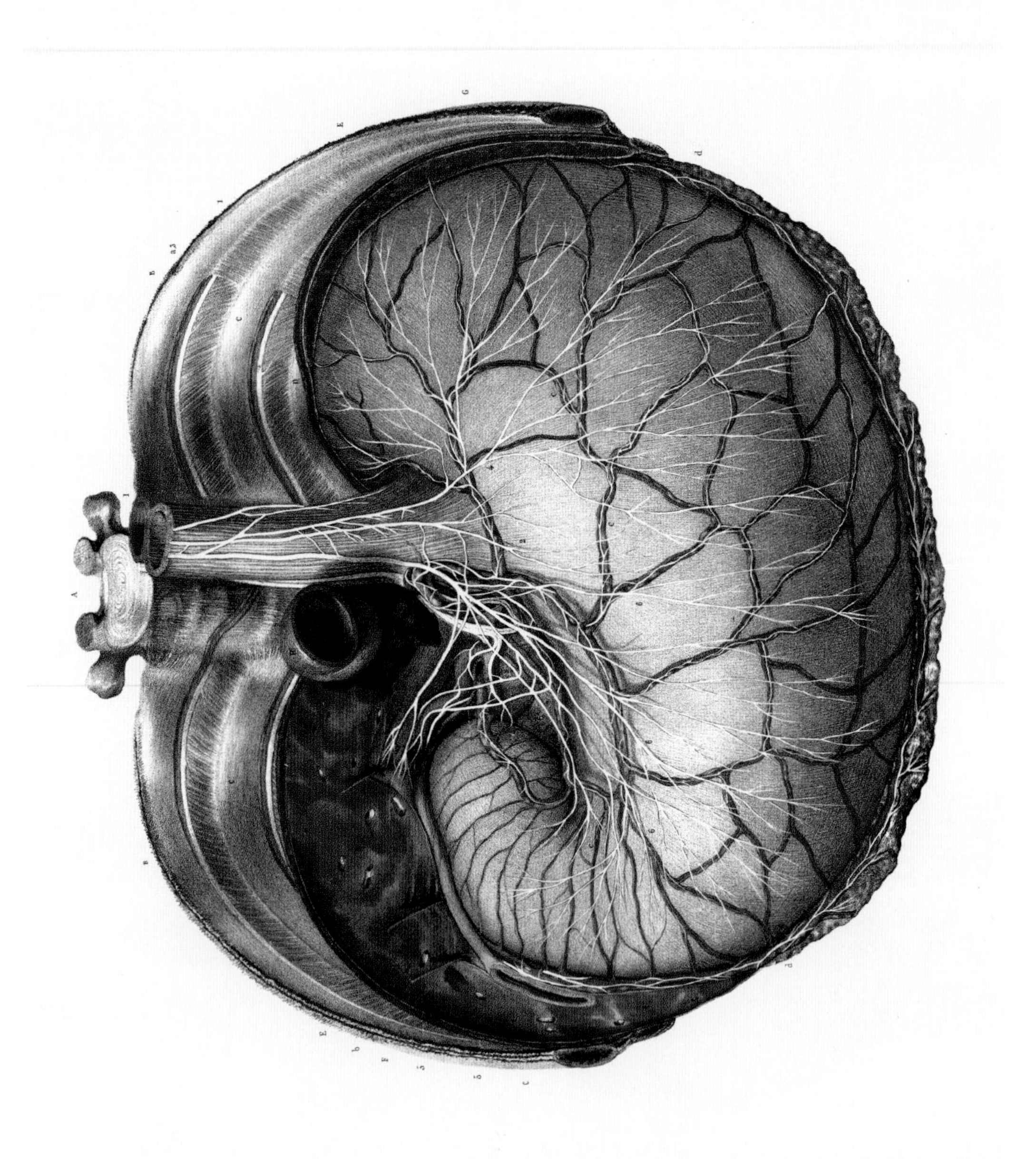

Stomach: Nerves / Estomac : Nerfs / Estómago: nervios

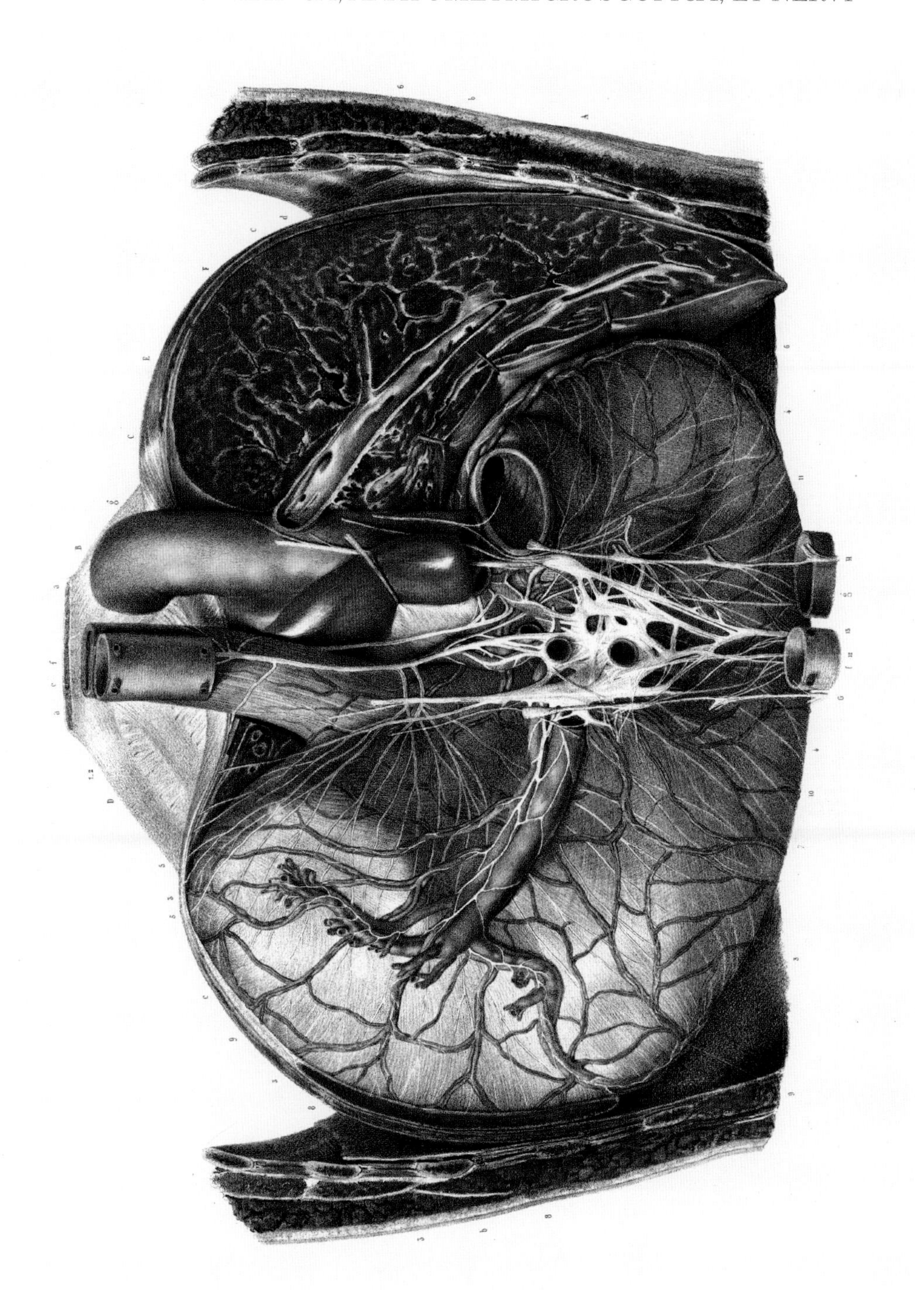

Stomach: Nerves / Estomac : Nerfs / Estómago: nervios

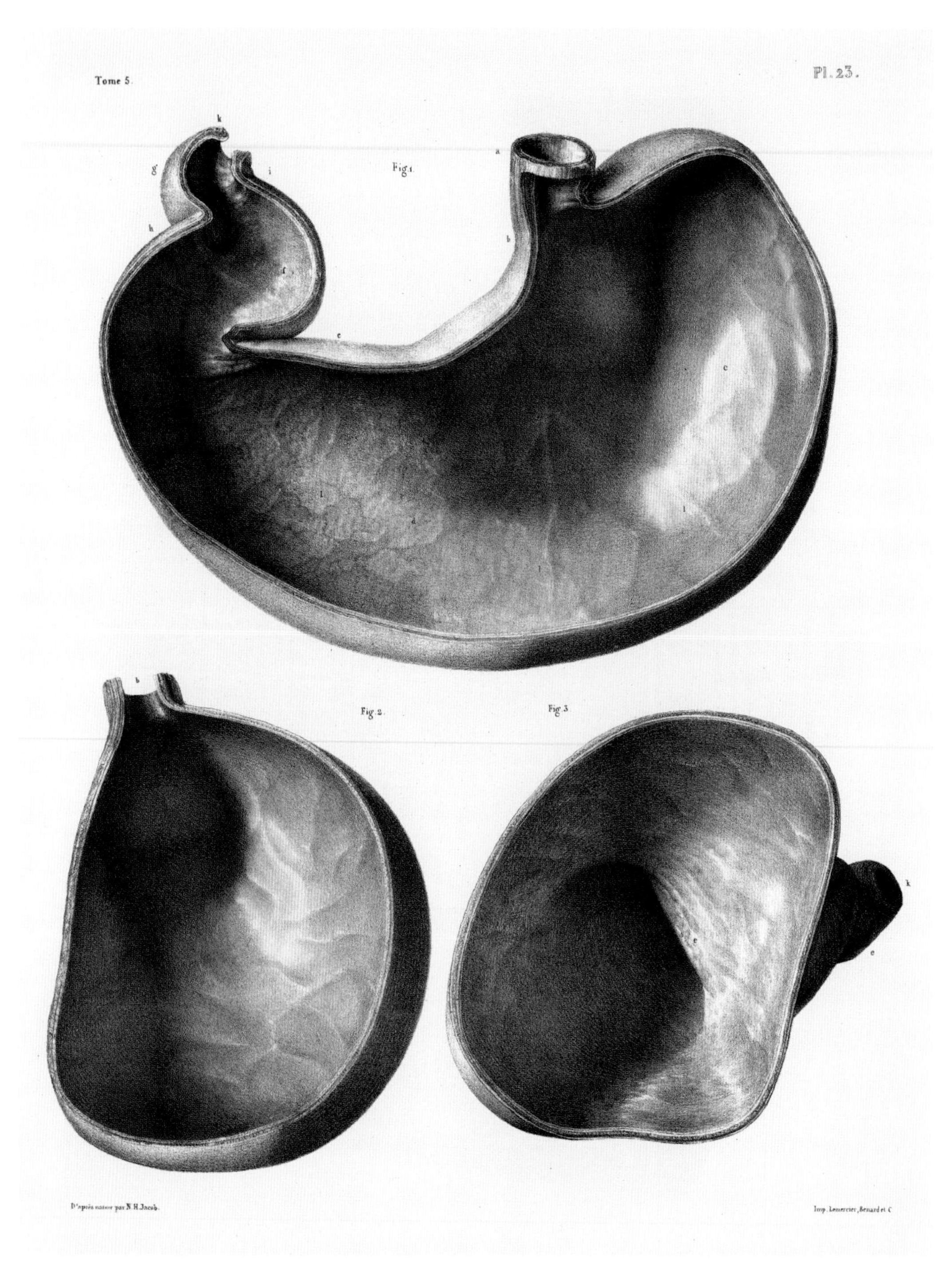

Stomach: Cavity / Estomac : Cavité
Estómago: cavidad

VENTRICULUS (GASTER): ANATOMIA MICROSCOPICA. DUODENUM: VASA. DUCTUS CHOLEDOCUS

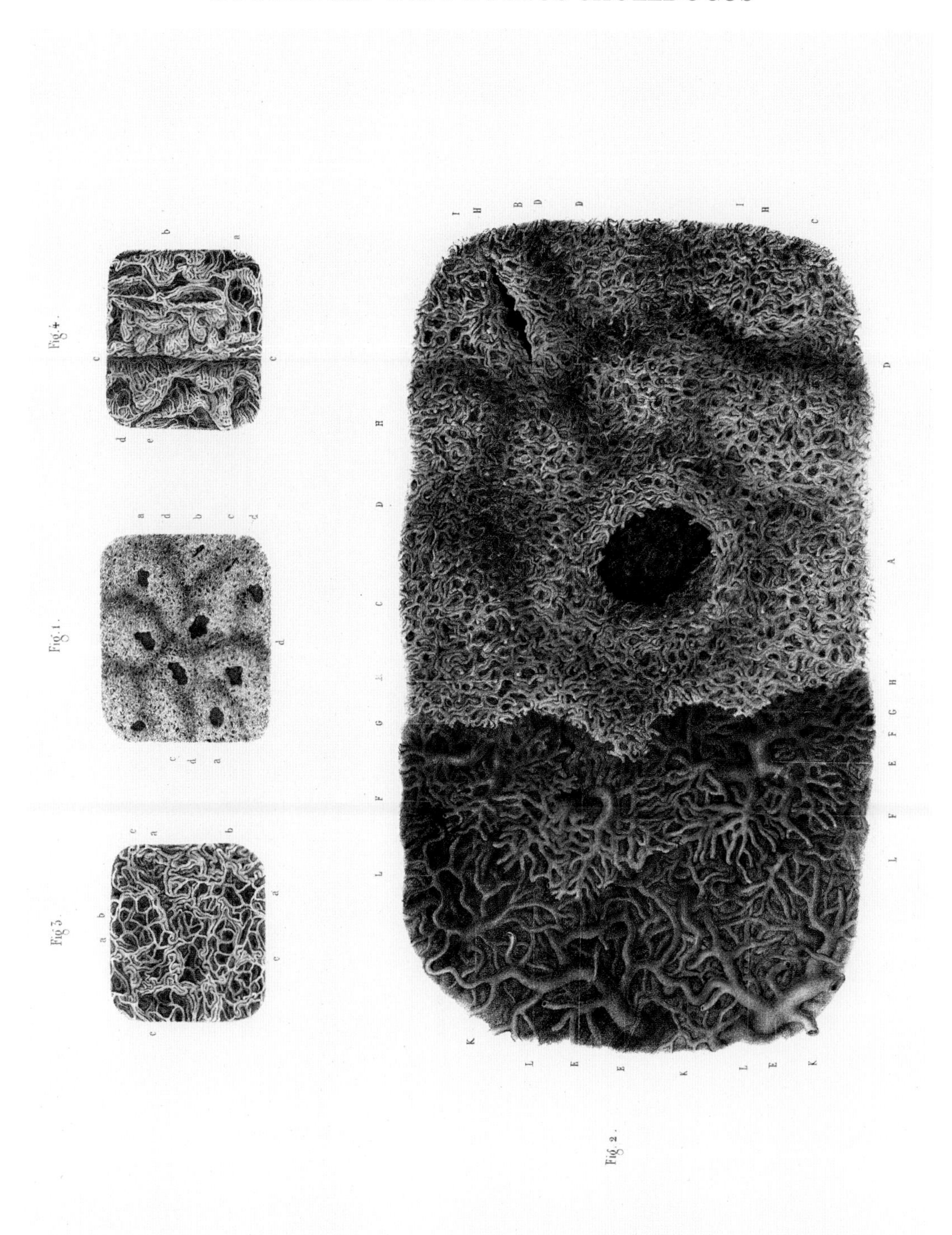

Stomach: Microscopic anatomy / Estomac : Anatomie microscopique
Estómago: anatomía microscópica

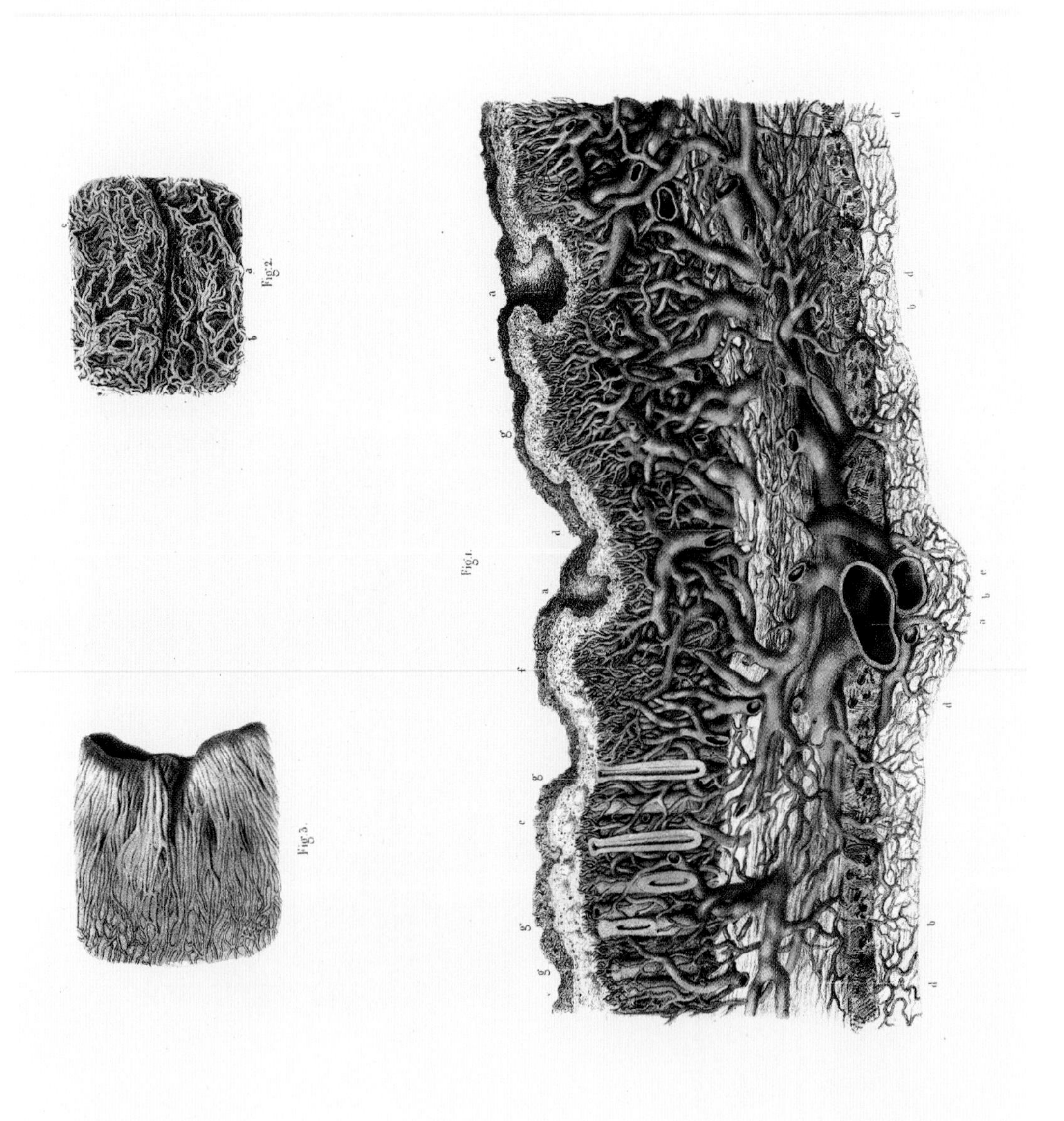

Stomach: Microscopic anatomy / Estomac : Anatomie microscopique
Estómago: anatomía microscópica

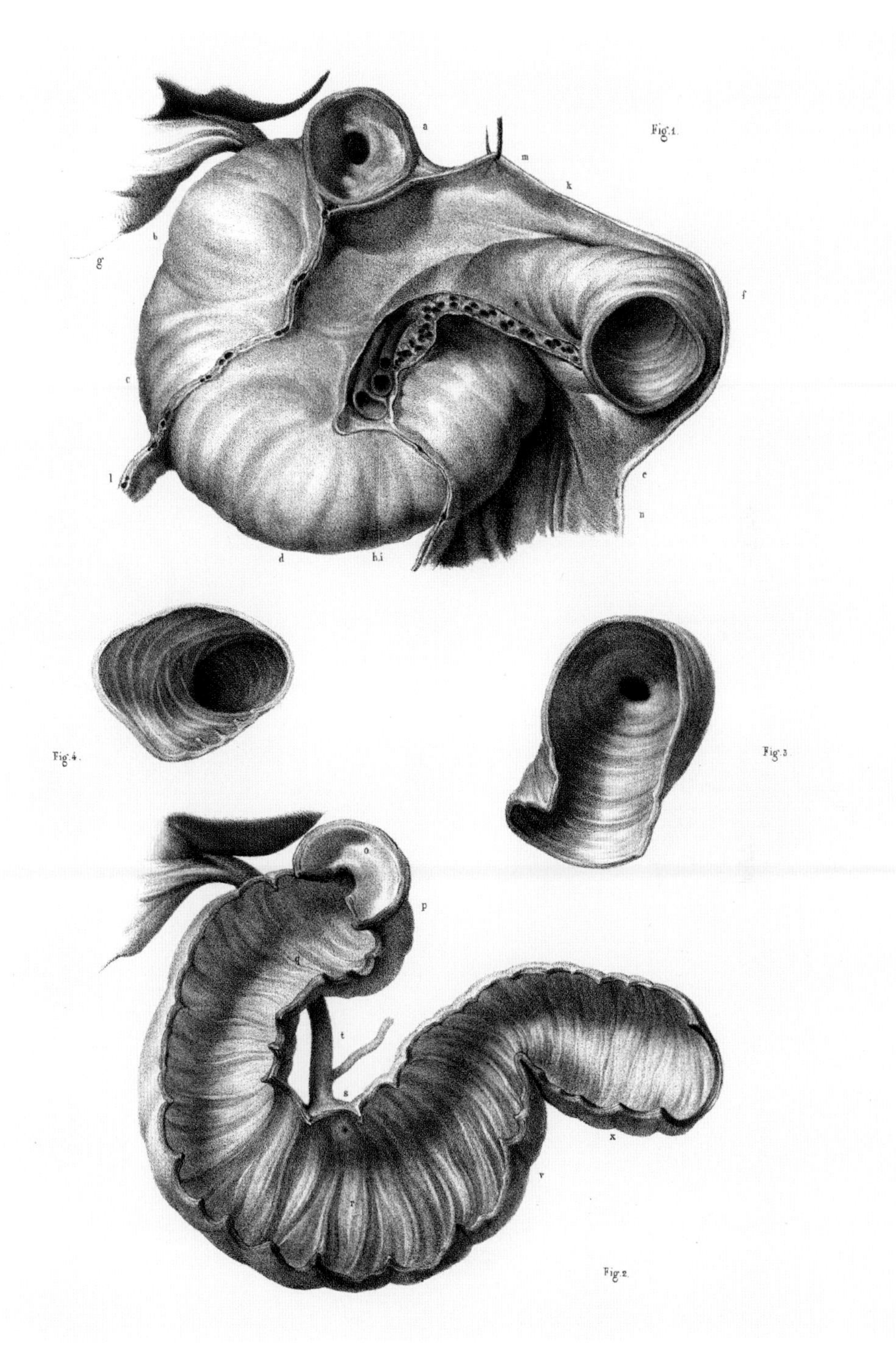

Duodenum / Duodénum / Duodeno

VENTRICULUS (GASTER): ANATOMIA MICROSCOPICA. DUODENUM: VASA. DUCTUS CHOLEDOCUS

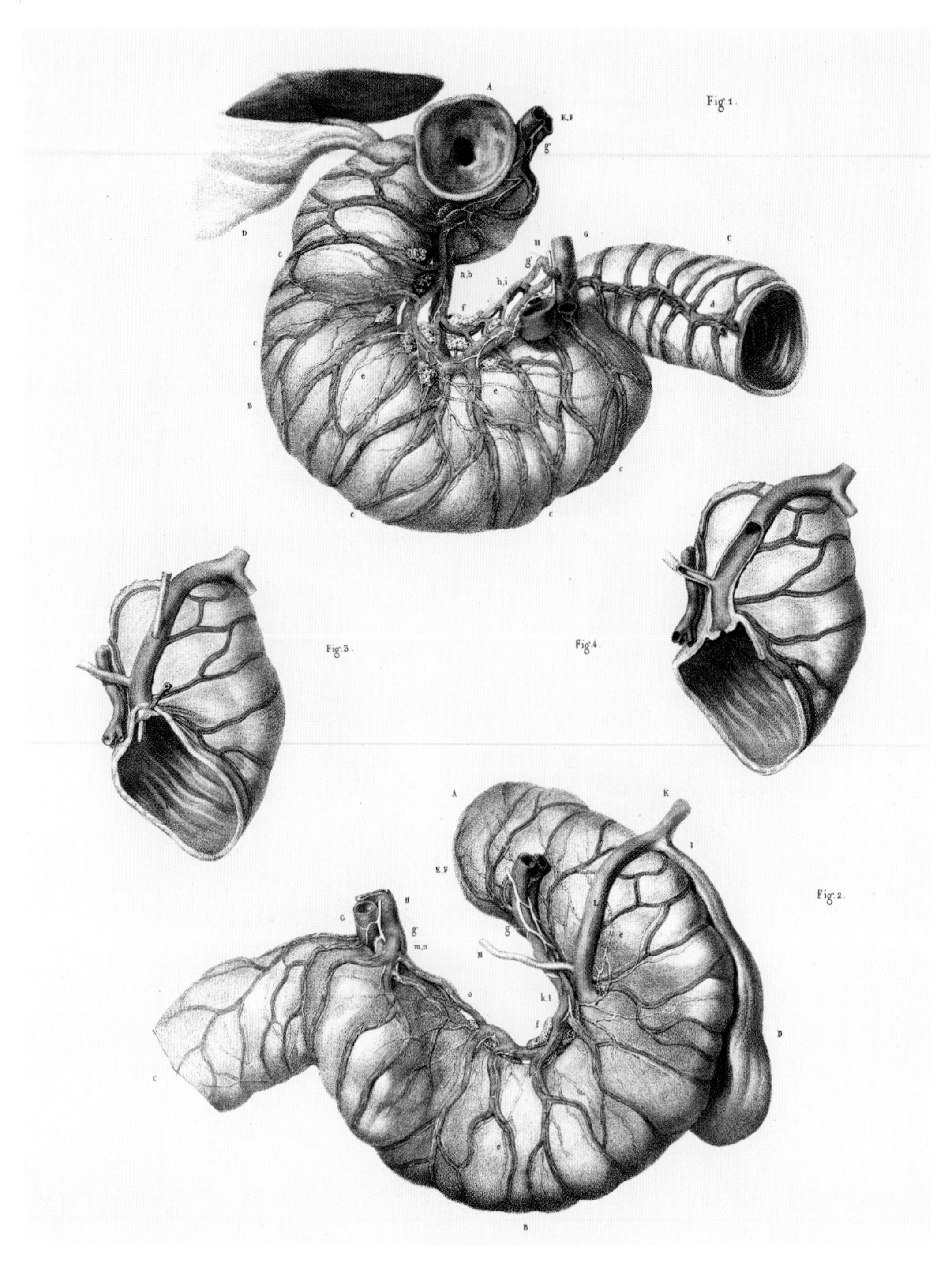

Duodenum: Vessels. Bile duct / Duodénum : Vaisseaux. Conduit cholédoque
Duodeno: vasos. Conducto colédoco

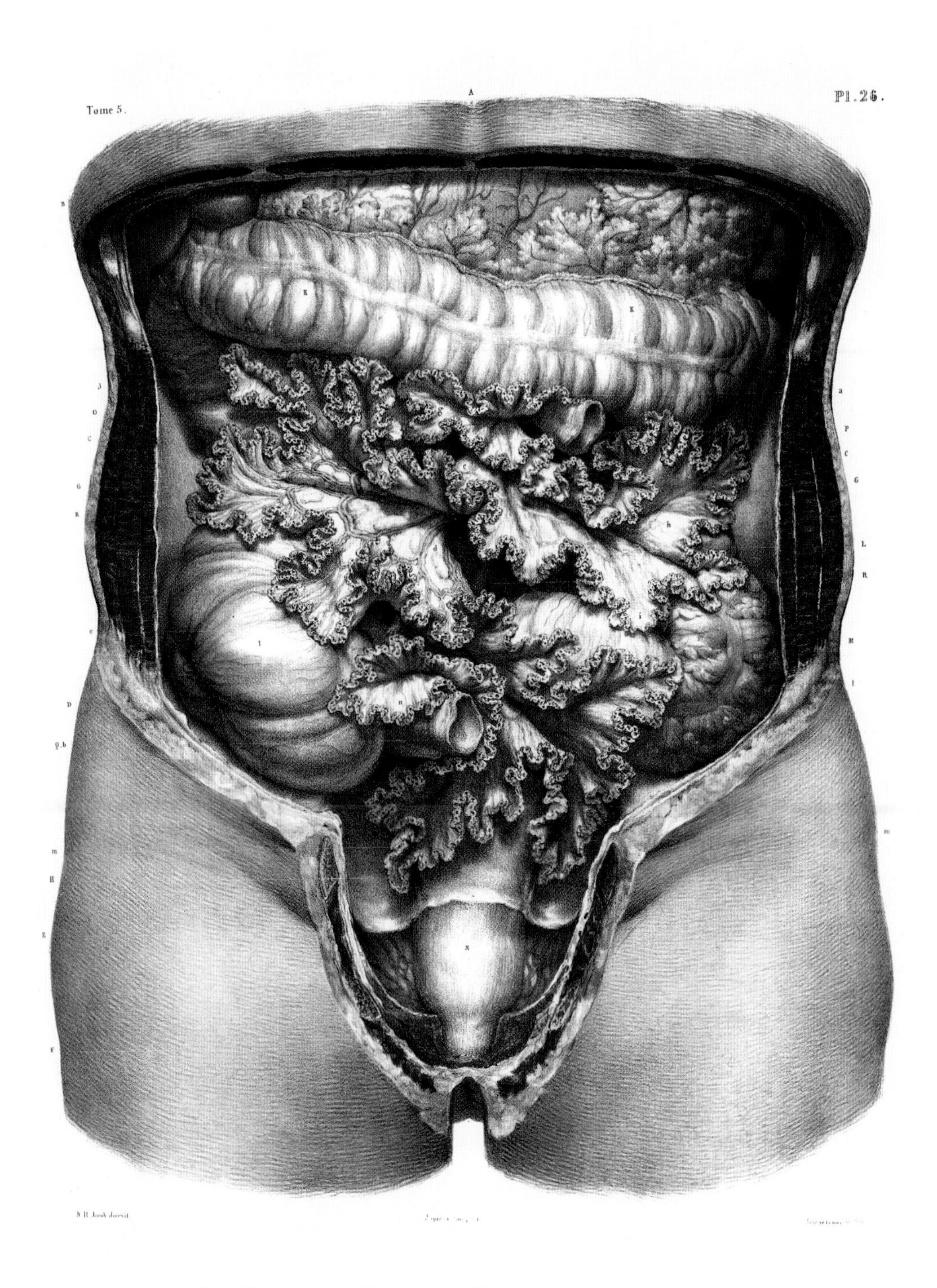

Small intestine: Mesentery / Intestin grêle : Mésentère
Intestino delgado: mesenterio

INTESTINUM TENUE: ANATOMIA MICROSCOPICA, ARTERIAE ET VENAE, VASA LYMPHATICA, ET NERVI

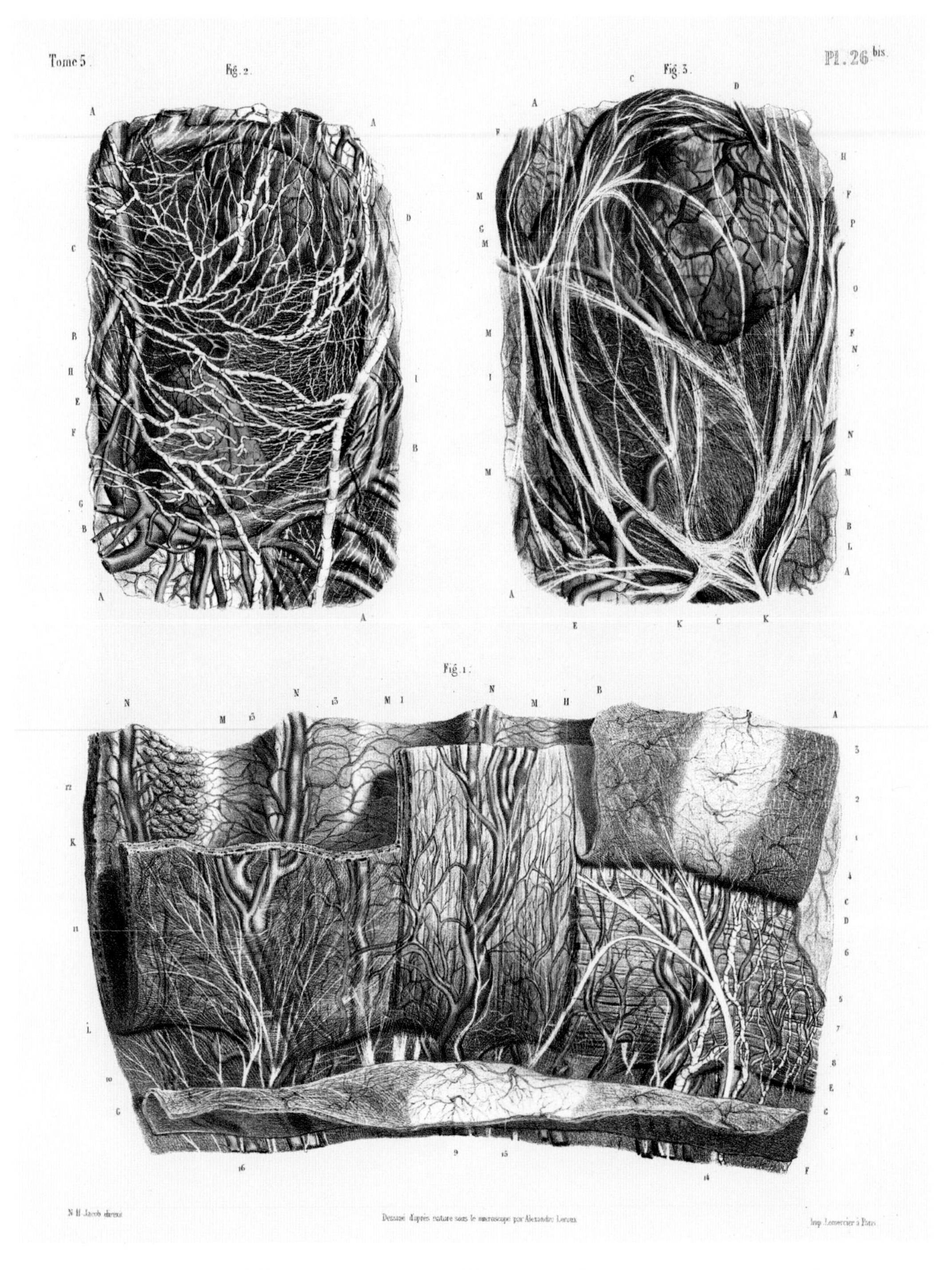

Small intestine: Microscopic anatomy / Intestin grêle : Anatomie microscopique
Intestino delgado: anatomía microscópica

INTESTINUM TENUE: ANATOMIA MICROSCOPICA, ARTERIAE ET VENAE, VASA LYMPHATICA, ET NERVI

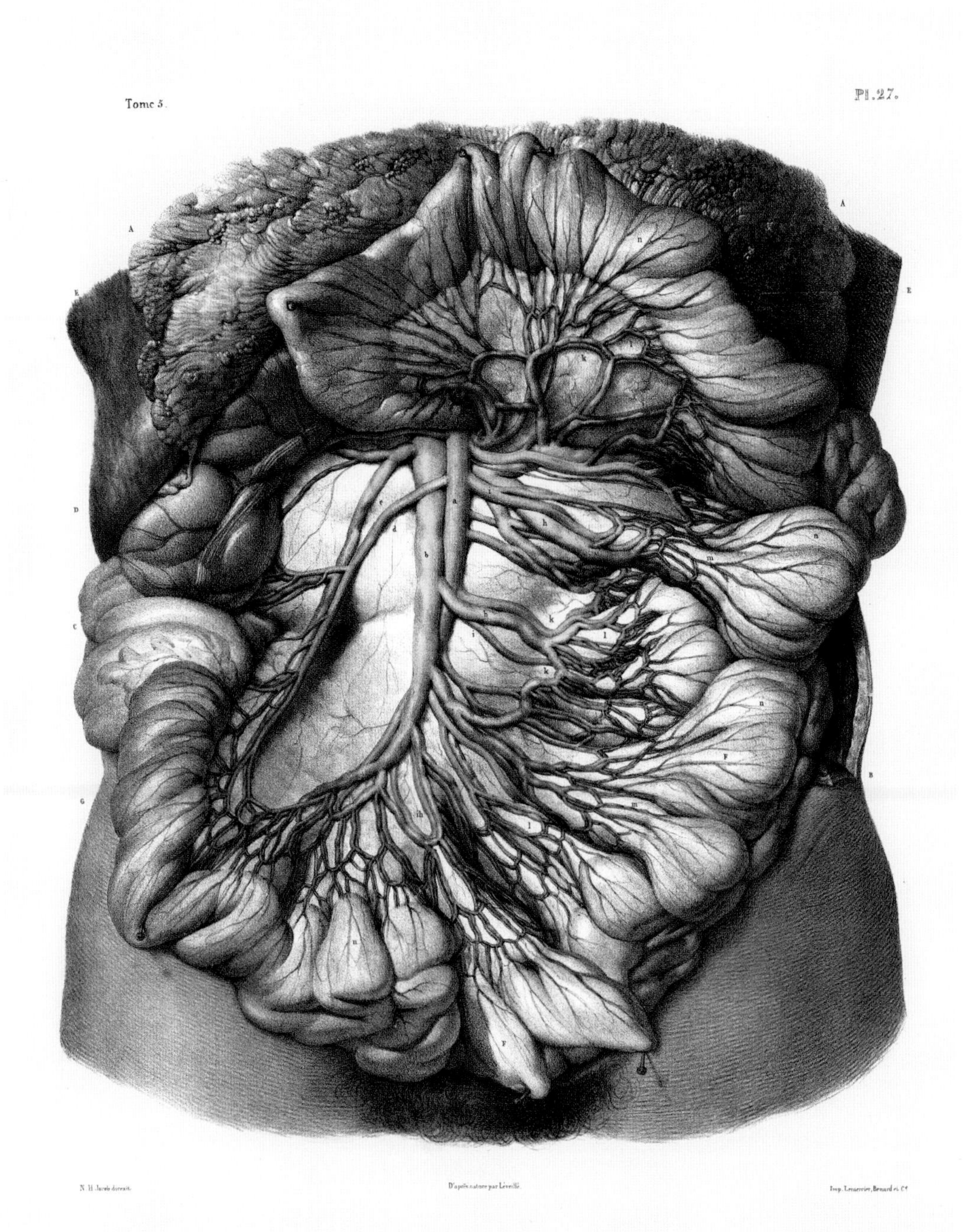

Small intestine: Arteries and veins / Intestin grêle : Artères et veines
Intestino delgado: arterias y venas

INTESTINUM TENUE: ANATOMIA MICROSCOPICA, ARTERIAE ET VENAE, VASA LYMPHATICA, ET NERVI

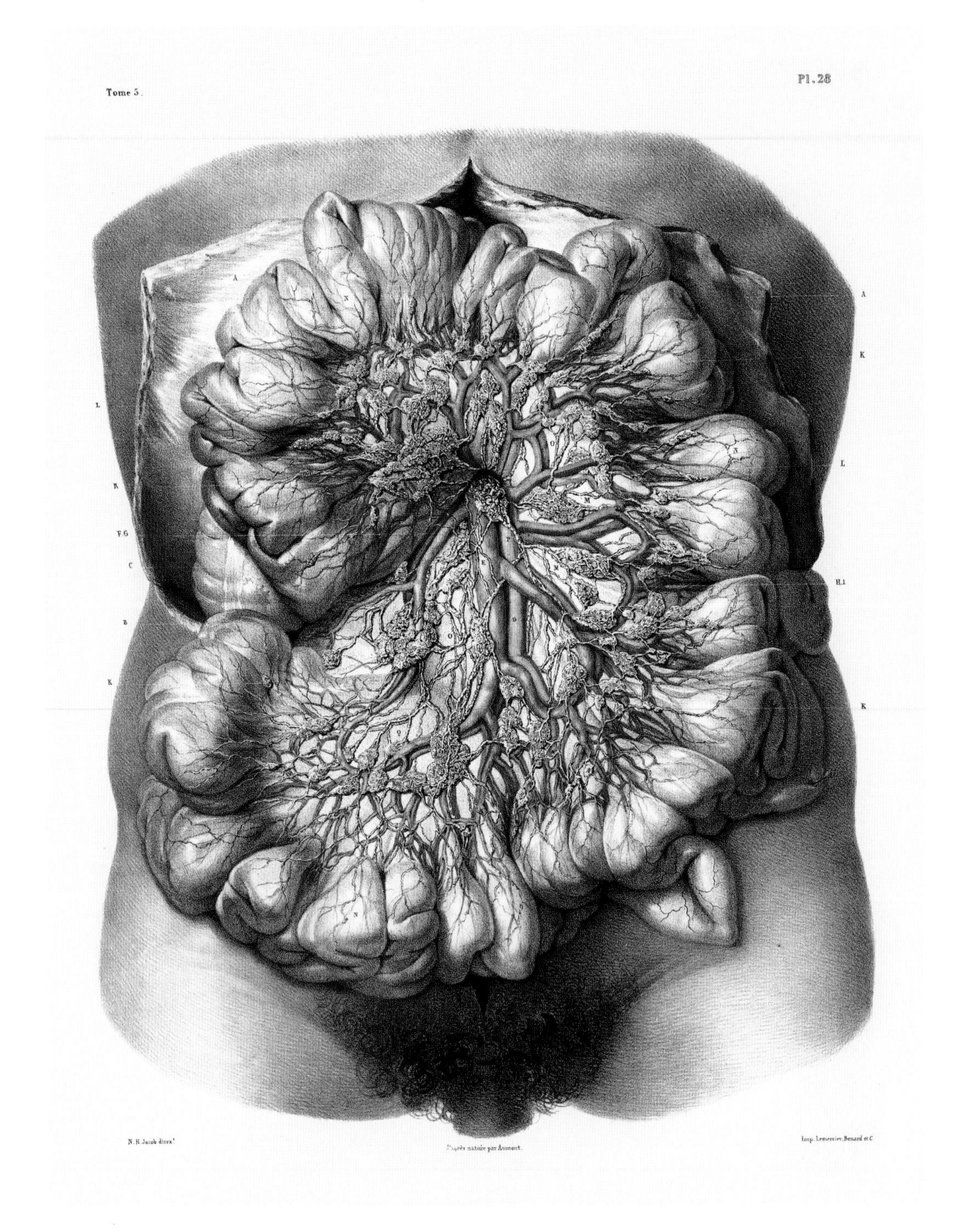

Small intestine: Lymph vessels / Intestin grêle : Vaisseaux lymphatiques
Intestino delgado: vasos linfáticos

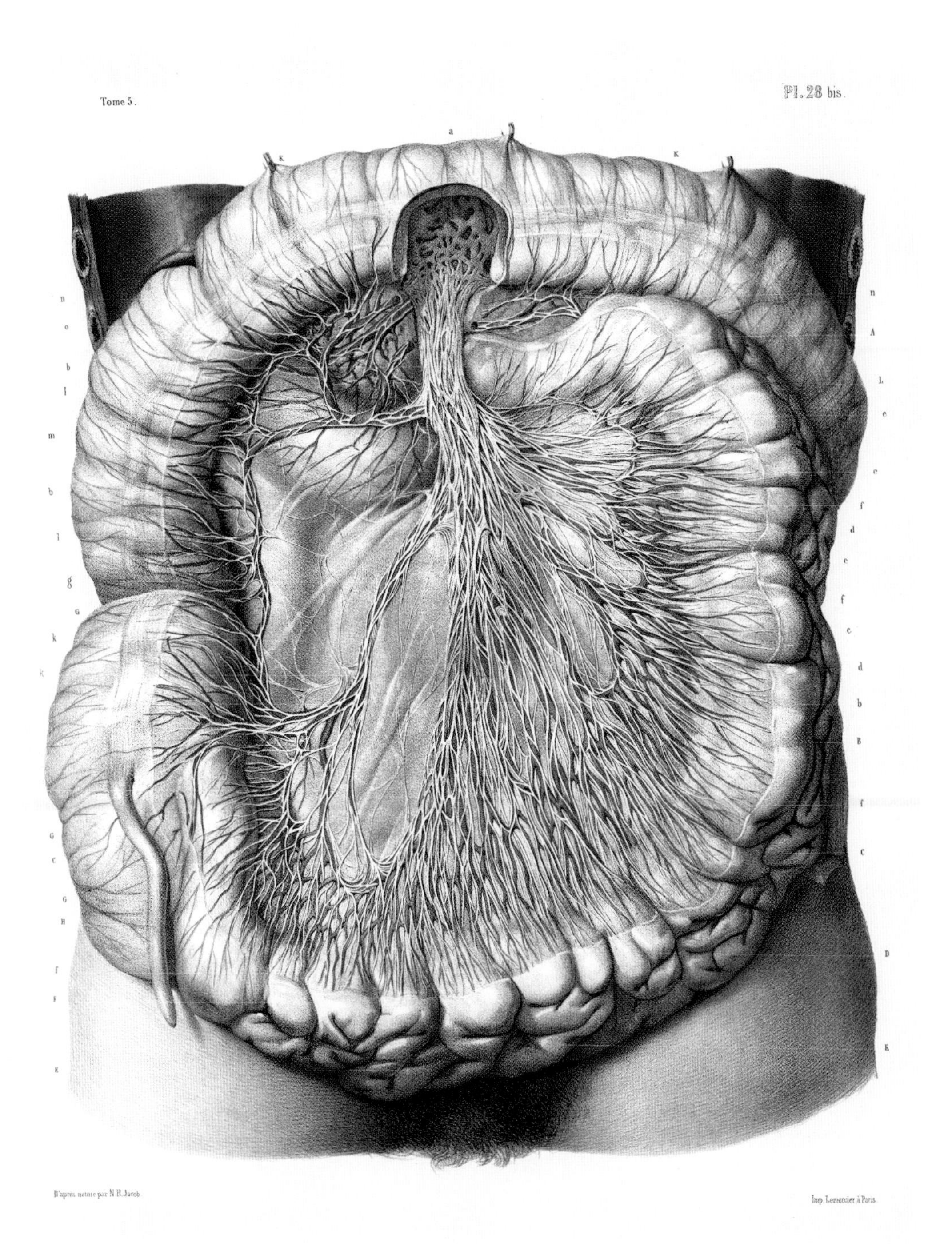

Small intestine: Nerves / Intestin grêle : Nerfs
Intestino delgado: nervios

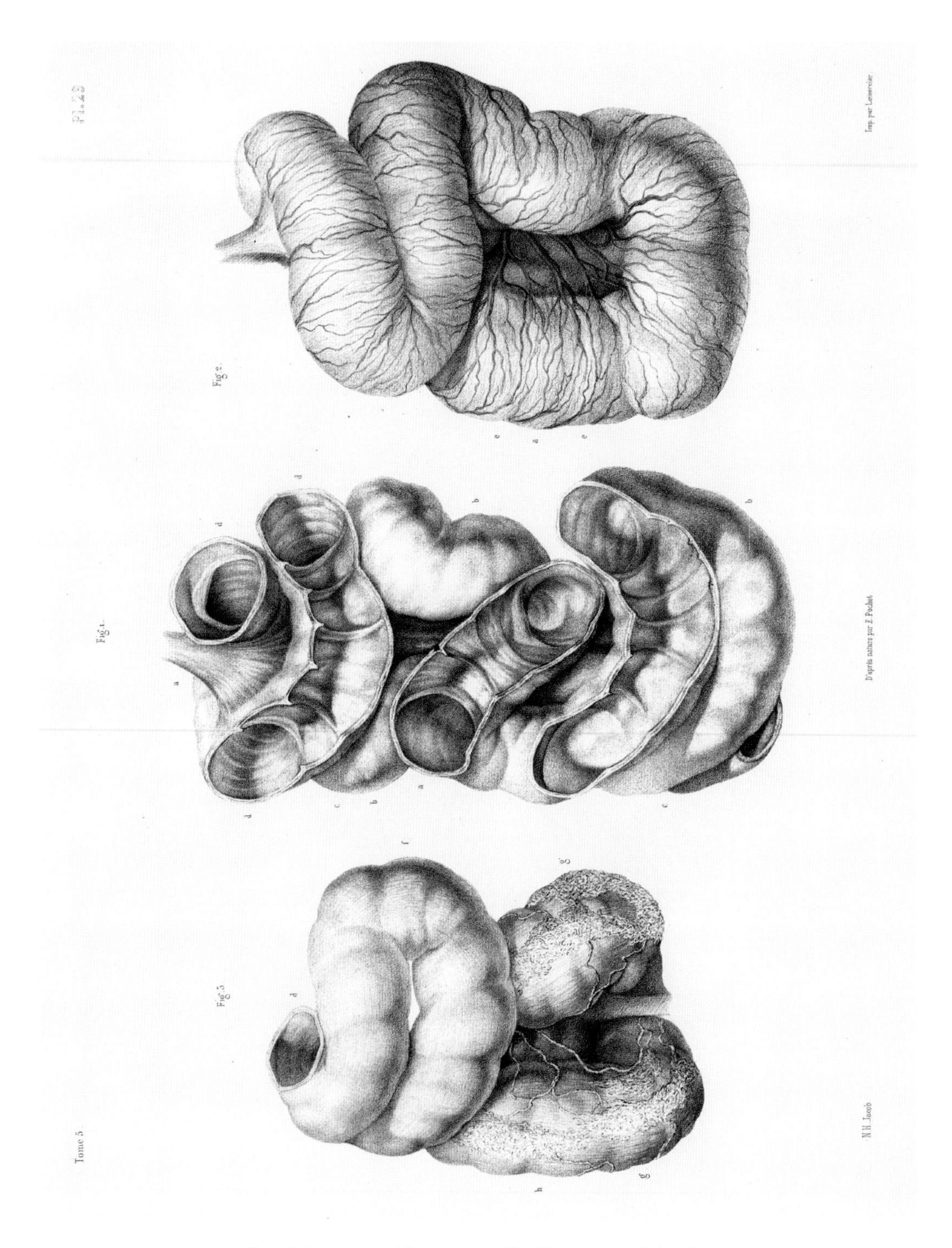

Small intestine / Intestin grêle / Intestino delgado

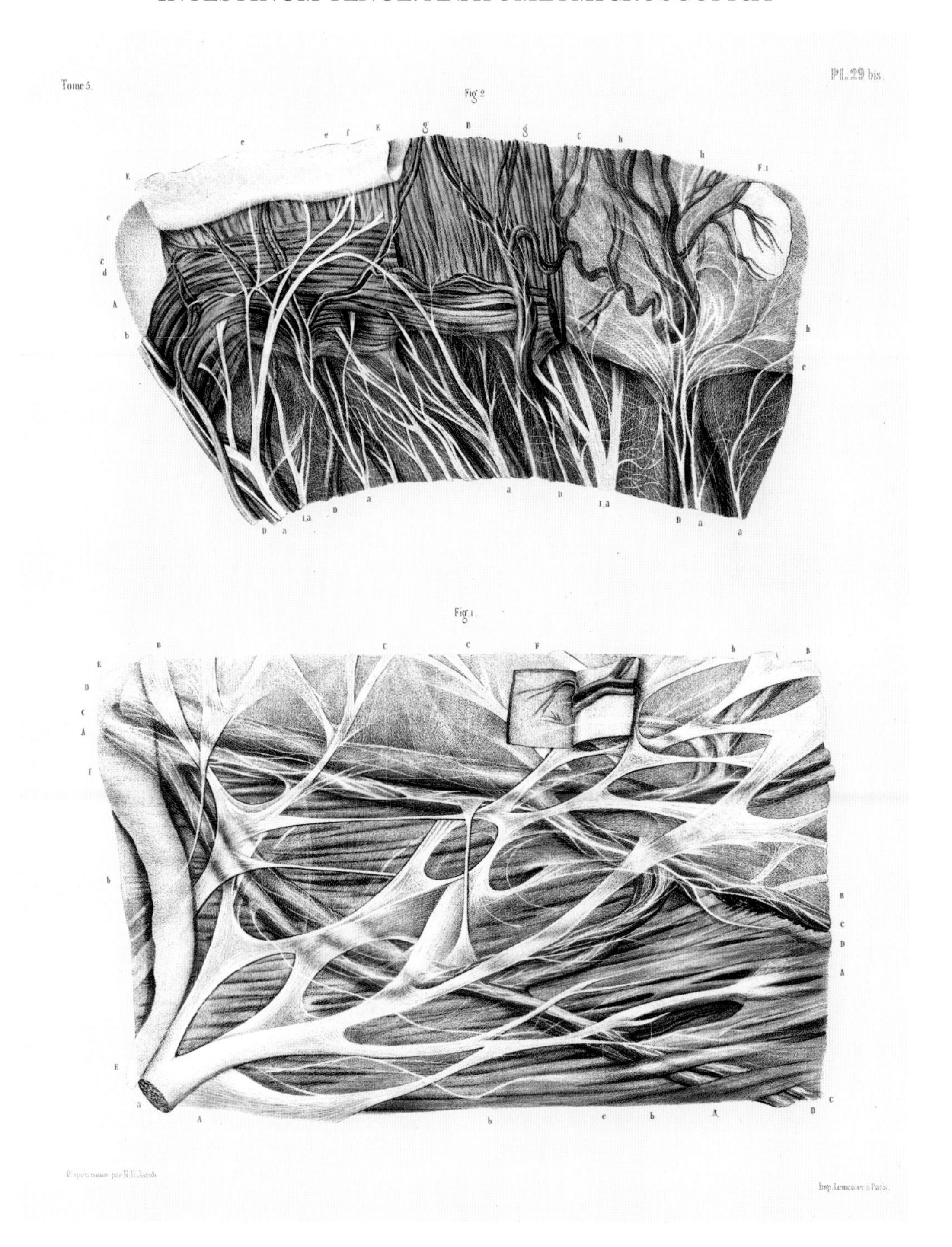

Stomach and small intestine: Microscopic anatomy
Estomac et intestin grêle : Anatomie microscopique
Estómago e intestino delgado: anatomía microscópica

INTESTINUM CRASSUM: ARTERIAE, VENAE, VASA LYMPHATICA, ET NERVI

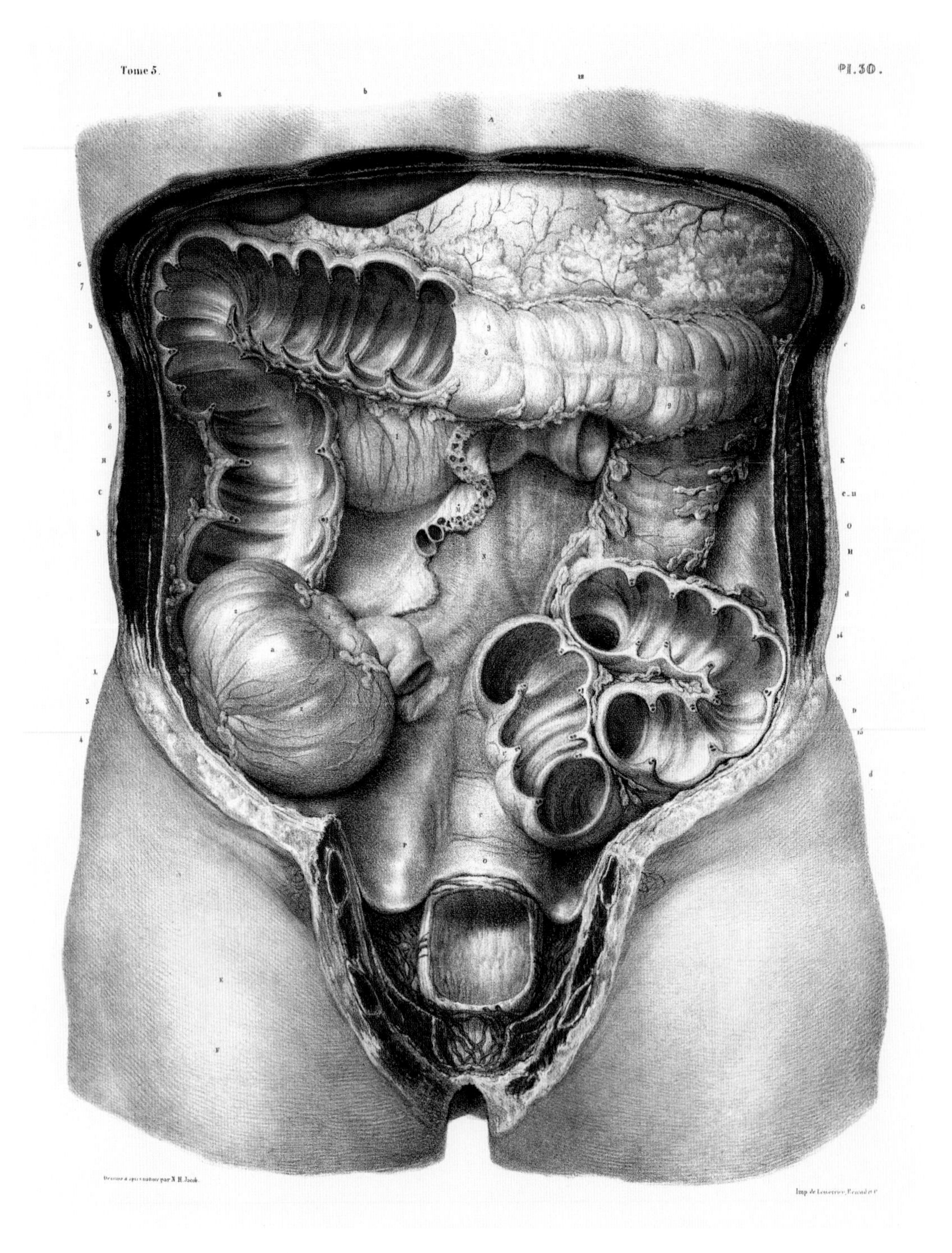

Large intestine / Gros intestin / Intestino grueso

INTESTINUM CRASSUM: ARTERIAE, VENAE, VASA LYMPHATICA, ET NERVI

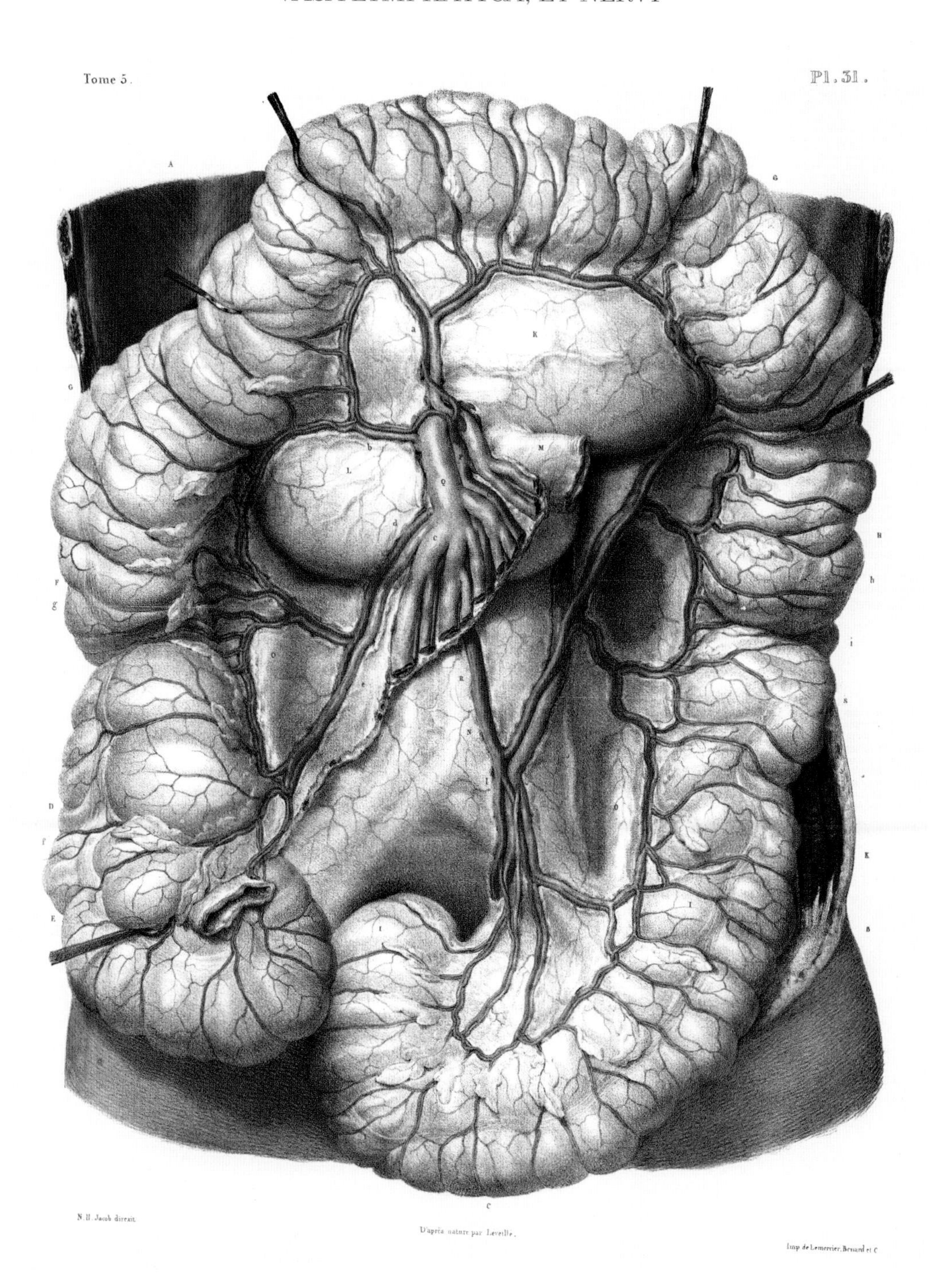

Large intestine: Arteries and veins / Gros intestin : Artères et veines
Intestino grueso: arterias y venas

INTESTINUM CRASSUM: ARTERIAE, VENAE, VASA LYMPHATICA, ET NERVI

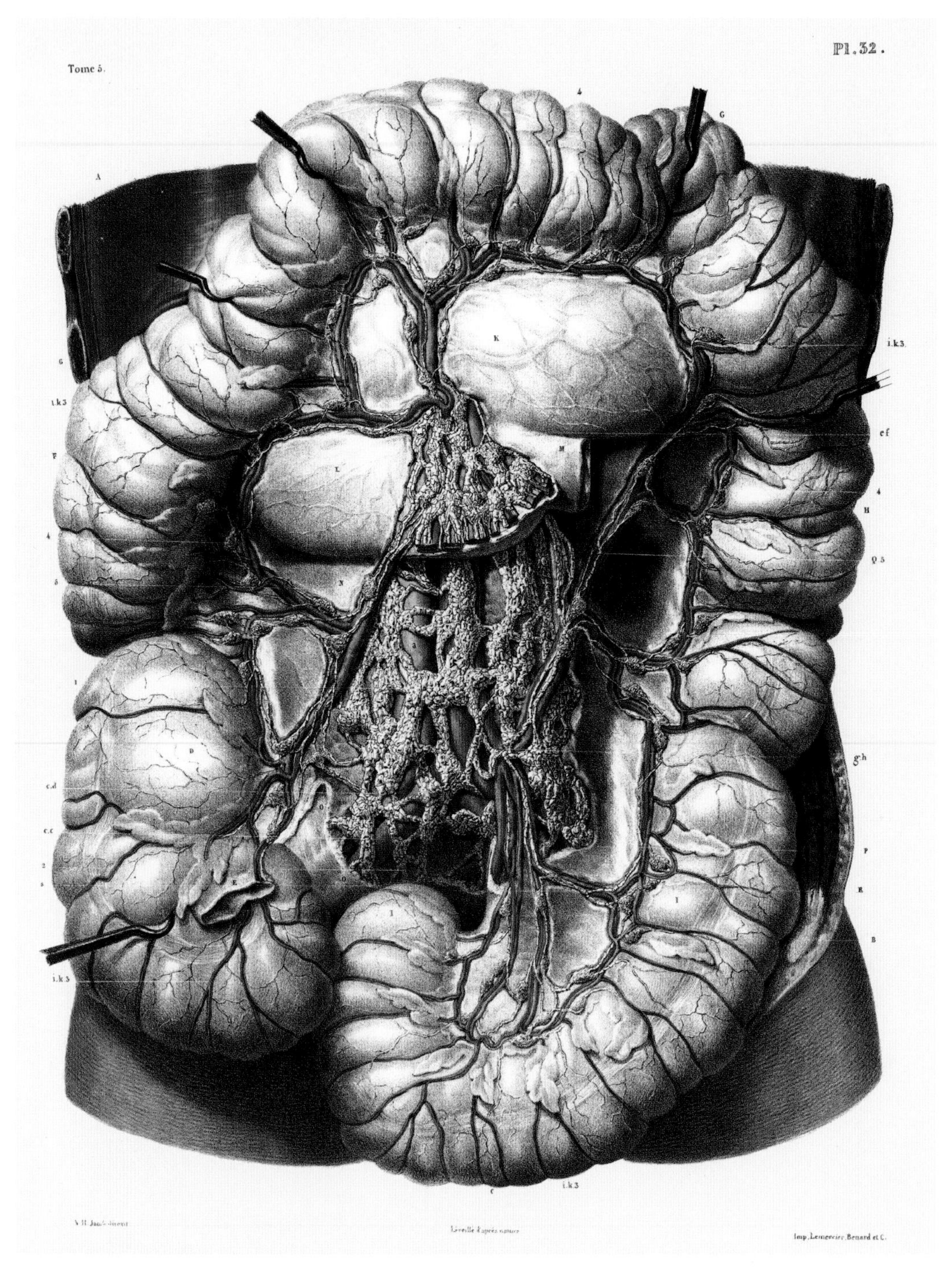

Large intestine: Lymph vessels / Gros intestin : Vaisseaux lymphatiques
Intestino grueso: vasos linfáticos

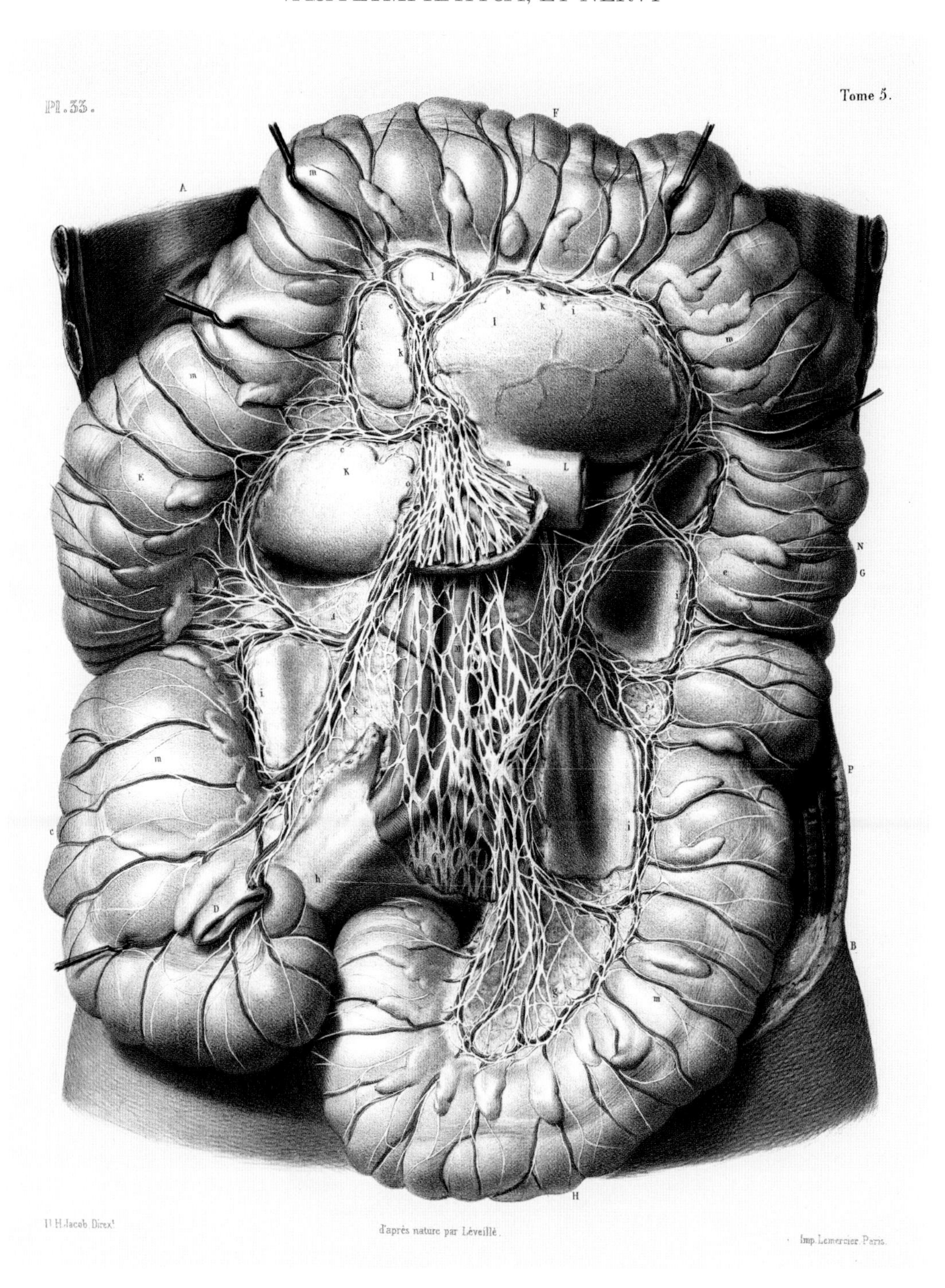

Large intestine: Nerves / Gros intestin : Nerfs
Intestino grueso: nervios

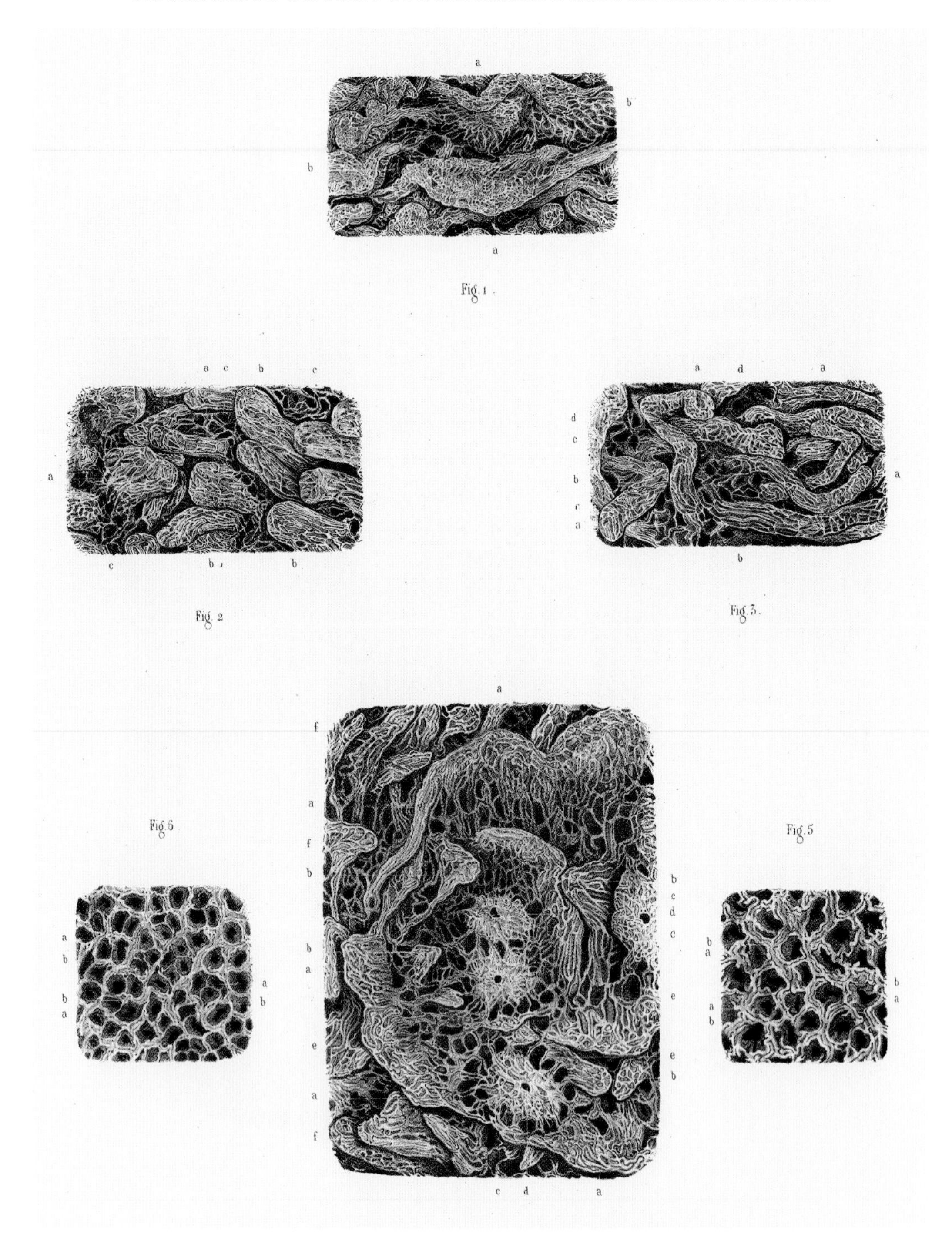

Small intestine and large intestine: Microscopic anatomy
Intestin grêle et gros intestin : Anatomie microscopique
Intestinos delgado y grueso: anatomía microscópica

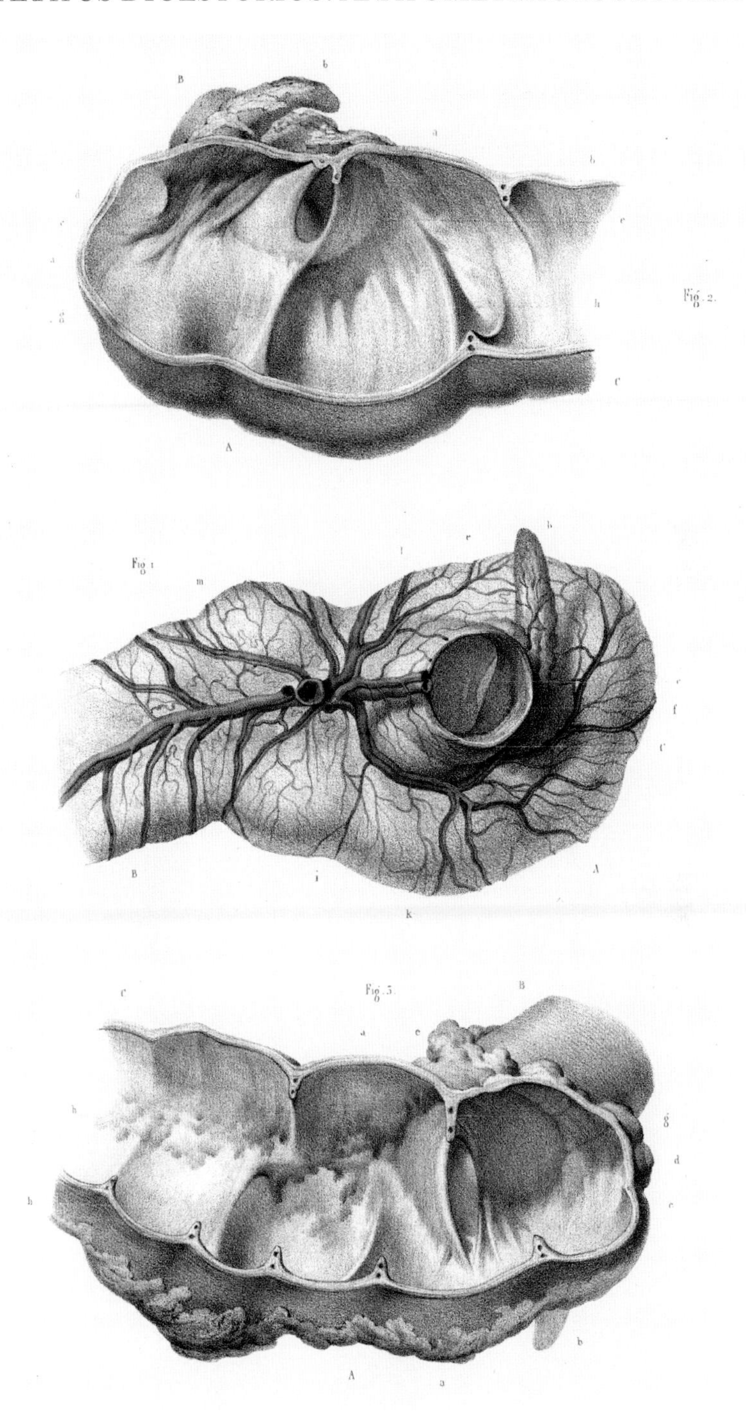

Large intestine / Gros intestin / Intestino grueso

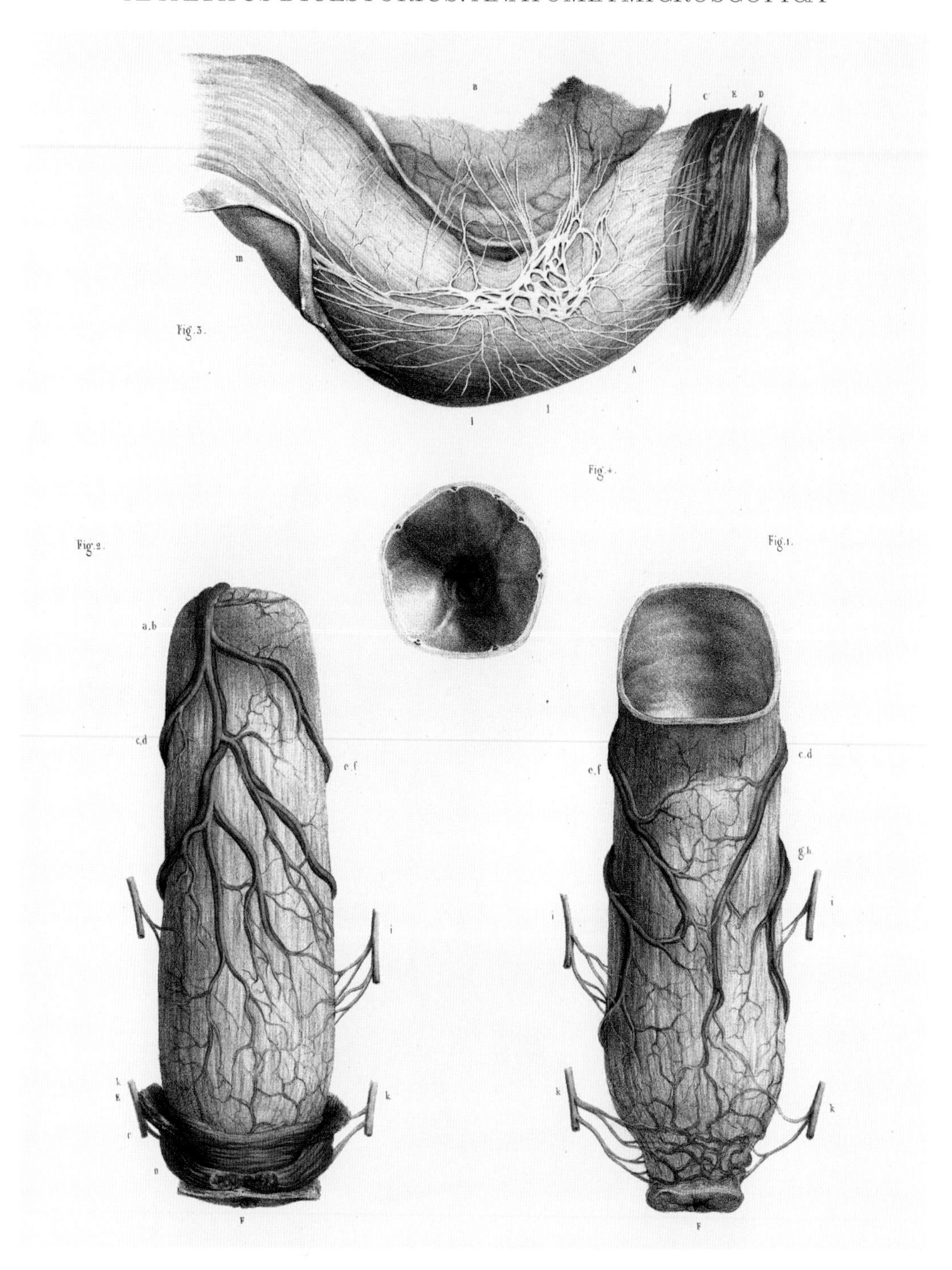

Rectum, anal canal, and anus / Rectum, canal anal et anus
Recto, canal anal y ano

Gastrointestinal tract: Microscopic anatomy
Appareil digestif : Anatomie microscopique
Aparato digestivo: anatomía microscópica

HEPAR ET VESICA FELLEA. HEPAR: ARTERIAE, VENAE, ET DUCTULI BILIFERI

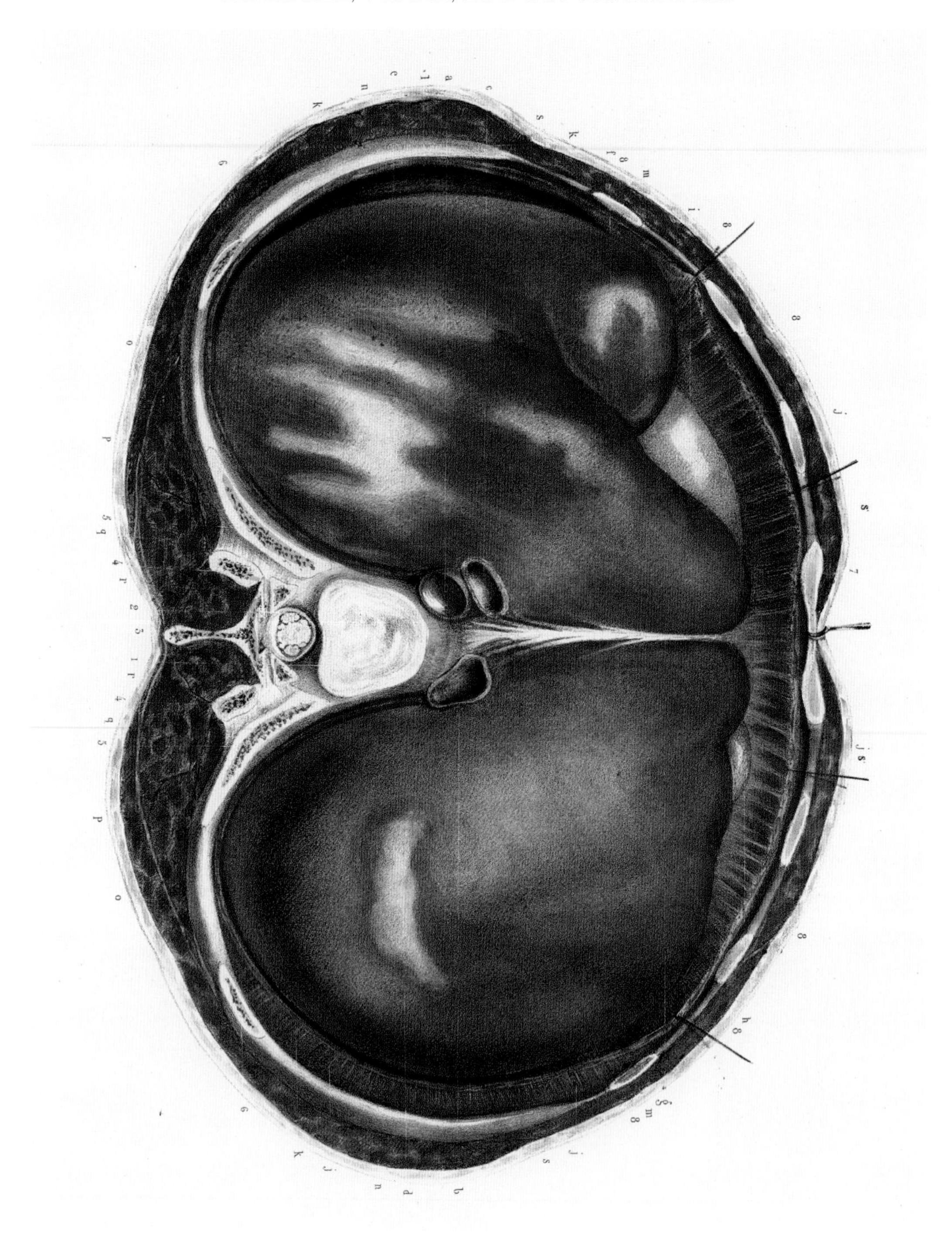

Liver / Foie / Hígado

HEPAR ET VESICA FELLEA. HEPAR: ARTERIAE, VENAE, ET DUCTULI BILIFERI

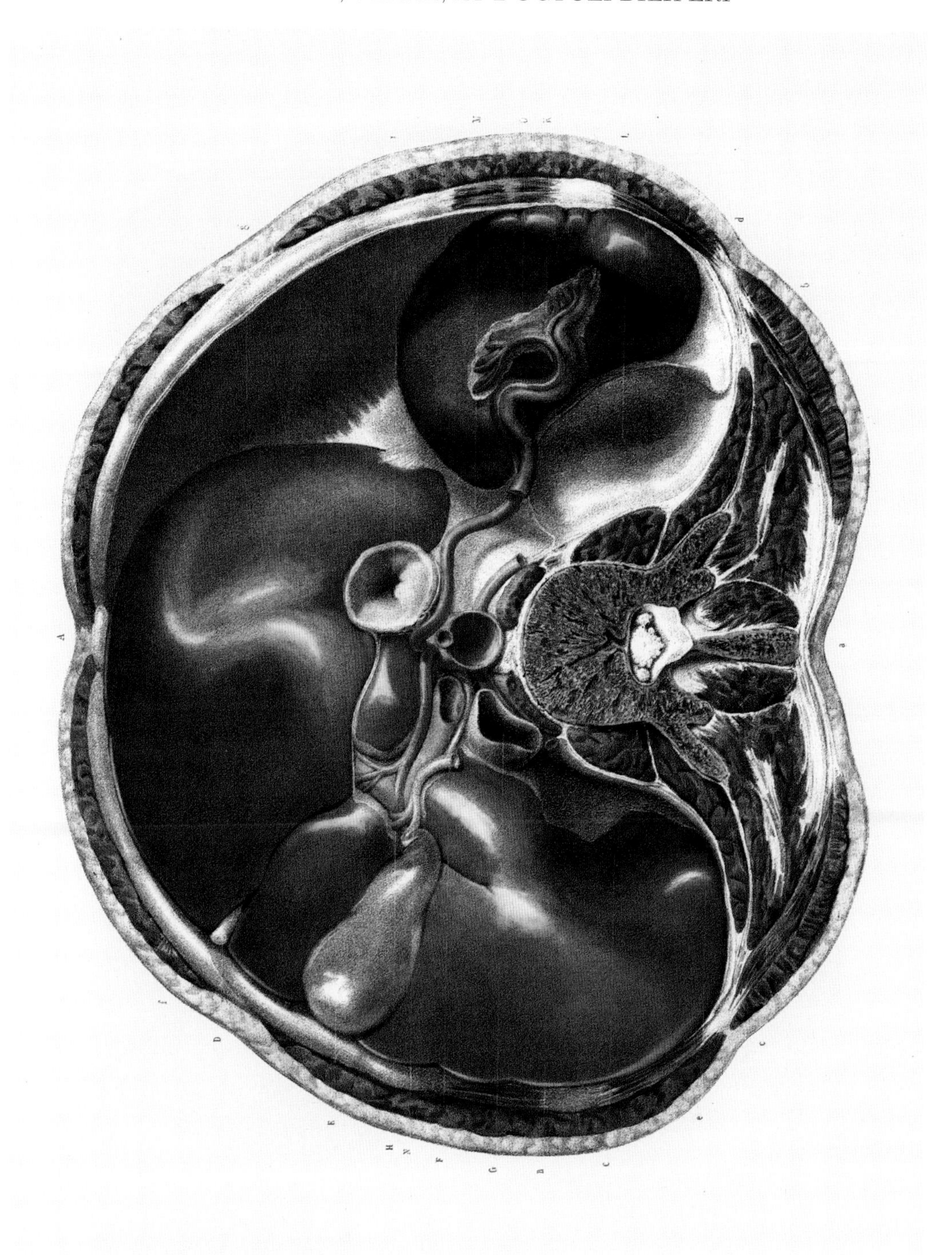

Liver and gallbladder / Foie et vésicule biliaire / Hígado y vesícula biliar

HEPAR ET VESICA FELLEA. HEPAR: ARTERIAE, VENAE, ET DUCTULI BILIFERI

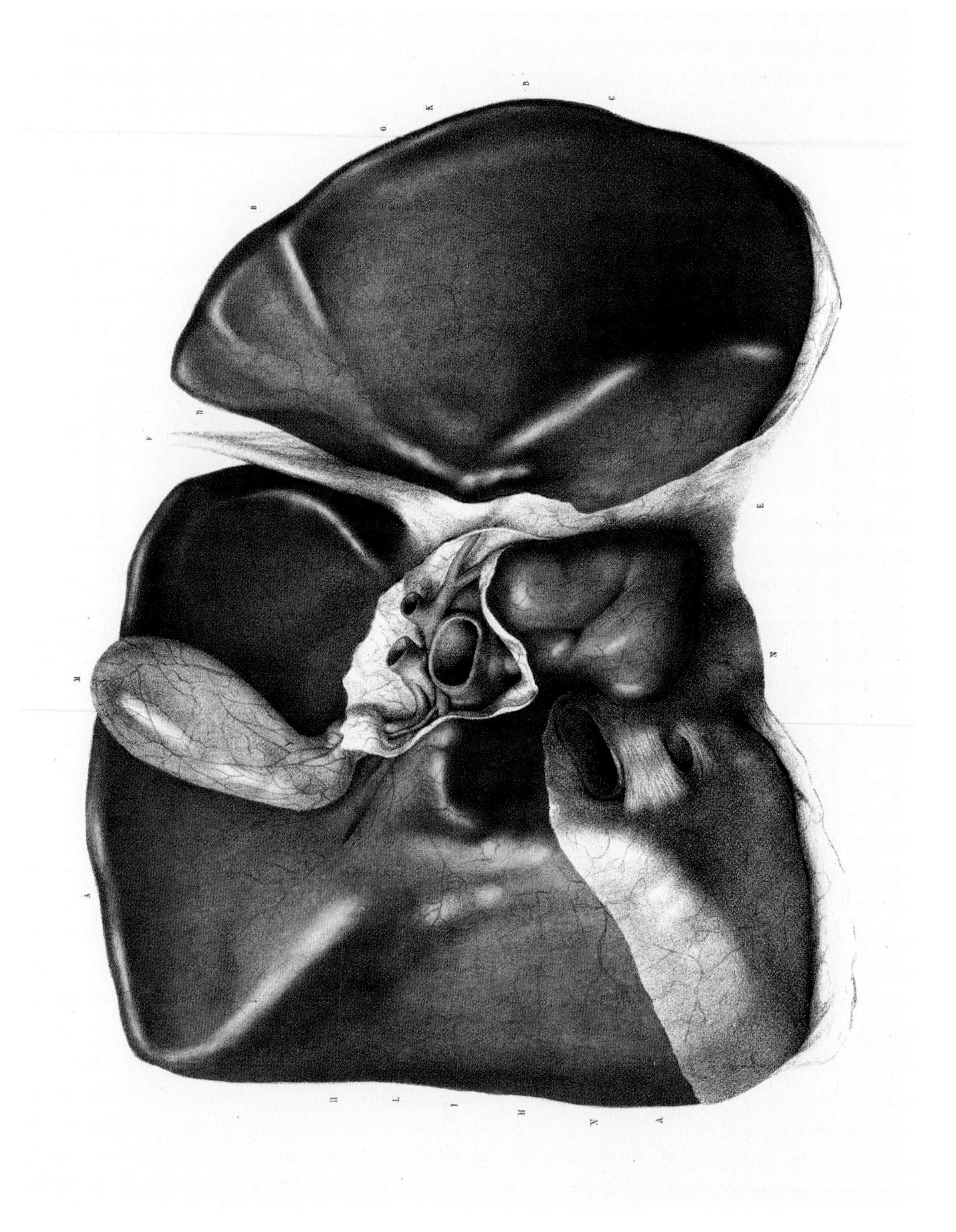

Liver and gallbladder / Foie et vésicule biliaire / Hígado y vesícula biliar

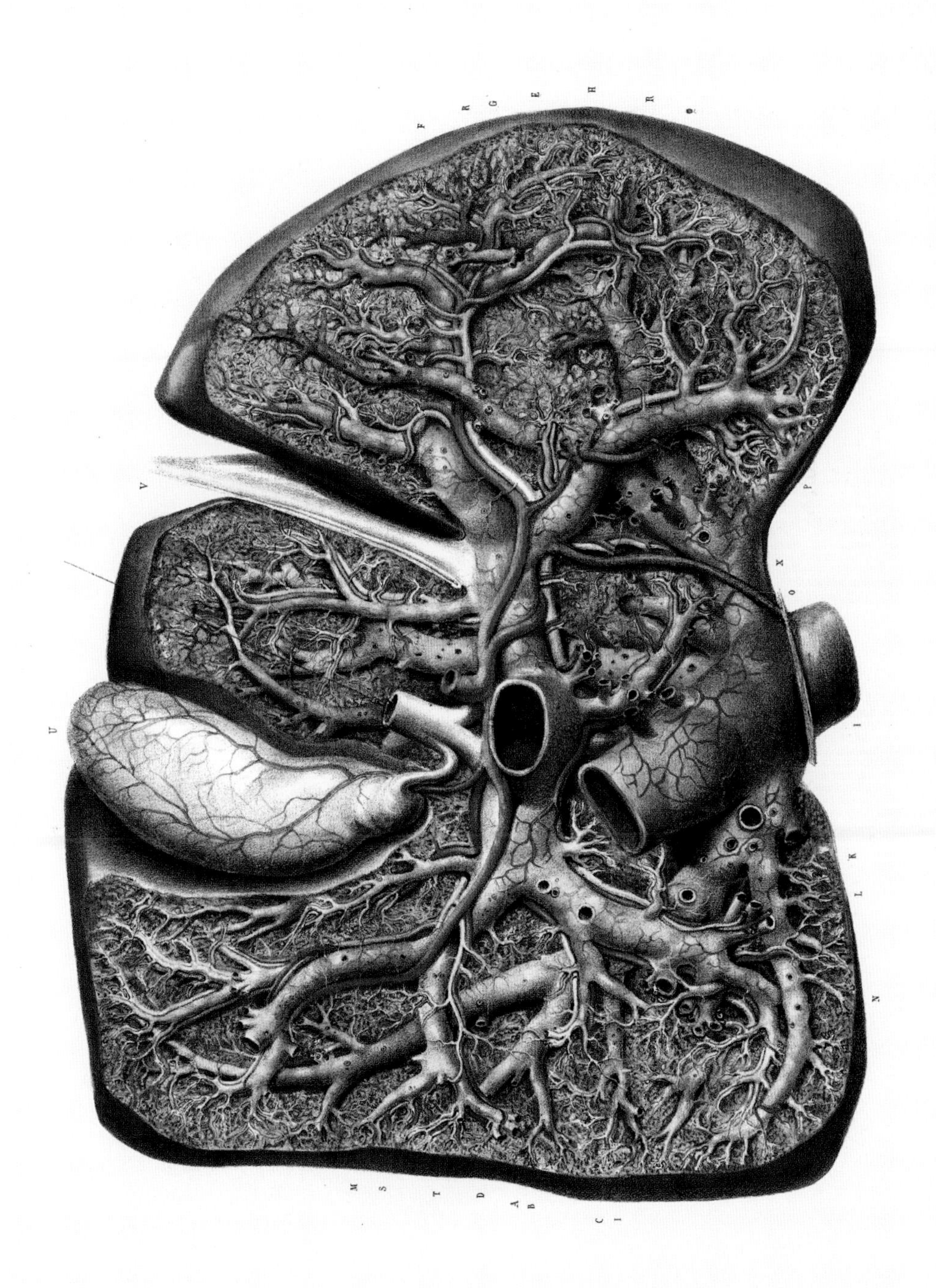

Liver: Arteries, veins, and bile canaliculi
Foie : Artères, veines et canalicules biliaires
Hígado: arterias, venas y canalículos biliares

HEPAR: ARTERIAE, VENAE, DUCTULI BILIFERI, VASA LYMPHATICA, ET ANATOMIA MICROSCOPICA. VESICA FELLEA, ET DUCTUS CHOLEDOCUS

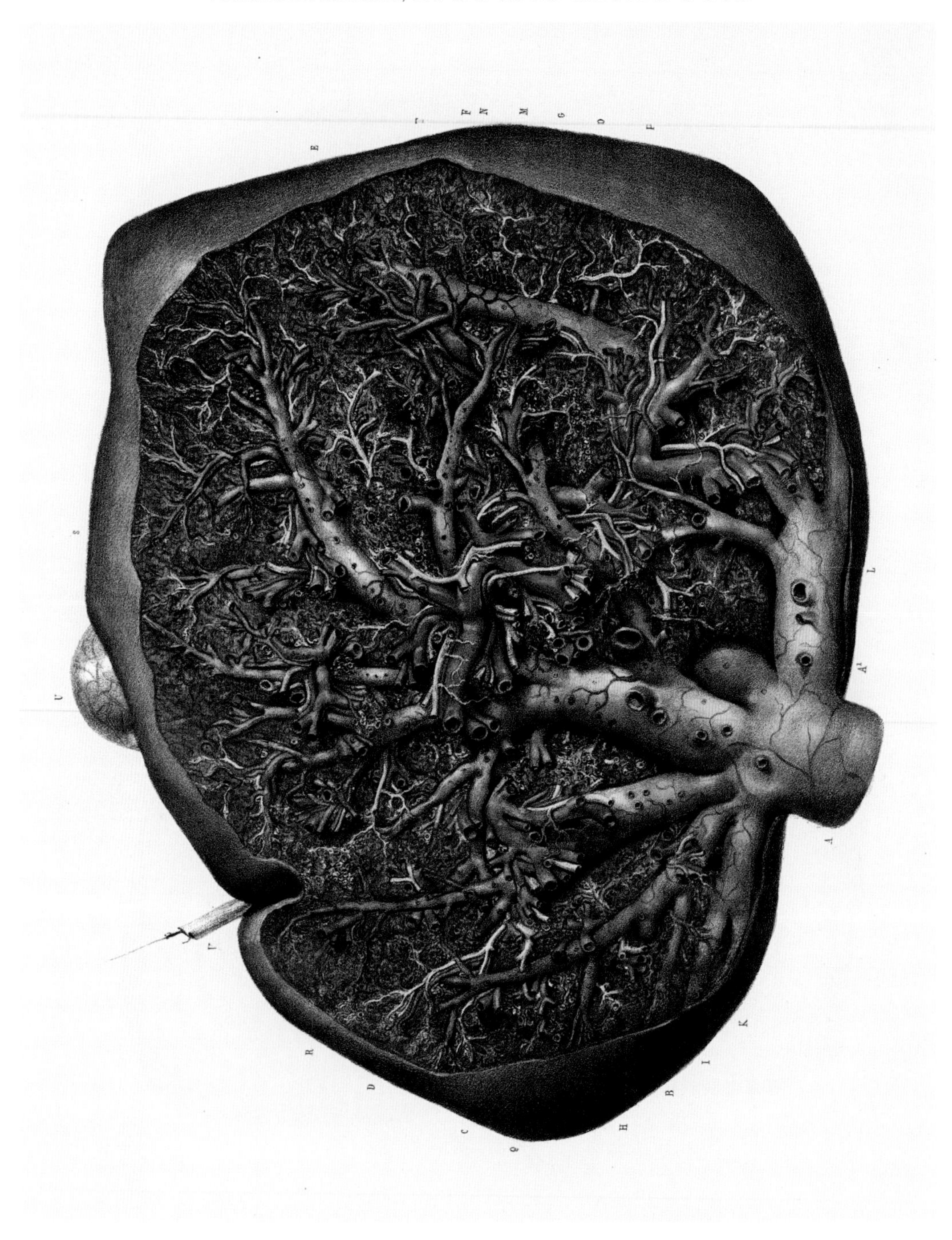

Liver: Arteries, veins, and bile canaliculi
Foie : Artères, veines et canalicules biliaires
Hígado: arterias, venas y canalículos biliares

HEPAR: ARTERIAE, VENAE, DUCTULI BILIFERI, VASA LYMPHATICA, ET ANATOMIA MICROSCOPICA. VESICA FELLEA, ET DUCTUS CHOLEDOCUS

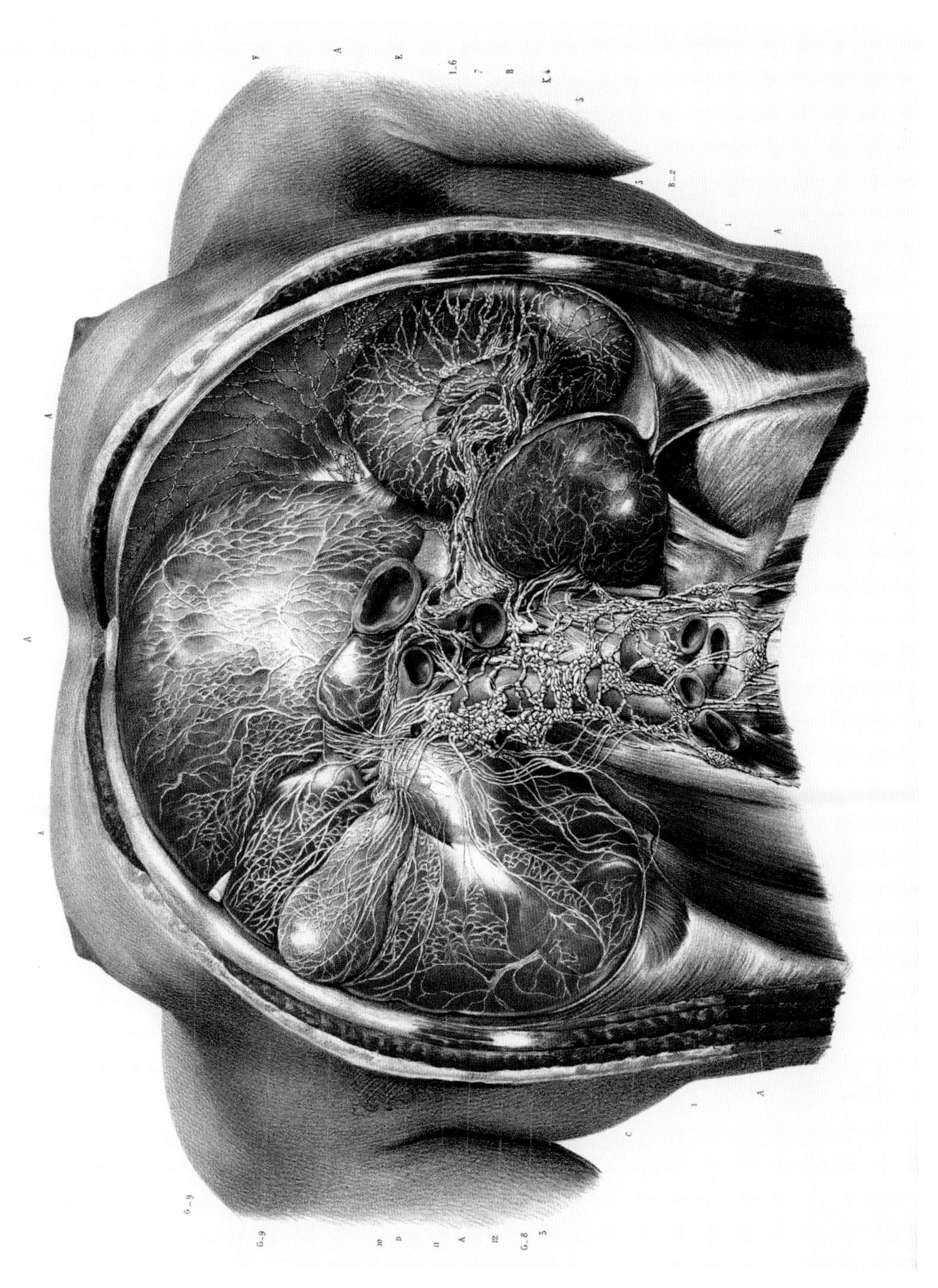

Liver: Lymph vessels / Foie : Vaisseaux lymphatiques
Hígado: vasos linfáticos

HEPAR: ARTERIAE, VENAE, DUCTULI BILIFERI, VASA LYMPHATICA, ET ANATOMIA MICROSCOPICA. VESICA FELLEA, ET DUCTUS CHOLEDOCUS

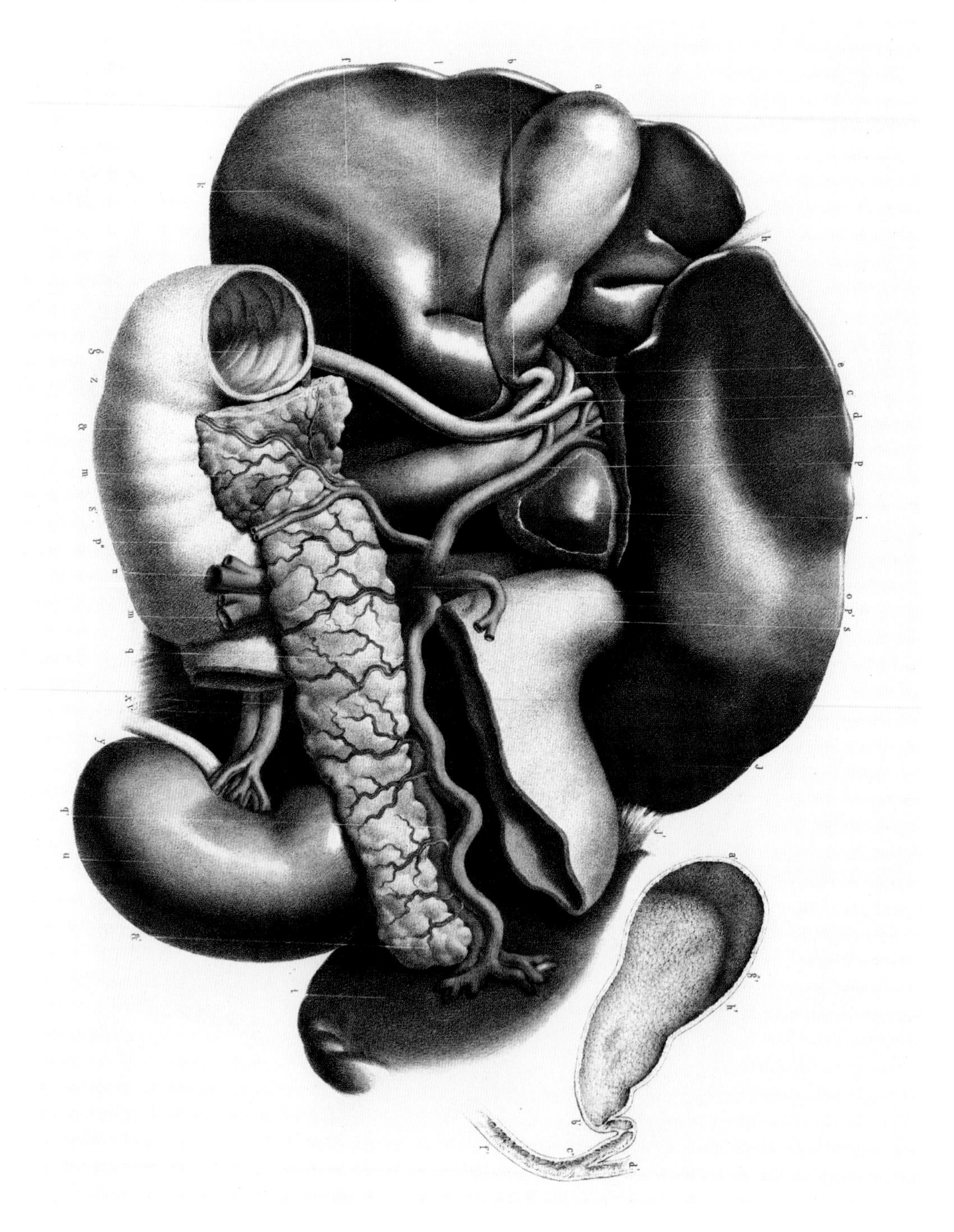

Liver: Gallbladder and bile duct / Foie : Vésicule biliaire et conduit cholédoque
Hígado: vesícula biliar y conducto colédoco

HEPAR: ARTERIAE, VENAE, DUCTULI BILIFERI, VASA LYMPHATICA, ET ANATOMIA MICROSCOPICA. VESICA FELLEA, ET DUCTUS CHOLEDOCUS

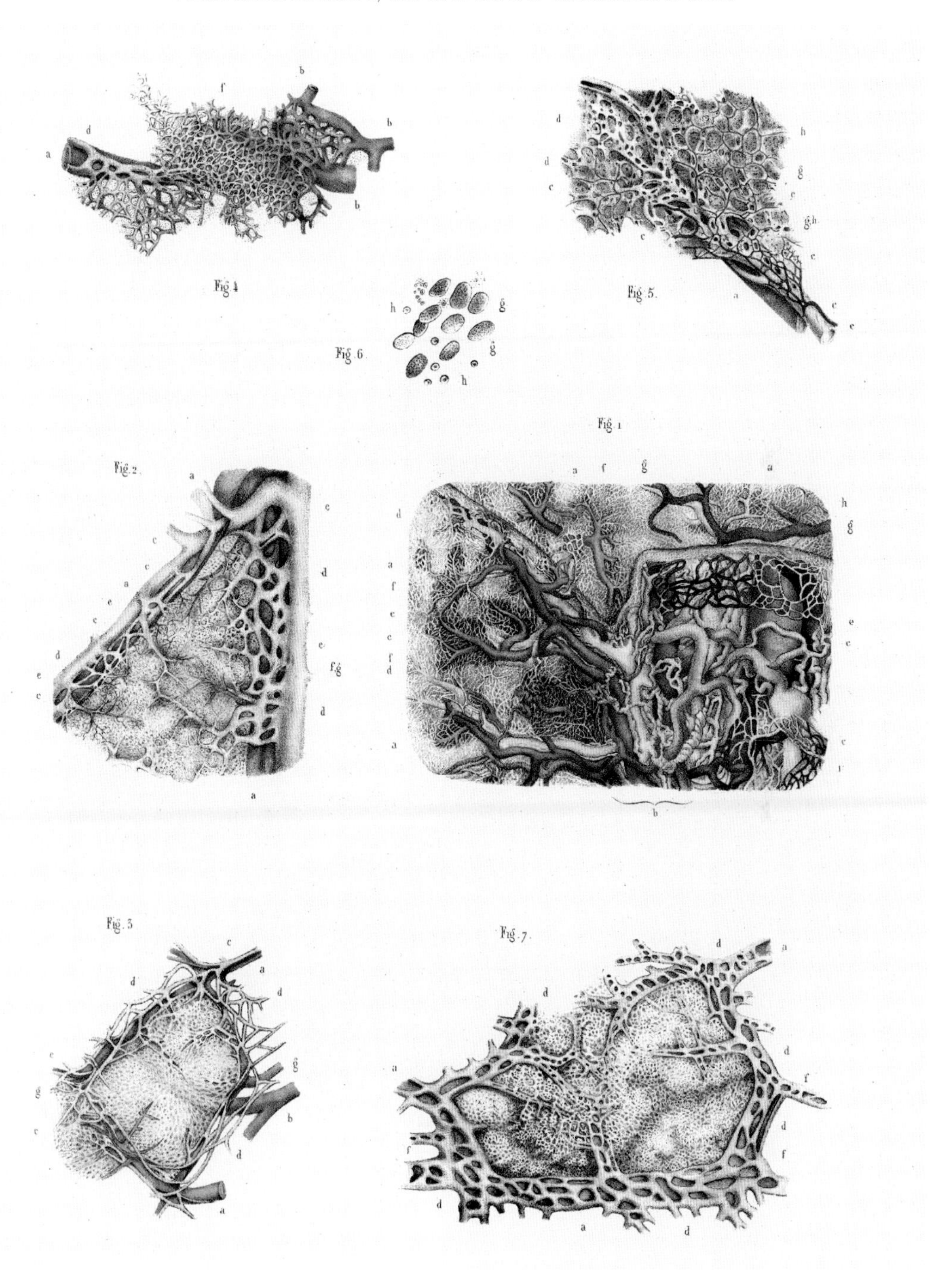

Liver: Microscopic Anatomy / Foie : Anatomie microscopique
Hígado: anatomía microscópica

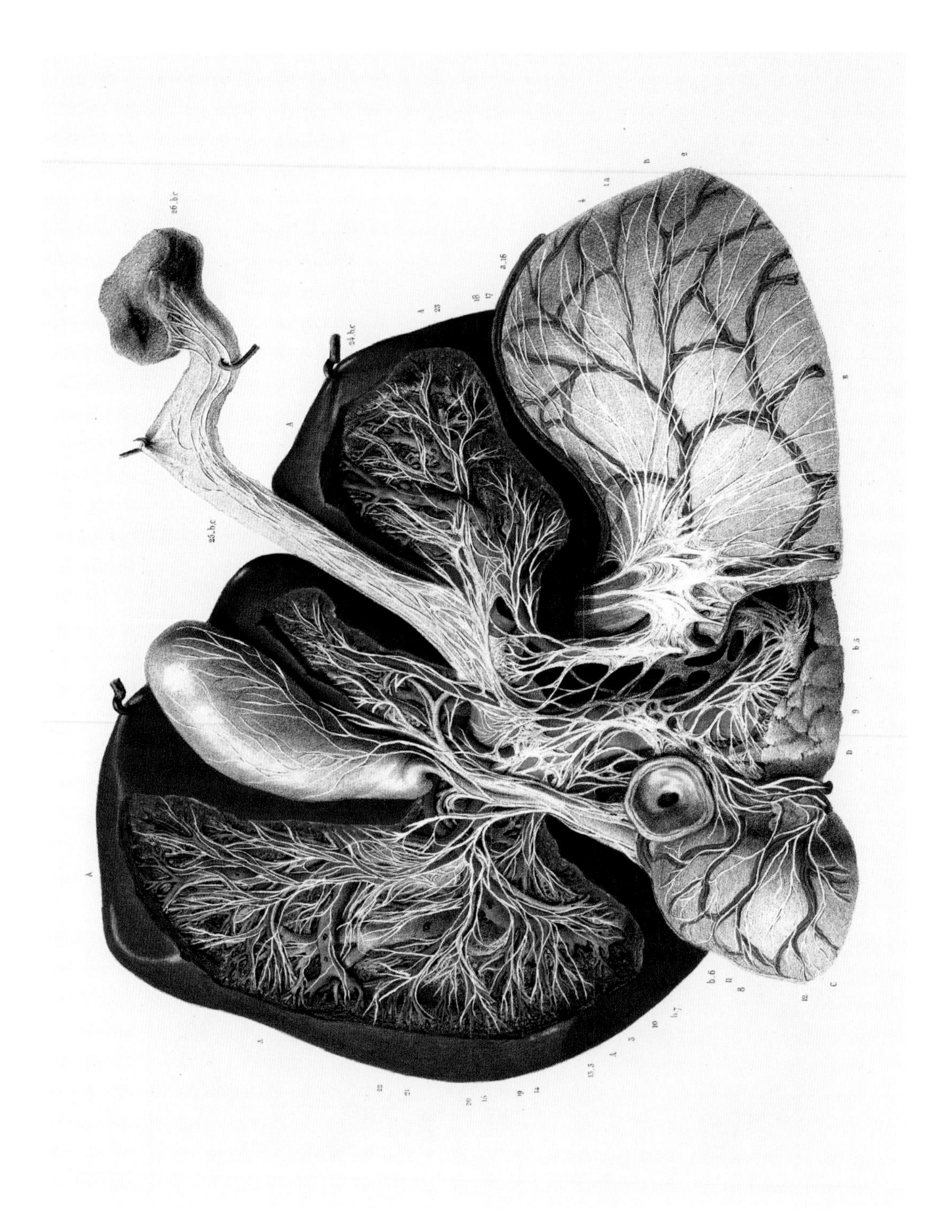

Liver: Nerves / Foie : Nerfs / Hígado: nervios

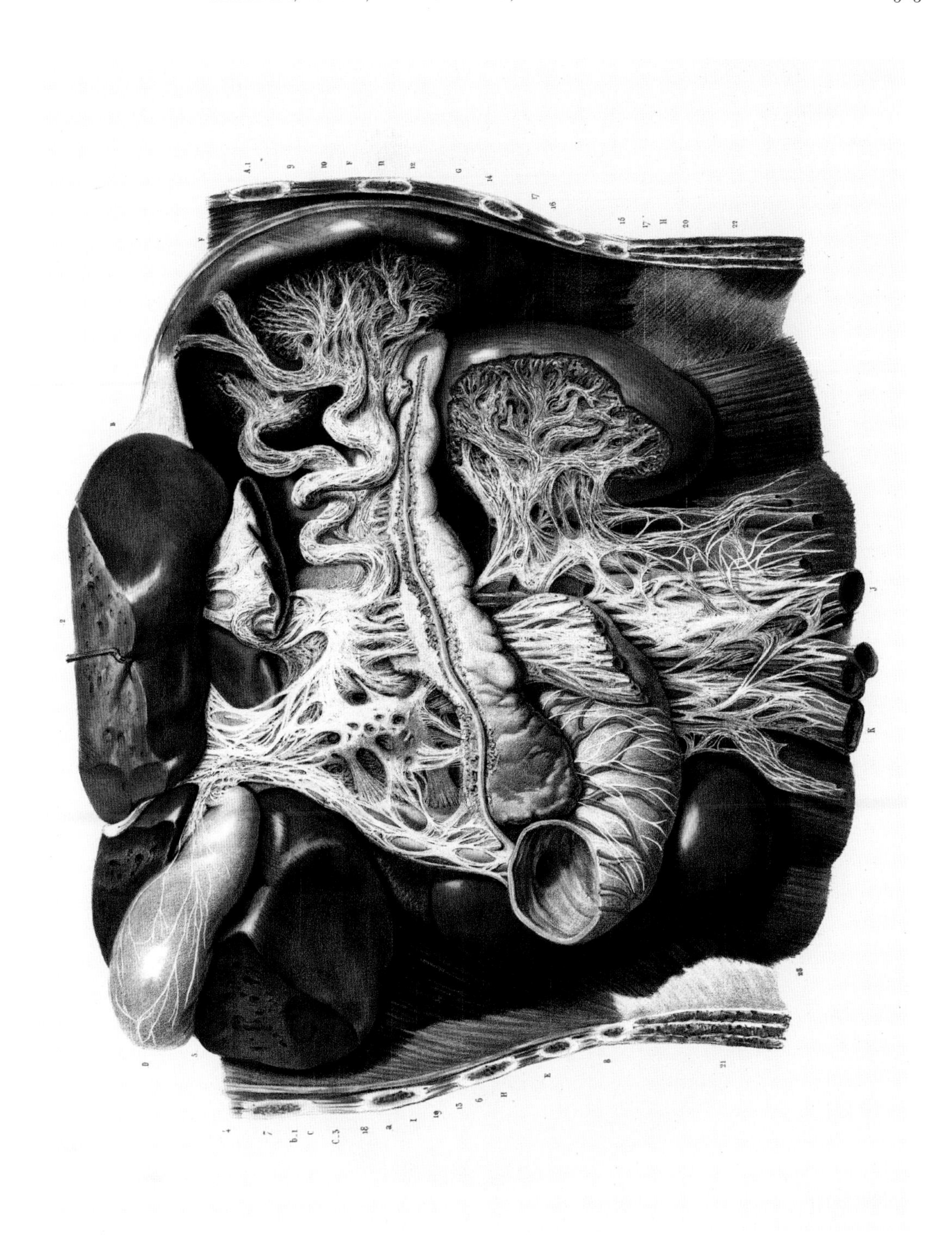

Liver, spleen, pancreas, and kidneys: Nerves / Foie, rate, pancréas et reins : Nerfs
Hígado, bazo, páncreas y riñones: nervios

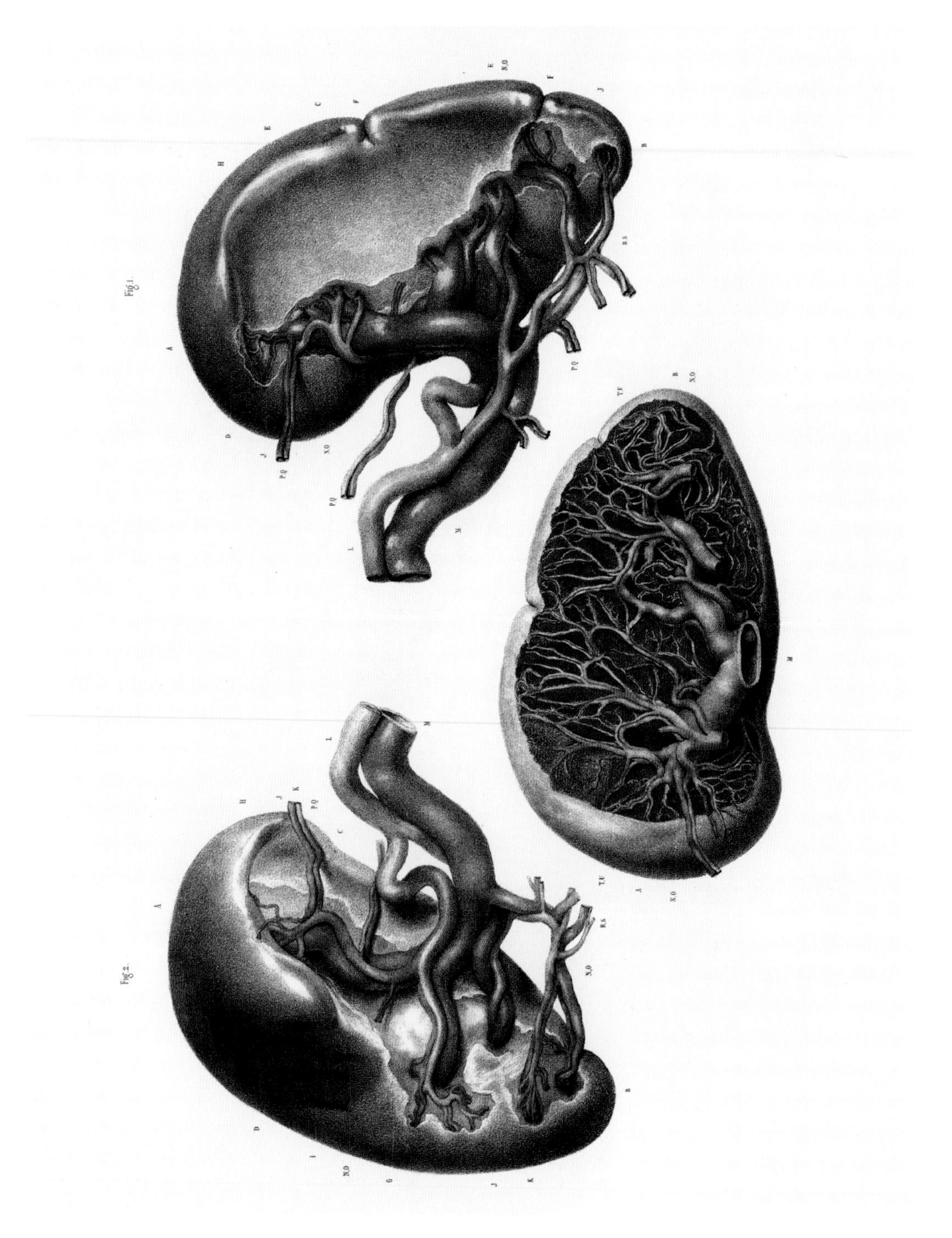

Spleen / Rate / Bazo

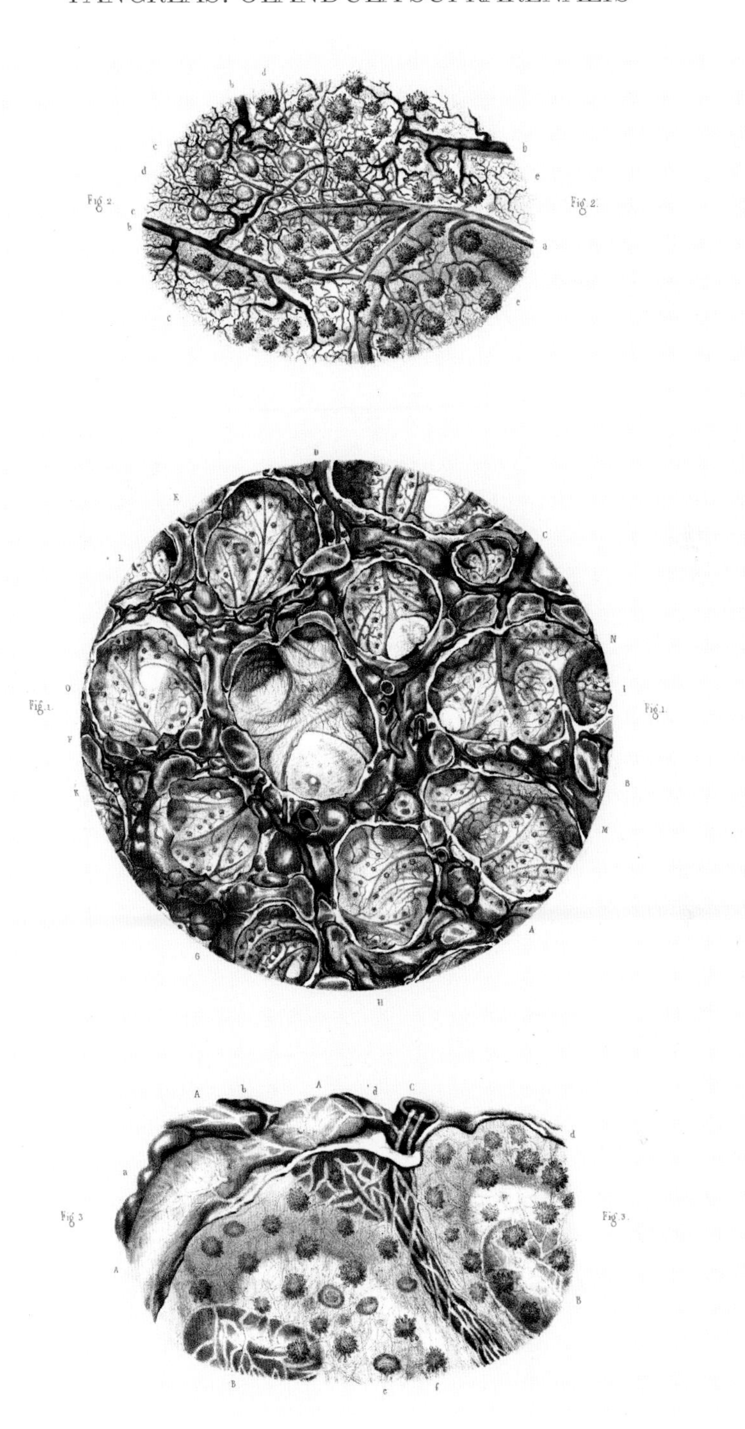

Spleen: Microscopic anatomy / Rate : Anatomie microscopique
Bazo: anatomía microscópica

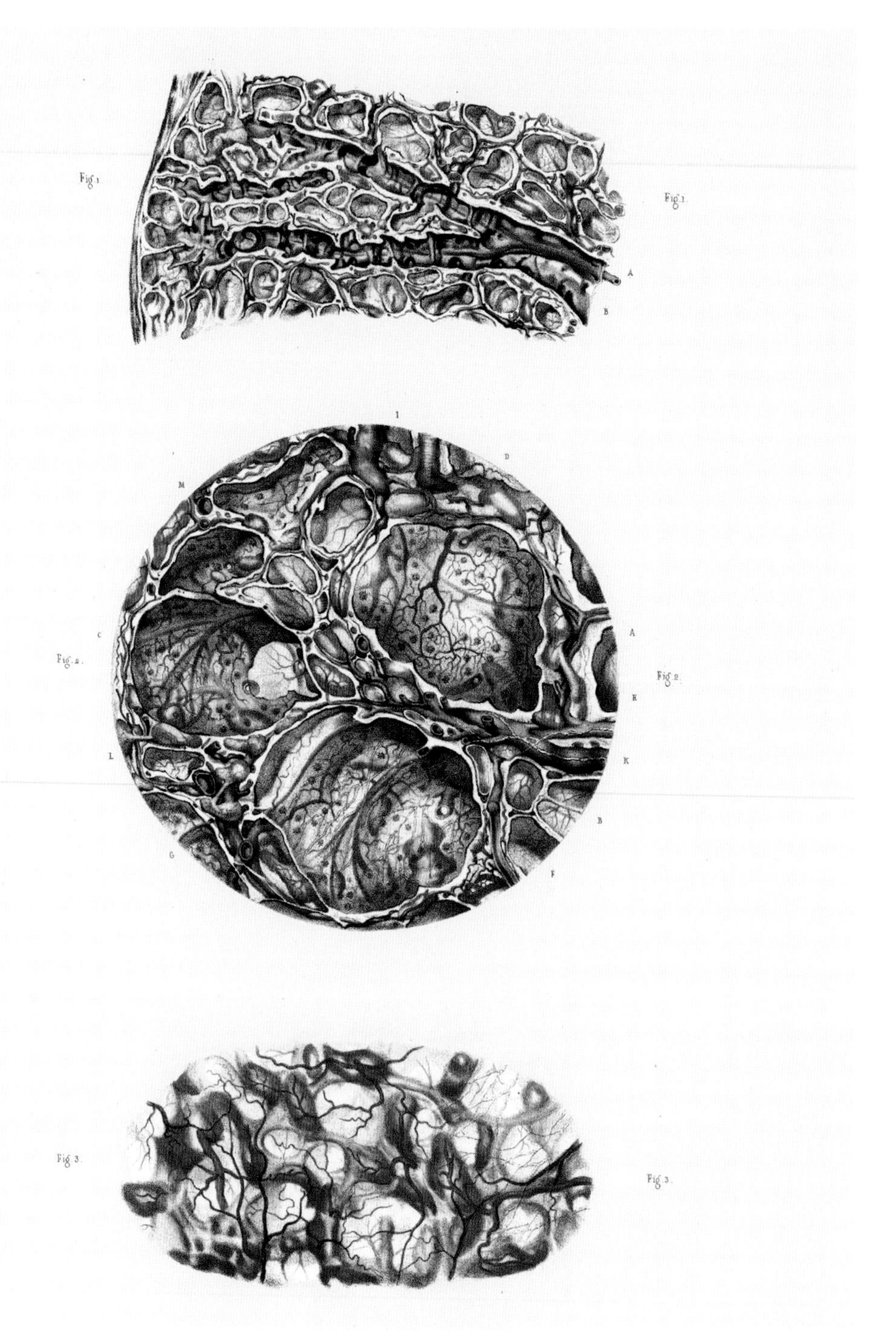

Spleen: Microscopic anatomy / Rate : Anatomie microscopique
Bazo: anatomía microscópica

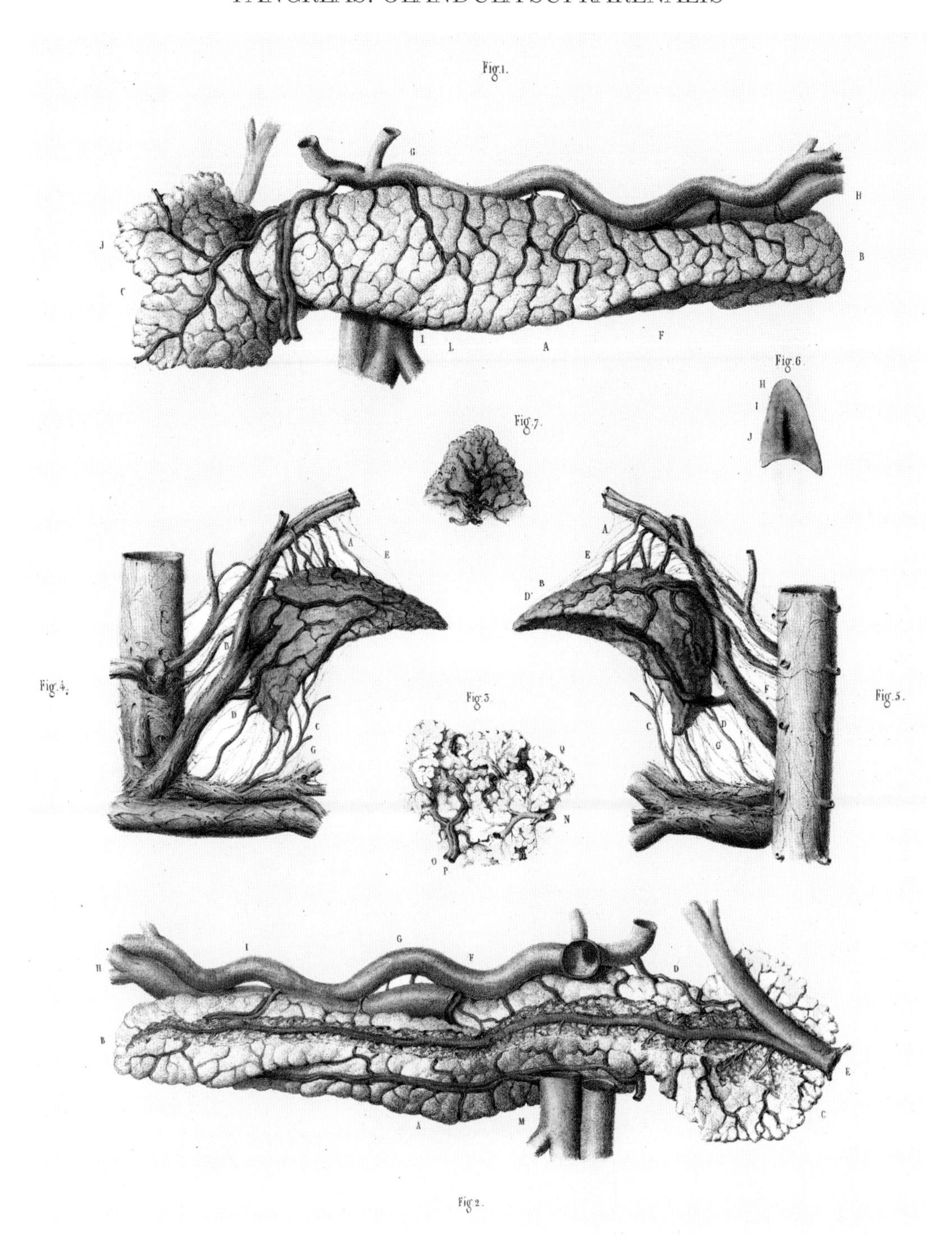

Pancreas. Adrenal gland / Pancréas. Glande surrénale
Páncreas. Glándula suprarrenal

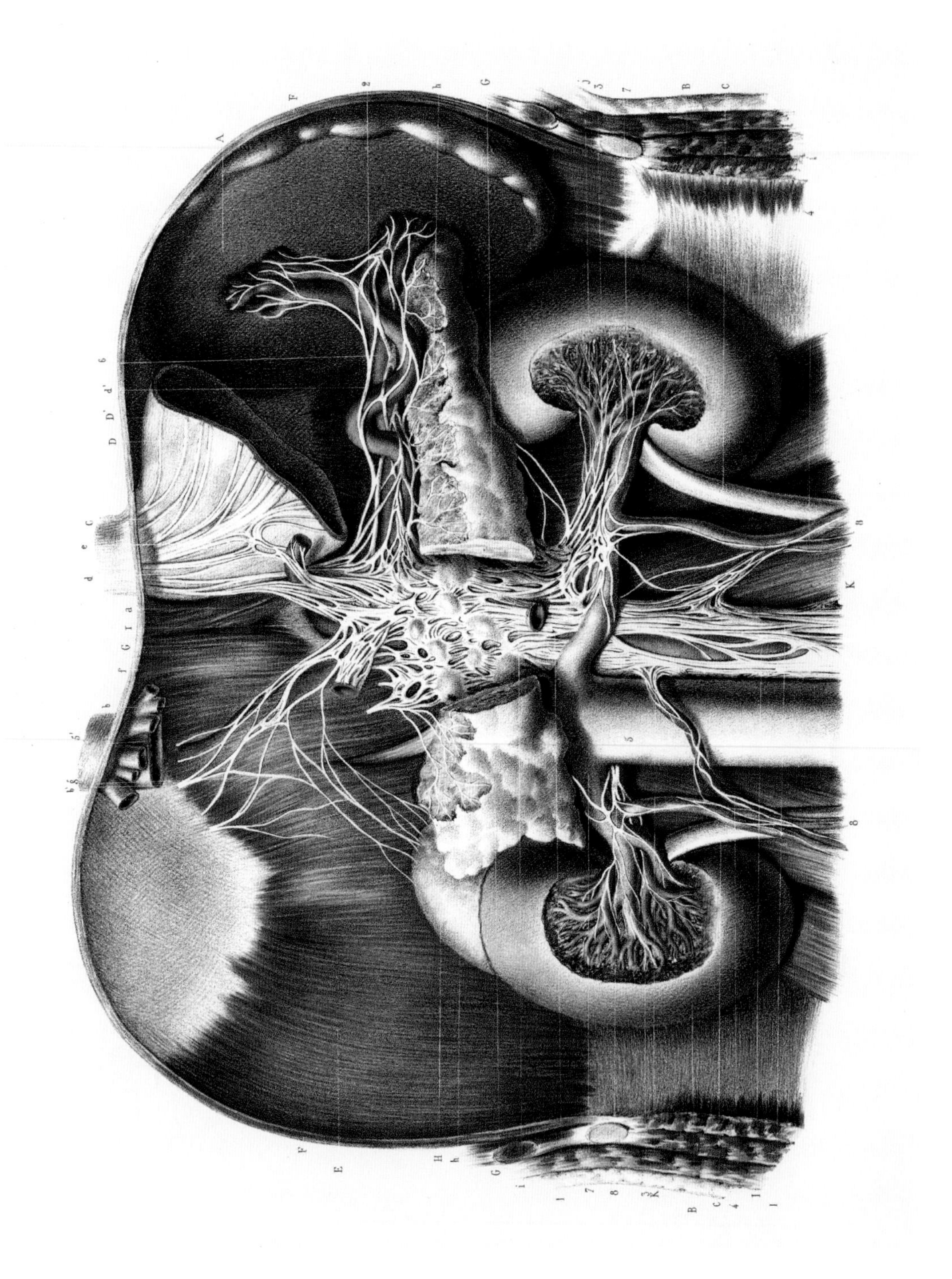

Pancreas, spleen, and kidneys: Nerves / Pancréas, rate et reins : Nerfs
Páncreas, bazo y riñones: nervios

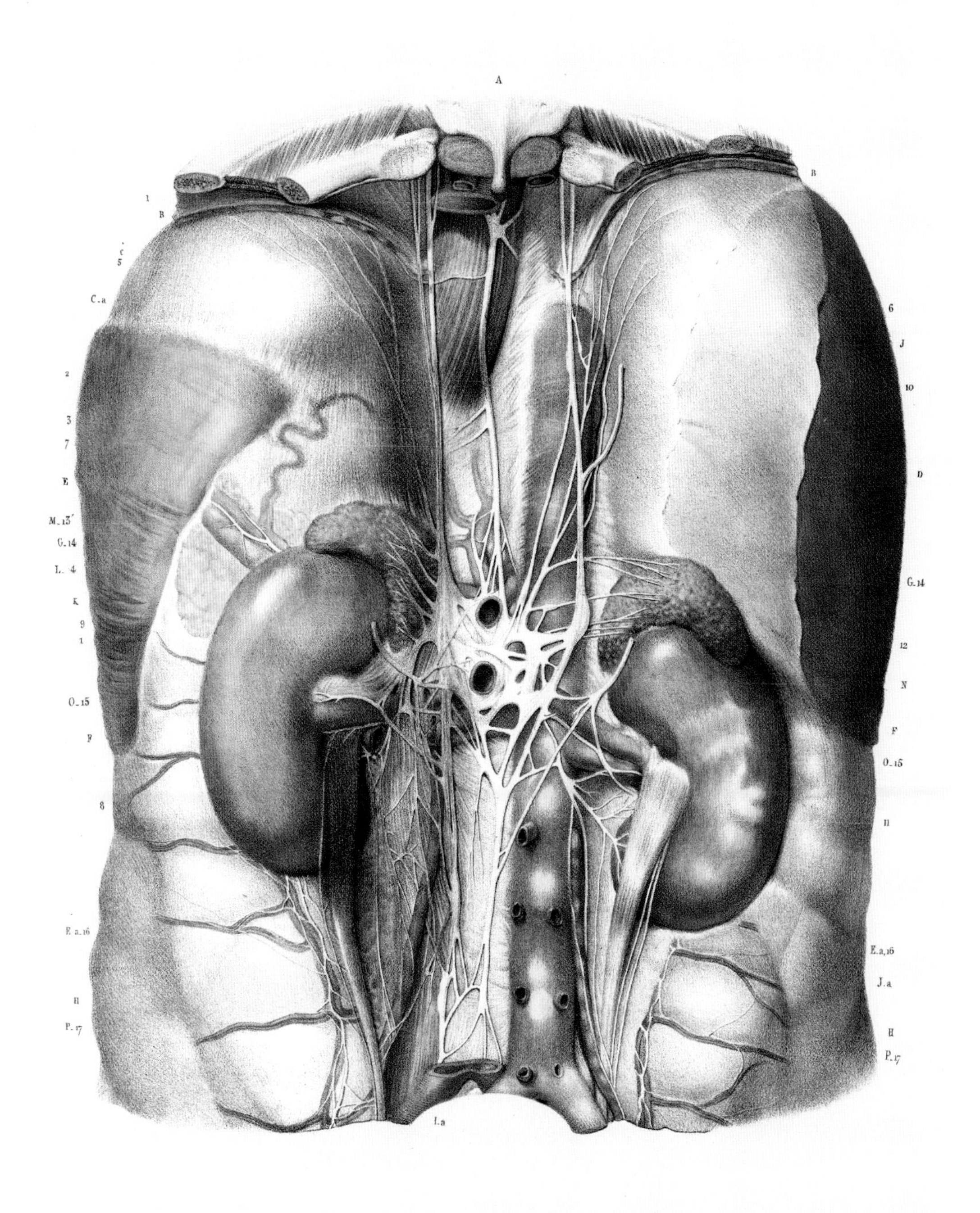

Retroperitoneal organs: Nerves / Viscères rétropéritonéaux : Nerfs
Vísceras retroperitoneales: nervios

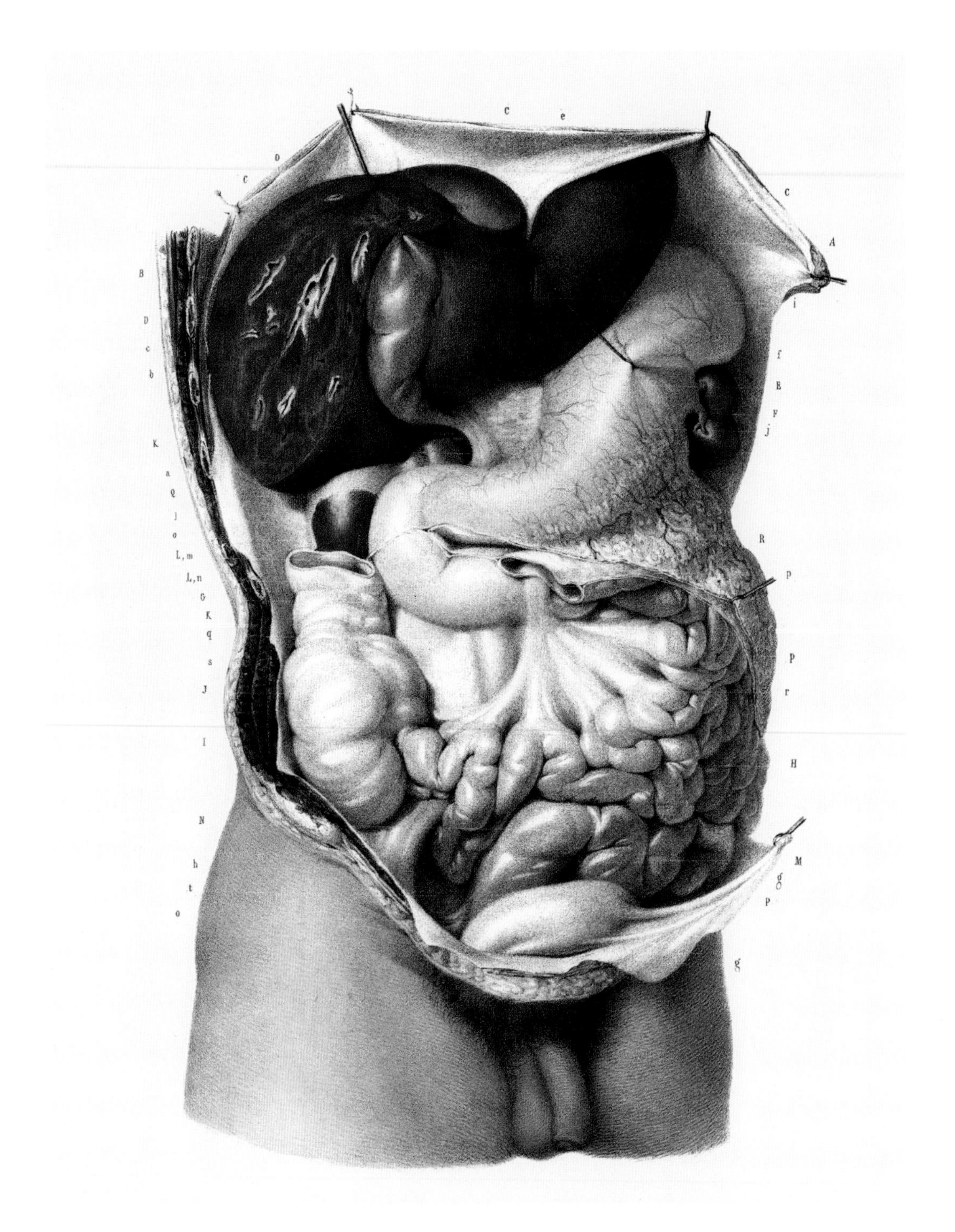

Peritoneum / Péritoine / Peritoneo

PERITONEUM: ANATOMIA MICROSCOPICA NERVORUM.
ORGANA URINARIA: RENES, URETERES, ET VESICA URINARIA.
REN: ANATOMIA MICROSCOPICA

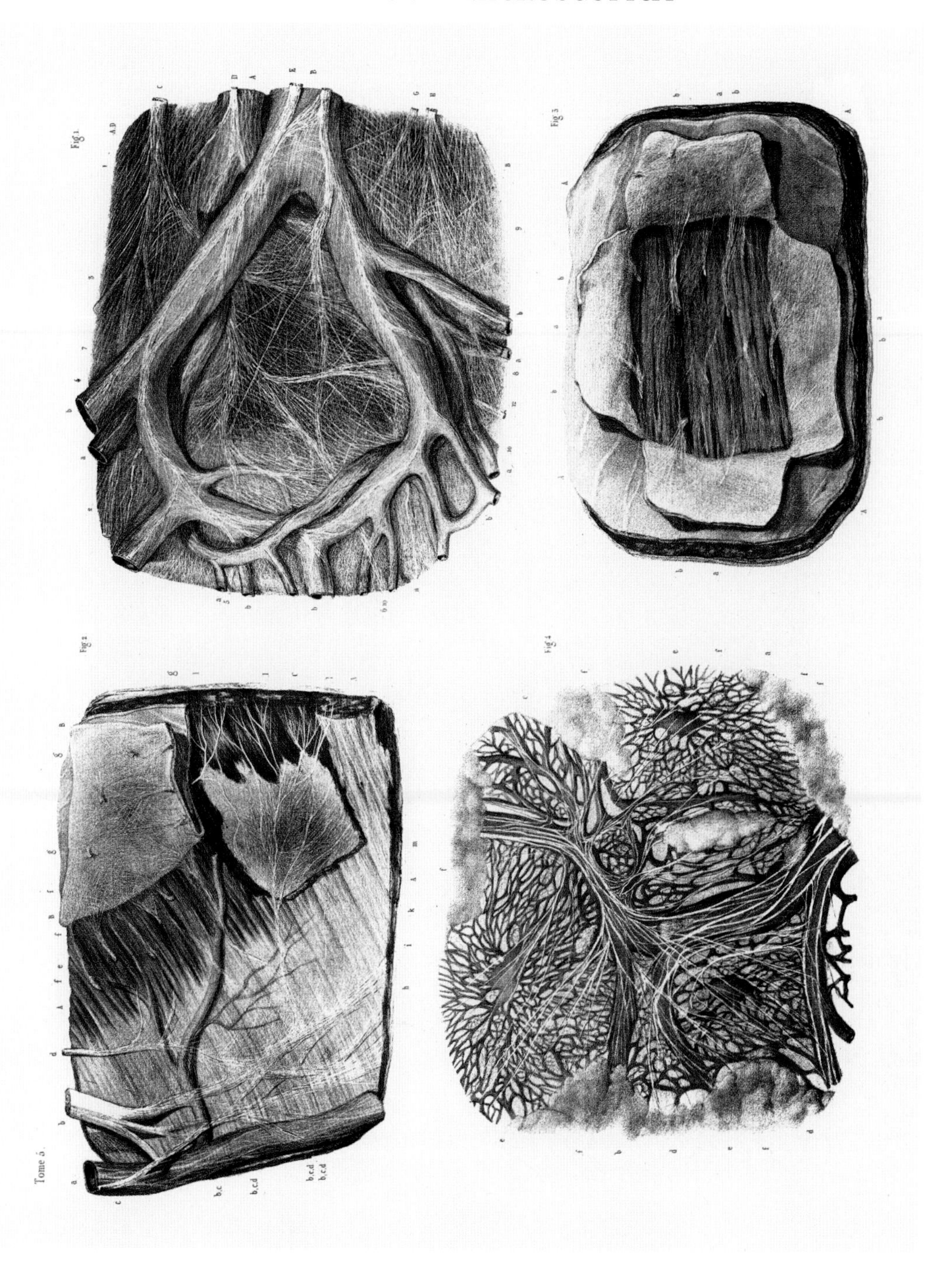

Peritoneum: Microscopic anatomy of the nerves
Péritoine : Anatomie microscopique des nerfs
Peritoneo: anatomía microscópica de los nervios

PERITONEUM: ANATOMIA MICROSCOPICA NERVORUM.
ORGANA URINARIA: RENES, URETERES, ET VESICA URINARIA.
REN: ANATOMIA MICROSCOPICA

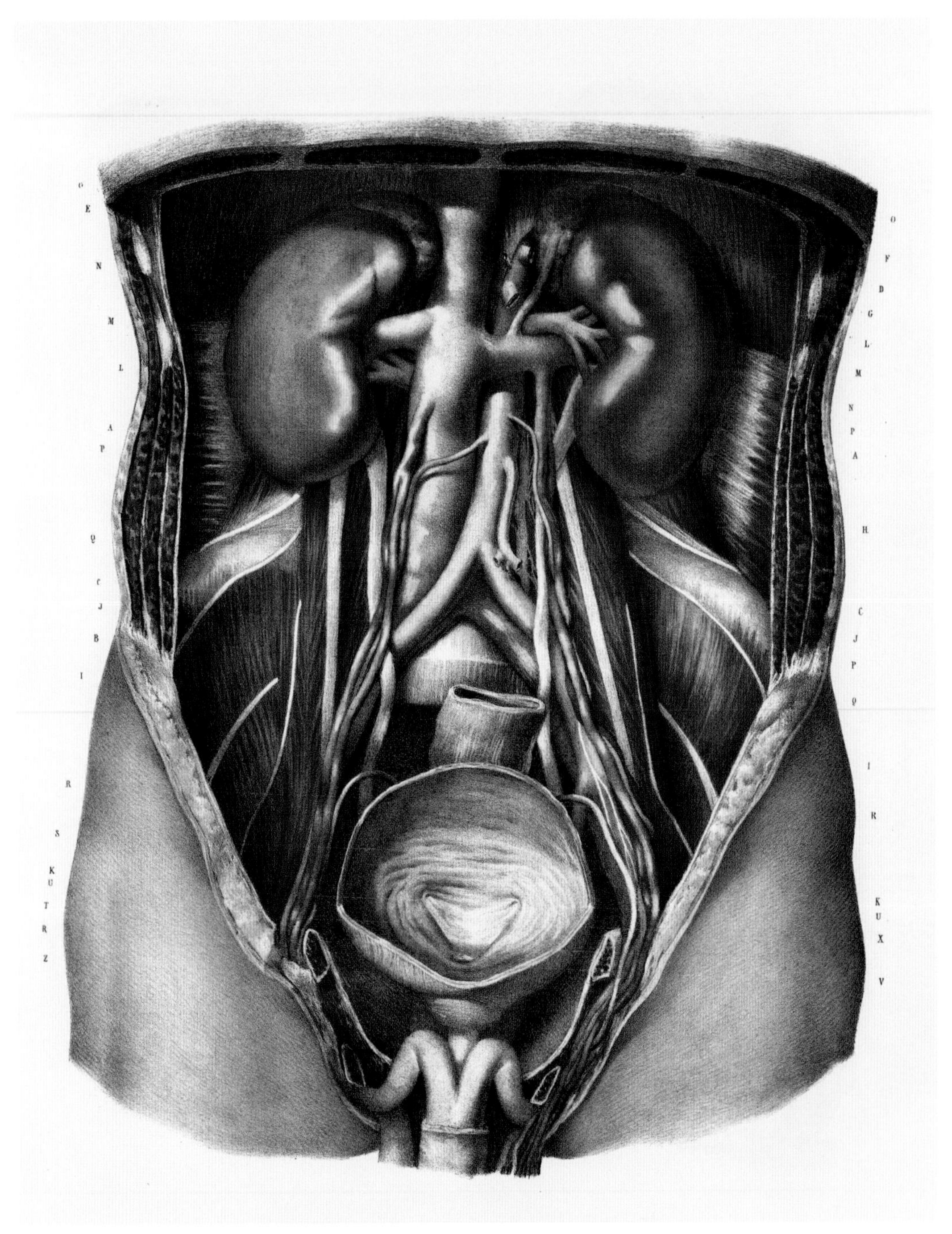

Urinary organs: Kidneys, ureters and bladder
Organes urinaires : Reins, uretères et vessie
Órganos urinarios: riñones, uréteres y vejiga

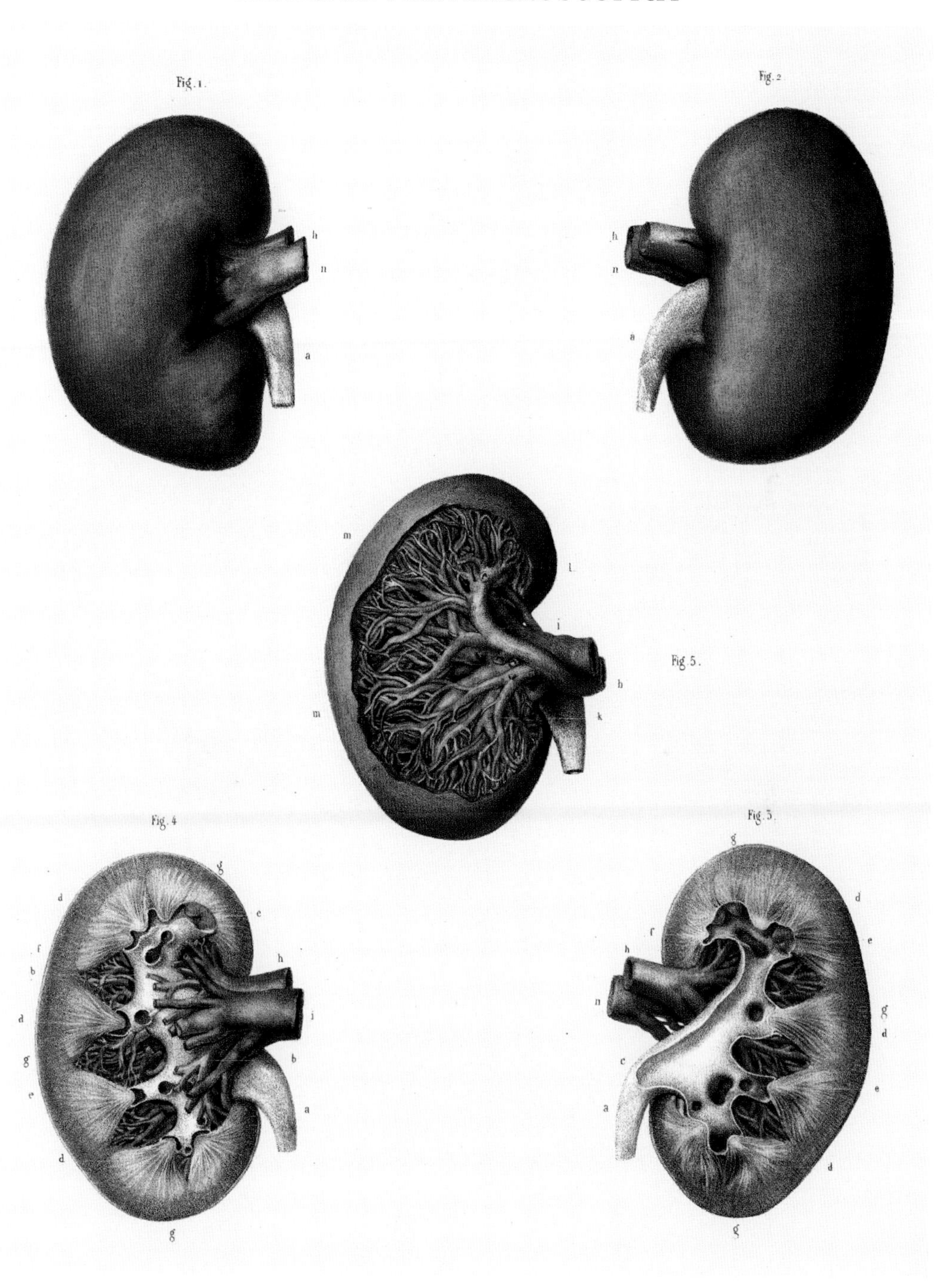

Kidney / Rein / Riñón

PERITONEUM: ANATOMIA MICROSCOPICA NERVORUM. ORGANA URINARIA: RENES, URETERES, ET VESICA URINARIA. REN: ANATOMIA MICROSCOPICA

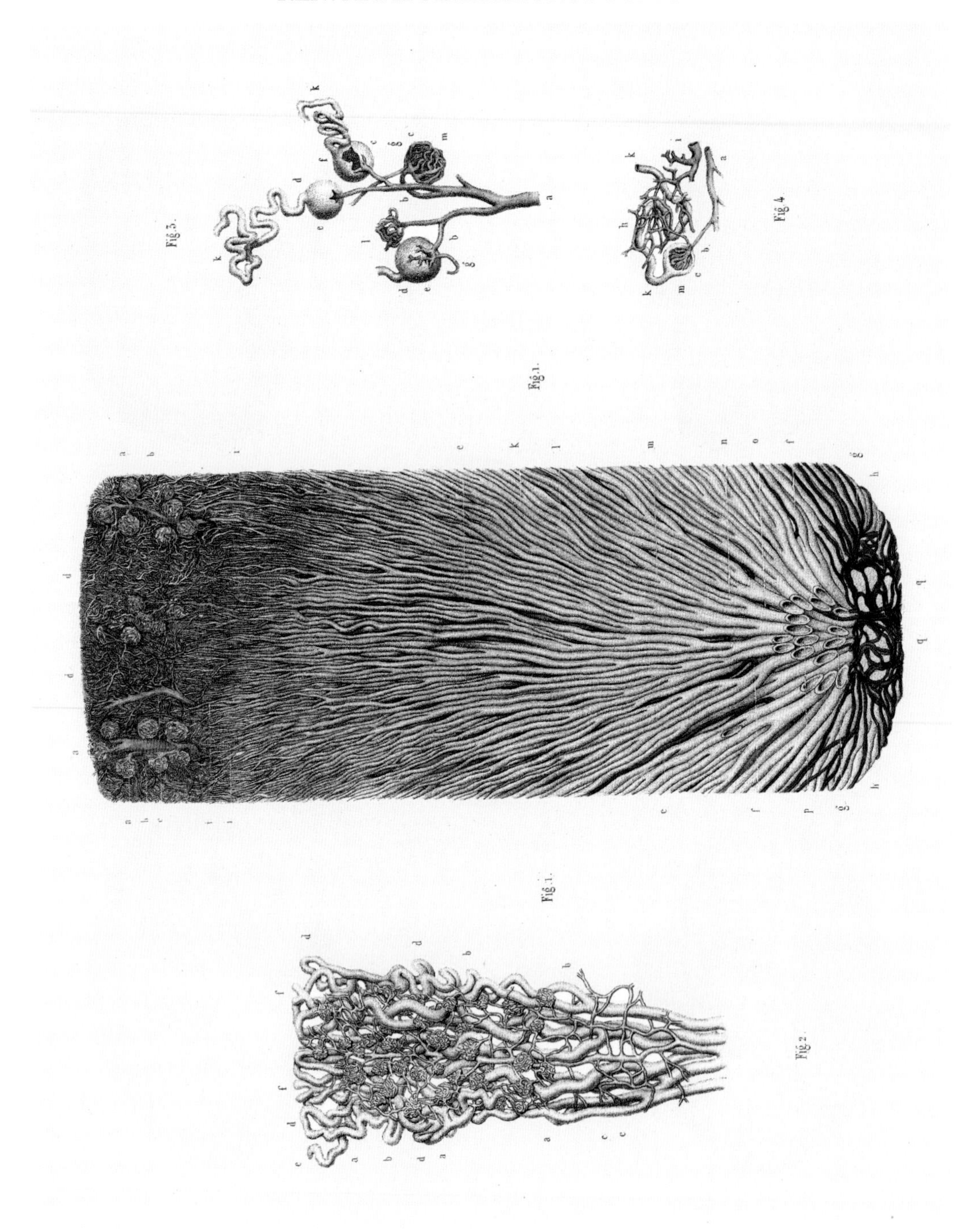

Kidney: Microscopic anatomy / Rein : Anatomie microscopique
Riñón: anatomía microscópica

Bladder / Vessie / Vejiga

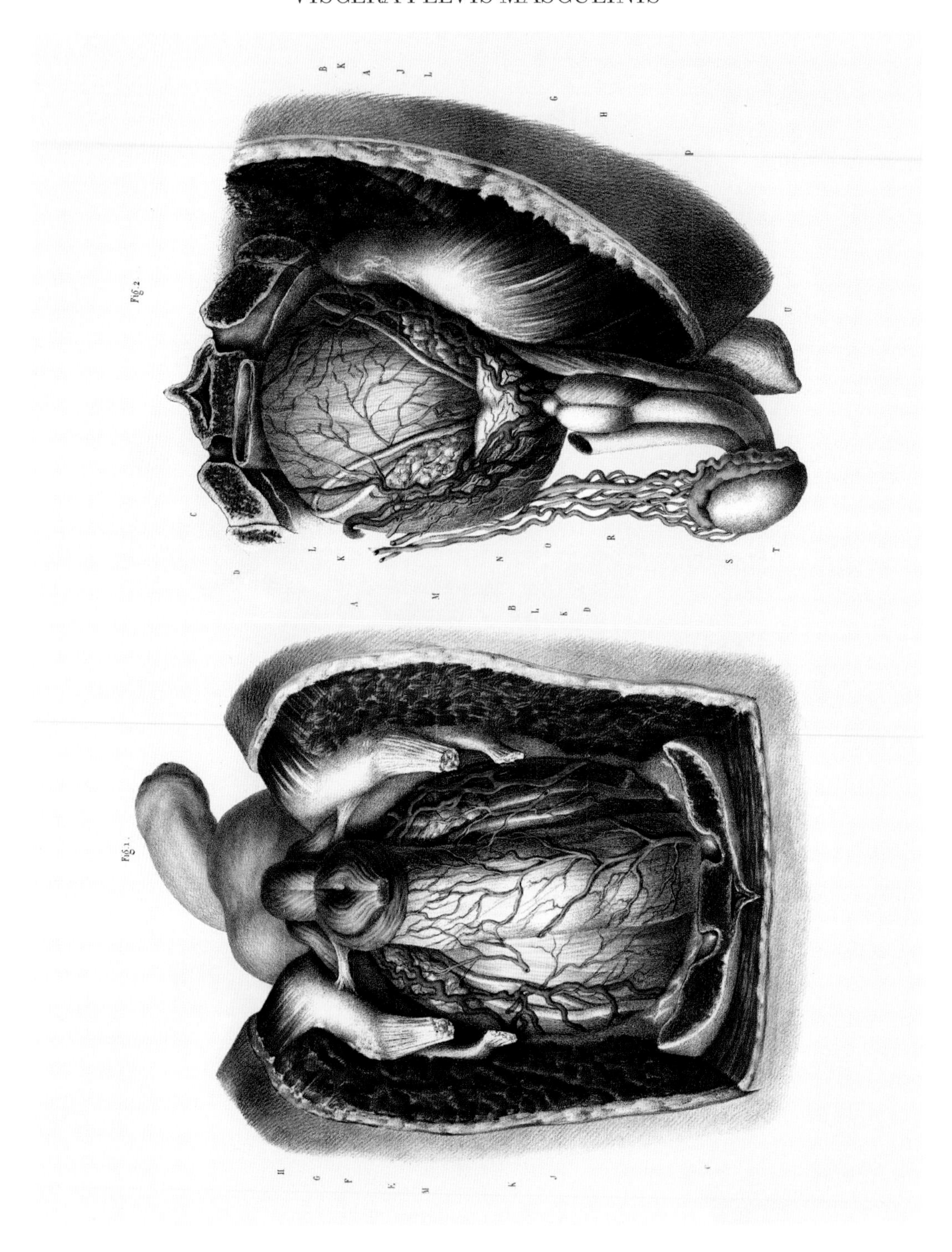

Bladder and male genital organs / Vessie et organes génitaux masculins
Vejiga y órganos genitales masculinos

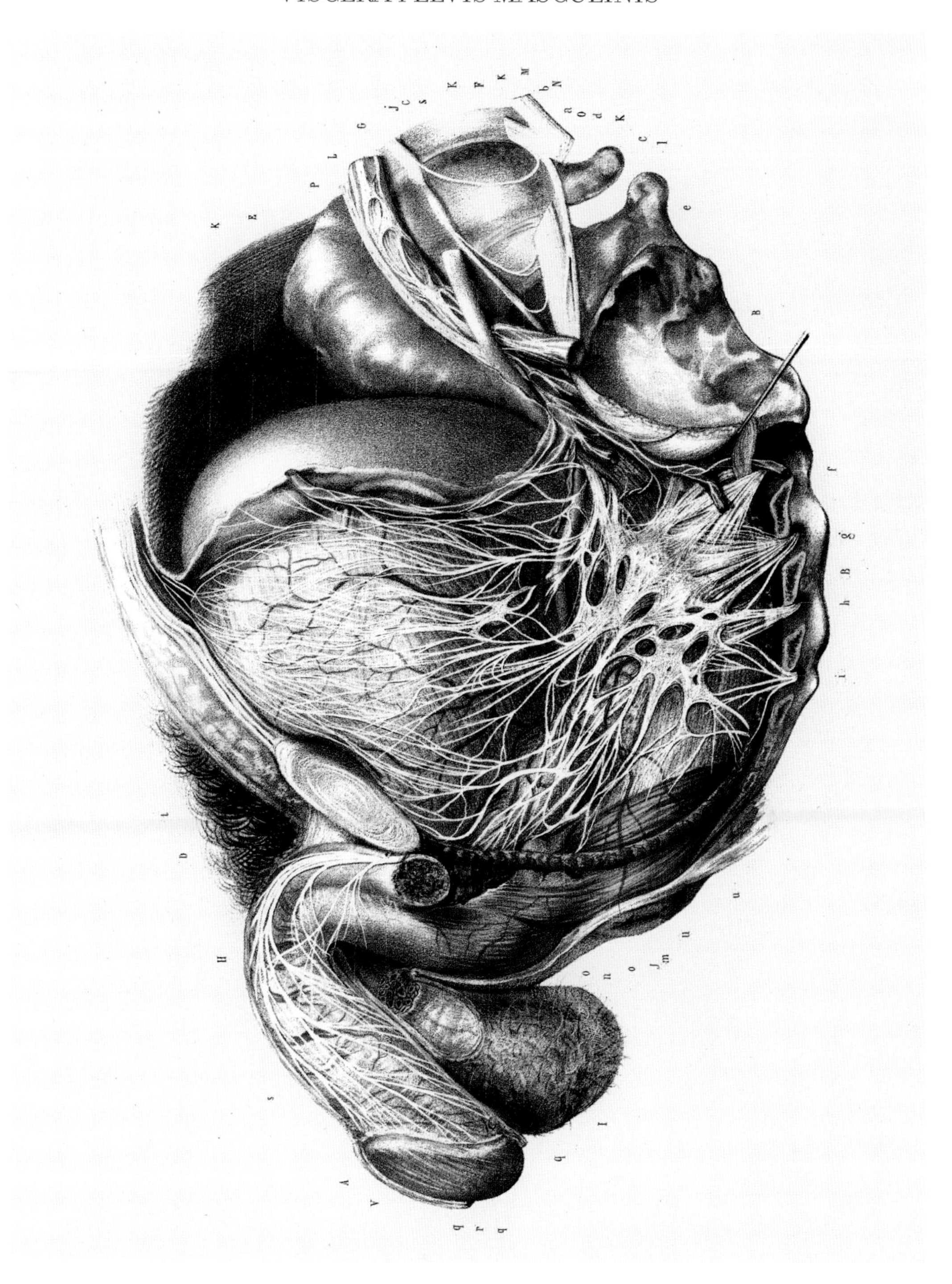

Organs of the male pelvis: Nerves / Viscères du bassin masculin : Nerfs
Vísceras de la pelvis masculina: nervios

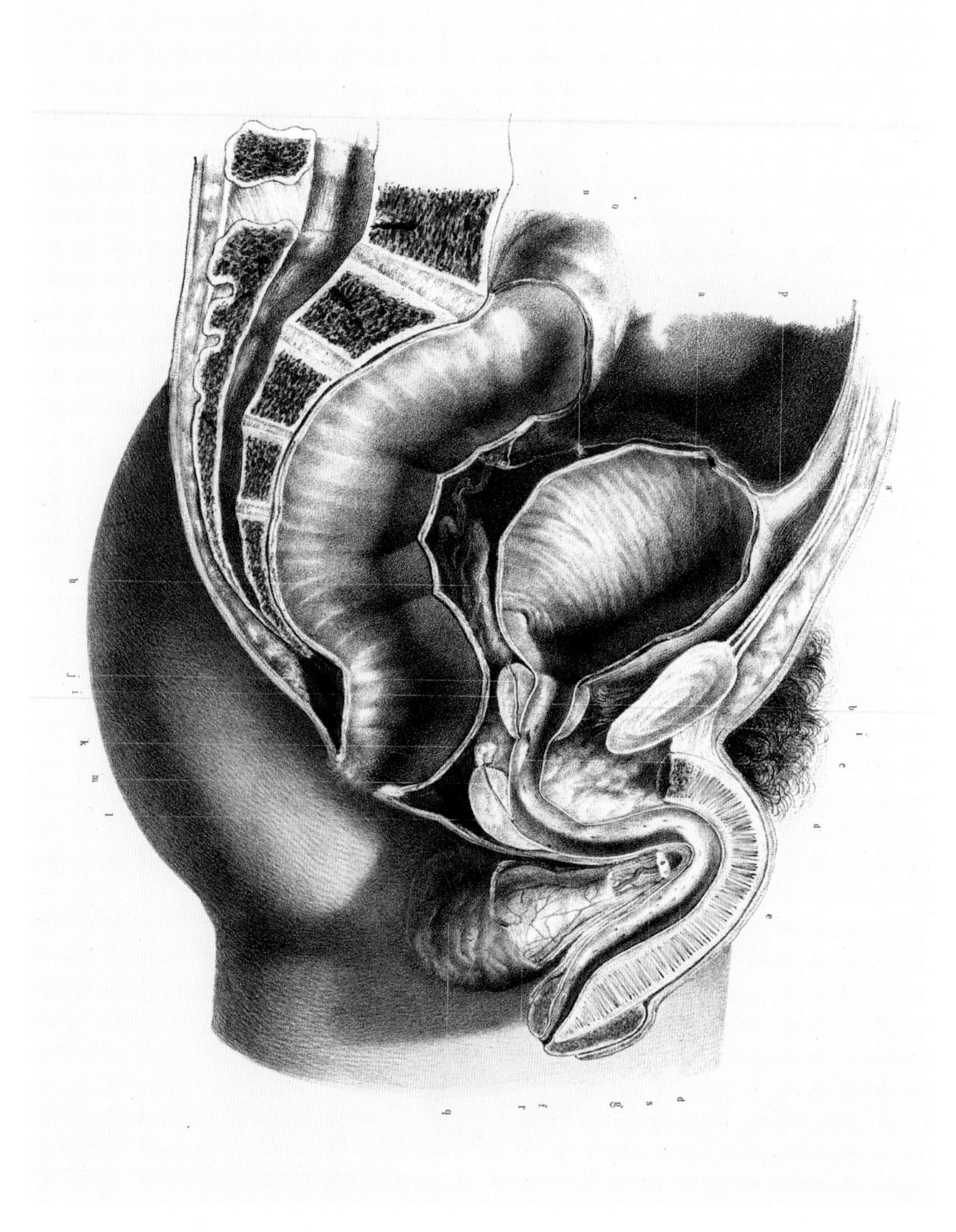

Organs of the male pelvis / Viscères du bassin masculin
Vísceras de la pelvis masculina

ORGANA GENITALIA MASCULINA EXTERNA ET FEMININA EXTERNA

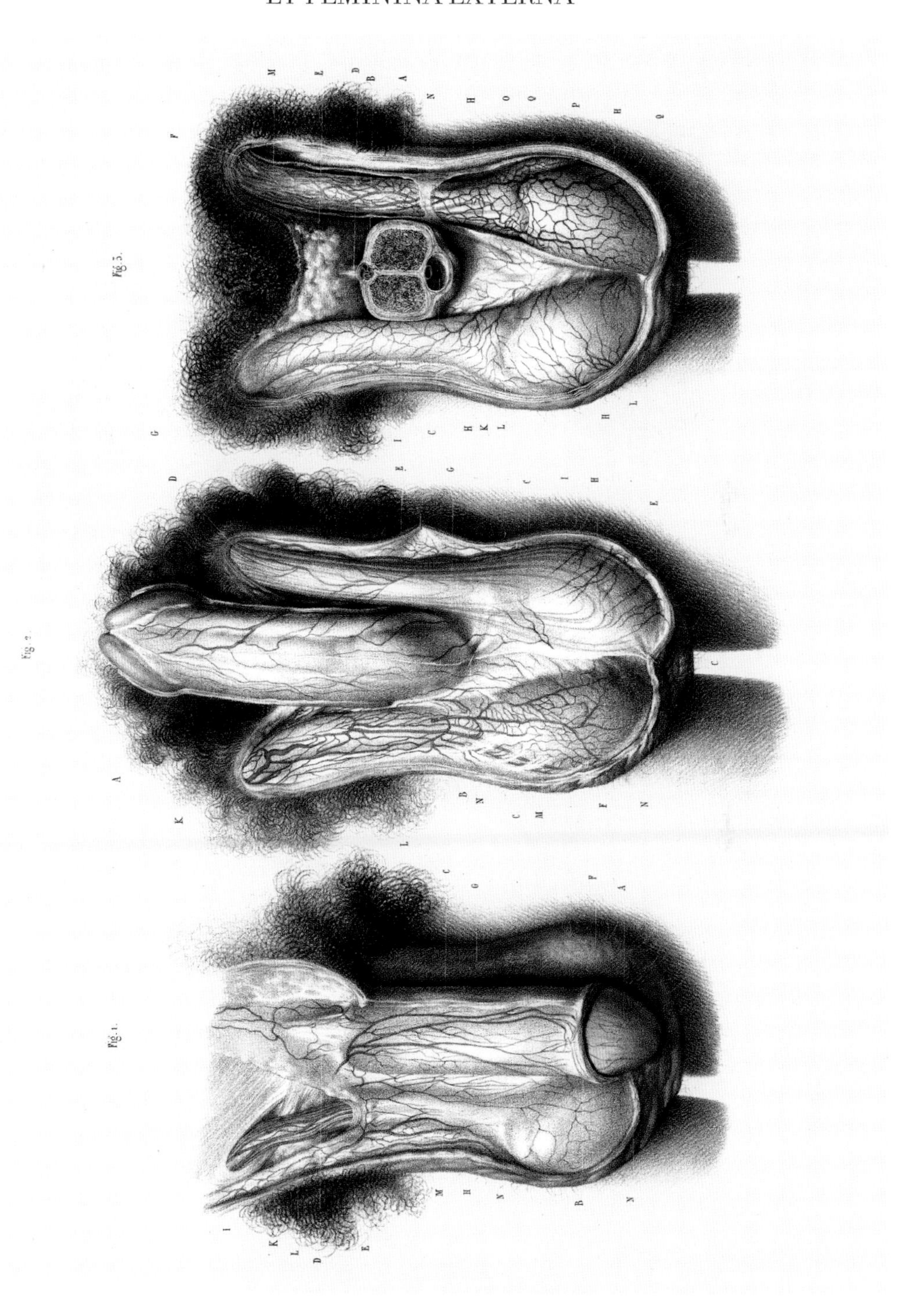

Male external genital organs / Organes génitaux externes masculins
Órganos genitales externos masculinos

ORGANA GENITALIA MASCULINA EXTERNA ET FEMININA EXTERNA

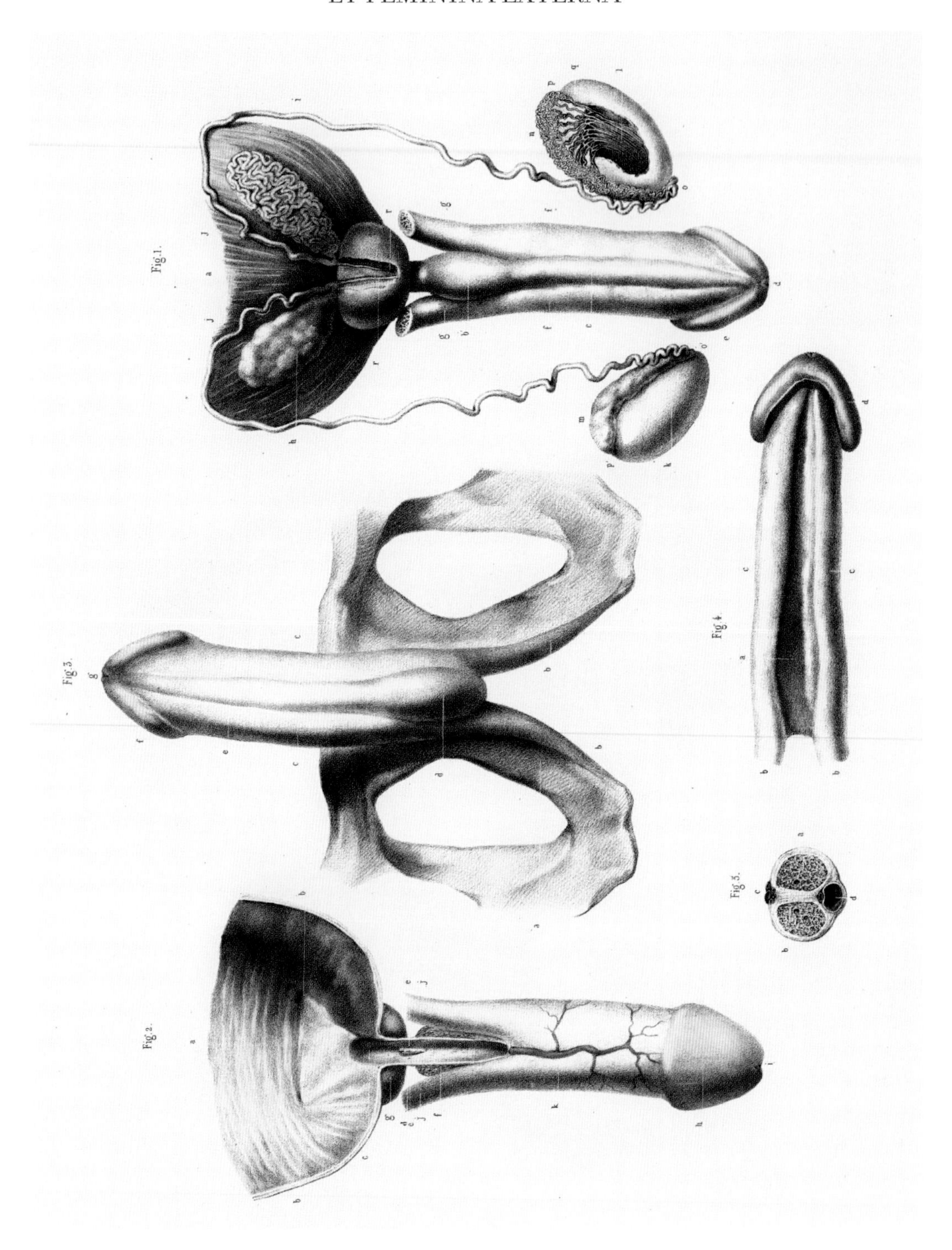

Male external genital organs / Organes génitaux externes masculins
Órganos genitales externos masculinos

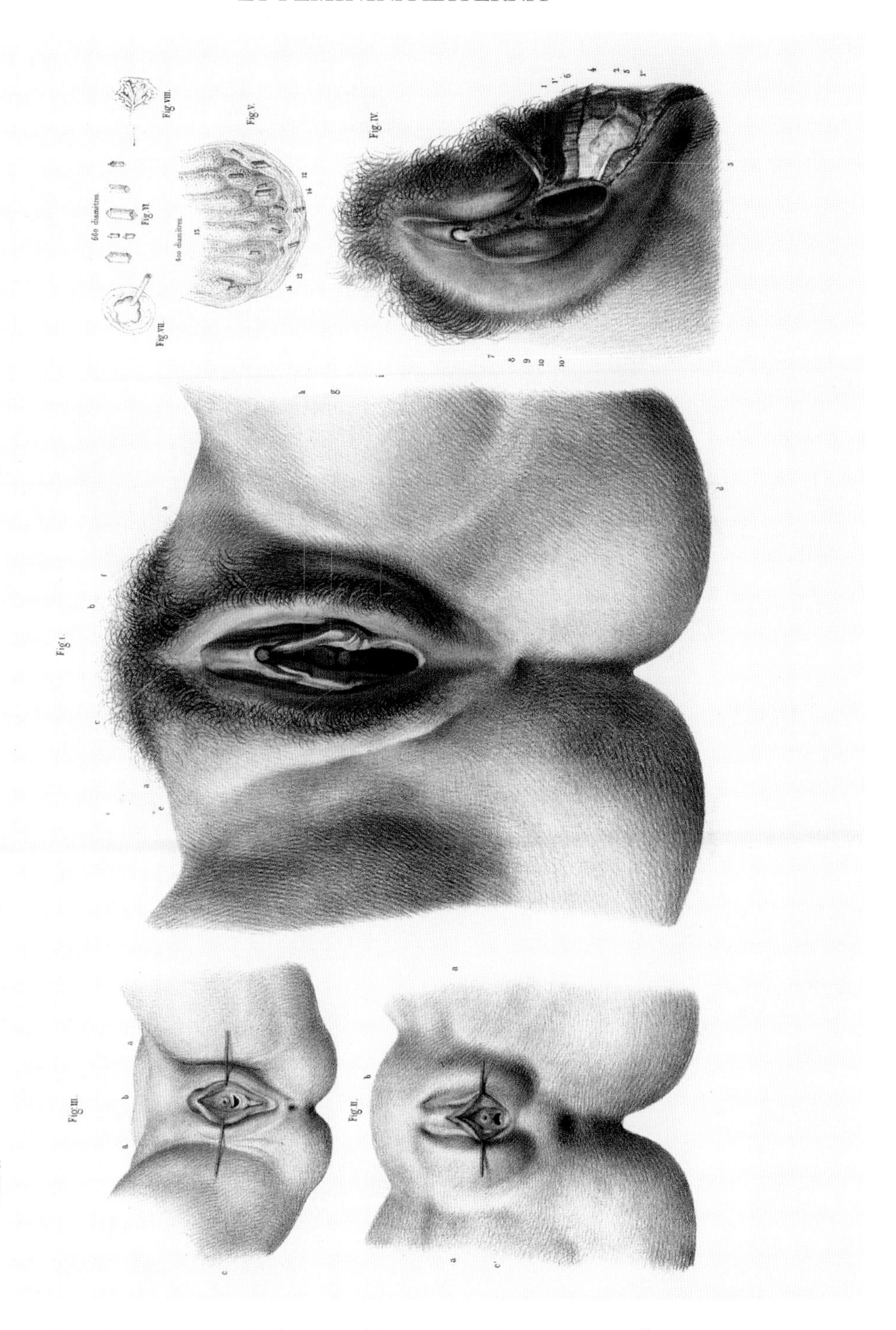

Female external genital organs / Organes génitaux externes féminins
Órganos genitales externos femeninos

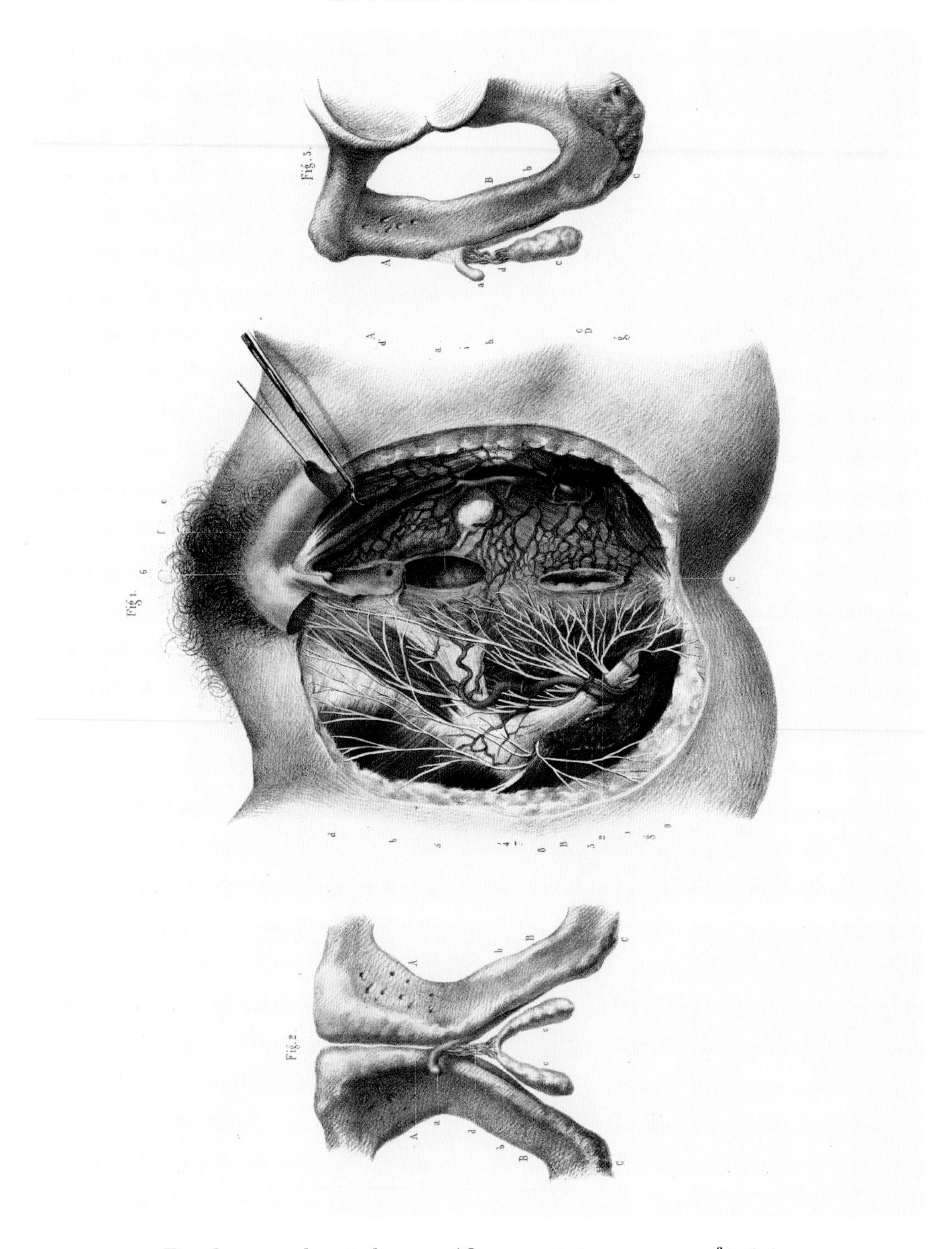

Female external genital organs / Organes génitaux externes féminins
Órganos genitales externos femeninos

VISCERA ABDOMINIS ET PELVIS: NERVI.
VISCERA PELVIS FEMININIS

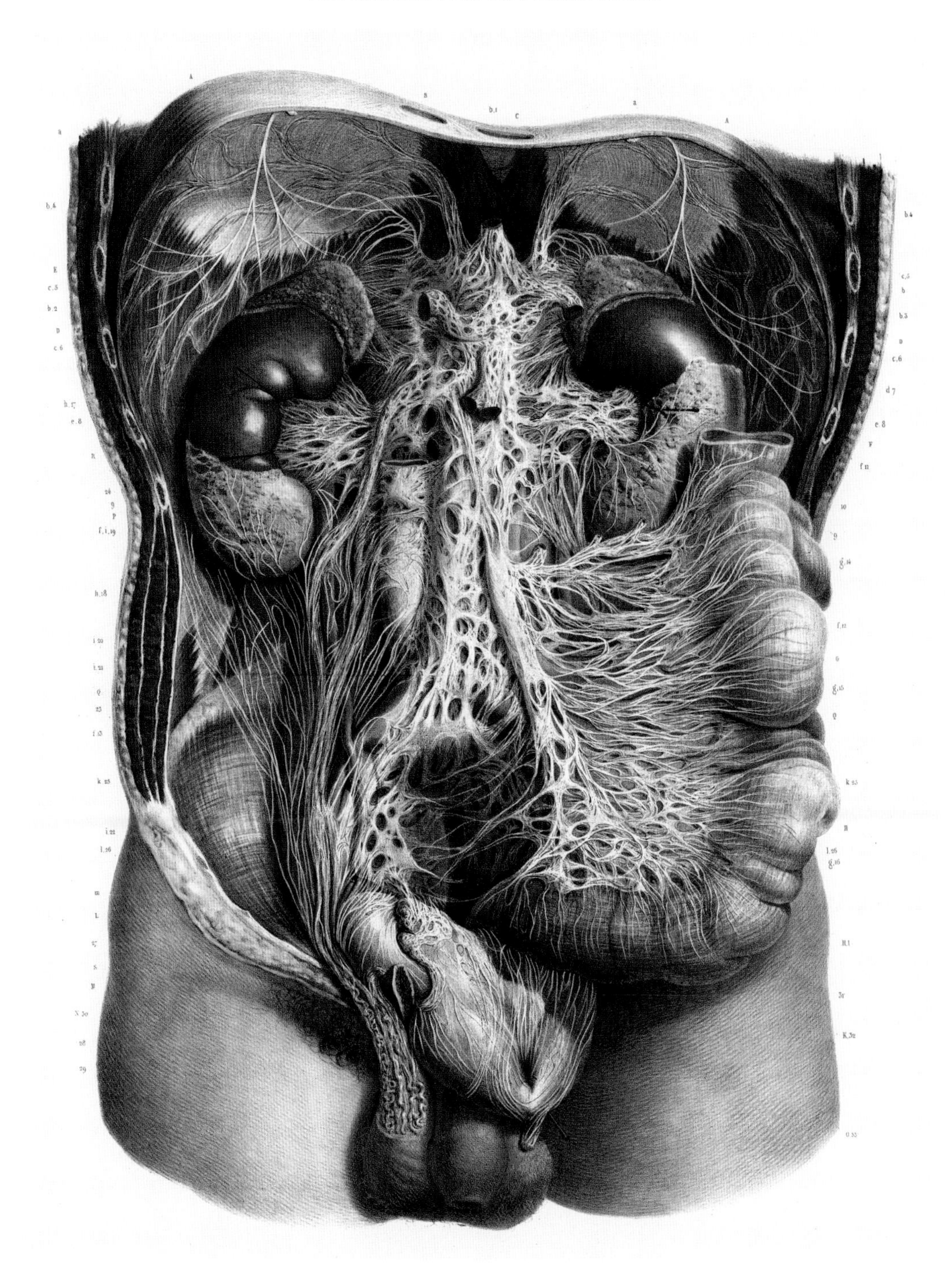

Abdominal and pelvic organs: Nerves / Viscères abdominaux et pelviens : Nerfs
Vísceras abdominales y pélvicas: nervios

VISCERA ABDOMINIS ET PELVIS: NERVI. VISCERA PELVIS FEMININIS

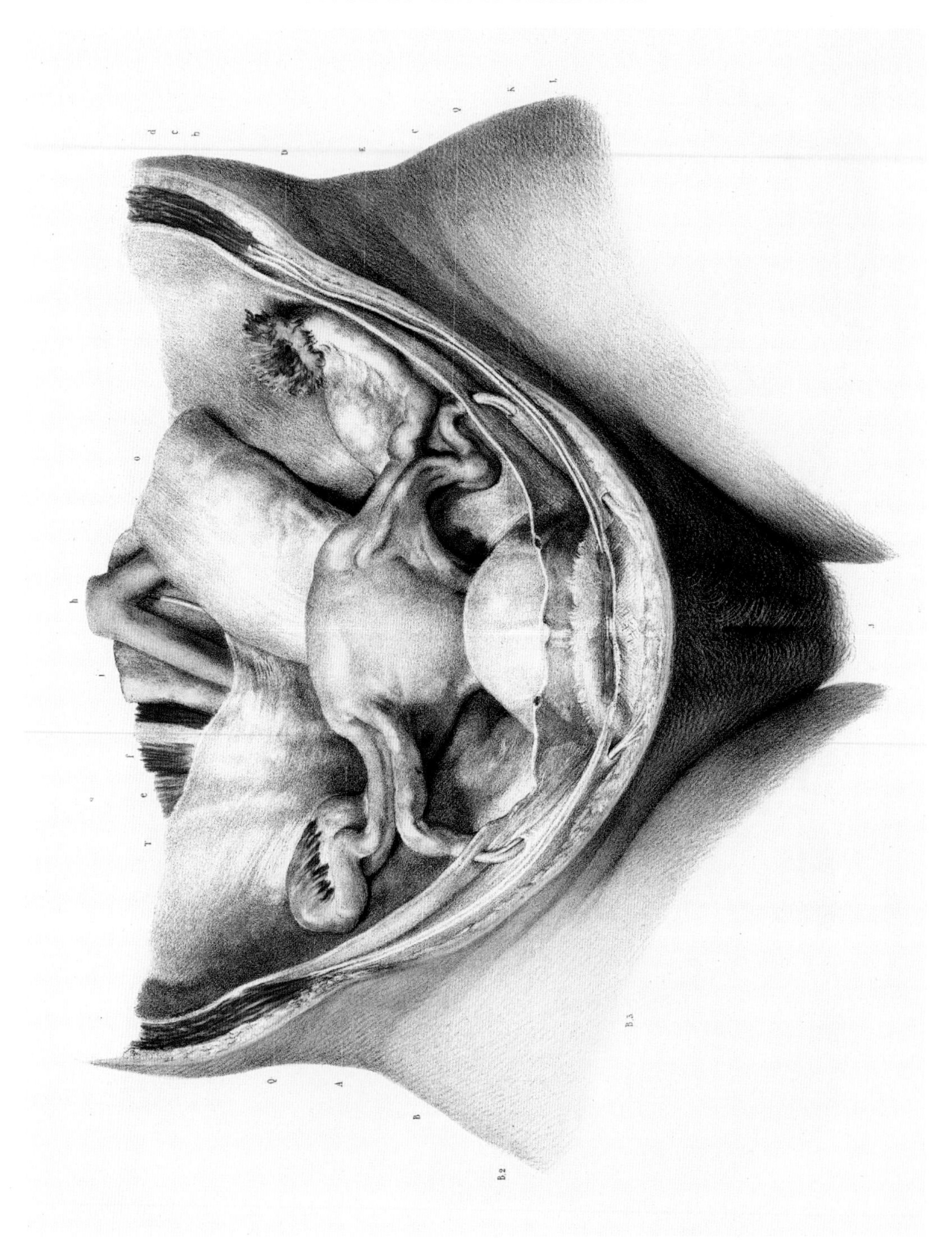

Organs of the female pelvis / Viscères du bassin féminin
Vísceras de la pelvis femenina

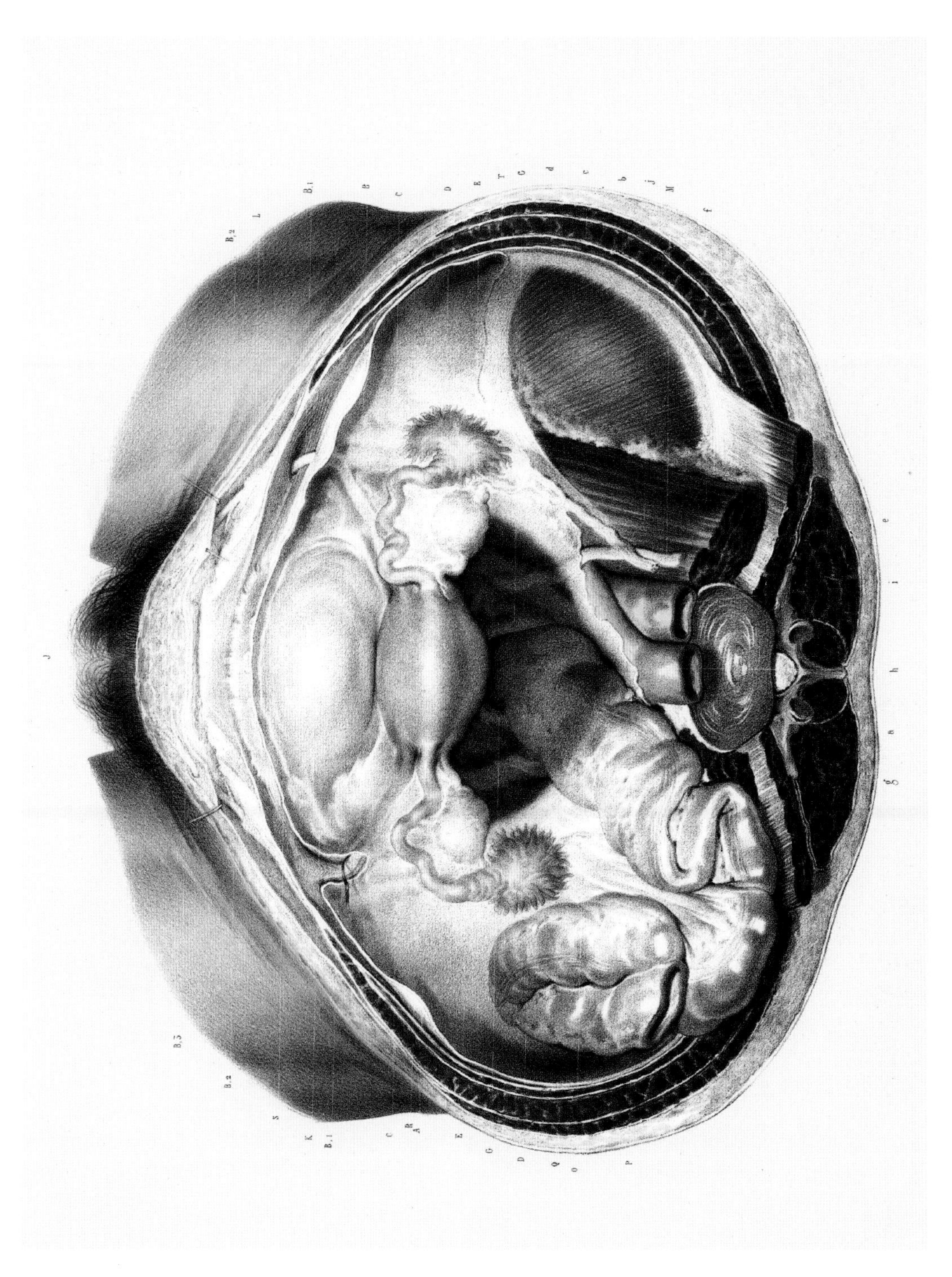

Organs of the female pelvis / Viscères du bassin féminin
Vísceras de la pelvis femenina

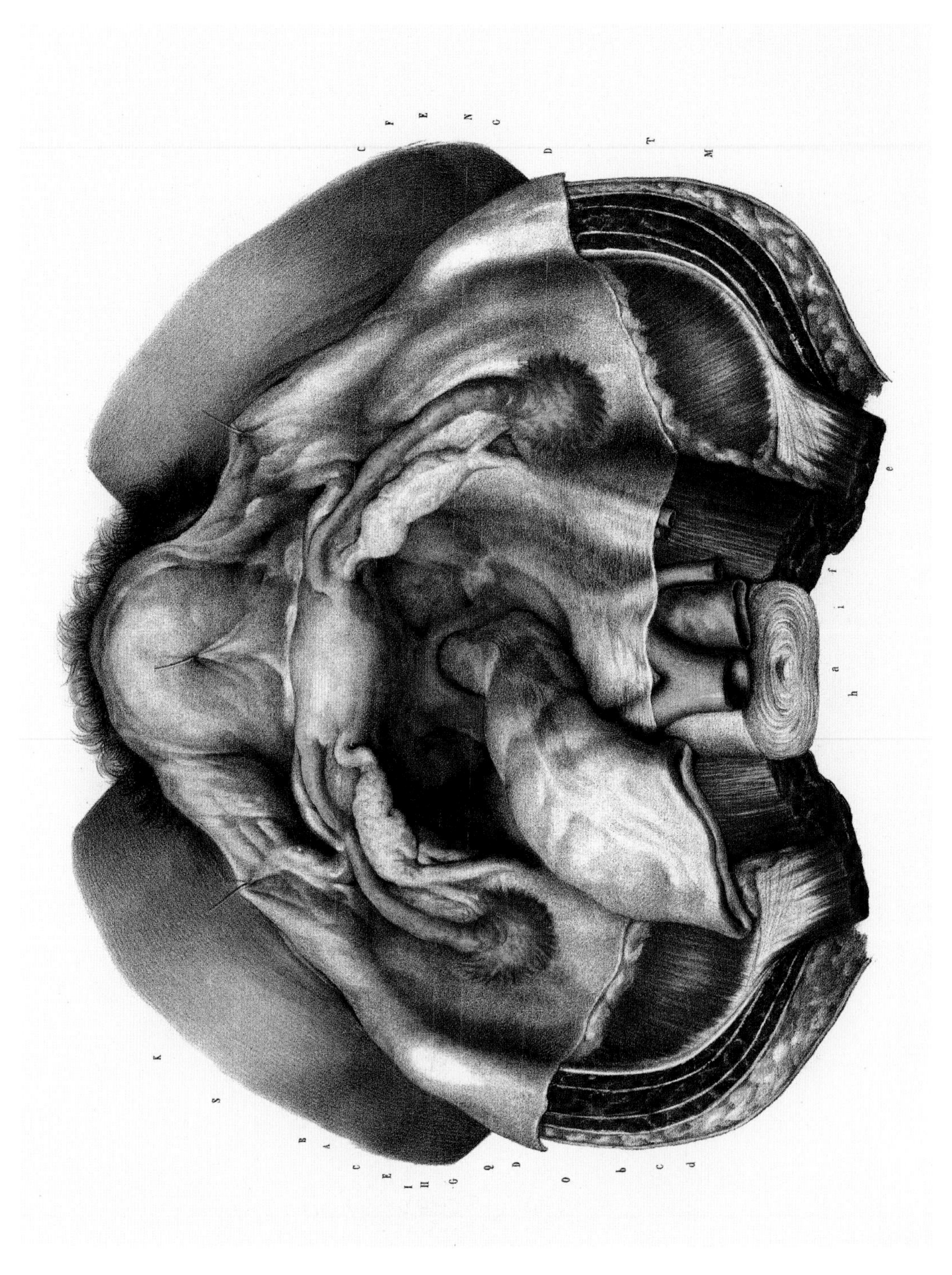

Organs of the female pelvis / Viscères du bassin féminin
Vísceras de la pelvis femenina

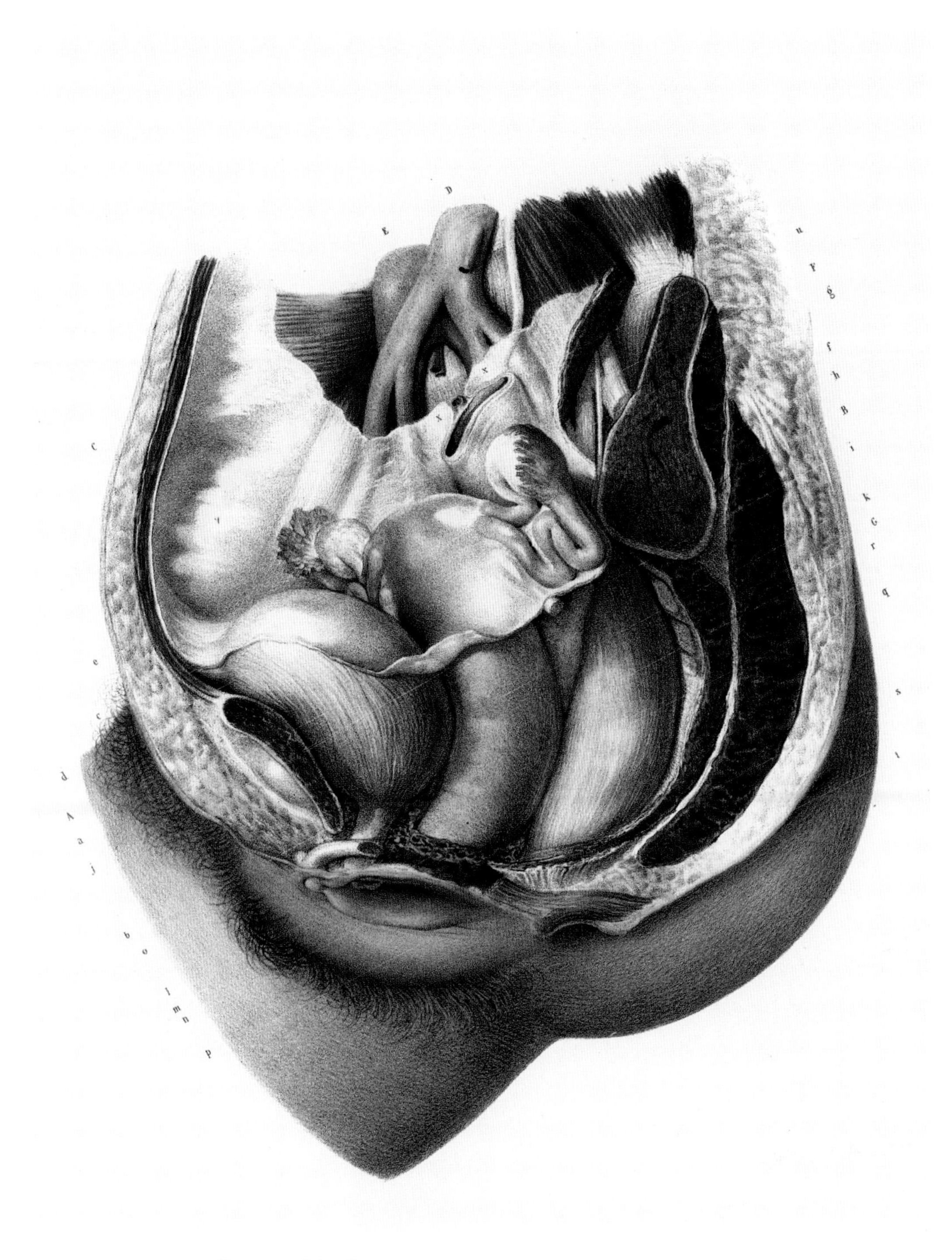

Organs of the female pelvis / Viscères du bassin féminin
Vísceras de la pelvis femenina

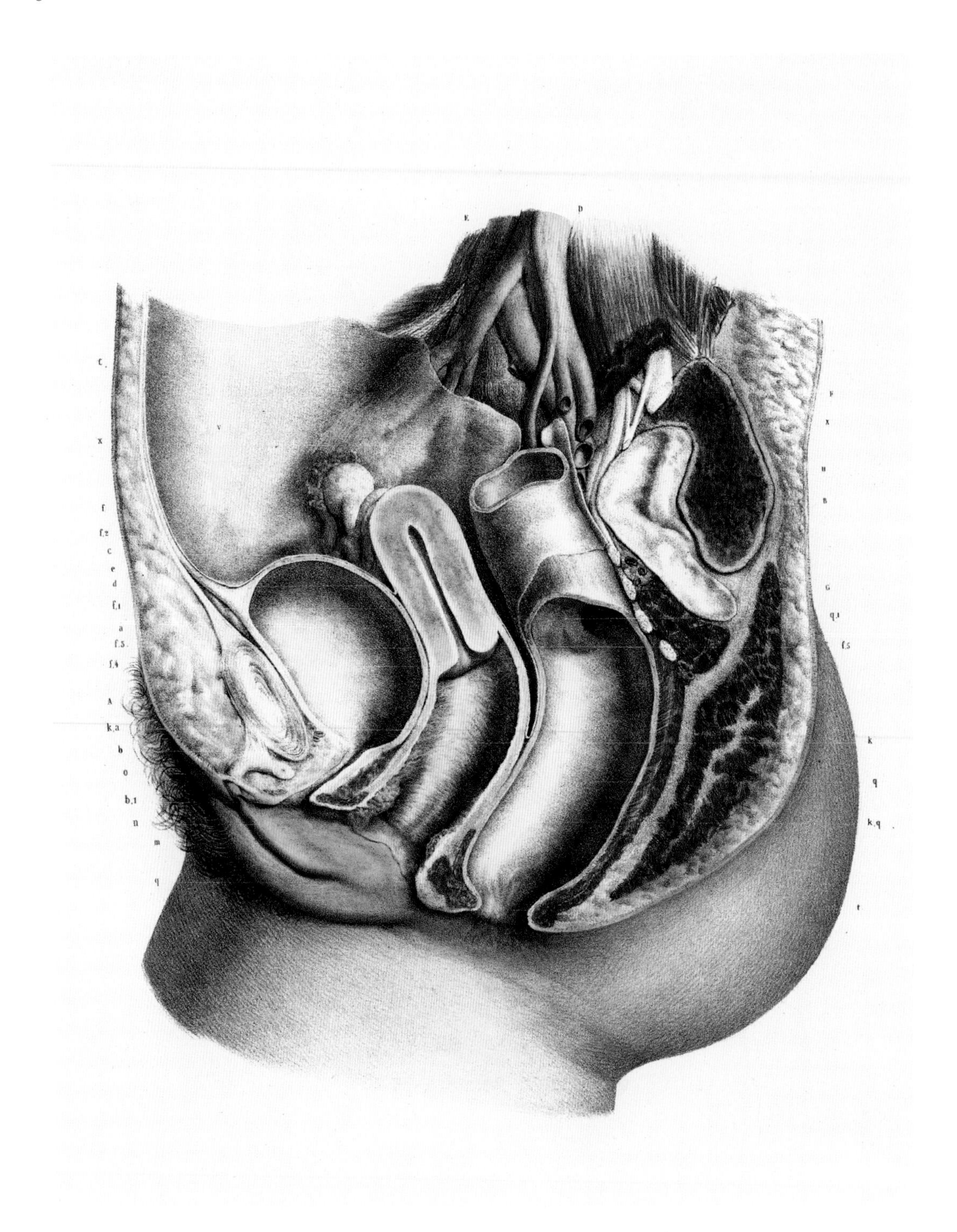

Organs of the female pelvis / Viscères du bassin féminin
Vísceras de la pelvis femenina

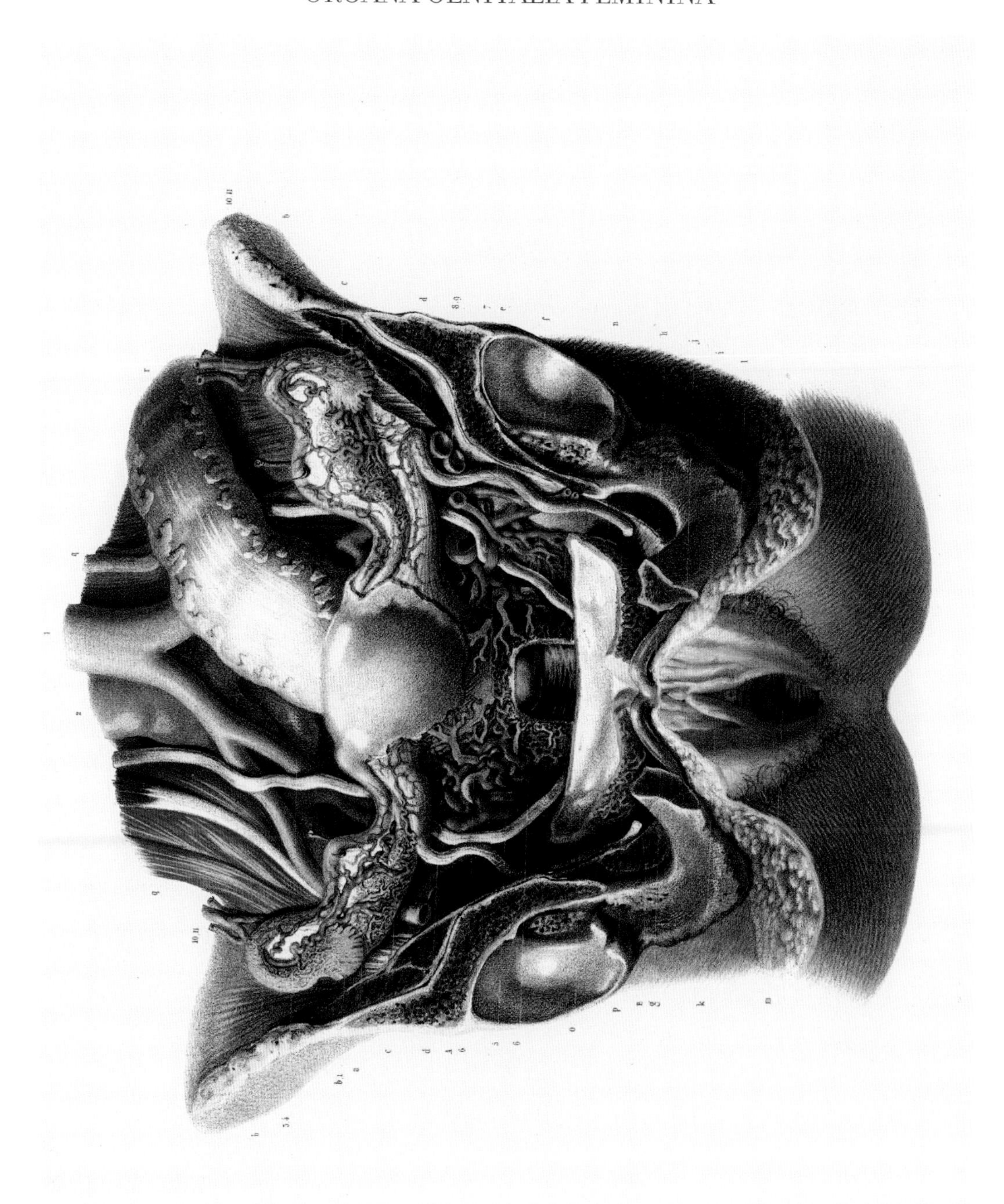

Organs of the female pelvis: Arteries and veins
Viscères du bassin féminin : Artères et veines
Vísceras de la pelvis femenina: arterias y venas

VISCERA PELVIS FEMININIS: ARTERIAE, VENAE, ET NERVI. ORGANA GENITALIA FEMININA

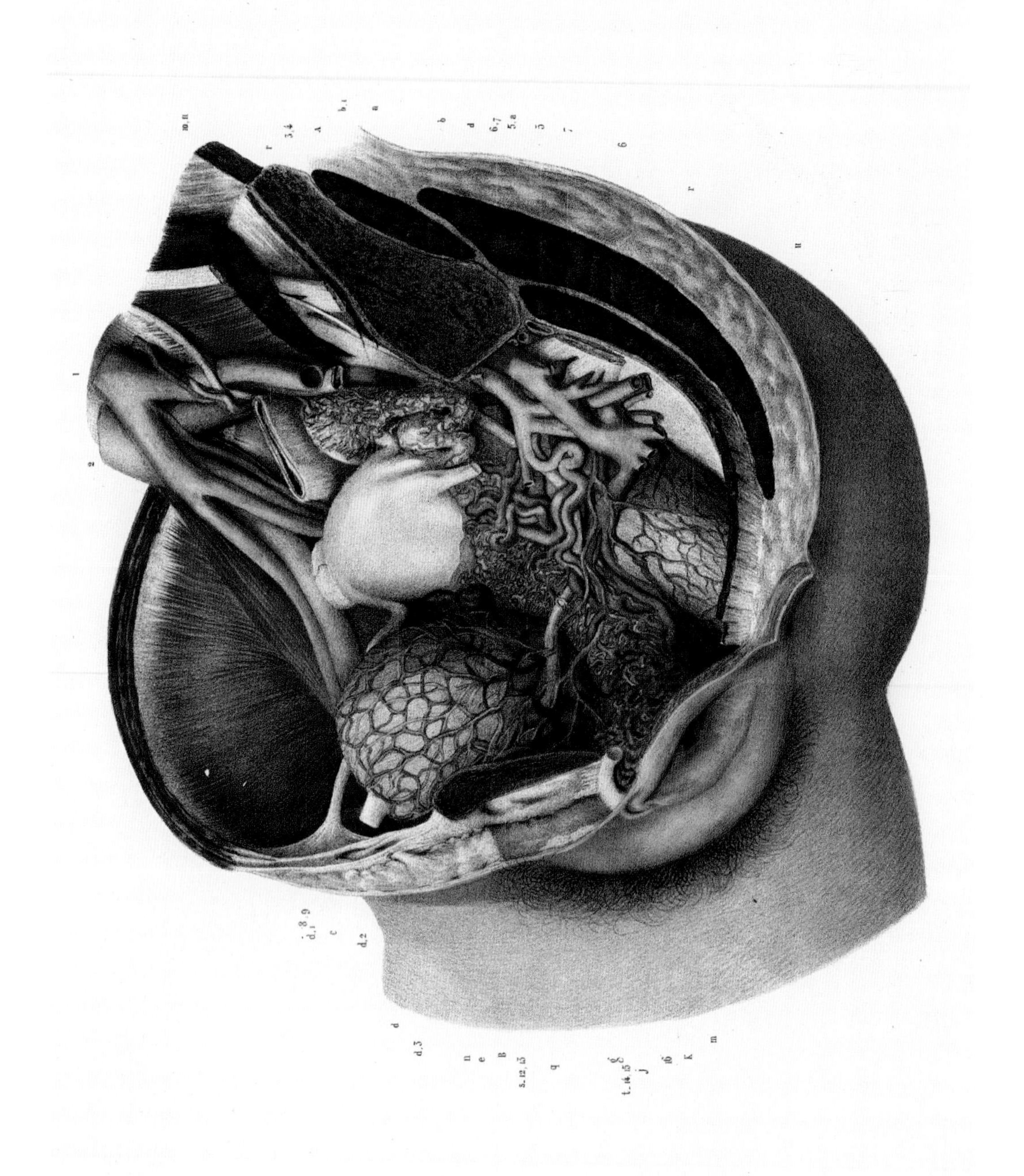

Organs of the female pelvis: Arteries and veins
Viscères du bassin féminin : Artères et veines
Vísceras de la pelvis femenina: arterias y venas

VISCERA PELVIS FEMININIS: ARTERIAE, VENAE, ET NERVI.
ORGANA GENITALIA FEMININA

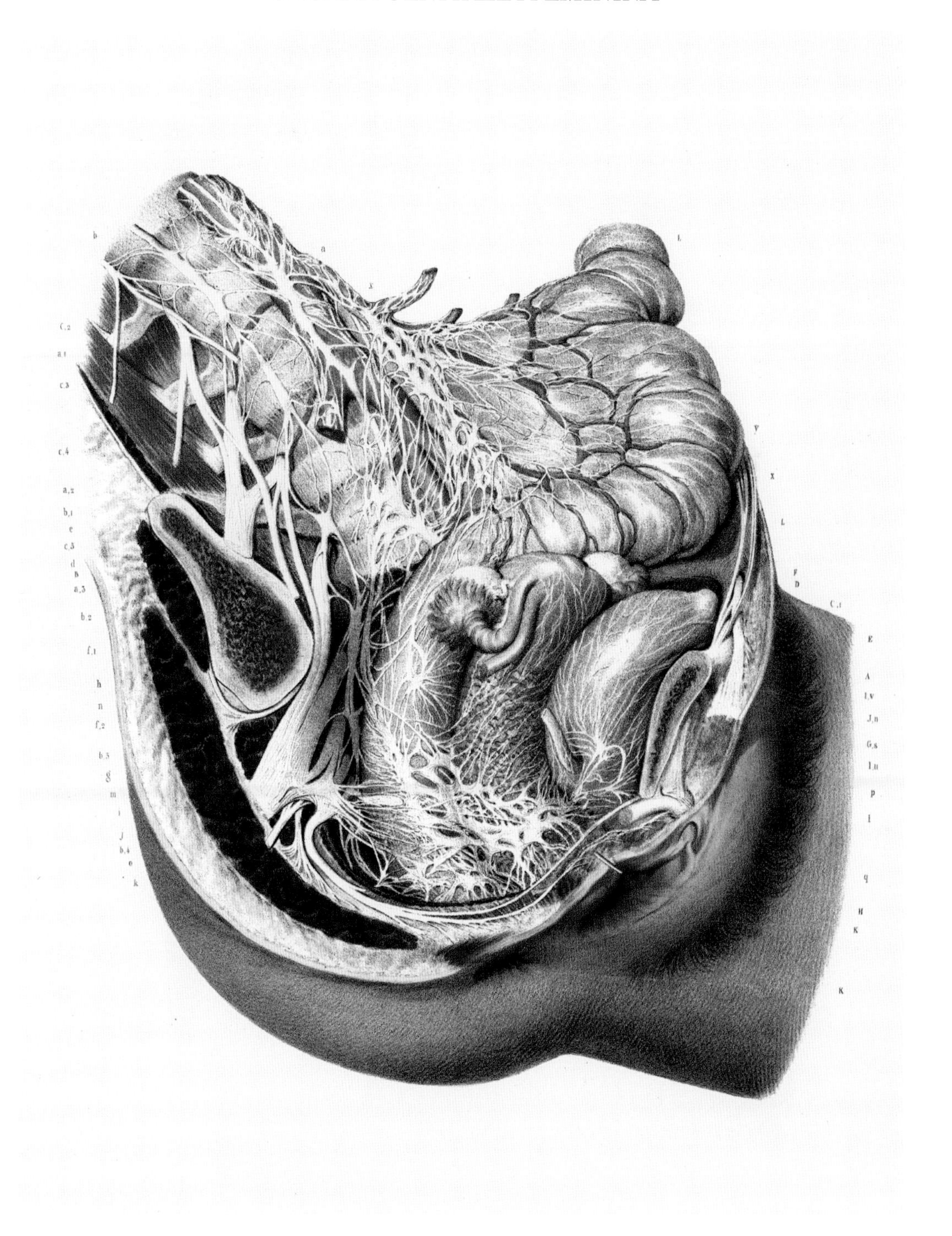

Organs of the female pelvis: Nerves / Viscères du bassin féminin : Nerfs
Vísceras de la pelvis femenina: nervios

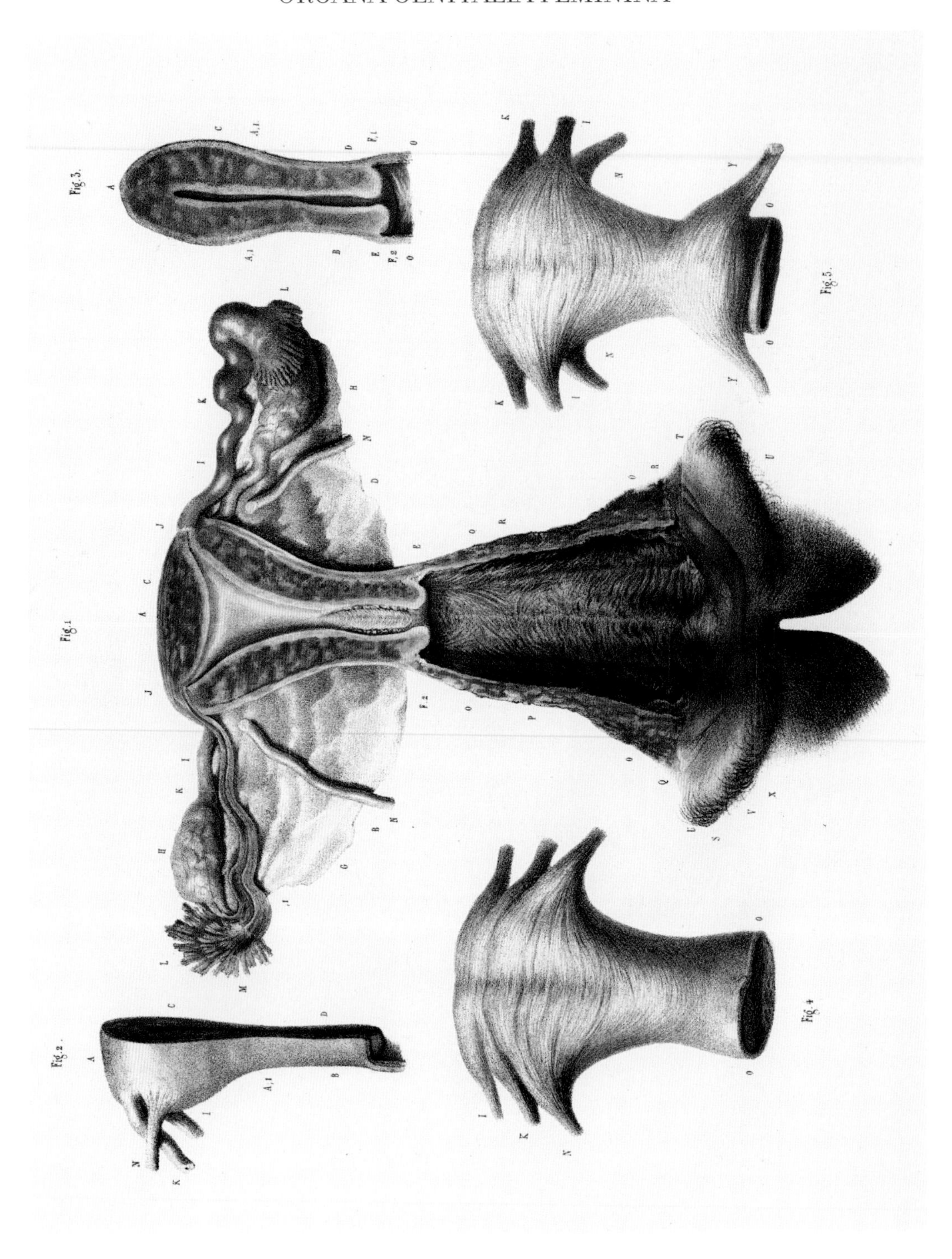

Female genital organs / Organes génitaux féminins
Órganos genitales femeninos

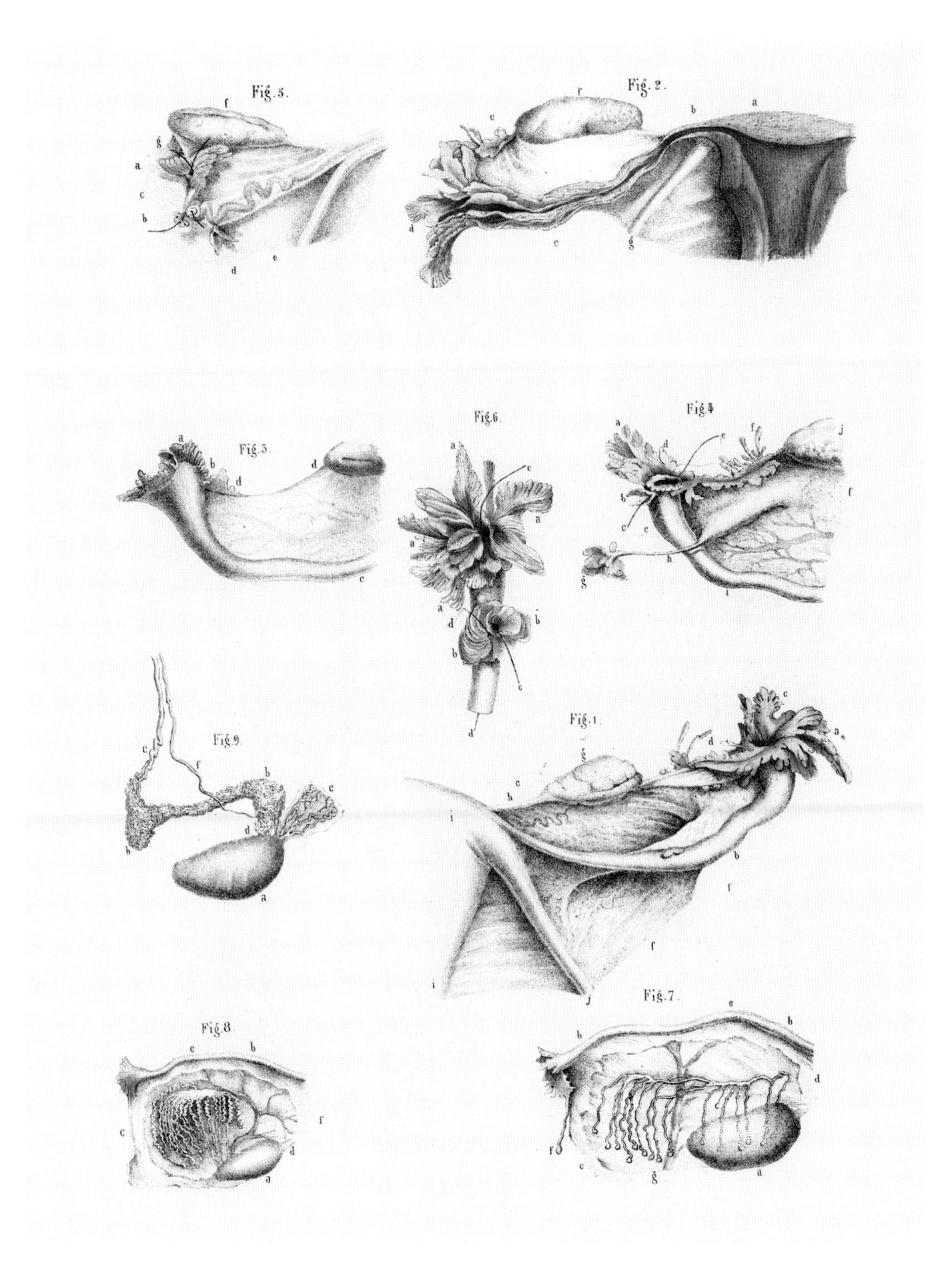

Uterine tube and ovary / Trompe utérine et ovaire / Trompa uterina y ovario

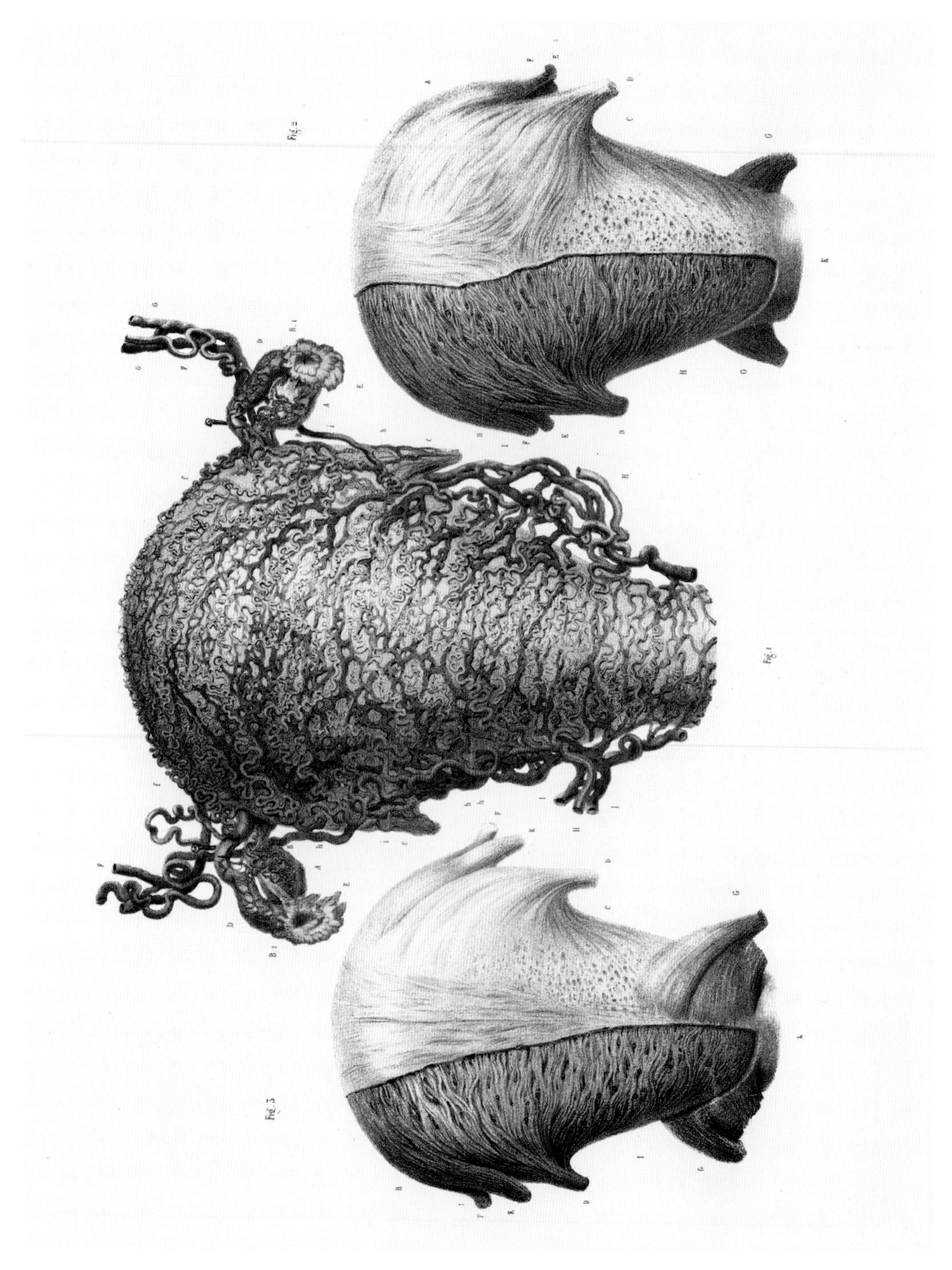

Uterus / Utérus / Útero

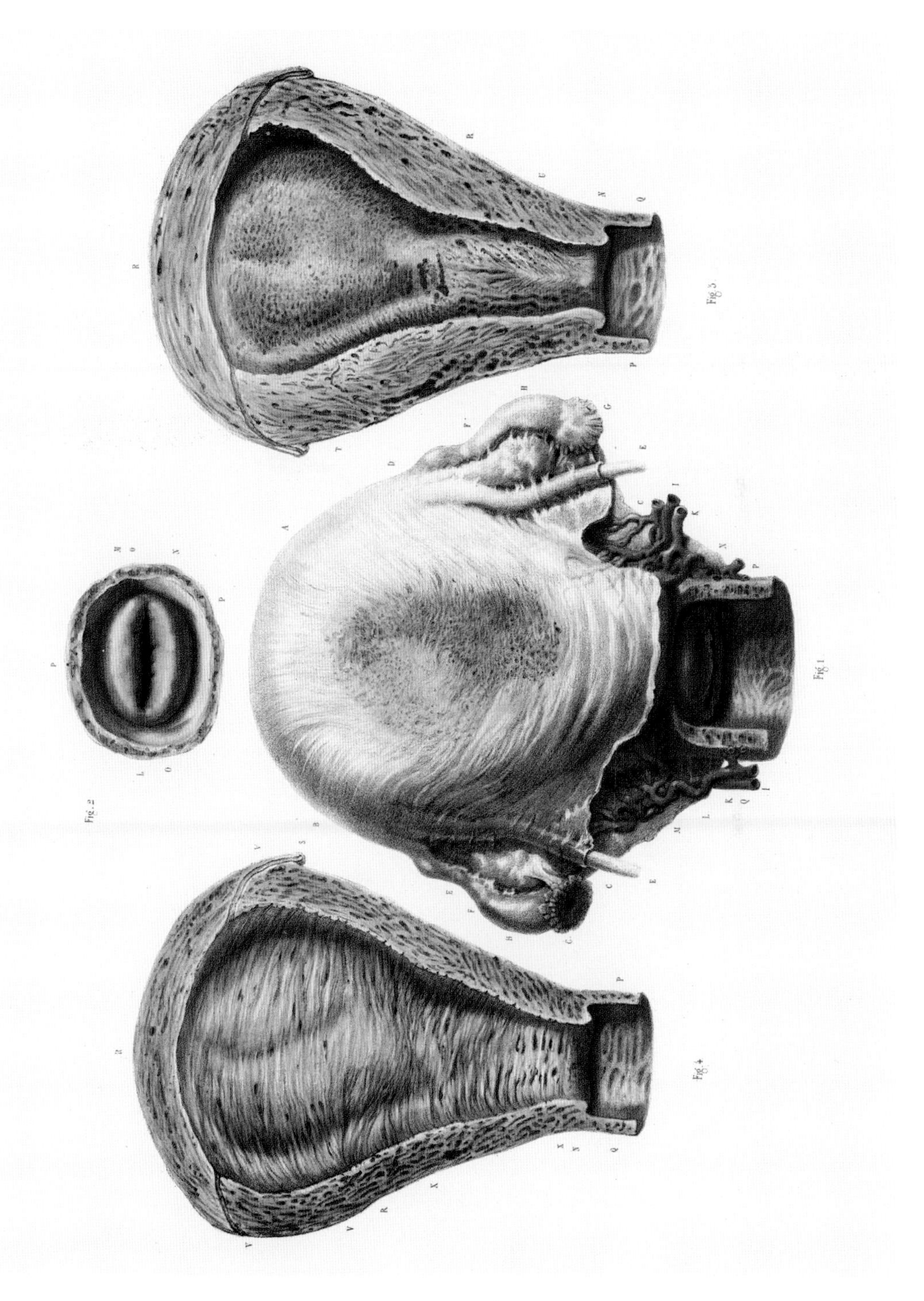

Uterus / Utérus / Útero

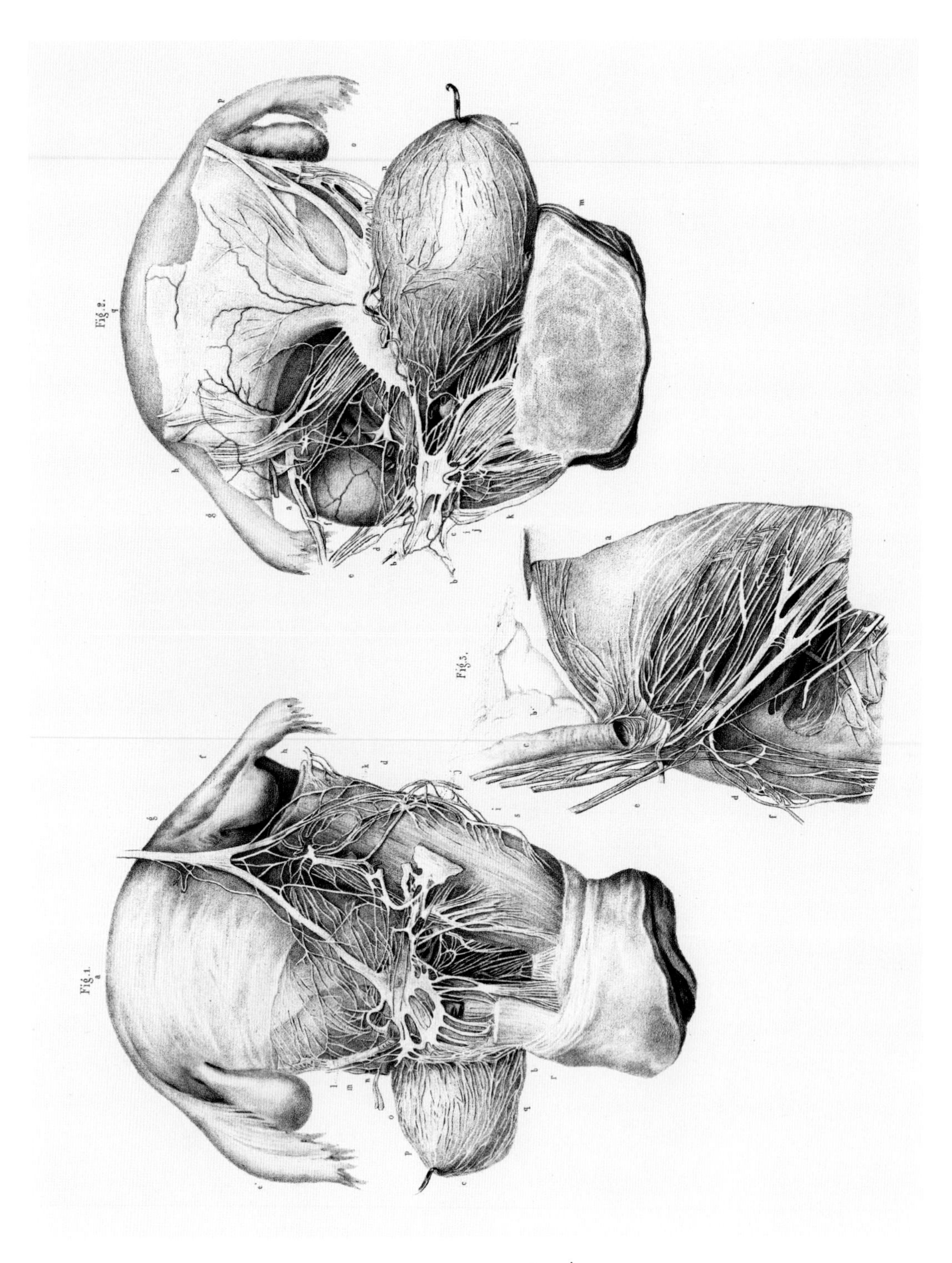

Uterus: Nerves / Utérus : Nerfs / Útero: nervios

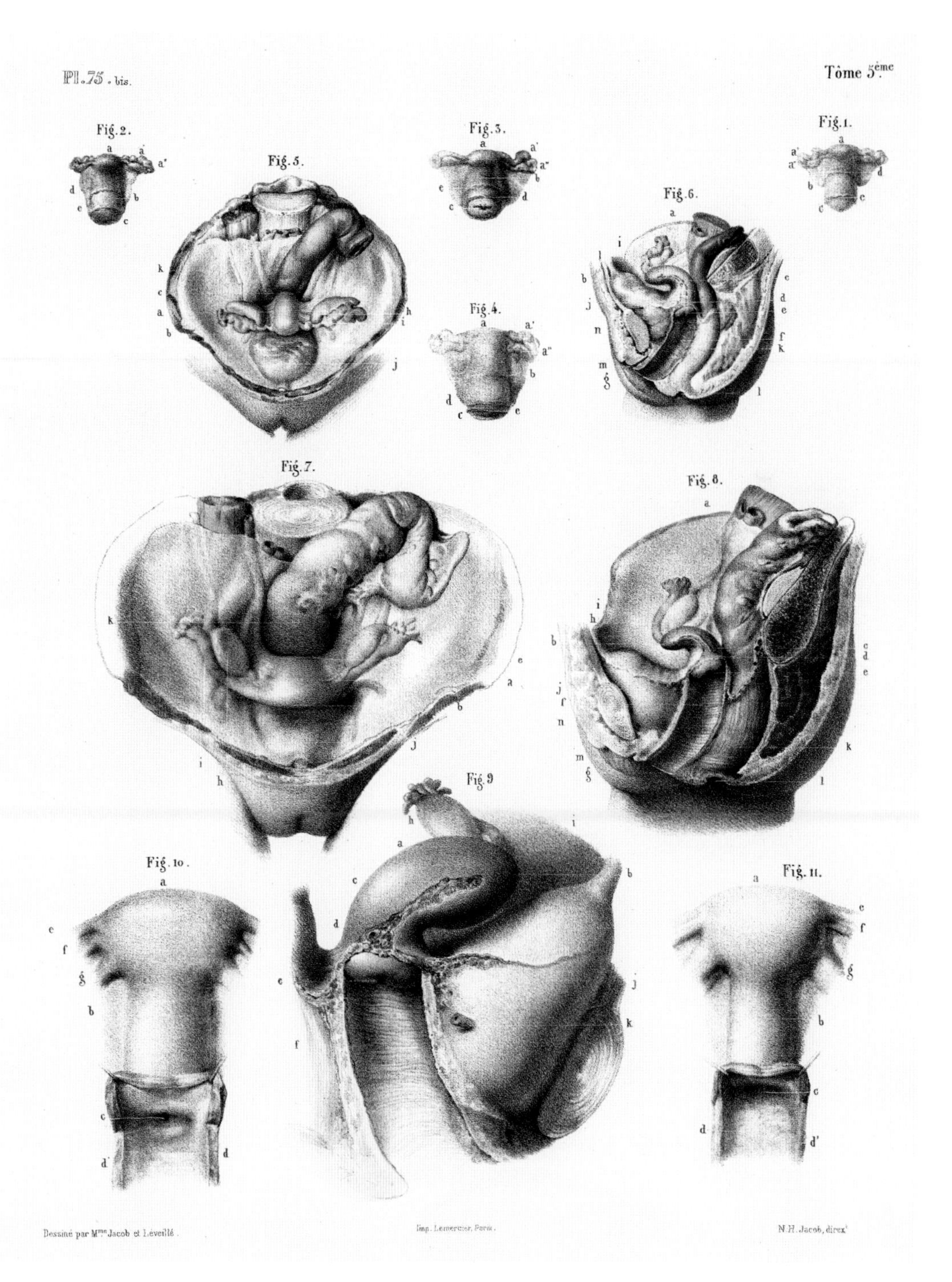

Uterus / Utérus / Útero

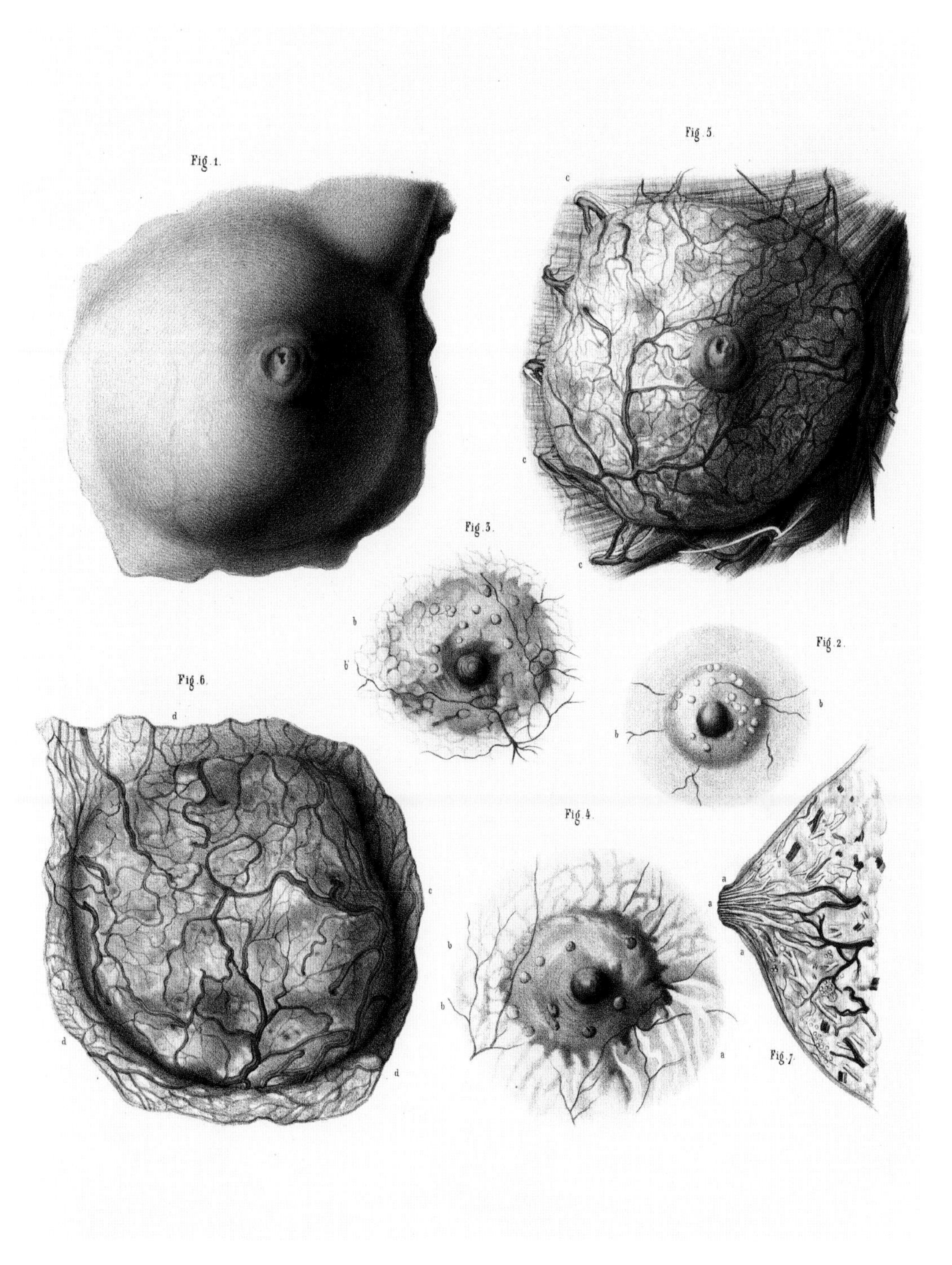

Breast and mammary gland / Sein et glande mammaire
Seno y glándula mamaria

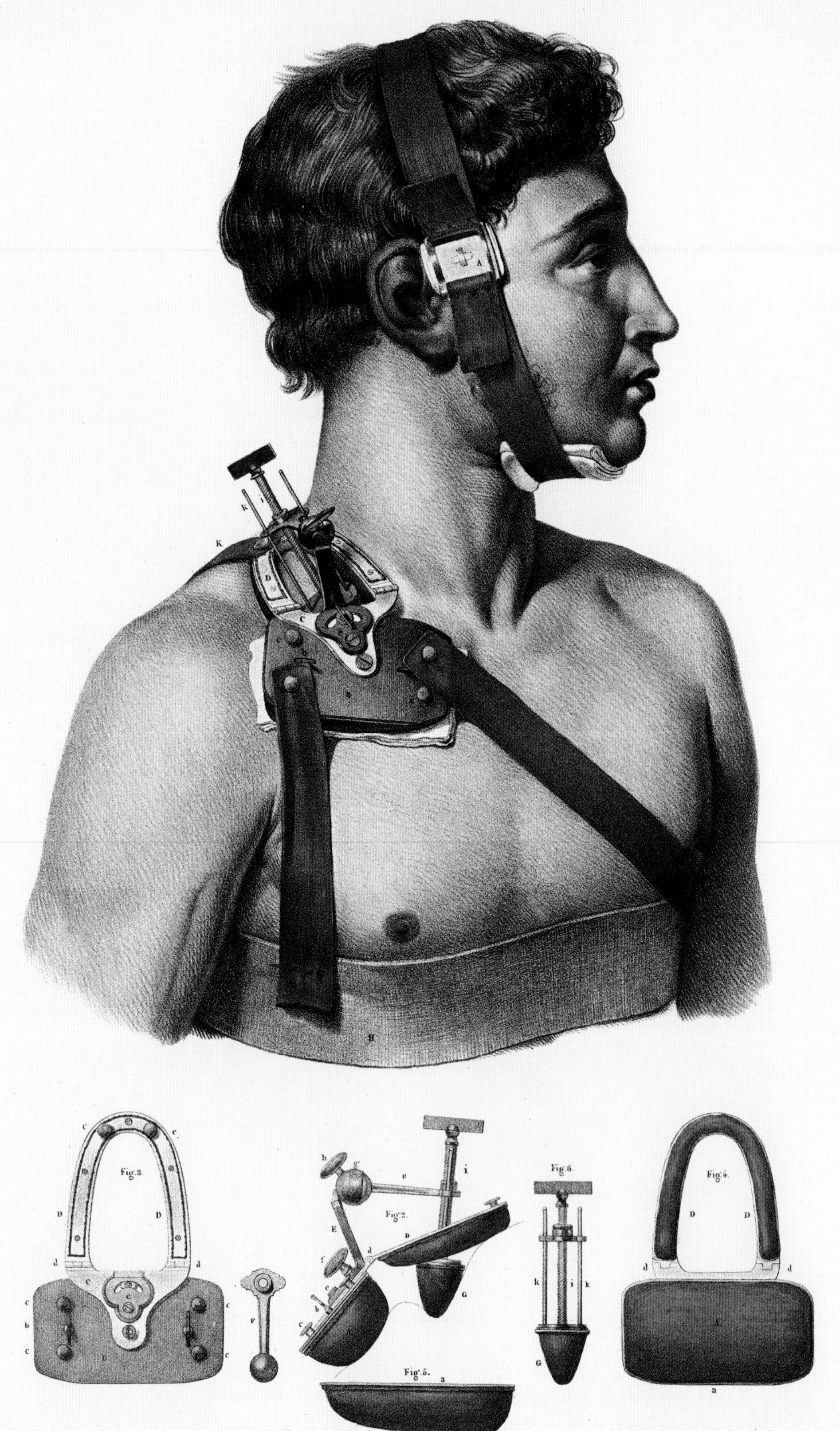

Dessiné par Rogat.
Dirigé par N.H. Jacob.

Instrument fabriqué par Mr. Charrière.

Lith. de Lemercier, Benard et Cie

VOL. 6

ANATOMIA CHIRURGICA. ARTES CHIRURGICAE

SURGICAL ANATOMY.
SURGICAL TECHNIQUES
(OPERATIVE MEDICINE)

ANATOMIE CHIRURGICALE.
TECHNIQUES CHIRURGICALES
(MEDECINE OPERATOIRE)

ANATOMÍA QUIRÚRGICA.
TÉCNICAS QUIRÚRGICAS
(MEDICINA OPERATORIA)

Left page / Ci-contre / Página contigua:
Compression of the arteries of the head and neck
Compressions des artères de la tête et du cou
Compresiones de las arterias de la cabeza y del cuello

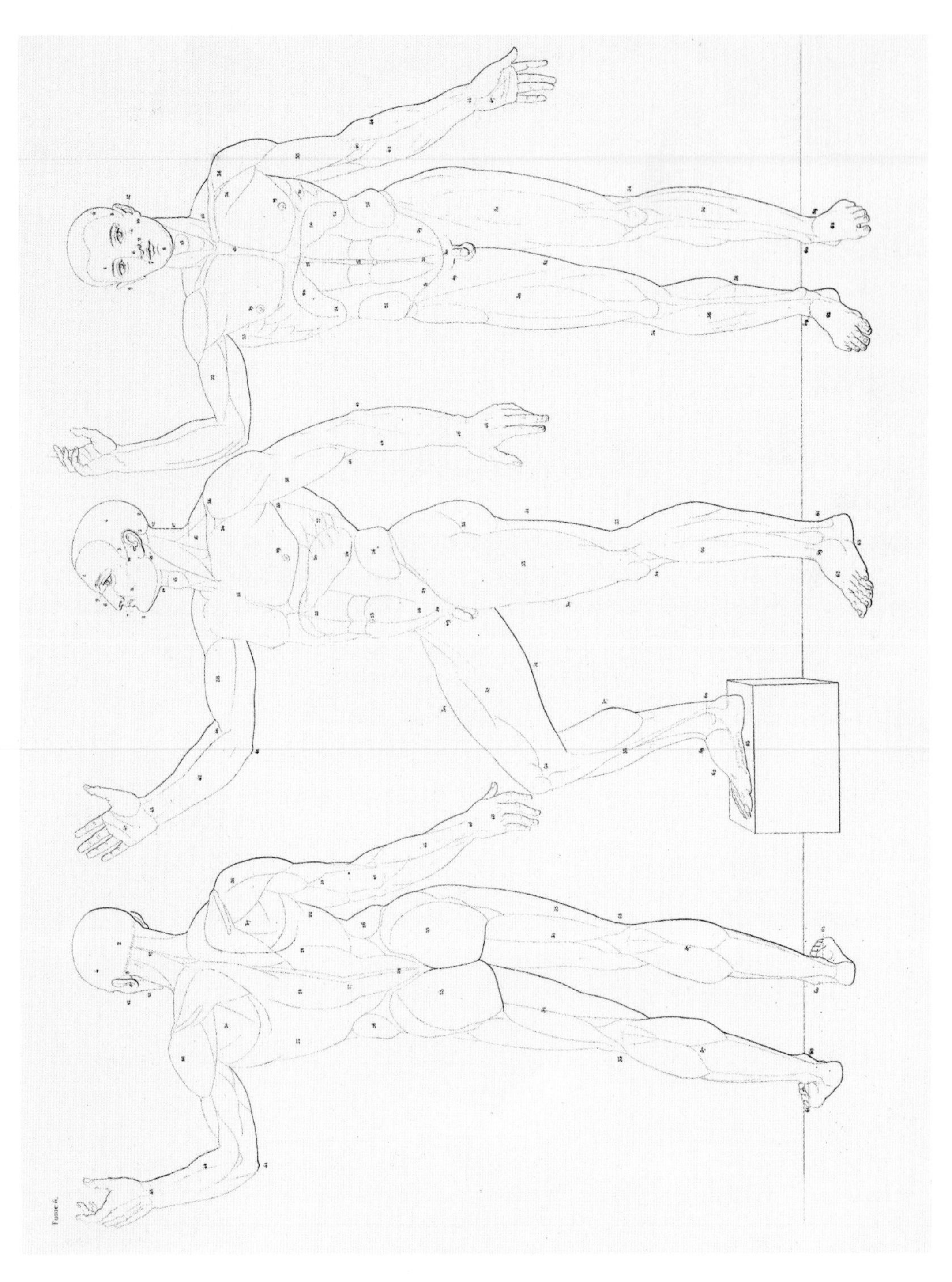

Regions and parts of the human body
Régions et parties du corps humain
Regiones y partes del cuerpo humano

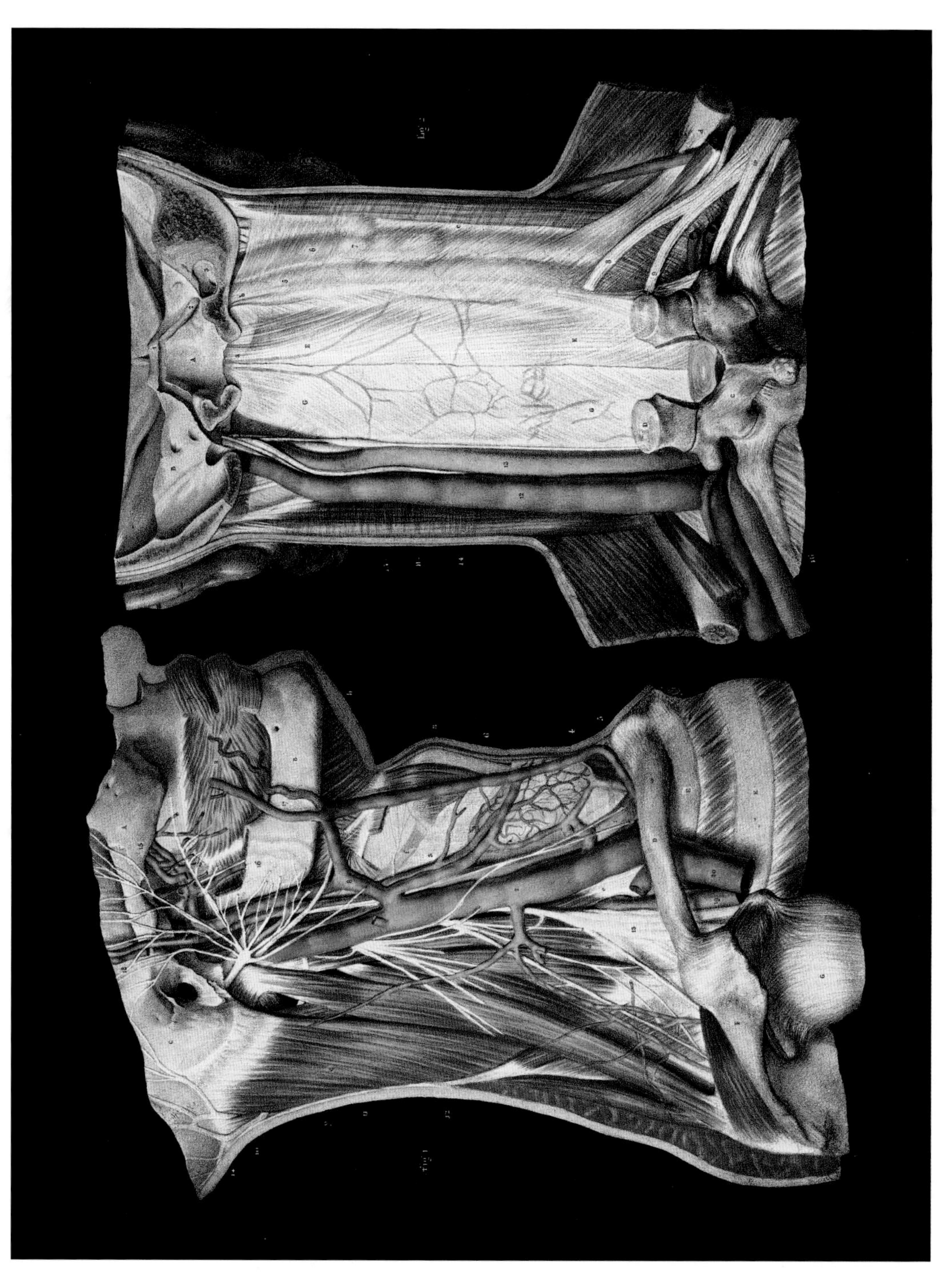

Topographical and surgical anatomy of the neck
Anatomie topographique et chirurgicale du cou
Anatomía topográfica y quirúrgica del cuello

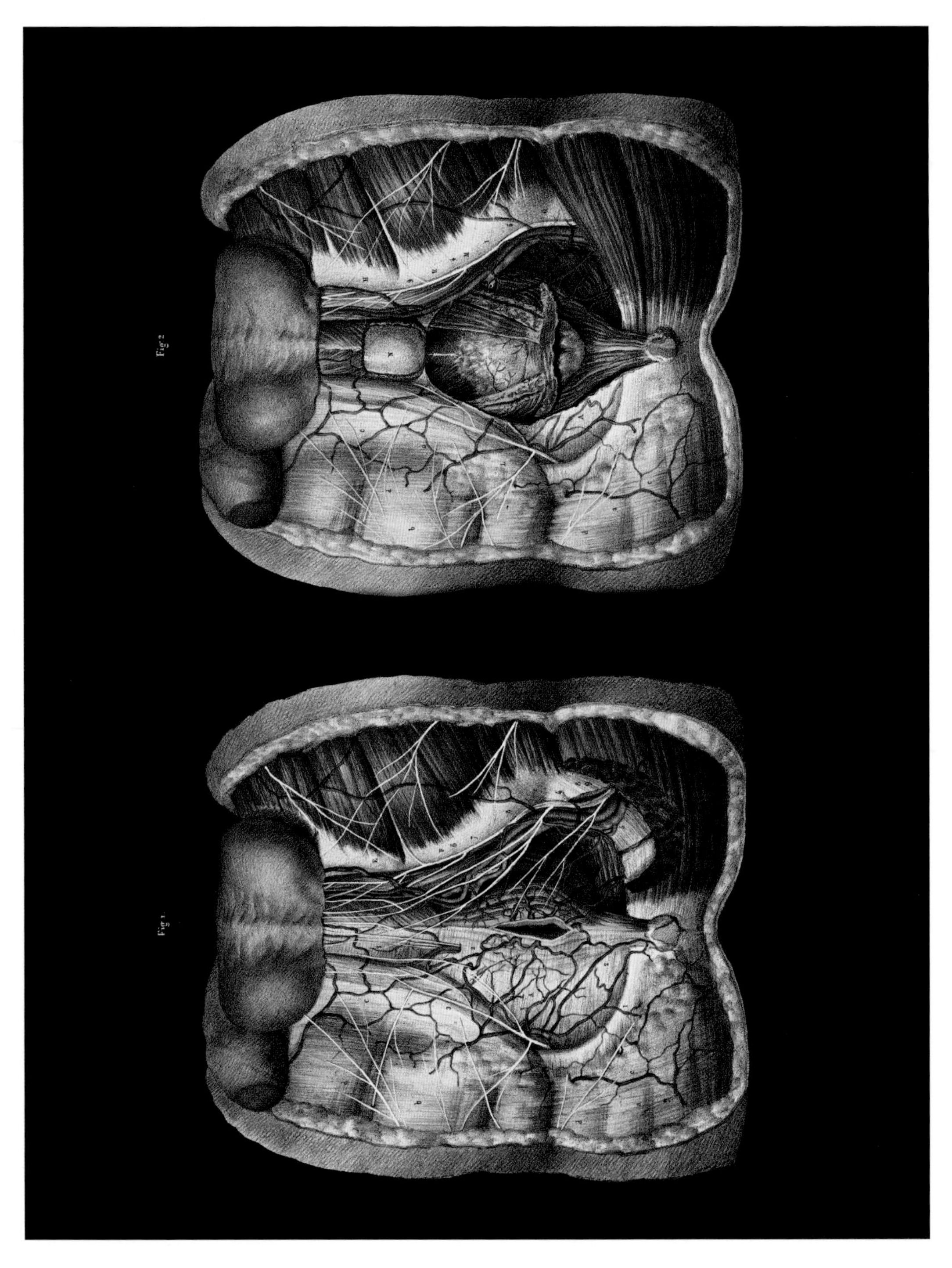

Topographical and surgical anatomy of the perineum
Anatomie topographique et chirurgicale du périnée
Anatomía topográfica y quirúrgica del periné

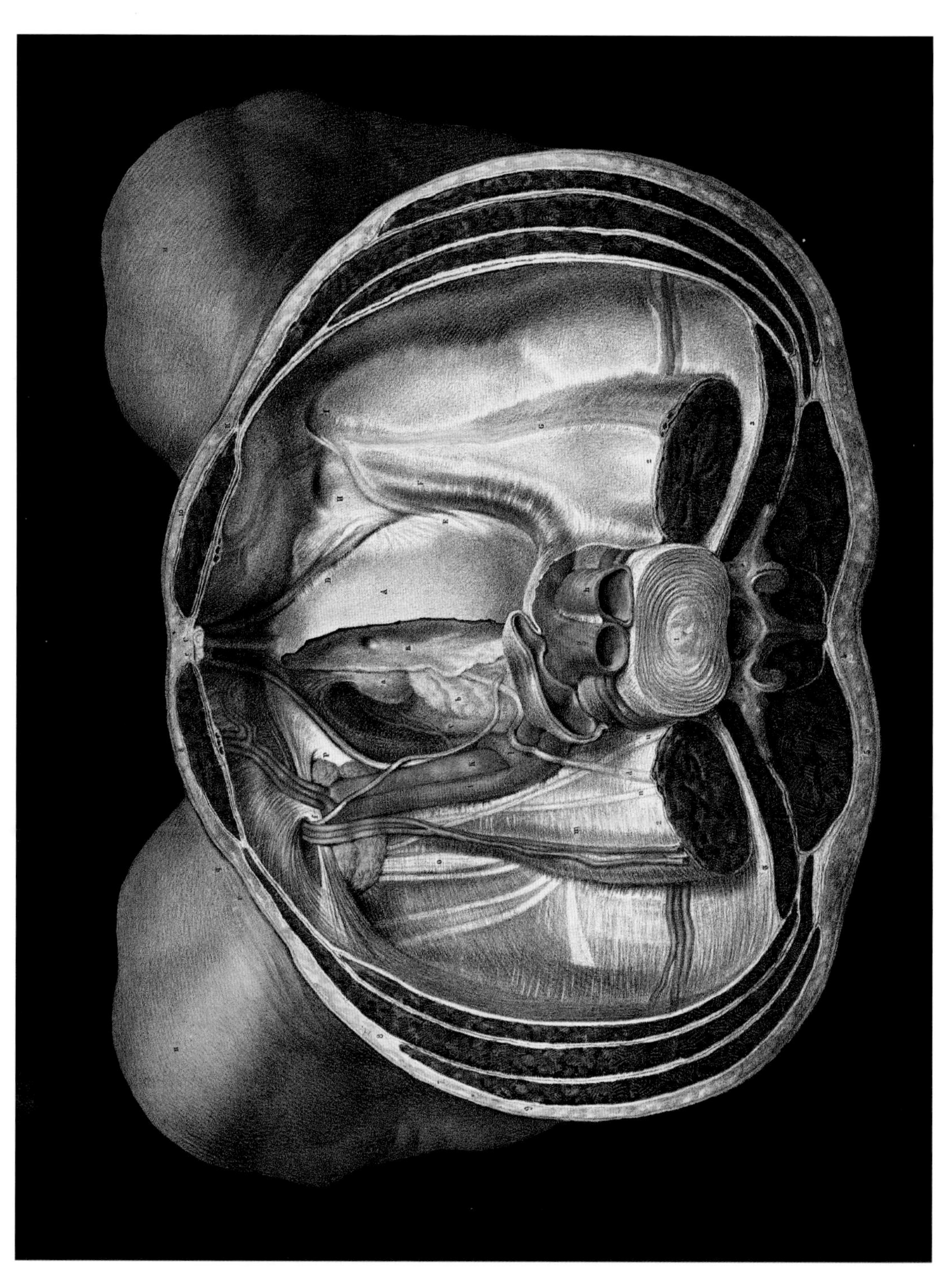

Topographical and surgical anatomy of the pelvis
Anatomie topographique et chirurgicale du pelvis
Anatomía topográfica y quirúrgica de la pelvis

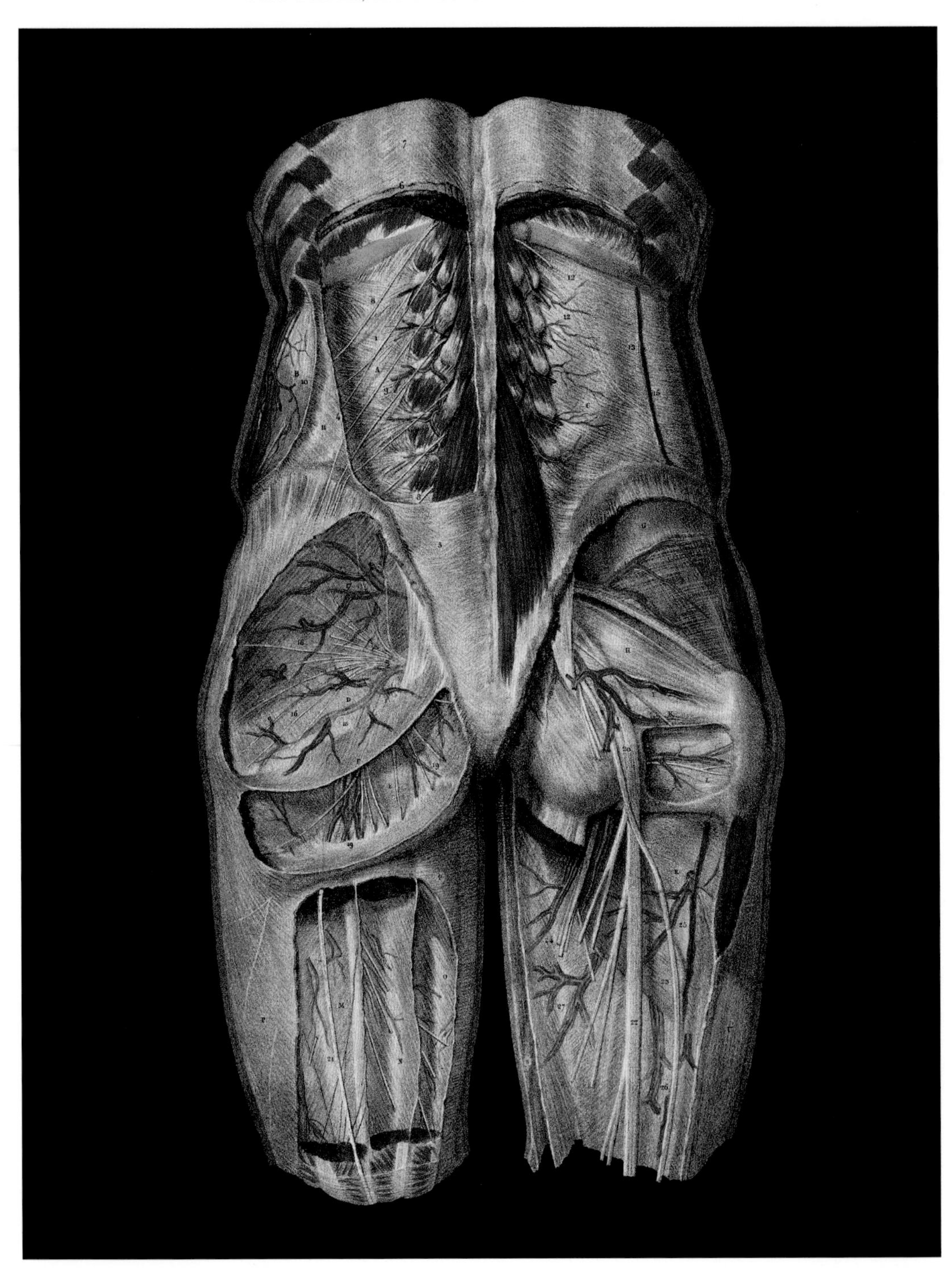

Topographical and surgical anatomy: Lumbar region, buttocks, and posterior femoral region
Anatomie topographique et chirurgicale : Régions lombaire, fessière et fémorale postérieure
Anatomía topográfica y quirúrgica: regiones lumbar, glútea y femoral posterior

ANATOMIA TOPOGRAPHICA
ET CHIRURGICA REGIONIS AXILLARIS ET COLLI

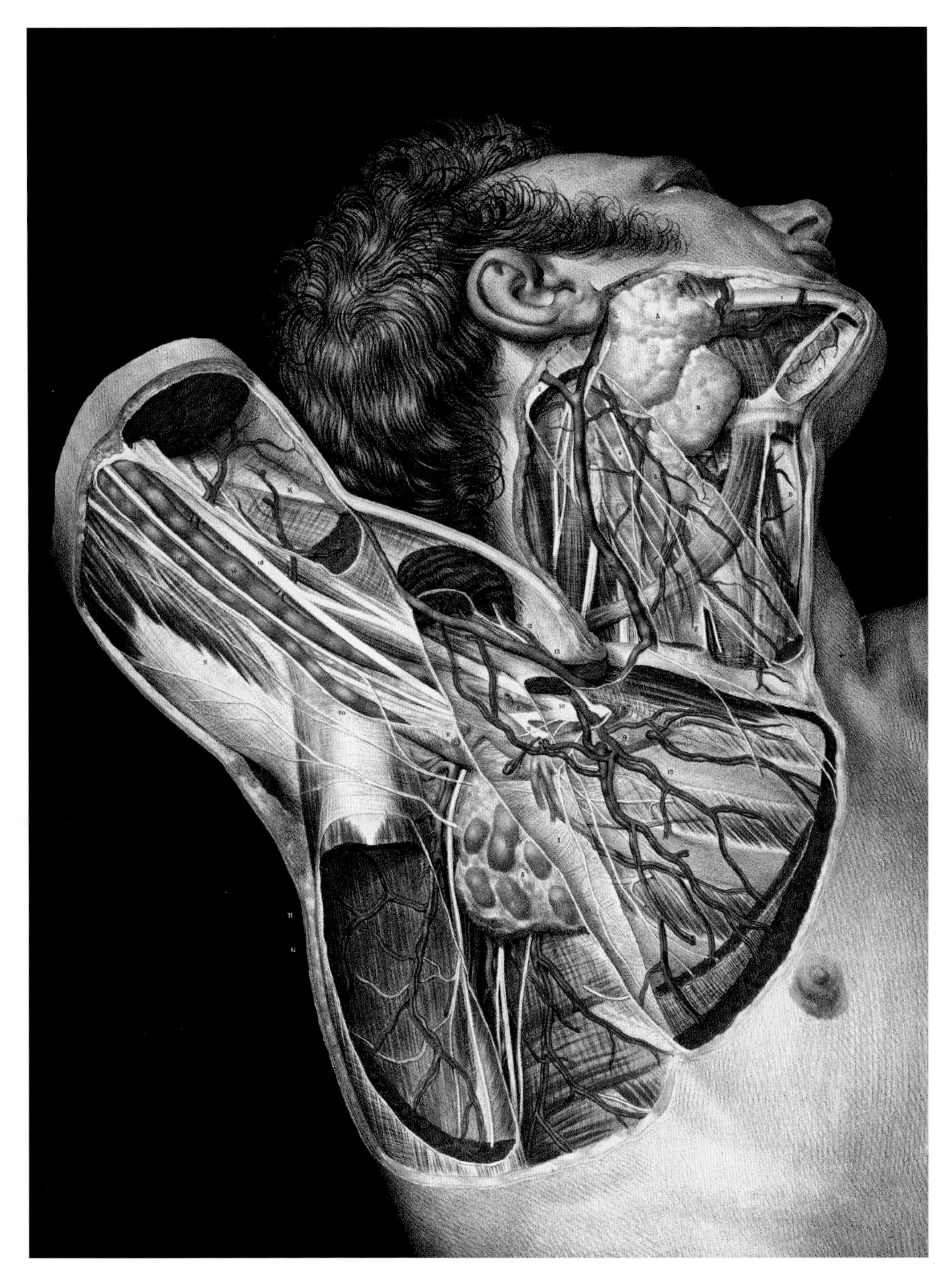

Topographical and surgical anatomy of the axillary region and the neck
Anatomie topographique et chirurgicale de la région axillaire et du cou
Anatomía topográfica y quirúrgica de la región axilar y cervical

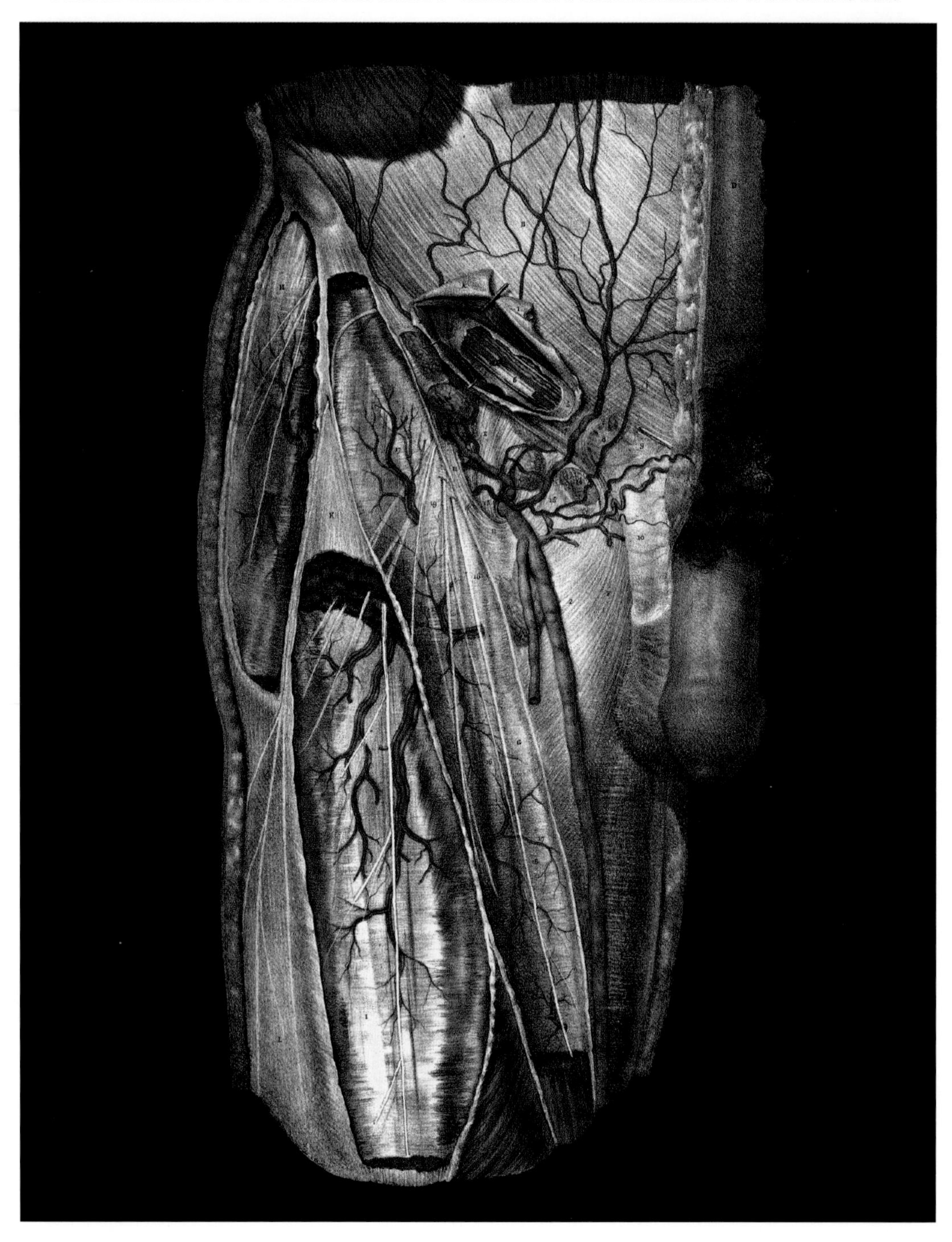

Topographical and surgical anatomy of the inguinal and anterior femoral regions
Anatomie topographique et chirurgicale des régions inguinale et fémorale antérieure
Anatomía topográfica y quirúrgica de las regiones inguinal y femoral anterior

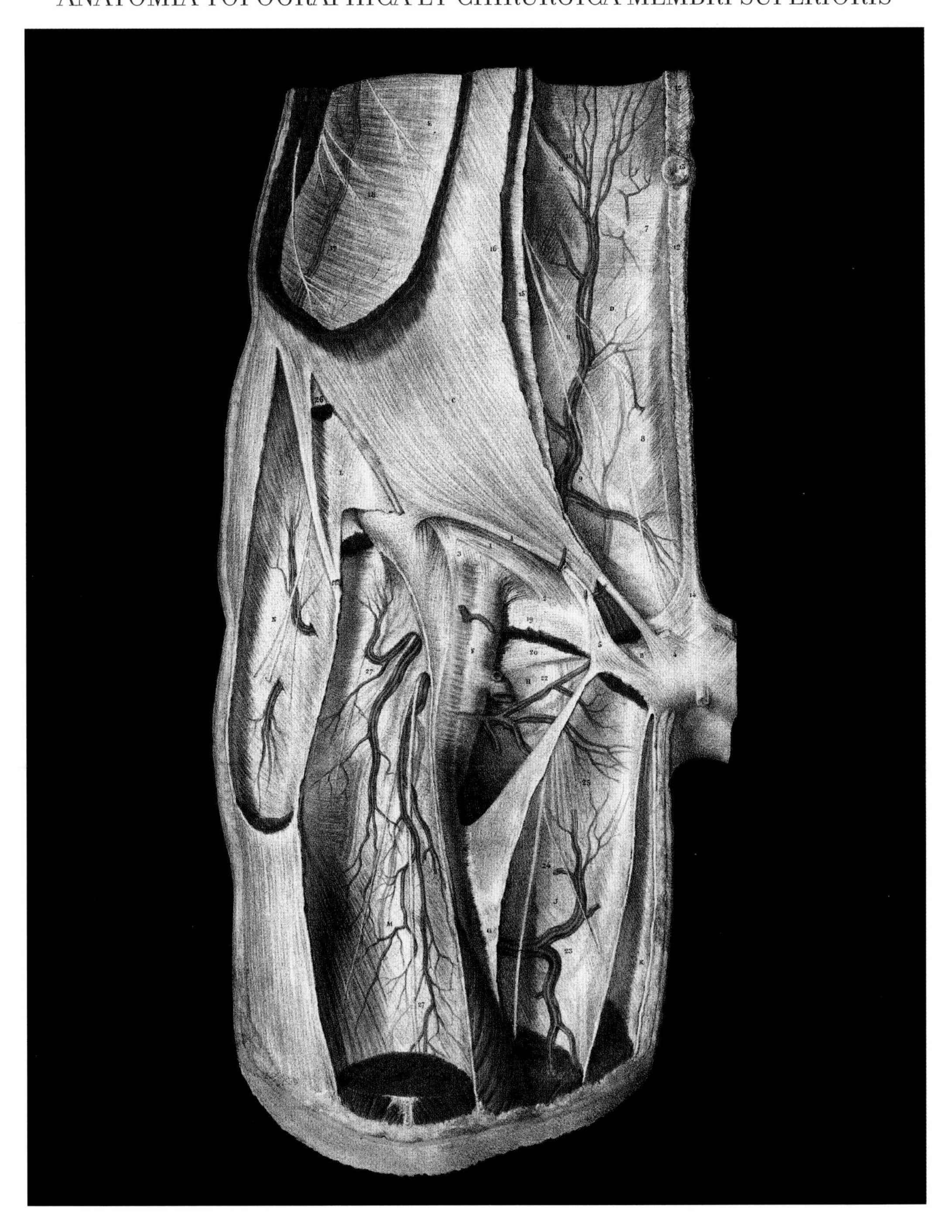

Topographical and surgical anatomy of the inguinal and anterior femoral regions
Anatomie topographique et chirurgicale des régions inguinale et fémorale antérieure
Anatomía topográfica y quirúrgica de las regiones inguinal y femoral anterior

ANATOMIA TOPOGRAPHICA ET CHIRURGICA REGIONUM INGUINALIS ET FEMORIS ANTERIORIS. ANATOMIA TOPOGRAPHICA ET CHIRURGICA MEMBRI SUPERIORIS

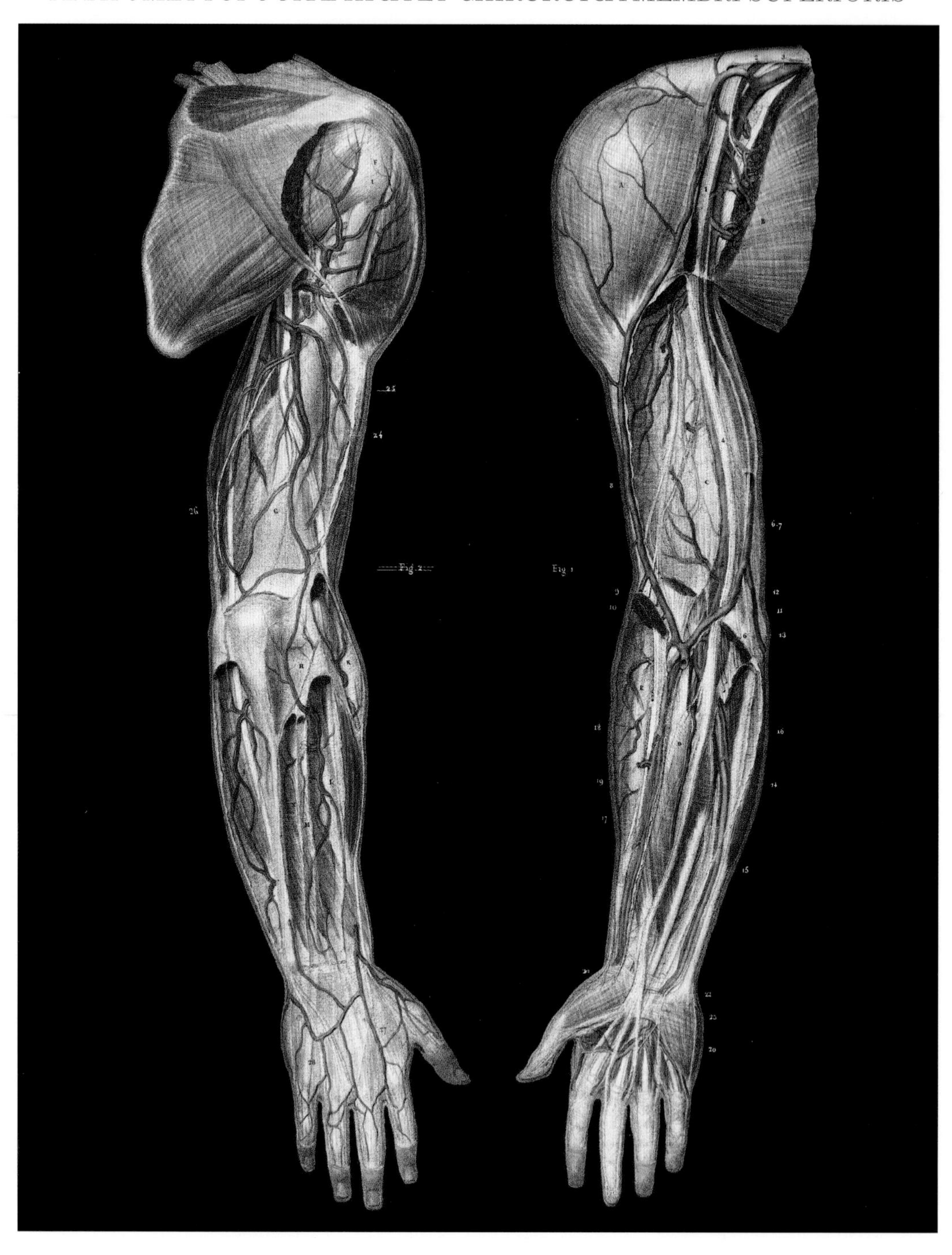

Topographical and surgical anatomy of the upper limb
Anatomie topographique et chirurgicale du membre supérieur
Anatomía topográfica y quirúrgica del miembro superior

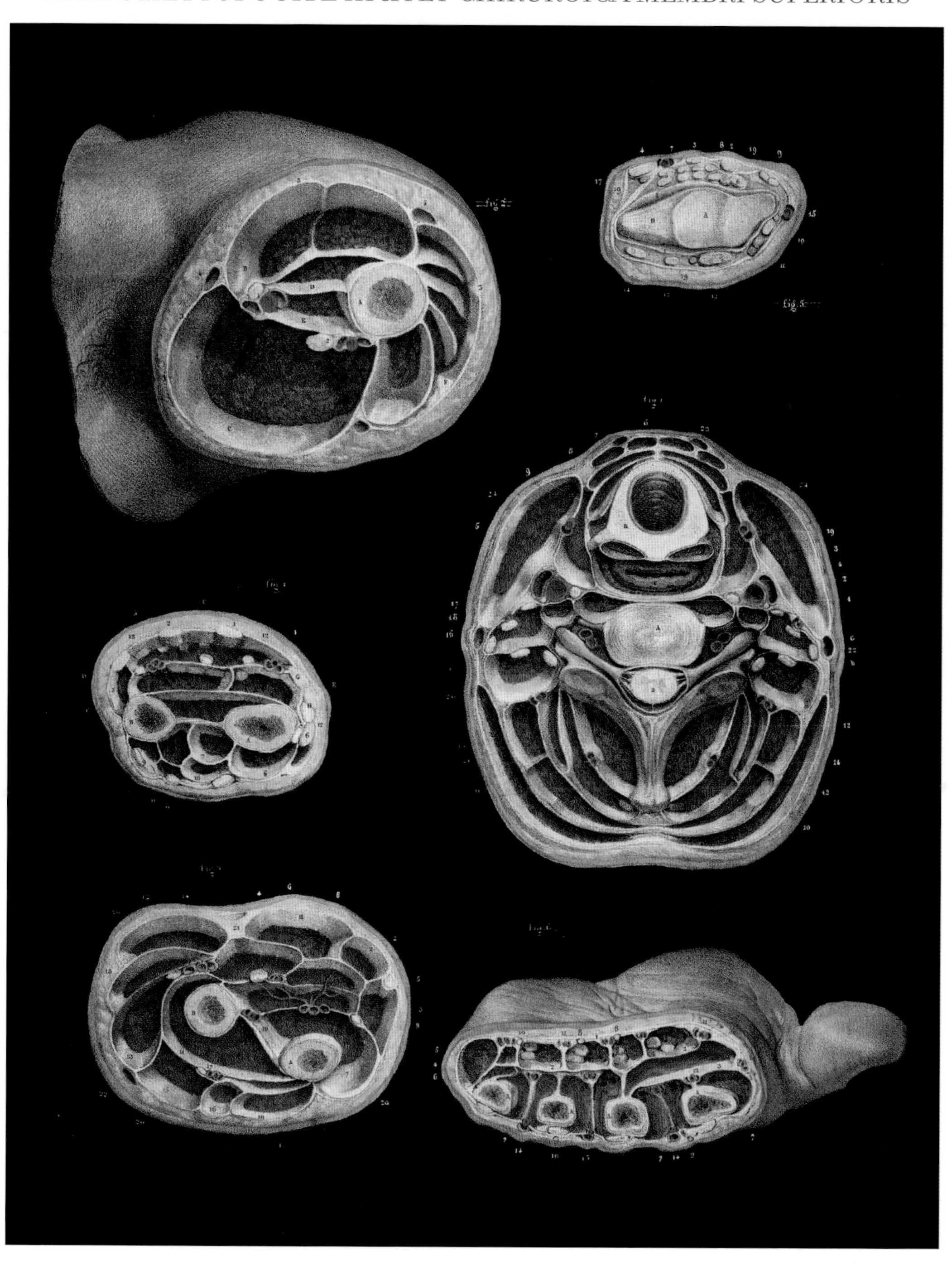

Topographical and surgical anatomy of the upper limb (and the neck)
Anatomie topographique et chirurgicale du membre supérieur (et du cou)
Anatomía topográfica y quirúrgica del miembro superior (y del cuello)

ANATOMIA TOPOGRAPHICA ET CHIRURGICA MEMBRI INFERIORIS

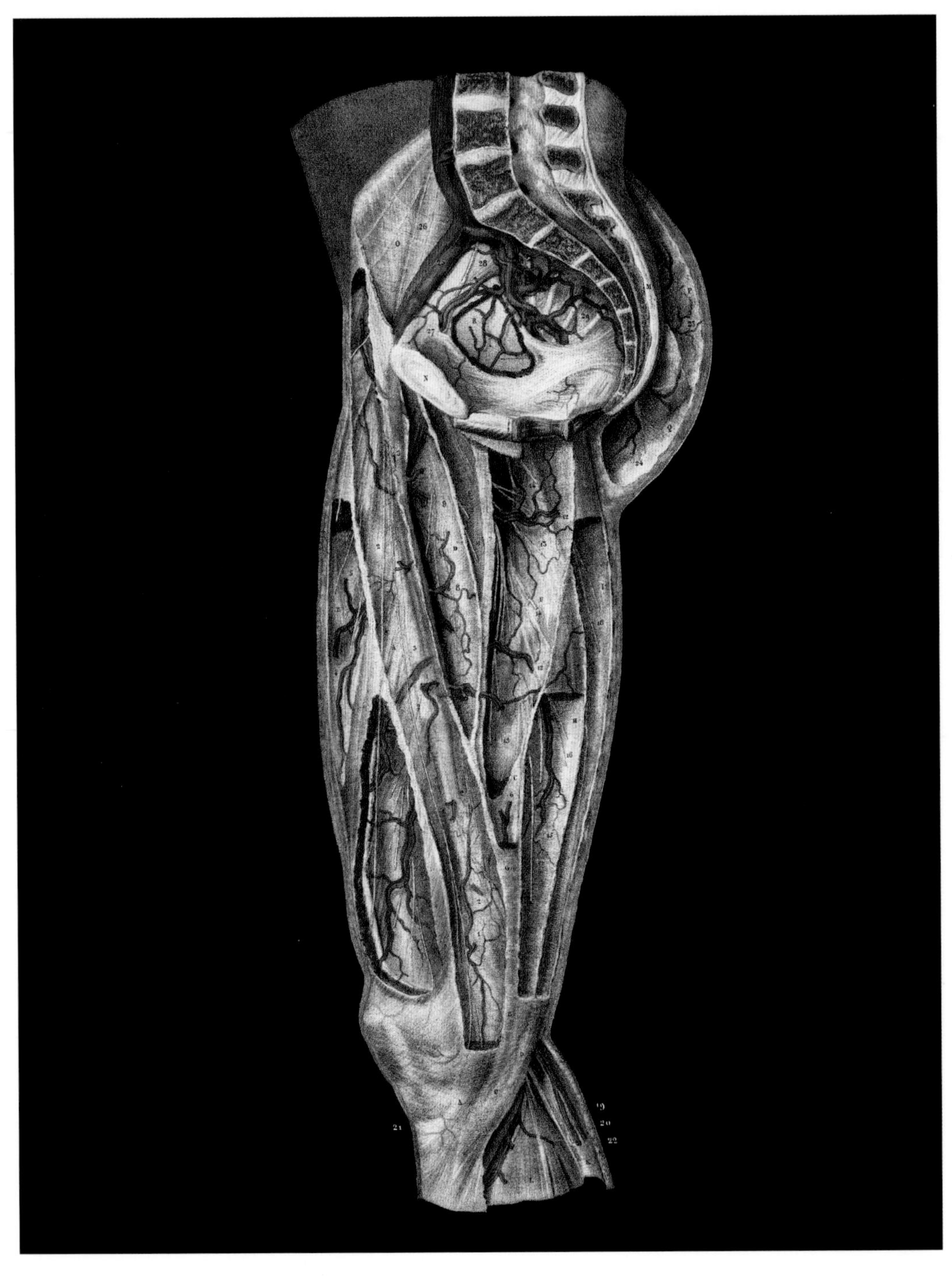

Topographical and surgical anatomy of the lower limb
Anatomie topographique et chirurgicale du membre inférieur
Anatomía topográfica y quirúrgica del miembro inferior

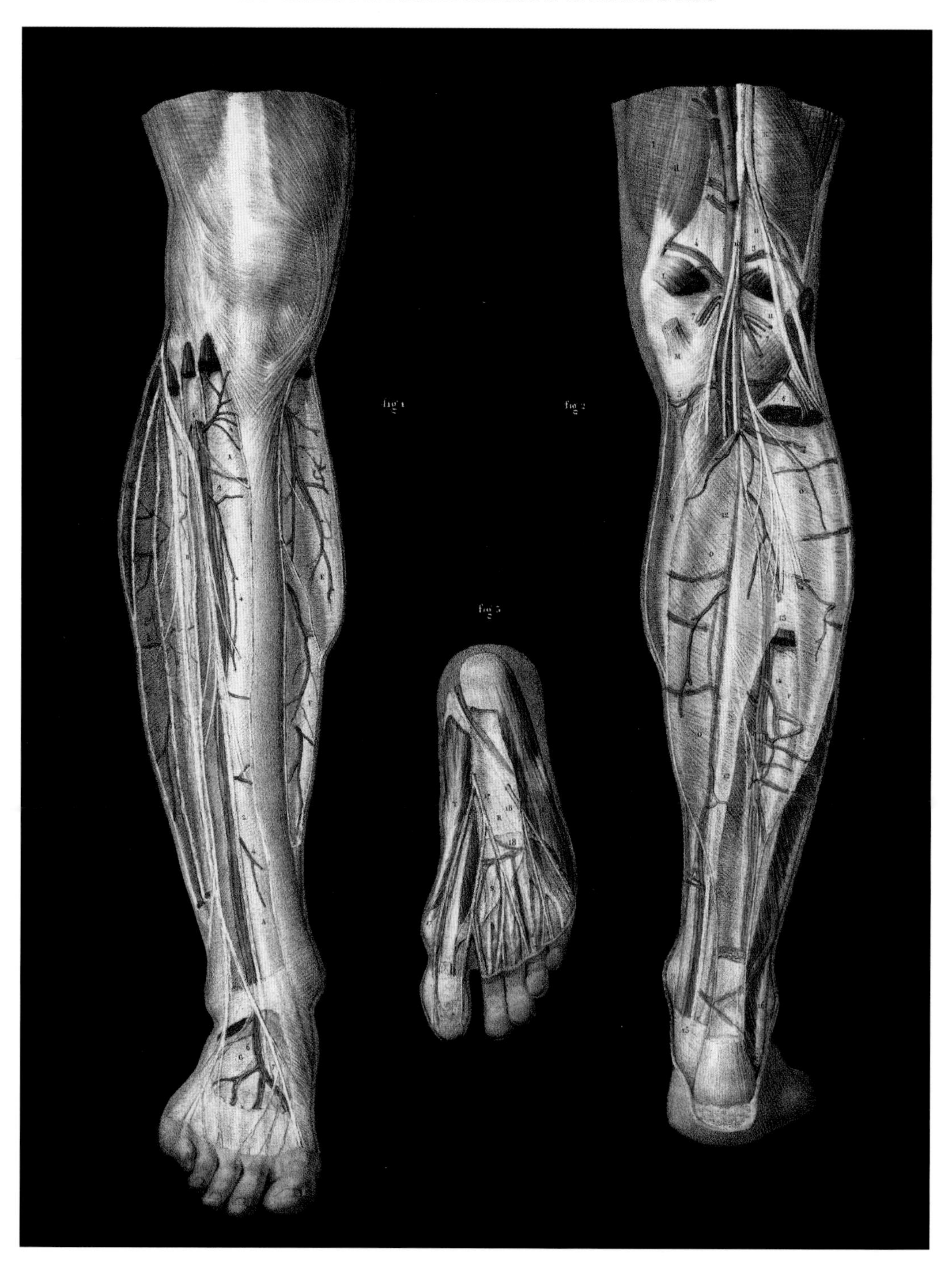

Topographical and surgical anatomy of the lower limb
Anatomie topographique et chirurgicale du membre inférieur
Anatomía topográfica y quirúrgica del miembro inferior

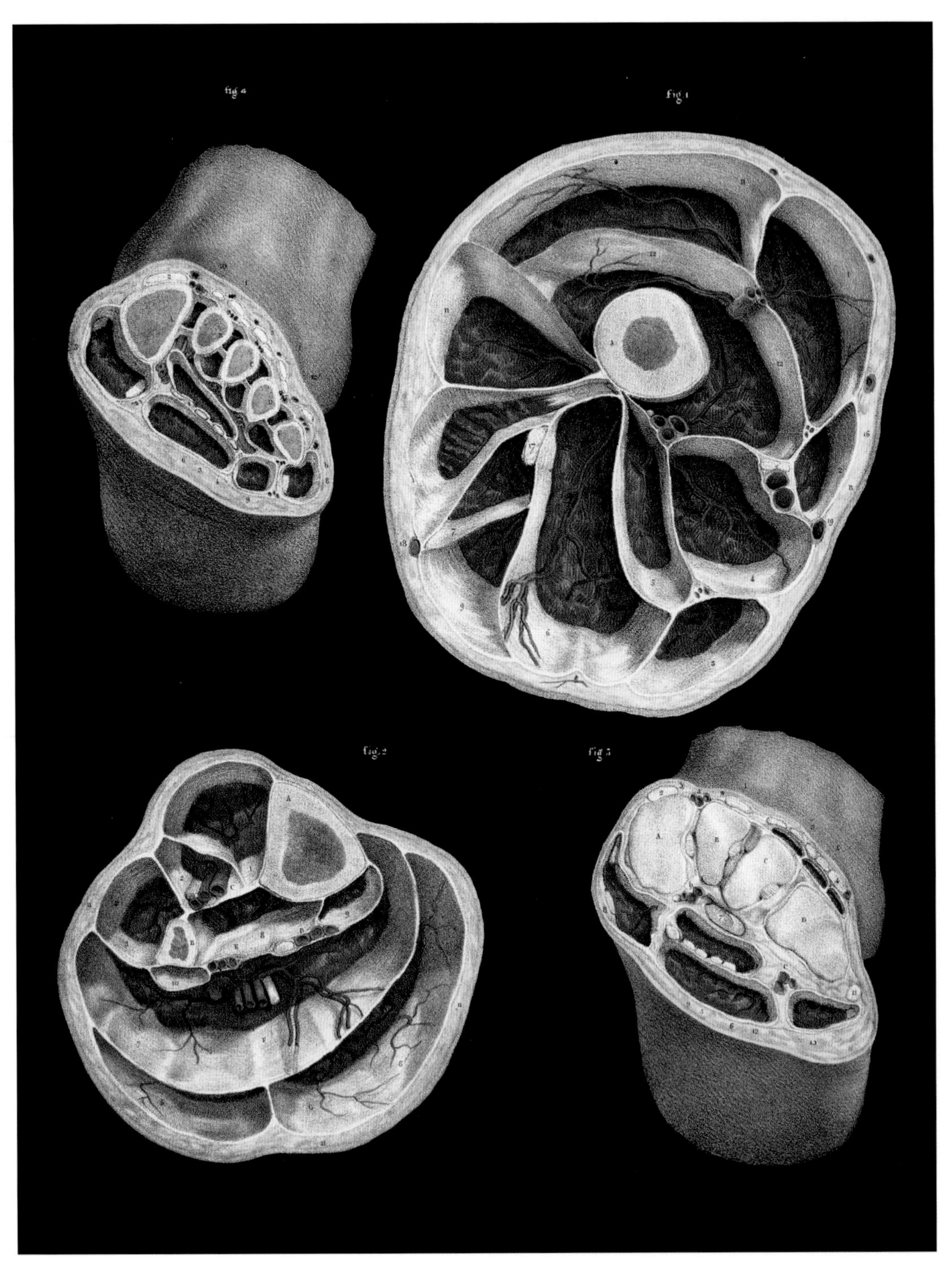

Topographical and surgical anatomy of the lower limb
Anatomie topographique et chirurgicale du membre inférieur
Anatomía topográfica y quirúrgica del miembro inferior

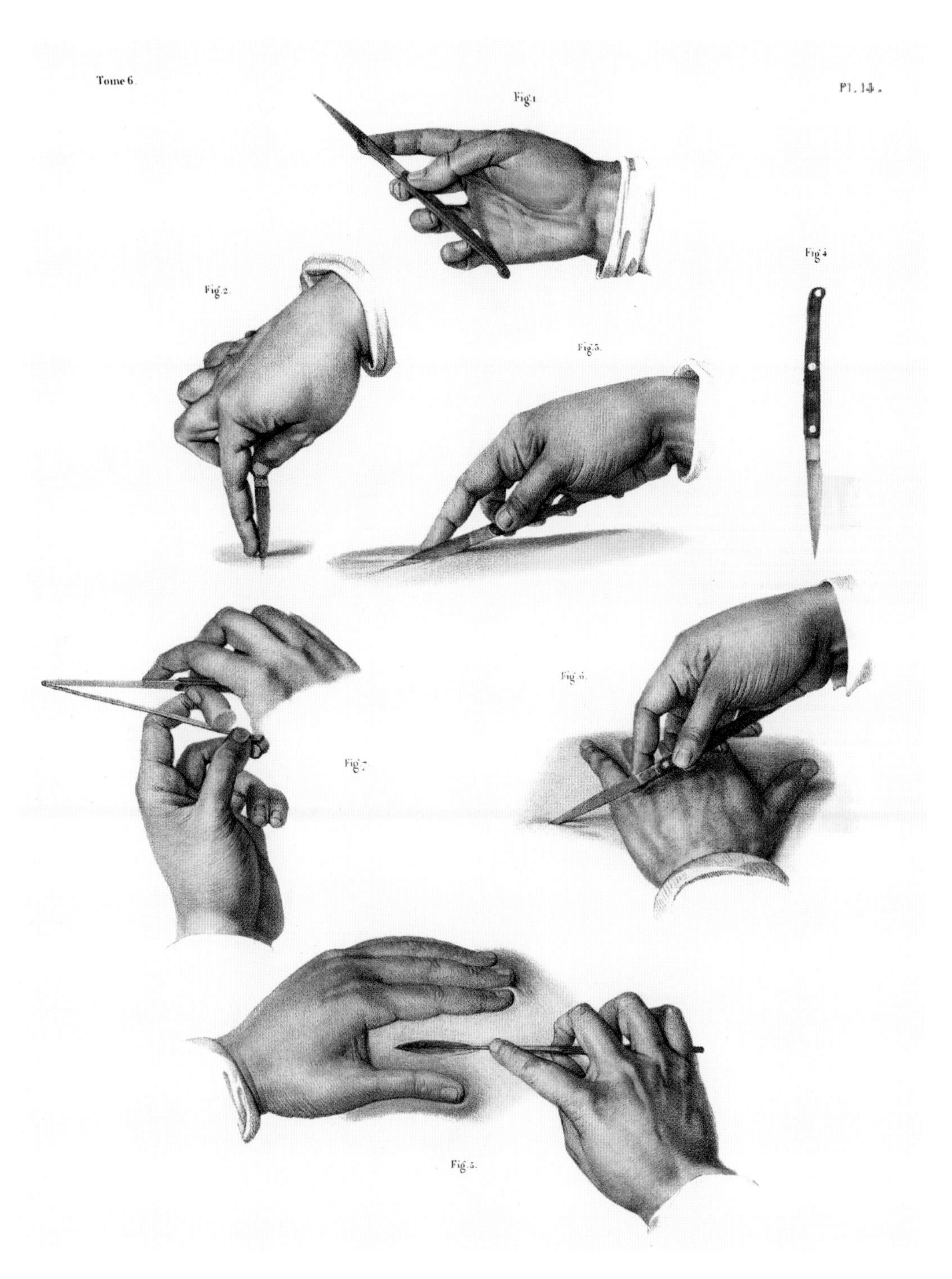

Incisions: Scalpel positions / Incisions : Positions du bistouri
Incisiones: posiciones del bisturí

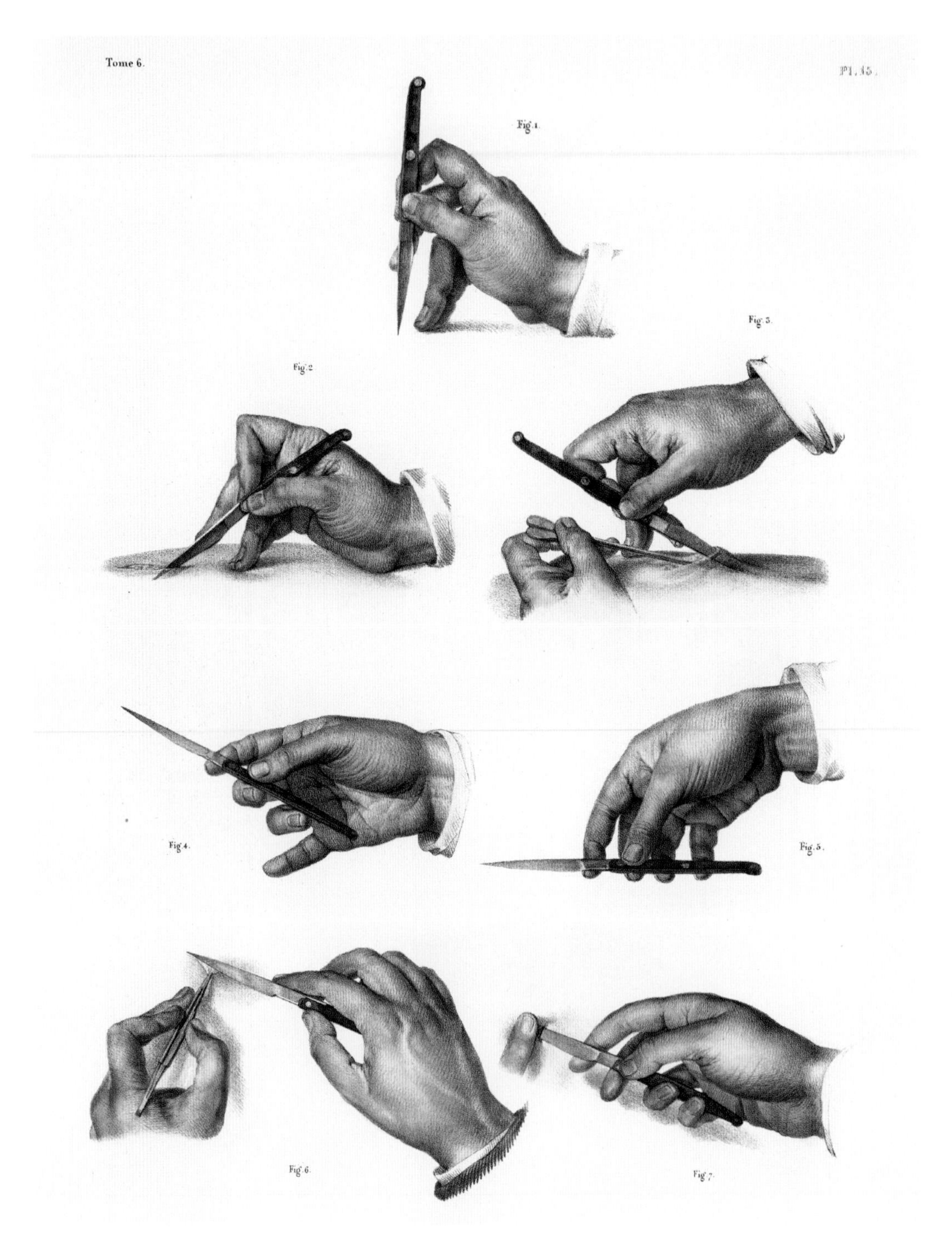

Incisions: Scalpel positions / Incisions : Positions du bistouri
Incisiones: posiciones del bisturí

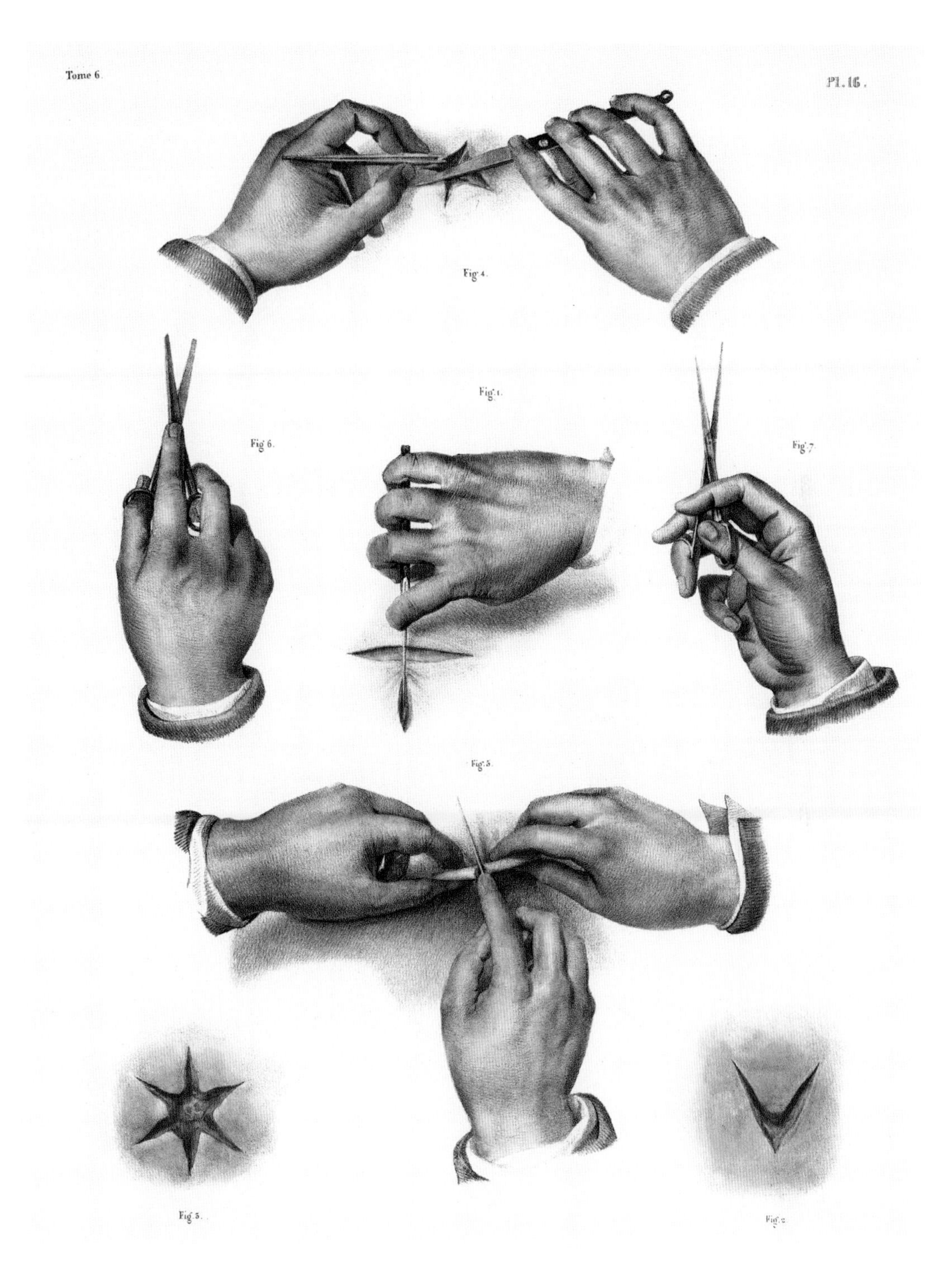

Incisions: Positions of scalpel and scissors
Incisions : Positions du bistouri et des ciseaux
Incisiones: posiciones del bisturí y de las tijeras

INCISIONES, CURATIONES PLAGARUM, ET USTIONES: INSTRUMENTA CHIRURGICA

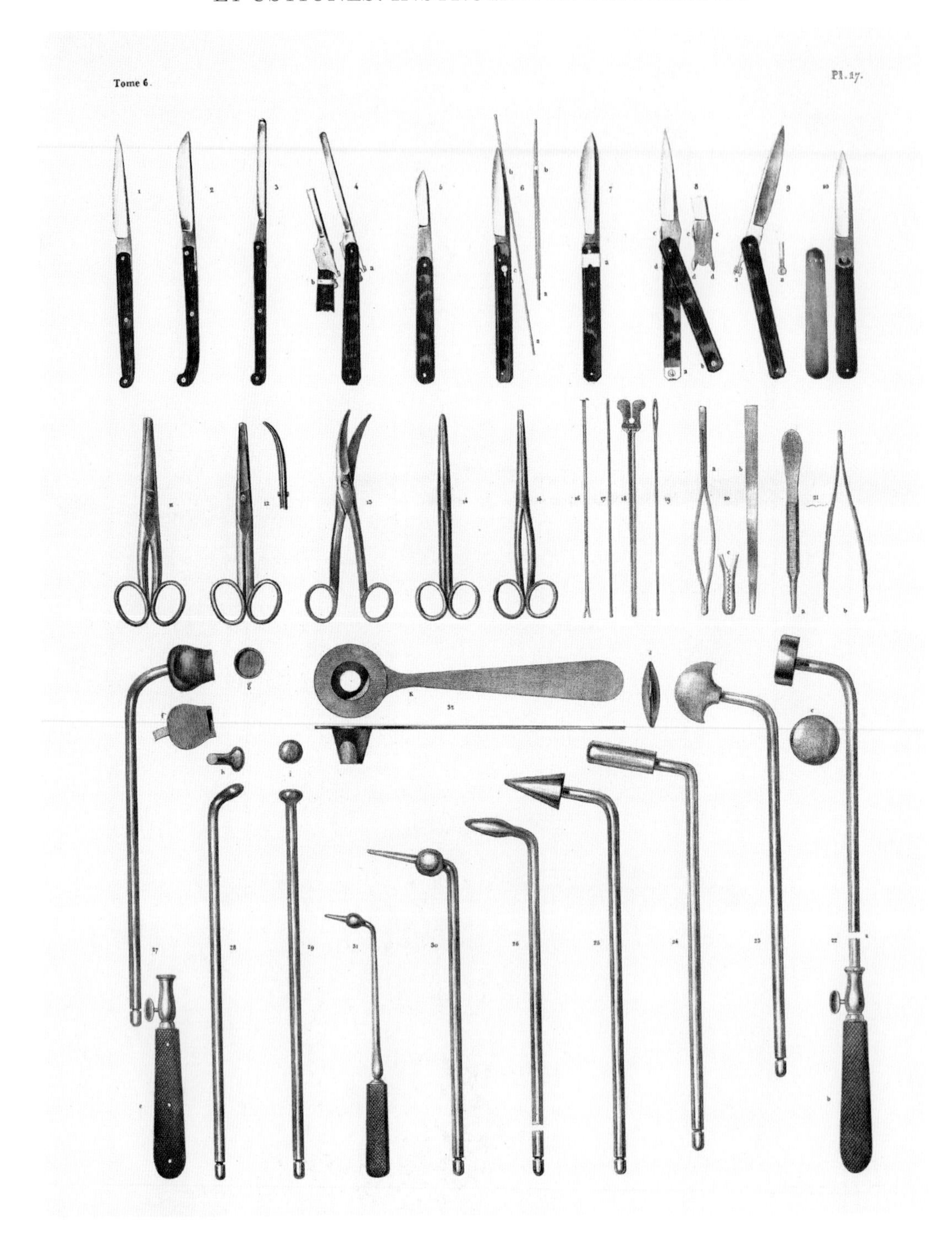

Incisions, treatment of wounds, and cauterisations: Surgical instruments
Incisions, traitements des plaies et cautérisations : Instruments chirurgicaux
Incisiones, tratamientos de las heridas y cauterizaciones: instrumentos quirúrgicos

COMPRESSIONES ARTERIARUM CAPITIS ET COLLI

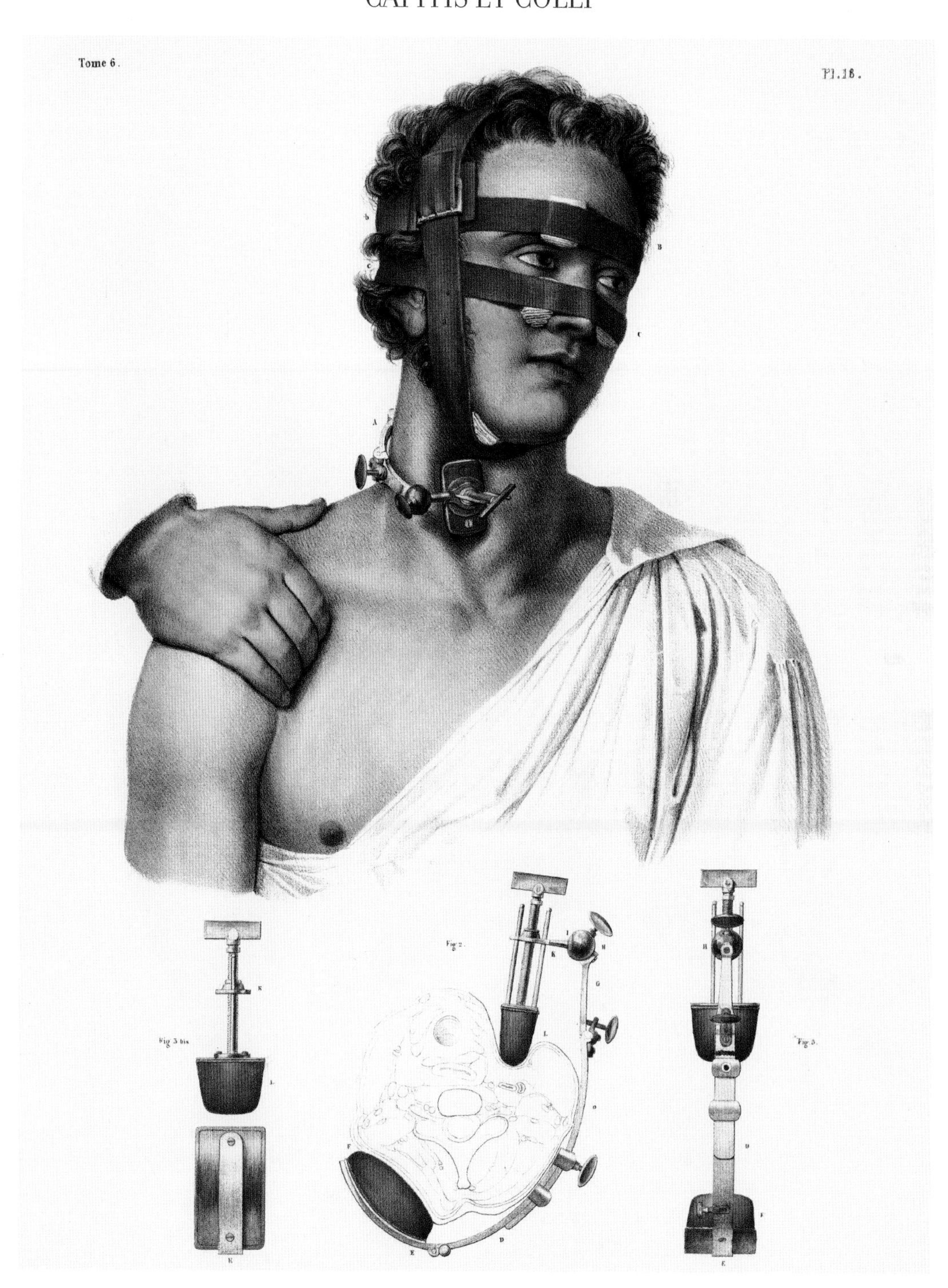

Compression of the arteries of the head and neck
Compressions des artères de la tête et du cou
Compresiones de las arterias de la cabeza y del cuello

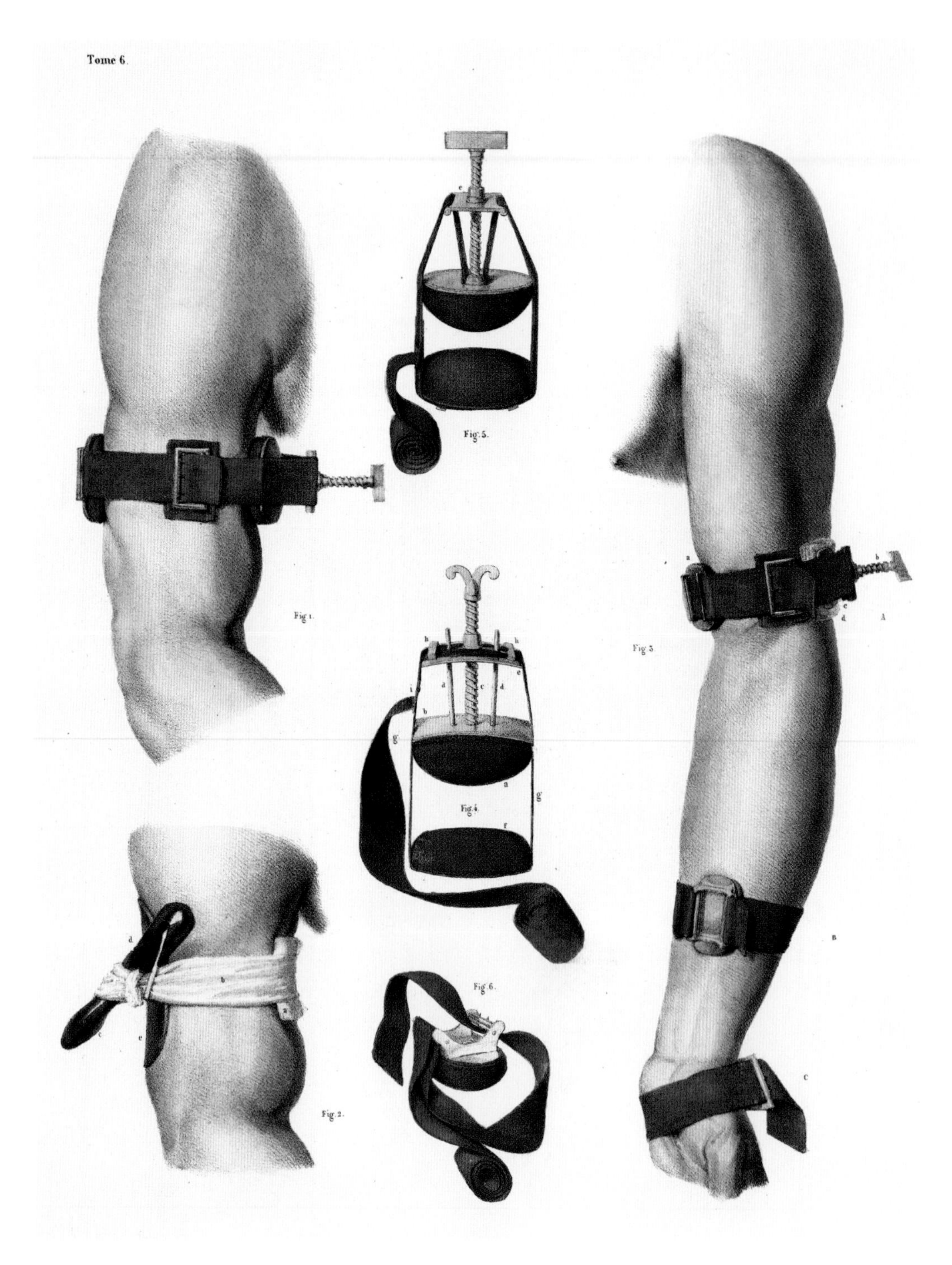

Compression of the arteries of the upper limb
Compressions des artères du membre supérieur
Compresiones de las arterias del miembro superior

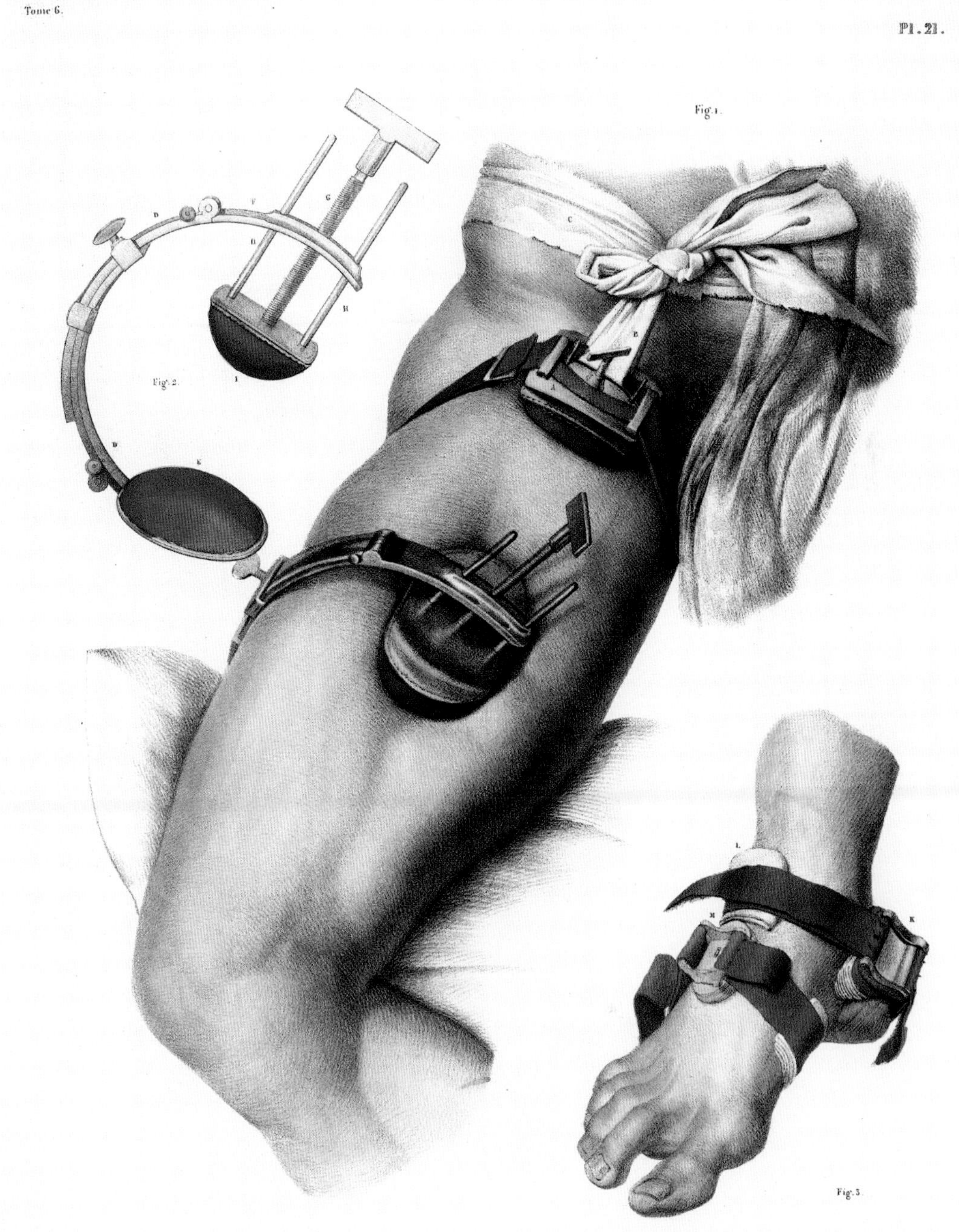

Tome 6.

Pl. 21.

Fig. 1.

Fig. 2.

Fig. 3.

Compression of the arteries of the lower limb
Compressions des artères du membre inférieur
Compresiones de las arterias del miembro inferior

ARTES CHIRURGICAE VARIAE.
INSTRUMENTA CHIRURGICA

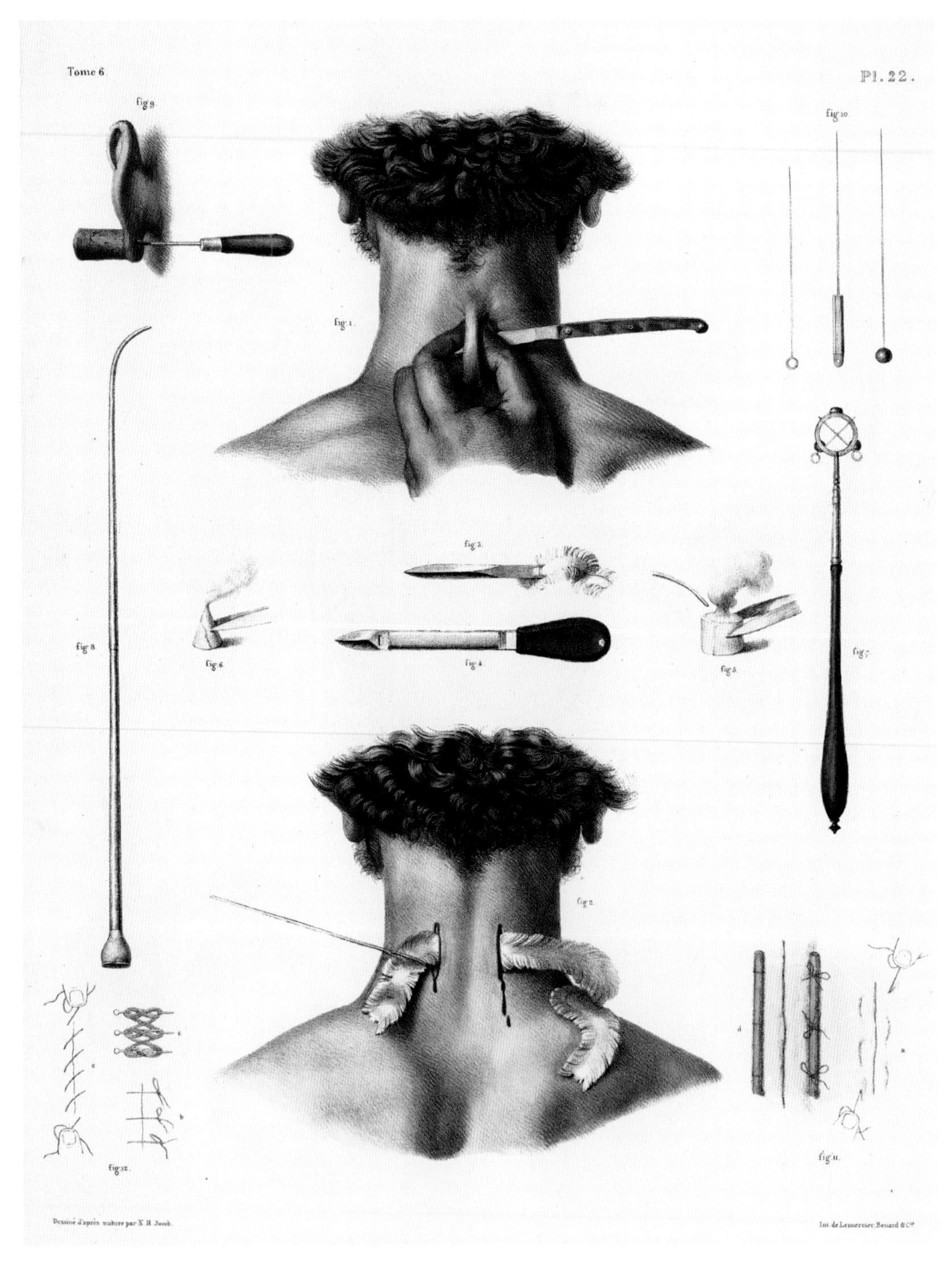

Various surgical techniques. Surgical instruments
Techniques chirurgicales diverses. Instruments chirurgicaux
Técnicas quirúrgicas diversas. Instrumentos quirúrgicos

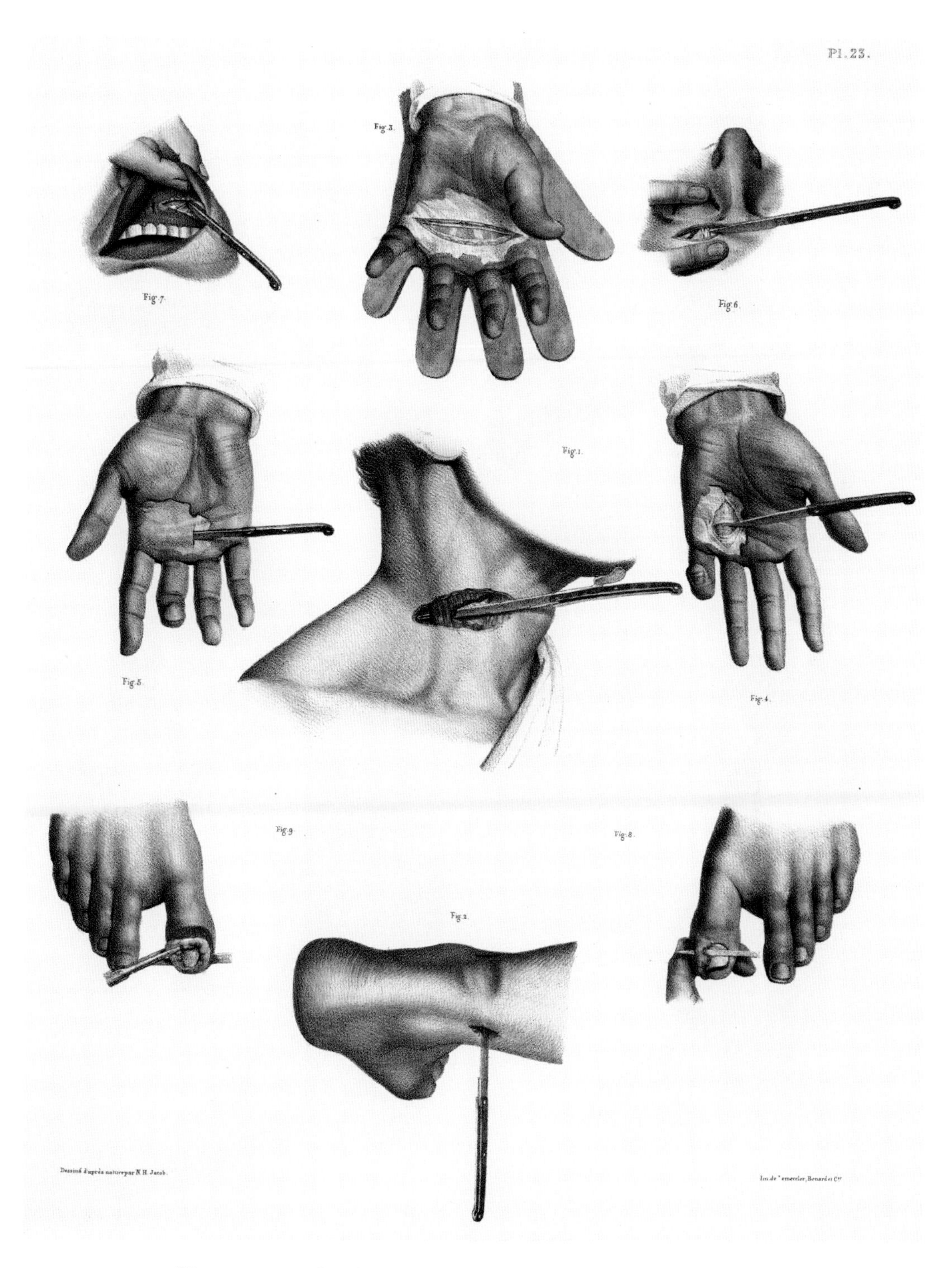

Various surgical techniques / Techniques chirurgicales diverses
Técnicas quirúrgicas diversas

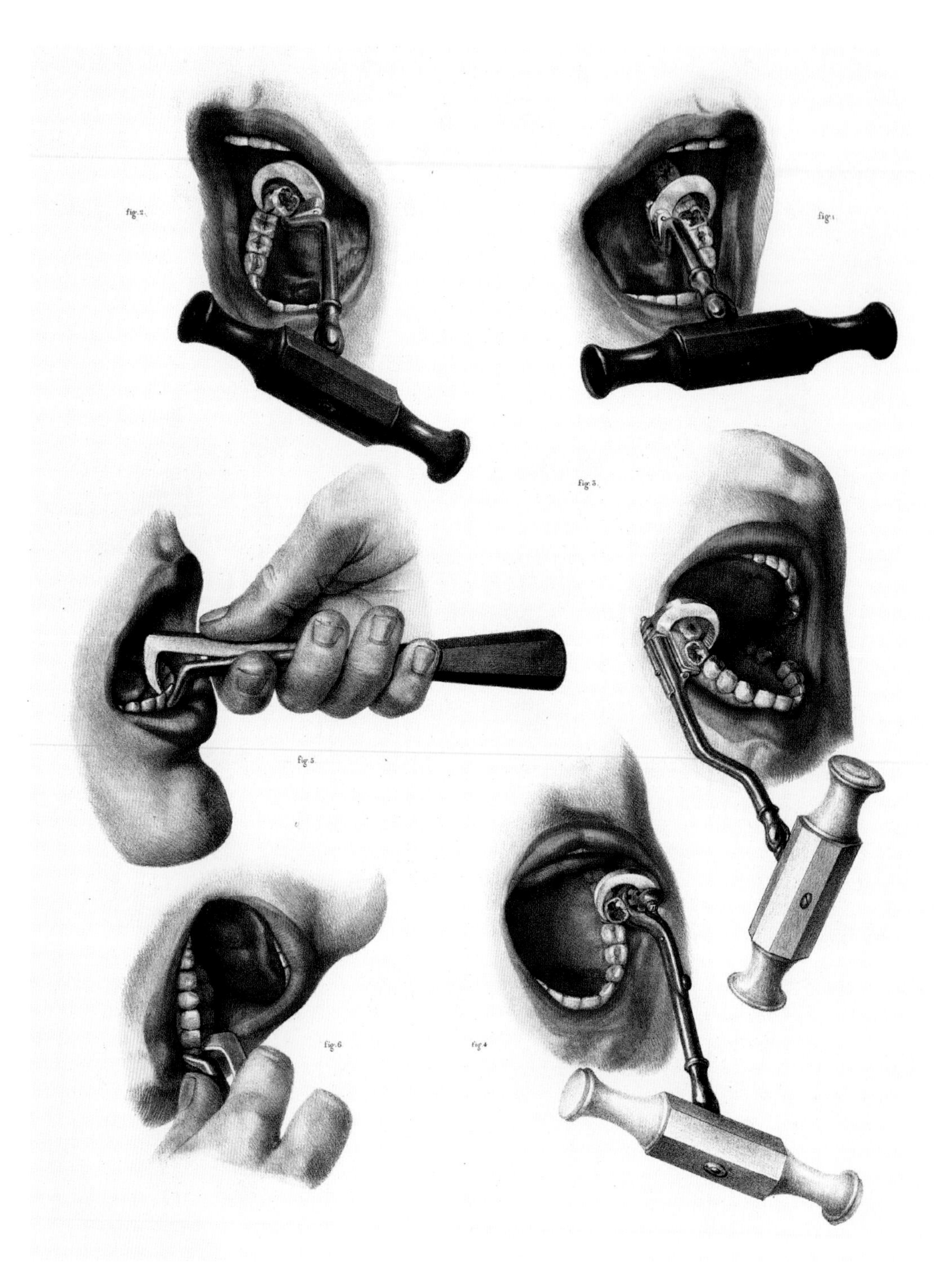

Tooth extraction / Avulsions de dents / Avulsiones dentales

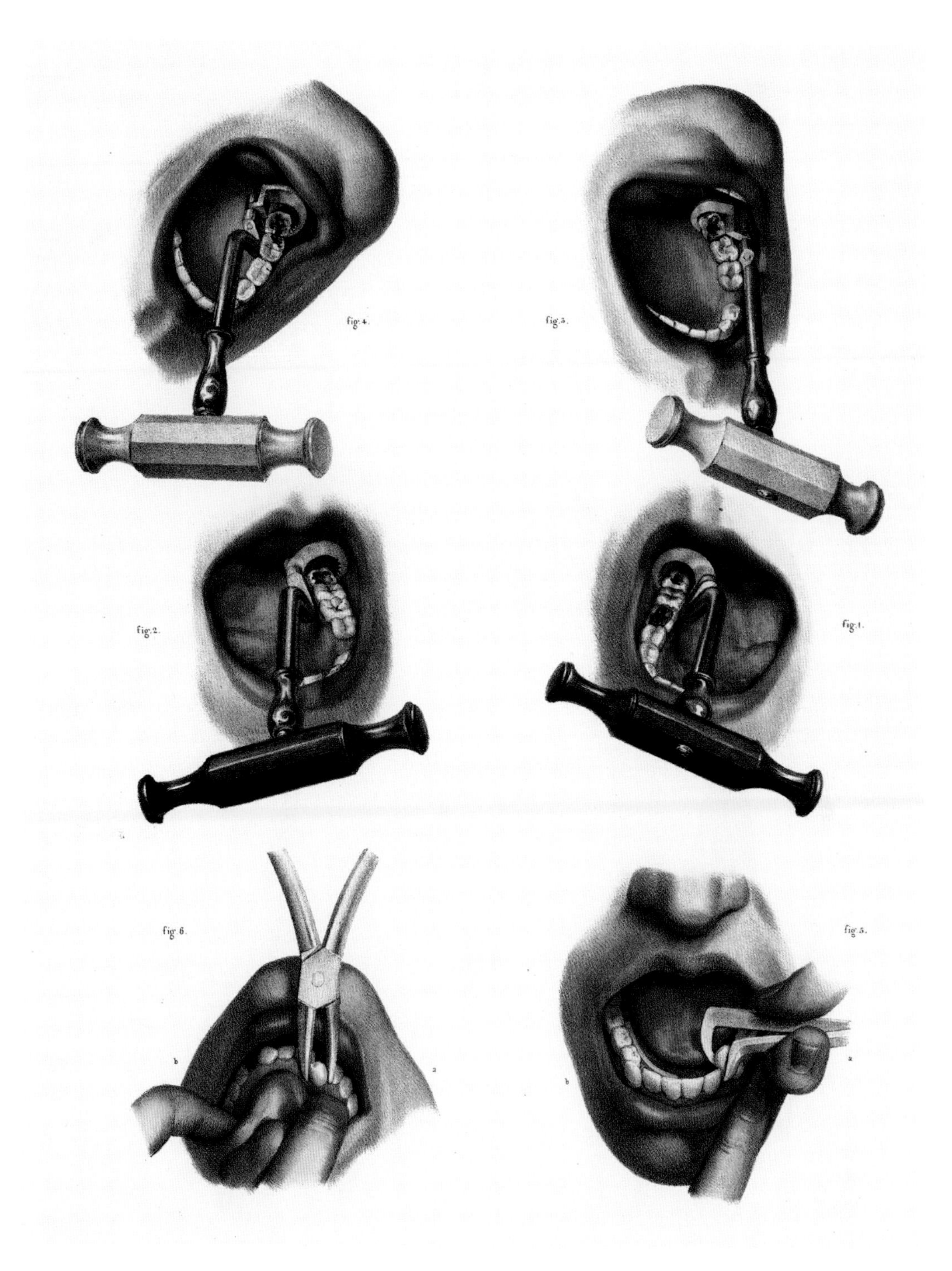

Tooth extraction / Avulsions de dents / Avulsiones dentales

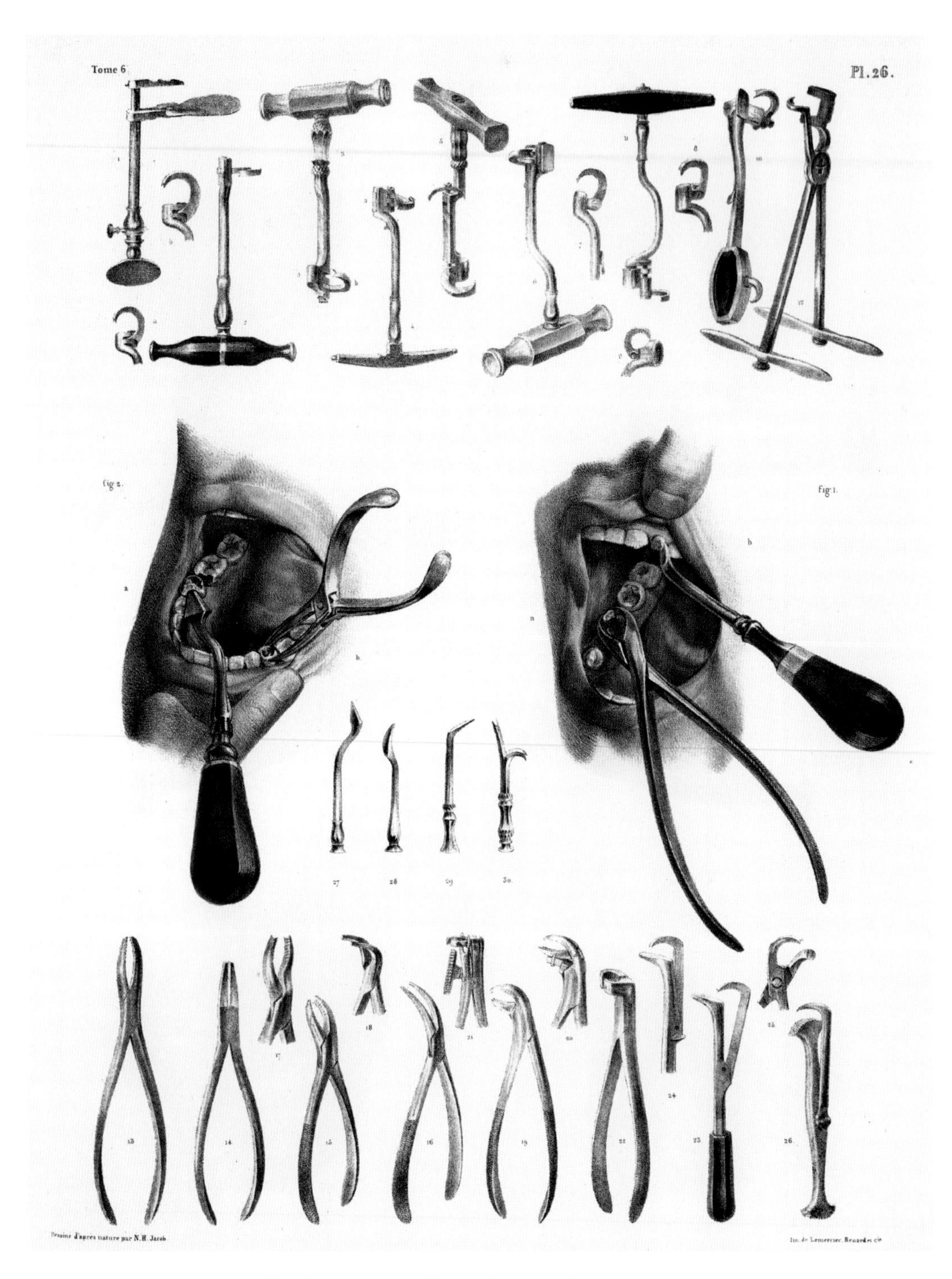

Tooth extraction. Dental surgical instruments
Avulsions de dents. Instruments chirurgicaux dentaires
Avulsiones dentales. Instrumentos quirúrgicos dentales

CUCURBITAE, INSTRUMENTA SCARIFICATIONIS, ET BDELLOMETRA

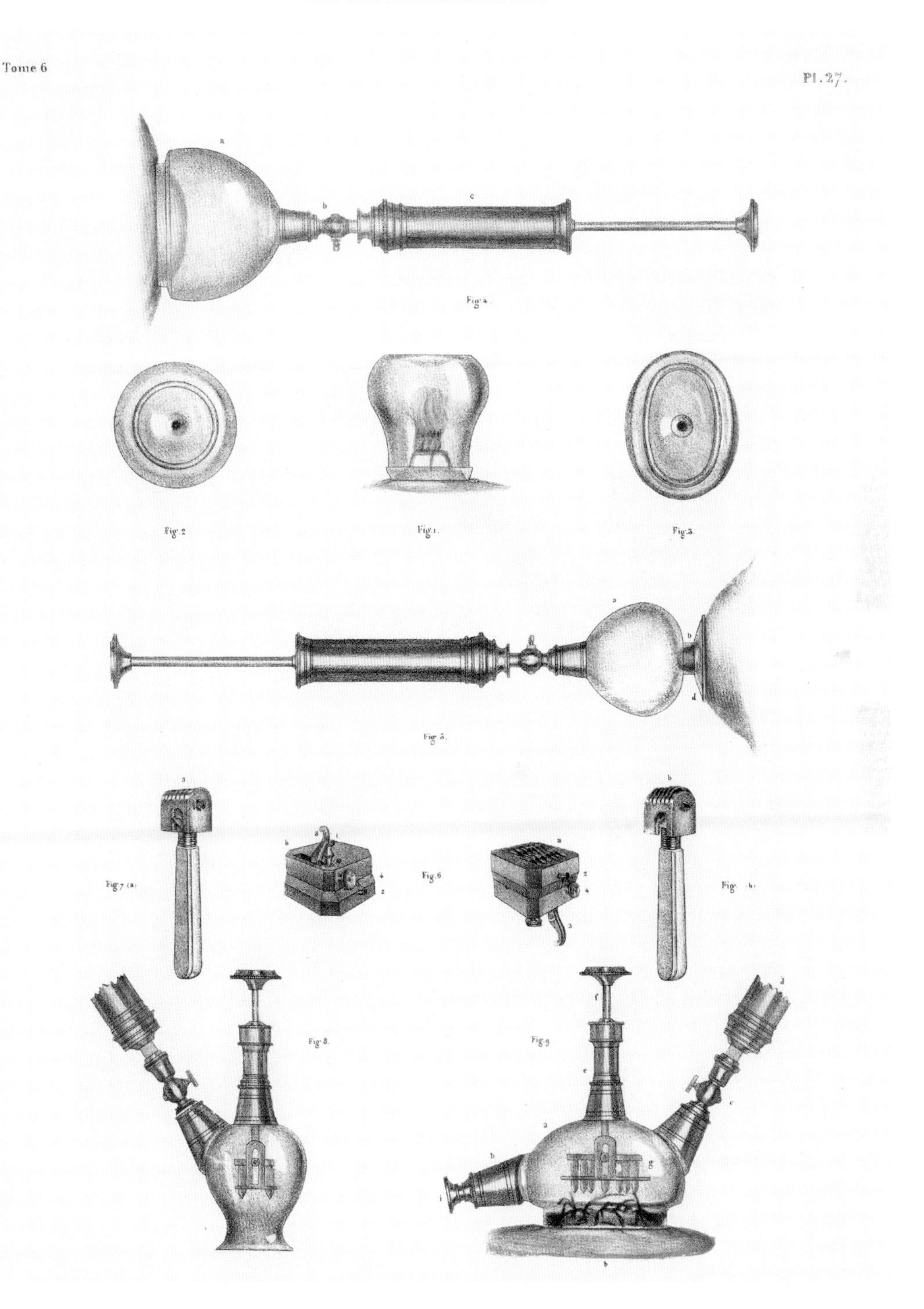

Ventouses, scarificators, and bdellometers
Ventouses, scarificateurs et bdellomètres
Ventosas, escarificadores y sanguijuelas mecánicas

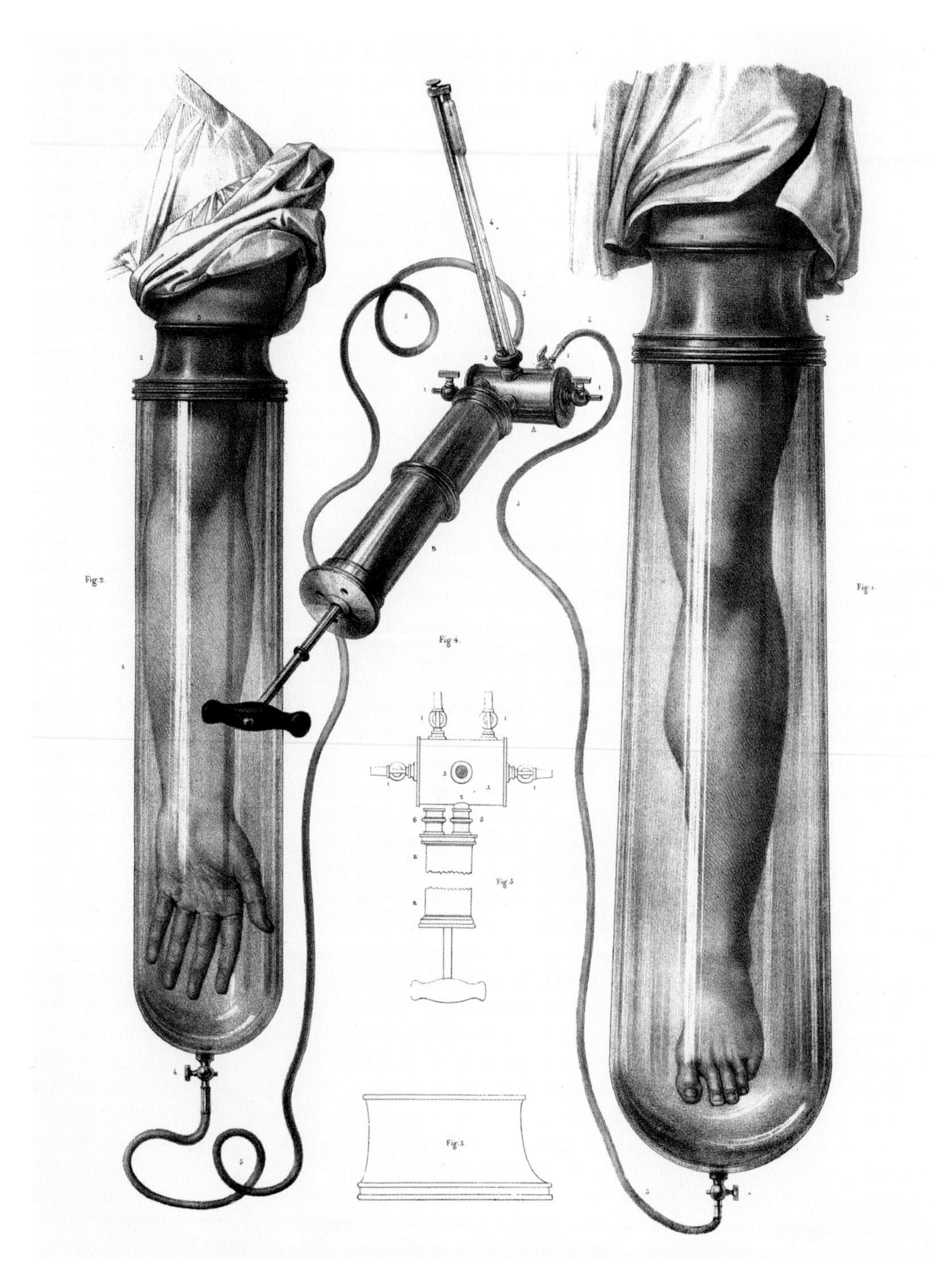

Junod's ventouse / Ventouses de Junod / Ventosas de Junod

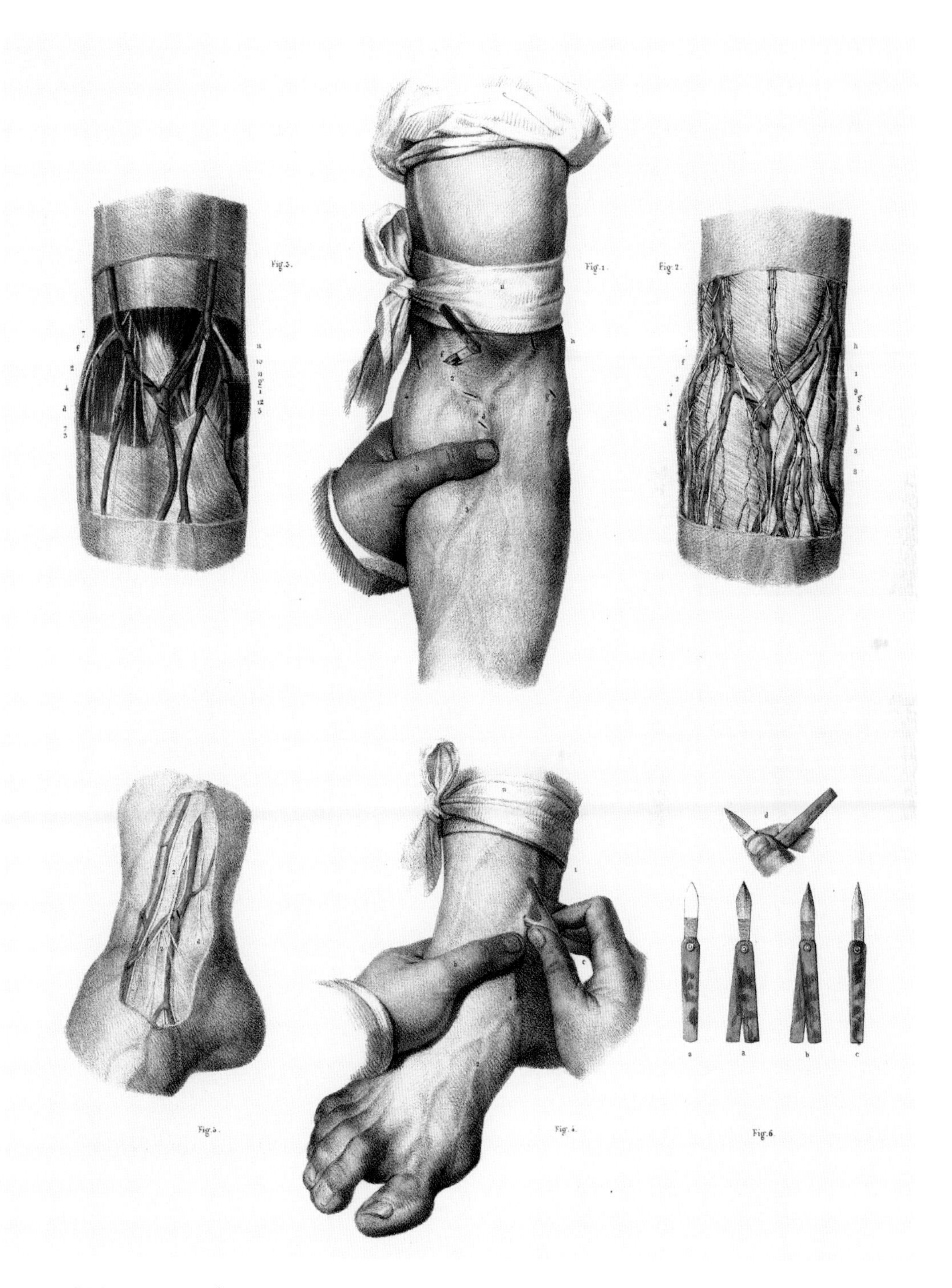

Phlebotomies (bloodletting) / Phlébotomies (saignées) / Flebotomías (sangrías)

Phlebotomies and arteriotomies (bloodletting)
Phlébotomies et artériotomies (saignées)
Flebotomías y arteriotomías (sangrías)

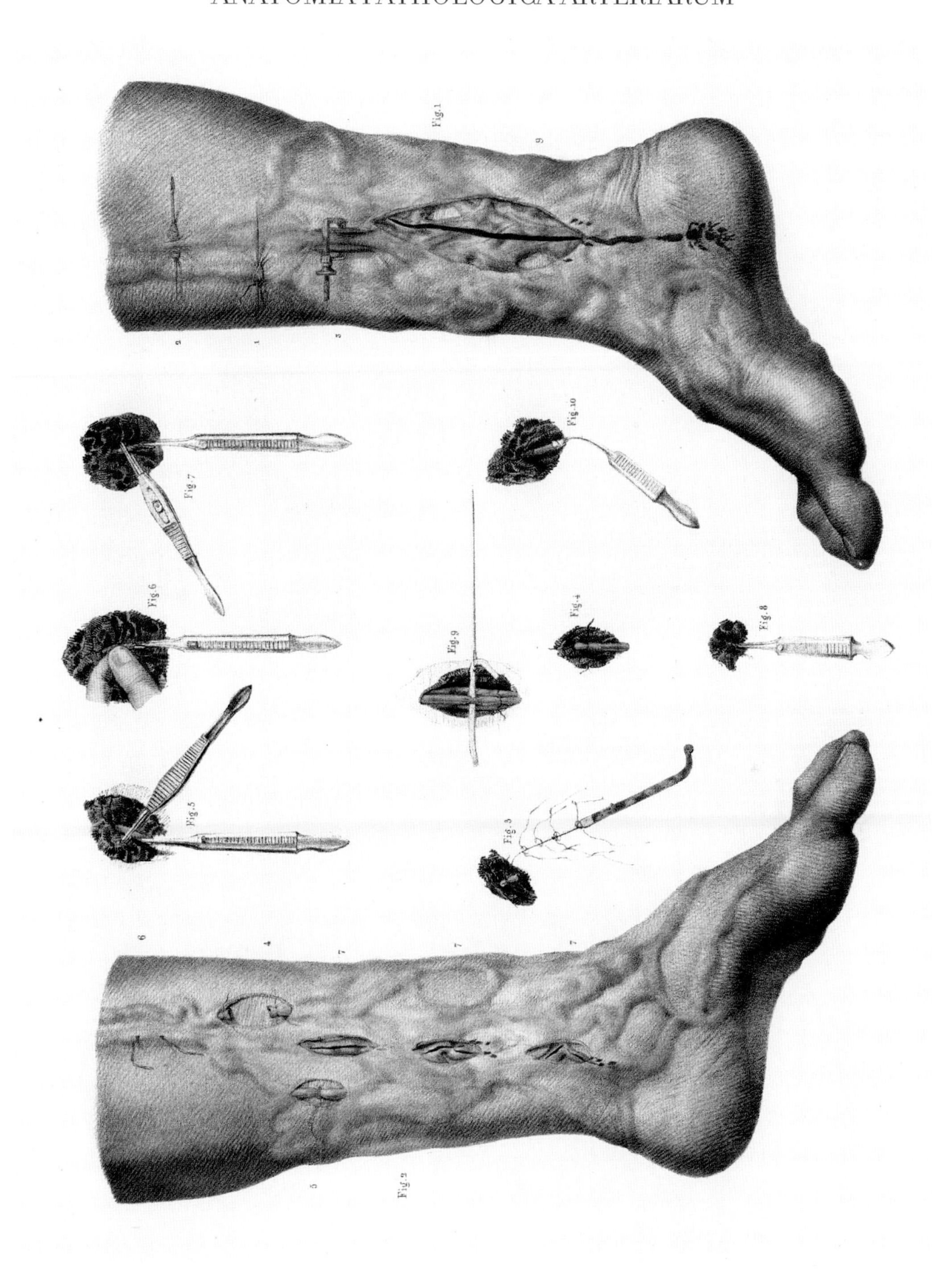

Vascular surgical techniques / Techniques chirurgicales vasculaires
Técnicas quirúrgicas vasculares

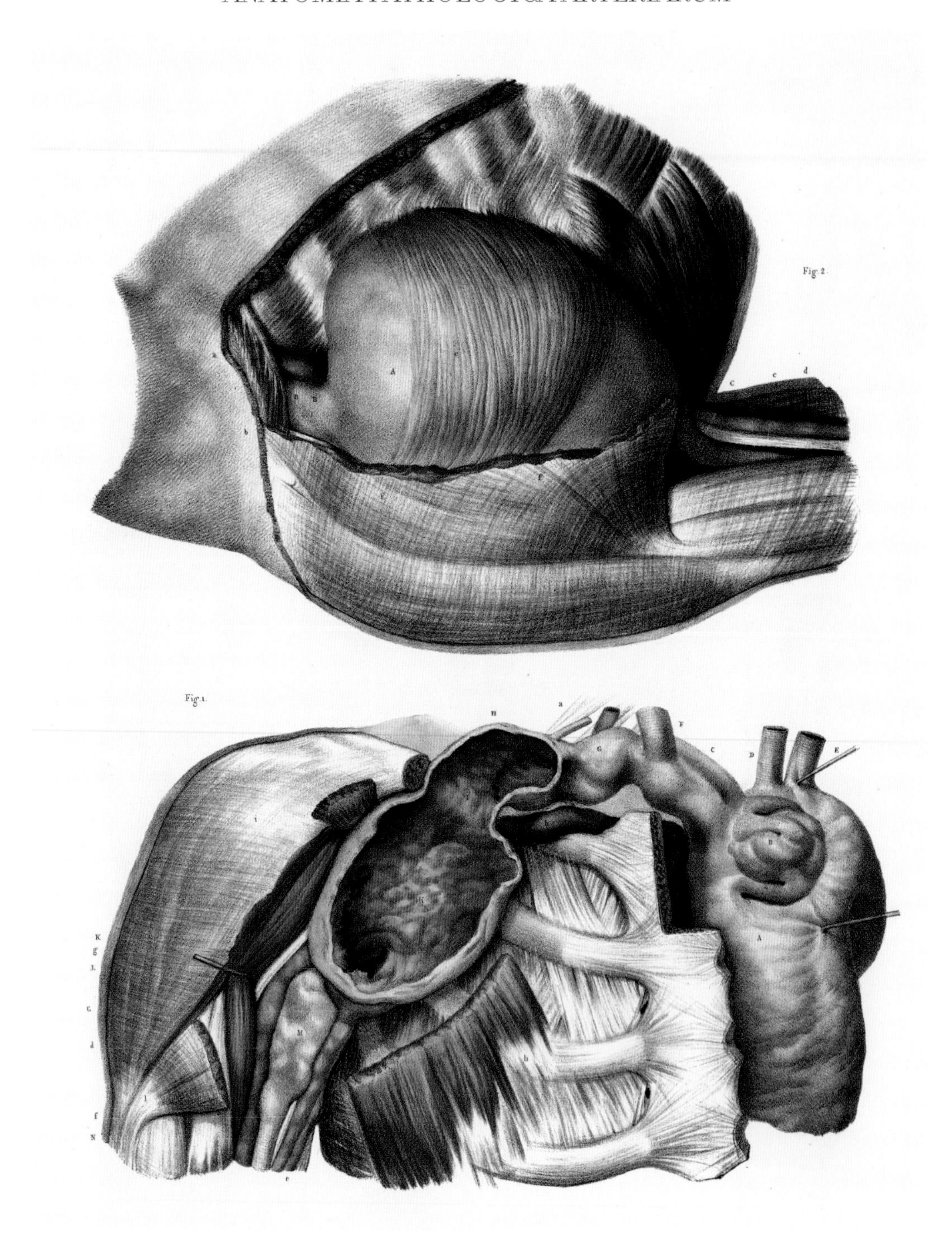

Pathological anatomy of the arteries: Aneurysms
Anatomie pathologique des artères : Anévrismes
Anatomía patológica de las arterias: aneurismas

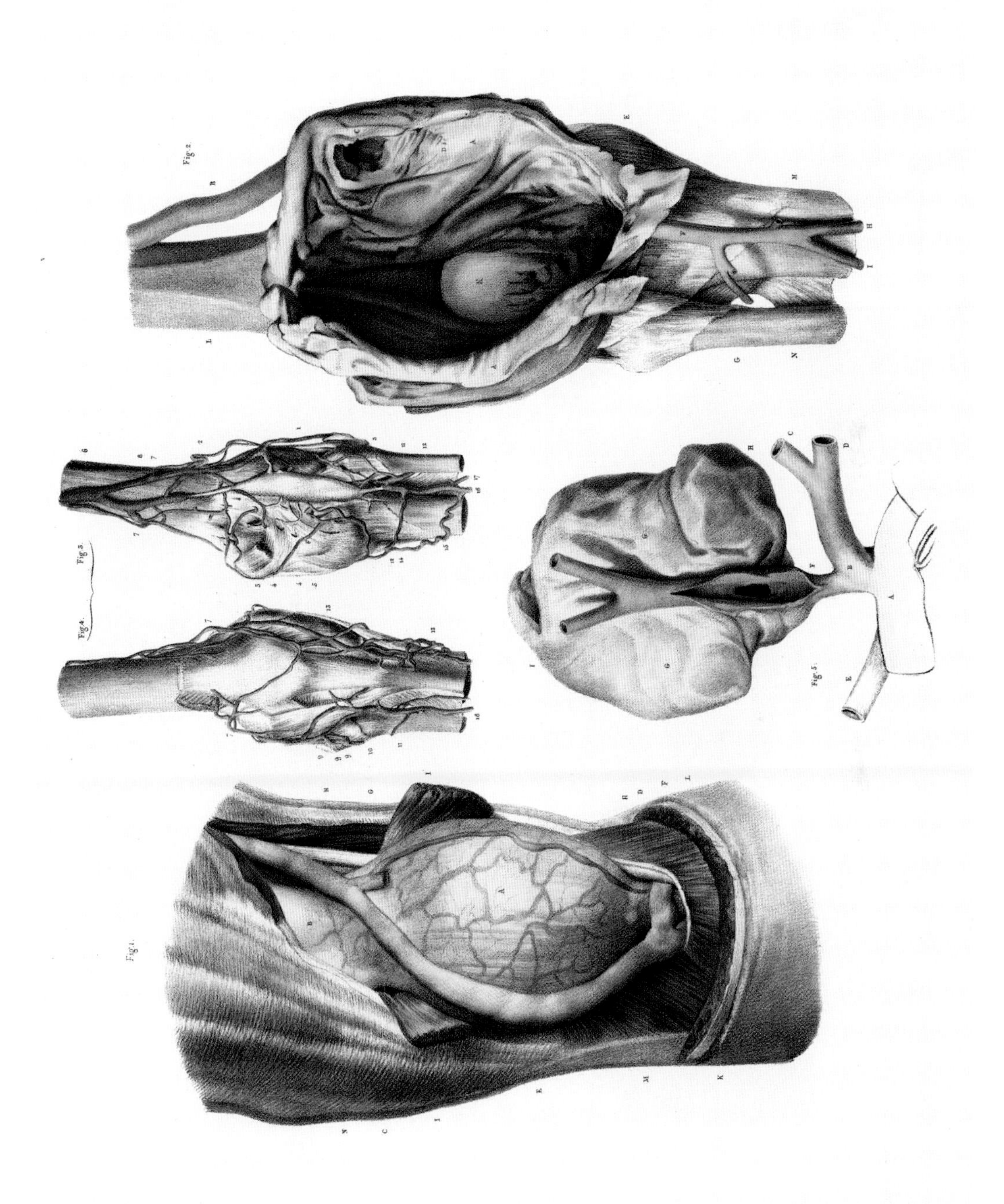

Pathological anatomy of the arteries: Aneurysms
Anatomie pathologique des artères : Anévrismes
Anatomía patológica de las arterias: aneurismas

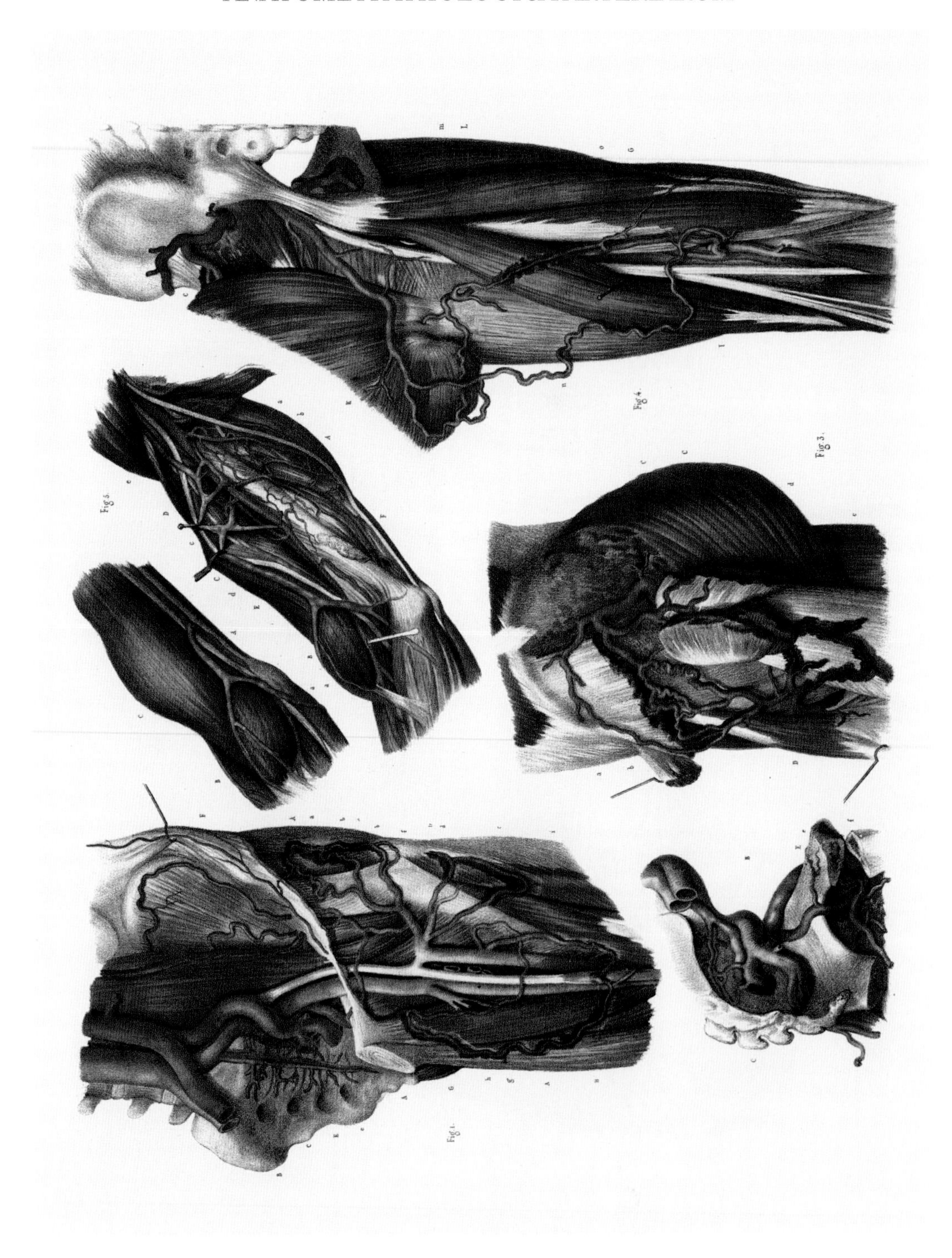

Ligations of arteries: Collateral circulations
Ligatures des artères : Circulations collatérales
Ligaduras arteriales: circulación colateral

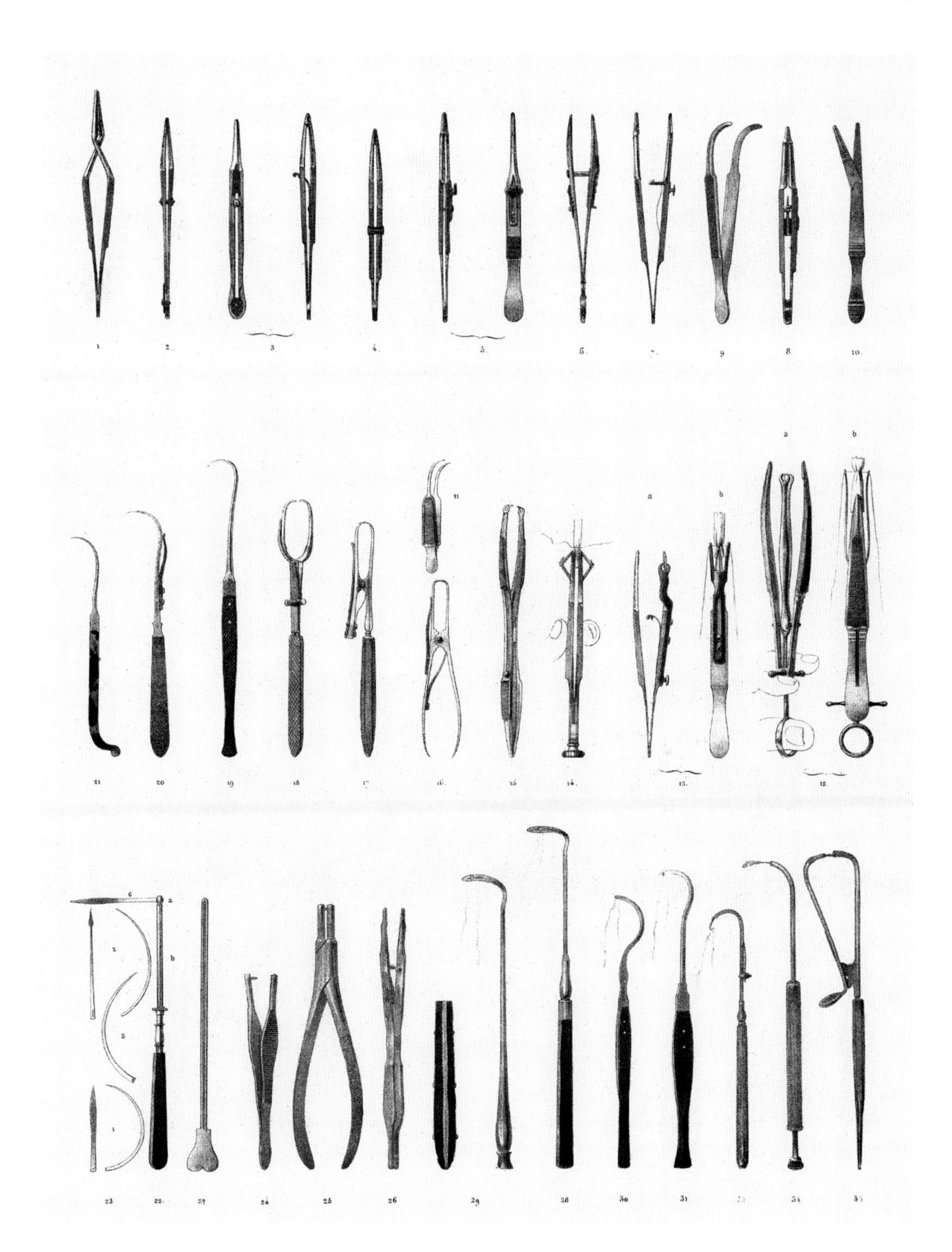

Ligations of arteries: Surgical instruments
Ligatures des artères : Instruments chirurgicaux
Ligaduras arteriales: instrumentos quirúrgicos

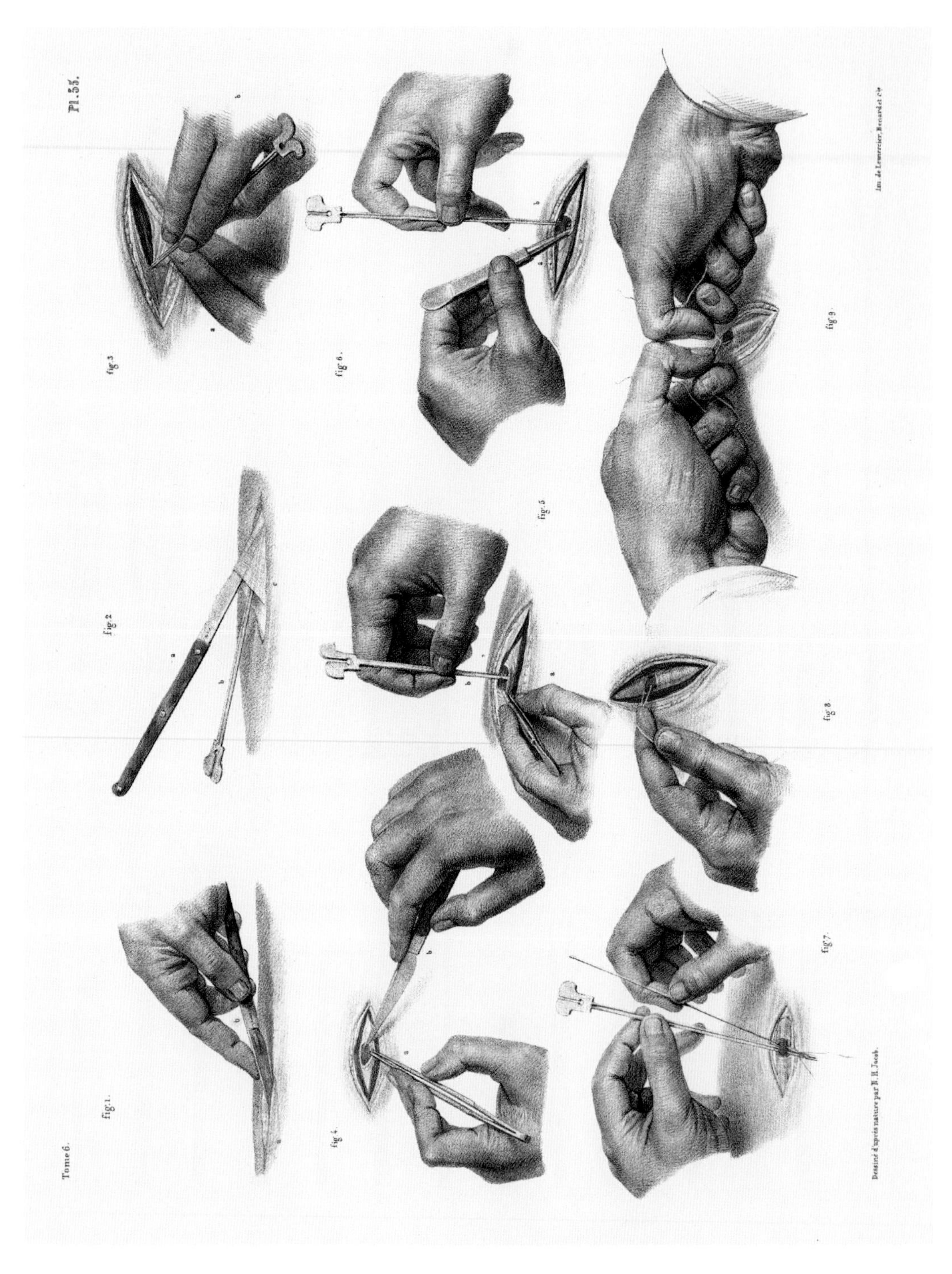

Ligation of arteries: Surgical techniques
Ligatures des artères : Techniques chirurgicales
Ligaduras arteriales: técnicas quirúrgicas

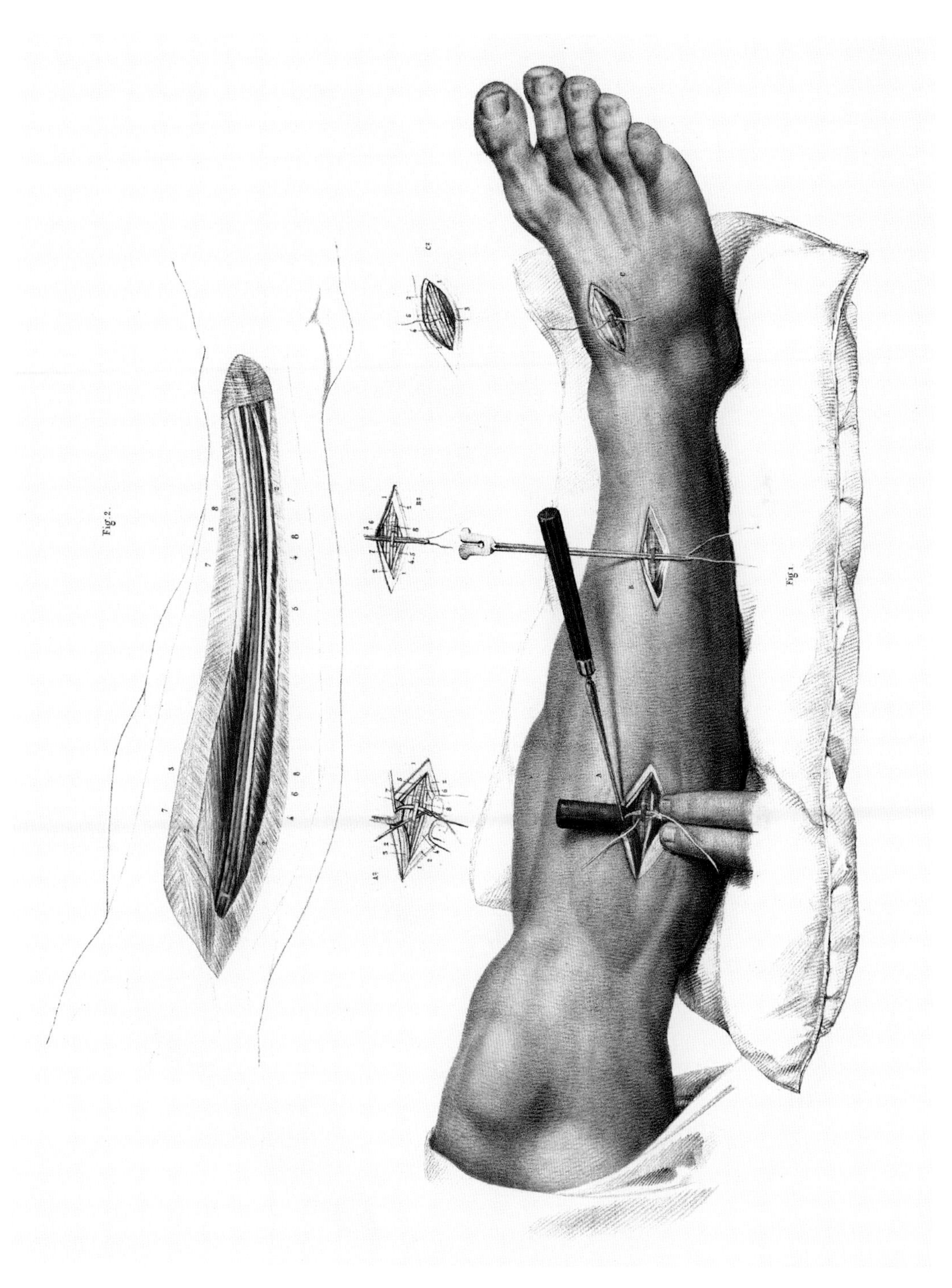

Ligation of arteries of the lower limb
Ligatures des artères du membre inférieur
Ligaduras arteriales del miembro inferior

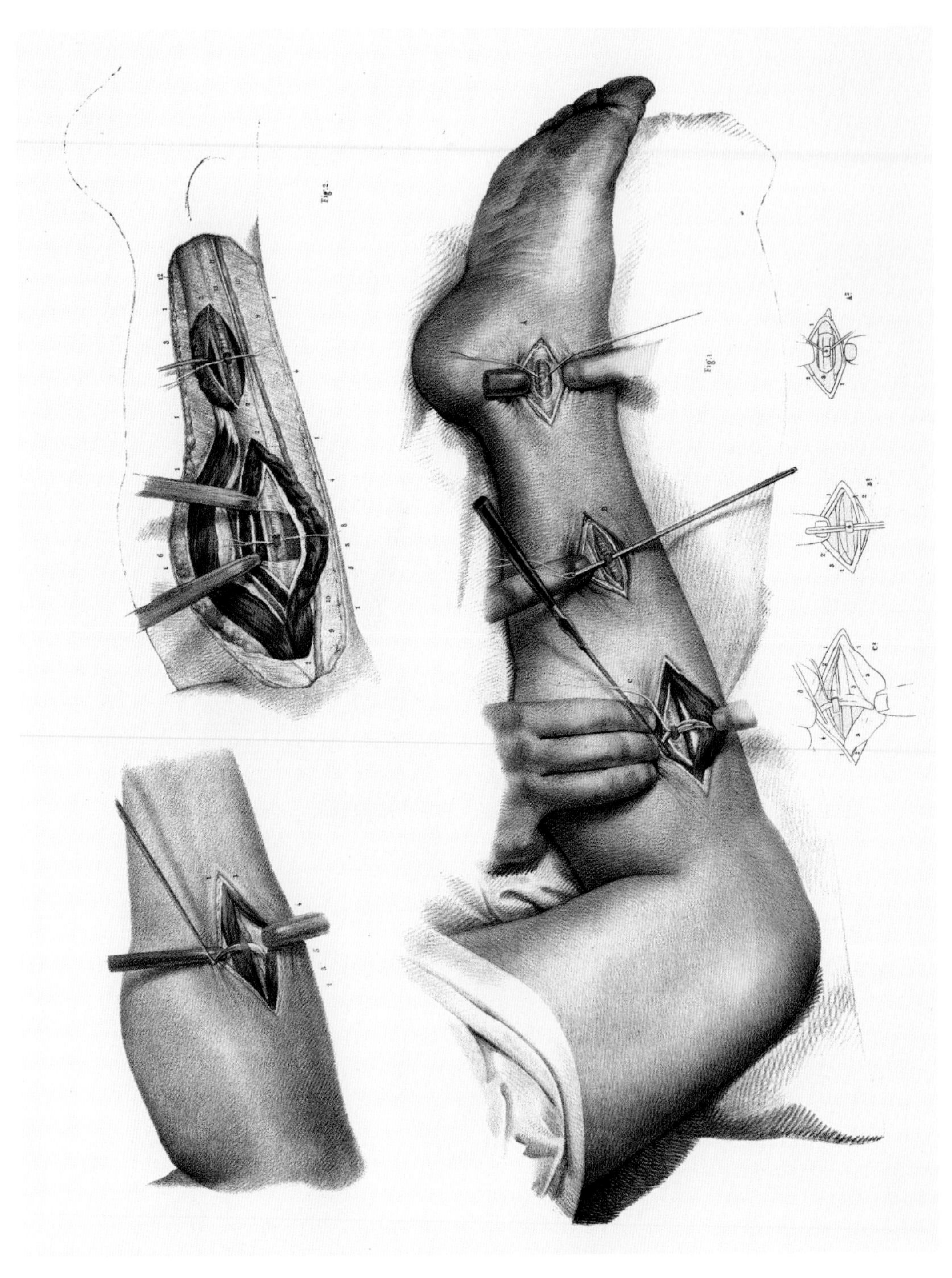

Ligation of arteries of the lower limb / Ligatures des artères du membre inférieur
Ligaduras arteriales del miembro inferior

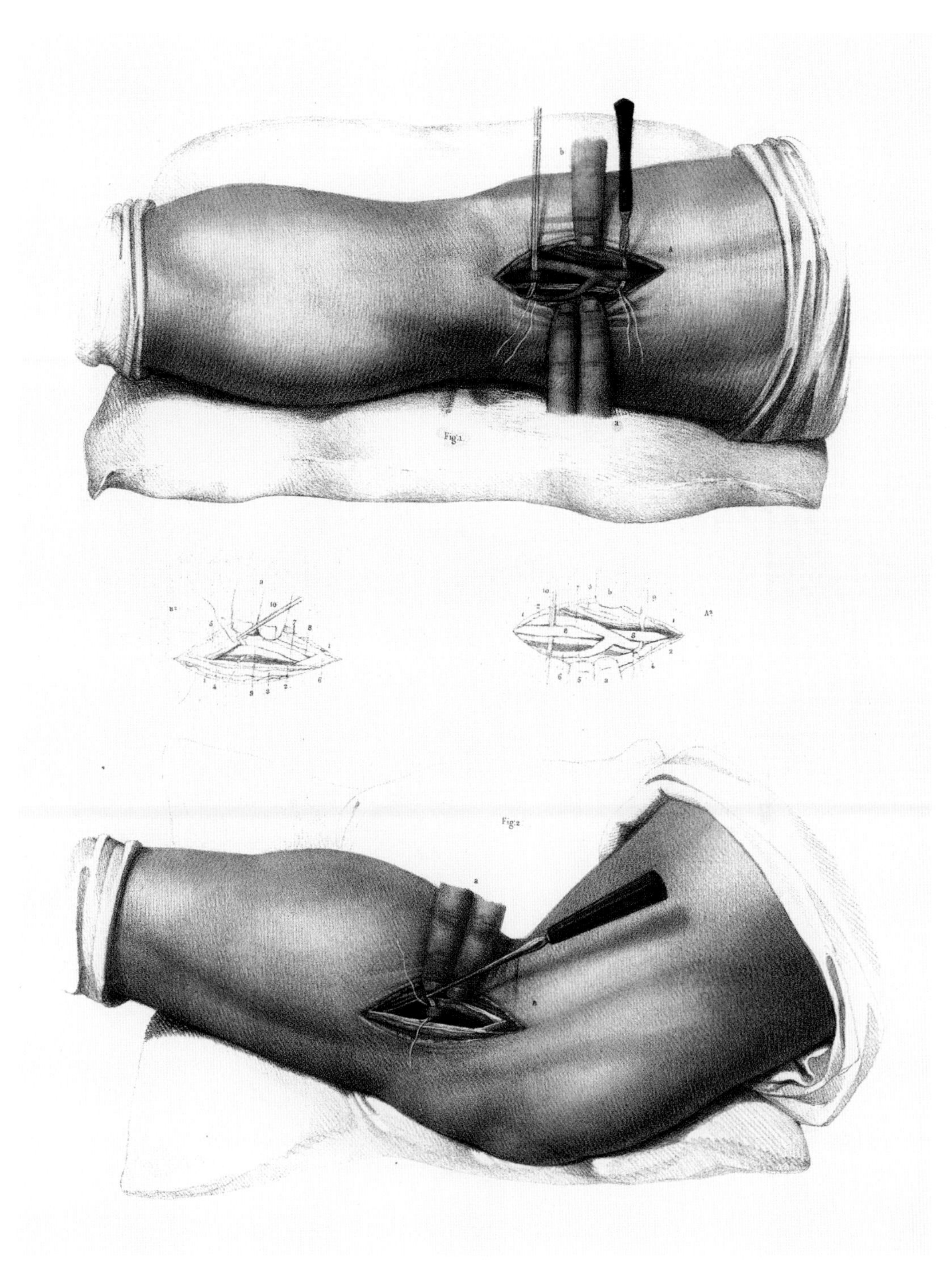

Ligation of arteries of the lower limb / Ligatures des artères du membre inférieur
Ligaduras arteriales del miembro inferior

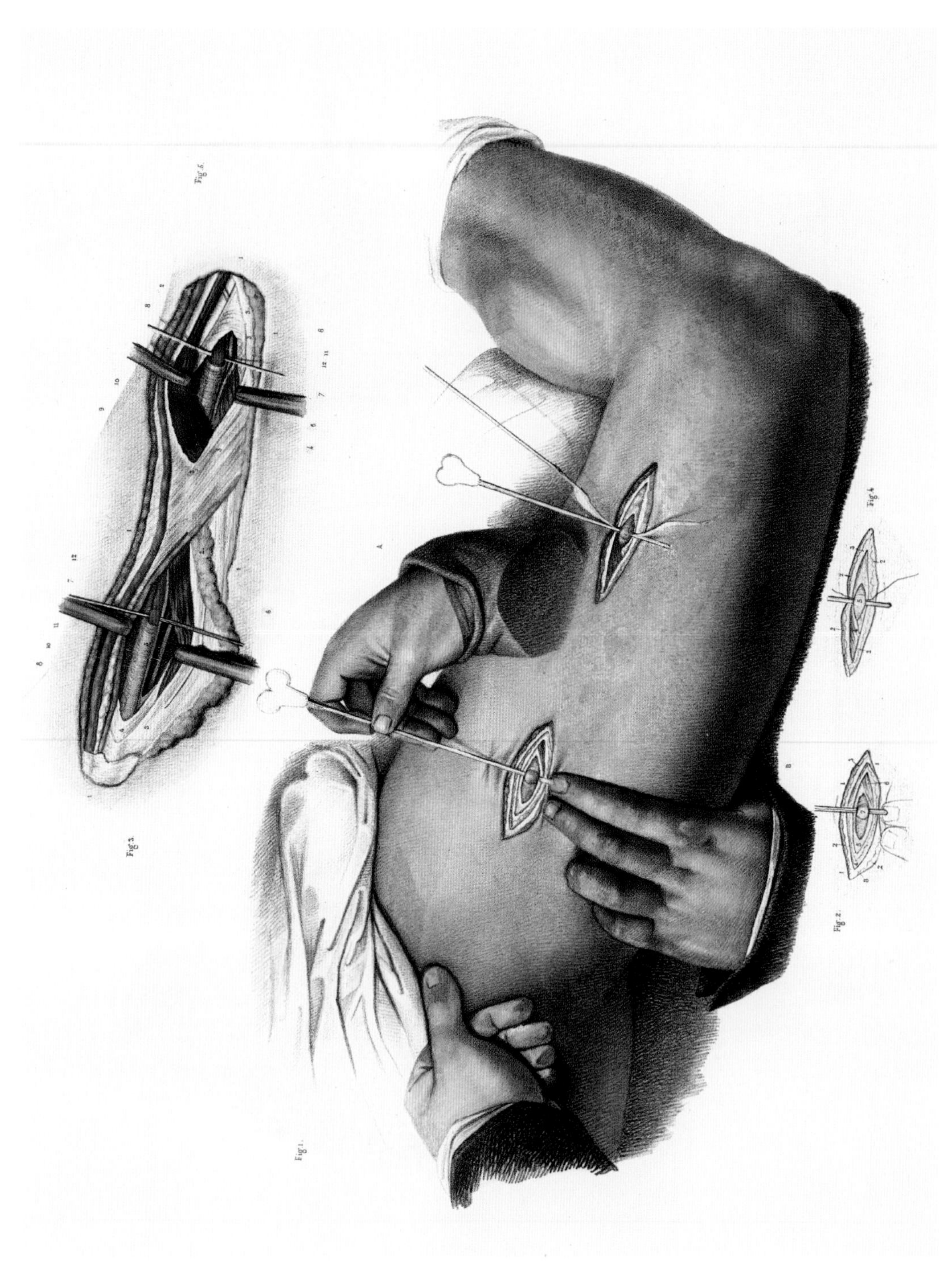

Ligation of arteries of the lower limb / Ligatures des artères du membre inférieur
Ligaduras arteriales del miembro inferior

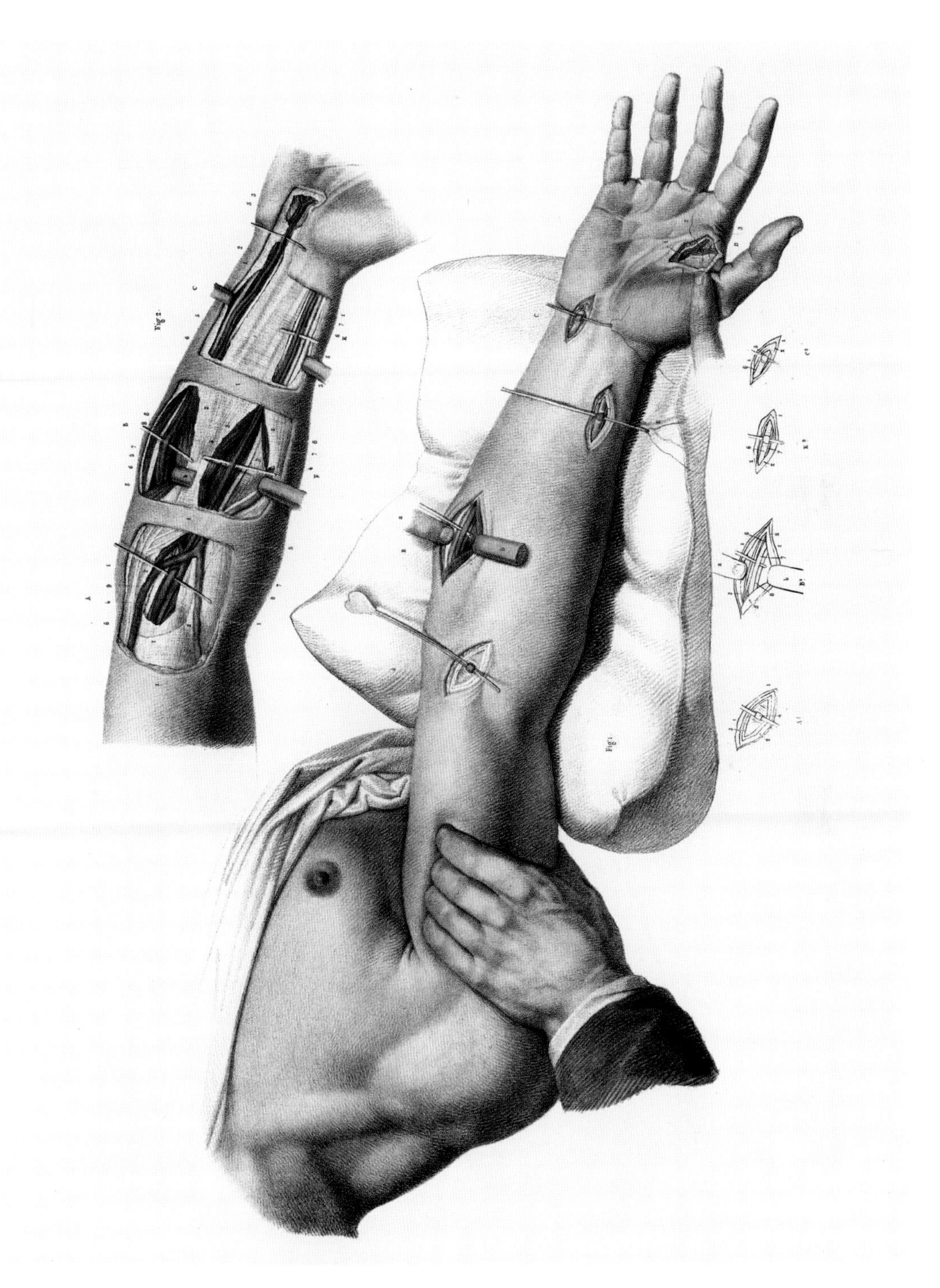

Ligation of arteries of the upper limb / Ligatures des artères du membre supérieur
Ligaduras arteriales del miembro superior

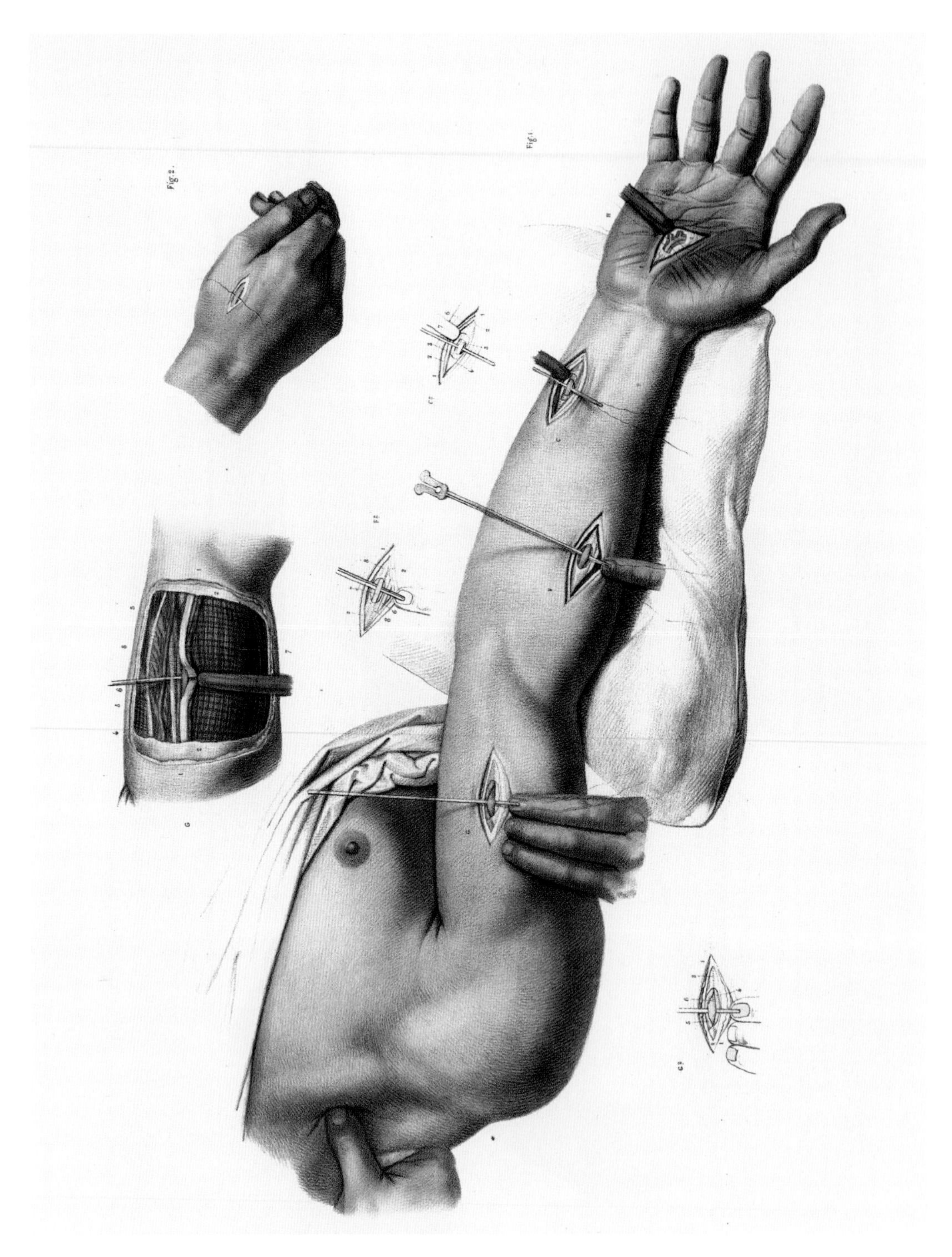

Ligation of arteries of the upper limb / Ligatures des artères du membre supérieur
Ligaduras arteriales del miembro superior

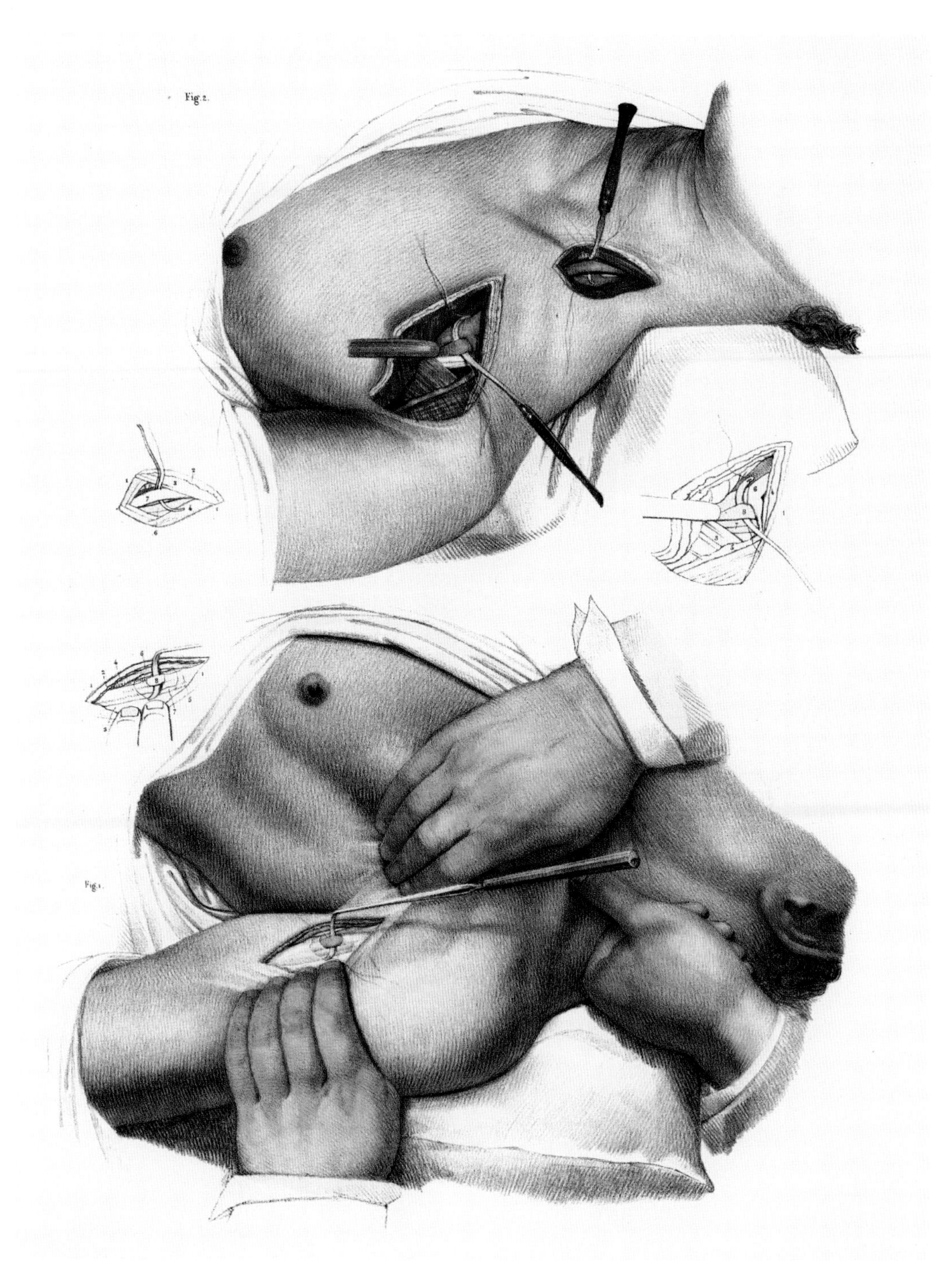

Ligation of arteries of the upper limb and neck
Ligatures des artères du membre supérieur et du cou
Ligaduras arteriales del miembro superior y del cuello

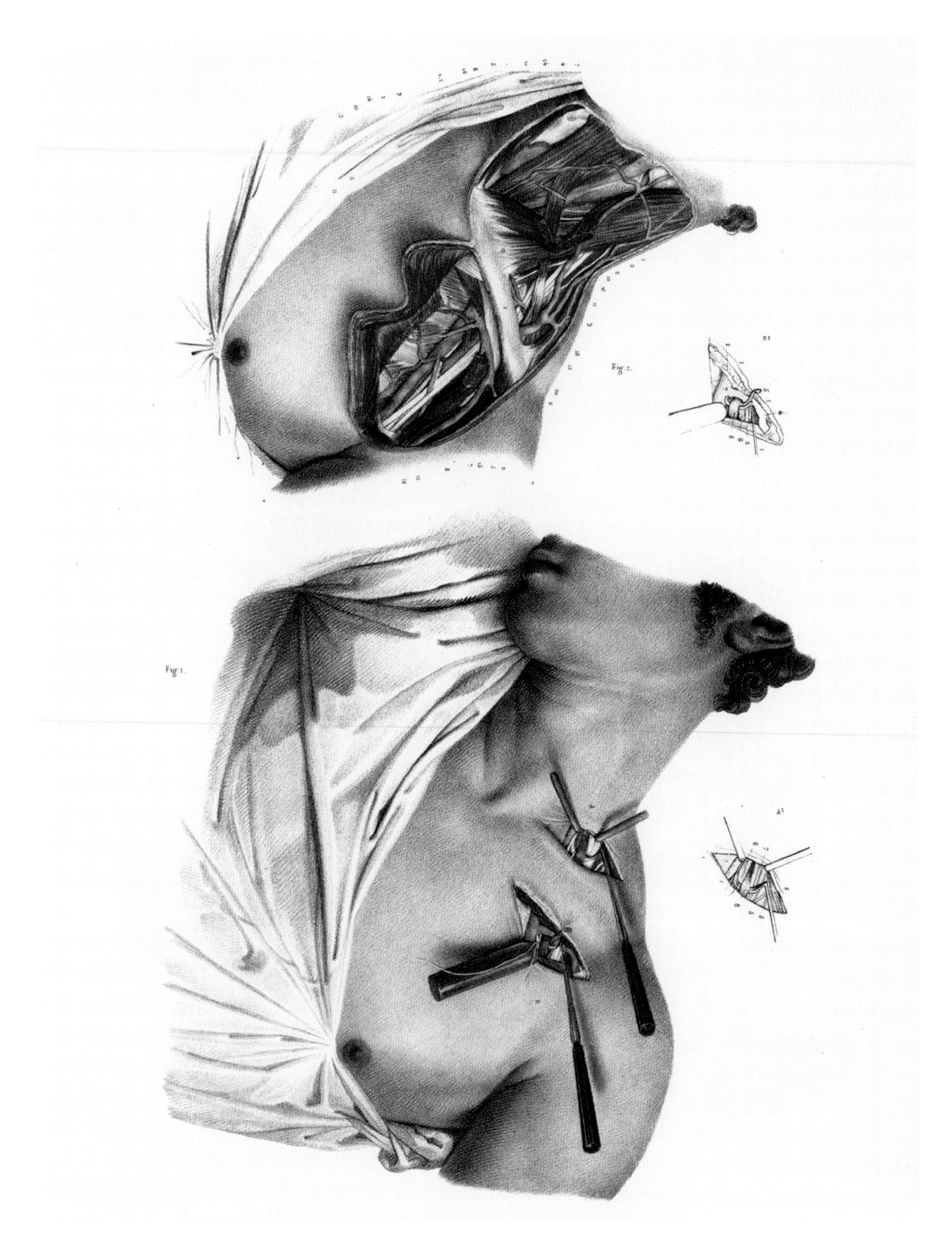

Ligation of arteries of the upper limb and neck
Ligatures des artères du membre supérieur et du cou
Ligaduras arteriales del miembro superior y del cuello

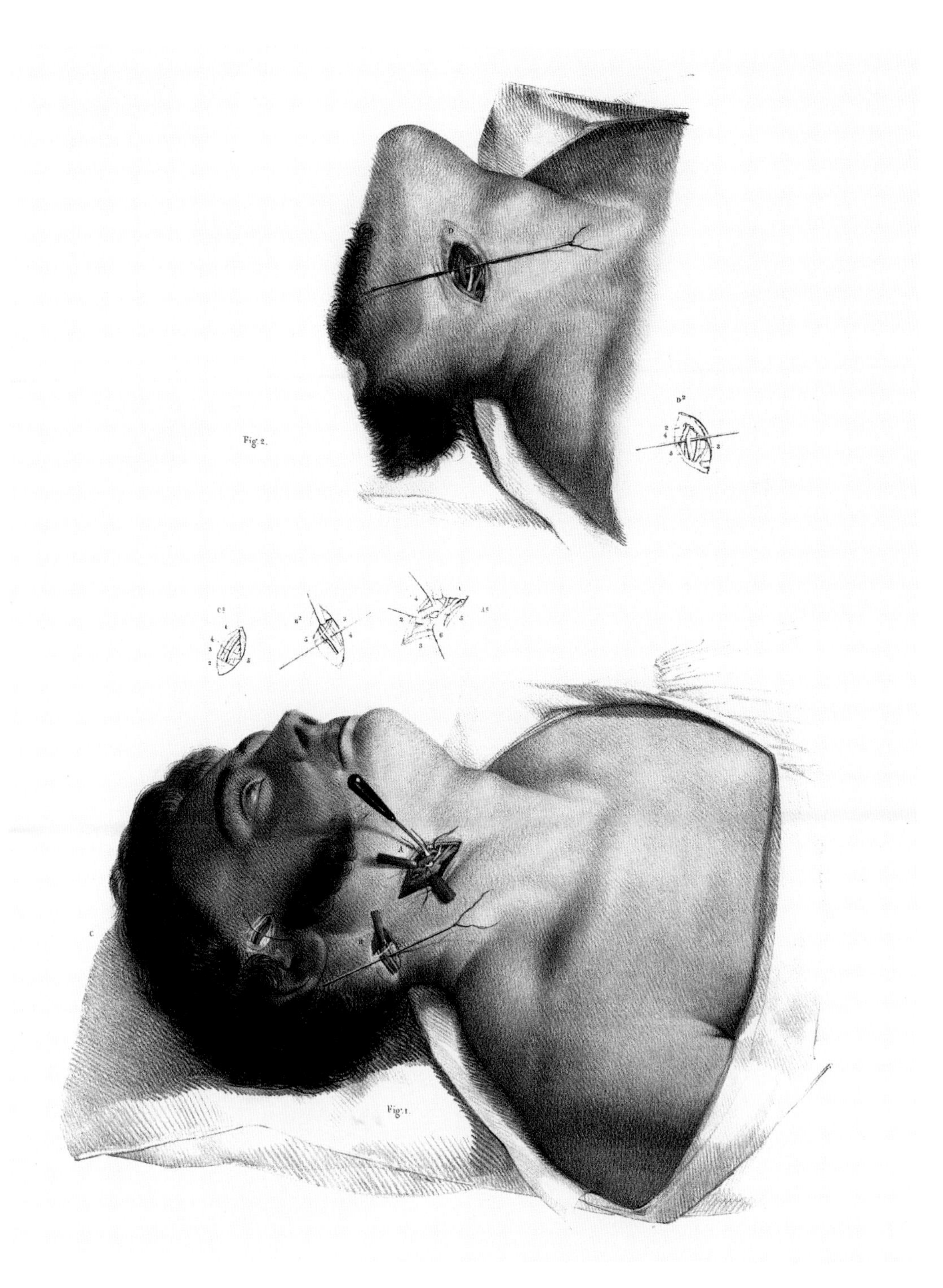

Ligation of arteries of the neck and head / Ligatures des artères du cou et de la tête
Ligaduras arteriales del cuello y de la cabeza

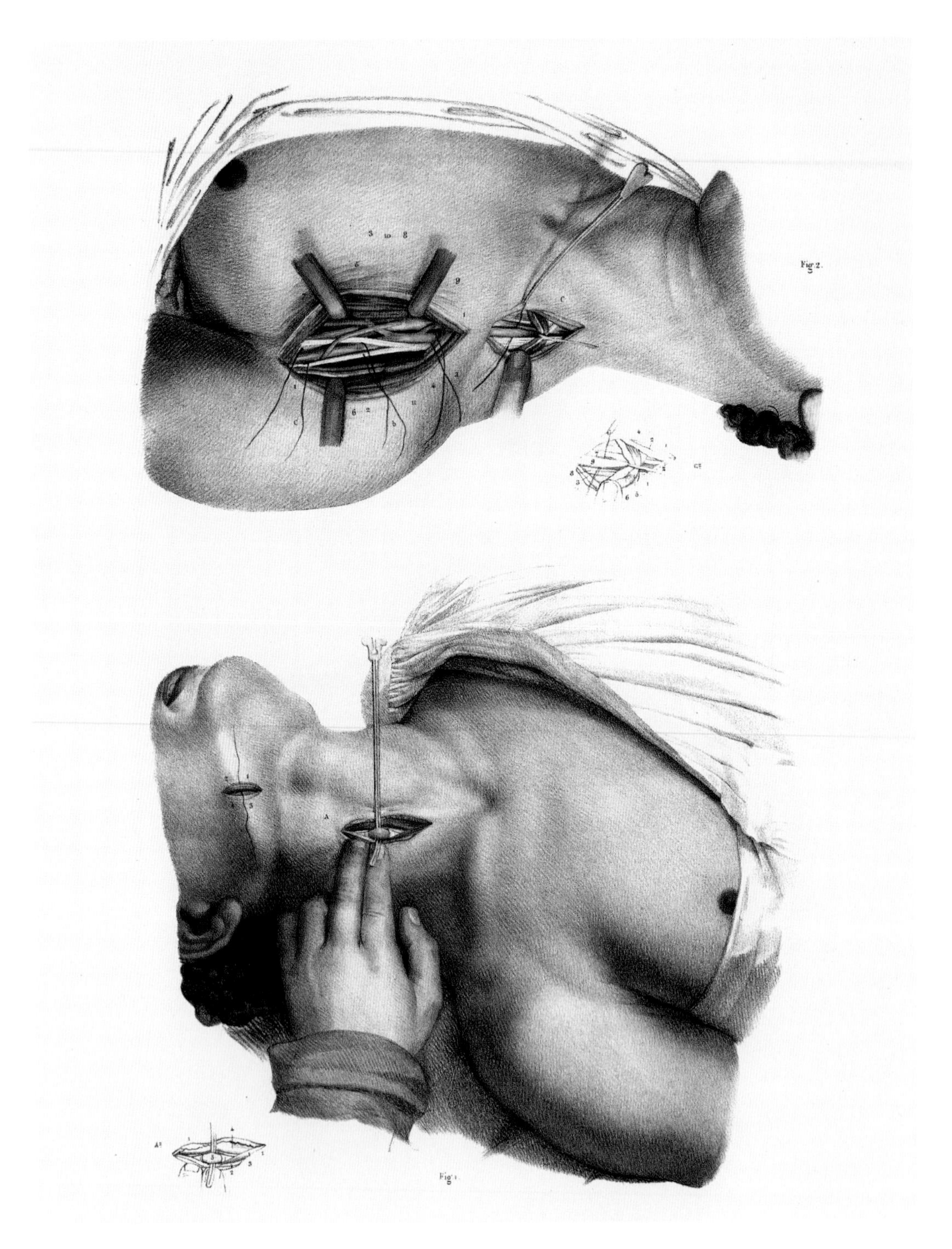

Ligation of arteries of the upper limb and neck
Ligatures des artères du membre supérieur et du cou
Ligaduras arteriales del miembro superior y del cuello

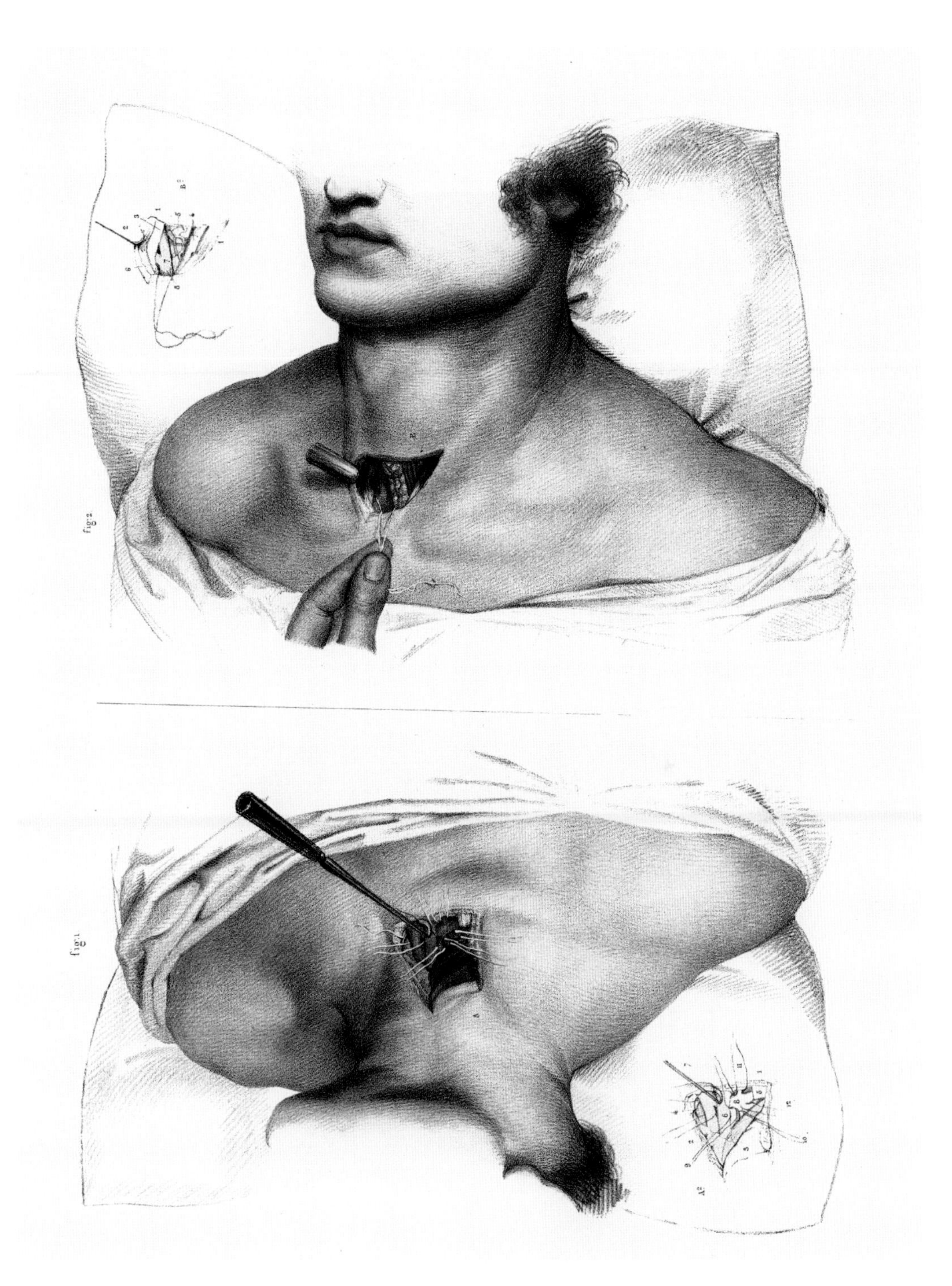

Ligation of arteries of the neck / Ligatures des artères du cou
Ligaduras arteriales del cuello

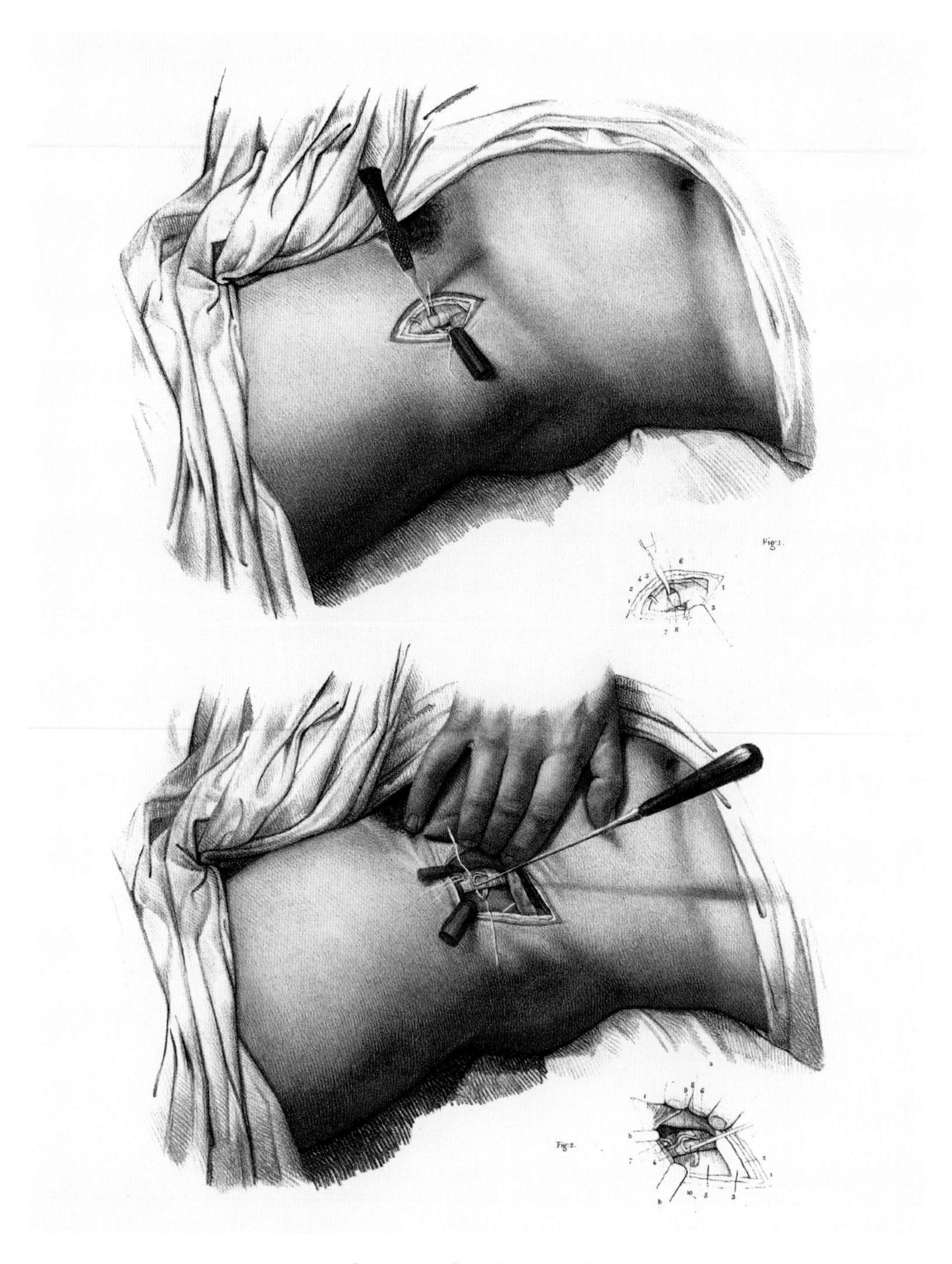

Ligation of arteries of the lower limb and pelvis
Ligatures des artères du membre inférieur et du pelvis
Ligaduras arteriales del miembro inferior y de la pelvis

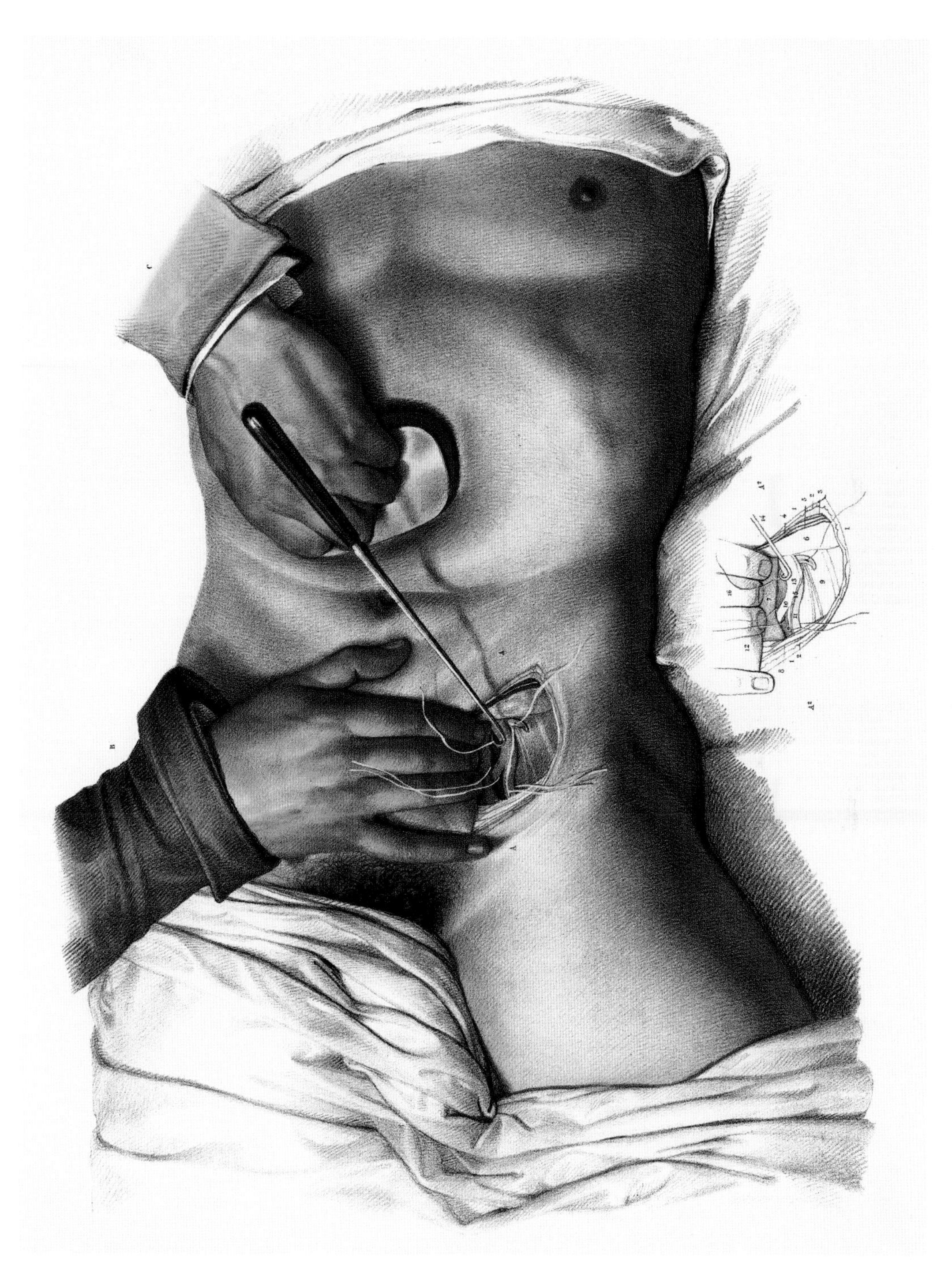

Ligation of arteries of the pelvis / Ligatures des artères du pelvis
Ligaduras arteriales de la pelvis

ARTES CHIRURGICAE VARIAE OSSIUM.
ABLATIONES FRAGMENTORUM OSSIUM

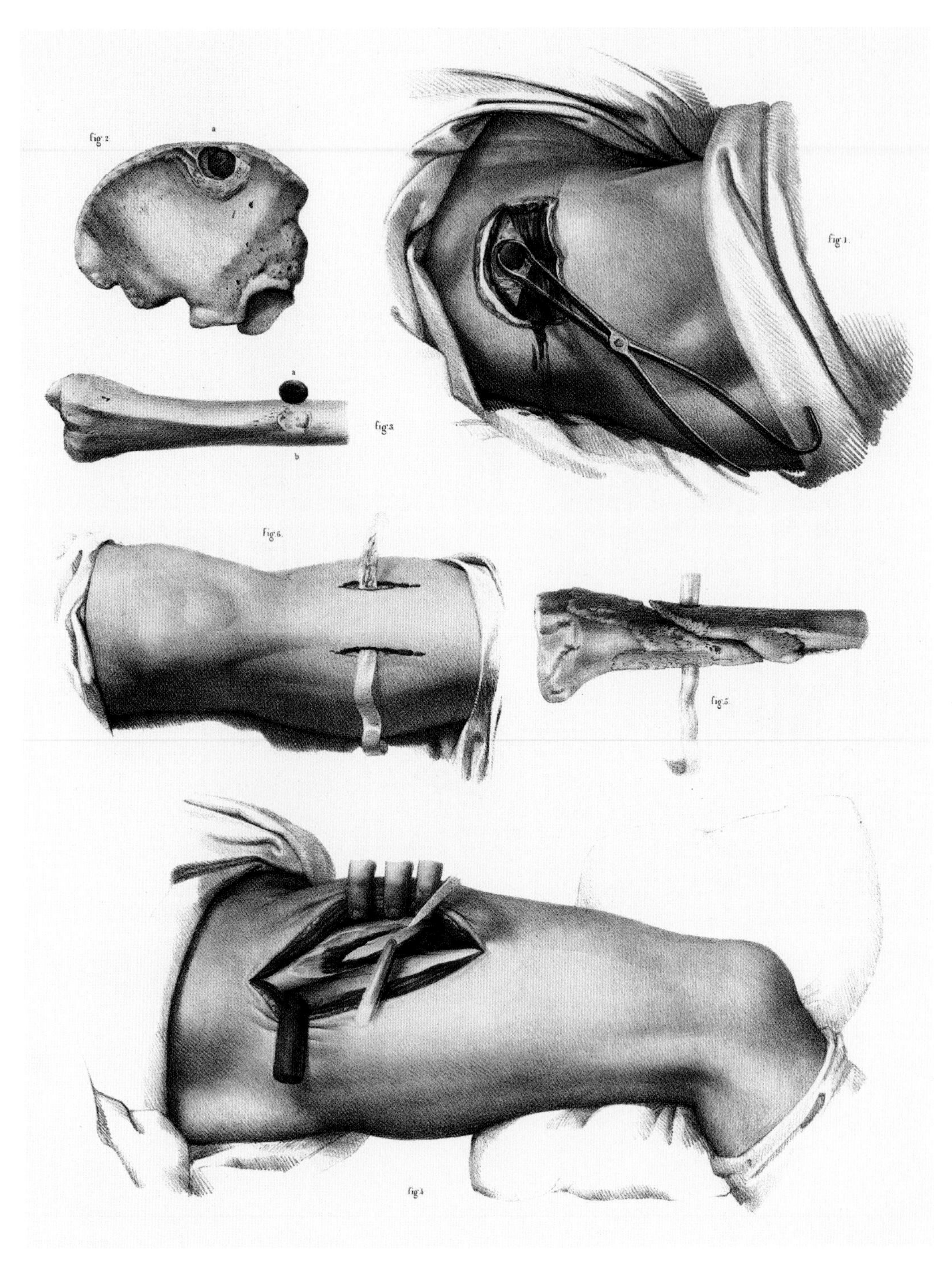

Various surgical techniques for the bones
Diverses techniques chirurgicales osseuses
Diversas técnicas quirúrgicas óseas

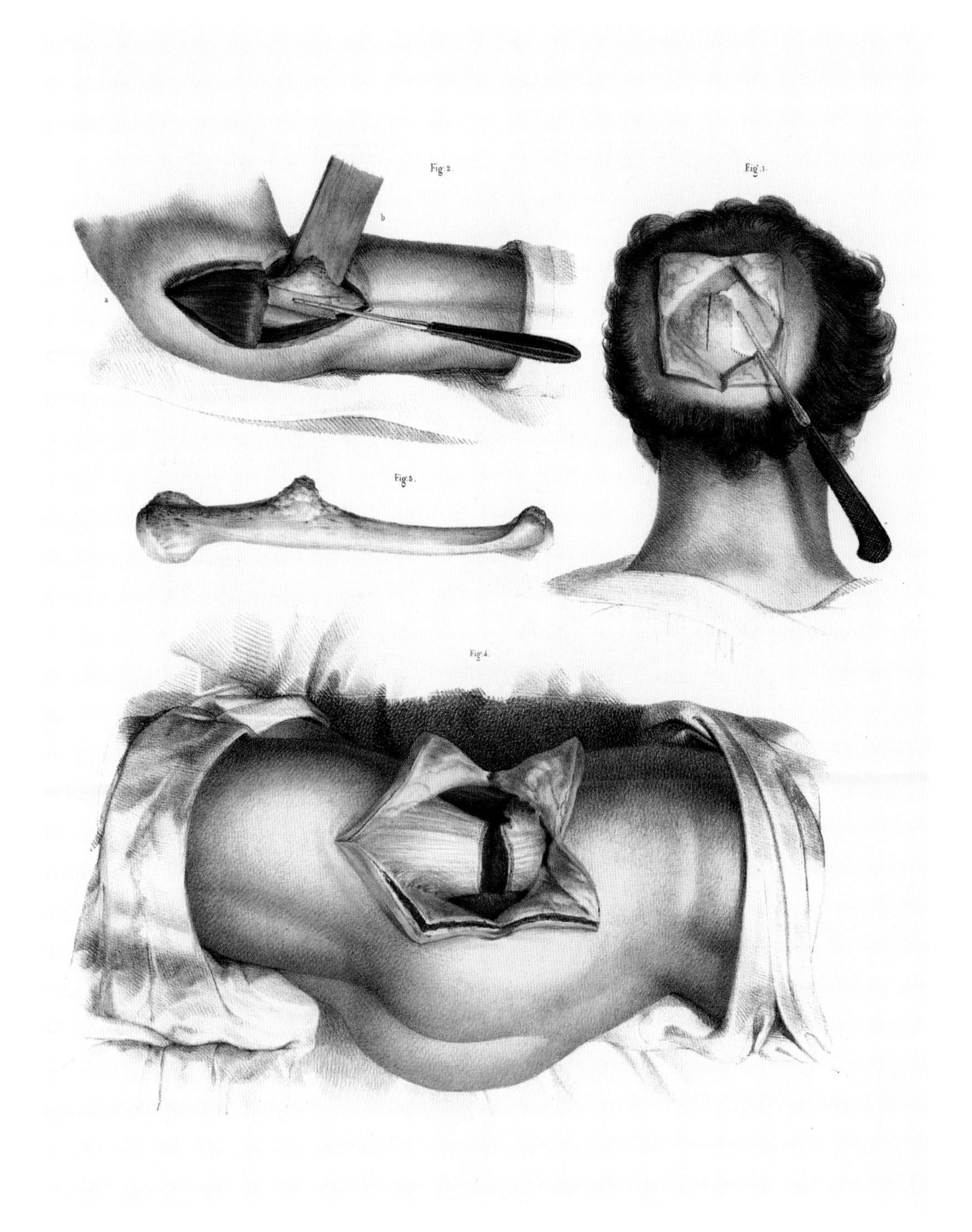

Various surgical techniques for the bones
Diverses techniques chirurgicales osseuses
Diversas técnicas quirúrgicas óseas

ARTES CHIRURGICAE VARIAE OSSIUM.
ABLATIONES FRAGMENTORUM OSSIUM

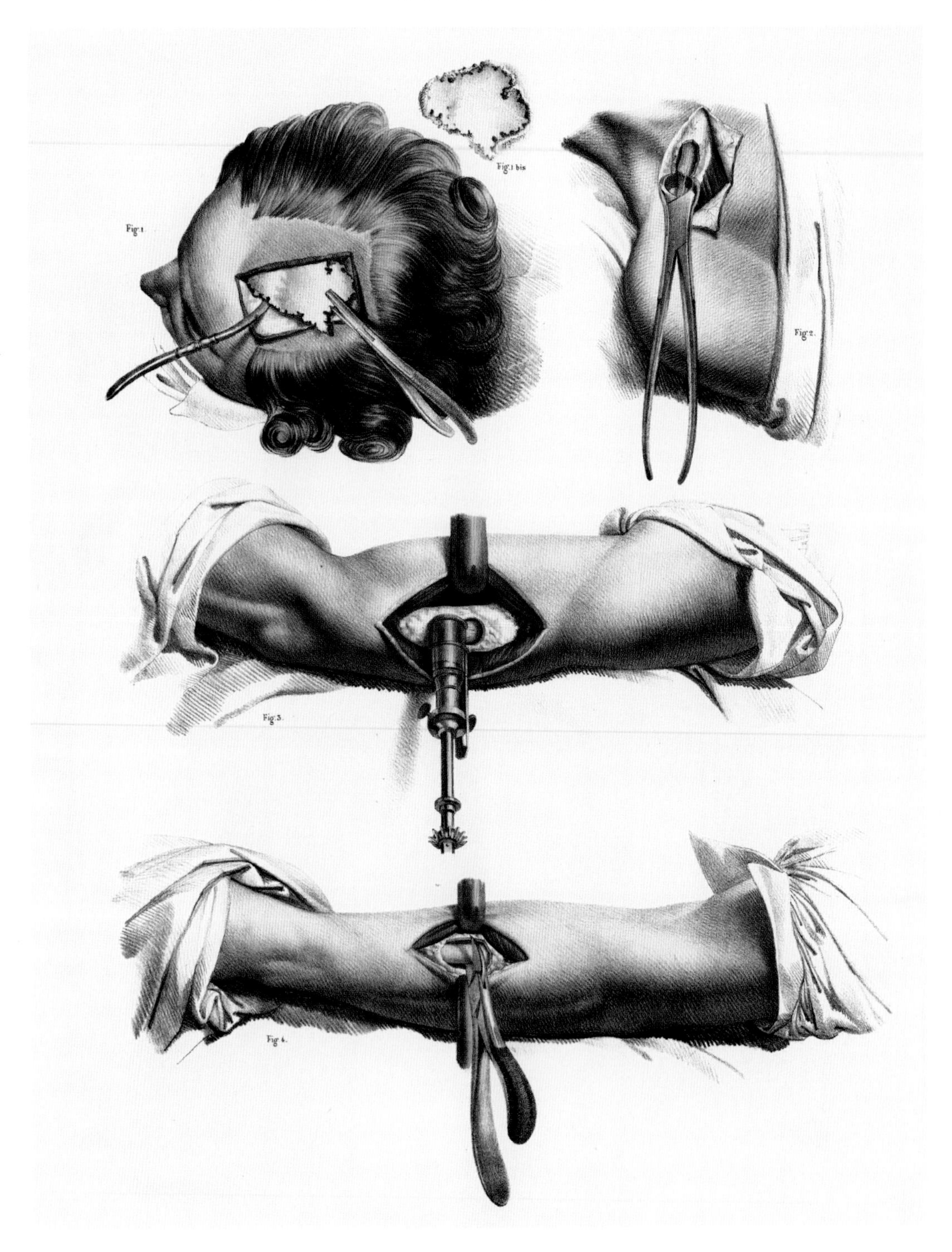

Ablation of bone fragments / Ablations de fragments osseux
Ablaciones de fragmentos óseos

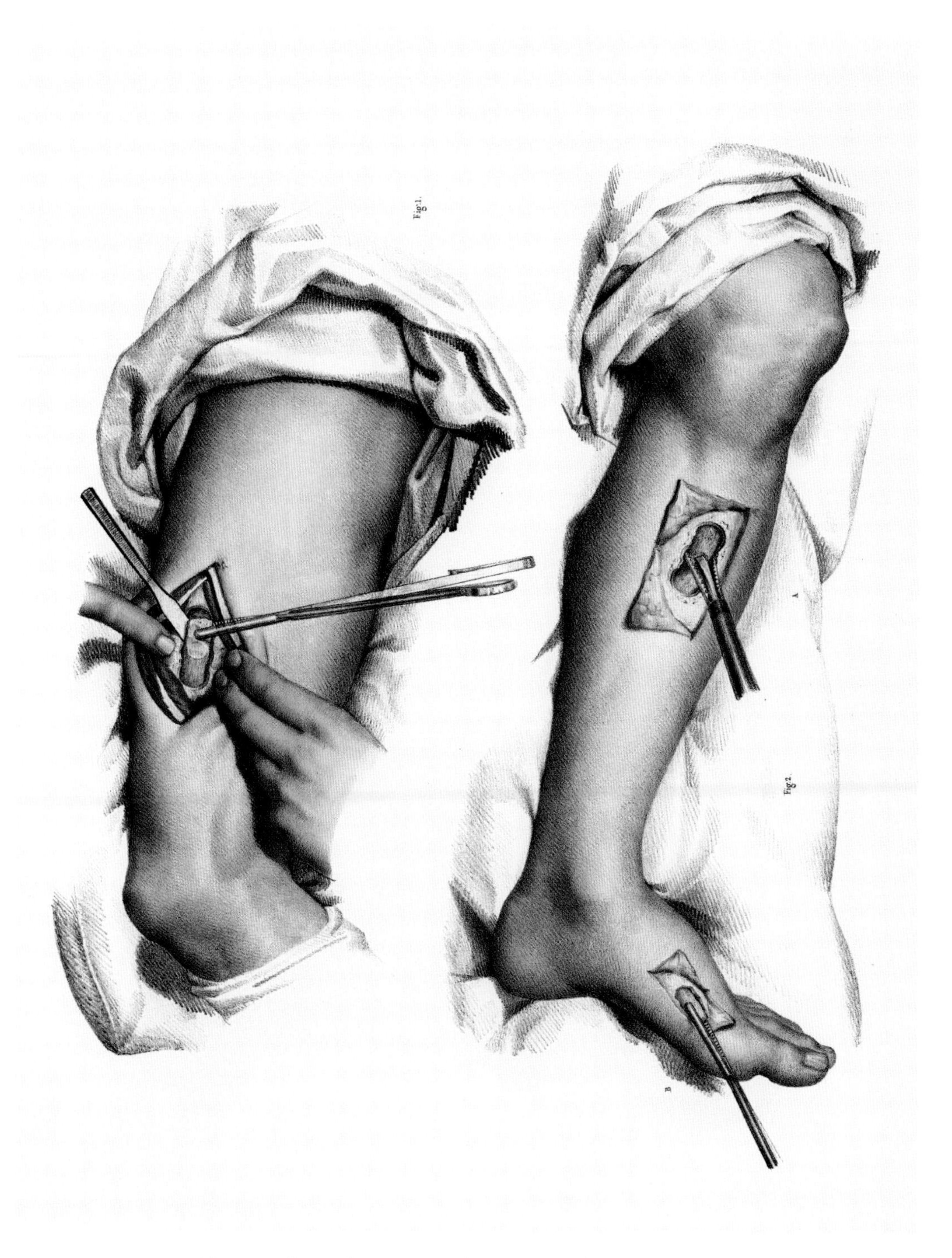

Ablation of bone fragments / Ablations de fragments osseux
Ablaciones de fragmentos óseos

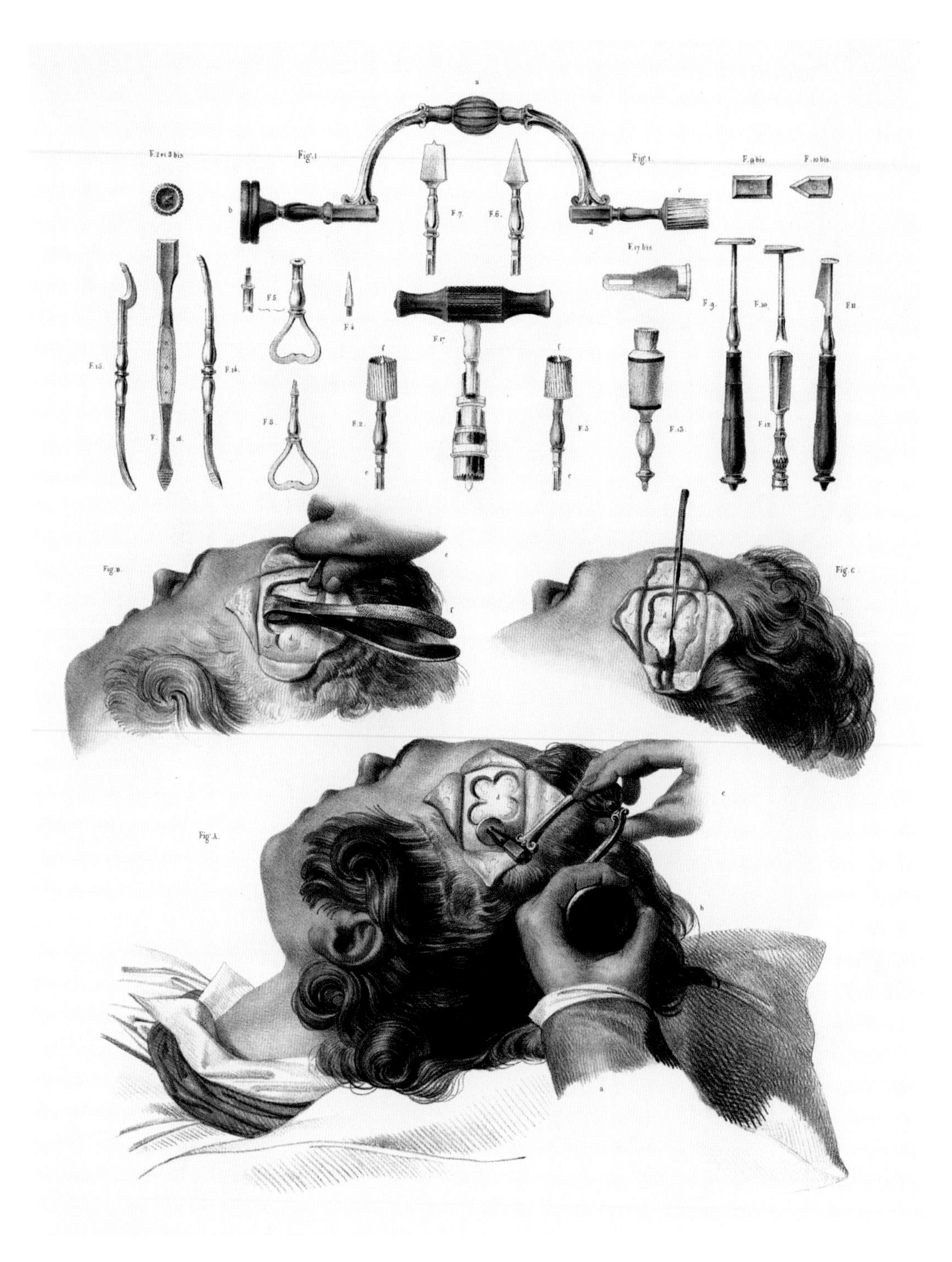

Skull trepanation and surgical instruments
Trépanation du crâne et instruments chirurgicaux
Trepanación del cráneo e instrumentos quirúrgicos

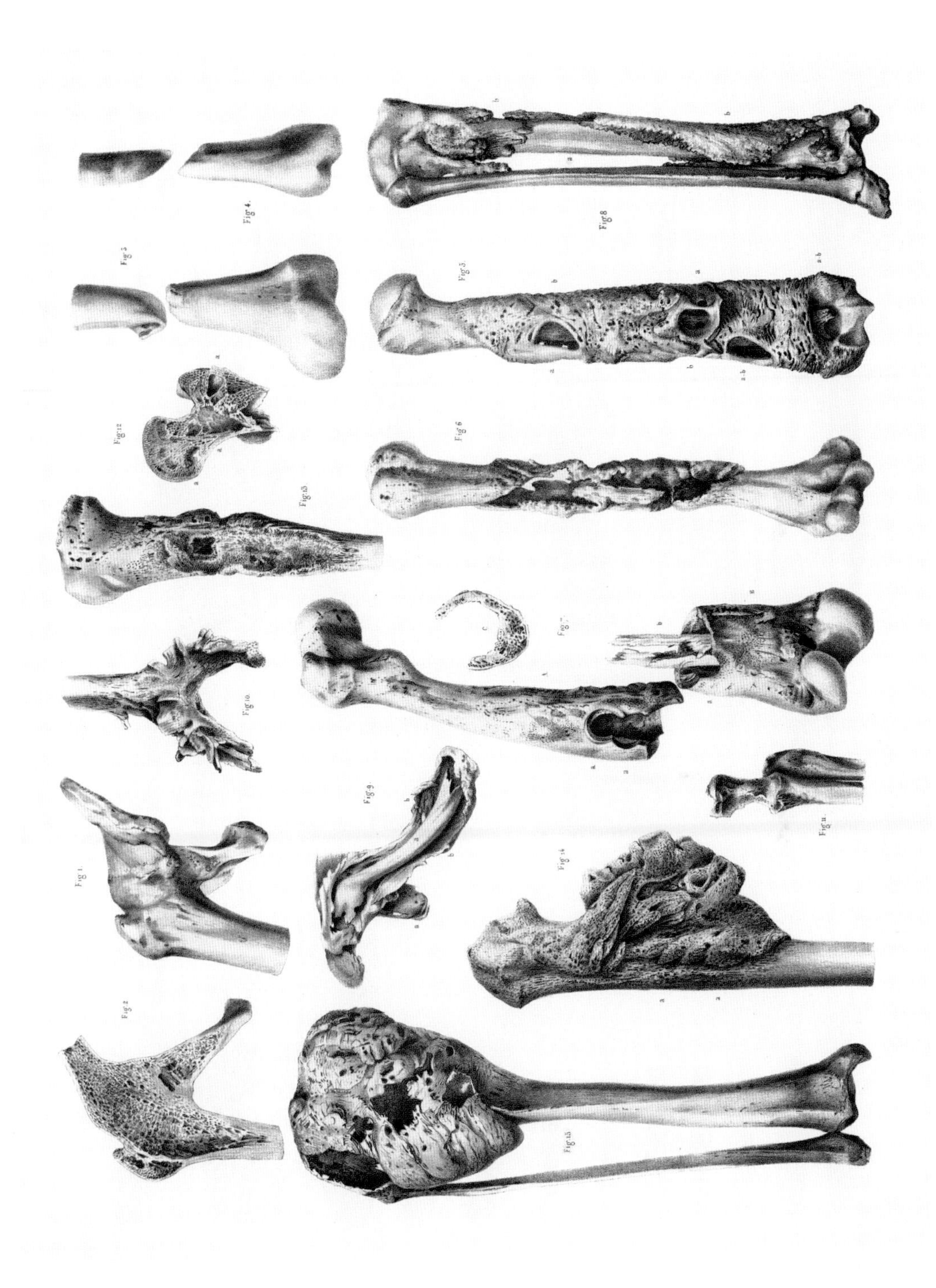

Pathological anatomy of the bones / Anatomie pathologique des os
Anatomía patológica de los huesos

ARTES CHIRURGICAE OSSIUM: INSTRUMENTA CHIRURGICA

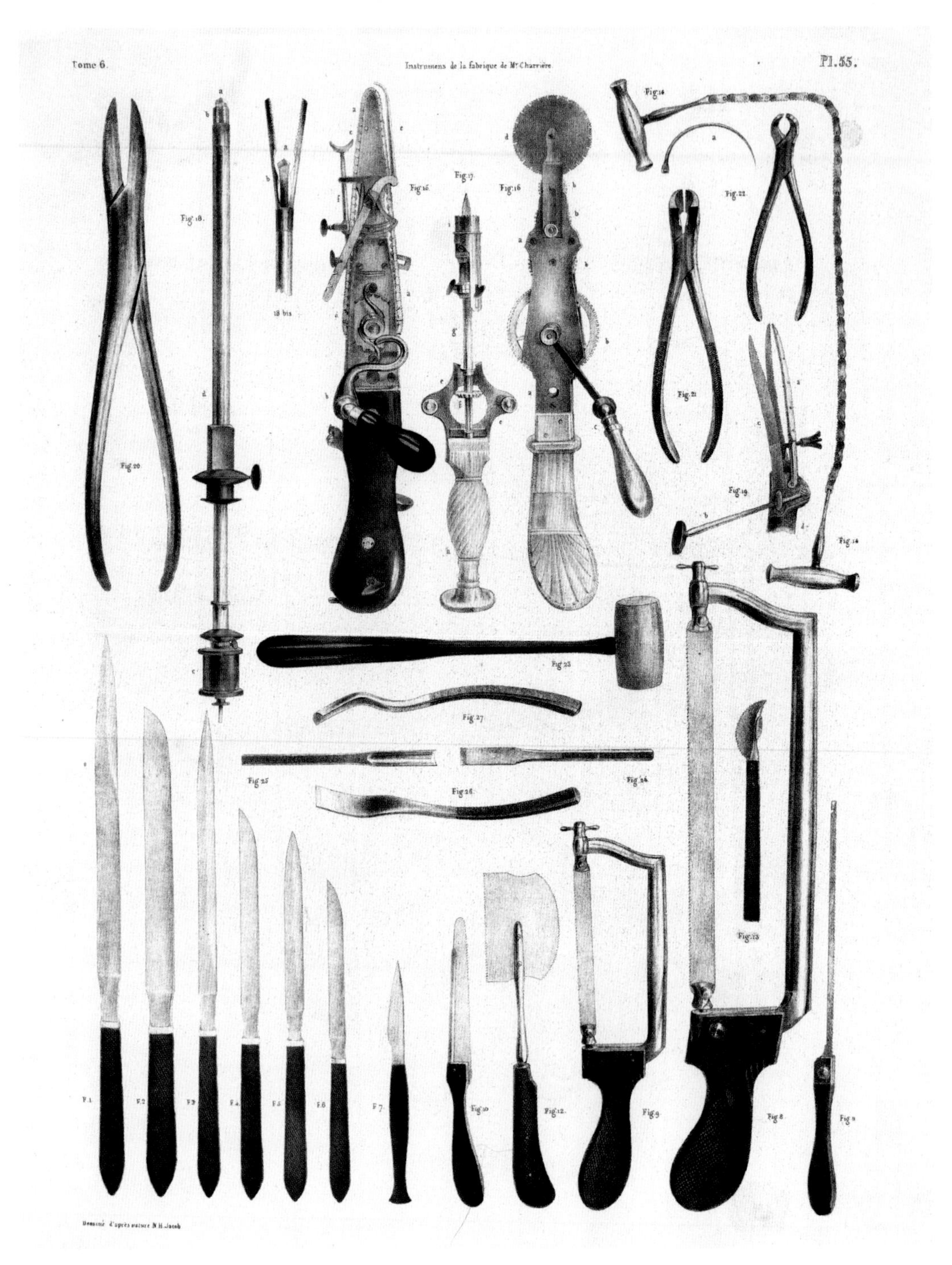

Surgical techniques for the bones: Surgical instruments
Techniques chirurgicales osseuses : Instruments chirurgicaux
Técnicas quirúrgicas óseas: instrumentos quirúrgicos

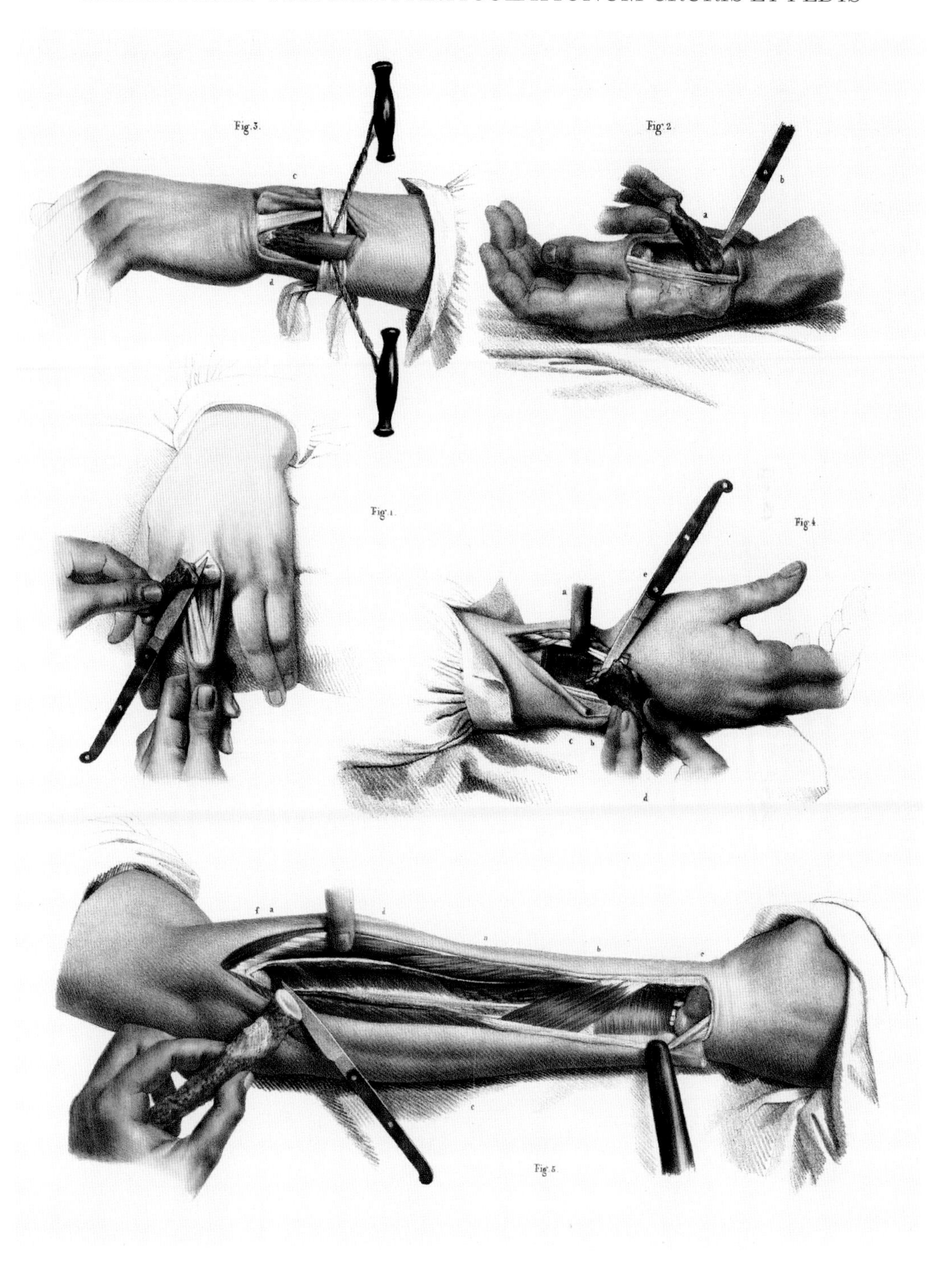

Resections of bones and joints of the hand and forearm
Résections osseuses et articulaires de la main et de l'avant-bras
Resecciones óseas y articulares de la mano y del antebrazo

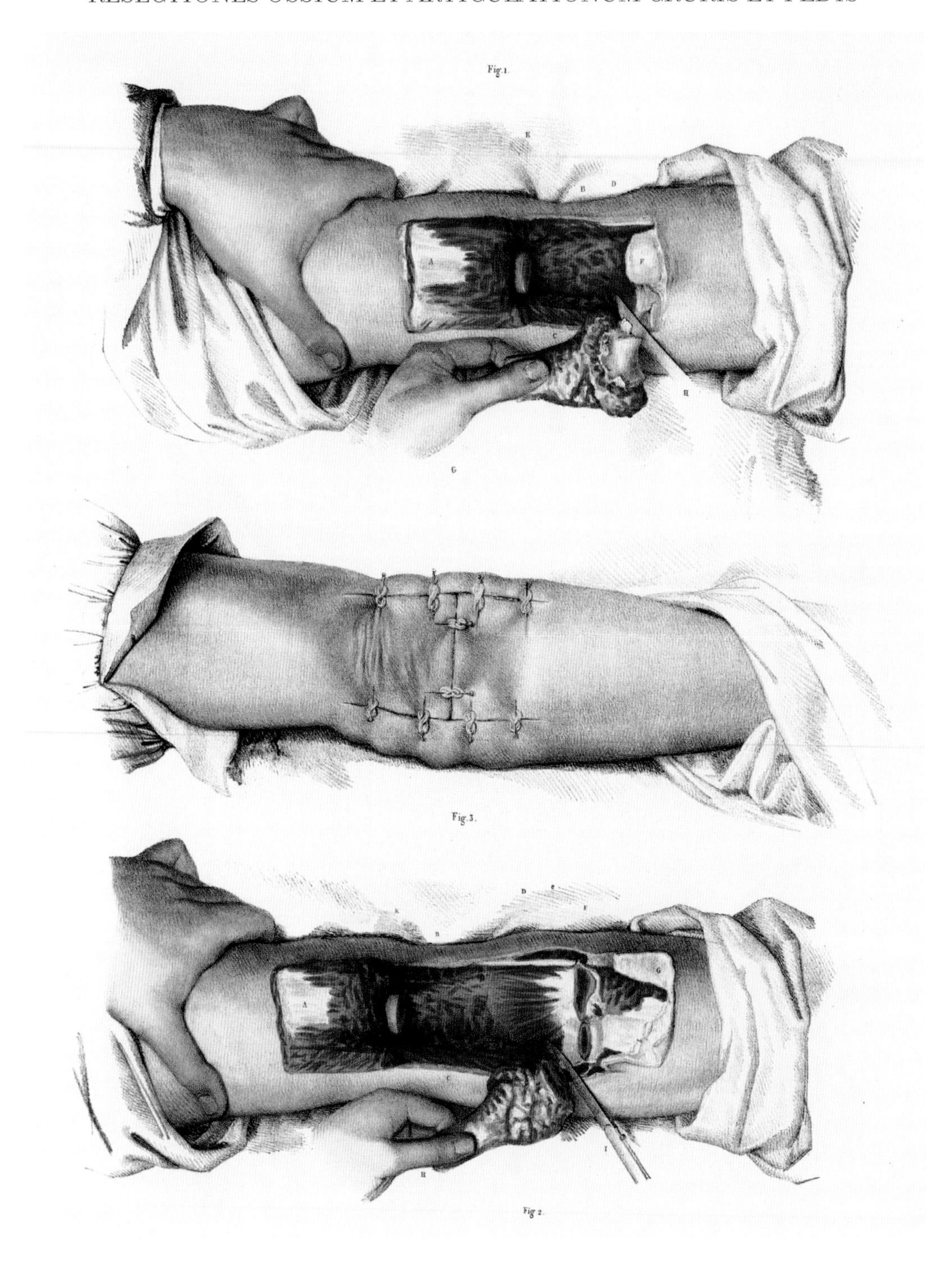

Resections of the elbow joint / Résections articulaires du coude
Resecciones articulares del codo

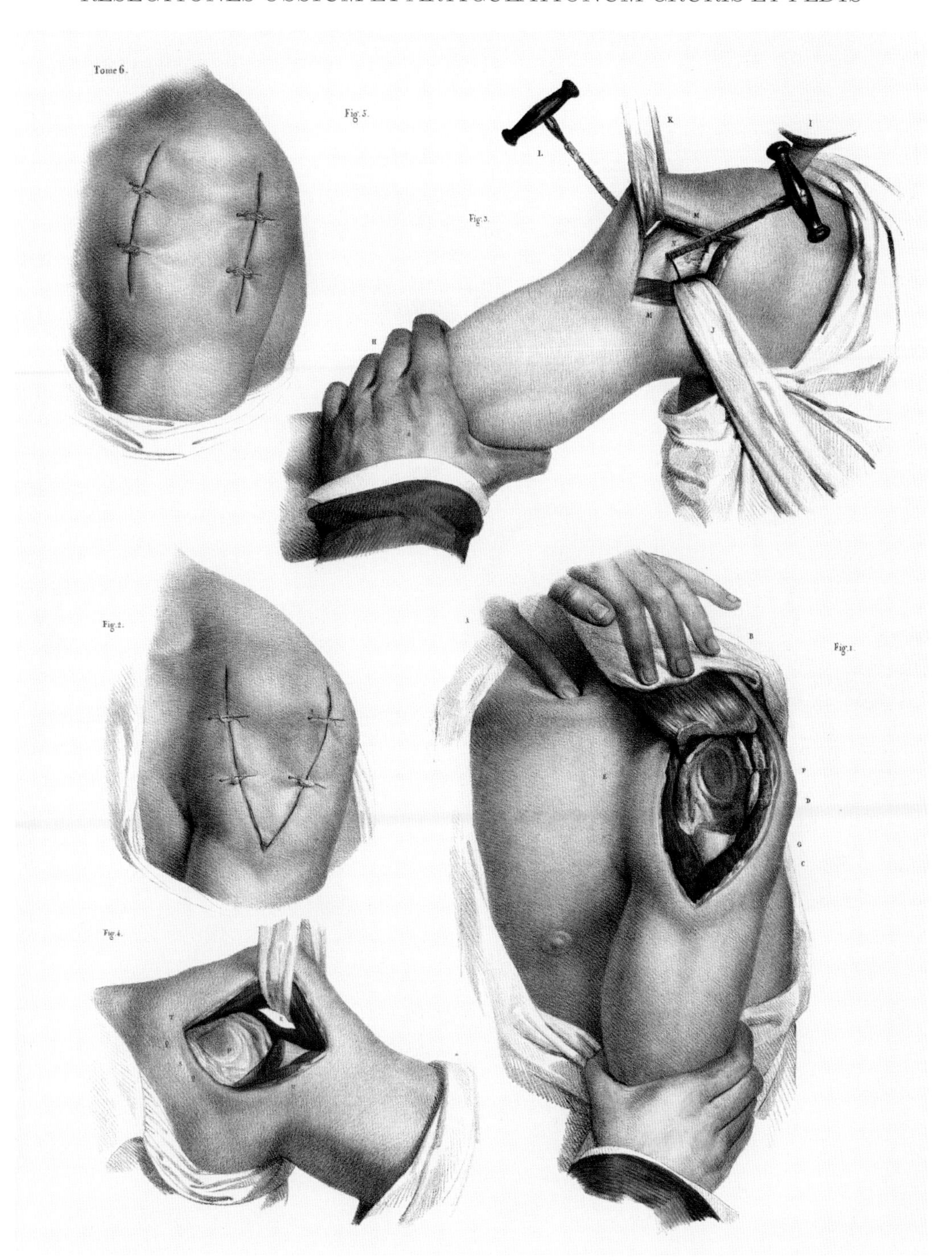

Resections of the humerus / Résections de l'humérus
Resecciones del húmero

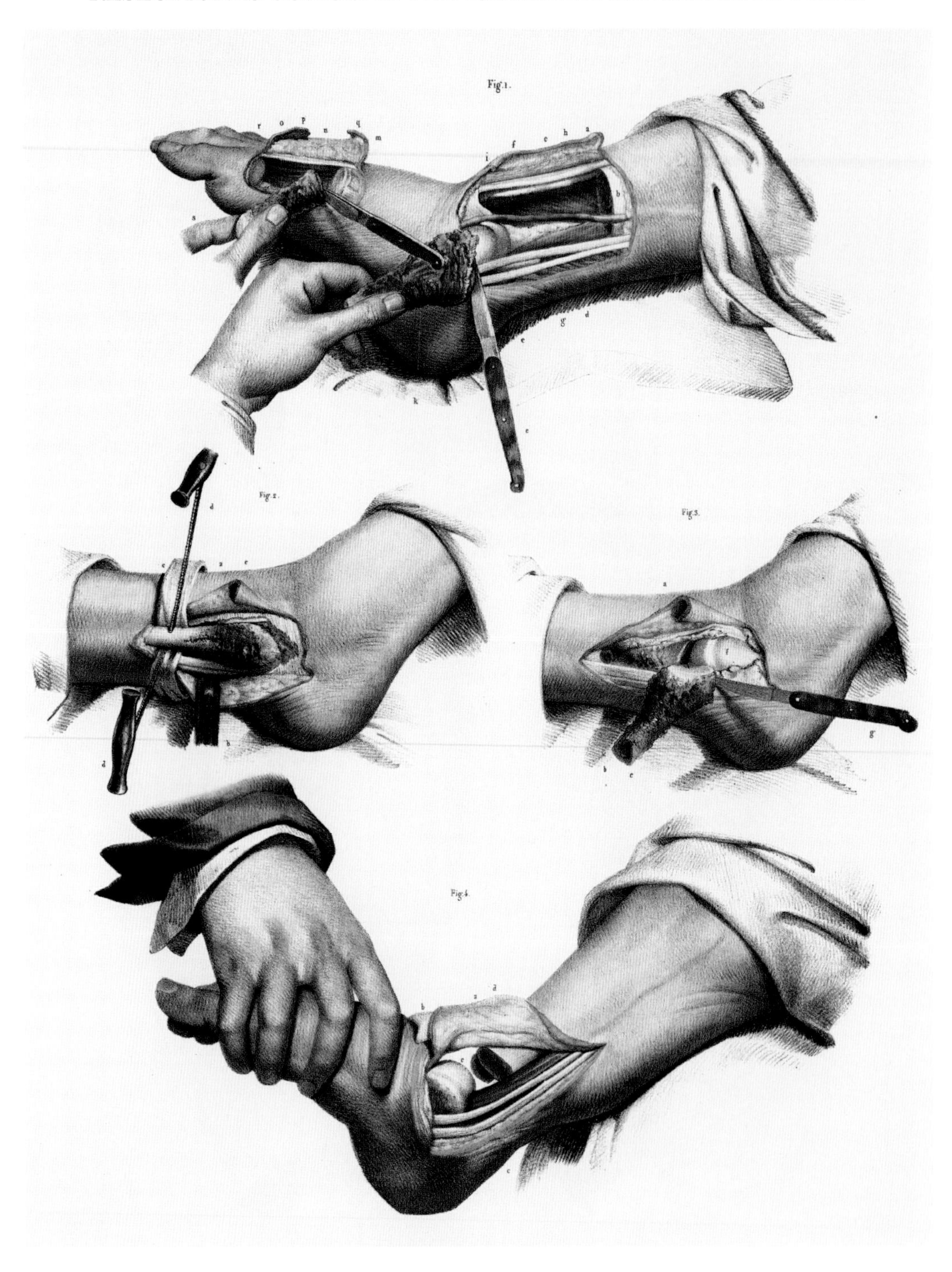

Resections of bones and joints of the lower leg and foot
Résections osseuses et articulaires de la jambe et du pied
Resecciones óseas y articulares de la pierna y del pie

RESECTIONES ARTICULATIONIS RADIOCARPEAE ET ARTICULATIONIS TALOCRURALIS. RESECTIONES OSSIUM CRURIS ET PEDIS. RESECTIO ARTICULATIONIS GENUS. RESECTIONES COSTARUM, SCAPULAE, ET CLAVICULAE

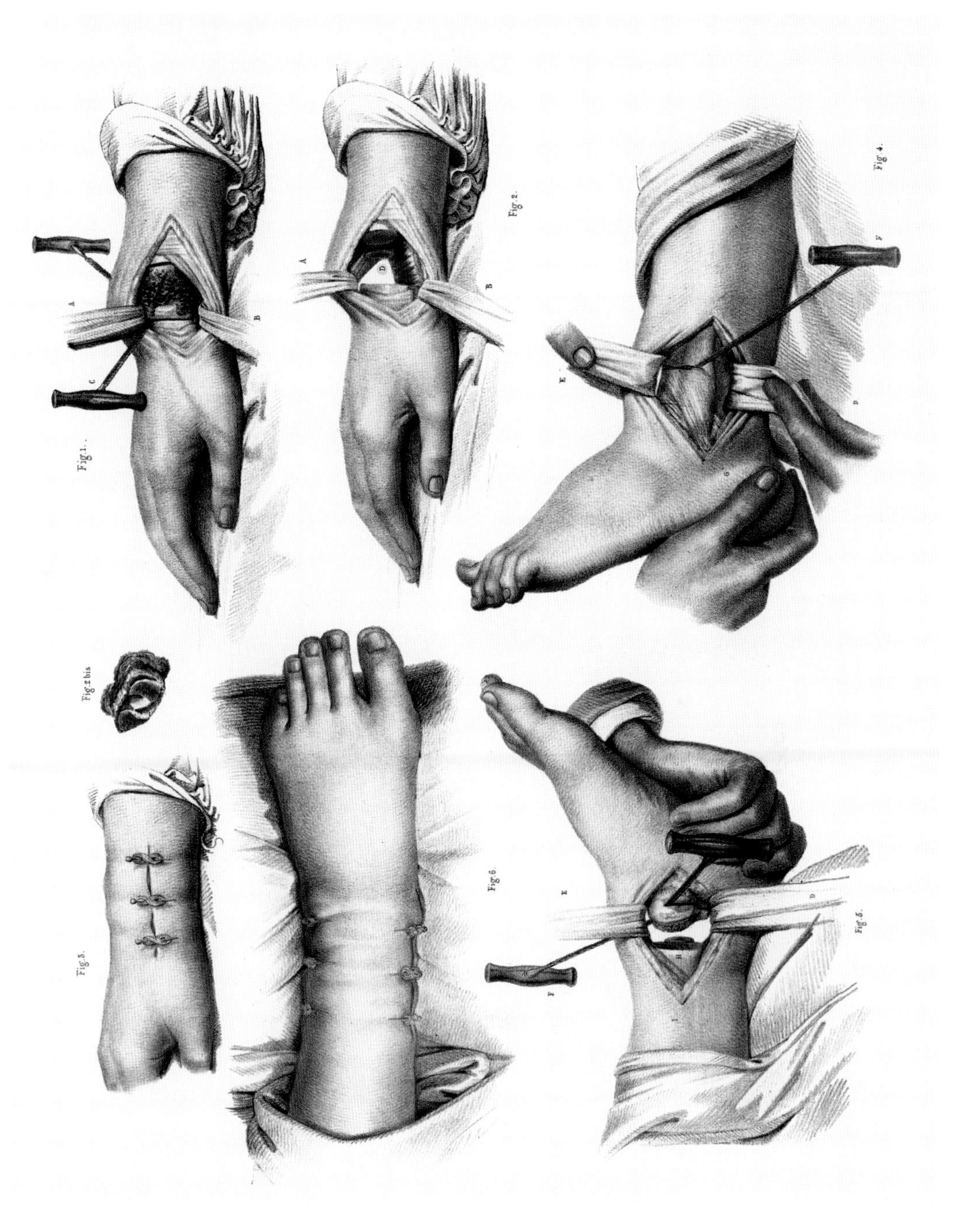

Resections of the wrist and ankle joint
Résections articulaires du poignet et de la cheville
Resecciones articulares de la muñeca y del tobillo

RESECTIONES ARTICULATIONIS RADIOCARPEAE ET ARTICULATIONIS TALOCRURALIS. RESECTIONES OSSIUM CRURIS ET PEDIS. RESECTIO ARTICULATIONIS GENUS. RESECTIONES COSTARUM, SCAPULAE, ET CLAVICULAE

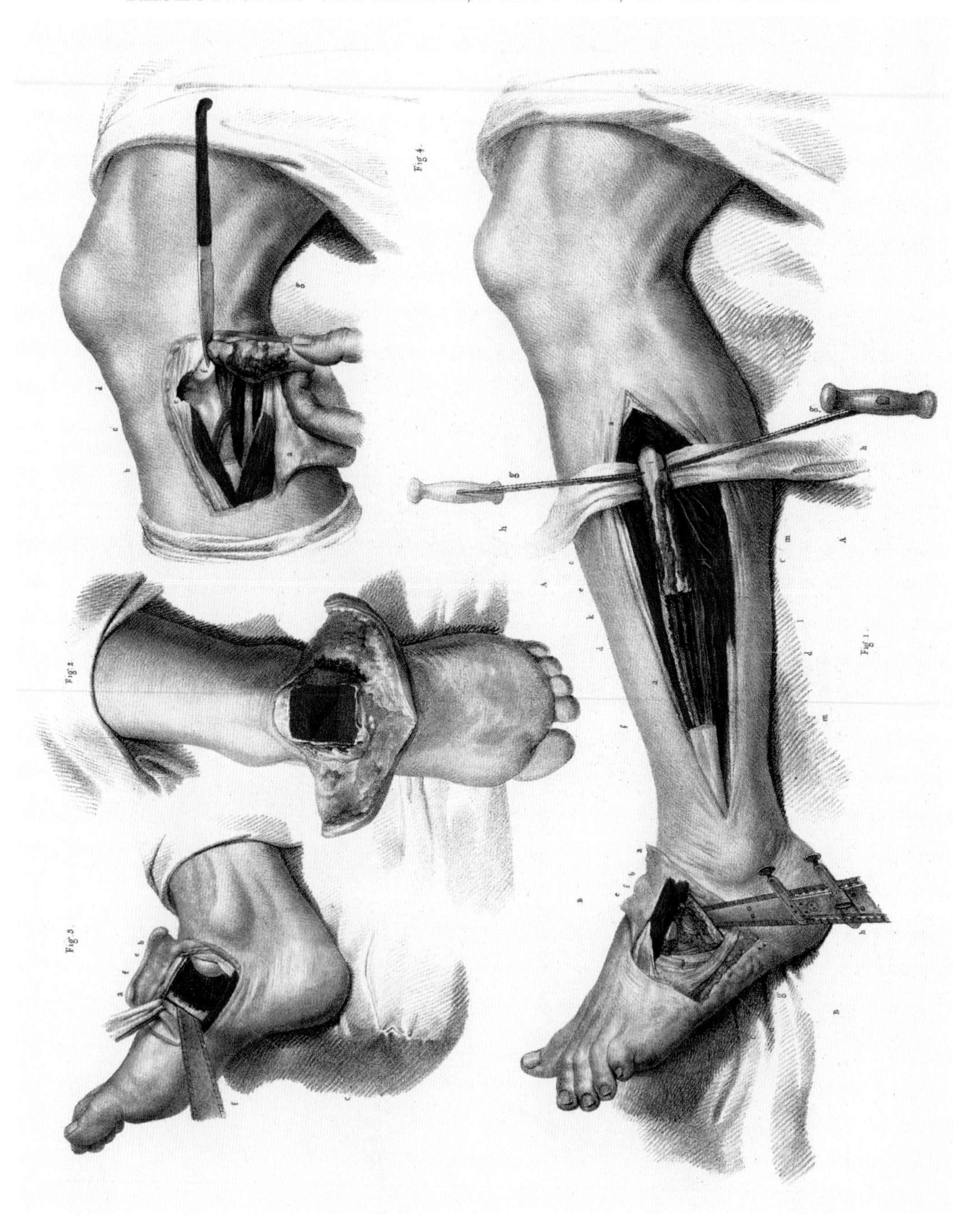

Resections of the bones of the lower leg and foot
Résections osseuses de la jambe et du pied
Resecciones óseas de la pierna y del pie

RESECTIONES ARTICULATIONIS RADIOCARPEAE ET ARTICULATIONIS TALOCRURALIS. RESECTIONES OSSIUM CRURIS ET PEDIS. RESECTIO ARTICULATIONIS GENUS. RESECTIONES COSTARUM, SCAPULAE, ET CLAVICULAE

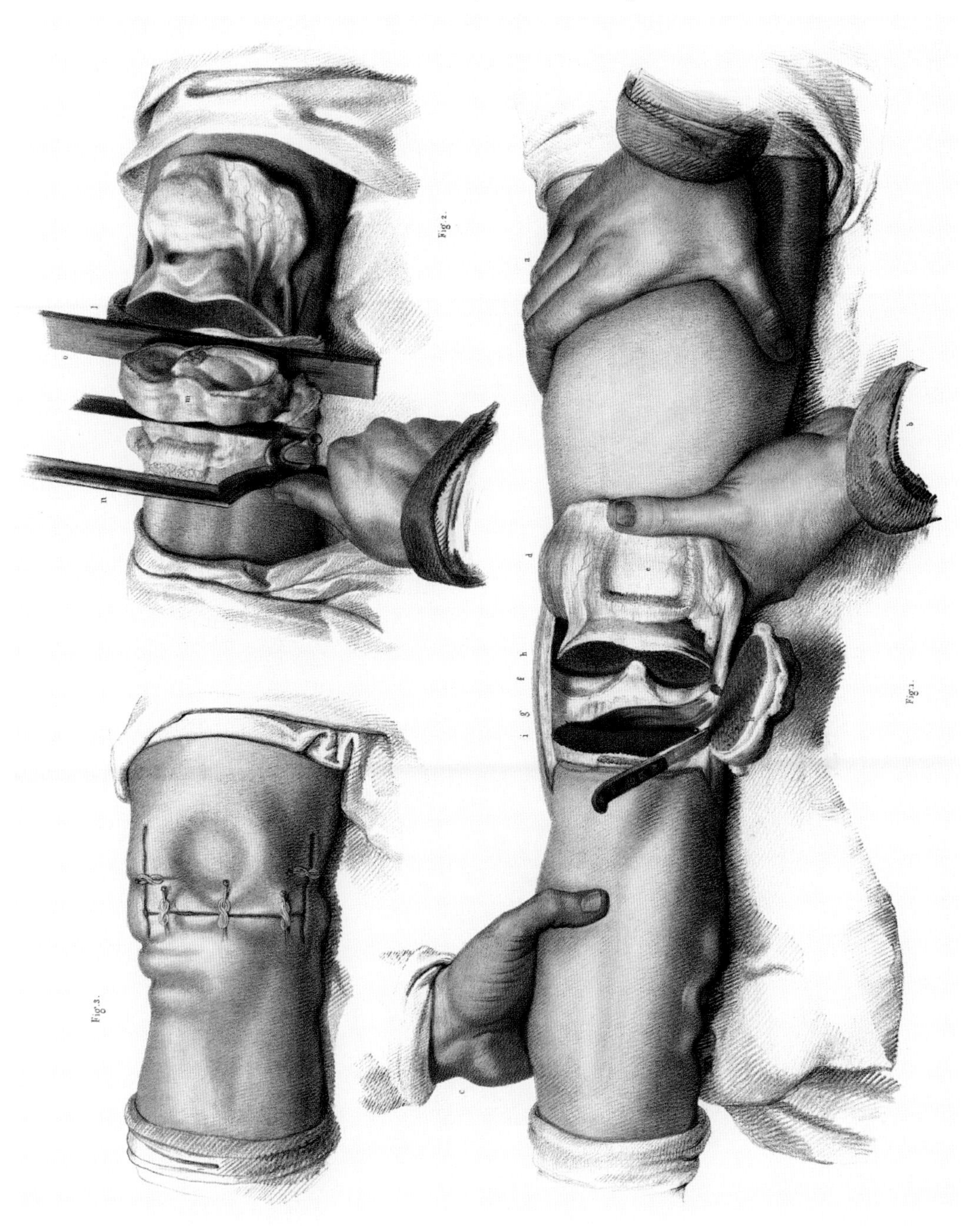

Resection of the knee joint / Résection articulaire du genou
Resección articular de la rodilla

RESECTIONES ARTICULATIONIS RADIOCARPEAE ET ARTICULATIONIS TALOCRURALIS. RESECTIONES OSSIUM CRURIS ET PEDIS. RESECTIO ARTICULATIONIS GENUS. RESECTIONES COSTARUM, SCAPULAE, ET CLAVICULAE

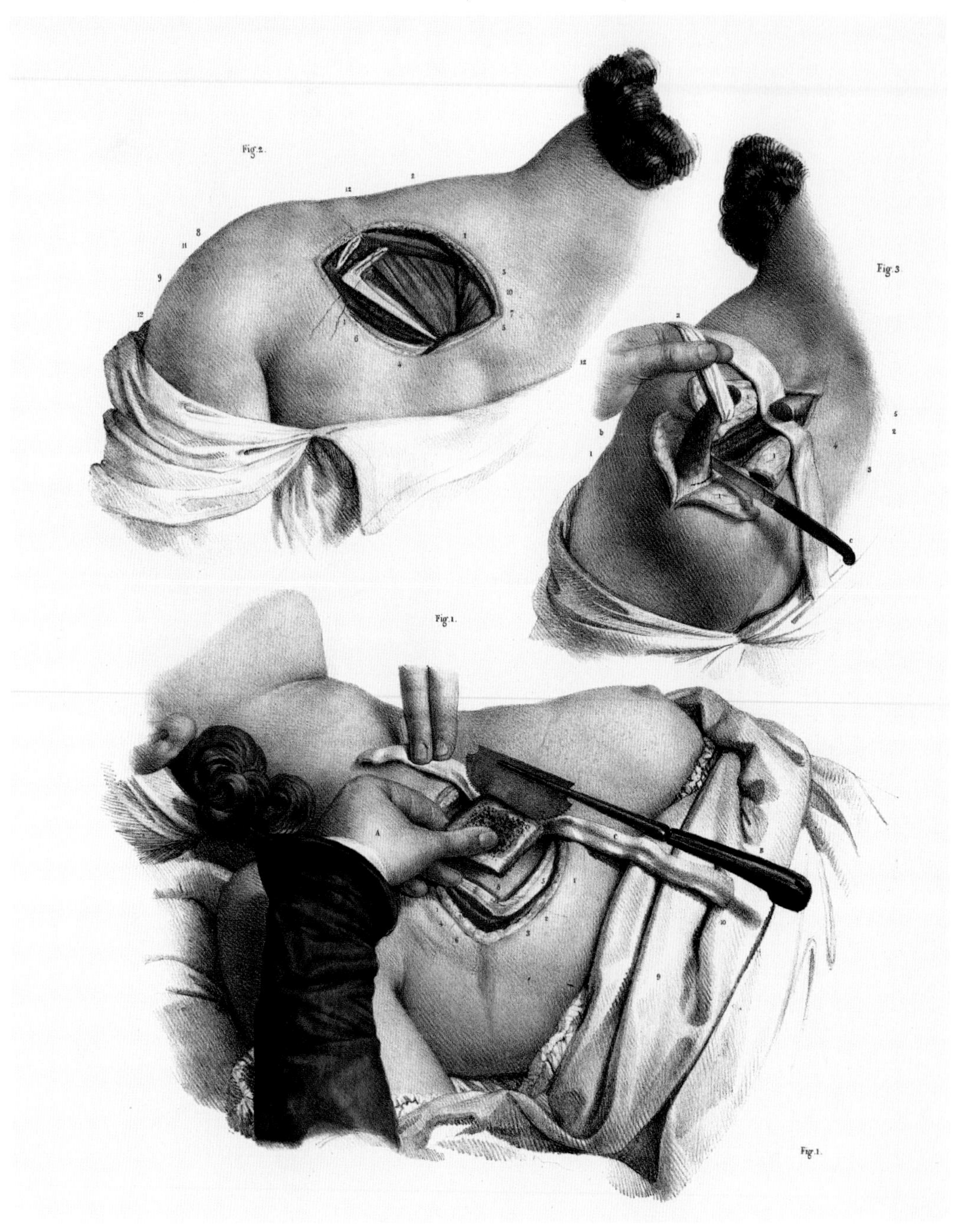

Resections of the ribs, the shoulder blade, and the collarbone
Résections de côtes, de la scapula et de la clavicule
Resecciones de las costillas, la escápula y la clavícula

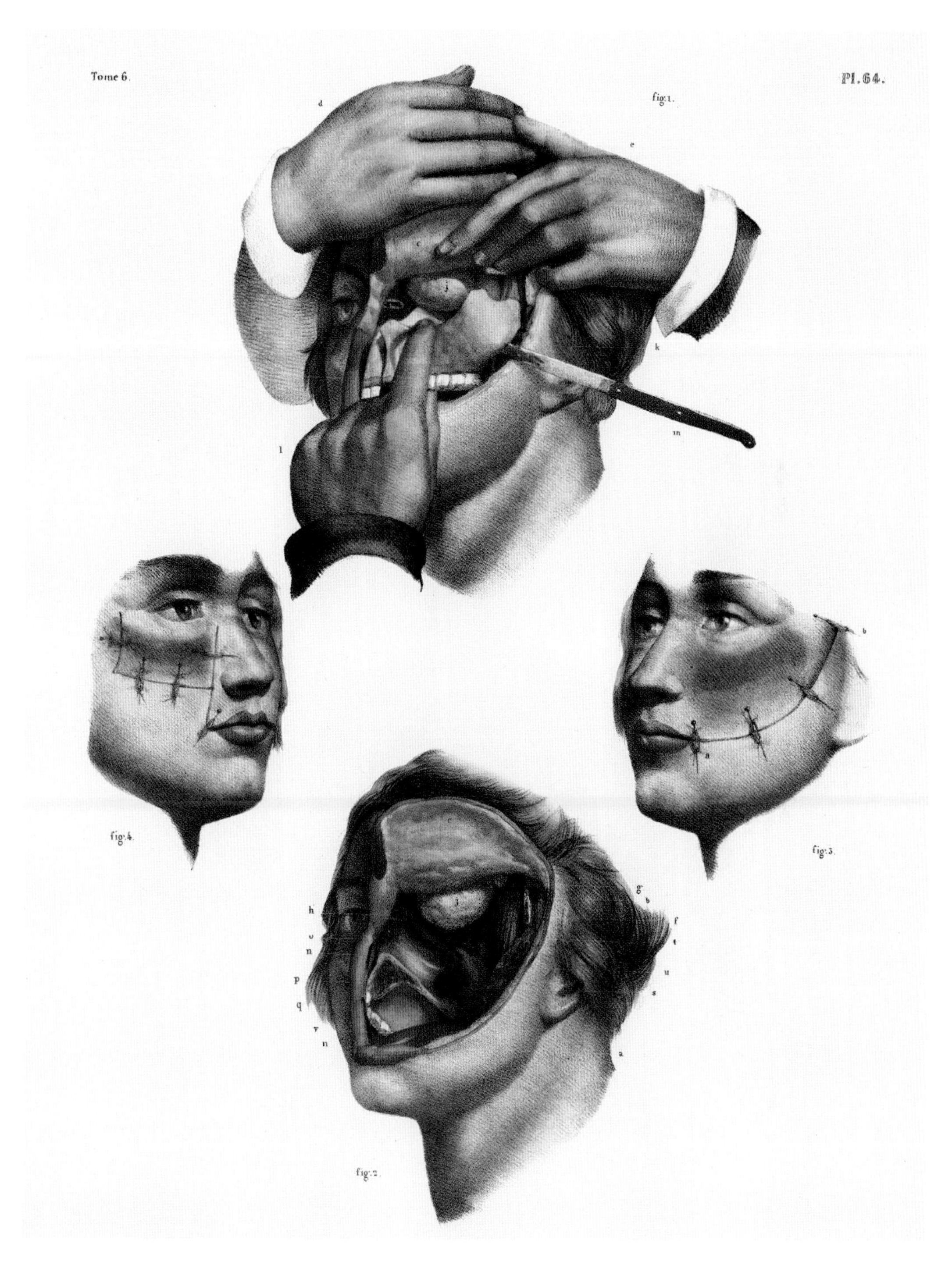

Resection of the maxillary bone / Résection de l'os maxillaire
Resección del hueso maxilar

Resections of the mandibular bone / Résections de la mandibule
Resecciones de la mandíbula

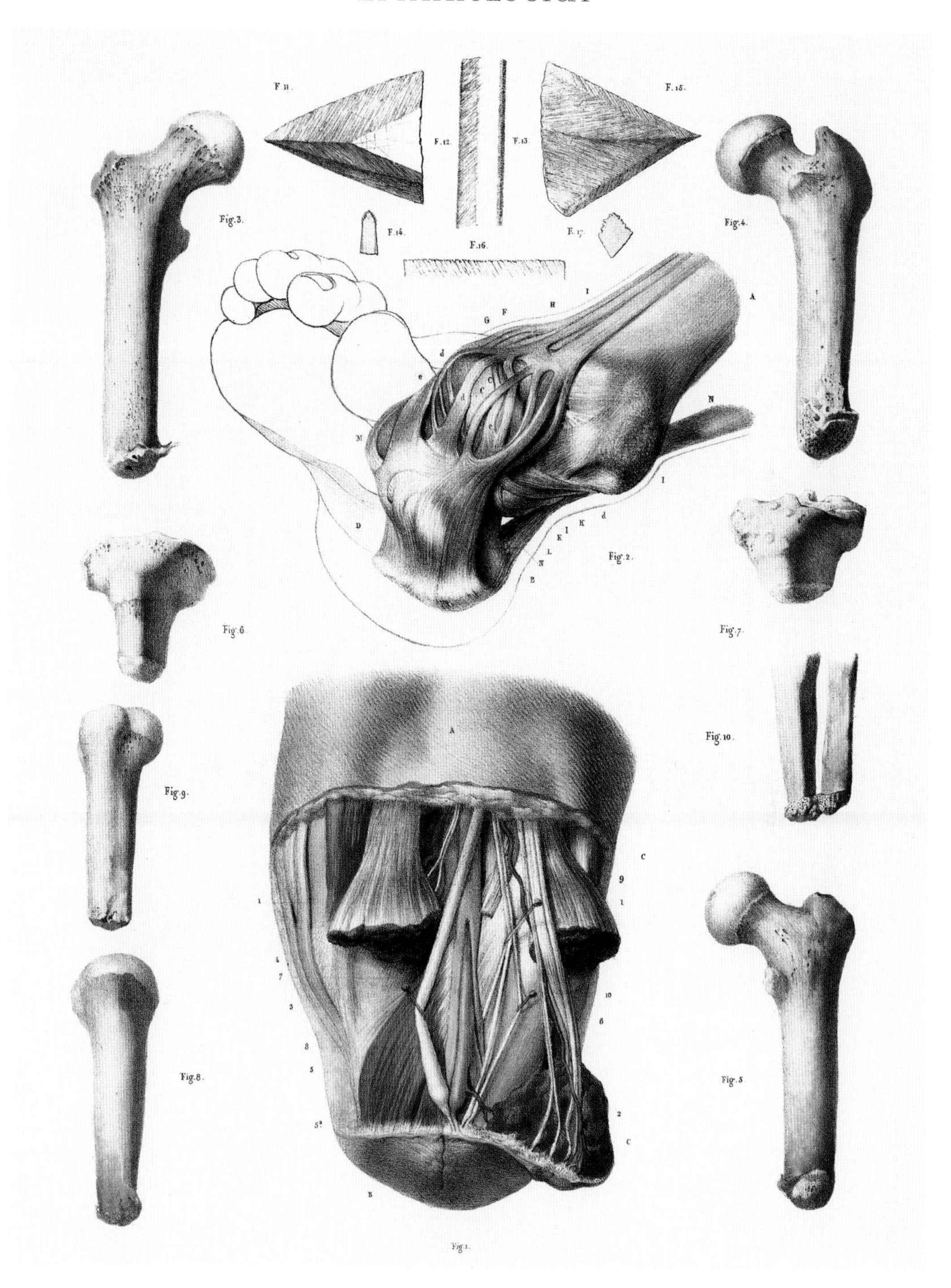

Amputations: Surgical and pathological anatomy
Amputations : Anatomie chirurgicale et pathologique
Amputaciones: anatomía quirúrgica y patológica

AMPUTATIONES ET DESARTICULATIONES PHALANGUM DIGITORUM MANUS

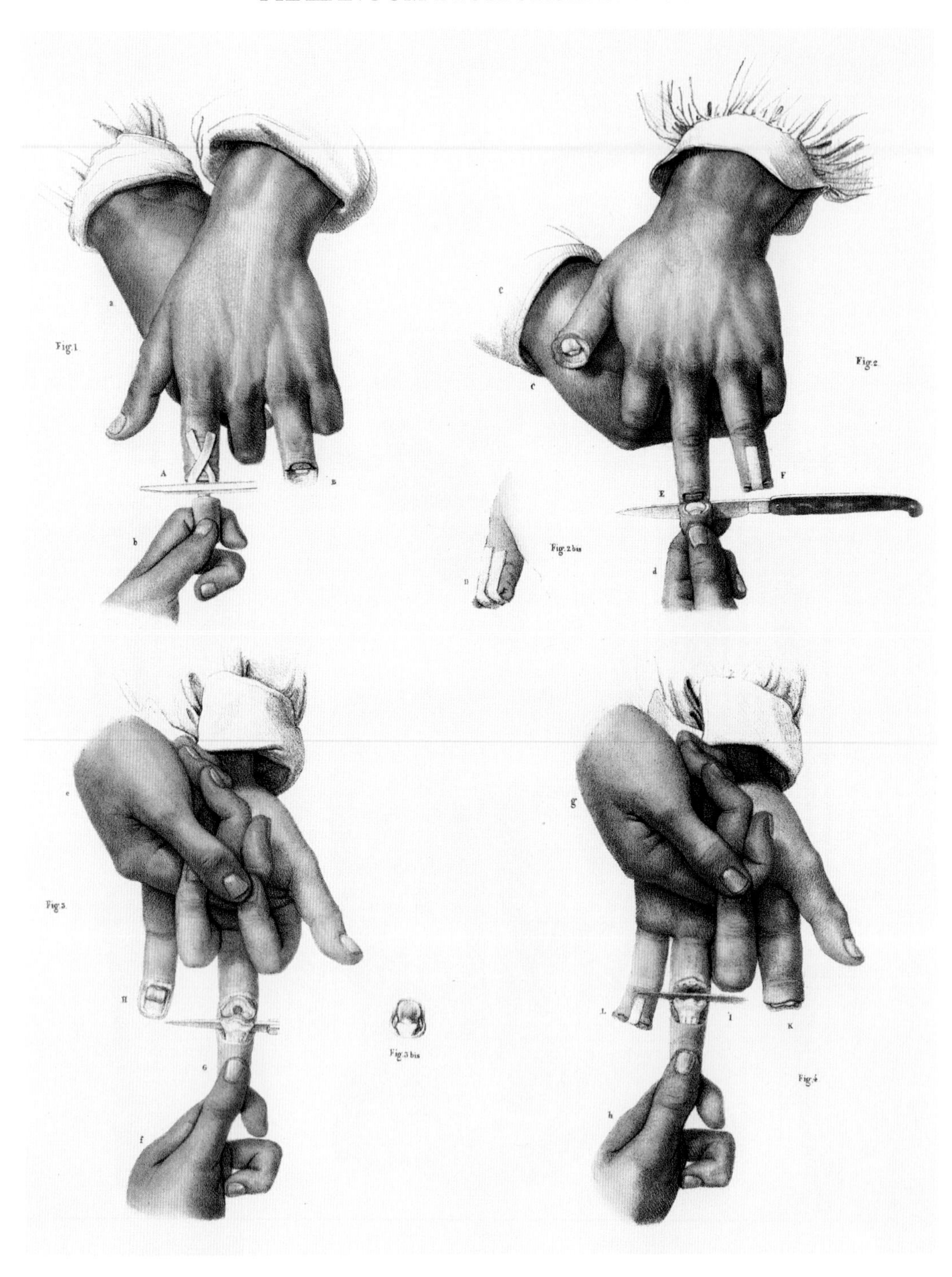

Amputations and disarticulations of phalanges of the fingers of the hand
Amputations et désarticulations de phalanges de doigts de la main
Amputaciones y desarticulaciones de las falanges de la mano

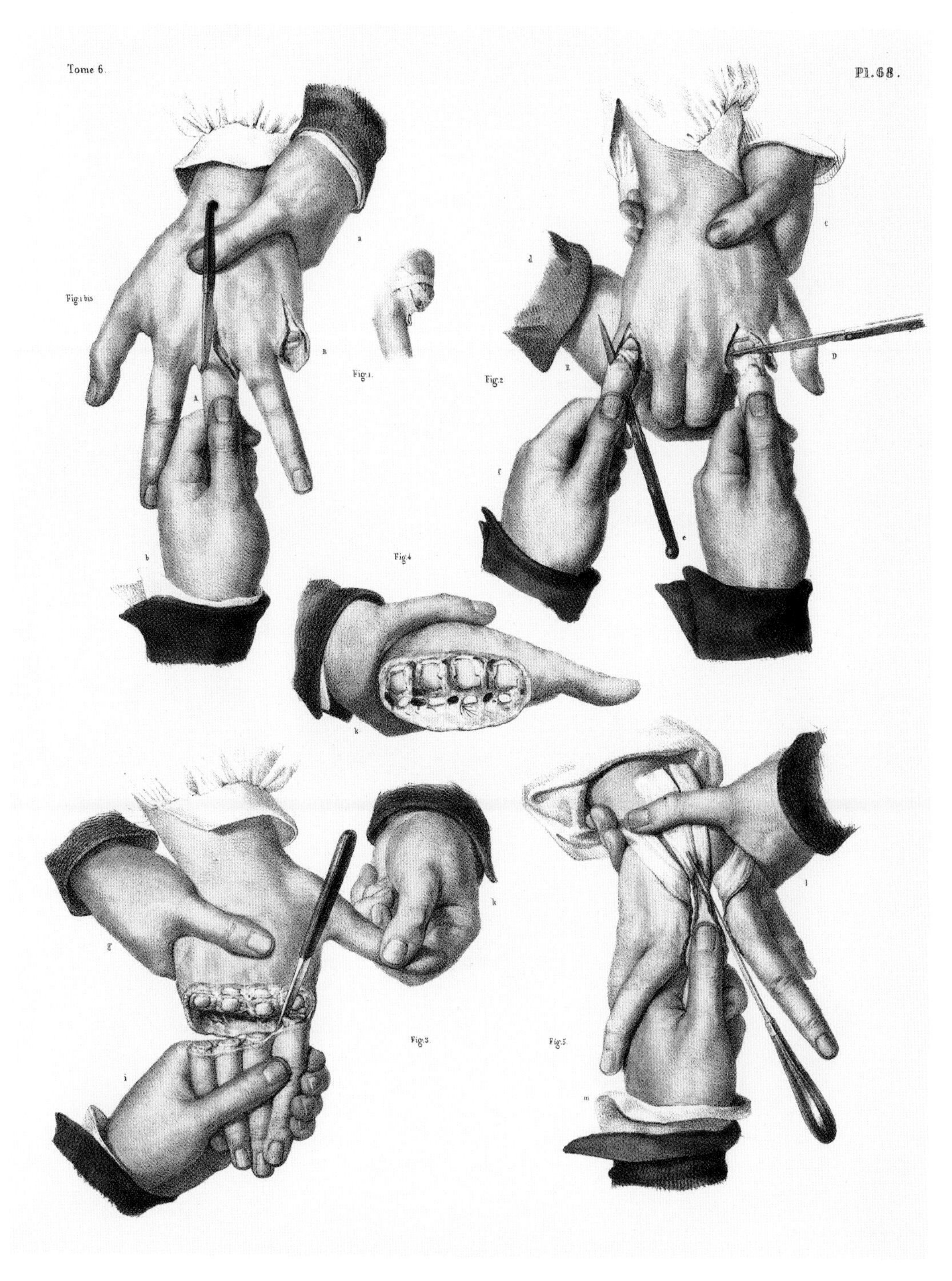

Amputations and disarticulations of the fingers of the hand
Amputations et désarticulations de doigts de la main
Amputaciones y desarticulaciones de los dedos de la mano

AMPUTATIONES ET DESARTICULATIONES METACARPII

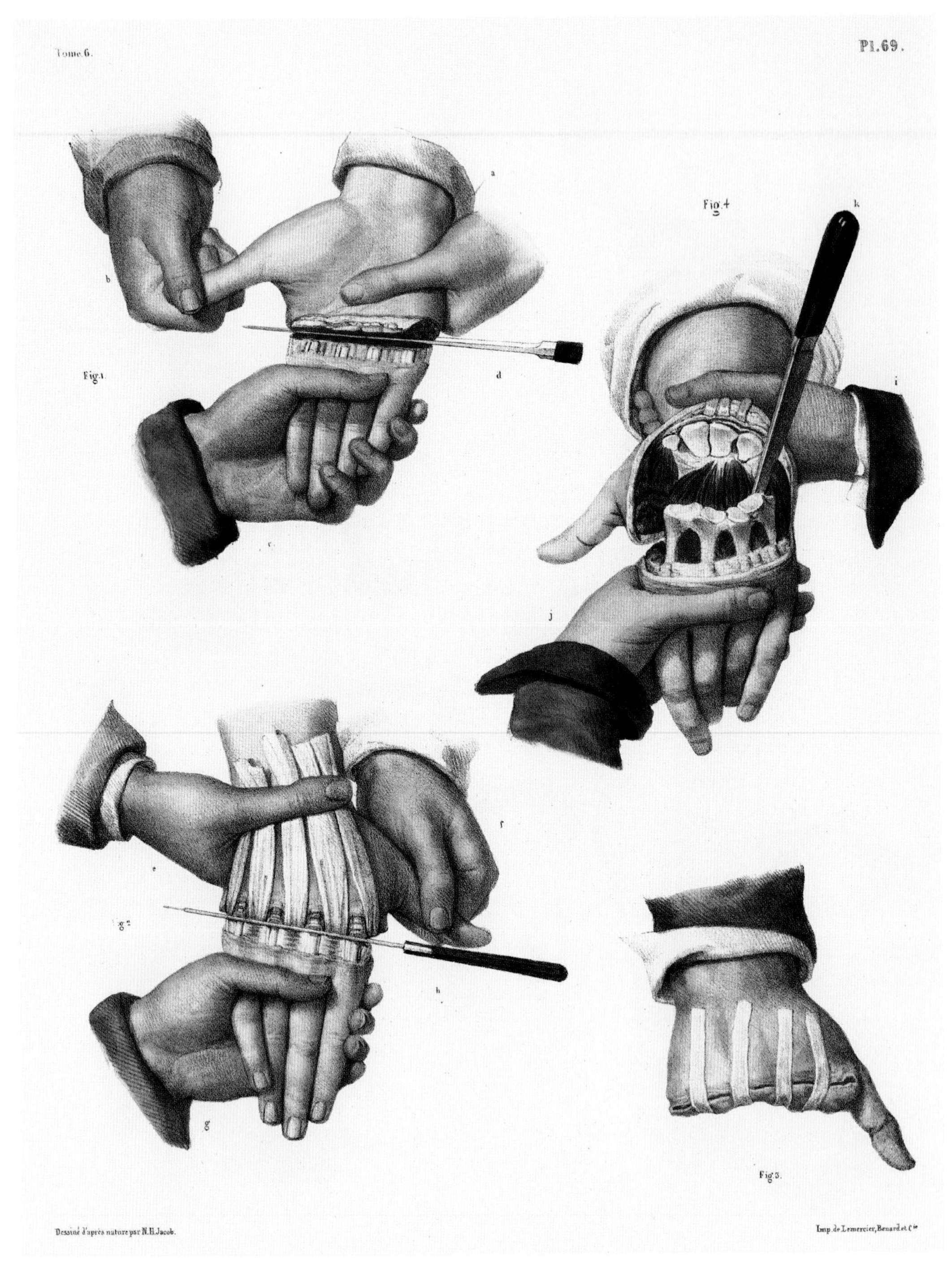

Amputations and disarticulations of the metacarpals
Amputations et désarticulations du métacarpe
Amputaciones y desarticulaciones del metacarpo

Disarticulations of the rays of the hand / Désarticulations de rayons de la main
Desarticulaciones de las radiaciones digitales de la mano

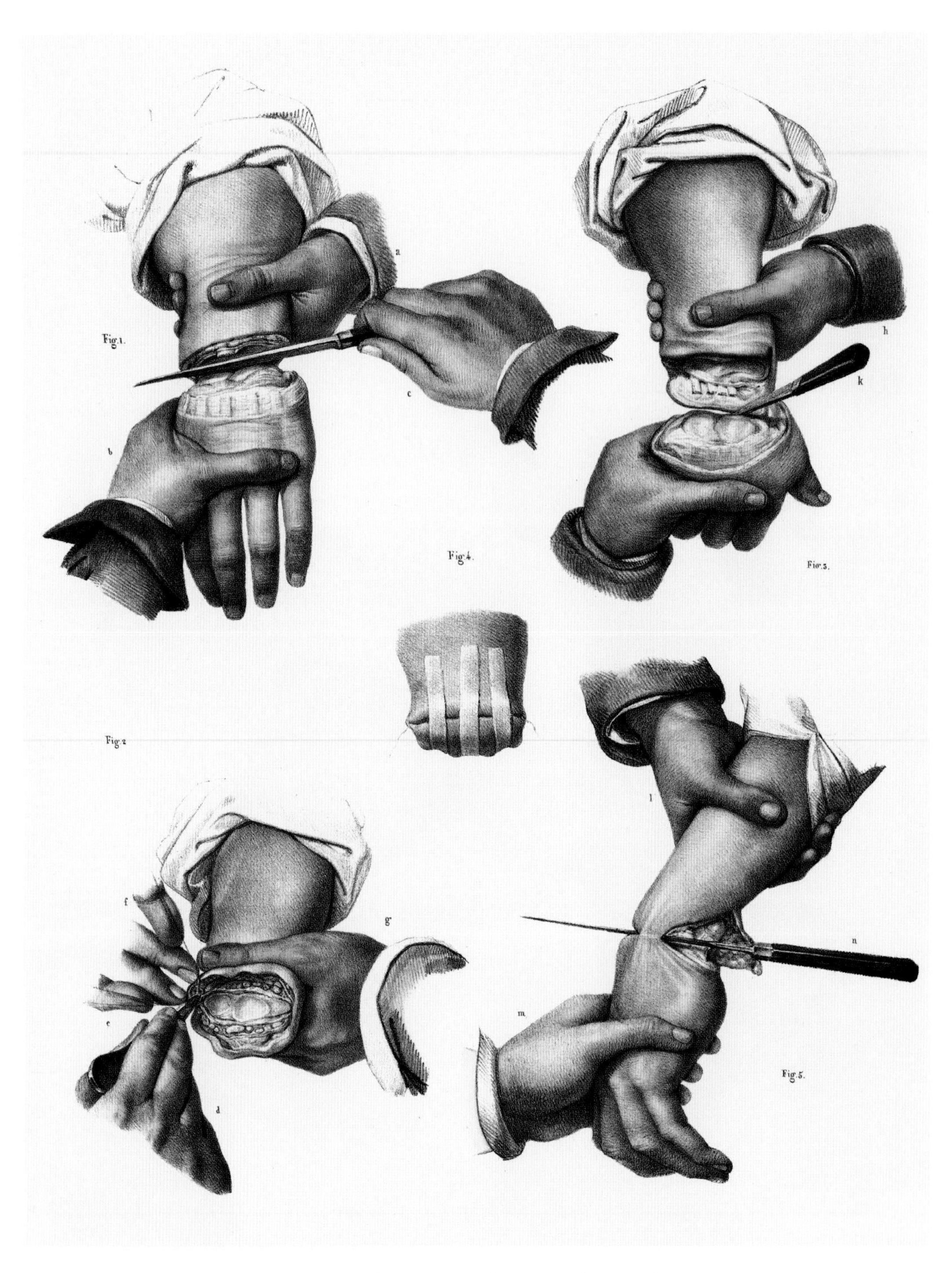

Disarticulations of the wrist / Désarticulations du poignet
Desarticulaciones de la muñeca

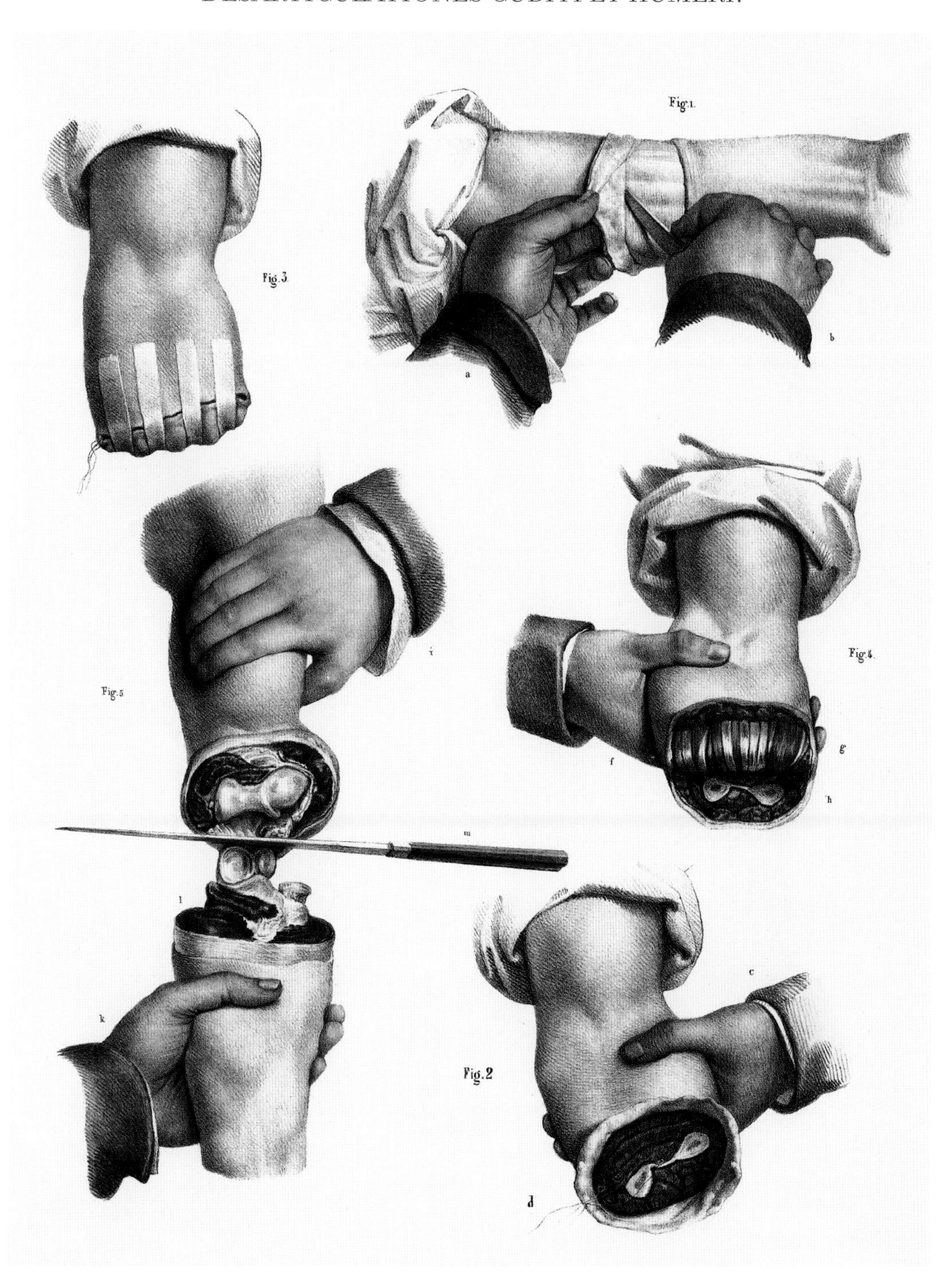

Amputations of the forearm and disarticulations of the elbow
Amputations de l'avant-bras et désarticulations du coude
Amputaciones del antebrazo y desarticulaciones del cod

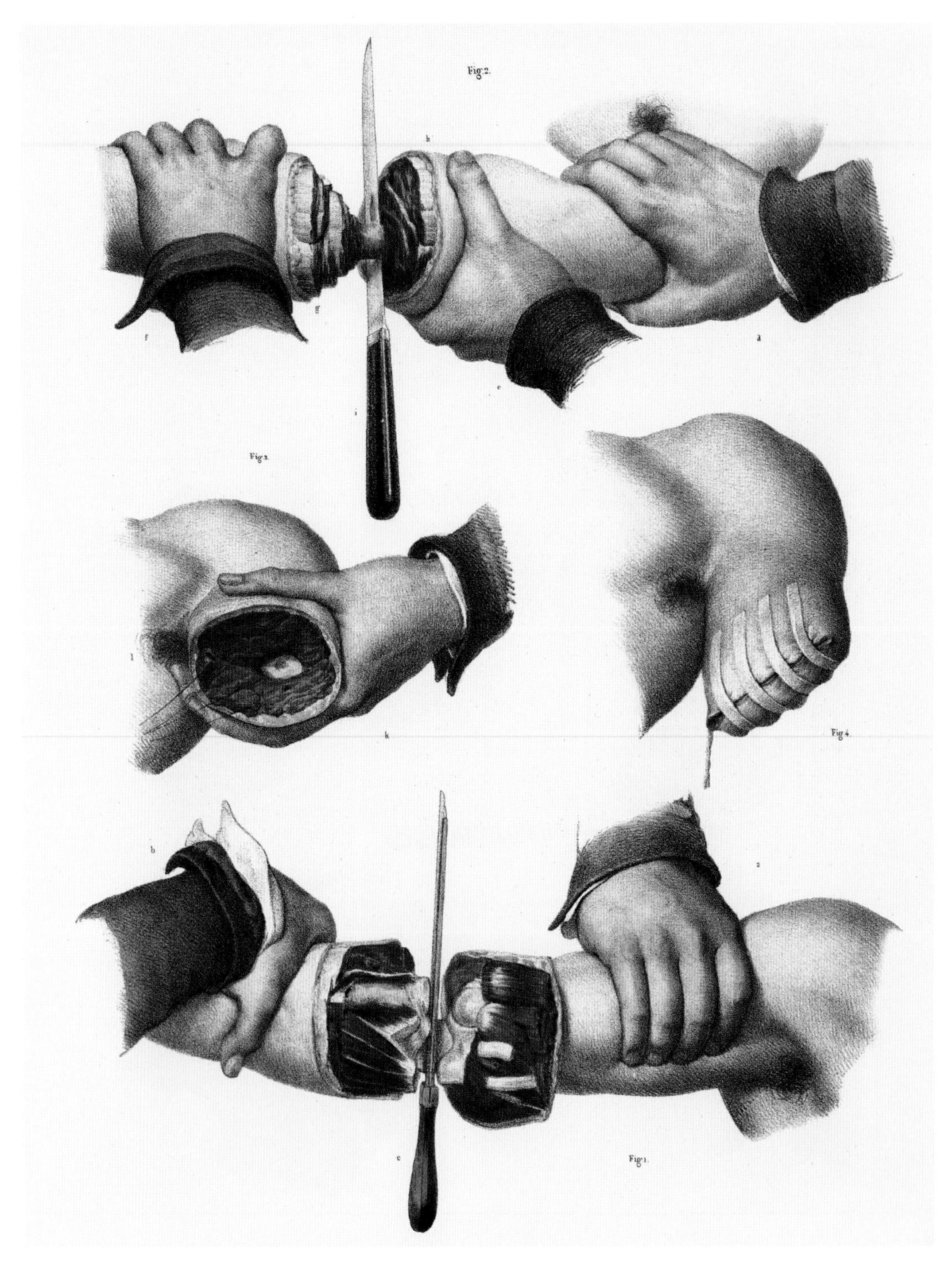

Disarticulations of the elbow and amputations of the arm
Désarticulations du coude et amputations du bras
Desarticulaciones del codo y amputaciones del brazo

AMPUTATIONES ANTEBRACHII ET BRACHII. DESARTICULATIONES CUBITI ET HUMERI.

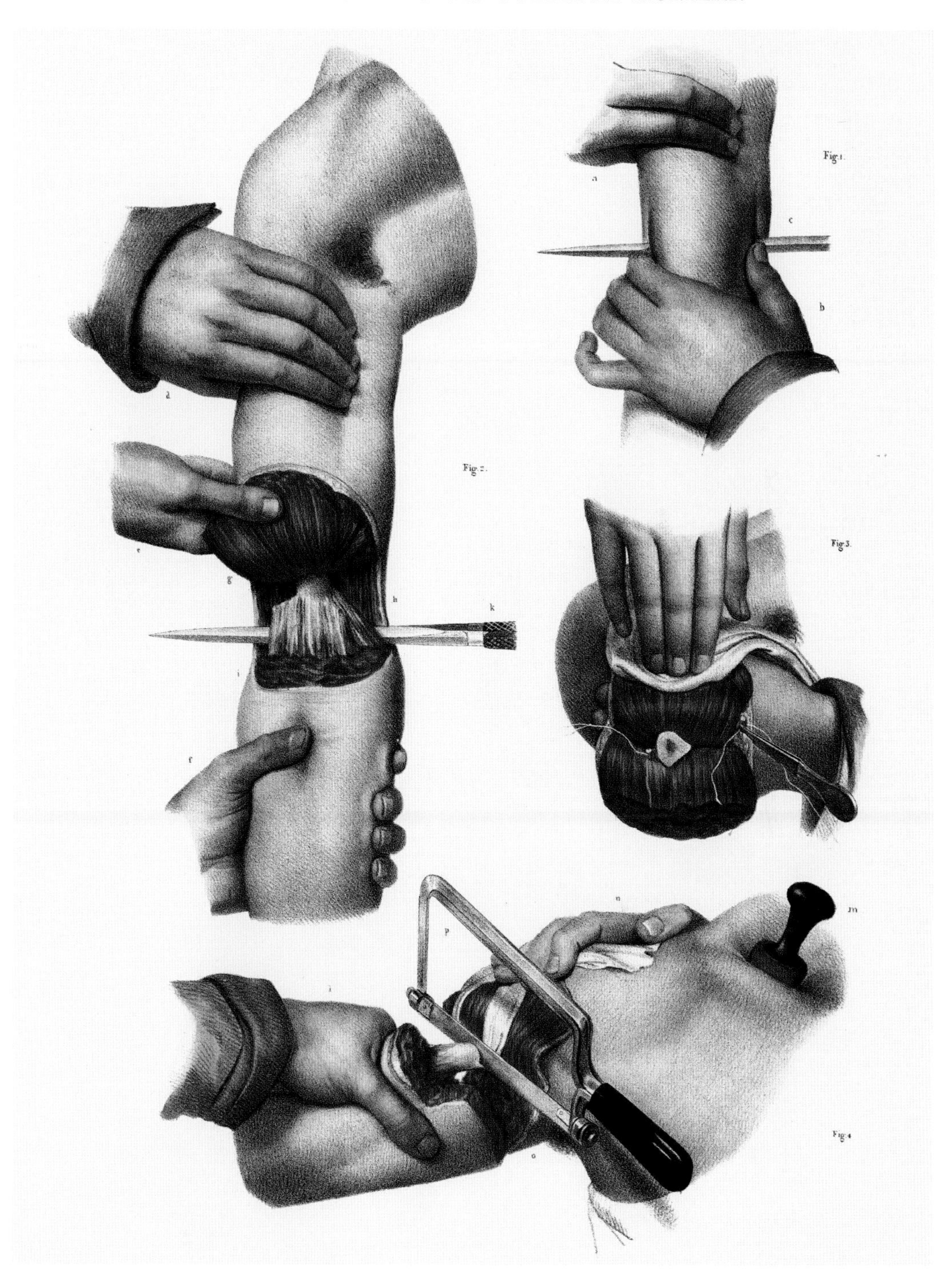

Amputations of the arm / Amputations du bras / Amputaciones del brazo

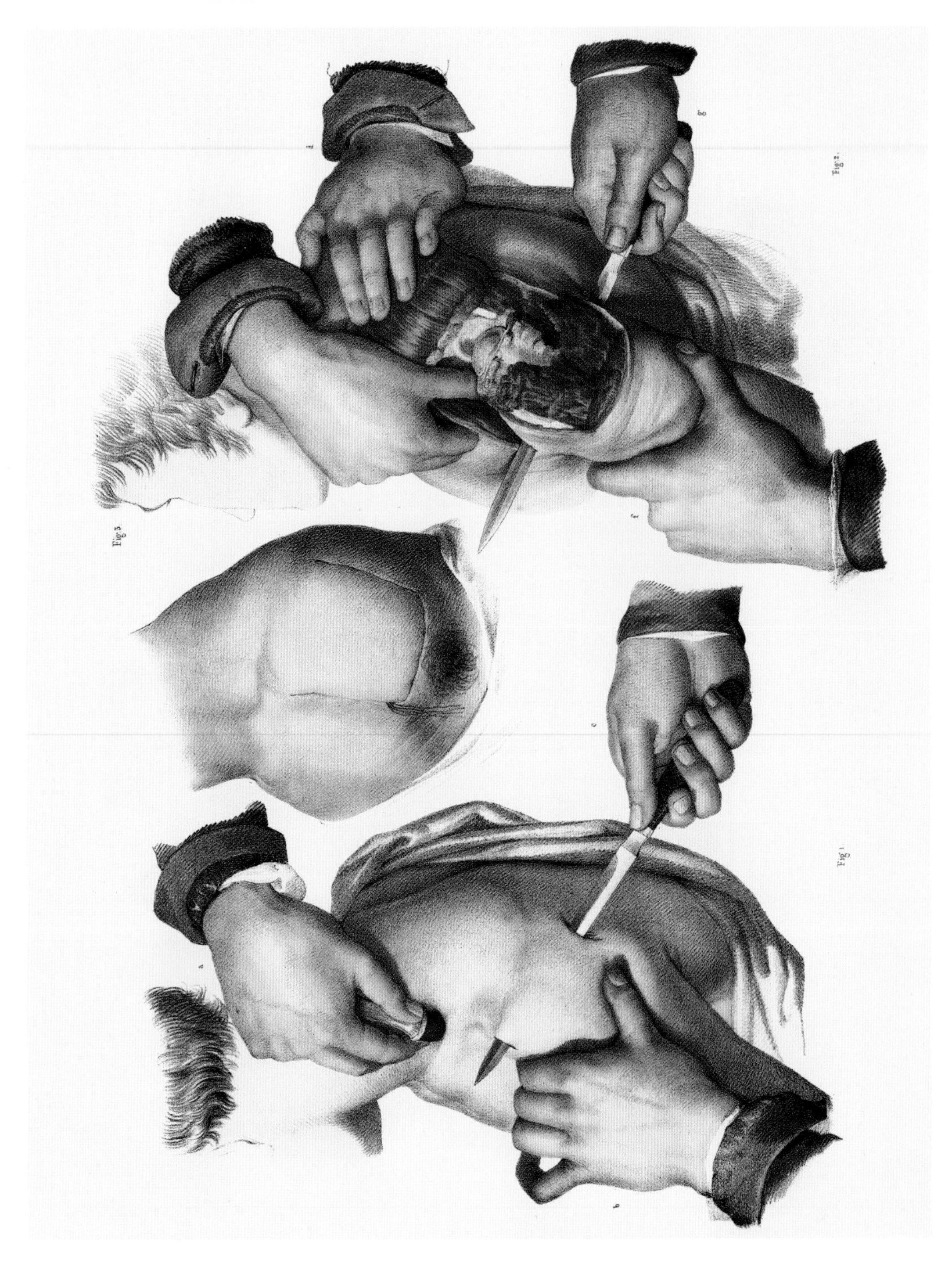

Disarticulations of the shoulder / Désarticulations de l'épaule
Desarticulaciones del hombro

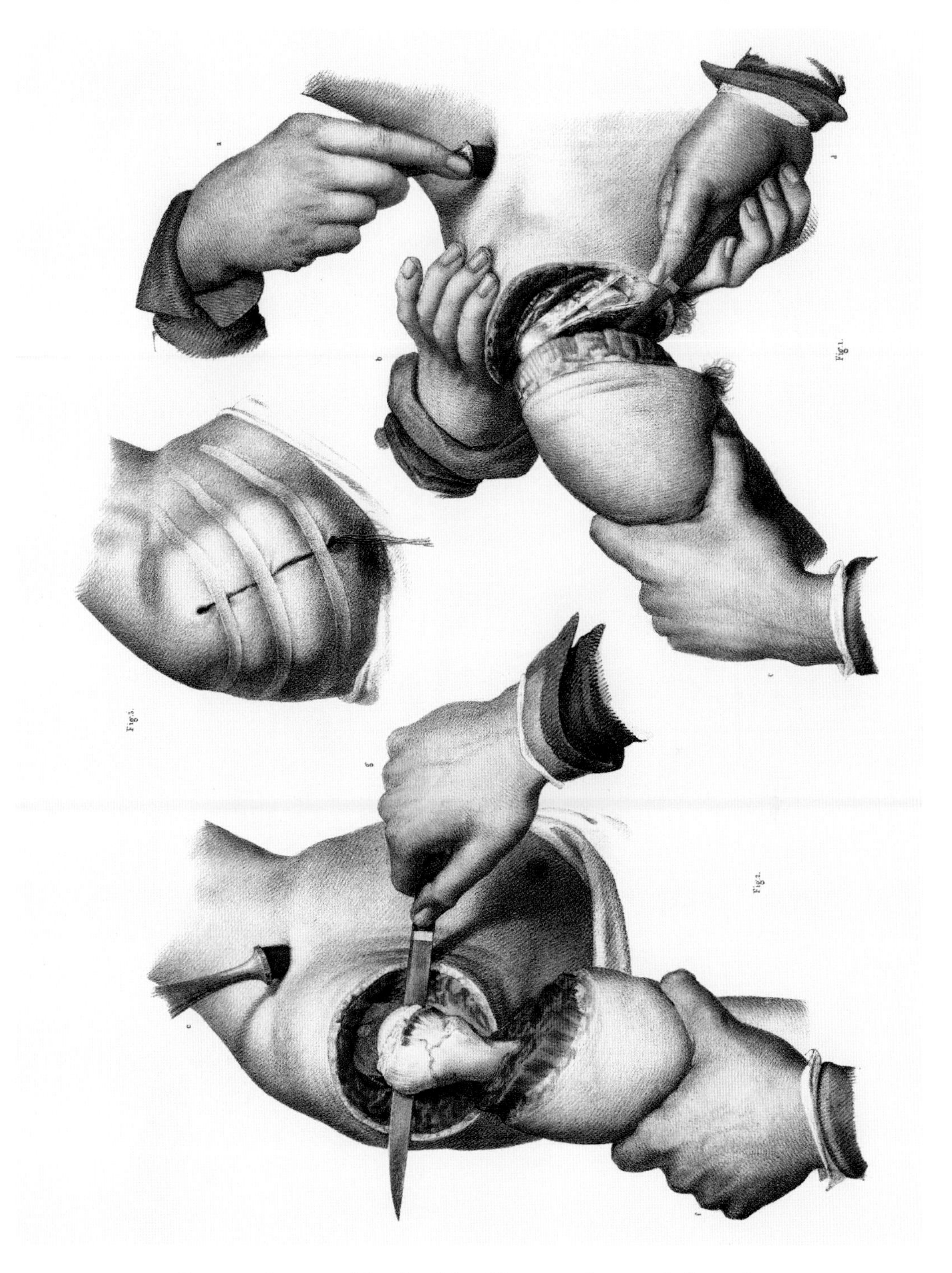

Disarticulations of the shoulder / Désarticulations de l'épaule
Desarticulaciones del hombro

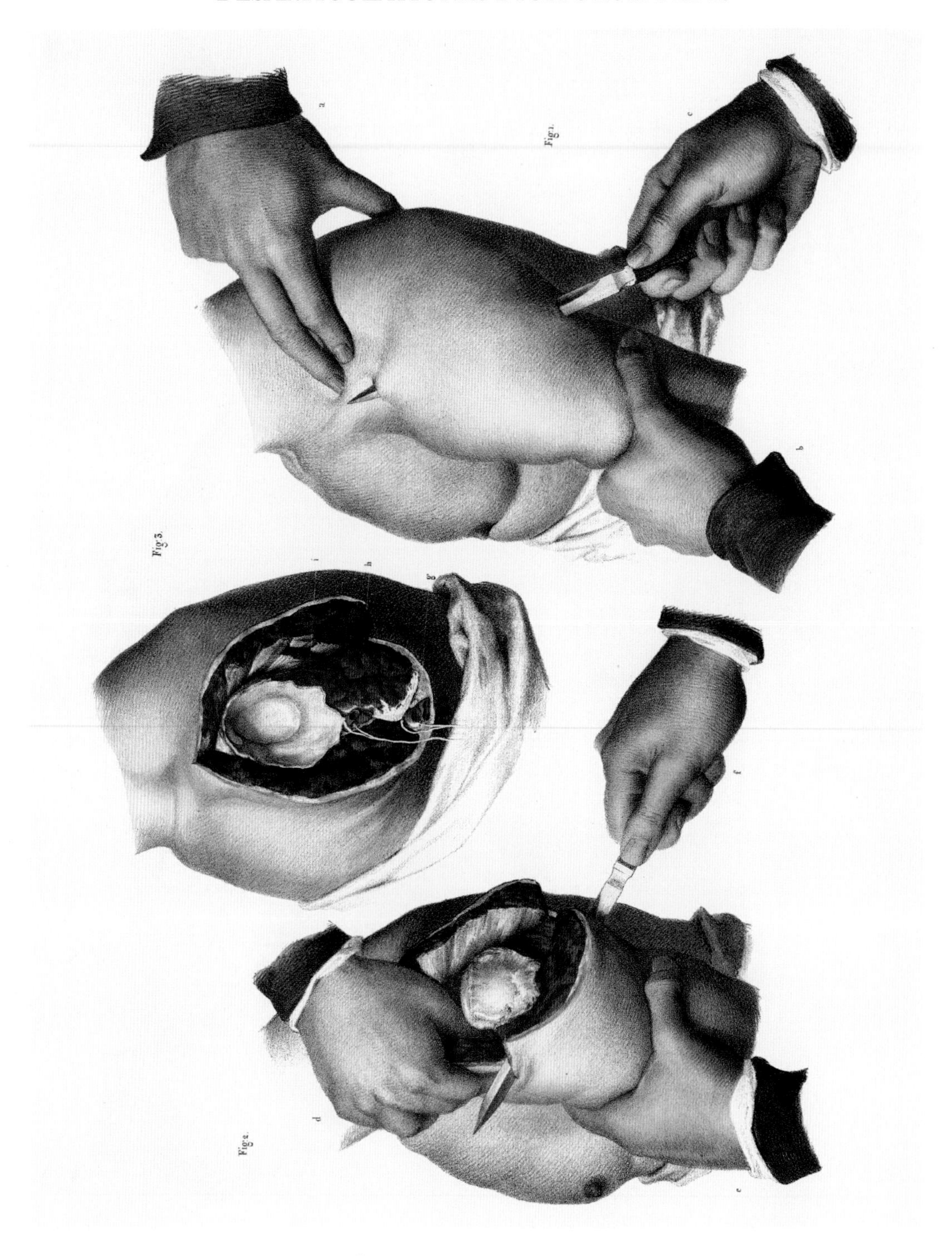

Disarticulations of the shoulder / Désarticulations de l'épaule
Desarticulaciones del hombro

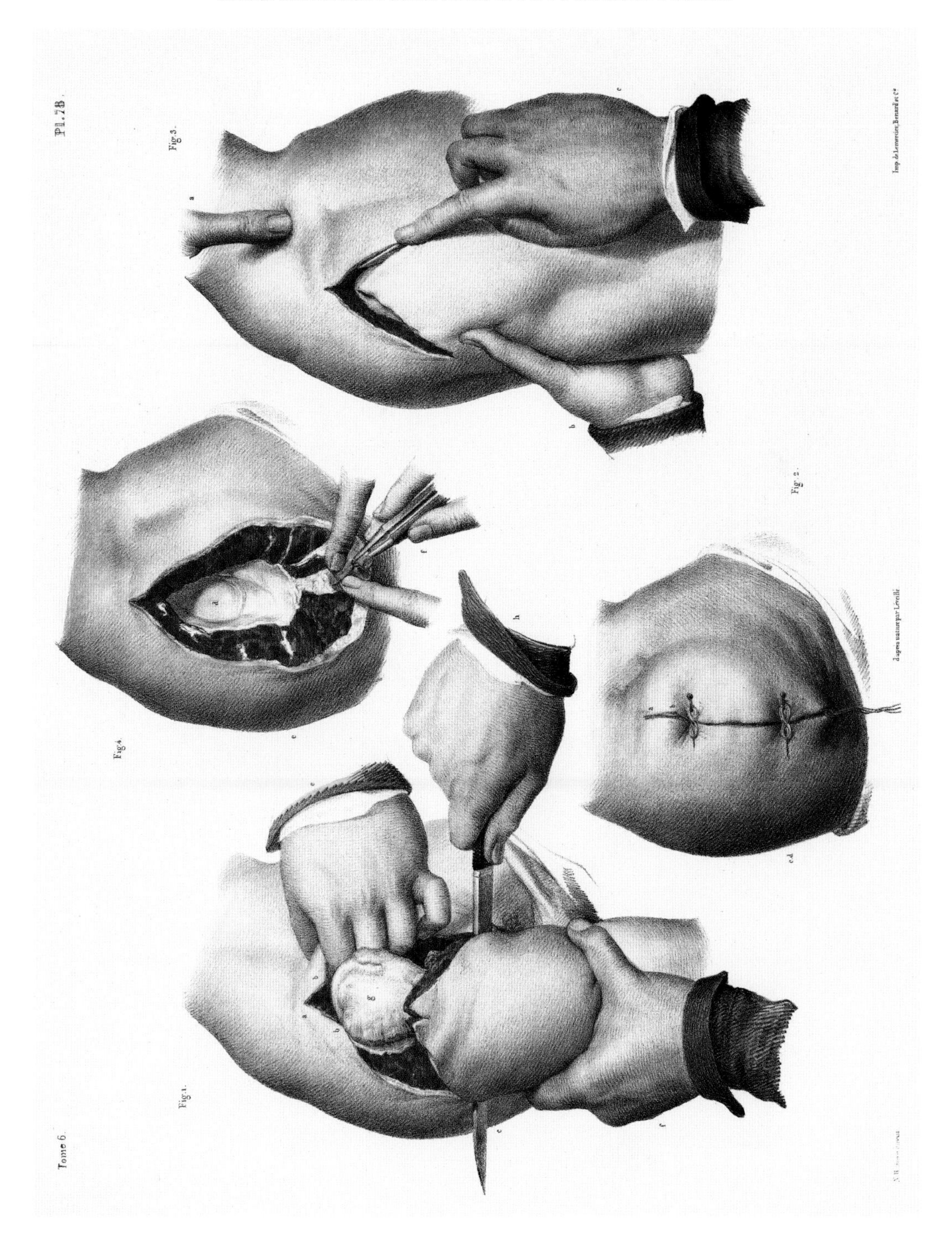

Disarticulations of the shoulder / Désarticulations de l'épaule
Desarticulaciones del hombro

DESARTICULATIONES HUMERI. DESARTICULATIONES DIGITORUM PEDIS

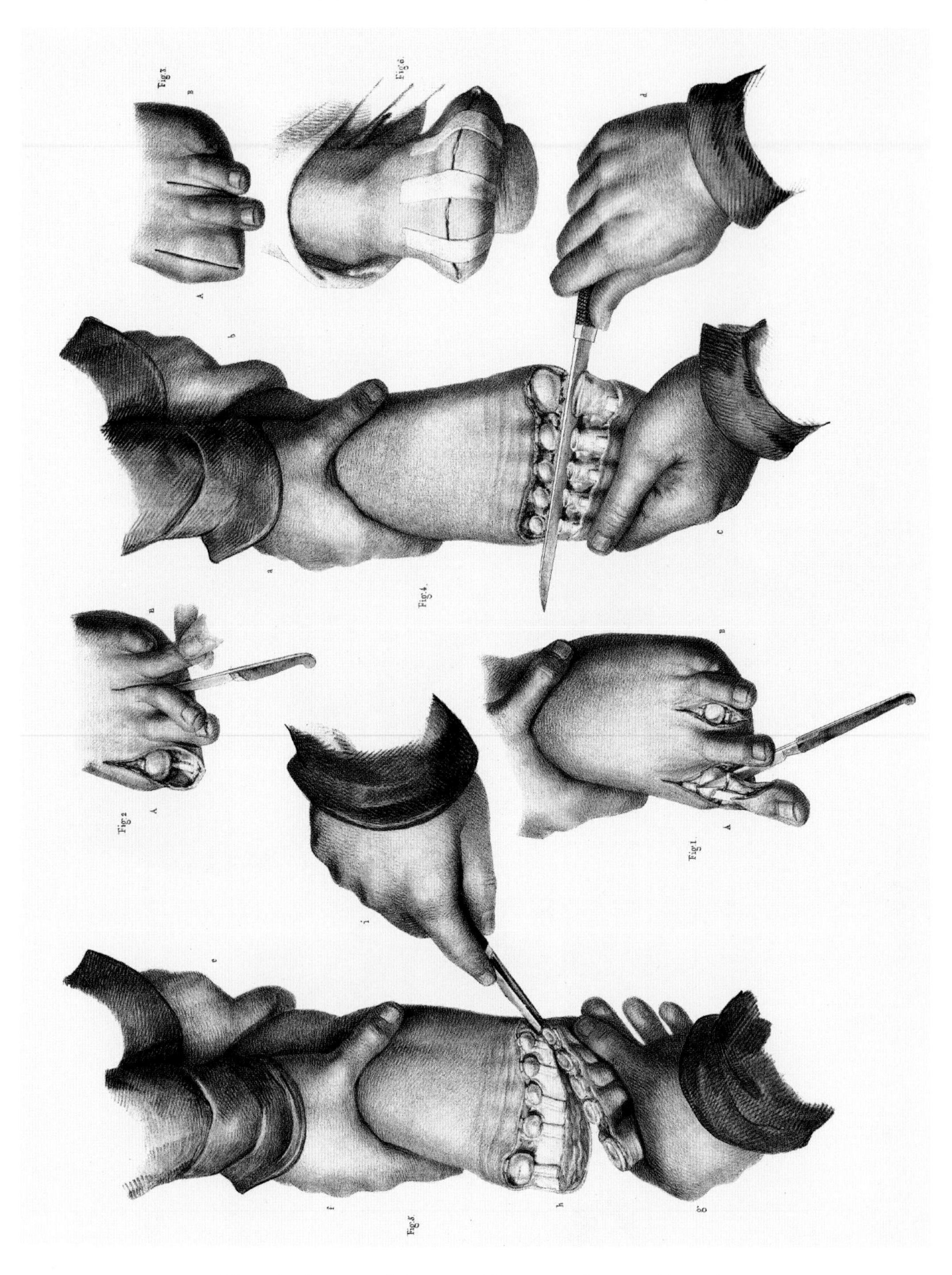

Disarticulations of the toes / Désarticulations d'orteils
Desarticulaciones de los dedos del pie

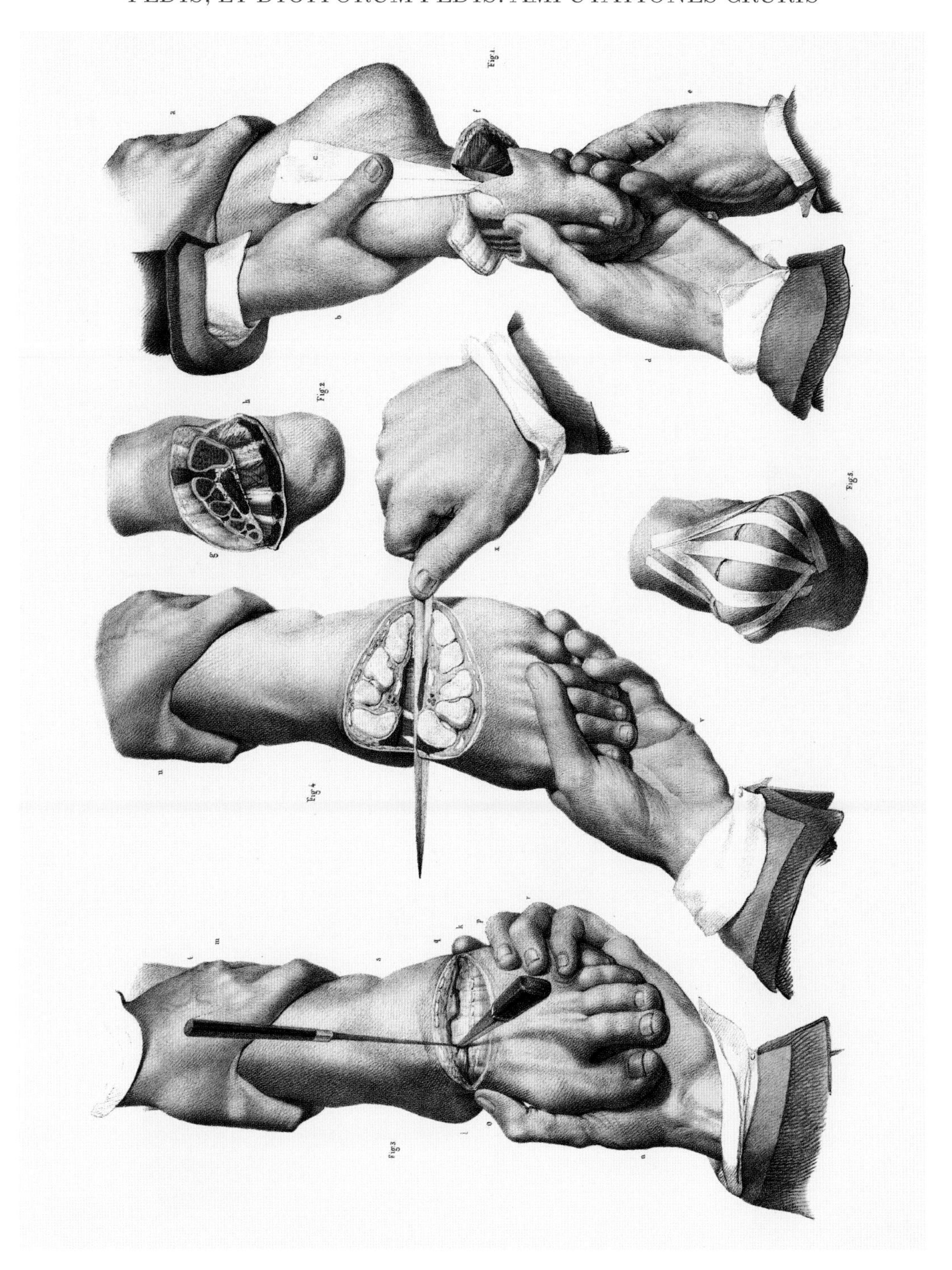

Amputation and disarticulation of the metatarsus
Amputation et désarticulation du métatarse
Amputación y desarticulación del metatarso

AMPUTATIONES ET DESARTICULATIONES METATARSII, PEDIS, ET DIGITORUM PEDIS. AMPUTATIONES CRURIS

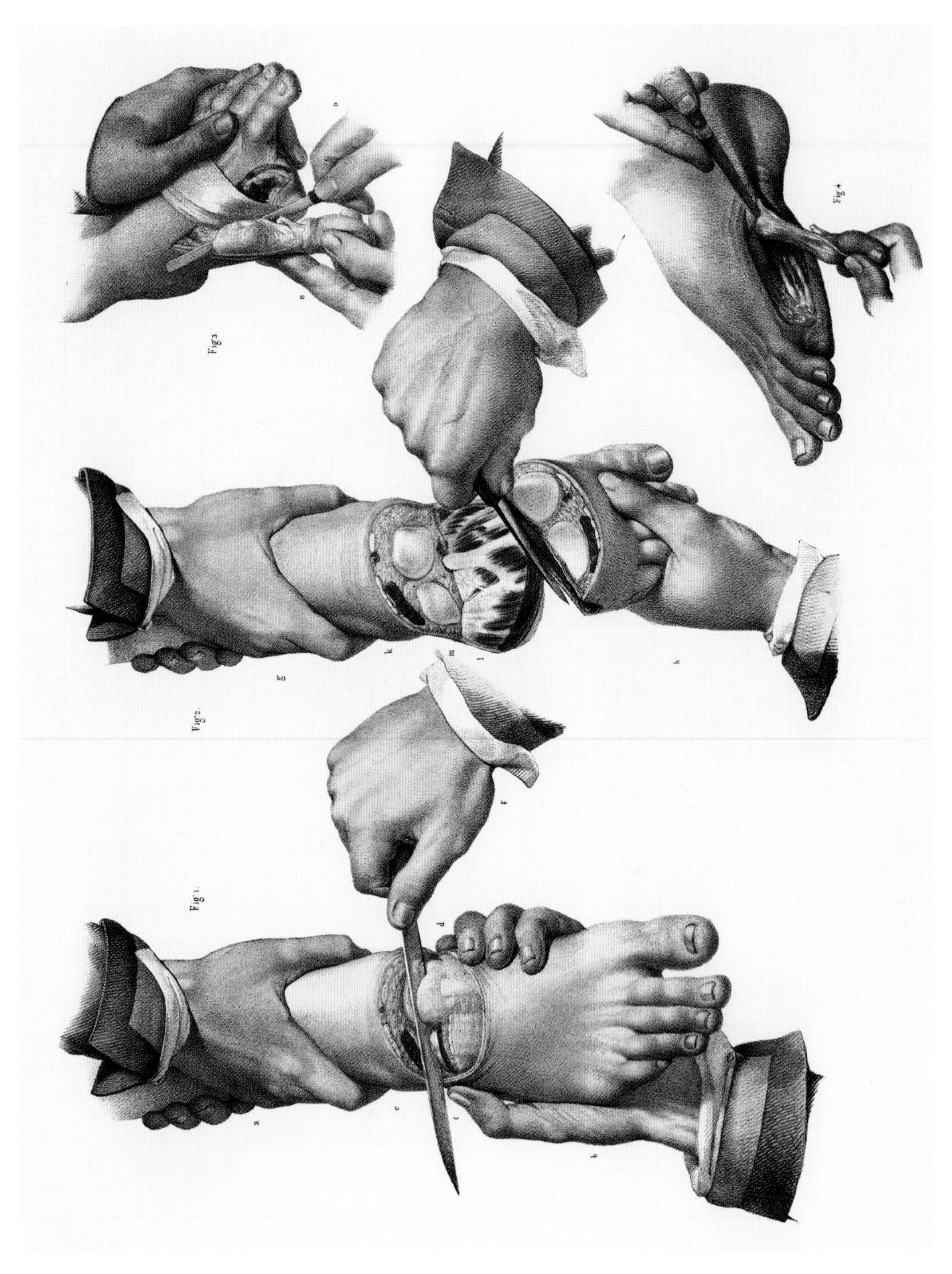

Amputations and disarticulations of the foot and rays of the foot
Amputations et désarticulations du pied et de rayons du pied
Amputaciones y desarticulaciones del pie y de sus radiaciones digitales

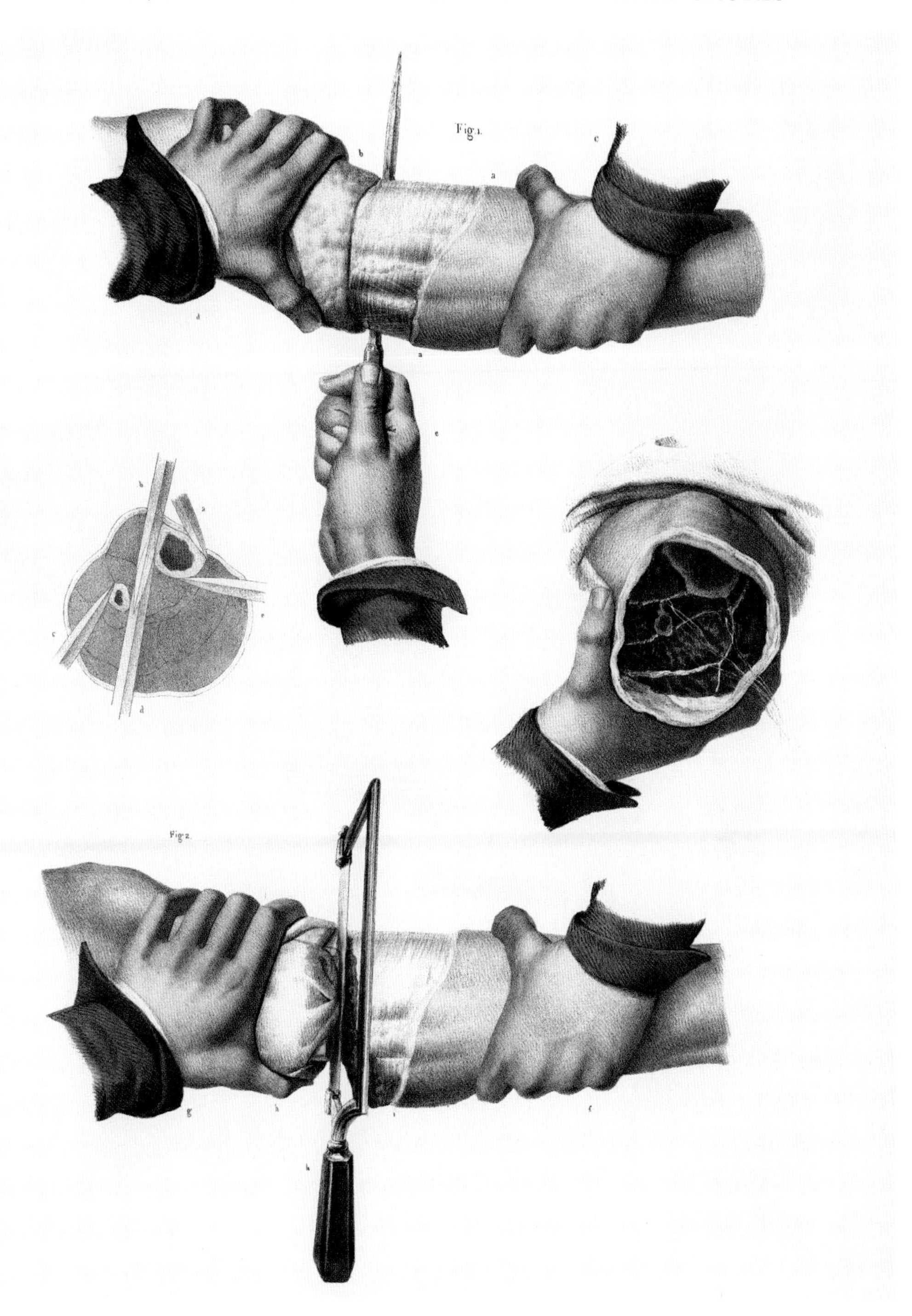

Amputations of the lower leg / Amputations de la jambe
Amputaciones de la pierna

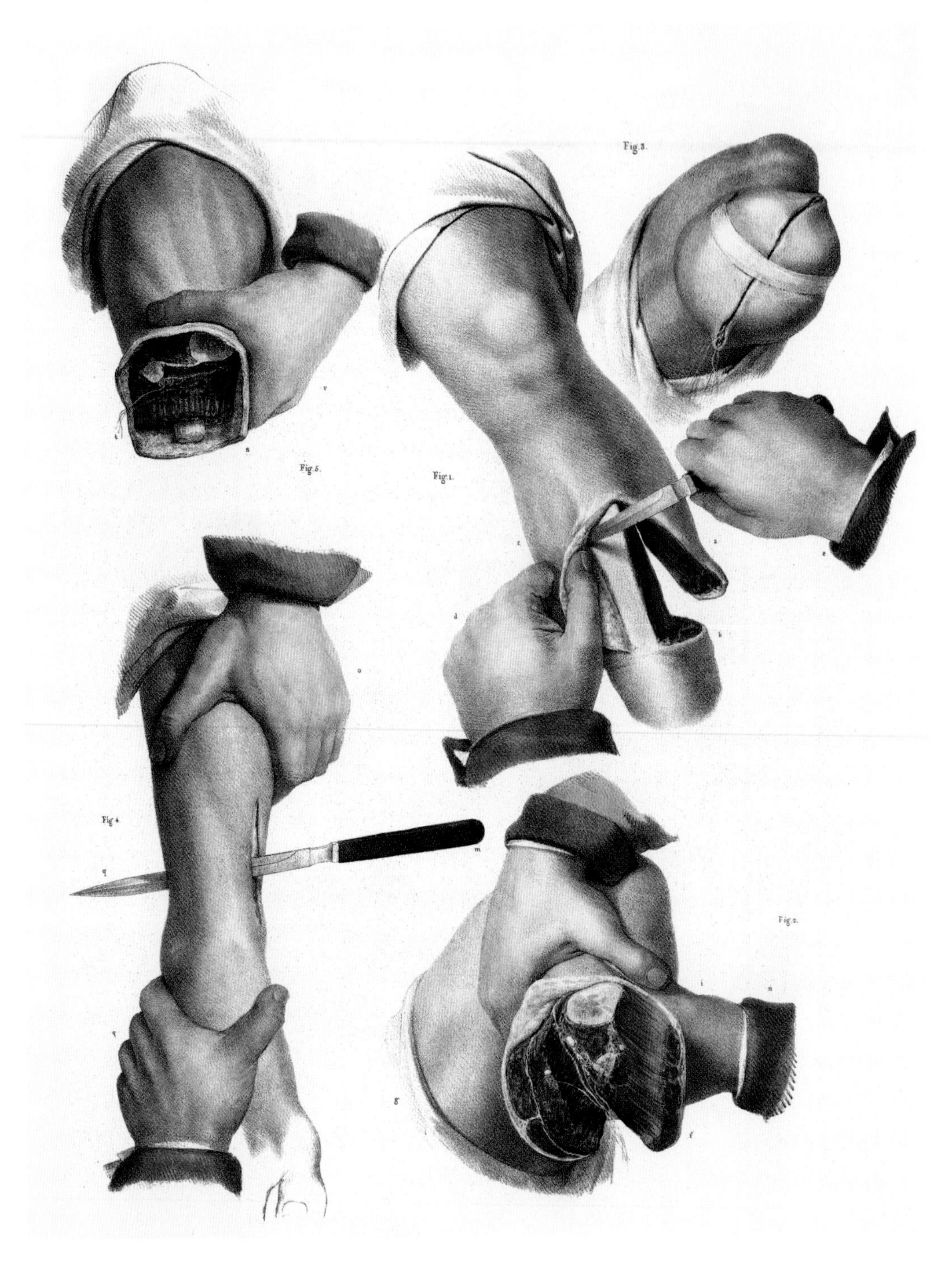

Amputations of the lower leg / Amputations de la jambe
Amputaciones de la pierna

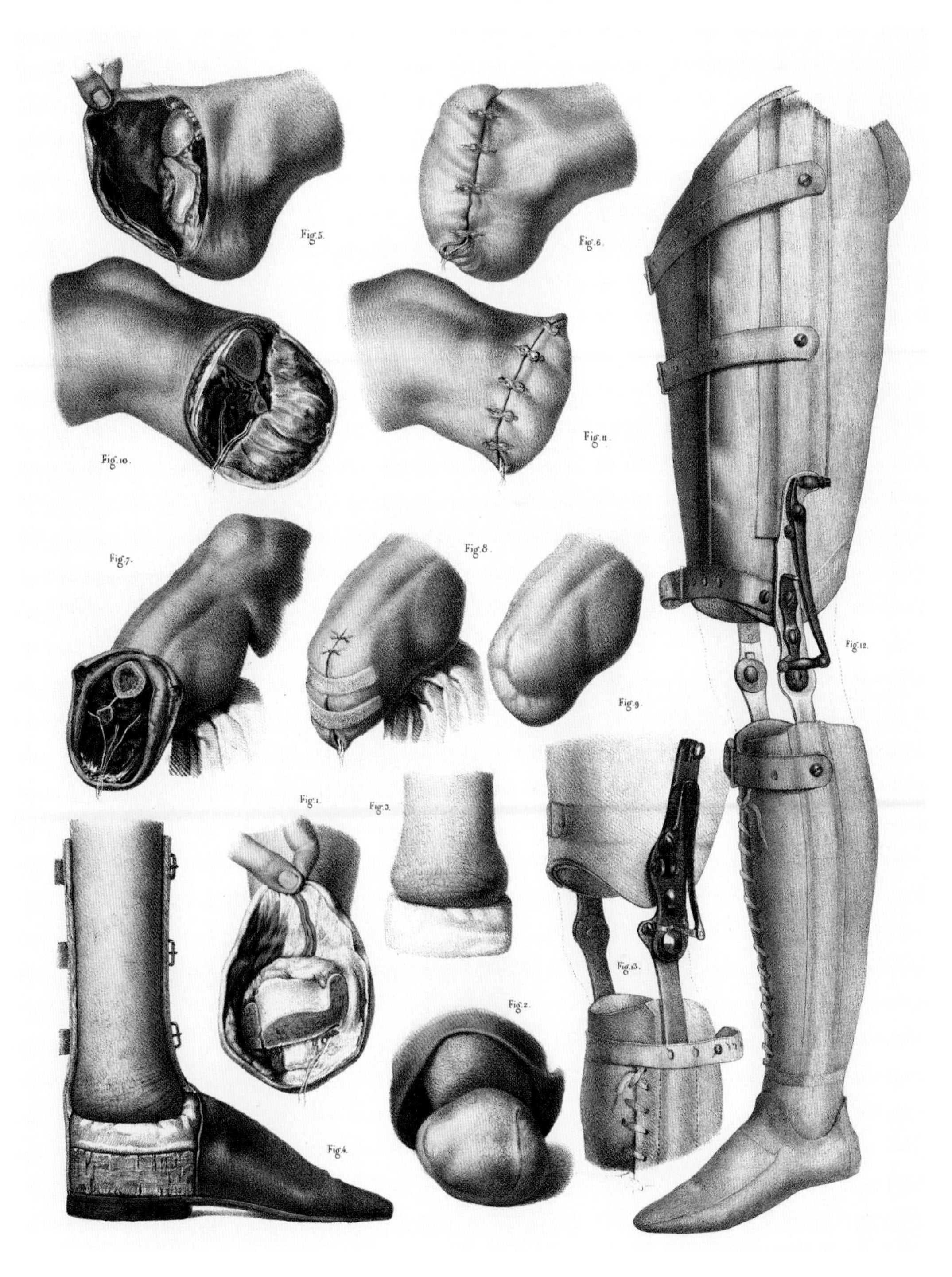

Disarticulations of the foot and amputations of the lower leg. Prostheses
Désarticulations du pied et amputations de la jambe. Prothèses
Desarticulaciones del pie y amputaciones de la pierna. Prótesis

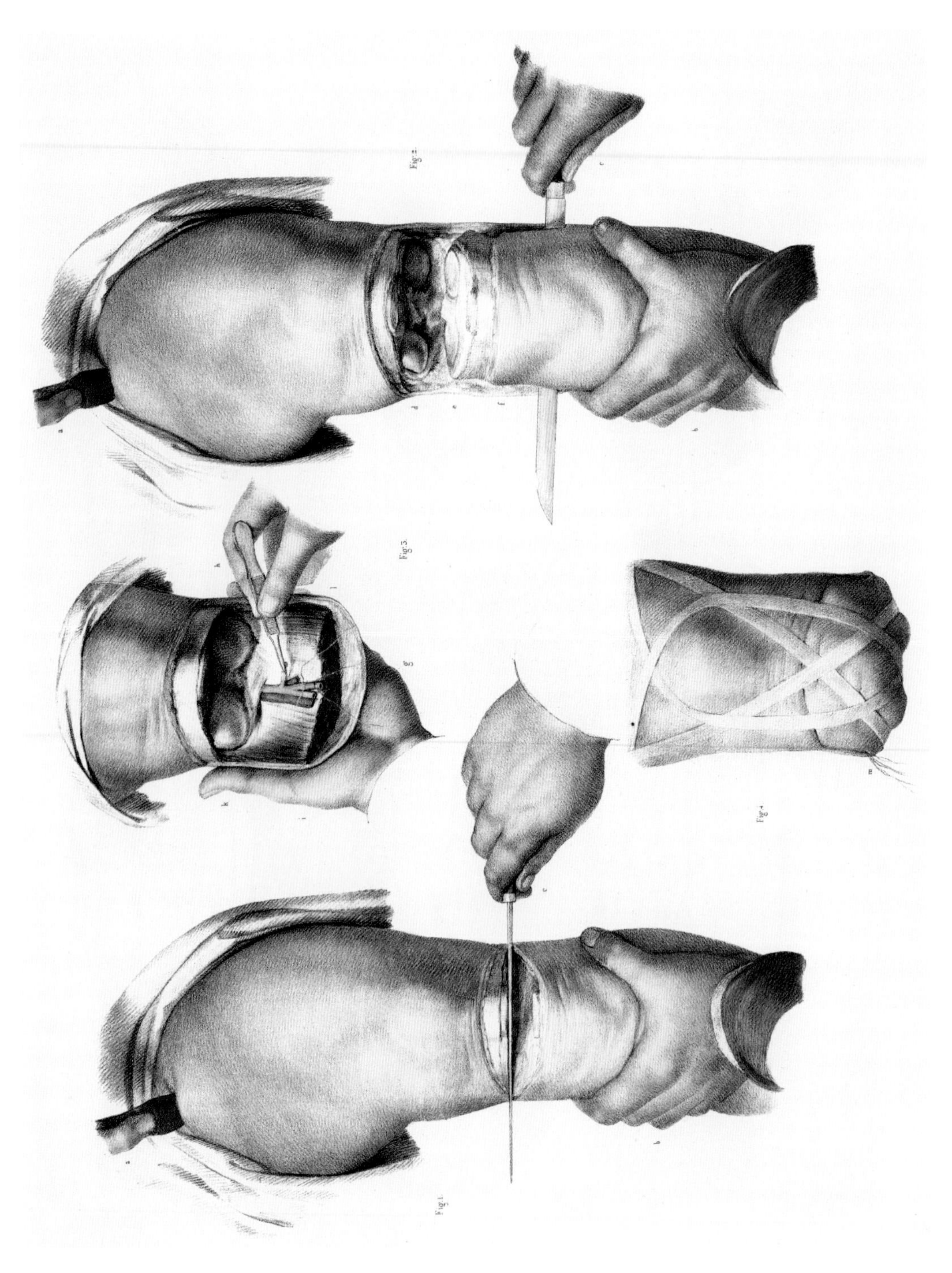

Disarticulation of the knee / Désarticulation du genou
Desarticulación de la rodilla

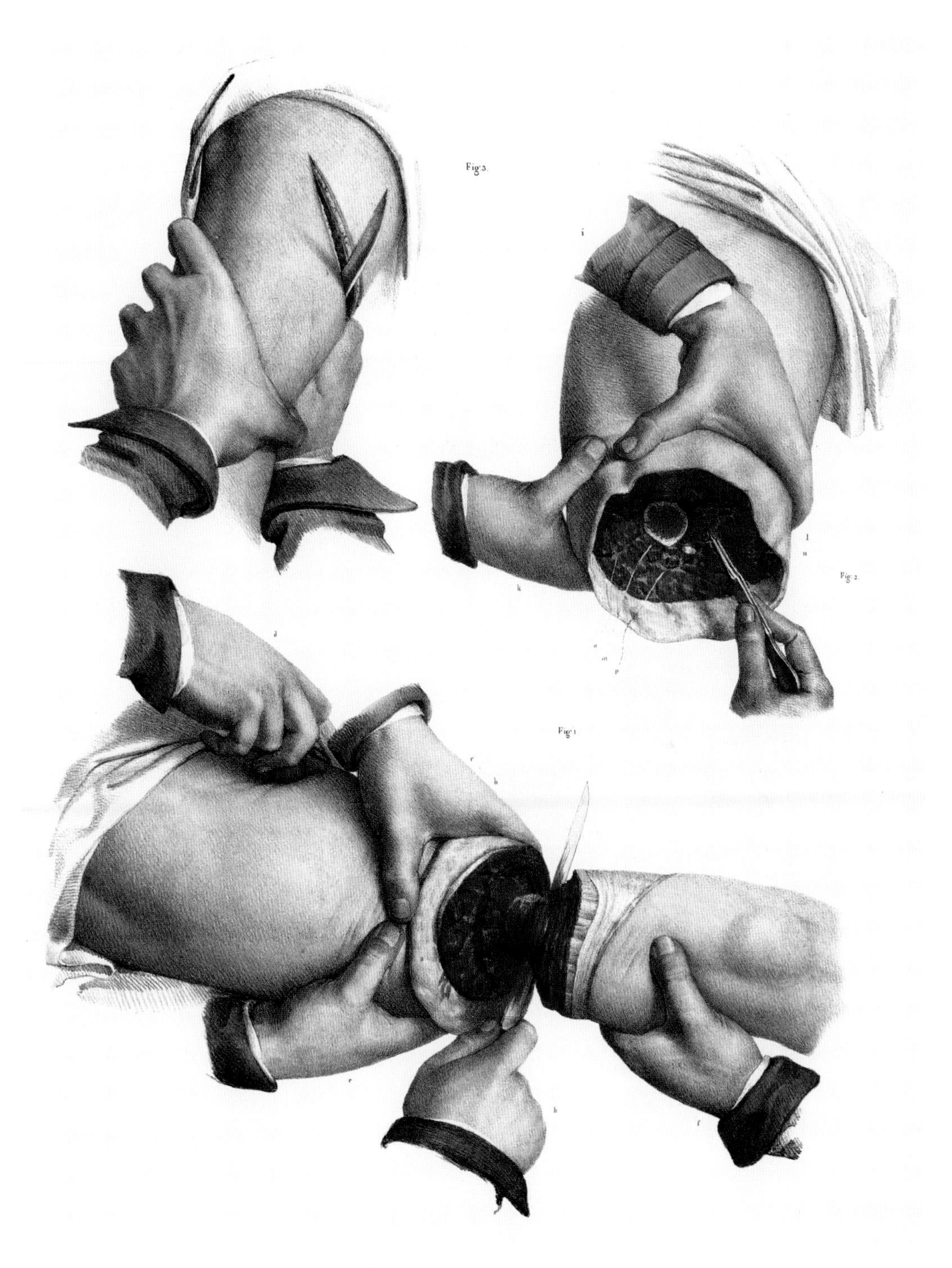

Amputations of the thigh / Amputations de la cuisse
Amputaciones del muslo

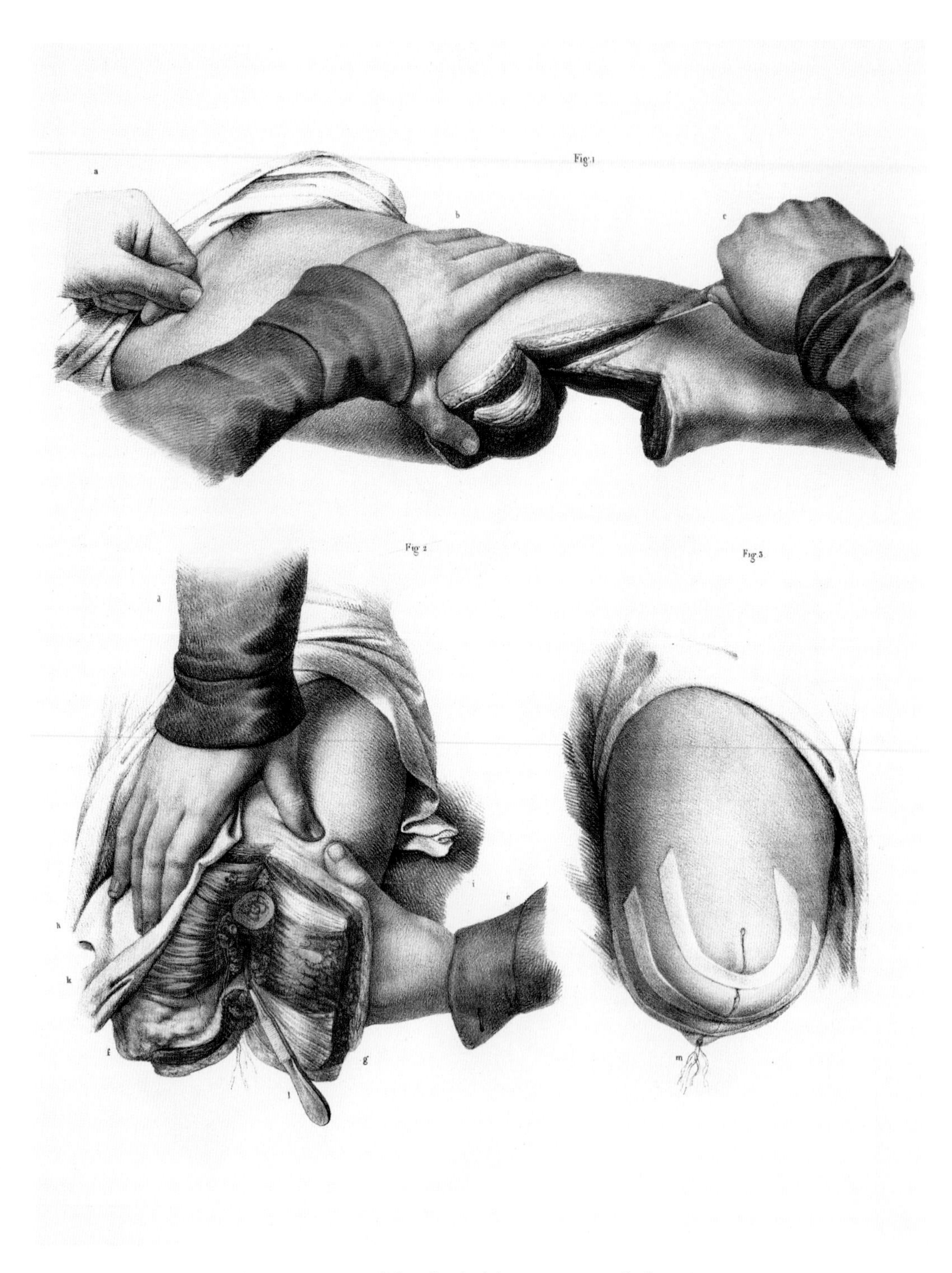

Amputations of the thigh / Amputations de la cuisse
Amputaciones del muslo

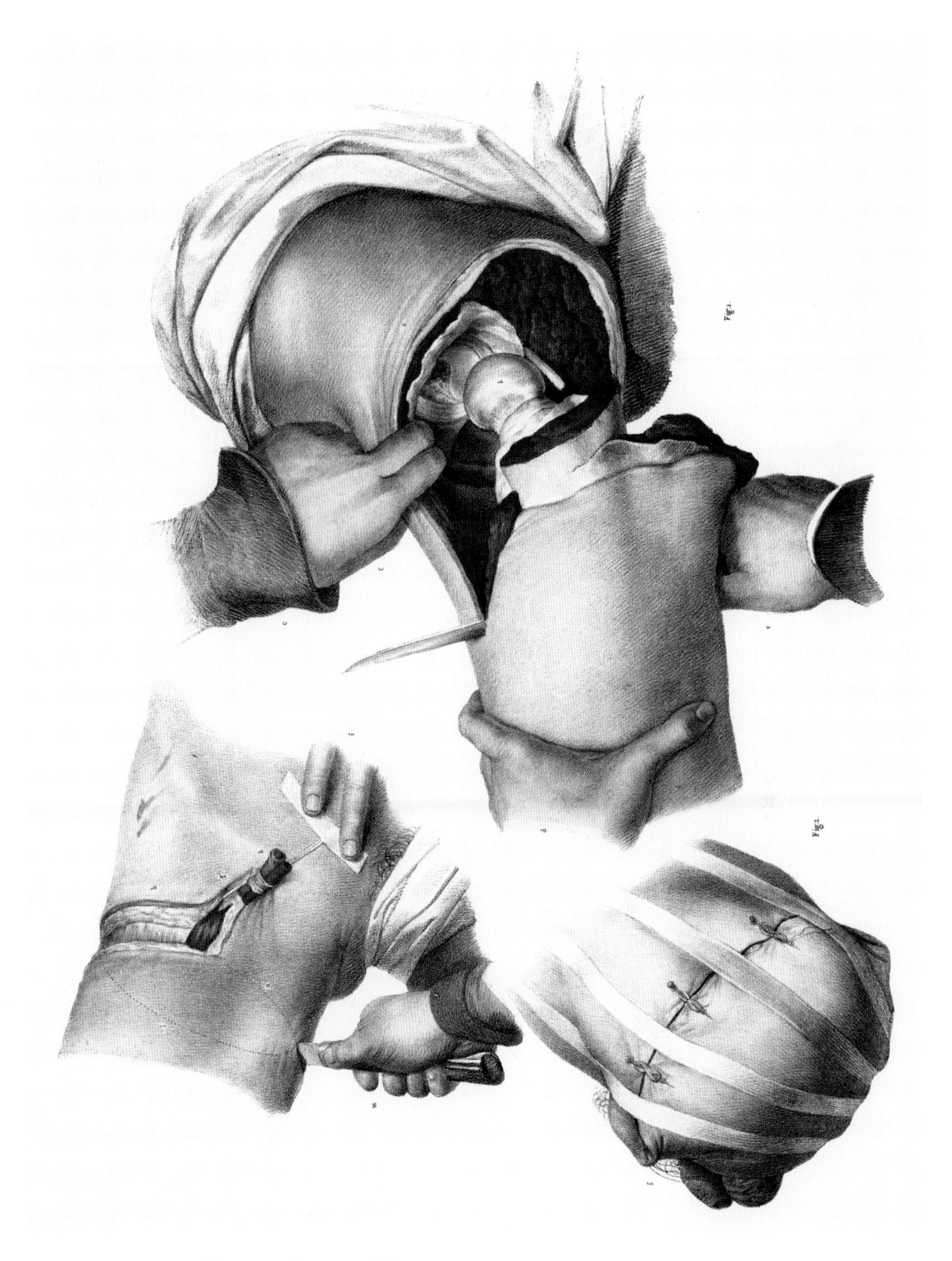

Disarticulations of the hip / Désarticulations de la hanche
Desarticulaciones de la cadera

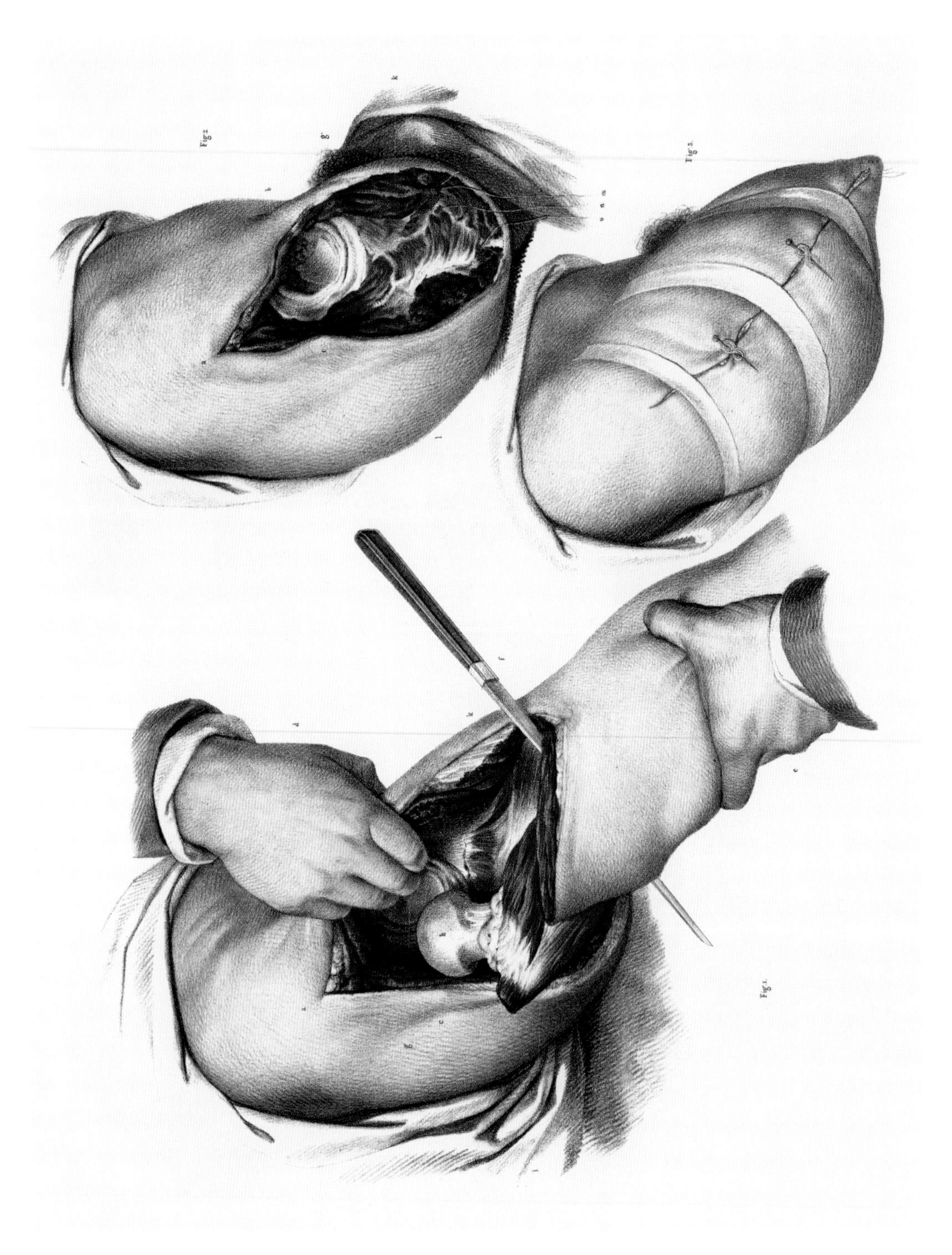

Disarticulations of the hip / Désarticulations de la hanche
Desarticulaciones de la cadera

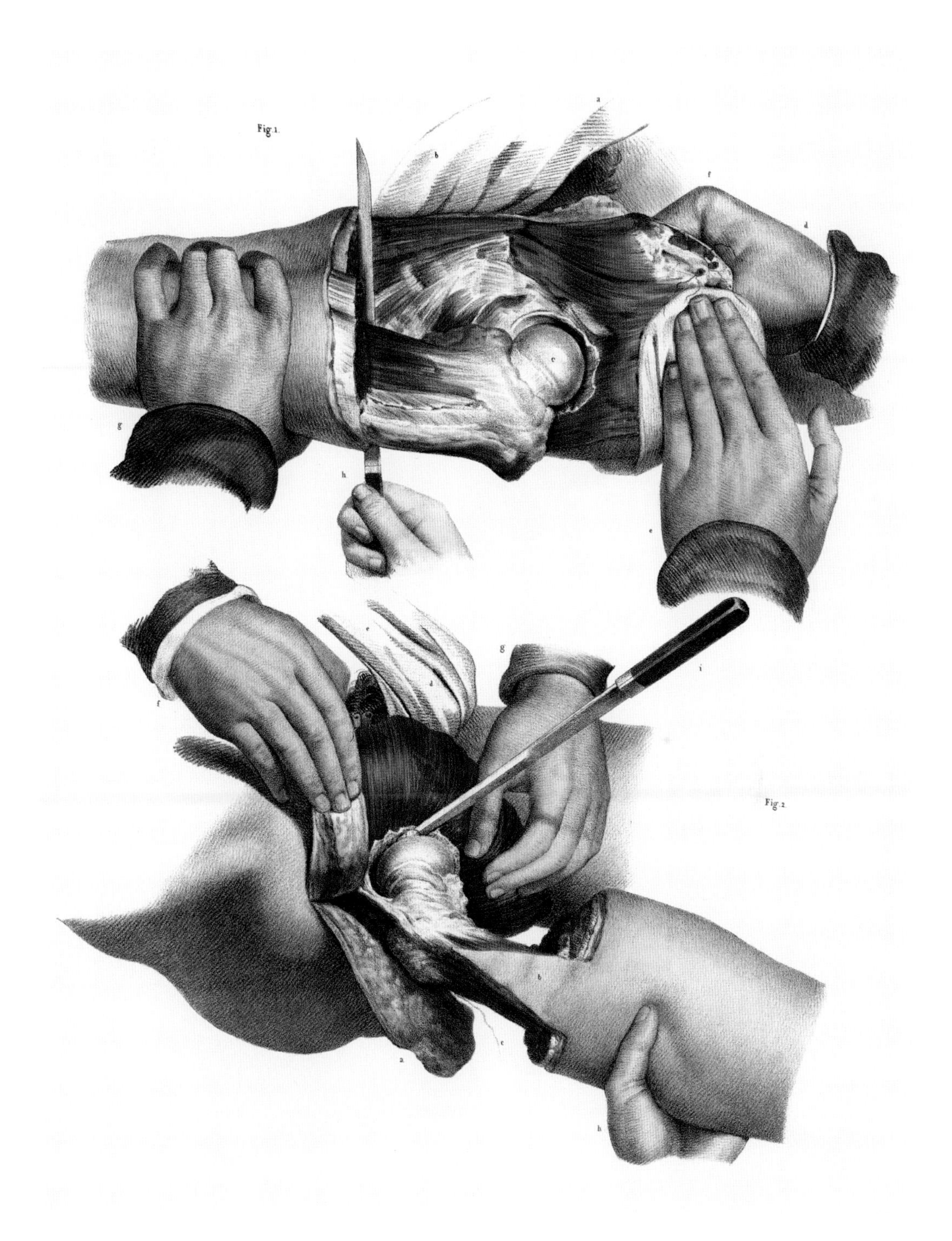

Disarticulations of the hip / Désarticulations de la hanche
Desarticulaciones de la cadera

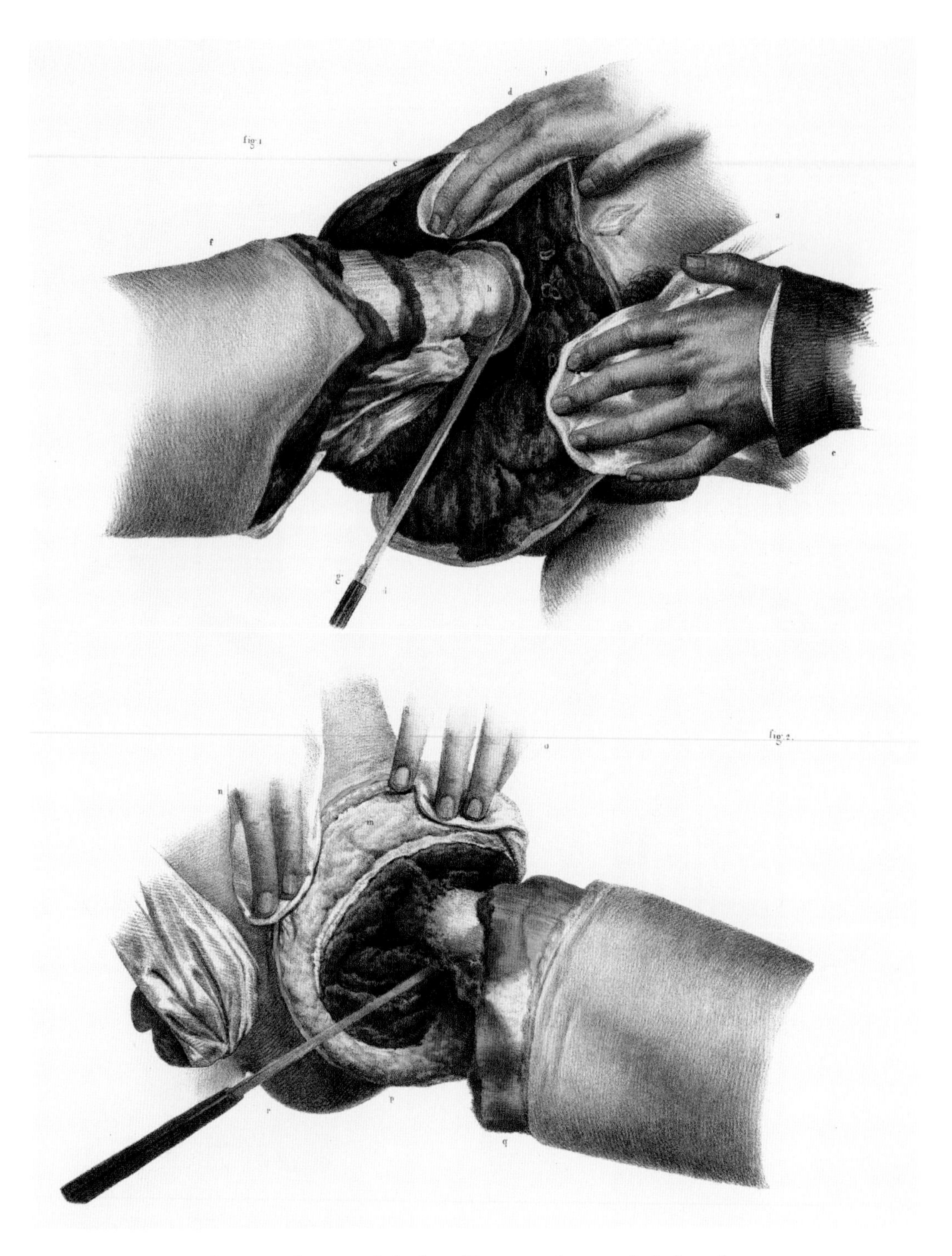

Disarticulations of the hip / Désarticulations de la hanche
Desarticulaciones de la cadera

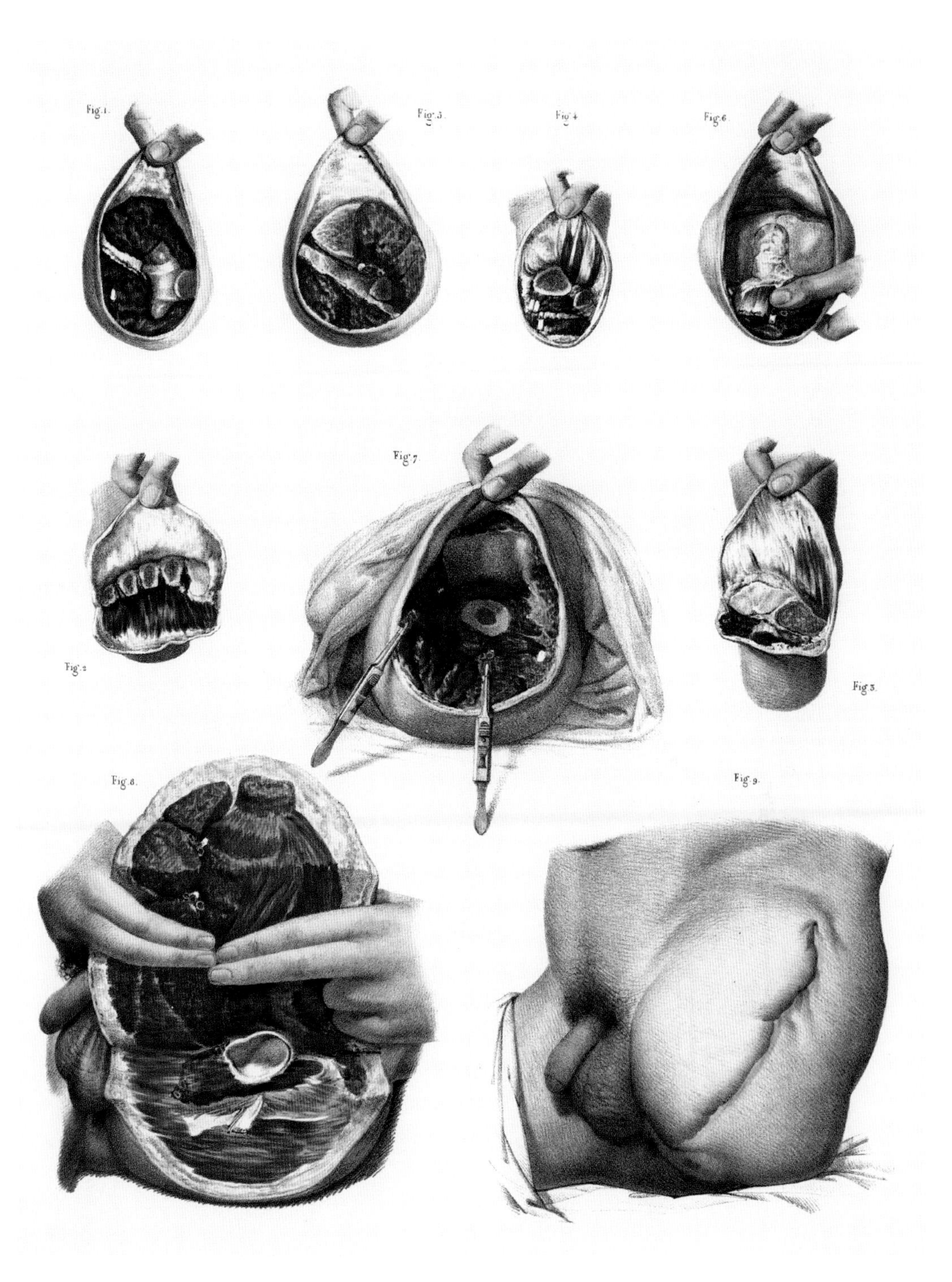

Various amputations and disarticulations / Amputations et désarticulations diverses
Amputaciones y desarticulaciones diversas

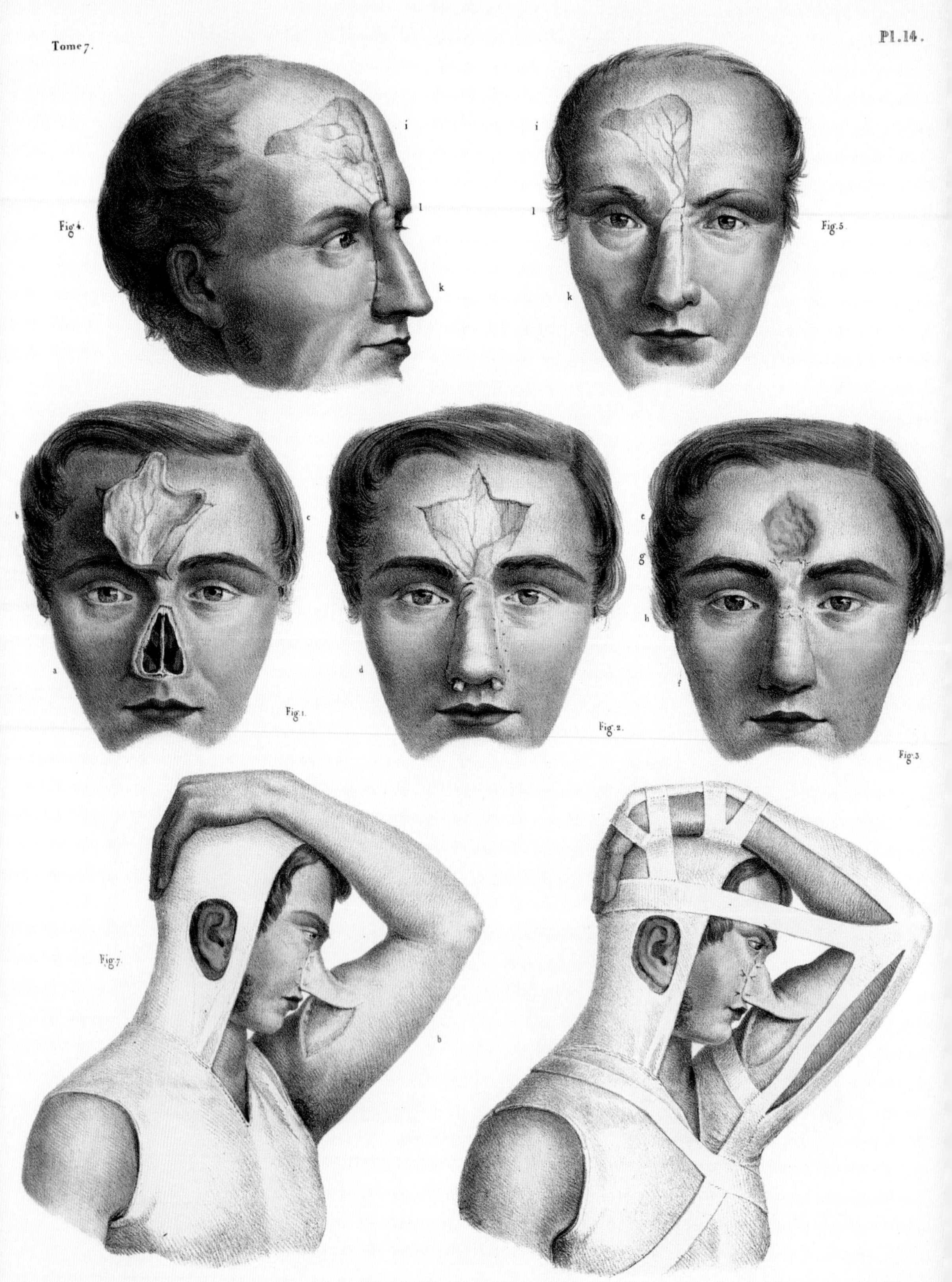

d'après nature par N. H. Jacob.

Imp. de Lemercier, Benard et Cie

VOL. 7

Anatomia Chirurgica. Artes Chirurgicae

SURGICAL ANATOMY.
SURGICAL TECHNIQUES
(OPERATIVE MEDICINE)

ANATOMIE CHIRURGICALE.
TECHNIQUES CHIRURGICALES
(MEDECINE OPERATOIRE)

ANATOMÍA QUIRÚRGICA.
TÉCNICAS QUIRÚRGICAS
(MEDICINA OPERATORIA)

Left page / Ci-contre / Página contigua:
Surgery of the nose / Chirurgie du nez / Cirugía de la nariz

CATHETERISMI CAVITATUM CAPITIS: ANATOMIA CHIRURGICA

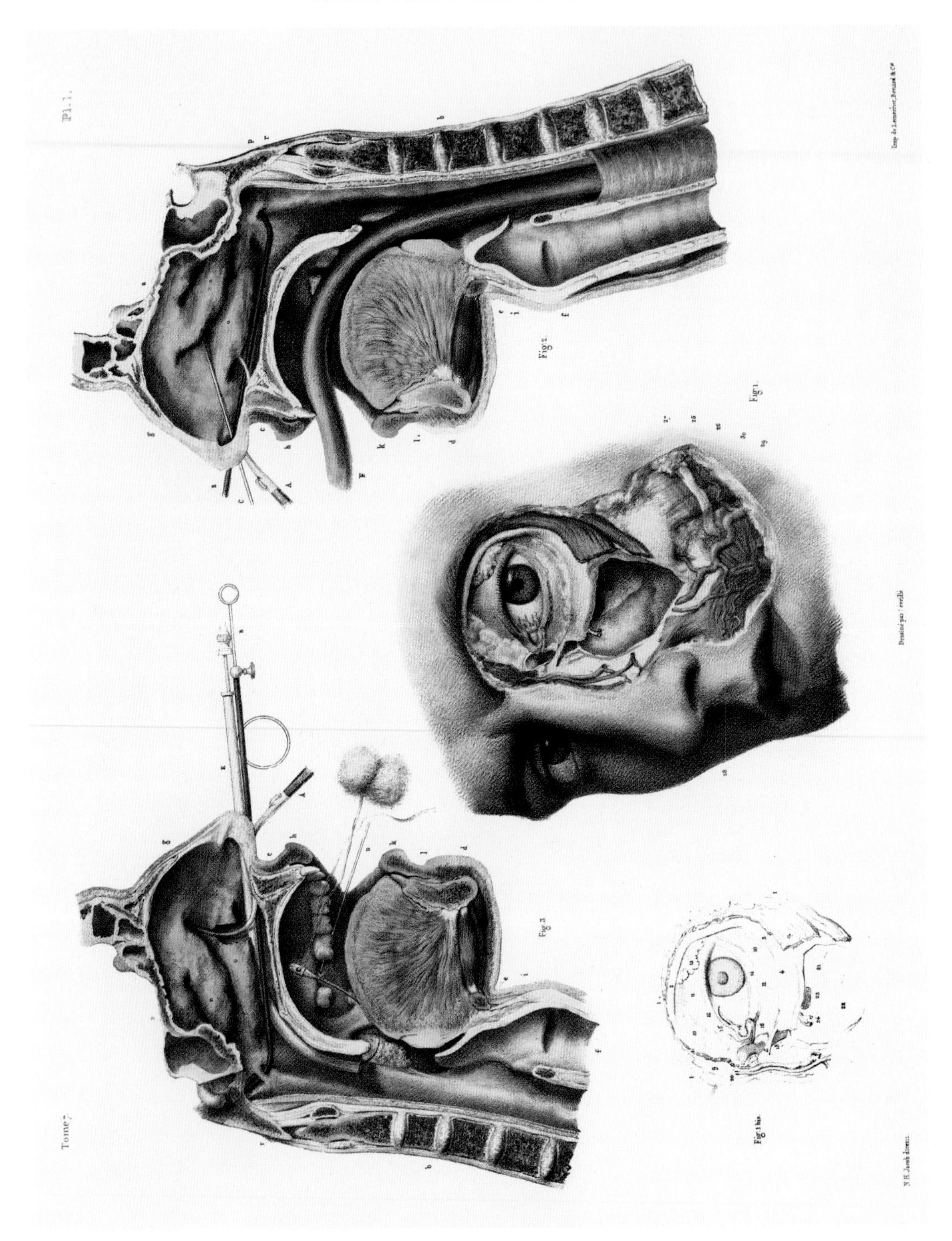

Catheterisations of the cavities and ducts of the head
Cathétérismes des cavités et conduits de la tête
Cateterismos de las cavidades y de los conductos de la cabeza

CHIRURGIA PALPEBRARUM, VIARUM LACRIMALIUM, ET OCULORUM: INSTRUMENTA CHIRURGICA

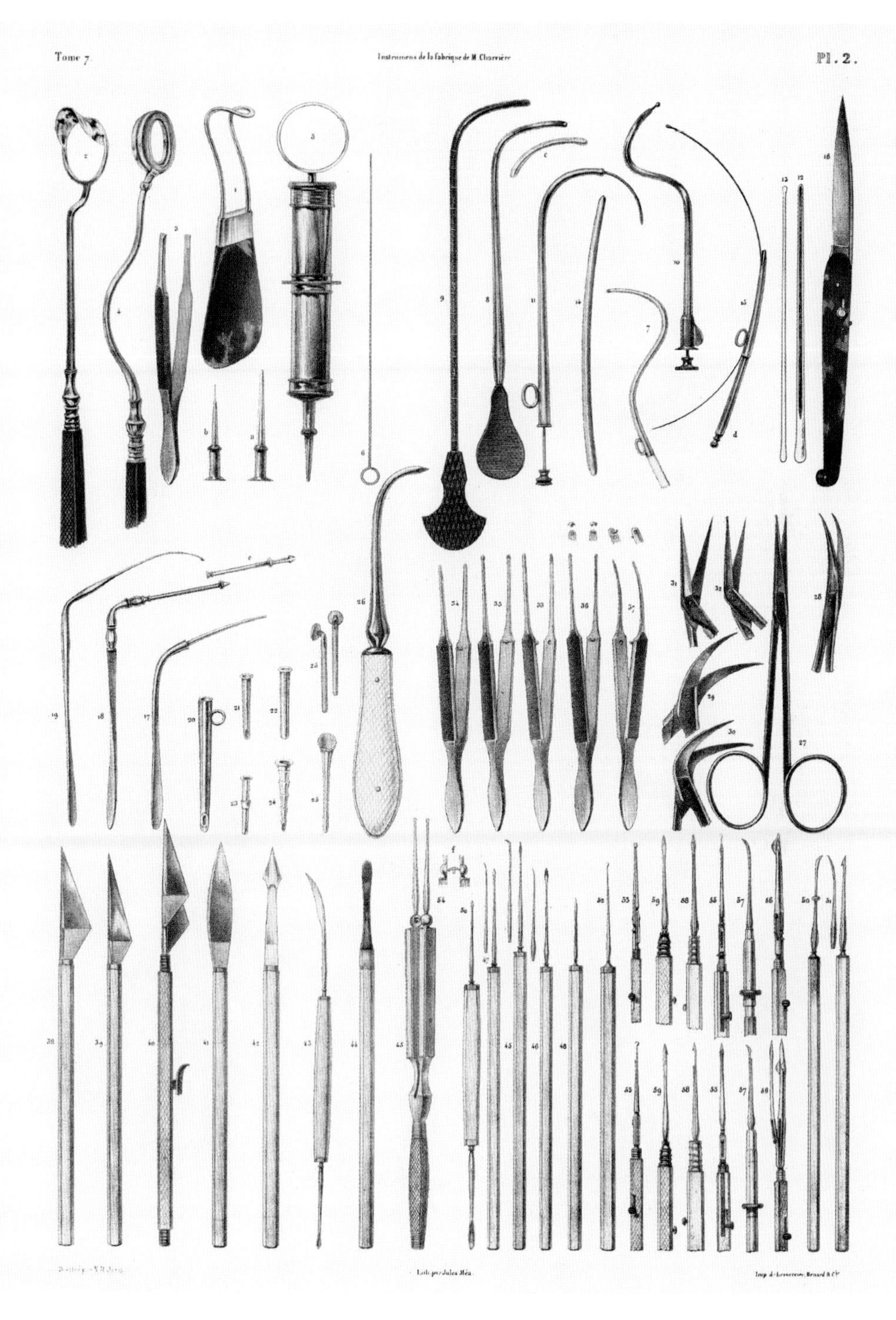

Surgery of the eyelids, the lacrimal pathways, and the eye: Surgical instruments
Chirurgie des paupières, des voies lacrymales et de l'œil : Instruments chirurgicaux
Cirugía de los párpados, de las vías lagrimales y del ojo: instrumentos quirúrgicos

Surgery of the eye and the lacrimal pathways / Chirurgie de l'œil et des voies lacrymales
Cirugía del ojo y de las vías lagrimales

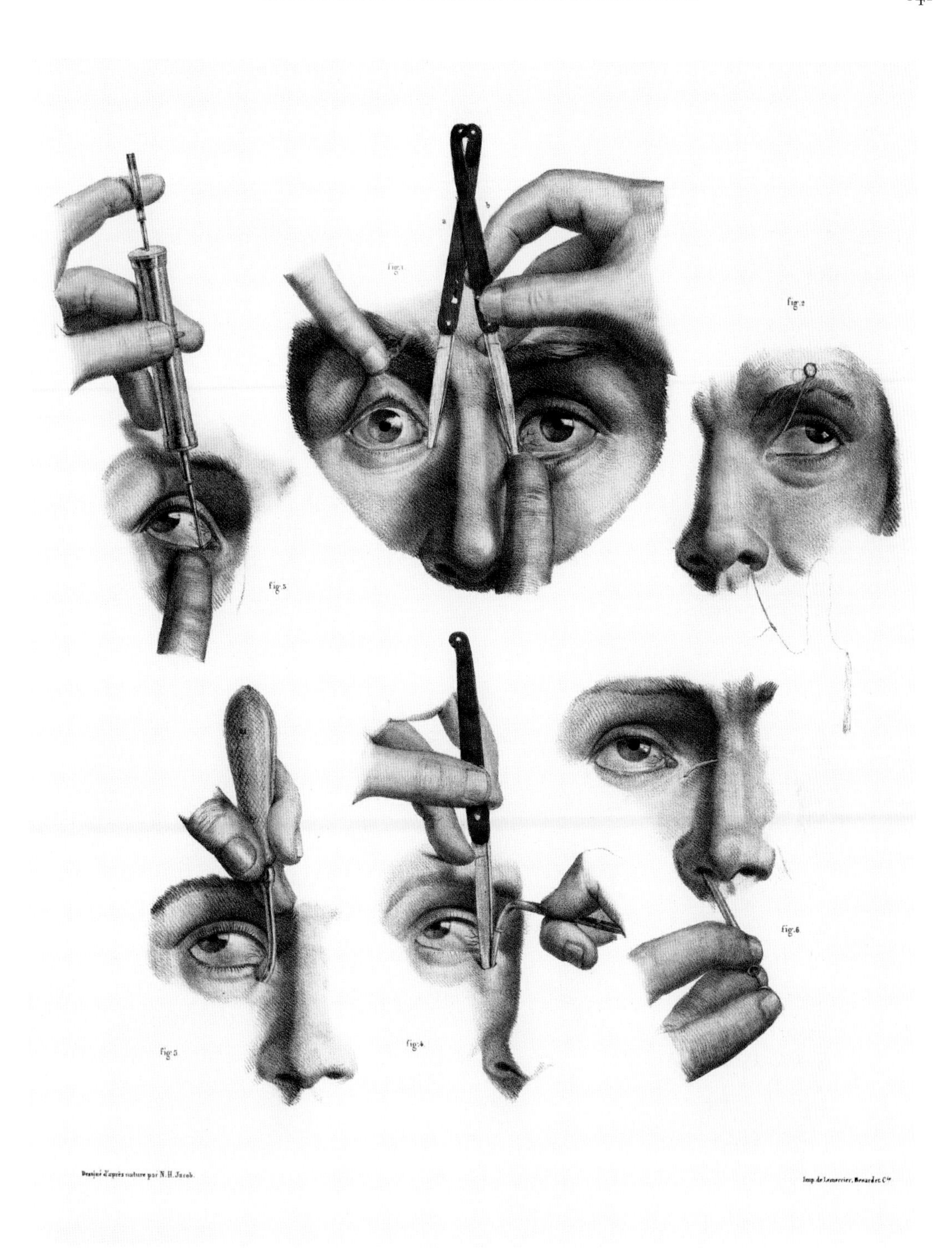

Surgery of the lacrimal pathways / Chirurgie des voies lacrymales
Cirugía de las vías lagrimales

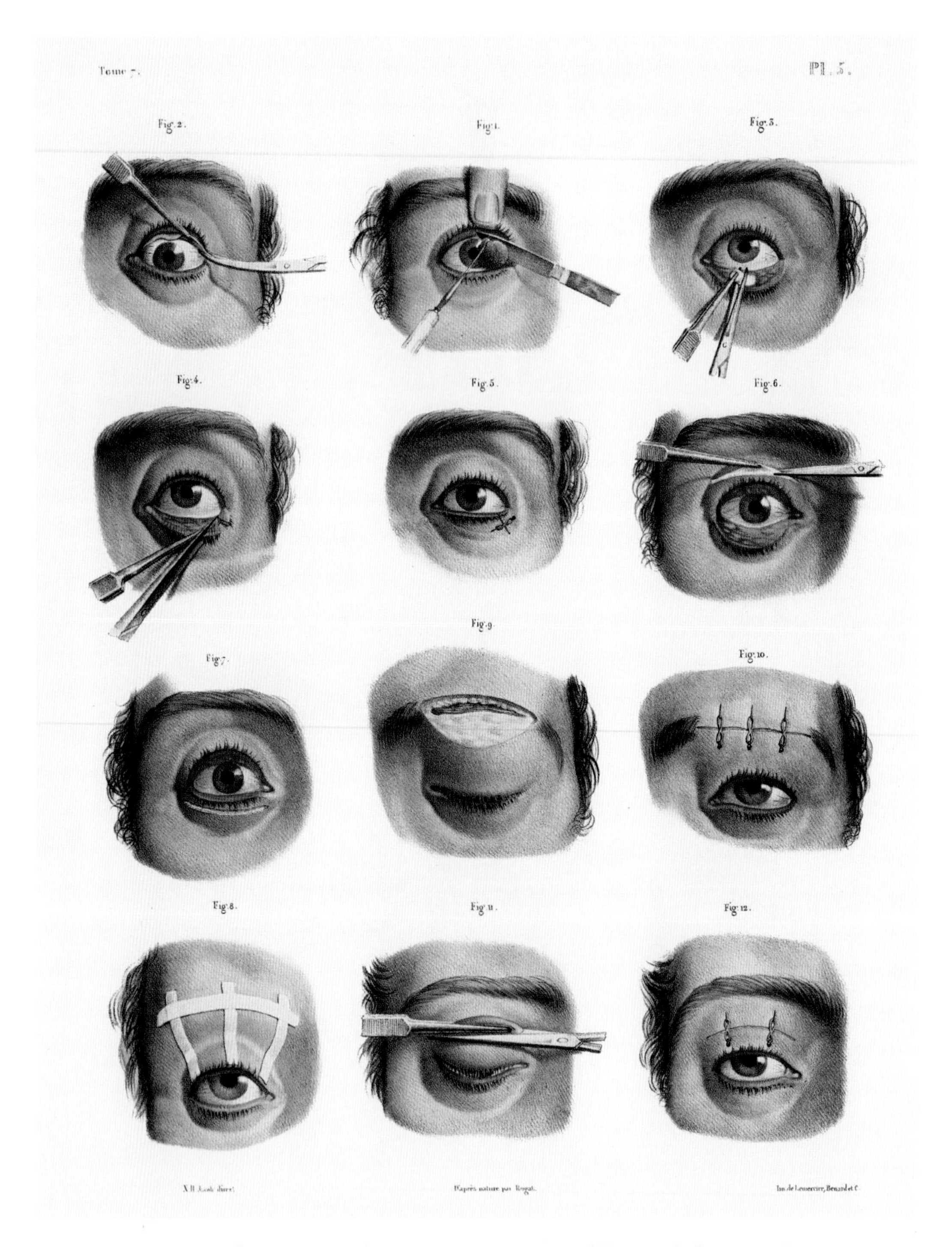

Surgery of the eyelids / Chirurgie des paupières / Cirugía de los párpados

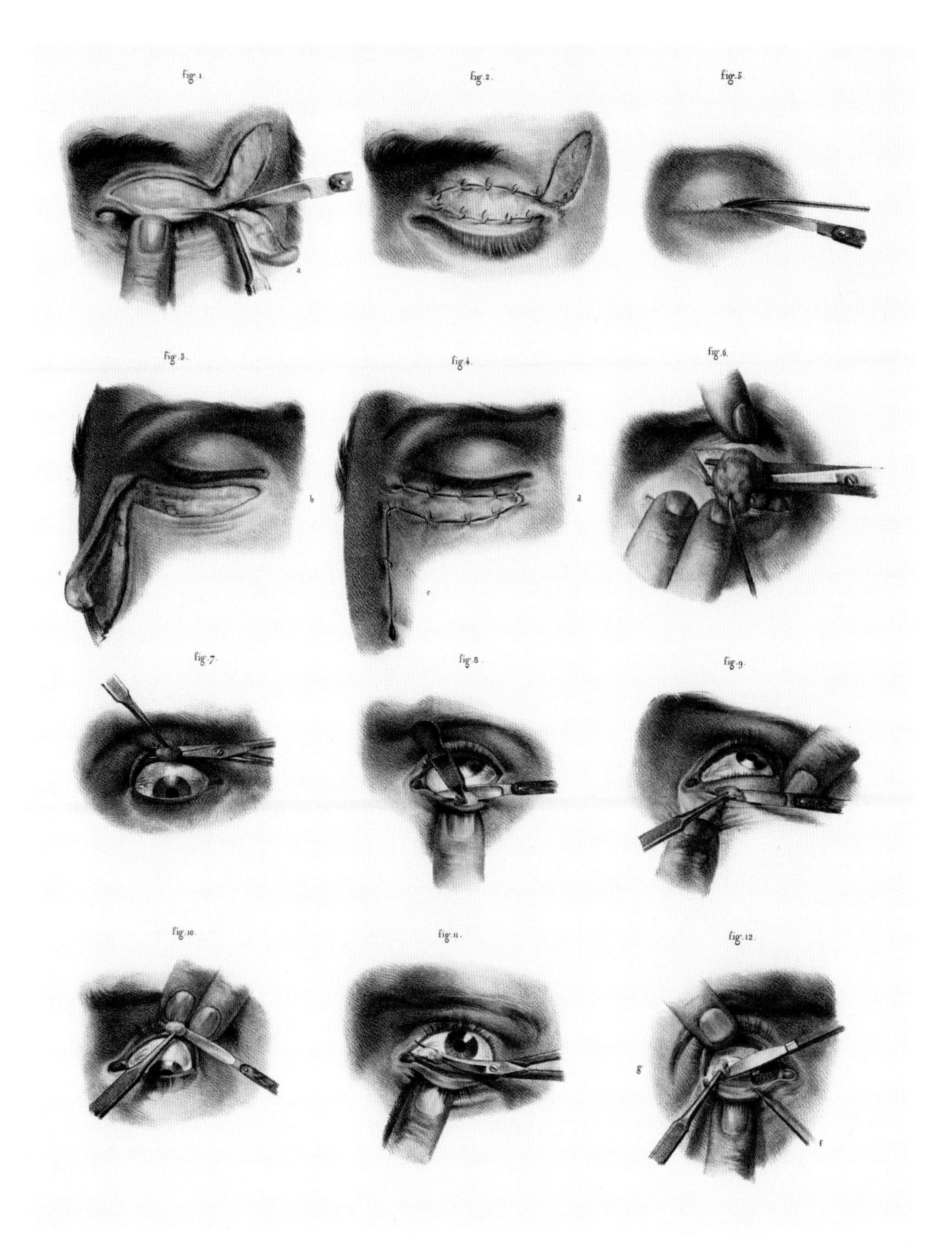

Surgery of the eyelids / Chirurgie des paupières / Cirugía de los párpados

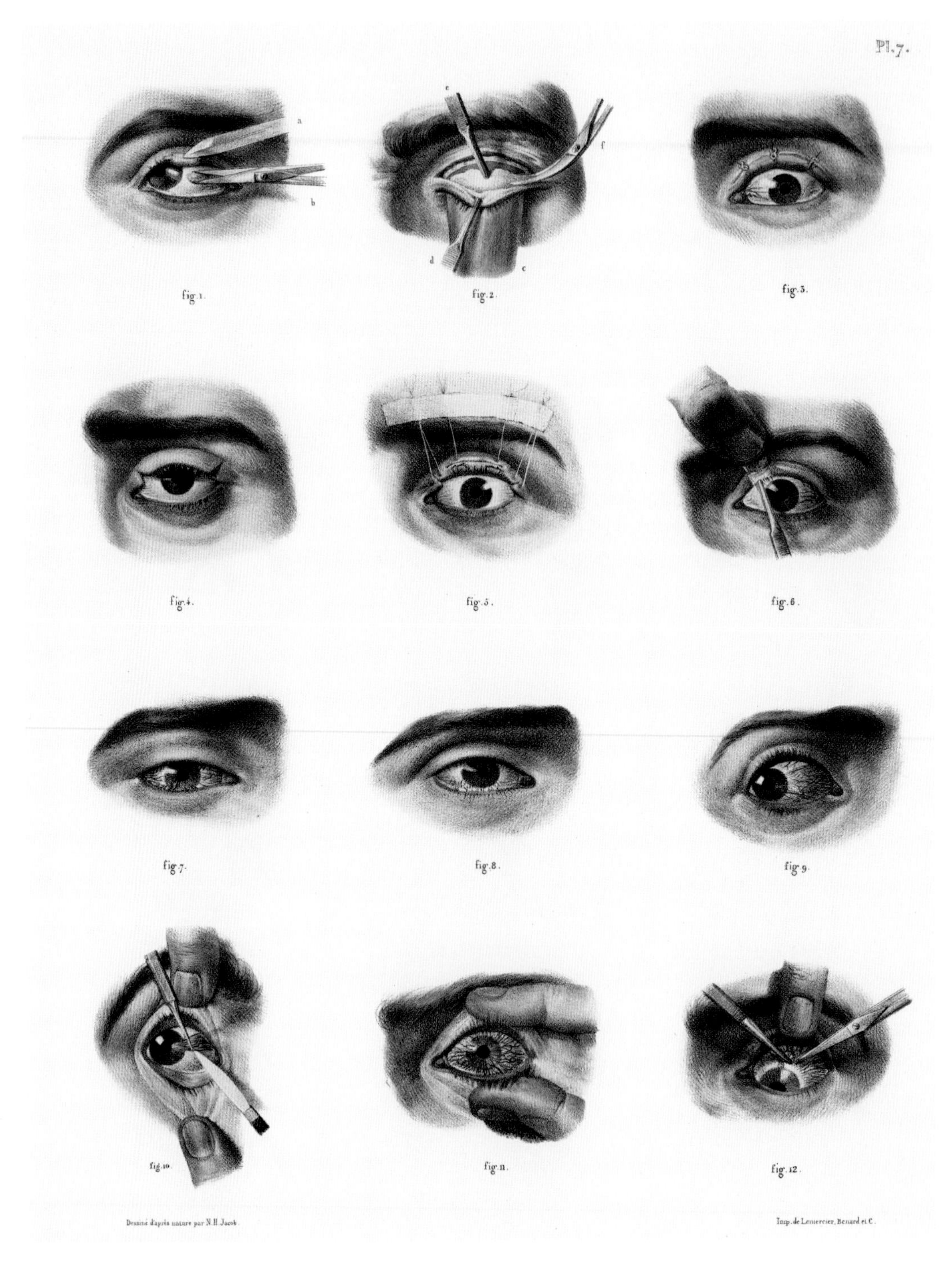

Surgery of the eyelids / Chirurgie des paupières / Cirugía de los párpados

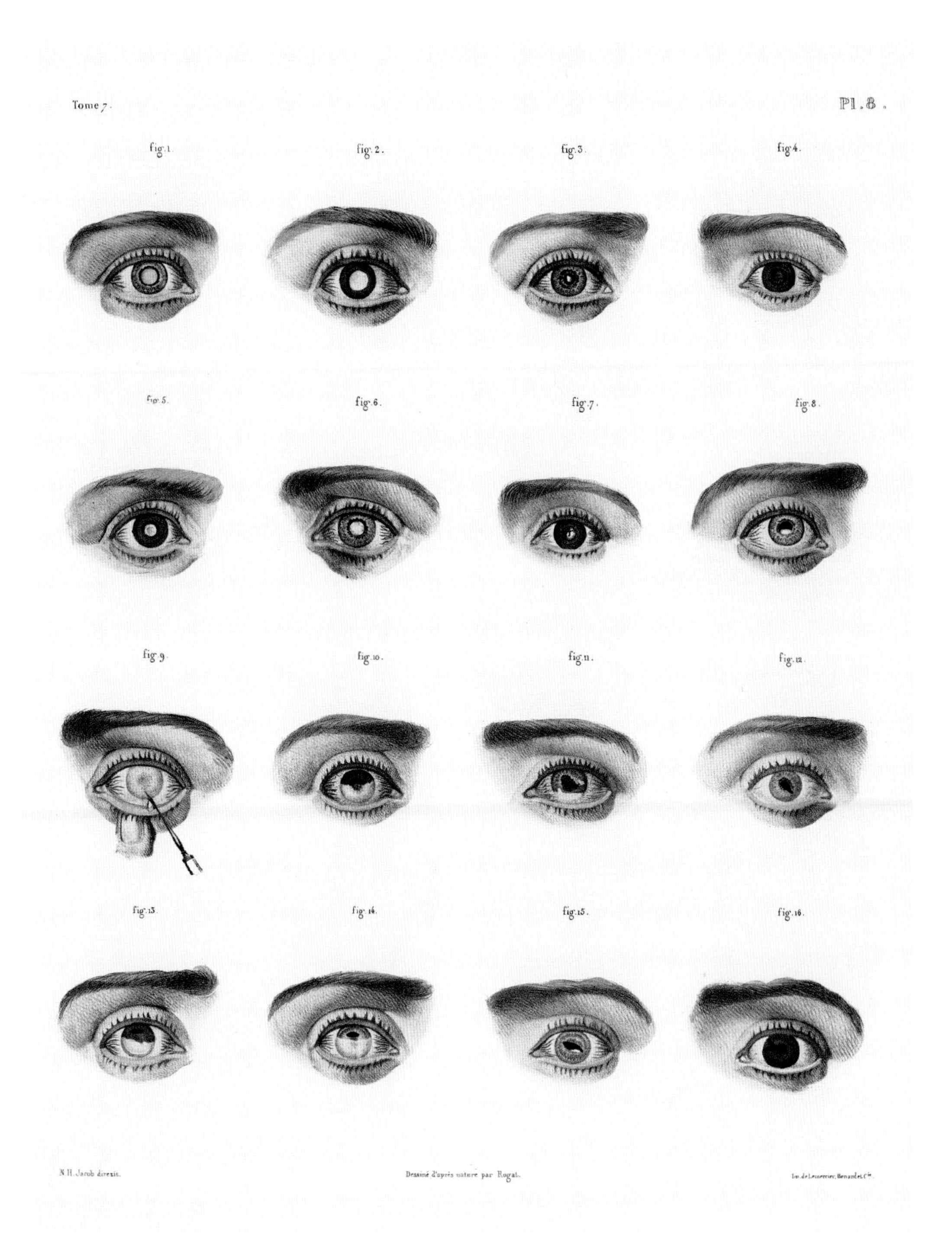

Pathological anatomy of the eye / Anatomie pathologique de l'œil
Anatomía patológica del ojo

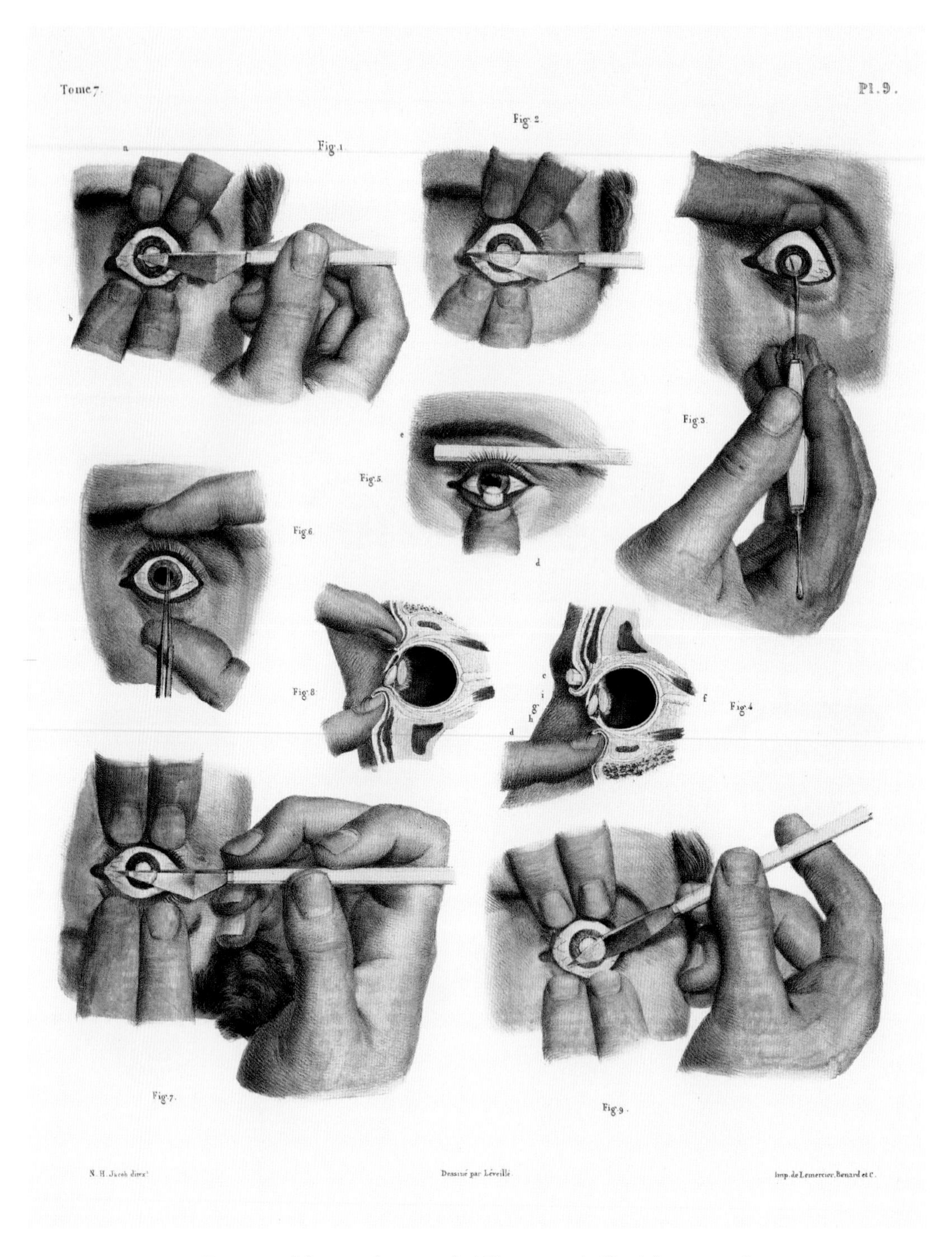

Surgery of the eye (cataract) / Chirurgie de l'œil (cataracte)
Cirugía del ojo (catarata)

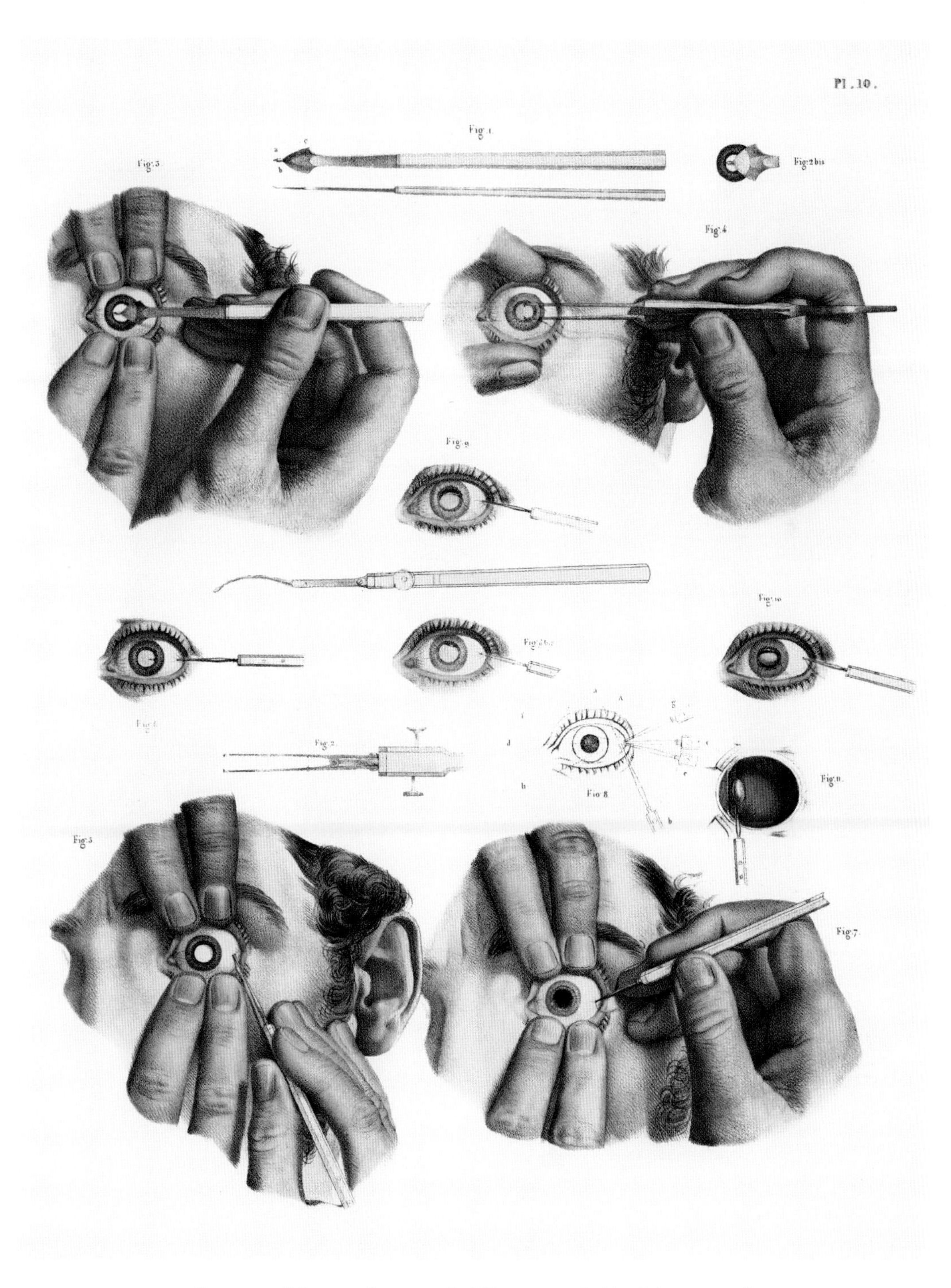

Surgery of the eye (cataract) / Chirurgie de l'œil (cataracte)
Cirugía del ojo (catarata)

CHIRURGIA OCULI: IRIS ET PUPILLA (IRIDOTOMIA)

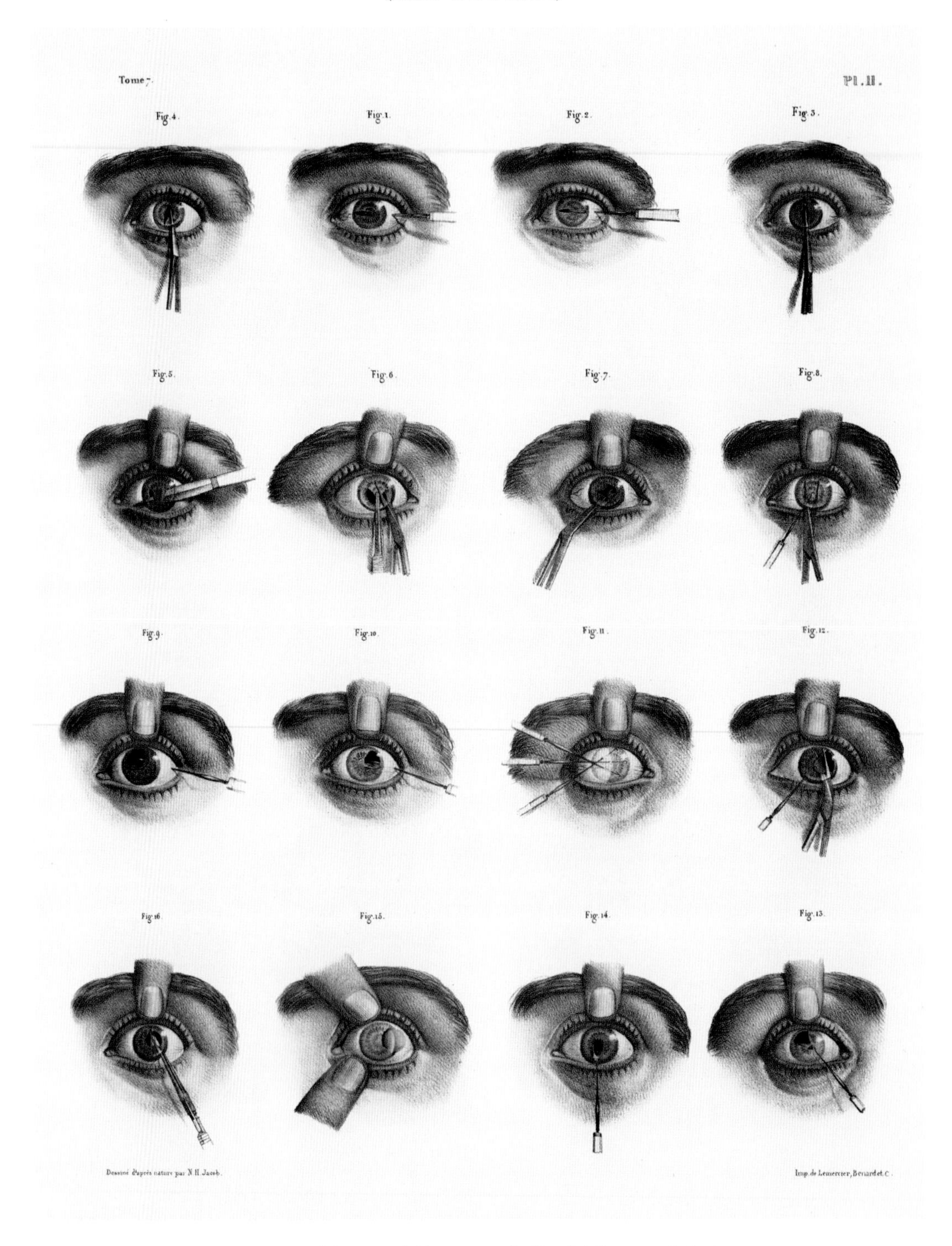

Surgery of the eye / Chirurgie de l'œil / Cirugía del ojo

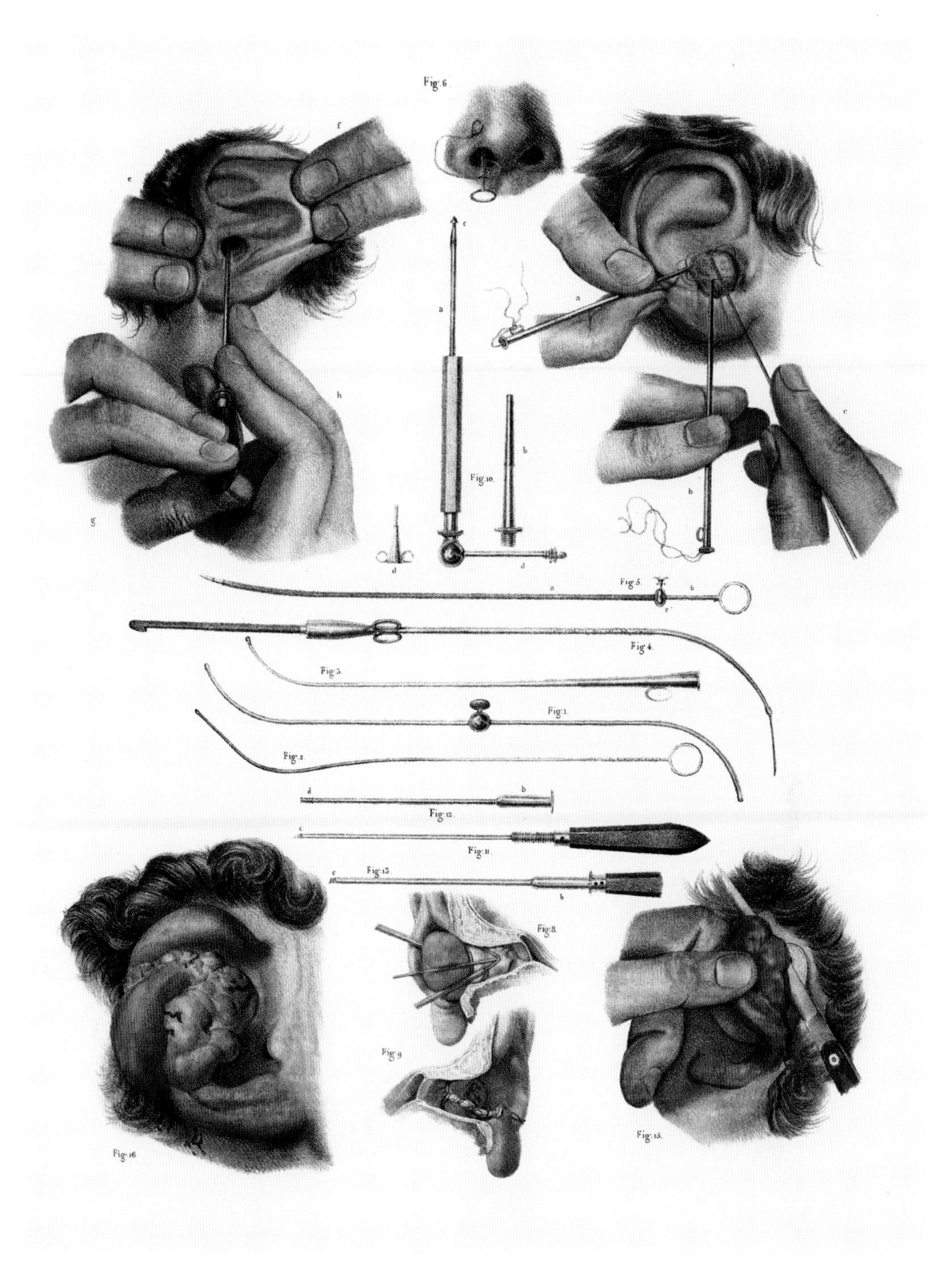

Surgery of the ear / Chirurgie de l'oreille / Cirugía del oído

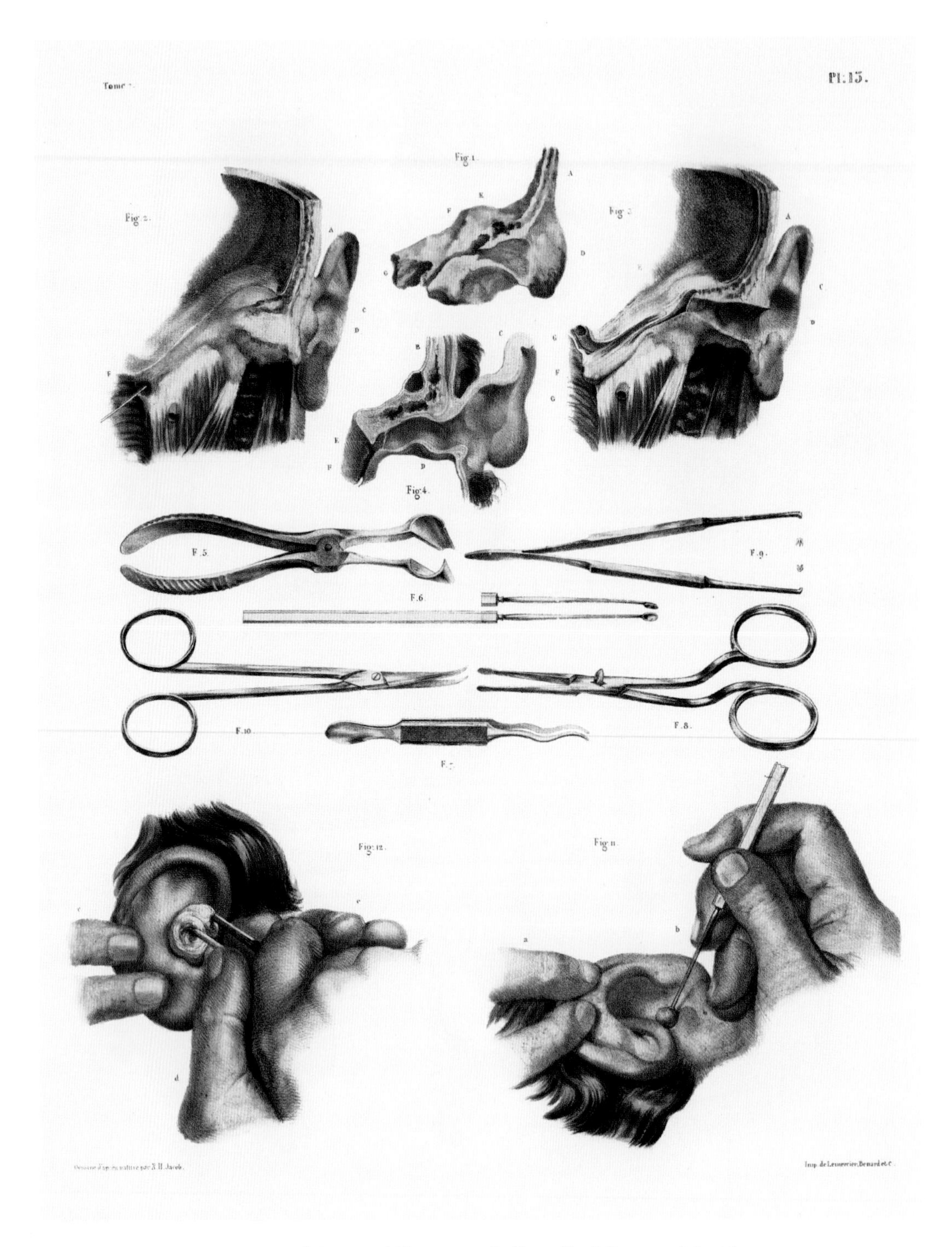

Surgery of the ear / Chirurgie de l'oreille / Cirugía del oído

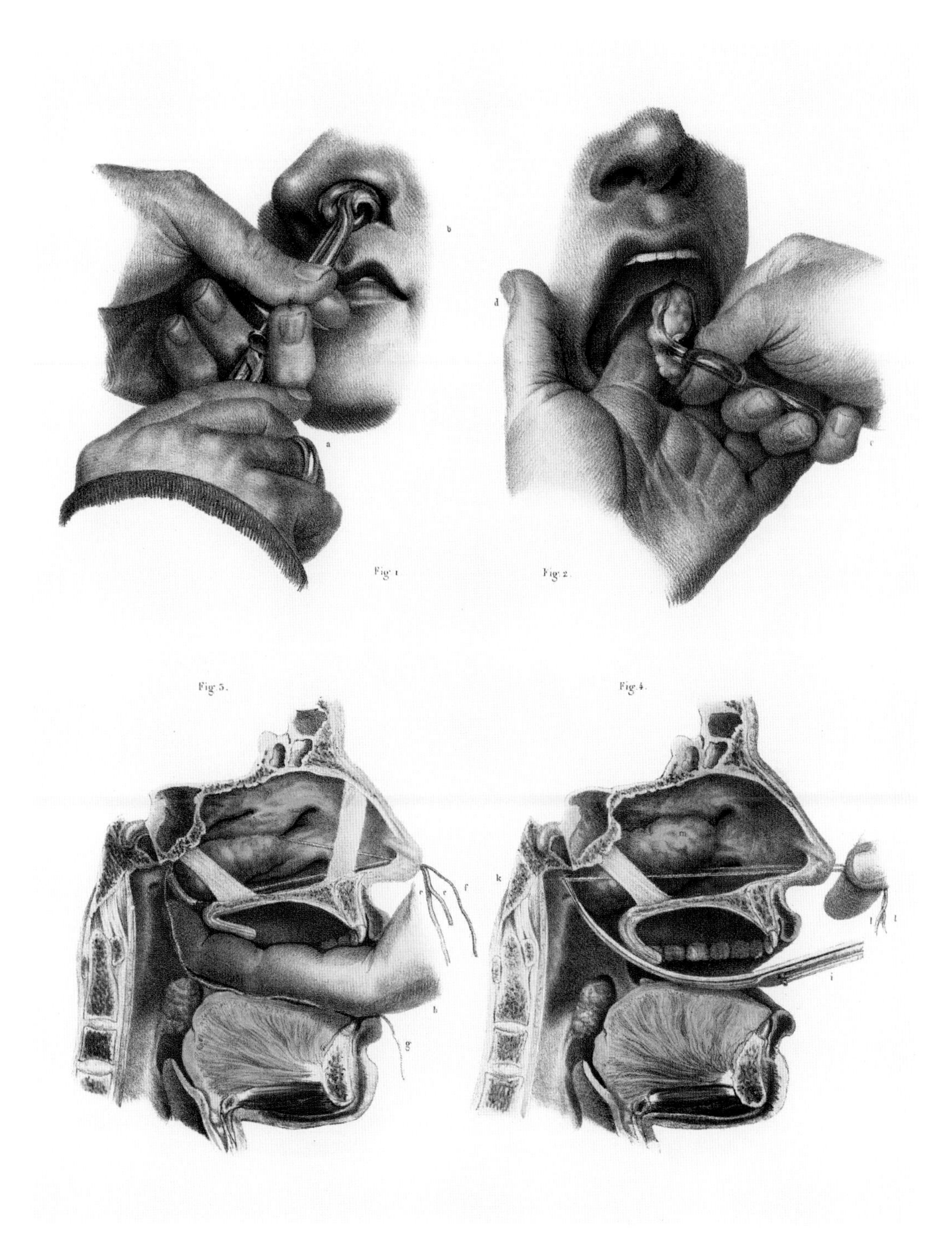

Surgery of the nose / Chirurgie du nez / Cirugía de la nariz

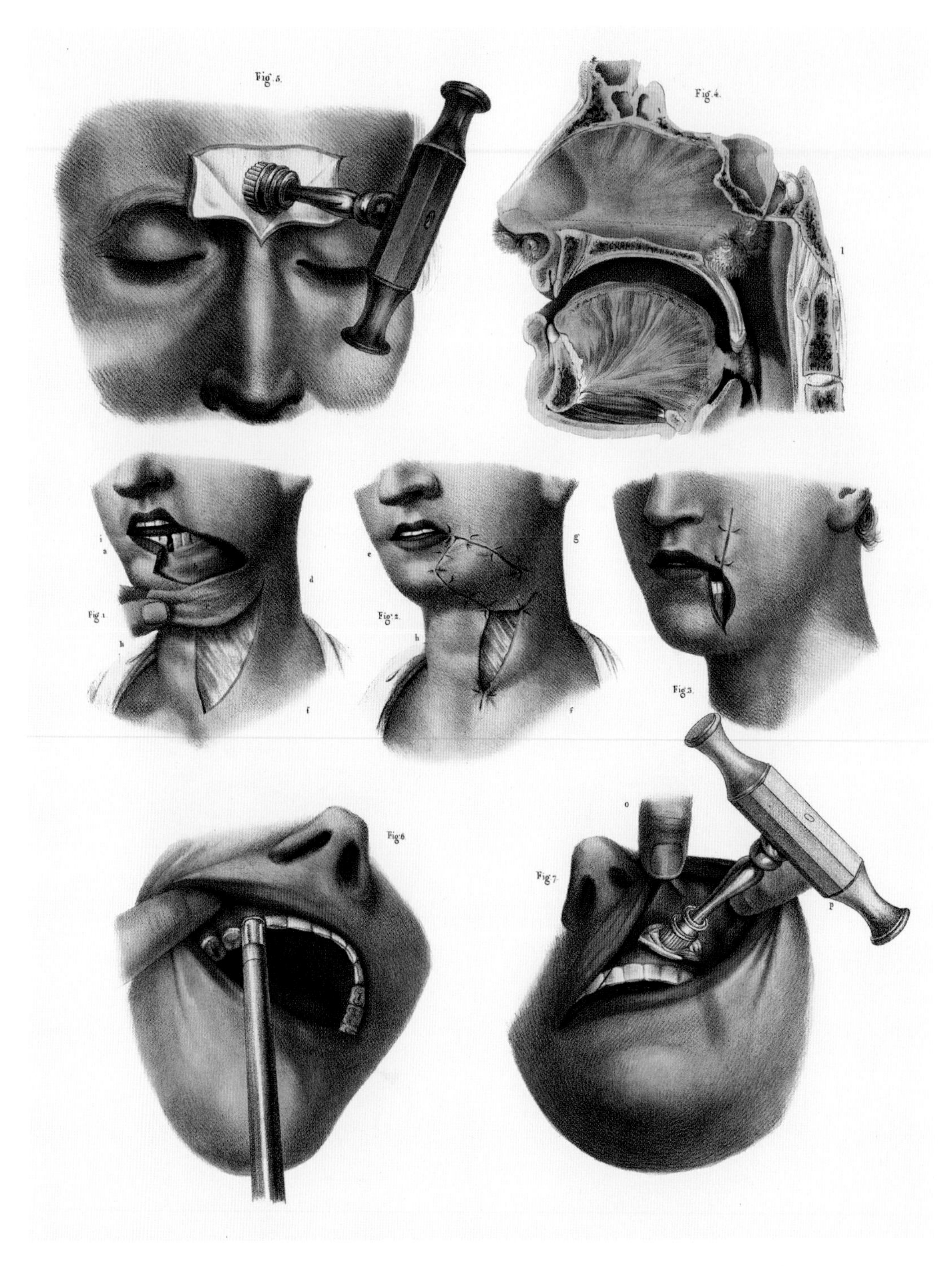

Surgery of the chin, nose, and sinuses / Chirurgie du menton, du nez et des sinus
Cirugía del mentón, de la nariz y de los senos

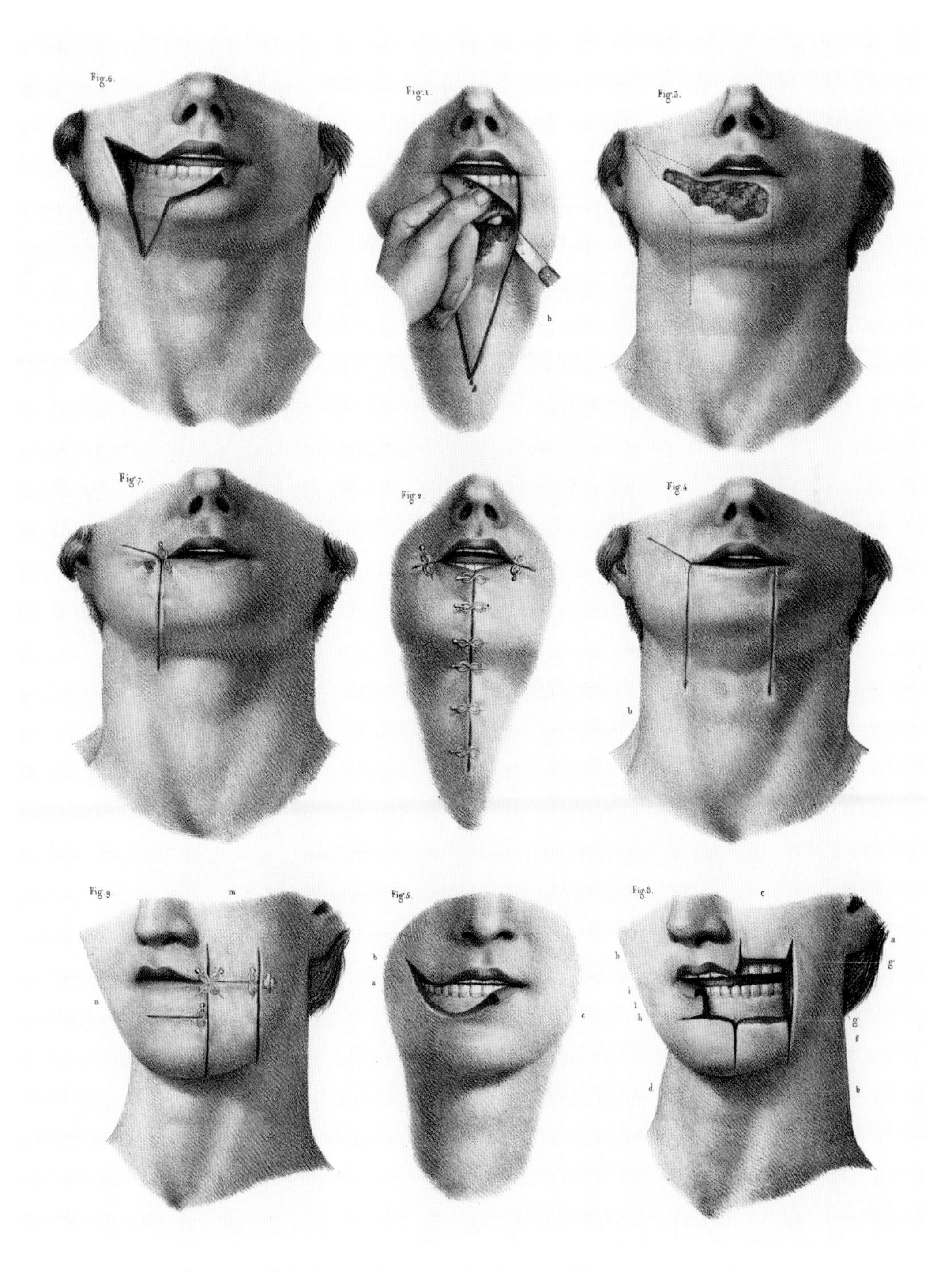

Surgery of the lips / Chirurgie des lèvres / Cirugía de los labios

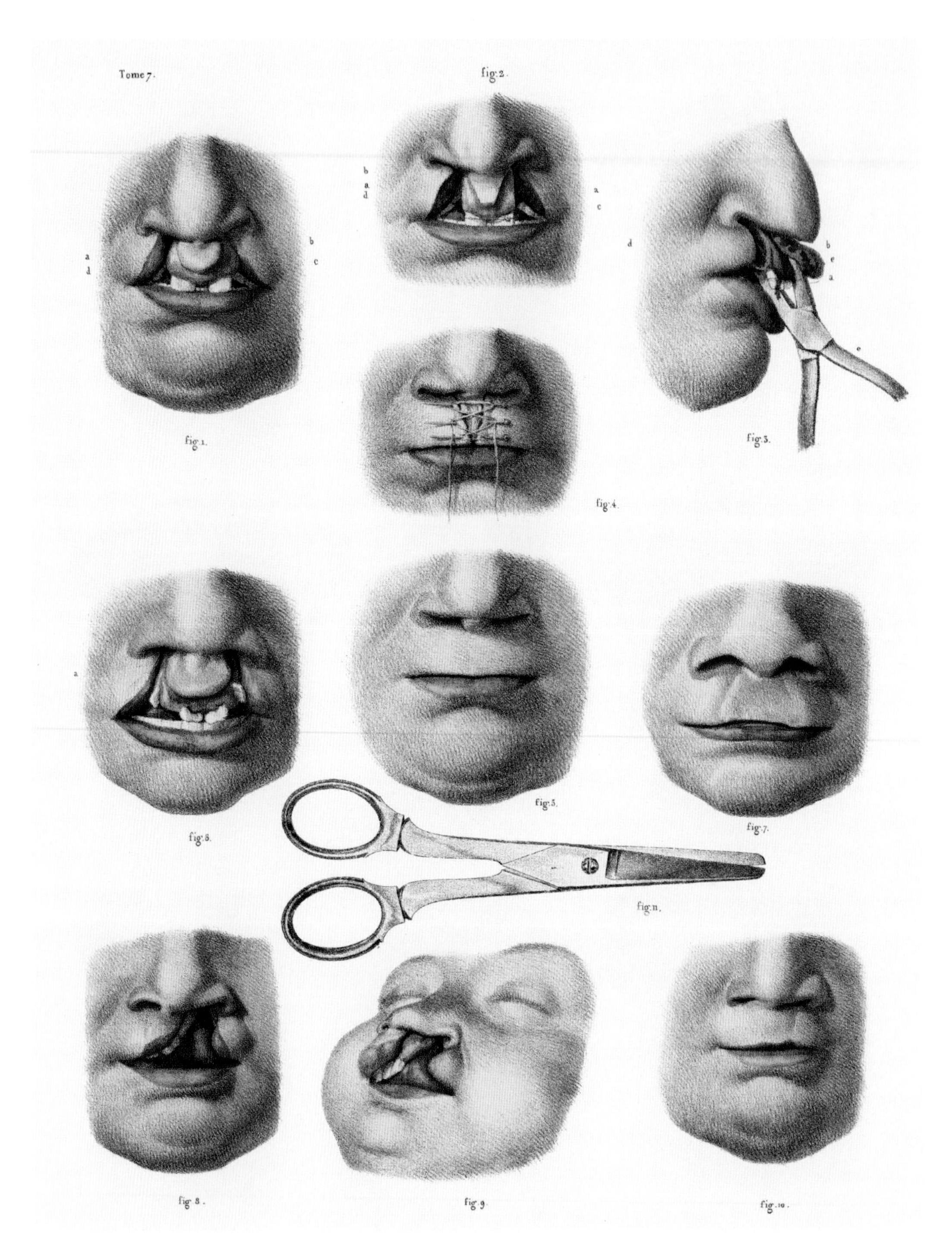

Surgery of the lips / Chirurgie des lèvres / Cirugía de los labios

CHIRURGIA NASI ET TONSILLARUM: INSTRUMENTA CHIRURGICA

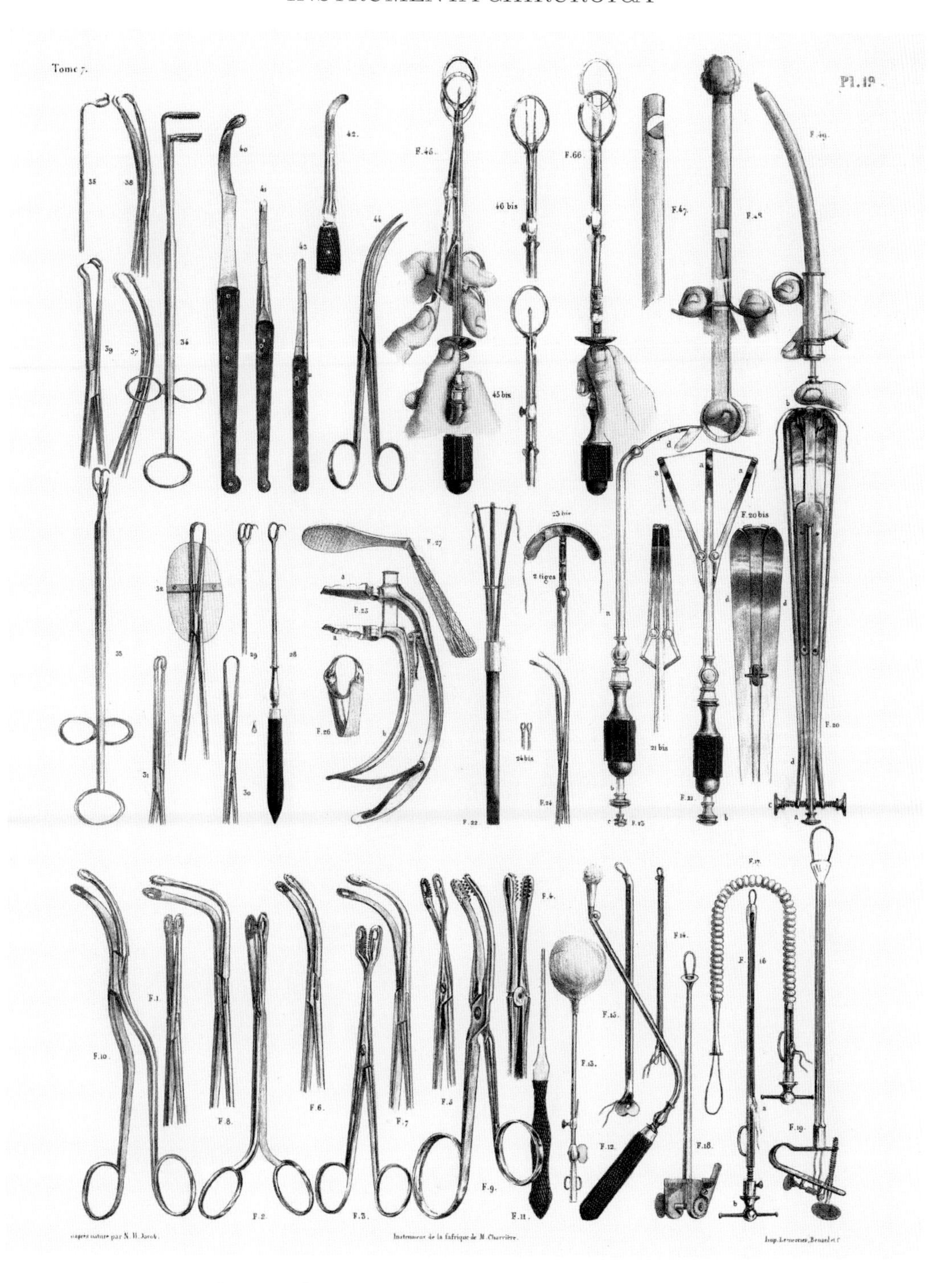

Surgery of the nose and tonsils: Surgical instruments
Chirurgie du nez et des amygdales : Instruments chirurgicaux
Cirugía de la nariz y de las amígdalas: instrumentos quirúrgicos

CHIRURGIA GLANDULAE PAROTIDEAE

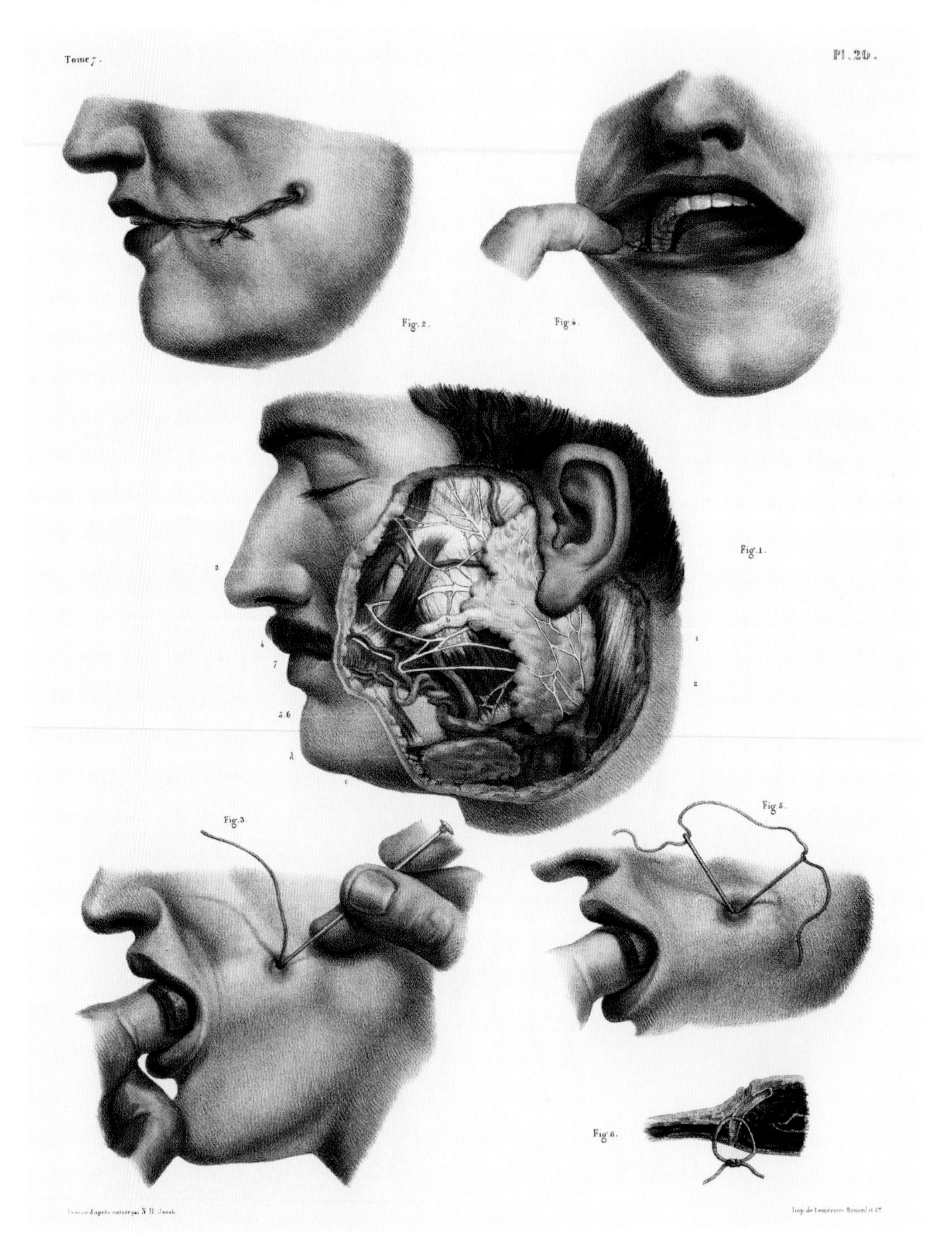

Surgery of the parotid gland / Chirurgie de la glande parotide
Cirugía de la glándula parótida

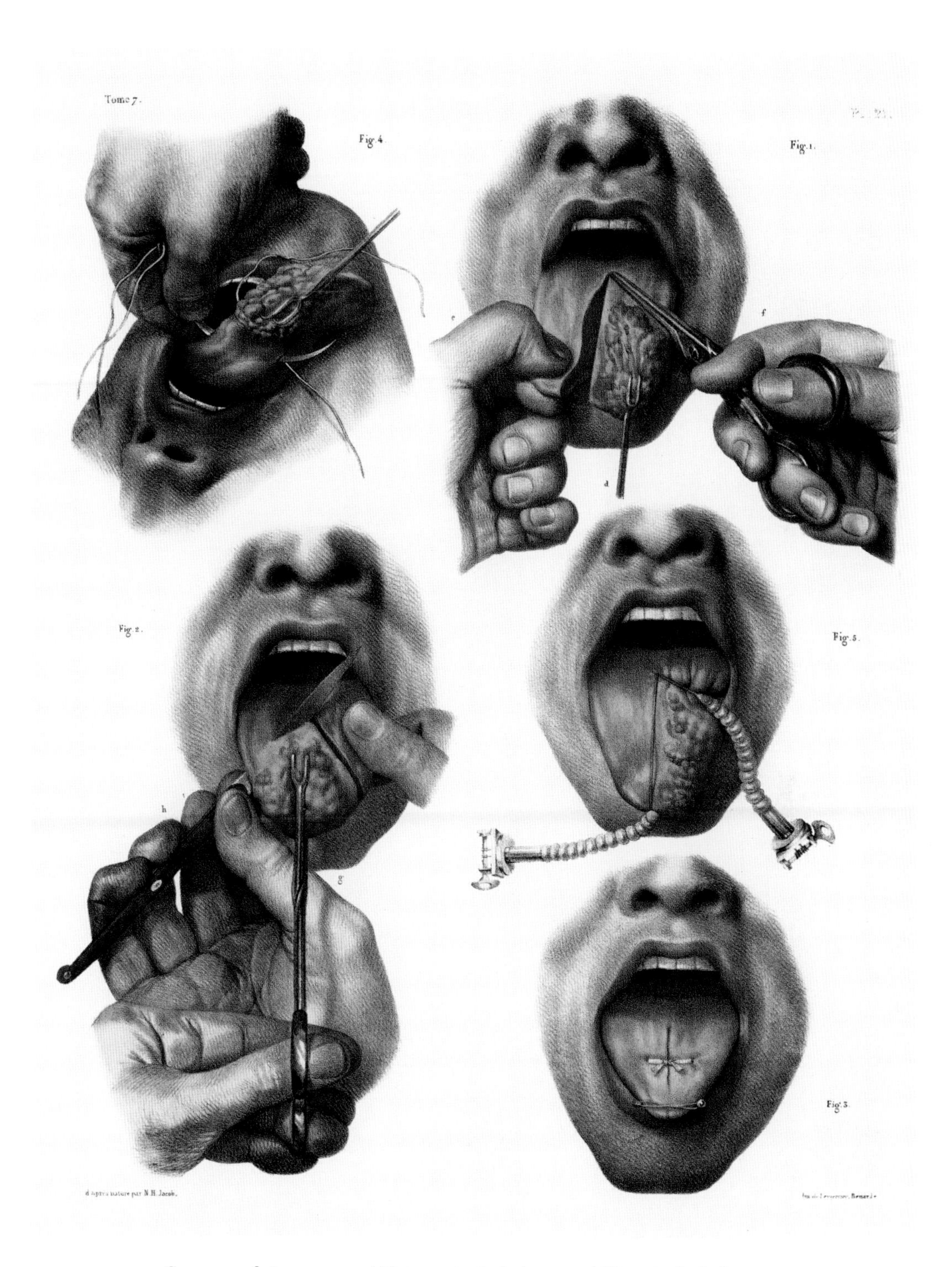

Surgery of the tongue / Chirurgie de la langue / Cirugía de la lengua

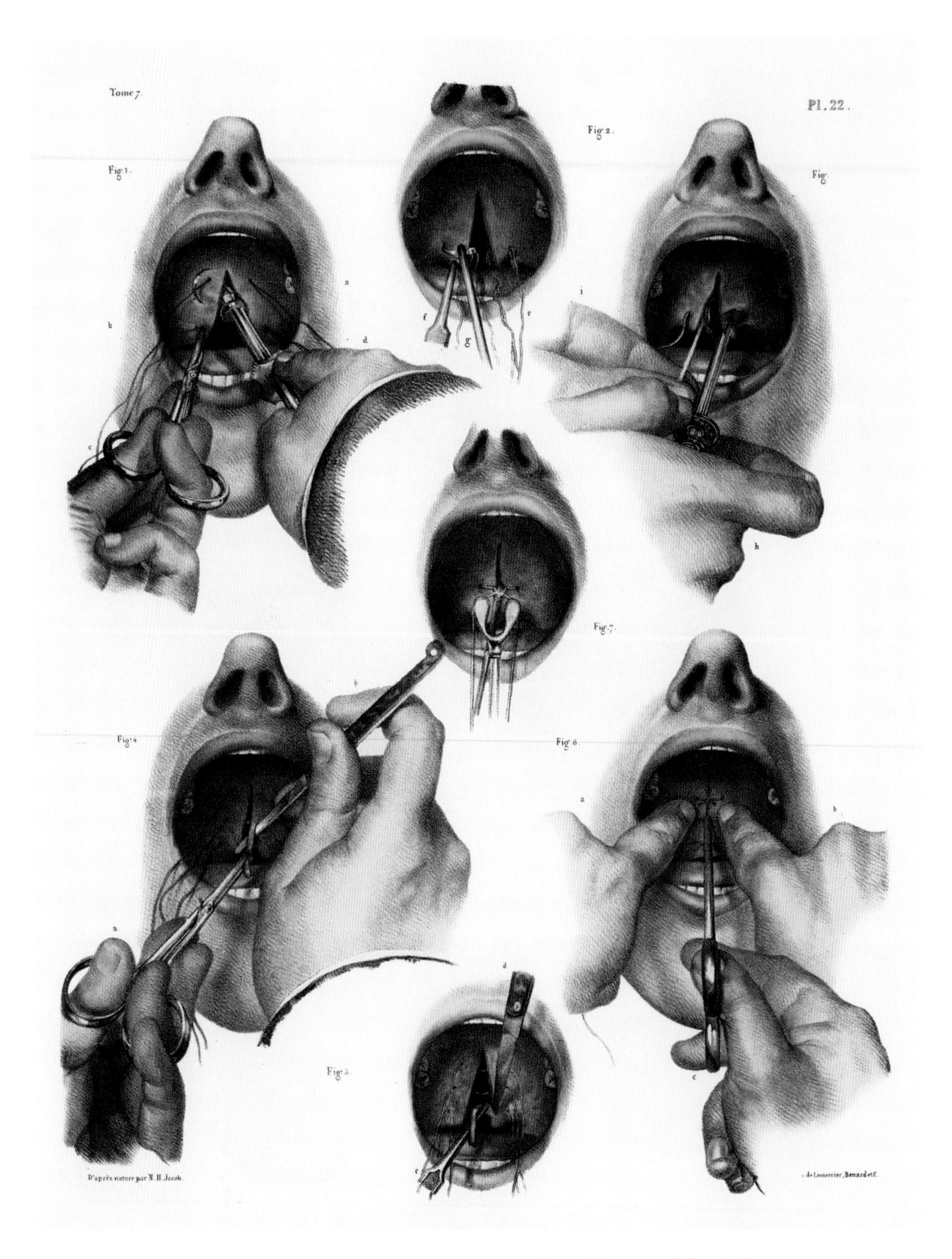

Surgery of the palate / Chirurgie du palais / Cirugía del paladar

CHIRURGIA PALATI: INSTRUMENTA CHIRURGICA

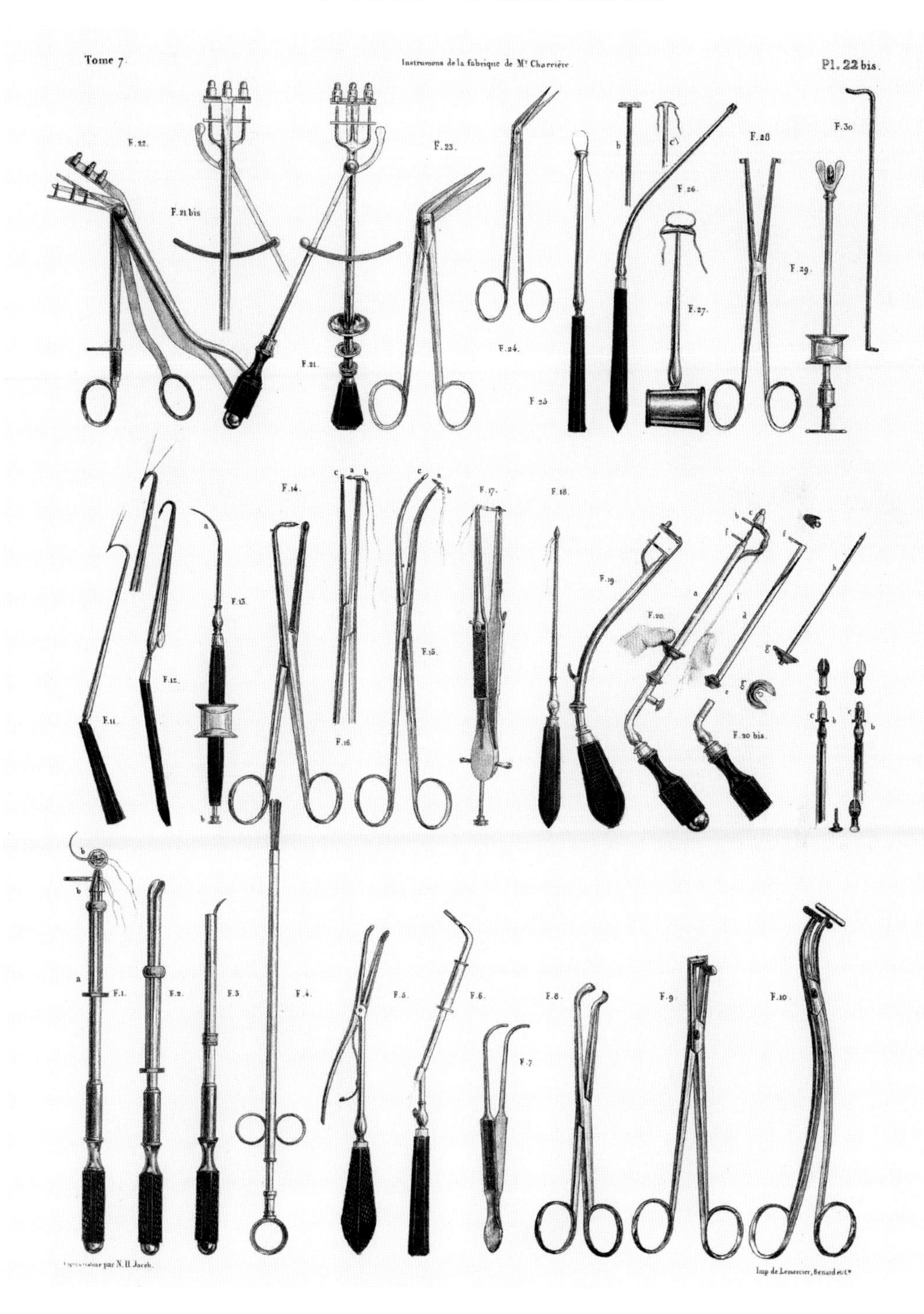

Surgery of the palate: Surgical instruments
Chirurgie du palais : Instruments chirurgicaux
Cirugía del paladar: instrumentos quirúrgicos

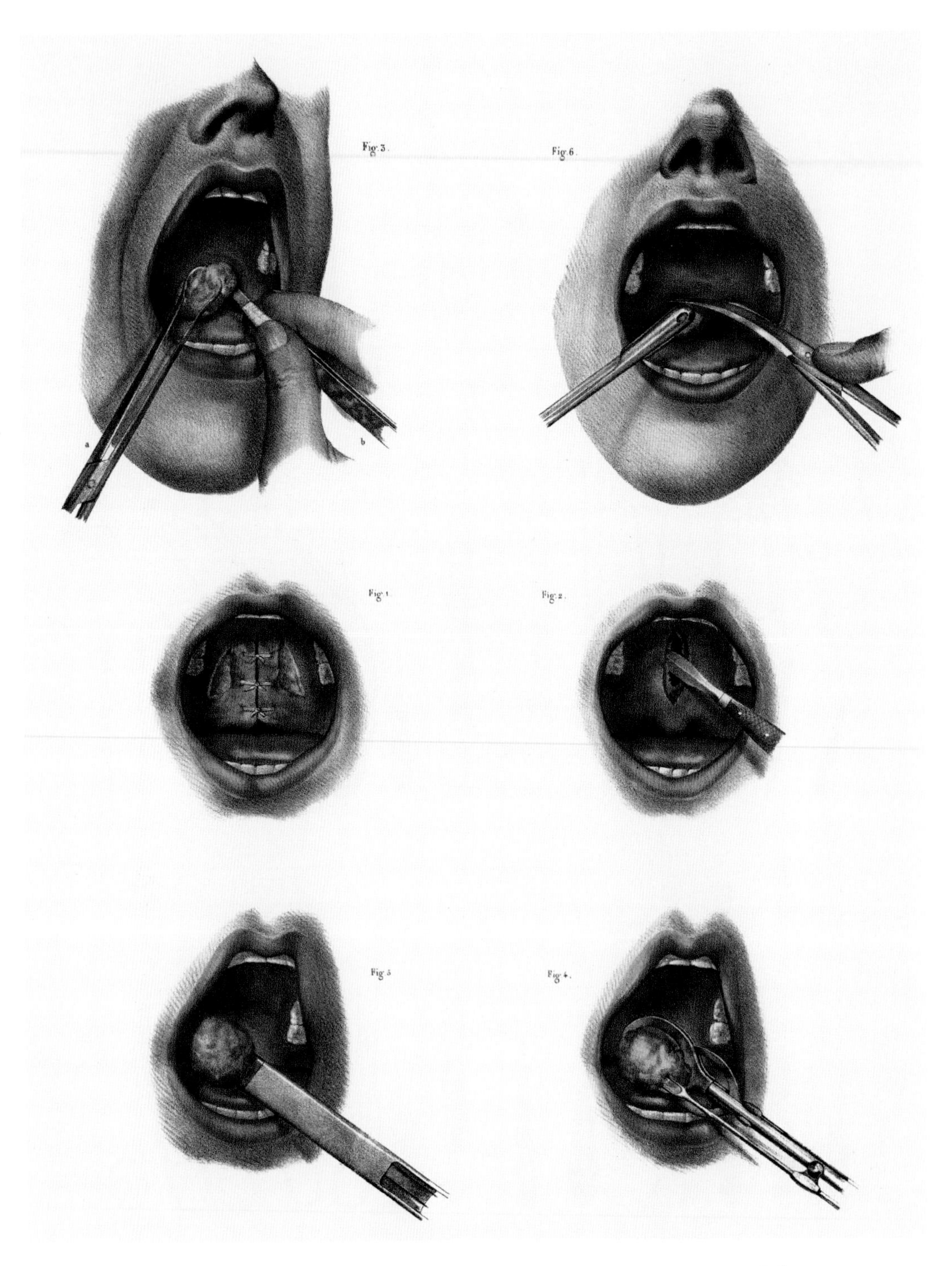

Surgery of the palate and tonsils / Chirurgie du palais et des amygdales
Cirugía del paladar y de las amígdalas

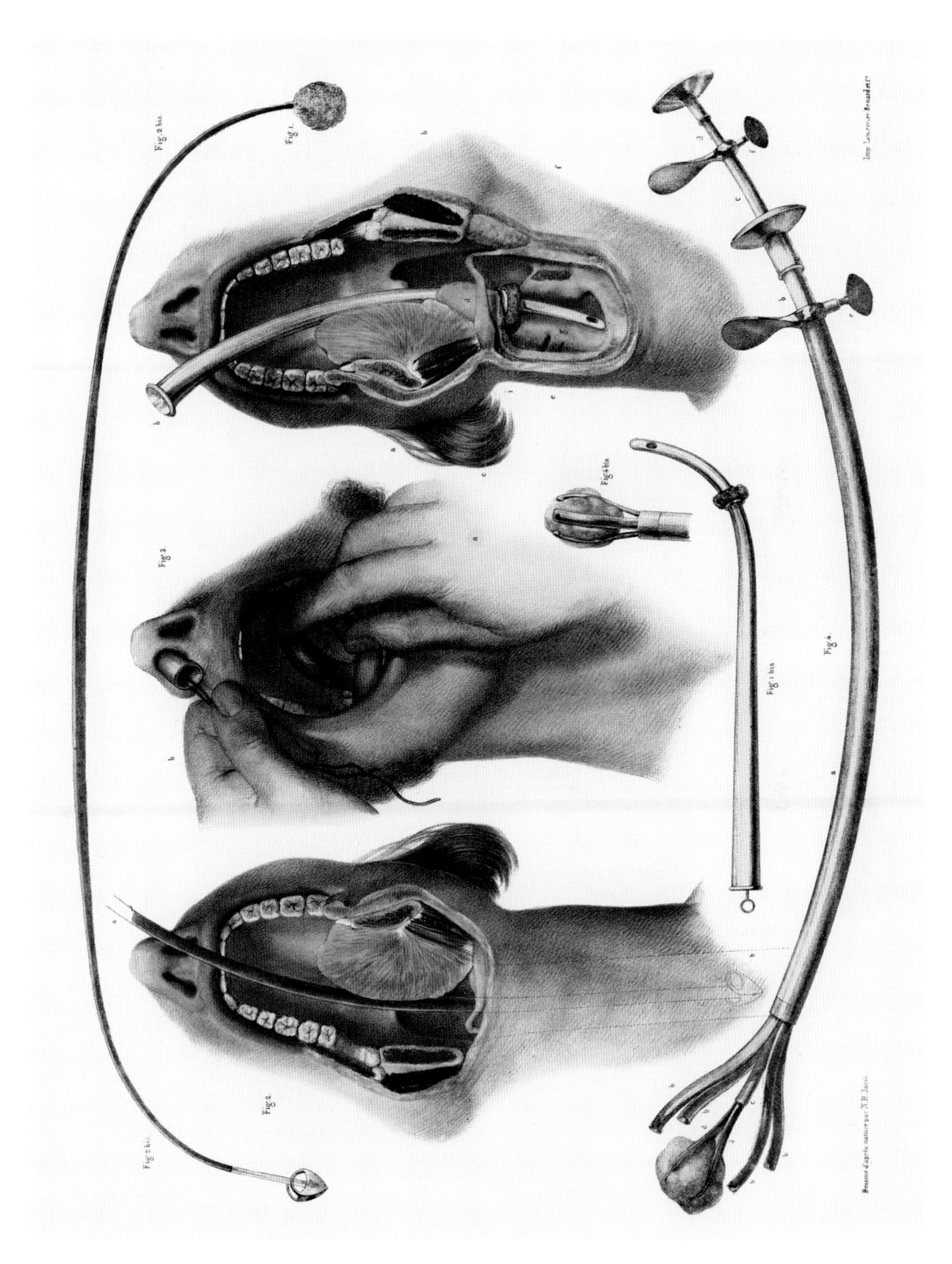

Catheterisations of the larynx and oesophagus
Cathétérismes du larynx et de l'œsophage
Cateterismos de la laringe y del esófago

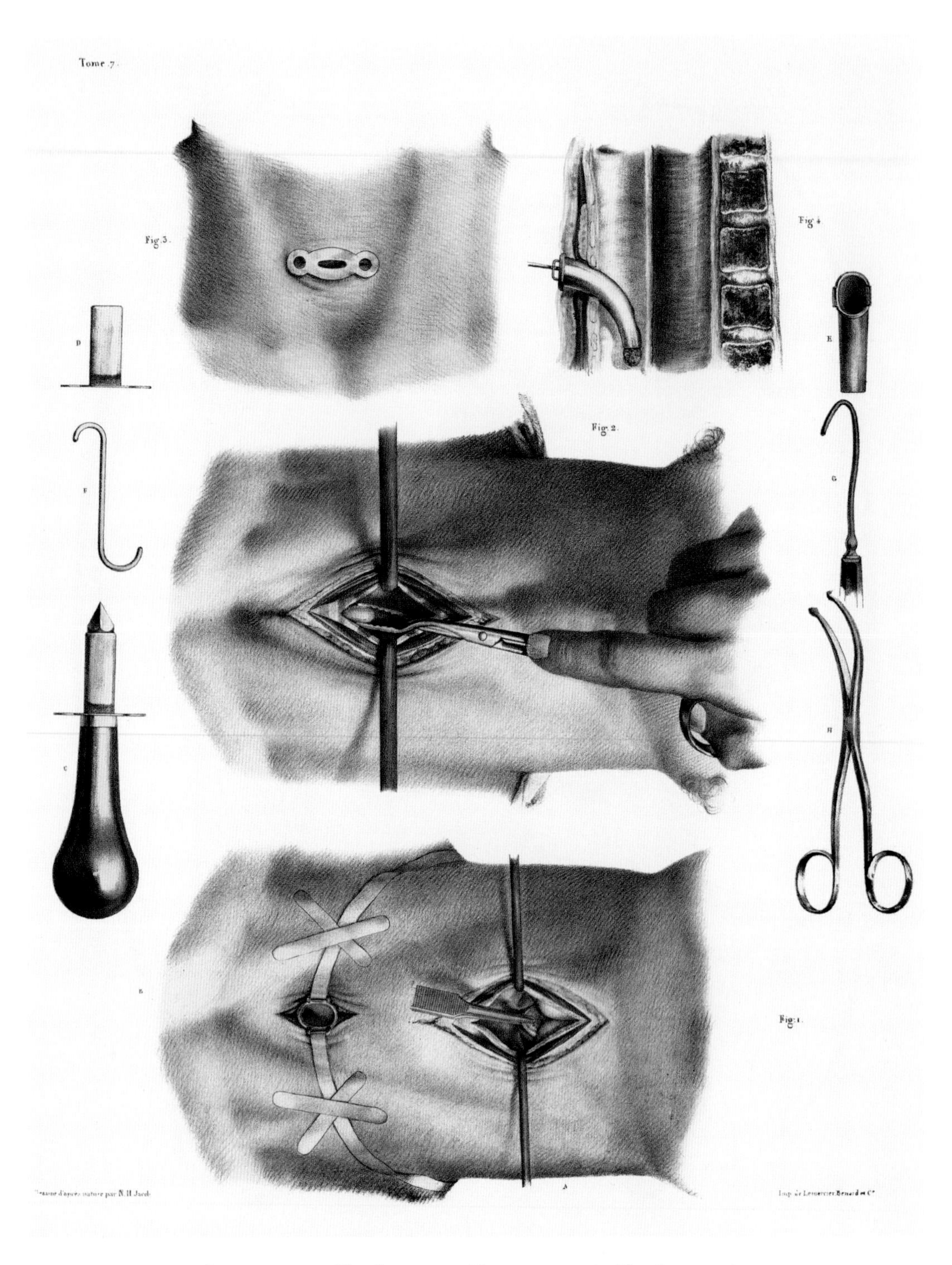

Laryngotomy. Tracheotomy / Laryngotomie. Trachéotomie
Laringotomía. Traqueotomía

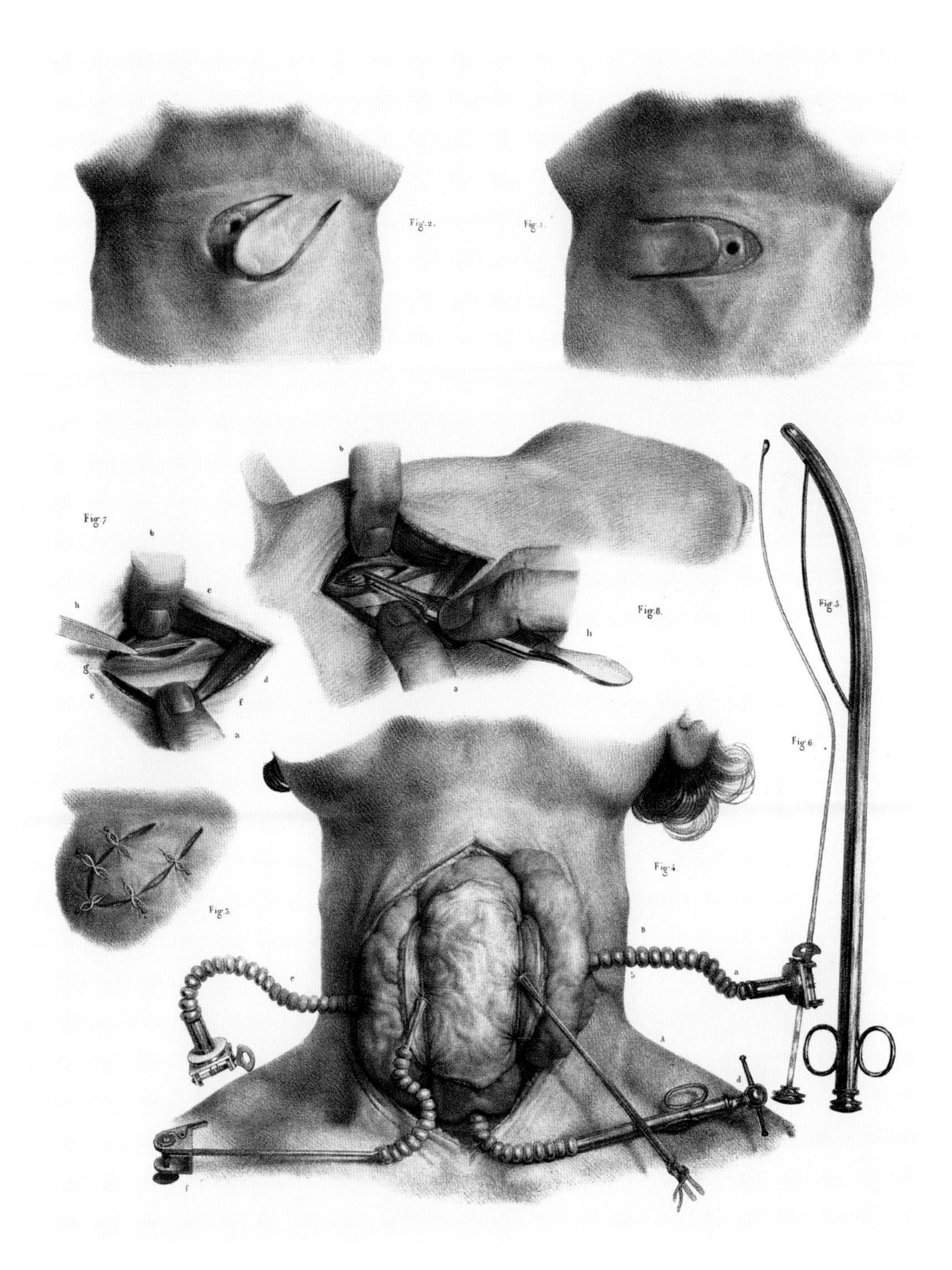

Surgery of the neck / Chirurgie du cou / Cirugía del cuello

Surgery of the breast / Chirurgie du sein / Cirugía mamaria

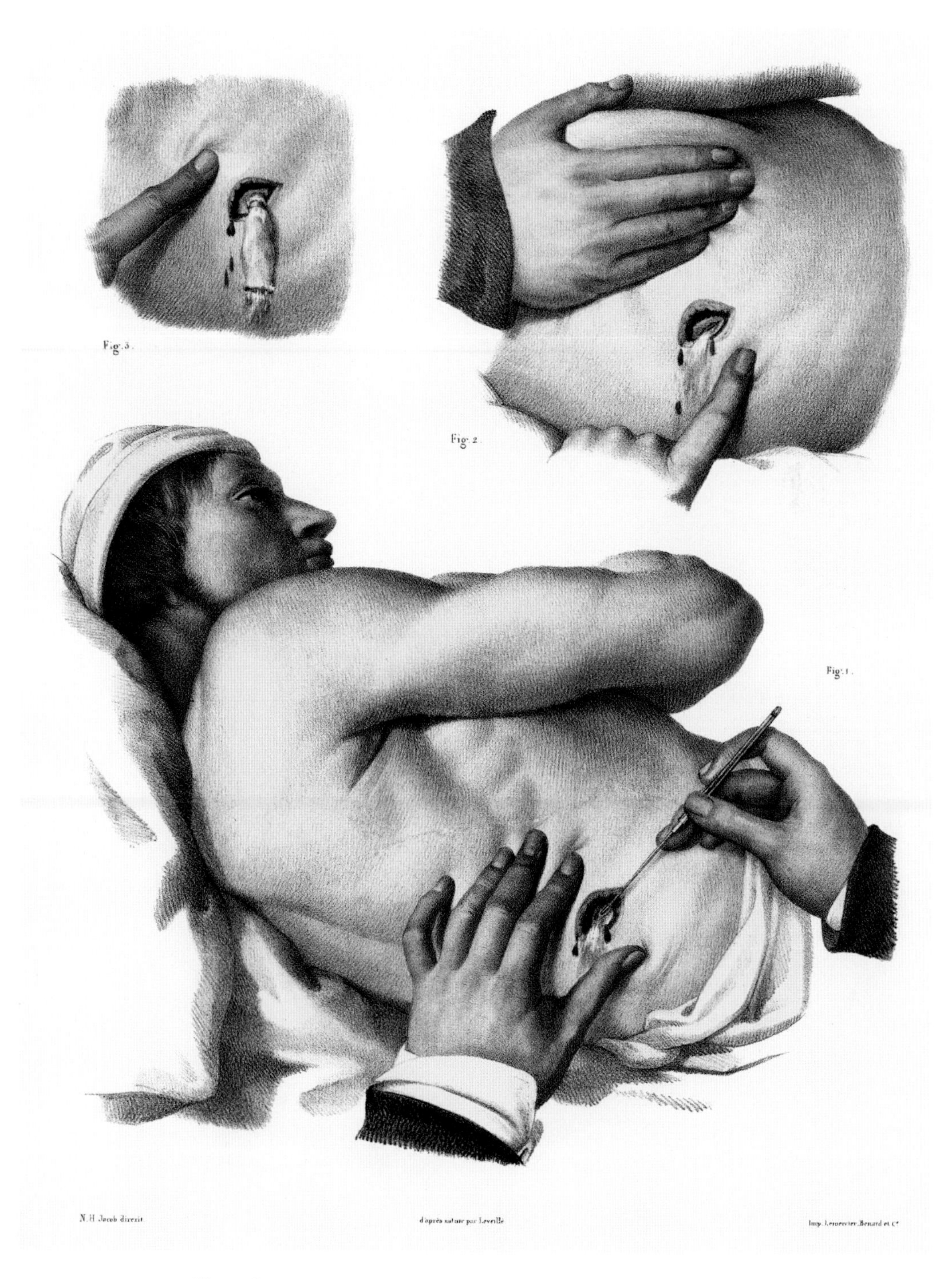

Pleural tap / Ponctions de la plèvre / Punciones de la pleura

PUNCTIONES PERITONEI ET PERICARDII. PUNCTIO ABSCESSUS HEPATIS

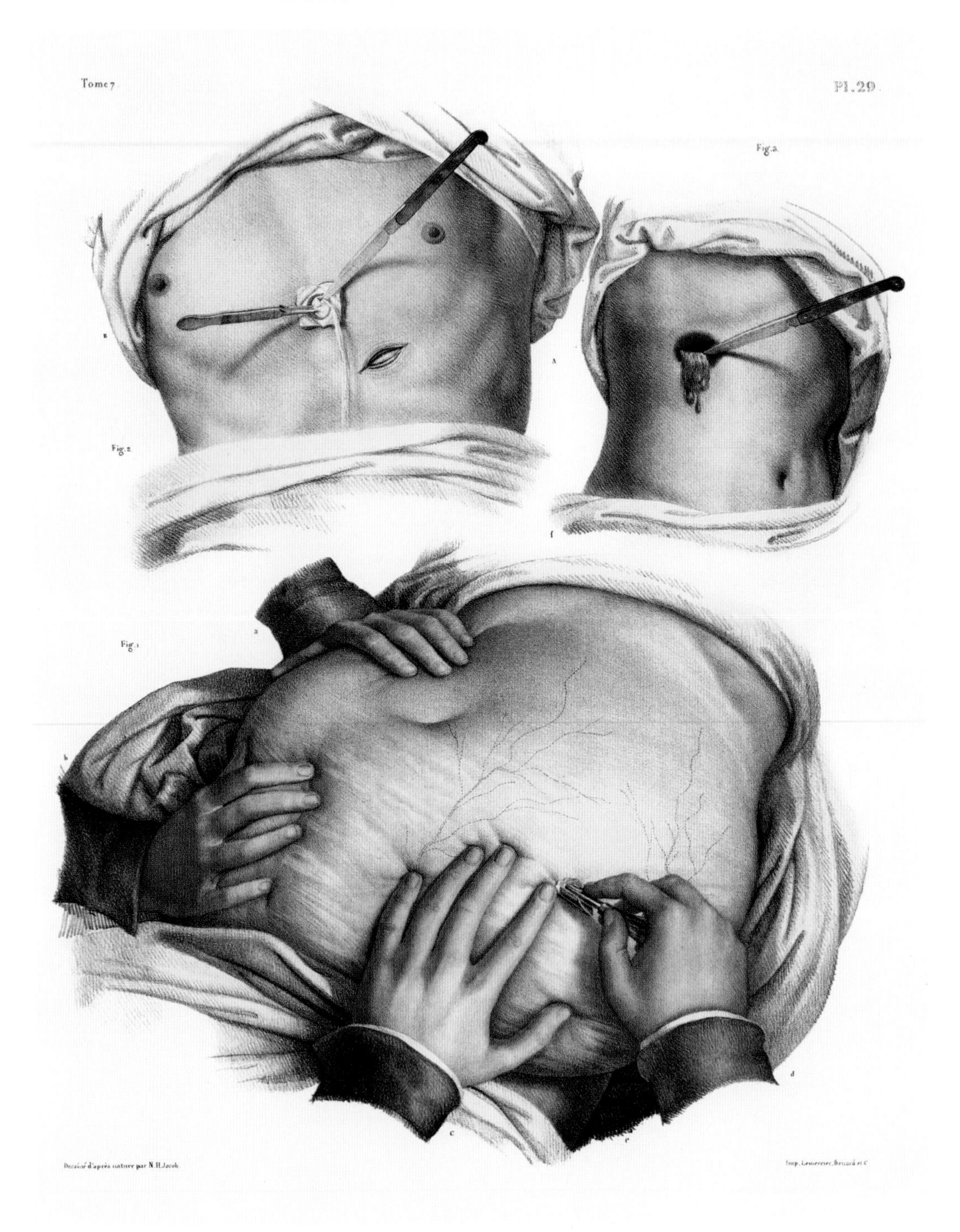

Peritoneal and pericardial taps. Liver abscess tap
Ponctions du péritoine et du péricarde. Ponction d'abcès du foie
Punciones del peritoneo y del pericardio. Punción de los abscesos del hígado

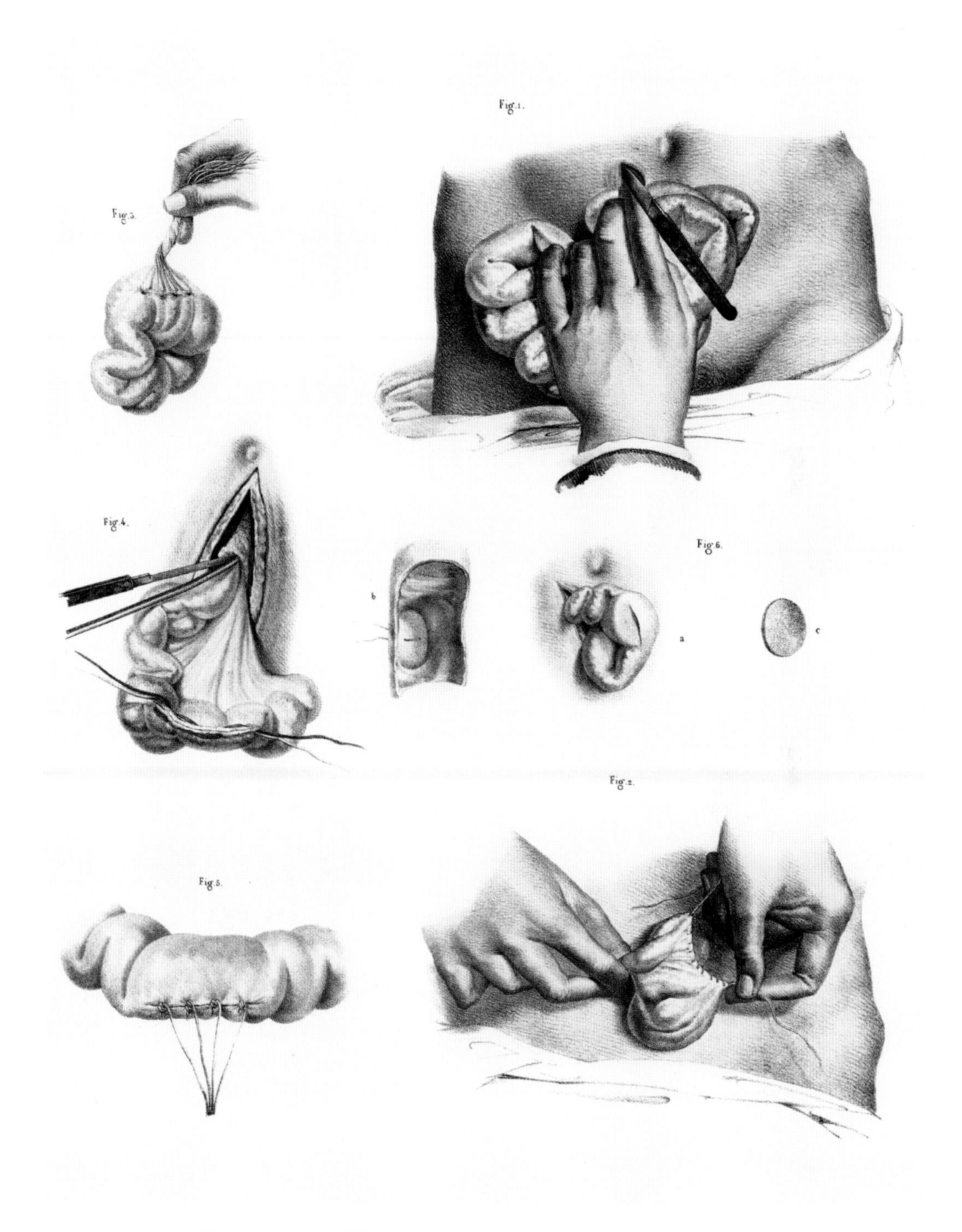

Bowel surgery / Chirurgie de l'intestin / Cirugía del intestino

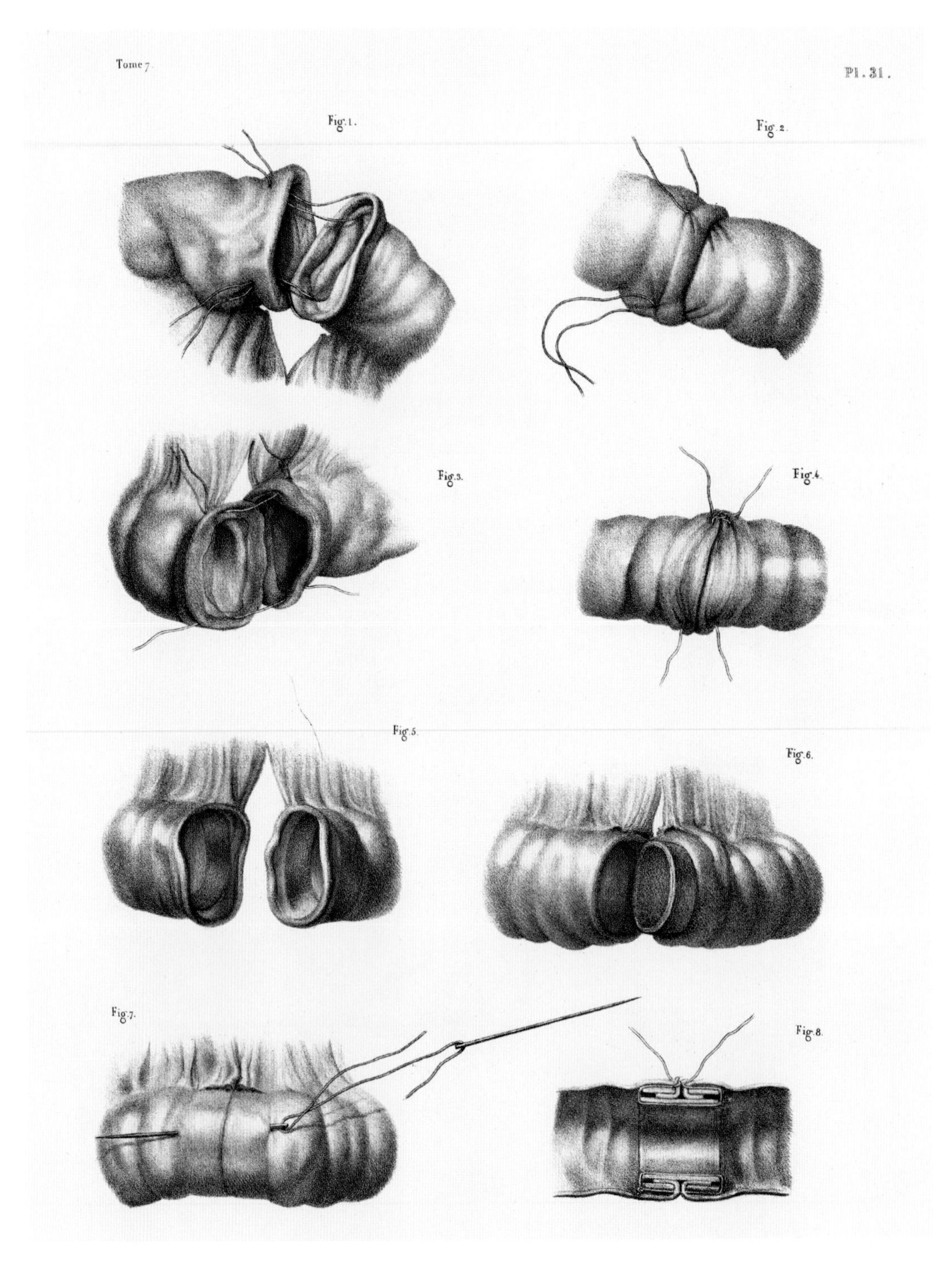

Bowel surgery / Chirurgie de l'intestin / Cirugía del intestino

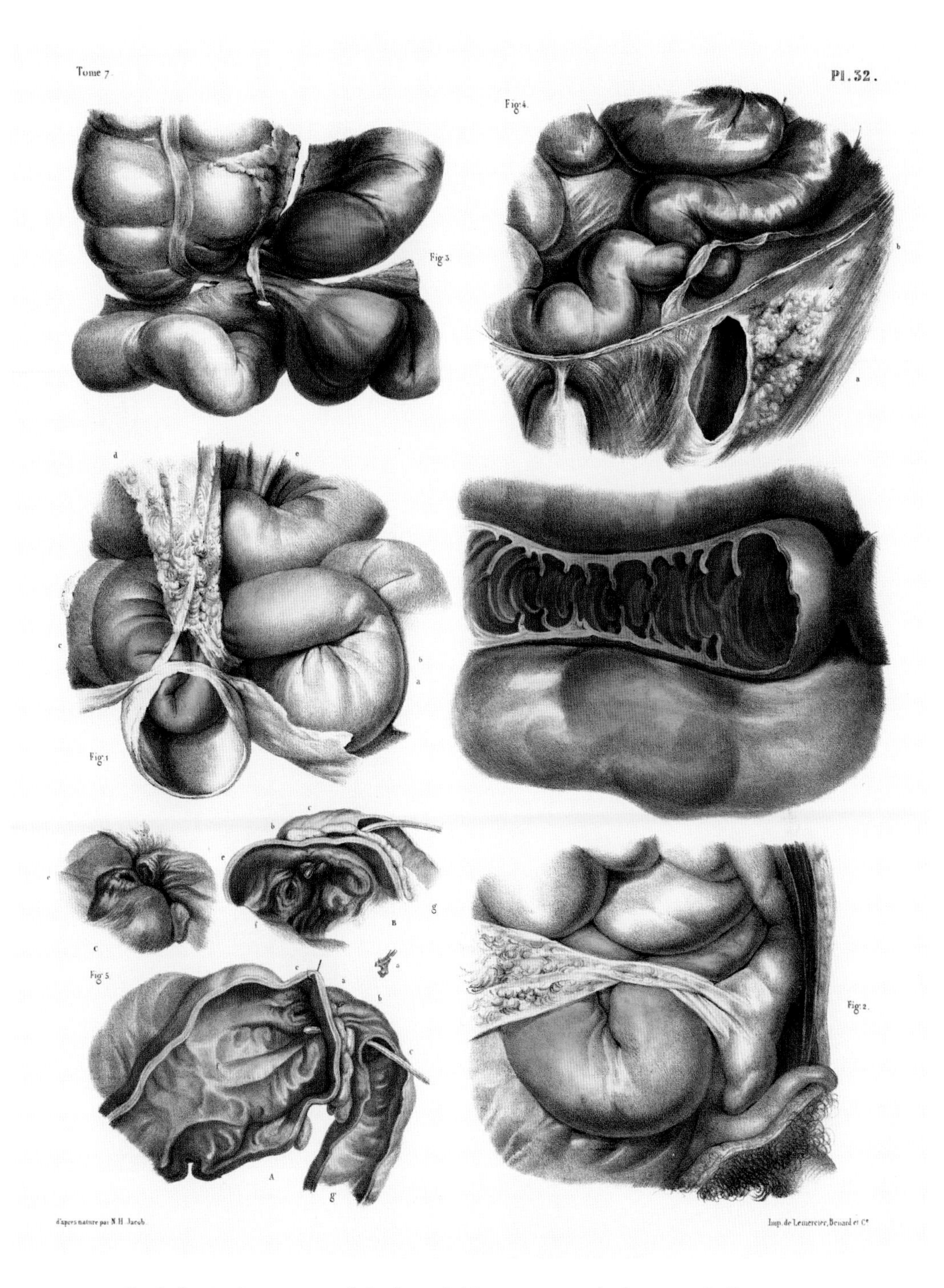

Pathological anatomy of the bowel / Anatomie pathologique de l'intestin
Anatomía patológica del intestino

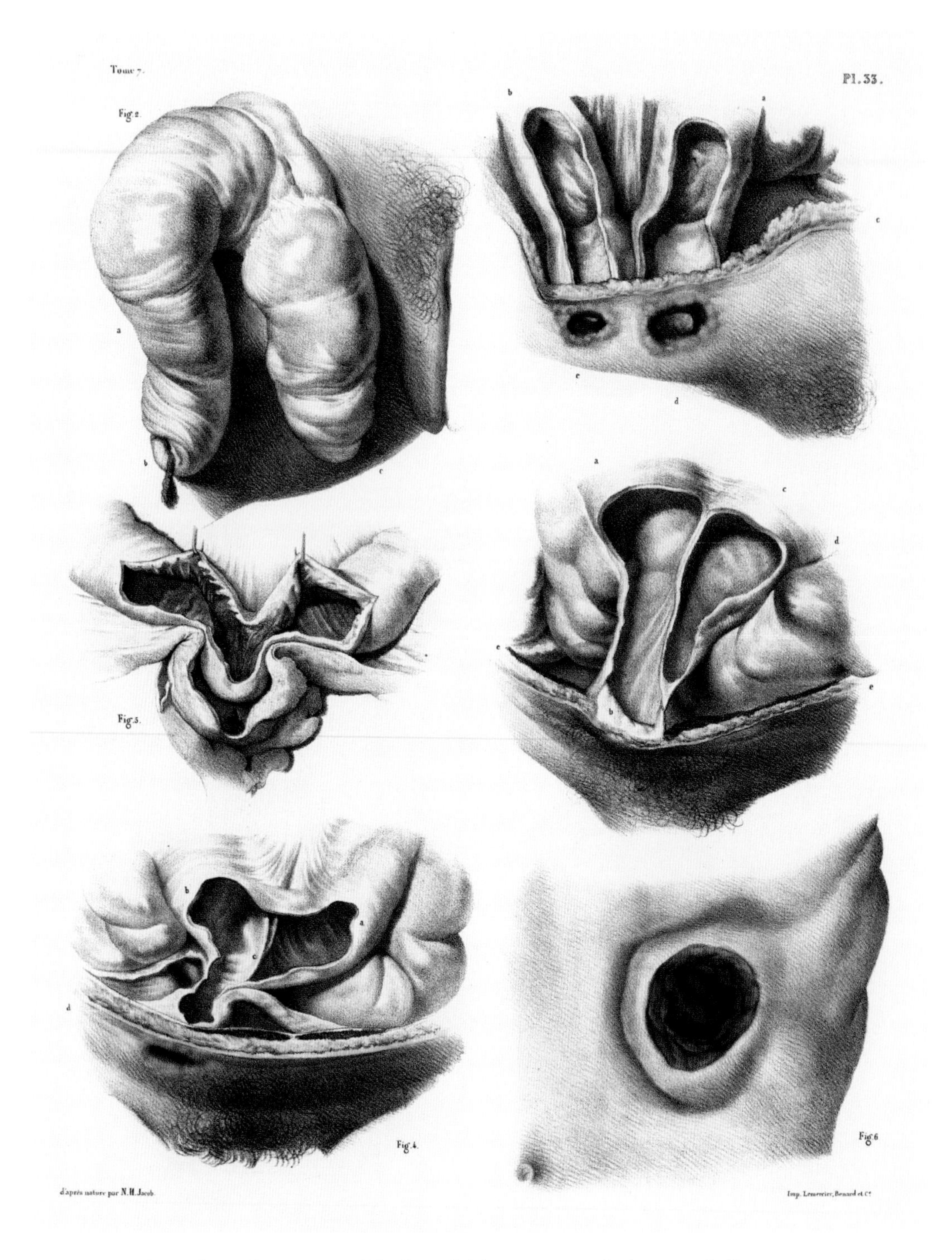

Pathological anatomy of the bowel / Anatomie pathologique de l'intestin
Anatomía patológica del intestino

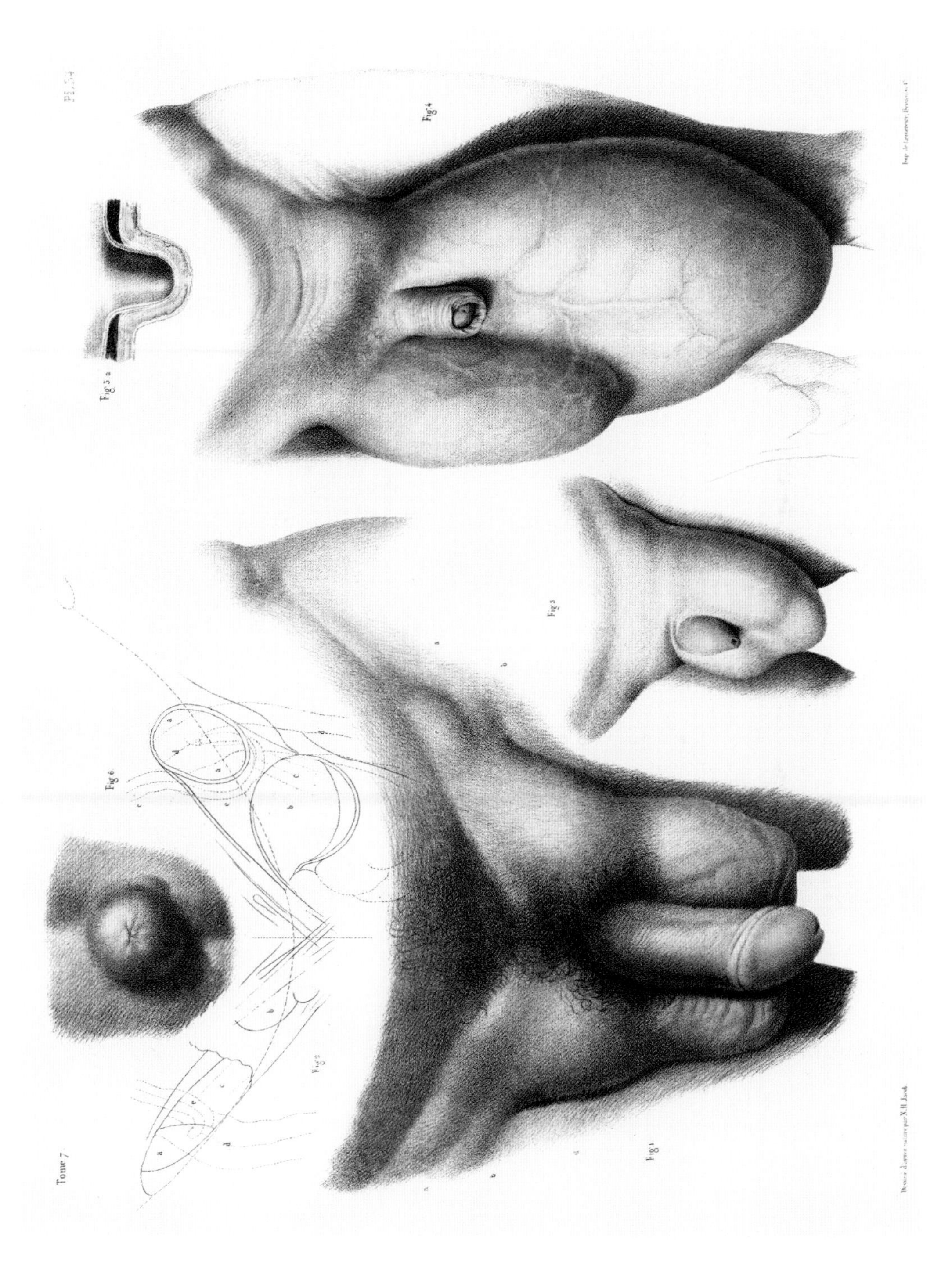

Pathological anatomy of abdominal hernias
Anatomie pathologique des hernies abdominales
Anatomía patológica de las hernias abdominales

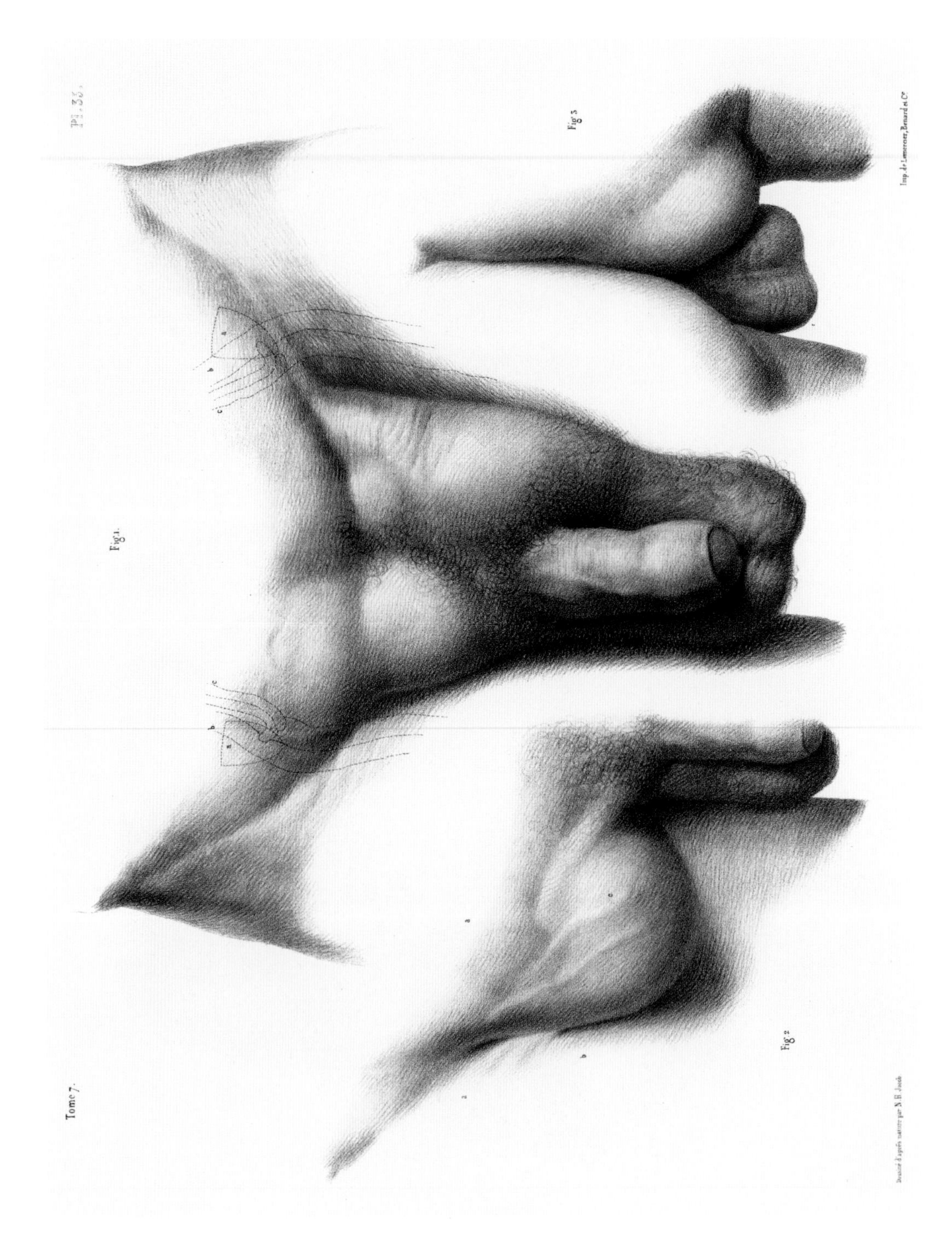

Pathological anatomy of abdominal hernias
Anatomie pathologique des hernies abdominales
Anatomía patológica de las hernias abdominales

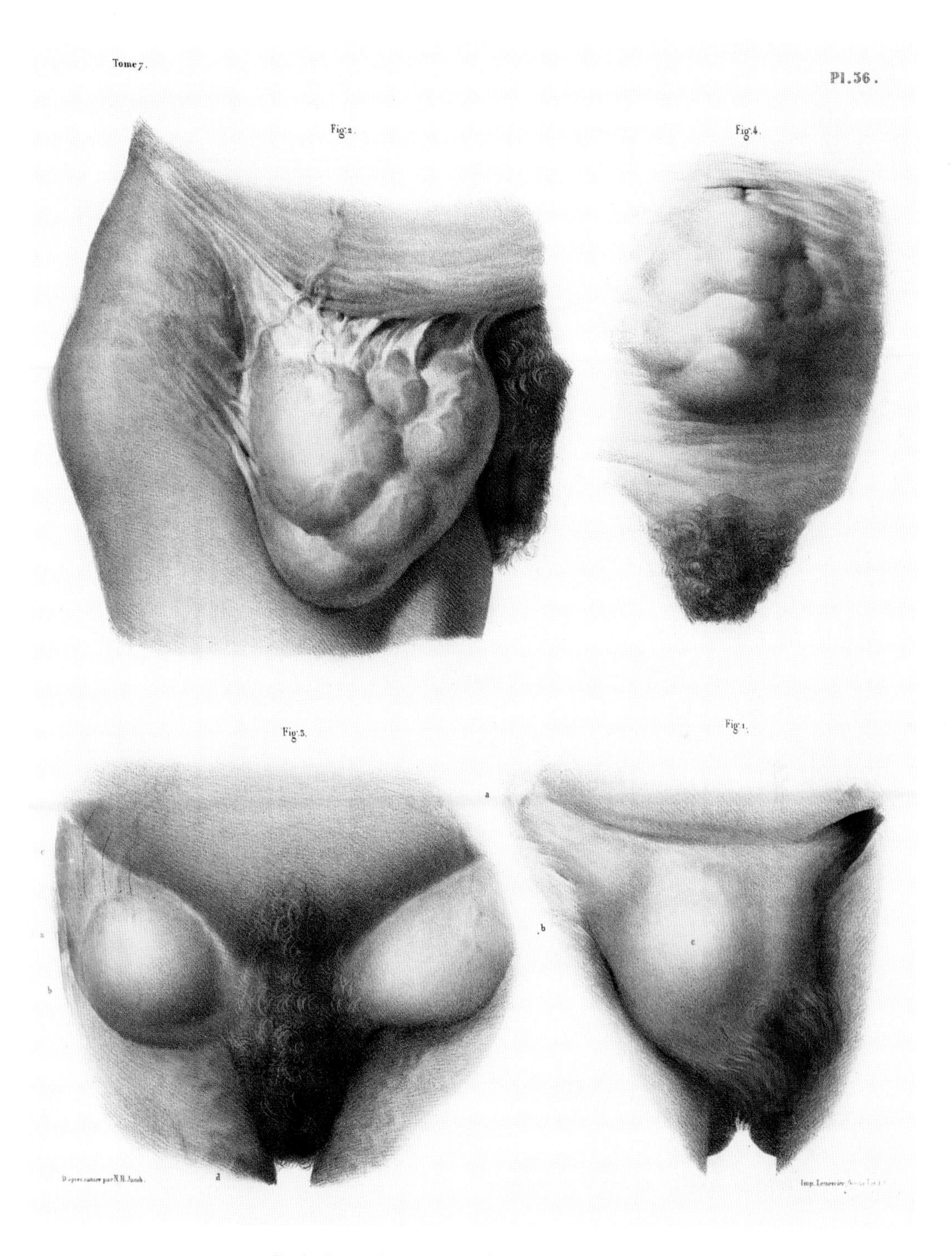

Pathological anatomy of abdominal hernias
Anatomie pathologique des hernies abdominales
Anatomía patológica de las hernias abdominales

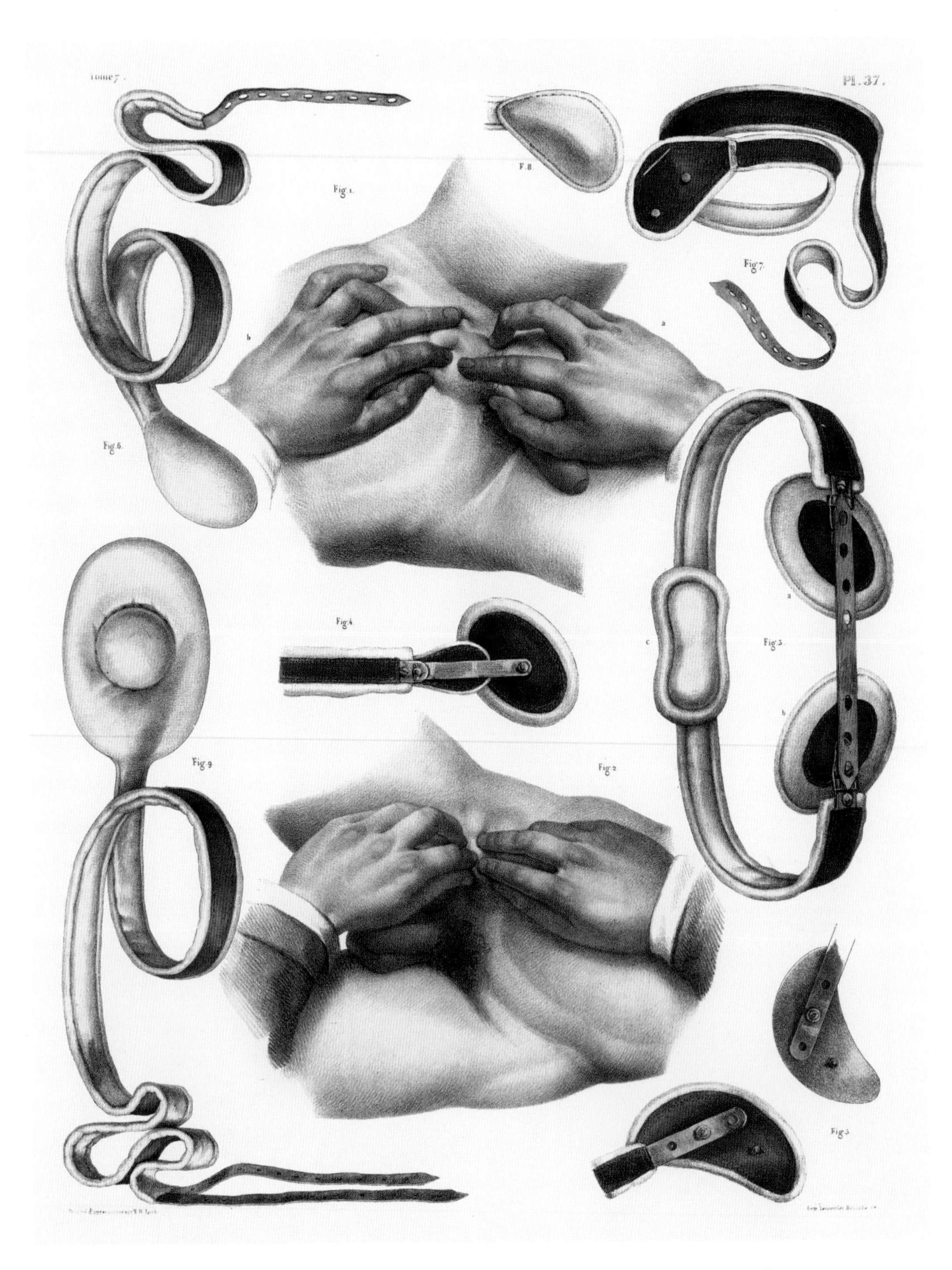

Surgery of abdominal hernias / Chirurgie des hernies abdominales
Cirugía de las hernias abdominales

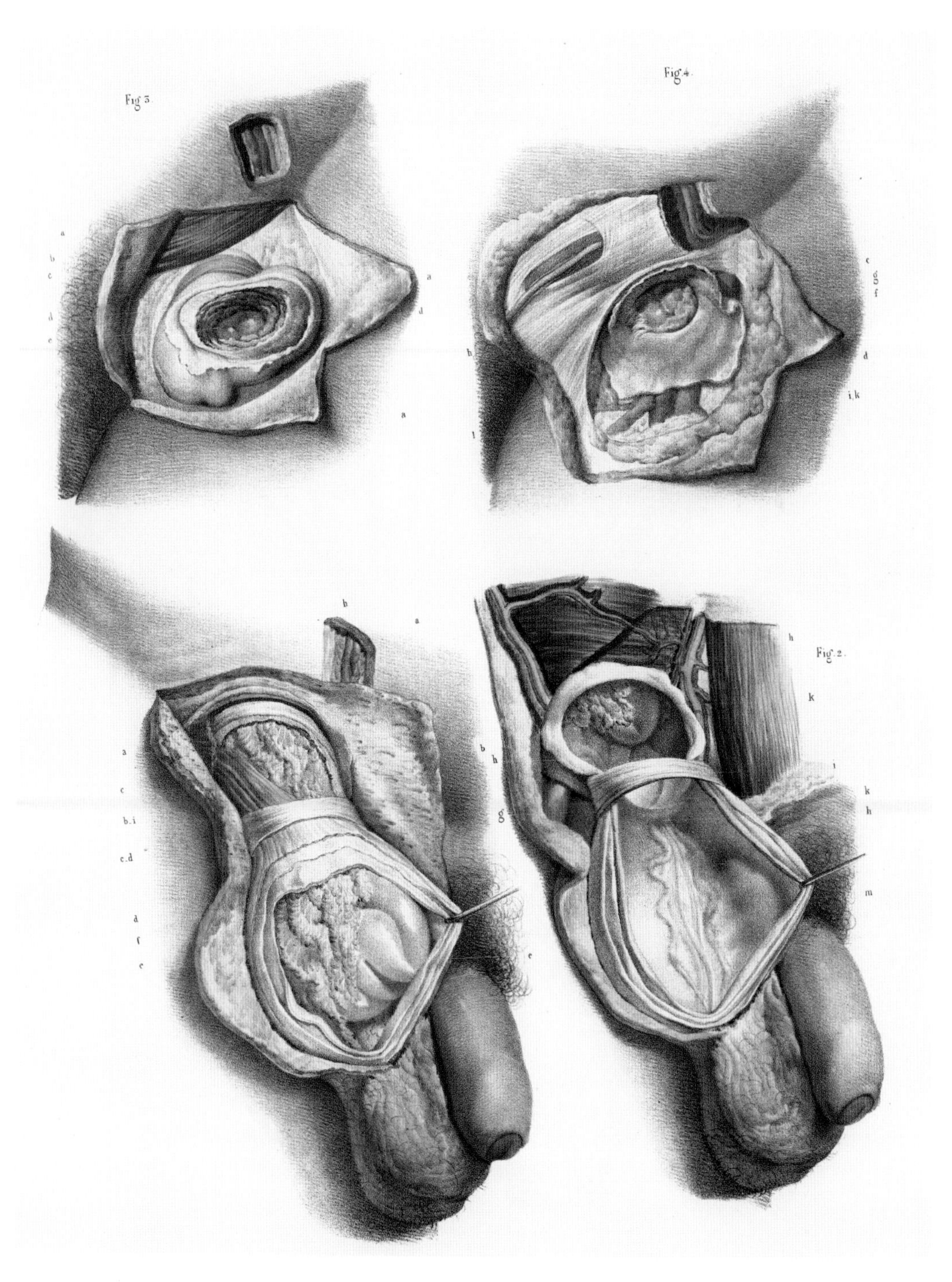

Pathological anatomy of abdominal hernias
Anatomie pathologique des hernies abdominales
Anatomía patológica de las hernias abdominales

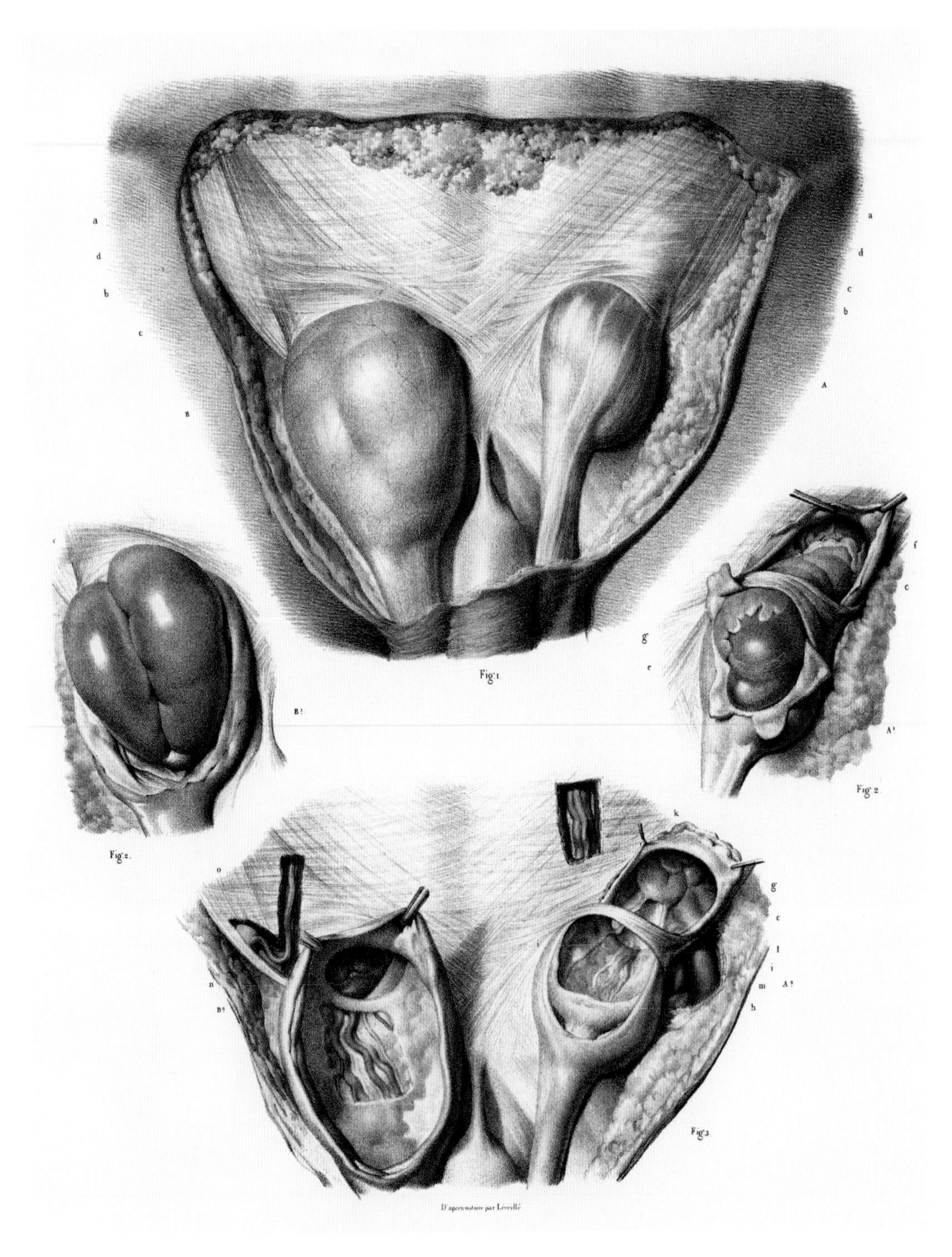

Pathological anatomy of abdominal hernias
Anatomie pathologique des hernies abdominales
Anatomía patológica de las hernias abdominales

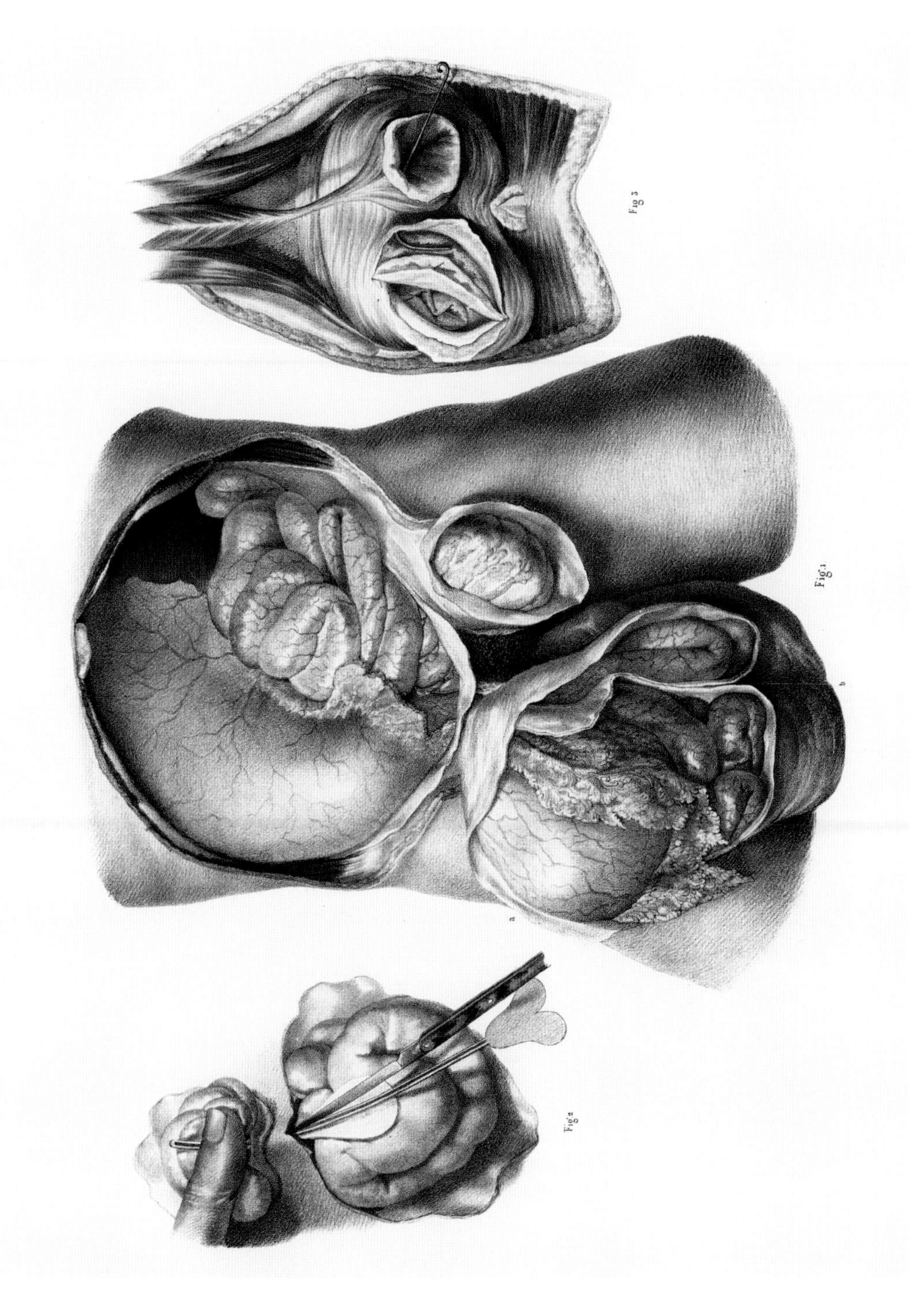

Pathological anatomy of abdominal hernias
Anatomie pathologique des hernies abdominales
Anatomía patológica de las hernias abdominales

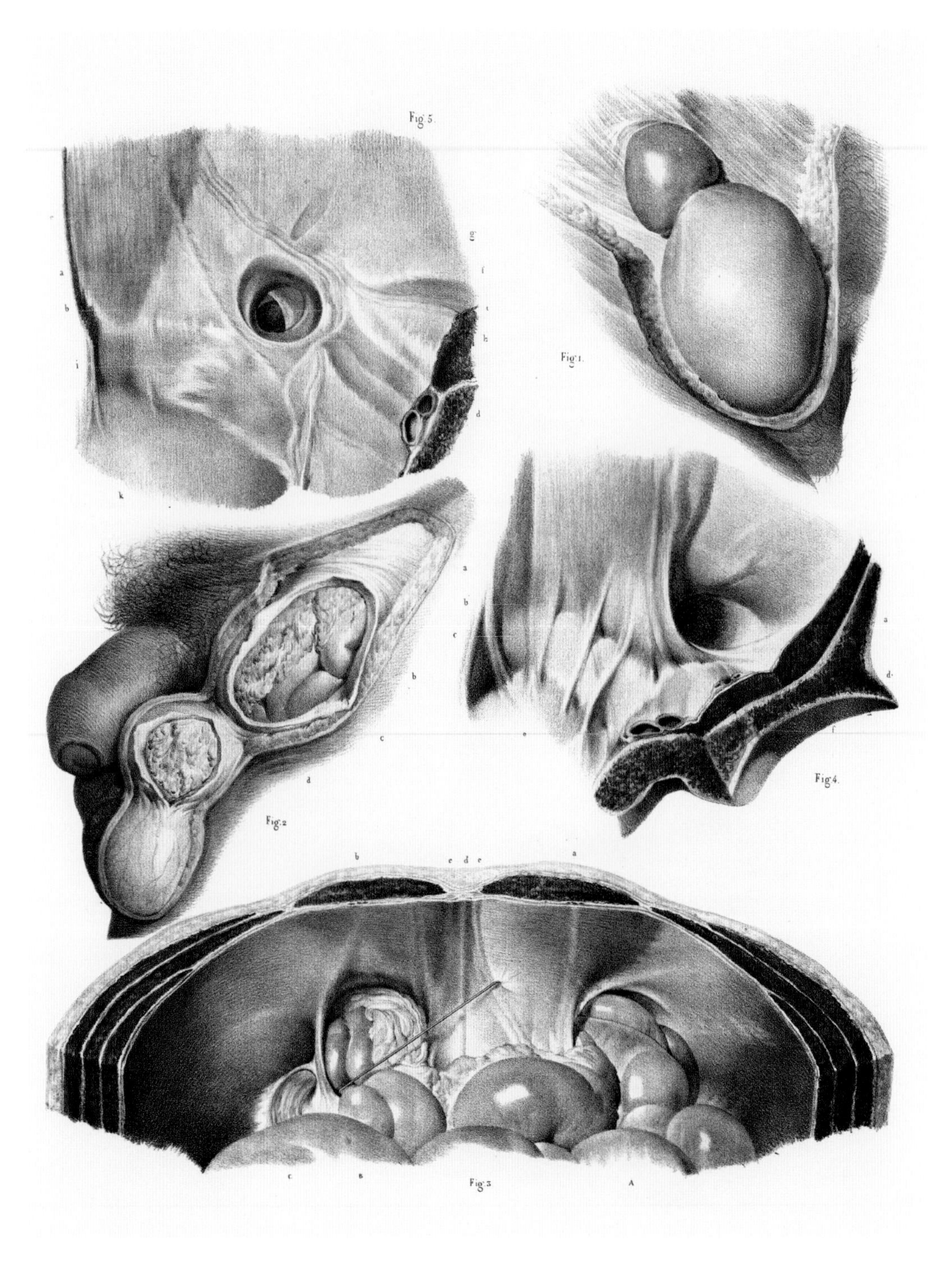

Pathological anatomy of abdominal hernias
Anatomie pathologique des hernies abdominales
Anatomía patológica de las hernias abdominales

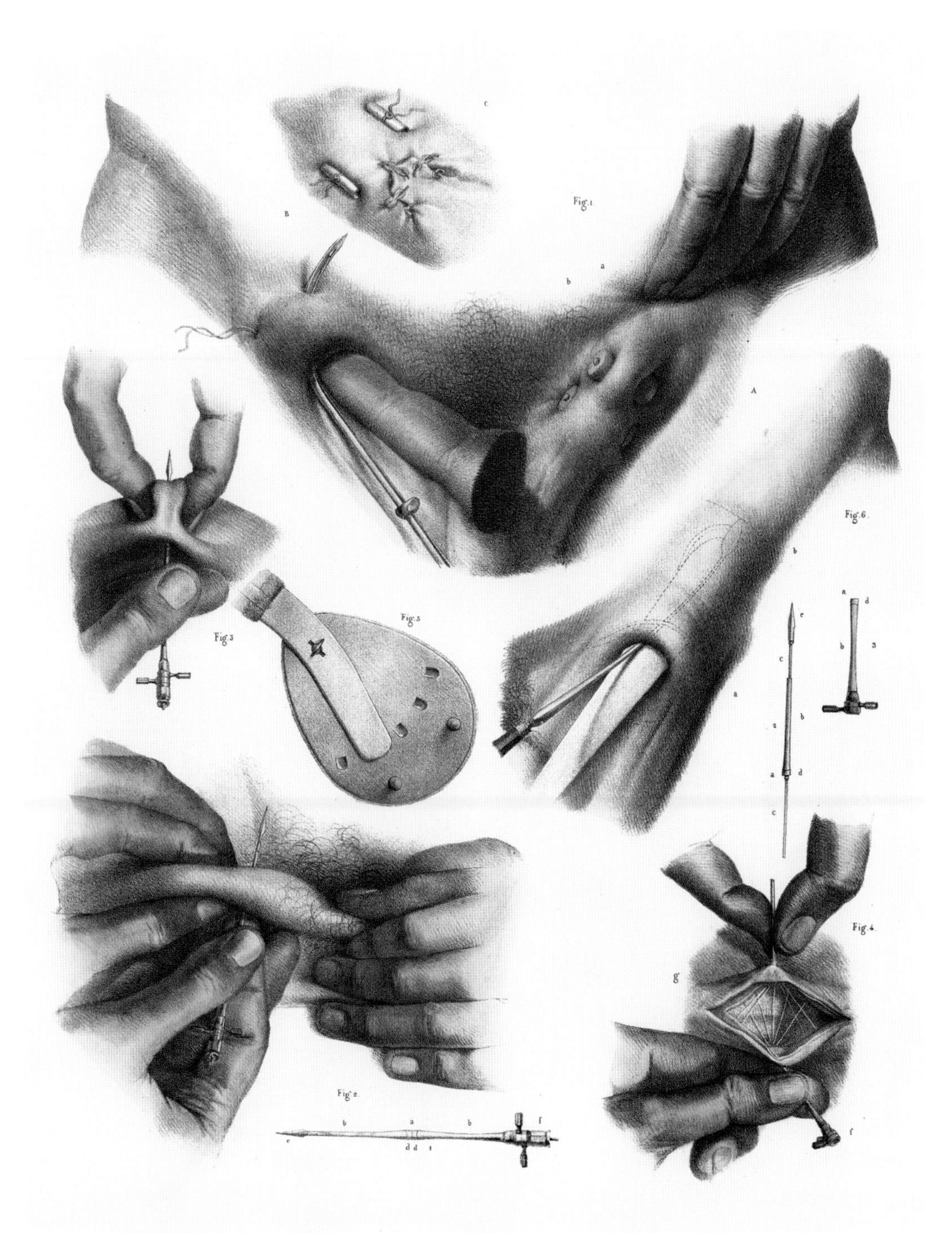

Surgery of abdominal hernias / Chirurgie des hernies abdominales
Cirugía de las hernias abdominales

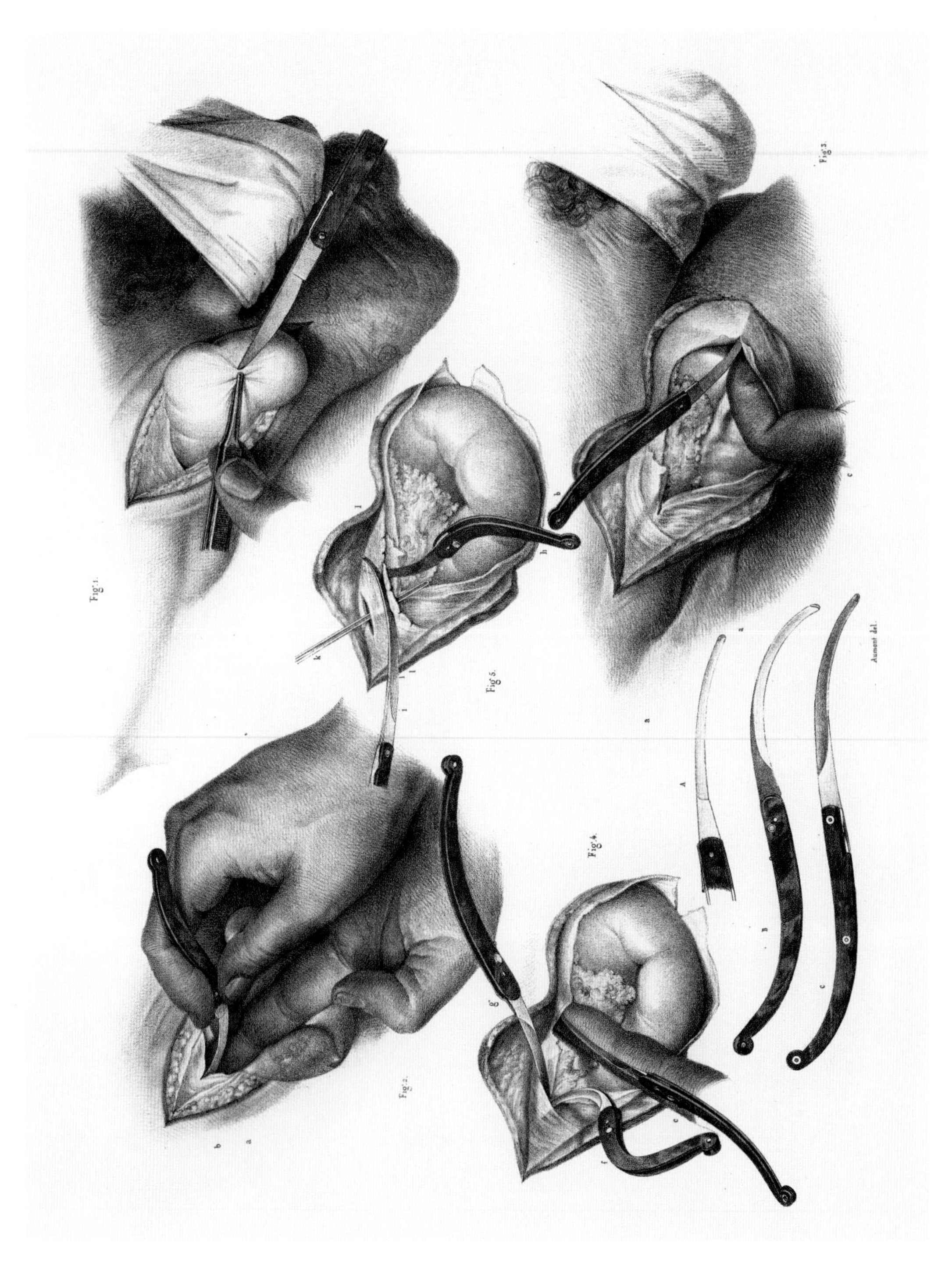

Surgery of abdominal hernias / Chirurgie des hernies abdominales
Cirugía de las hernias abdominales

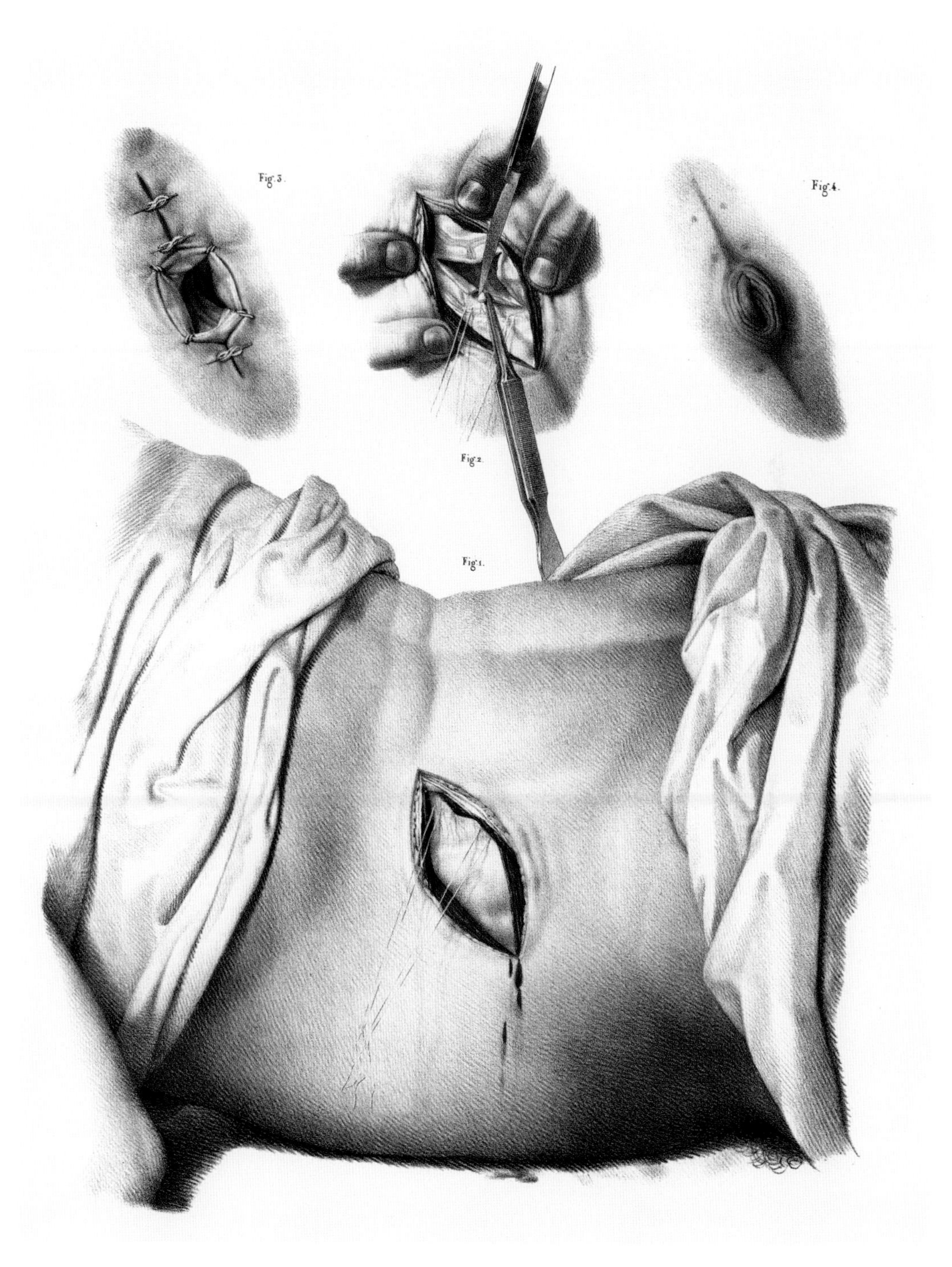

Surgery of the colon / Chirurgie du côlon / Cirugía del colon

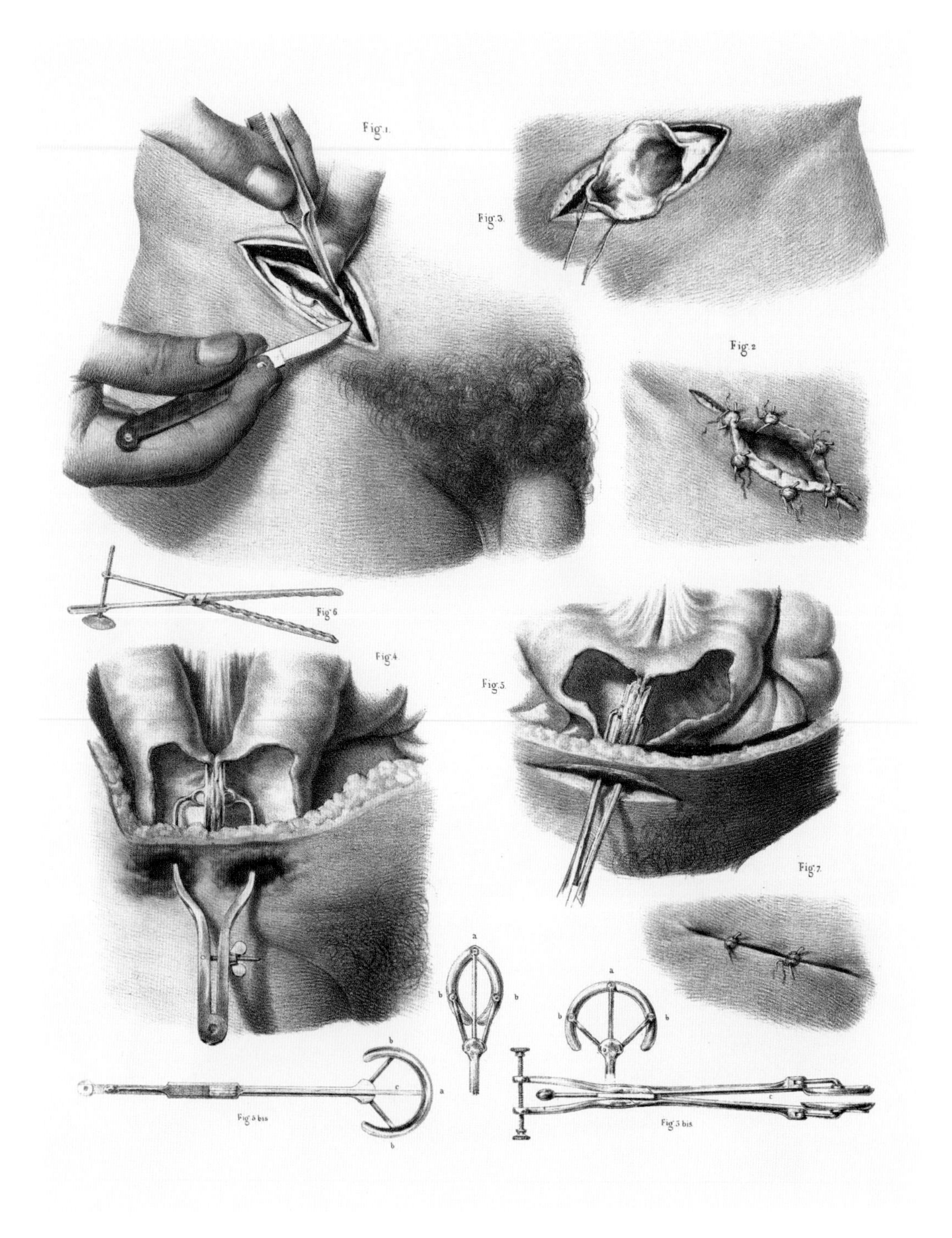

Surgery of the colon / Chirurgie du côlon / Cirugía del colon

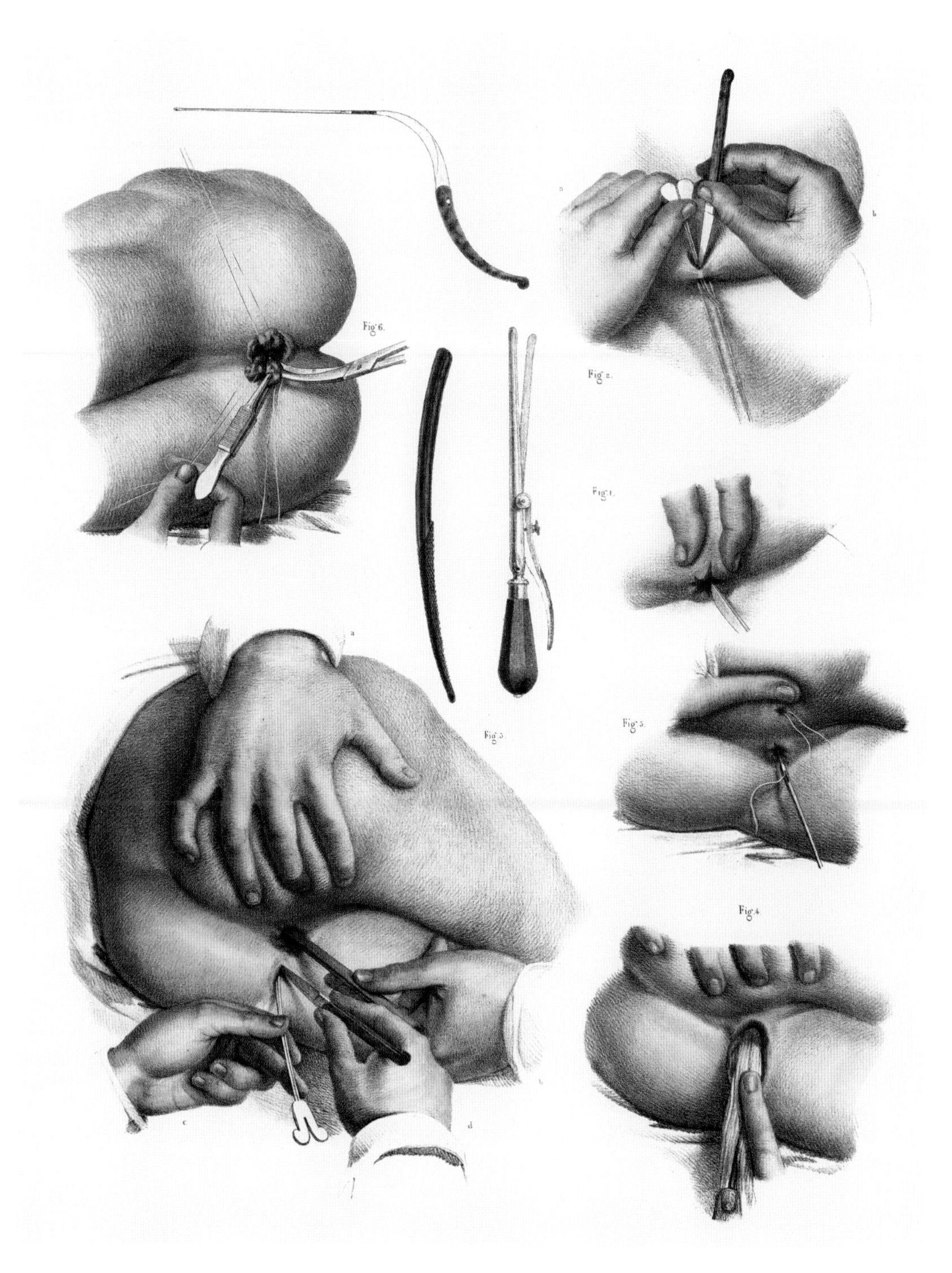

Surgery of the anus / Chirurgie de l'anus / Cirugía del ano

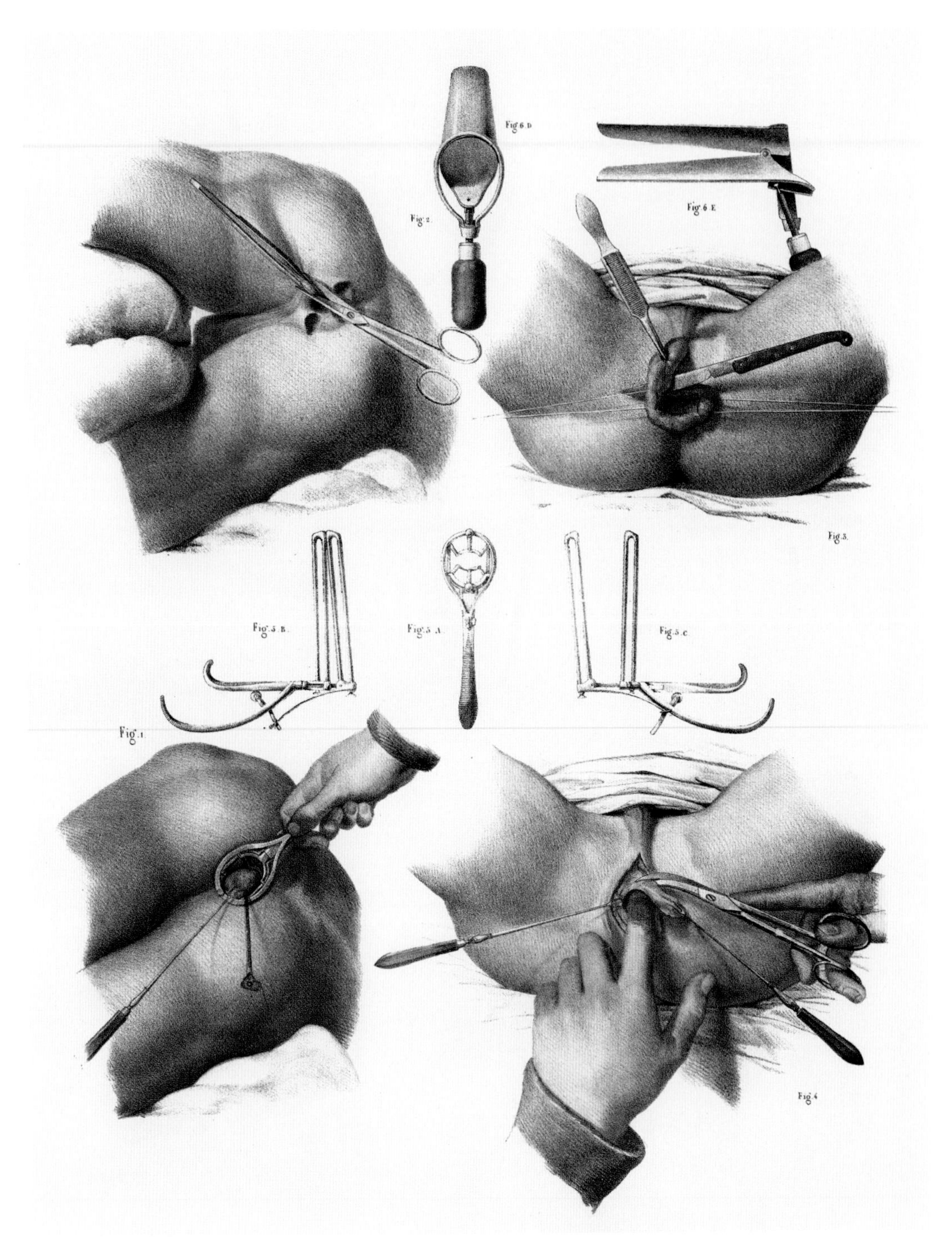

Surgery of the rectum and anus / Chirurgie du rectum et de l'anus
Cirugía del recto y del ano

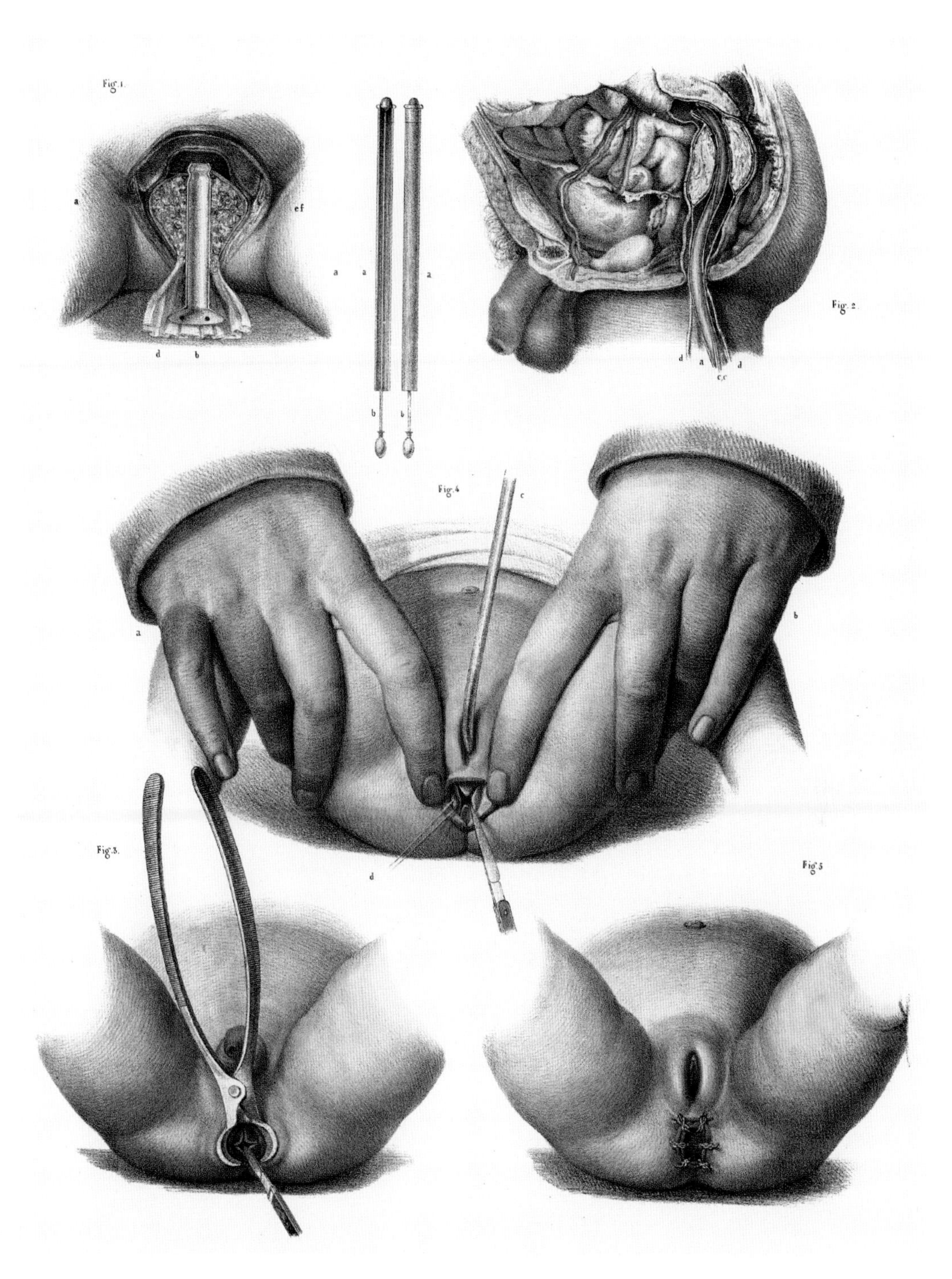

Surgery of the rectum and anus / Chirurgie du rectum et de l'anus
Cirugía del recto y del ano

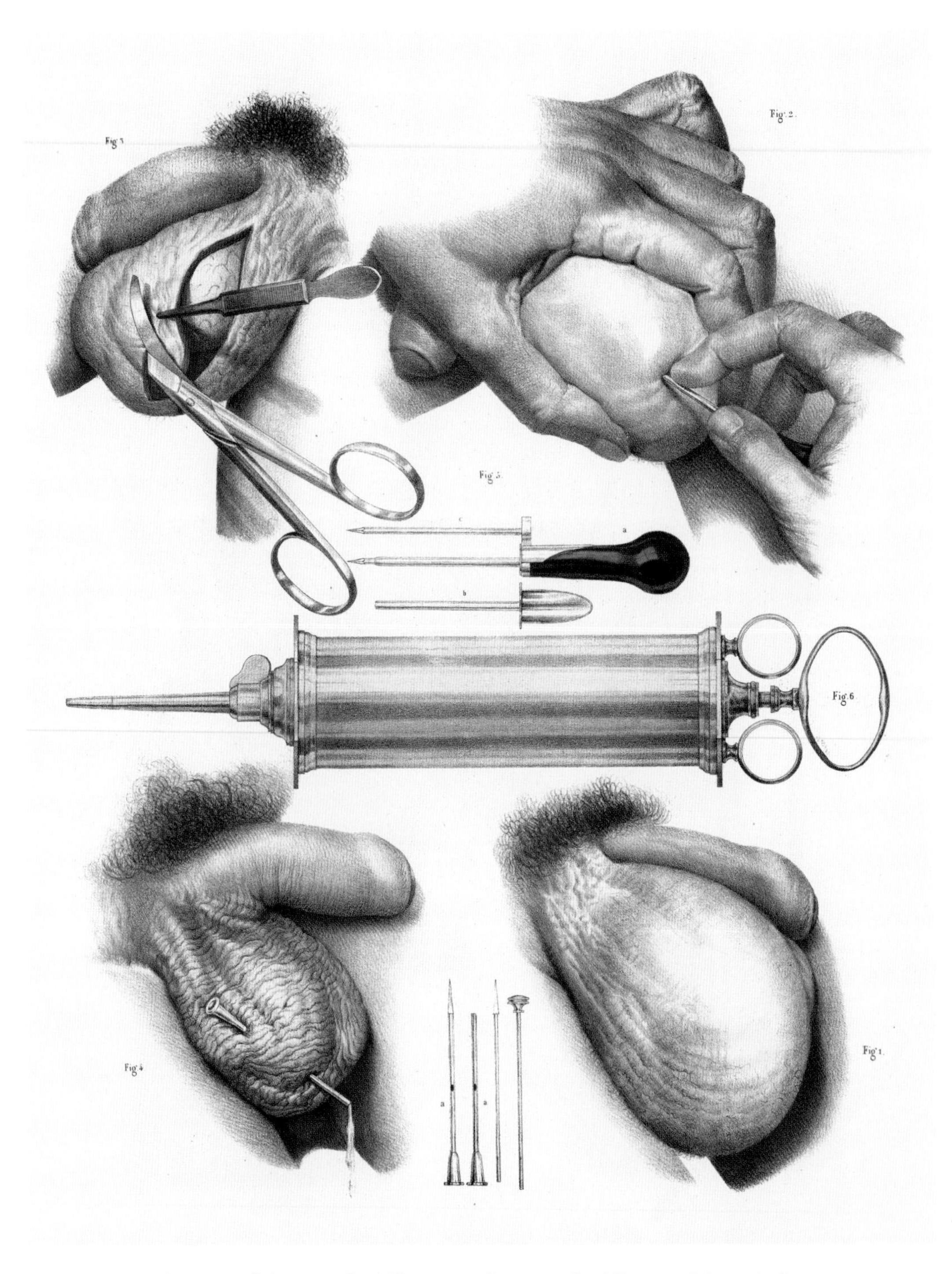

Surgery of the testicle / Chirurgie du testicule / Cirugía del testículo

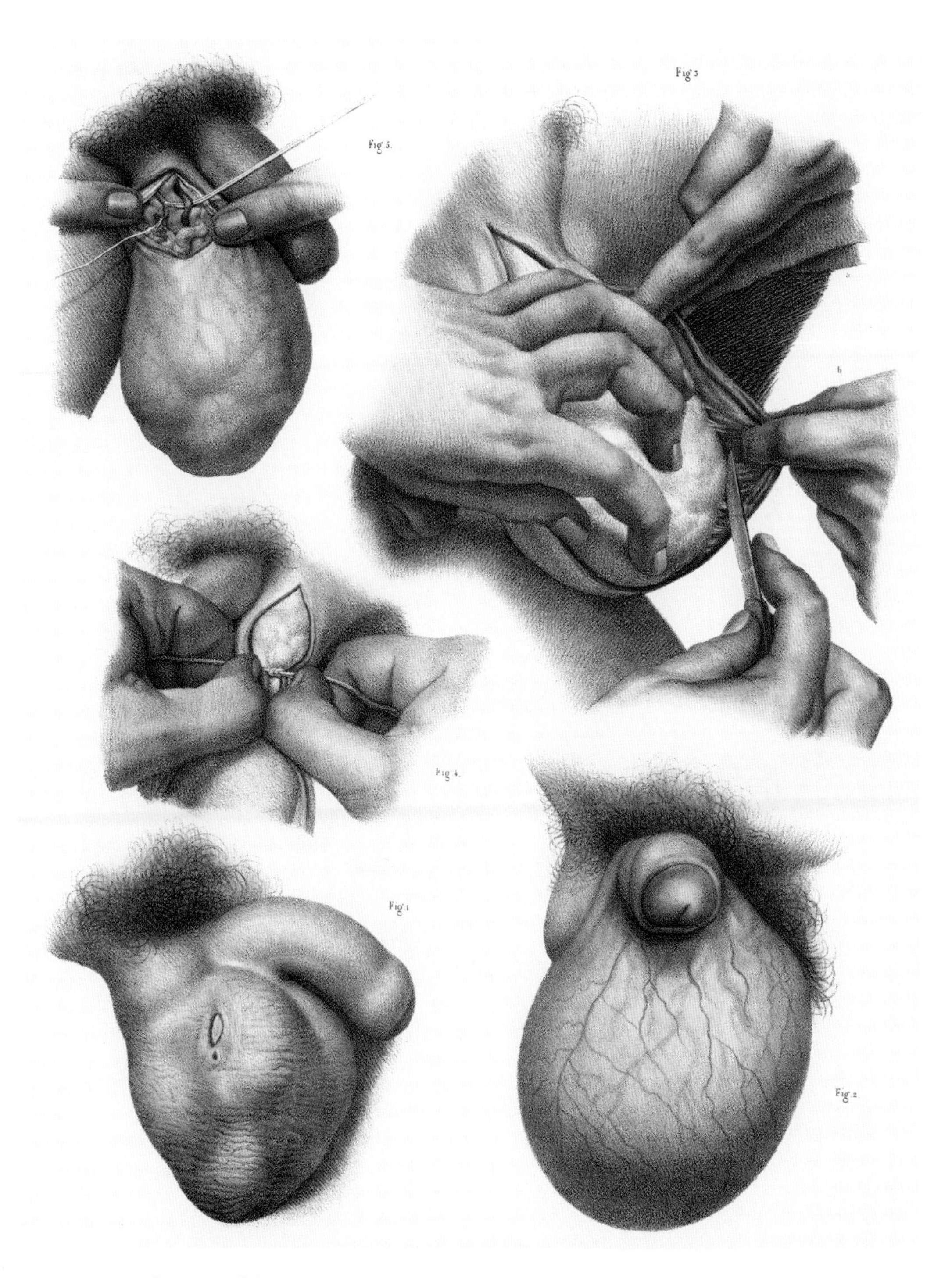

Surgery of the testicle / Chirurgie du testicule / Cirugía del testículo

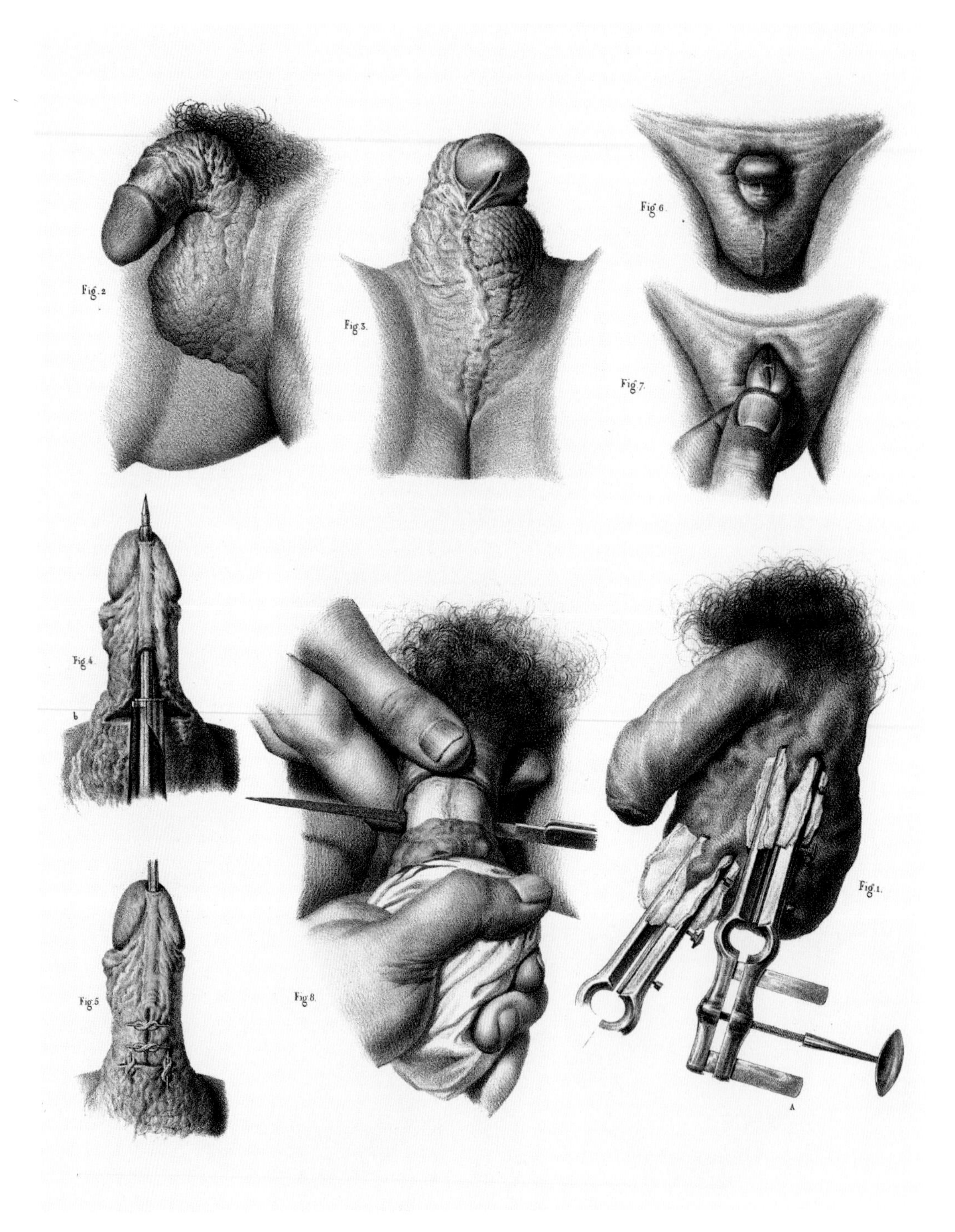

Surgery of the testicle. Surgery of the penis
Chirurgie du testicule. Chirurgie du pénis
Cirugía del testículo. Cirugía del pene

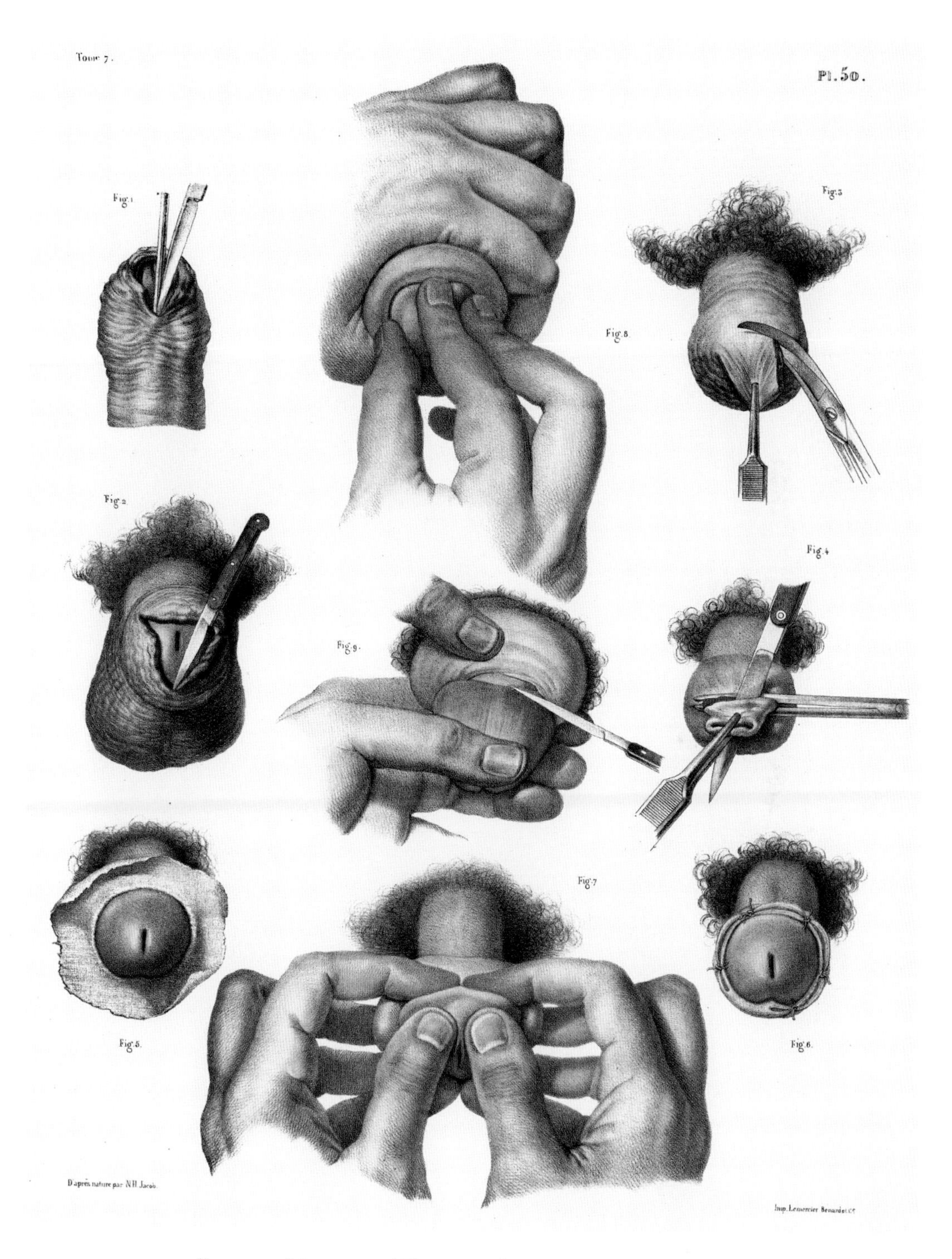

Surgery of the penis / Chirurgie du pénis / Cirugía del pene

ANATOMIA CHIRURGICA ORGANORUM URO-GENITALIORUM MASCULINORUM

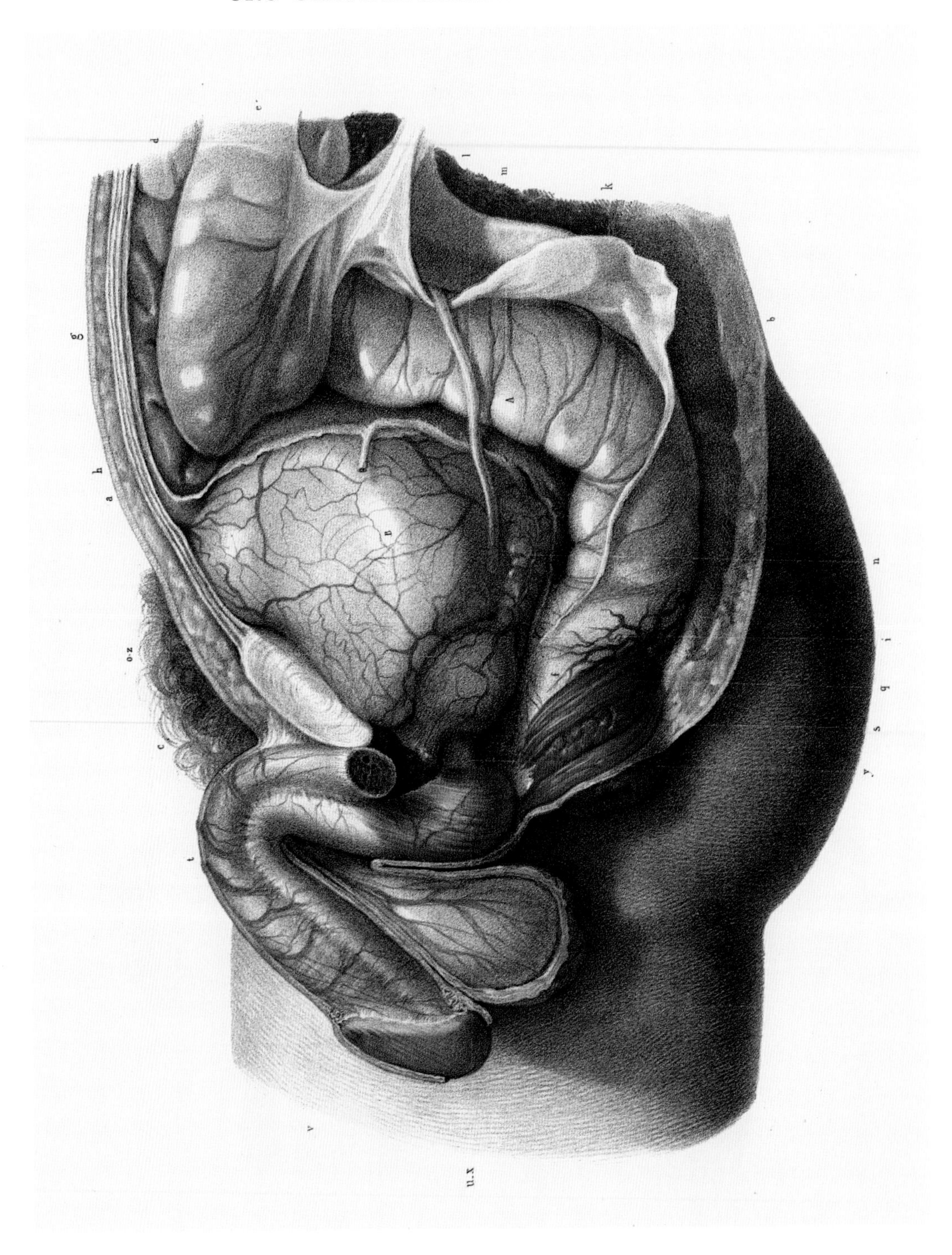

Surgical anatomy of the male genitourinary organs
Anatomie chirurgicale des organes génito-urinaires masculins
Anatomía quirúrgica de los órganos genitourinarios masculinos

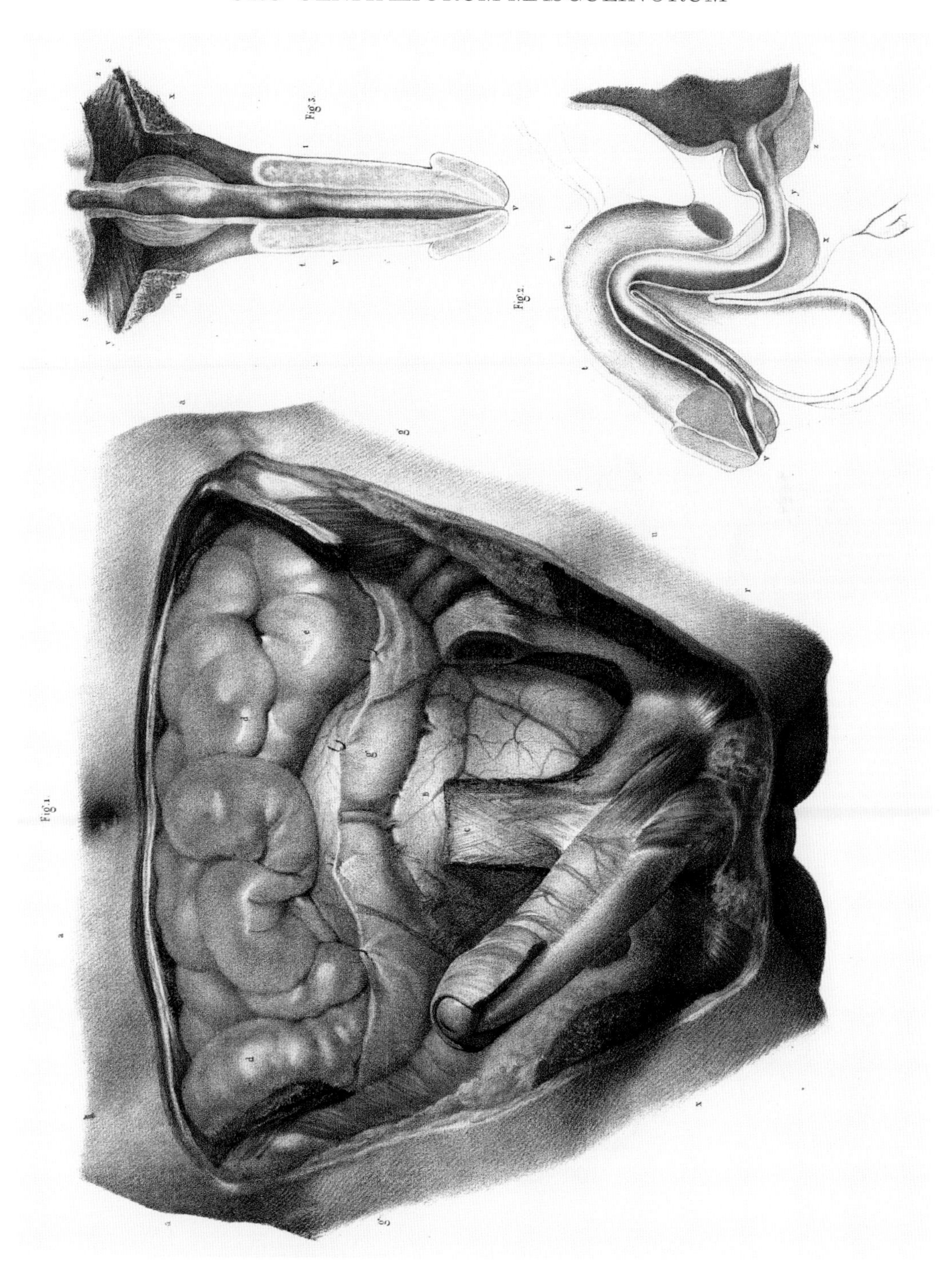

Surgical anatomy of the male genitourinary organs
Anatomie chirurgicale des organes génito-urinaires masculins
Anatomía quirúrgica de los órganos genitourinarios masculinos

ANATOMIA PATHOLOGICA ORGANORUM URO-GENITALIORUM MASCULINORUM

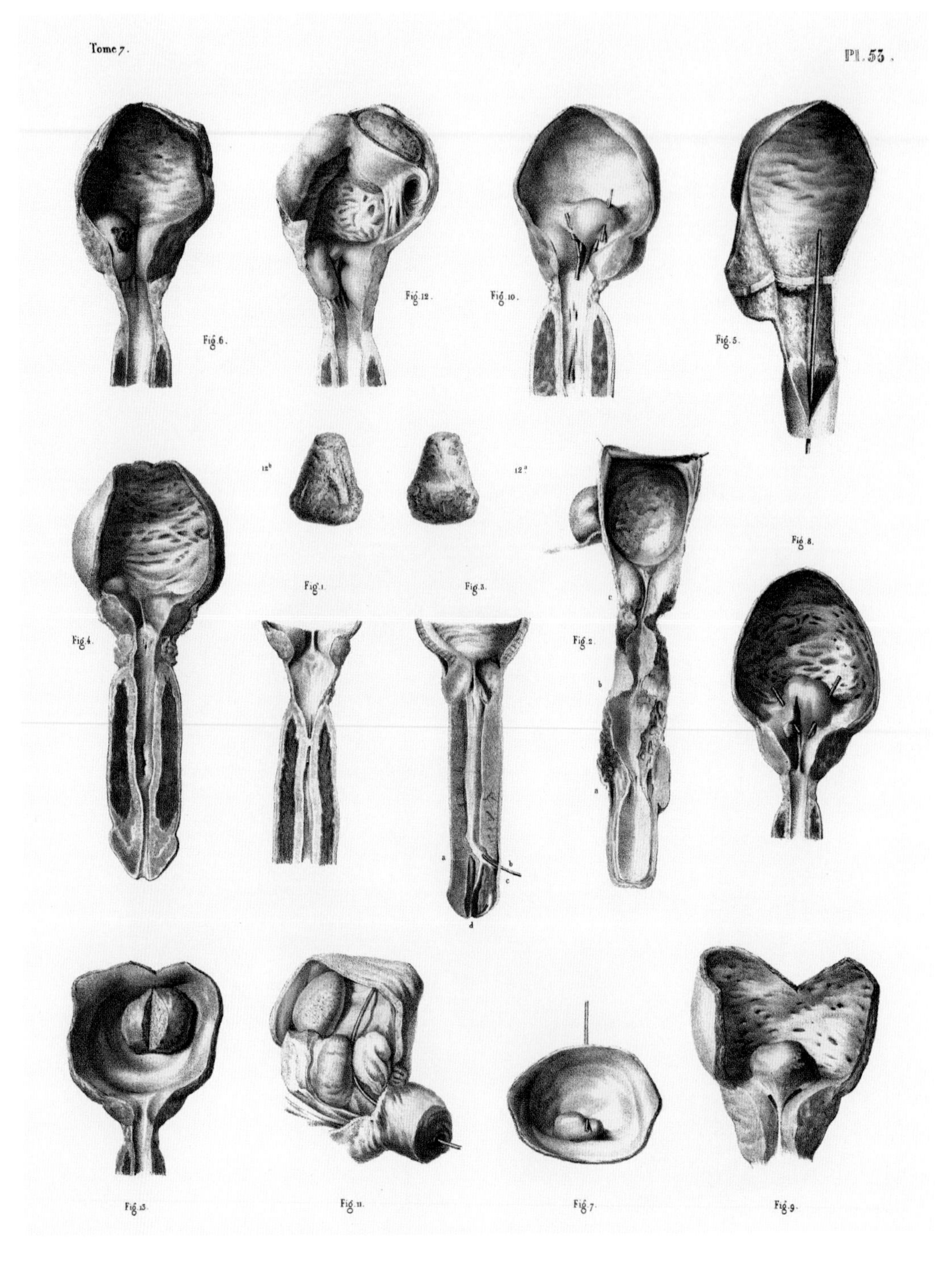

Pathological anatomy of the male genitourinary organs
Anatomie pathologique des organes génito-urinaires masculins
Anatomía patológica de los órganos genitourinarios masculinos

CHIRURGIA ORGANORUM URO-GENITALIORUM MASCULINORUM: INSTRUMENTA CHIRURGICA

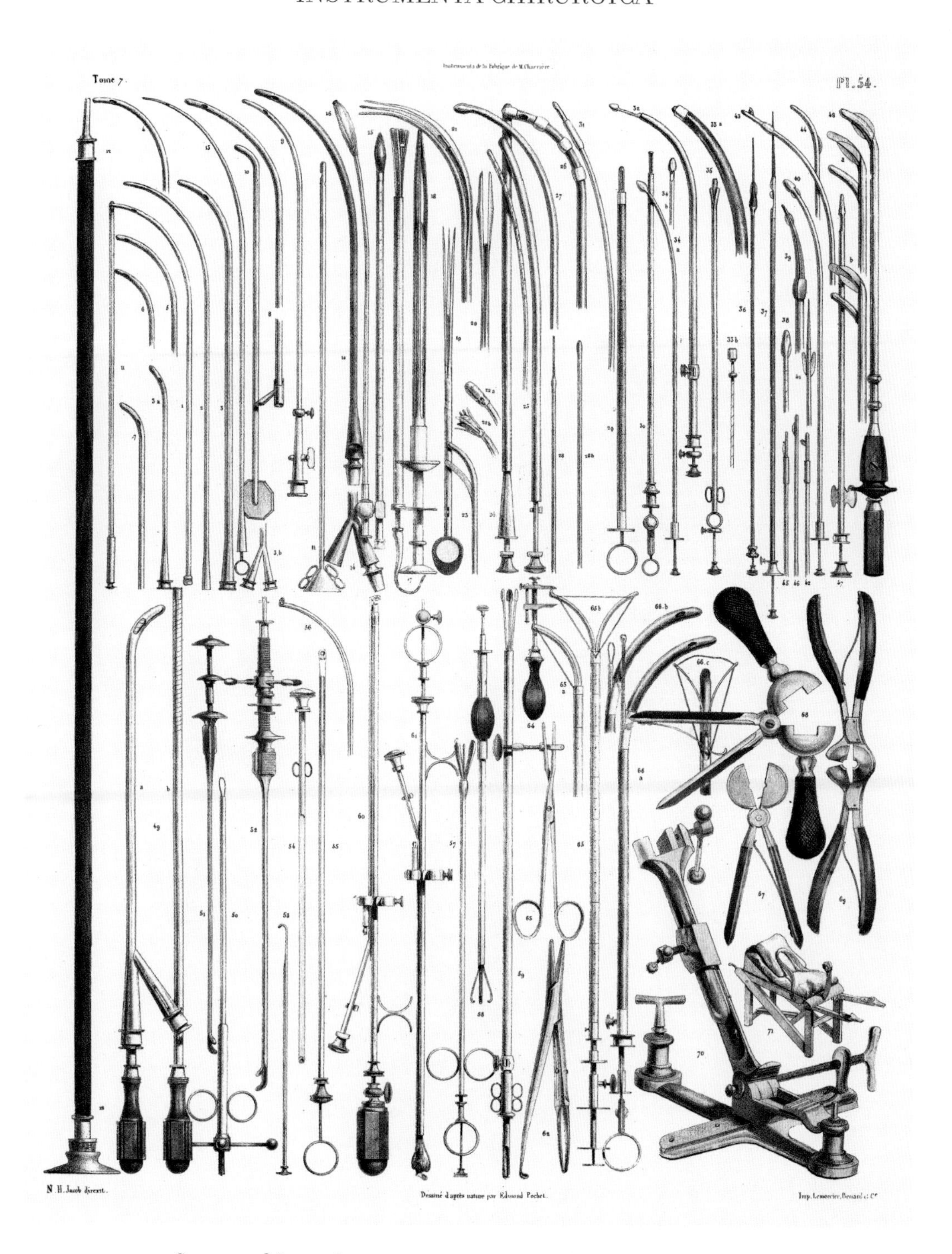

Surgery of the male genitourinary organs: Surgical instruments
Chirurgie des organes génito-urinaires masculins : Instruments chirurgicaux
Cirugía de los órganos genitourinarios masculinos: instrumentos quirúrgicos

ANATOMIA PATHOLOGICA
CALCULI VESICAE URINARIAE ET PROSTATAE

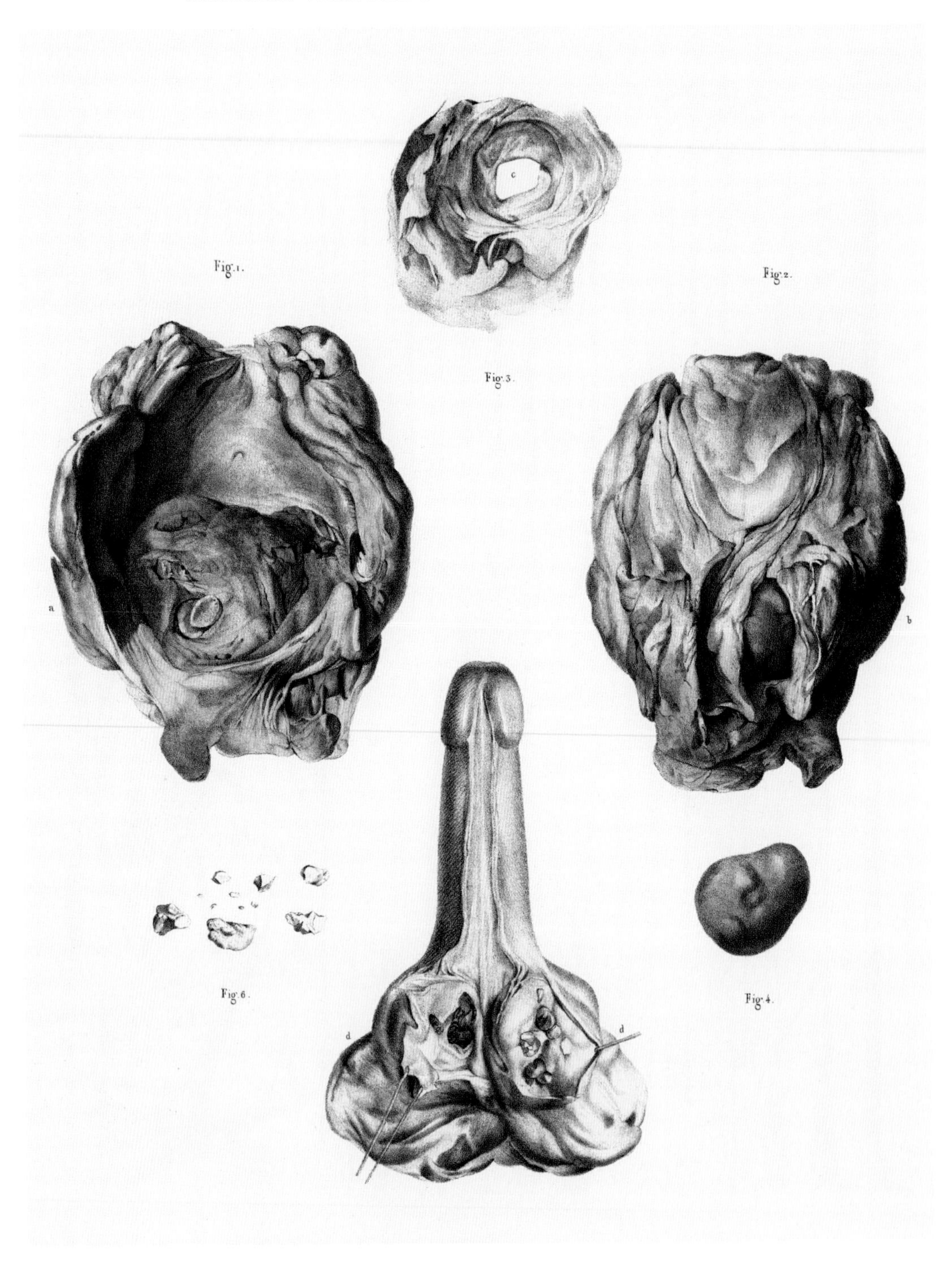

Pathological anatomy of bladder and prostate stones
Anatomie pathologique des calculs de la vessie et de la prostate
Anatomía patológica de los cálculos de la vejiga y de la próstata

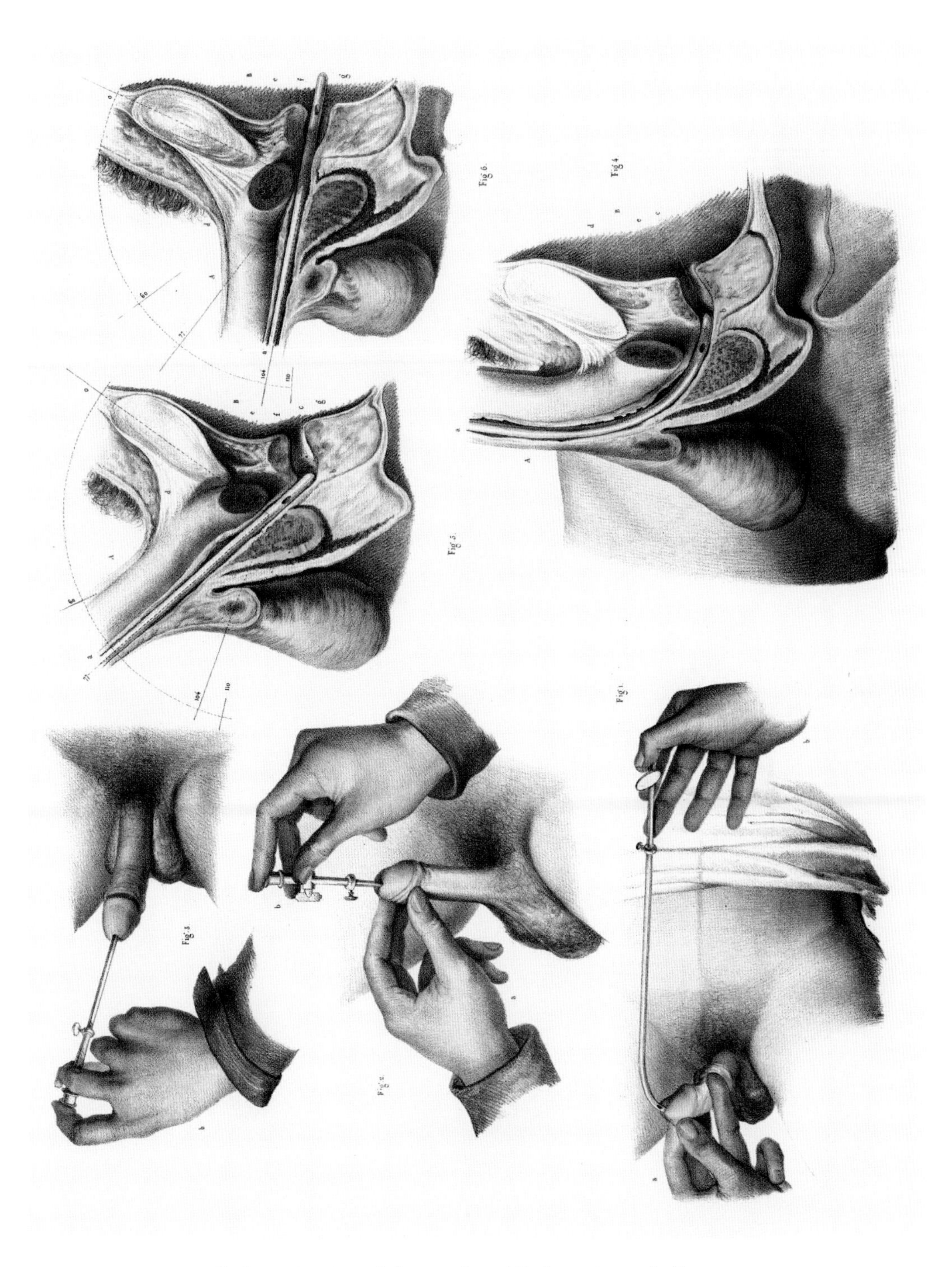

Catheterisation of the urethra / Cathétérisme de l'urètre
Cateterismo de la uretra

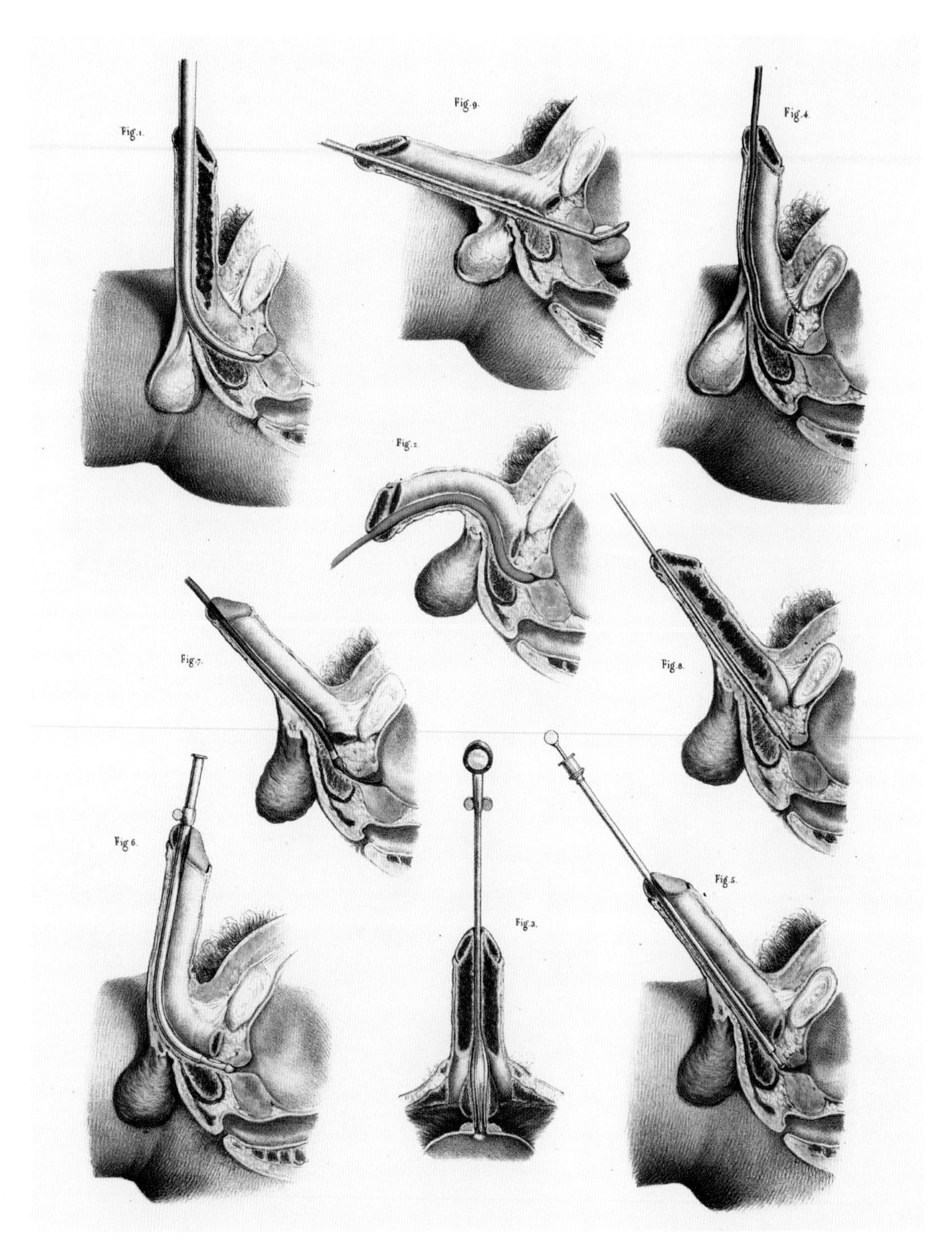

Surgery of the urethra / Chirurgie de l'urètre / Cirugía de la uretra

CHIRURGIA PROSTATAE.
PONCTIONES VESICAE URINARIAE

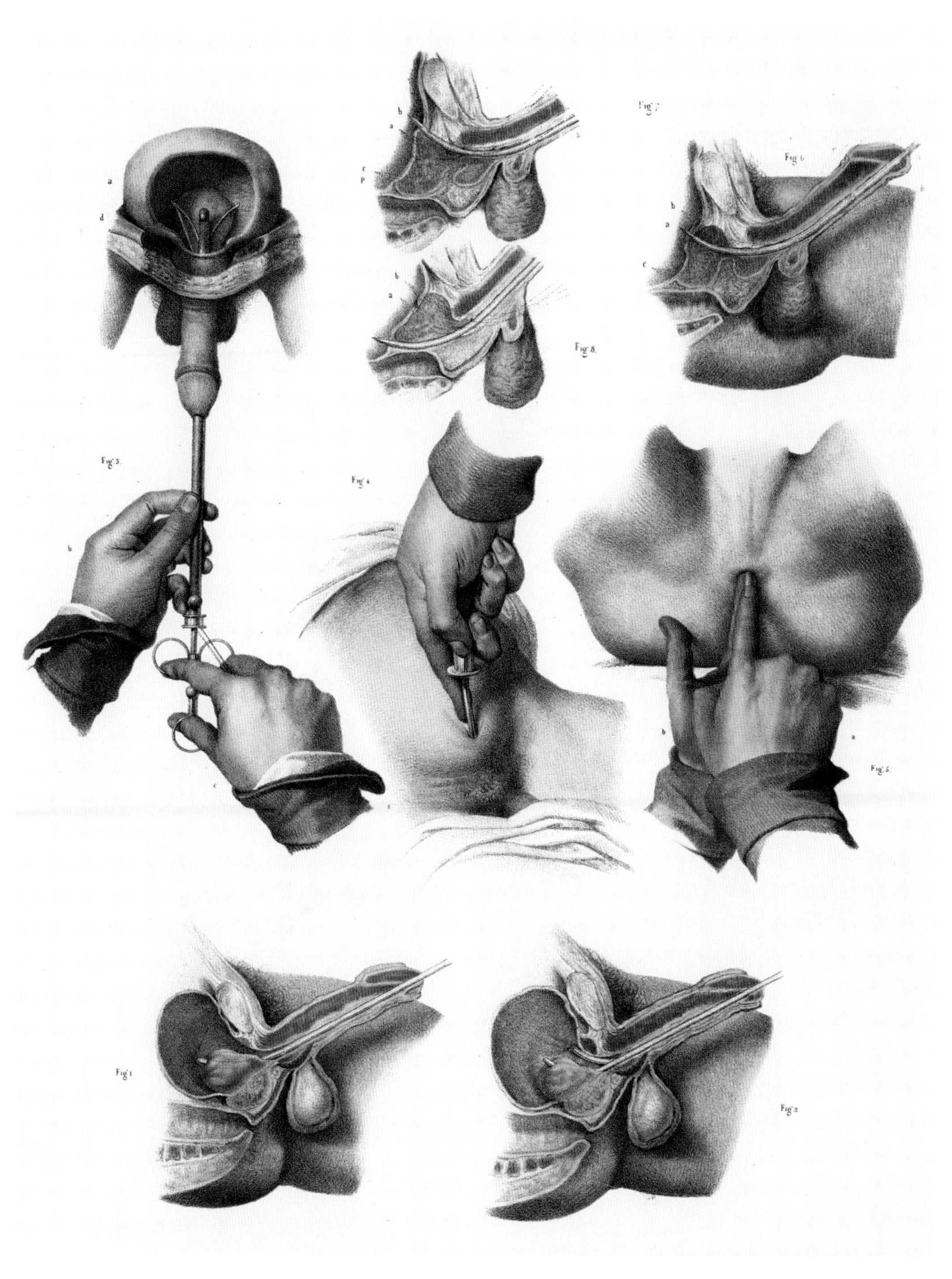

Surgery of the prostate. Bladder punctures
Chirurgie de la prostate. Ponctions de la vessie
Cirugía de la próstata. Punciones de la vejiga

CHIRURGIA CALCULORUM URETHRAE

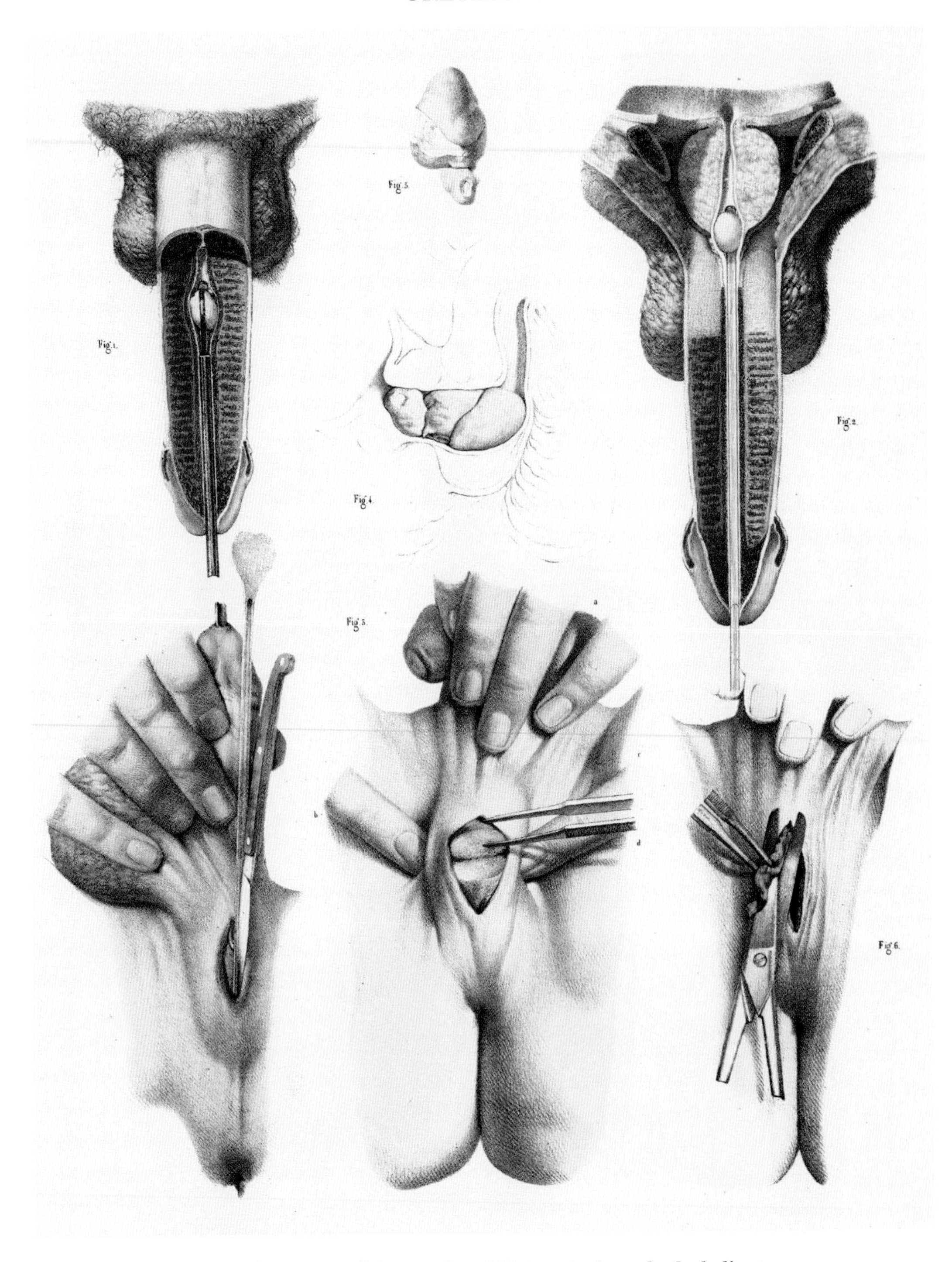

Surgery for stones of the urethra / Chirurgie des calculs de l'urètre
Cirugía de los cálculos uretrales

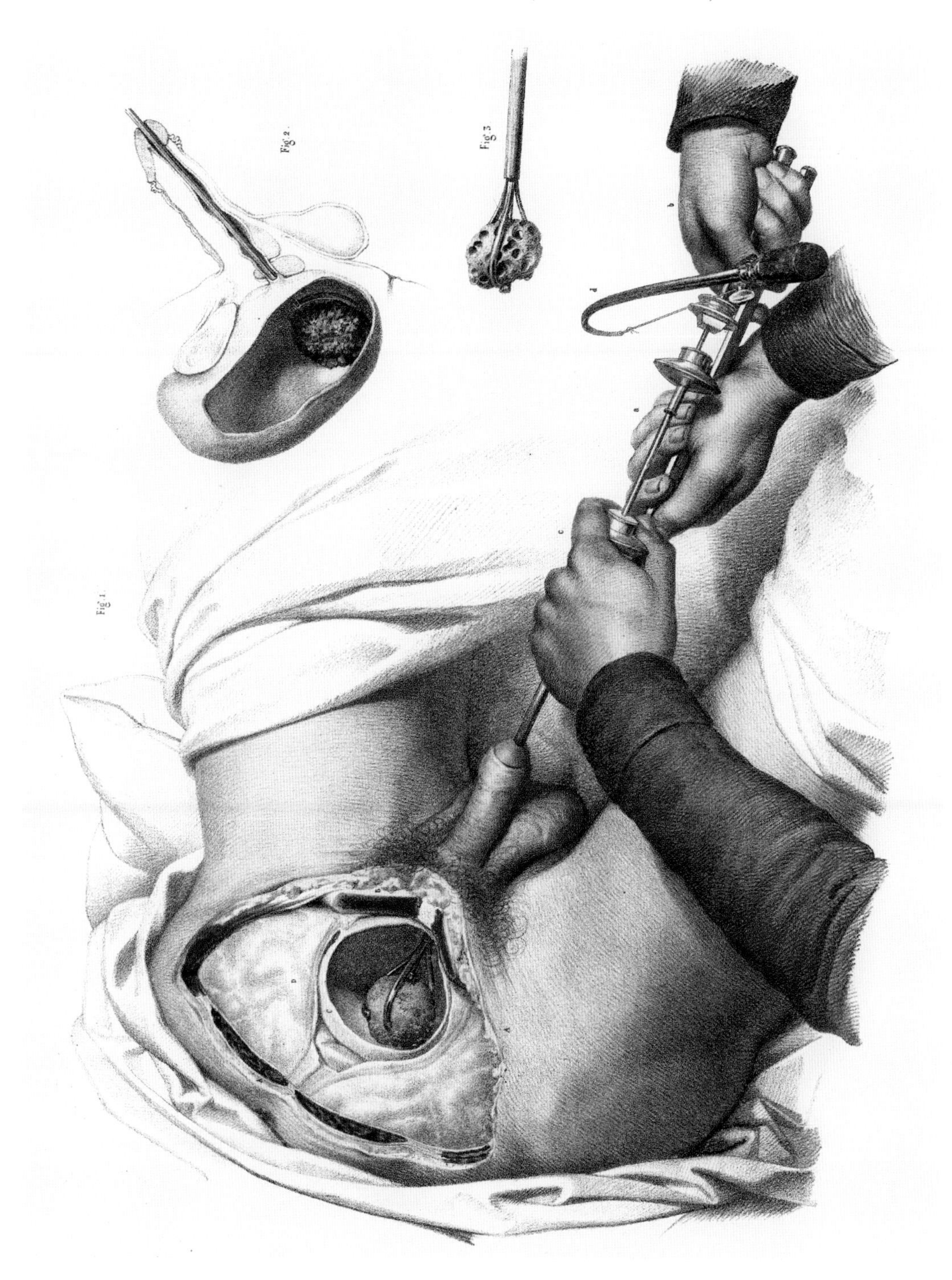

Surgery for bladder stones (lithotripsy)
Chirurgie des calculs de la vessie (lithotritie)
Cirugía de los cálculos de la vejiga (litotricia)

CHIRURGIA CALCULORUM VESICAE URINARIAE (LITHOTRITIA)

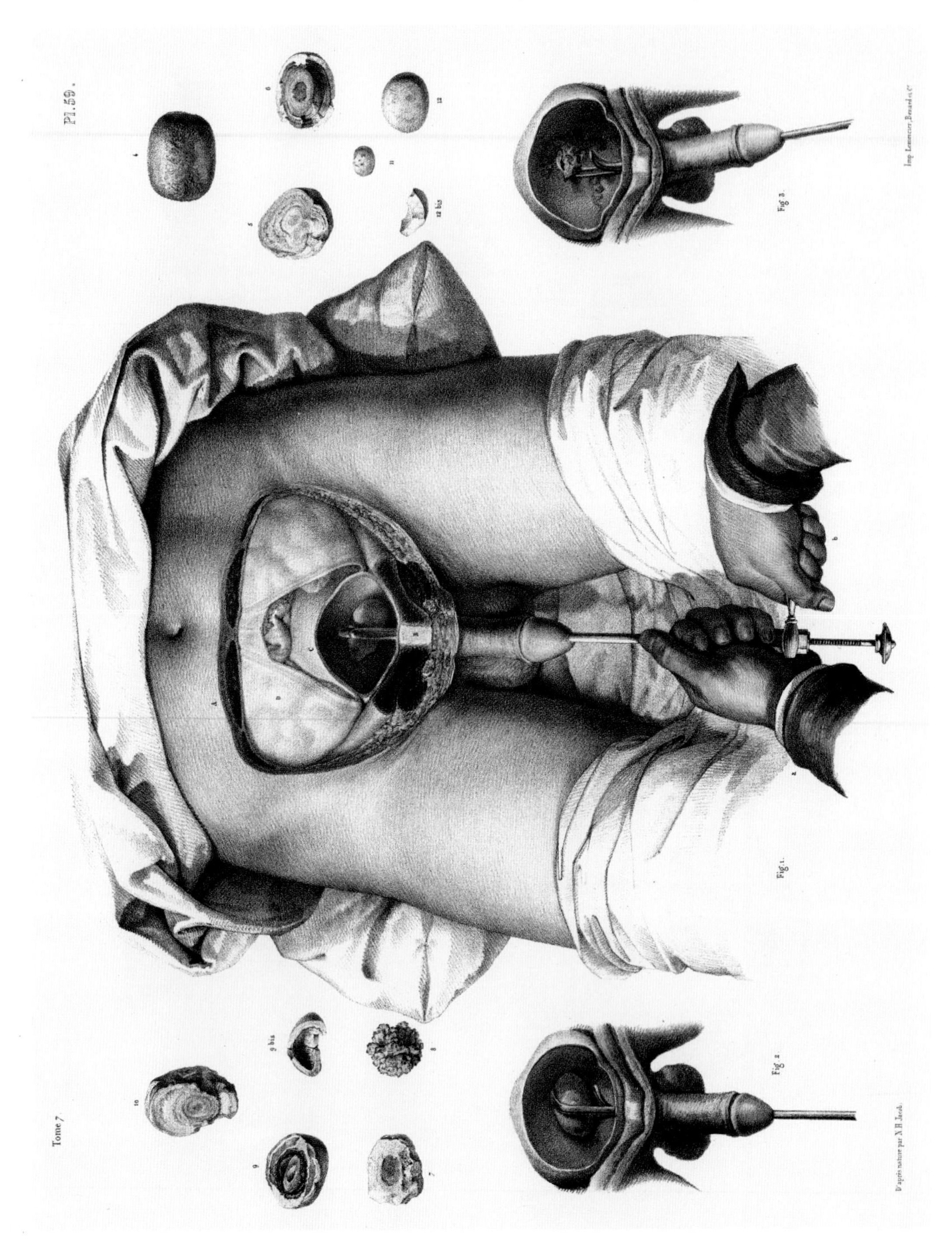

Surgery for bladder stones (lithotripsy)
Chirurgie des calculs de la vessie (lithotritie)
Cirugía de los cálculos vesicales (litotricia)

CHIRURGIA CALCULORUM VESICAE URINARIAE (LITHOTRITIA)

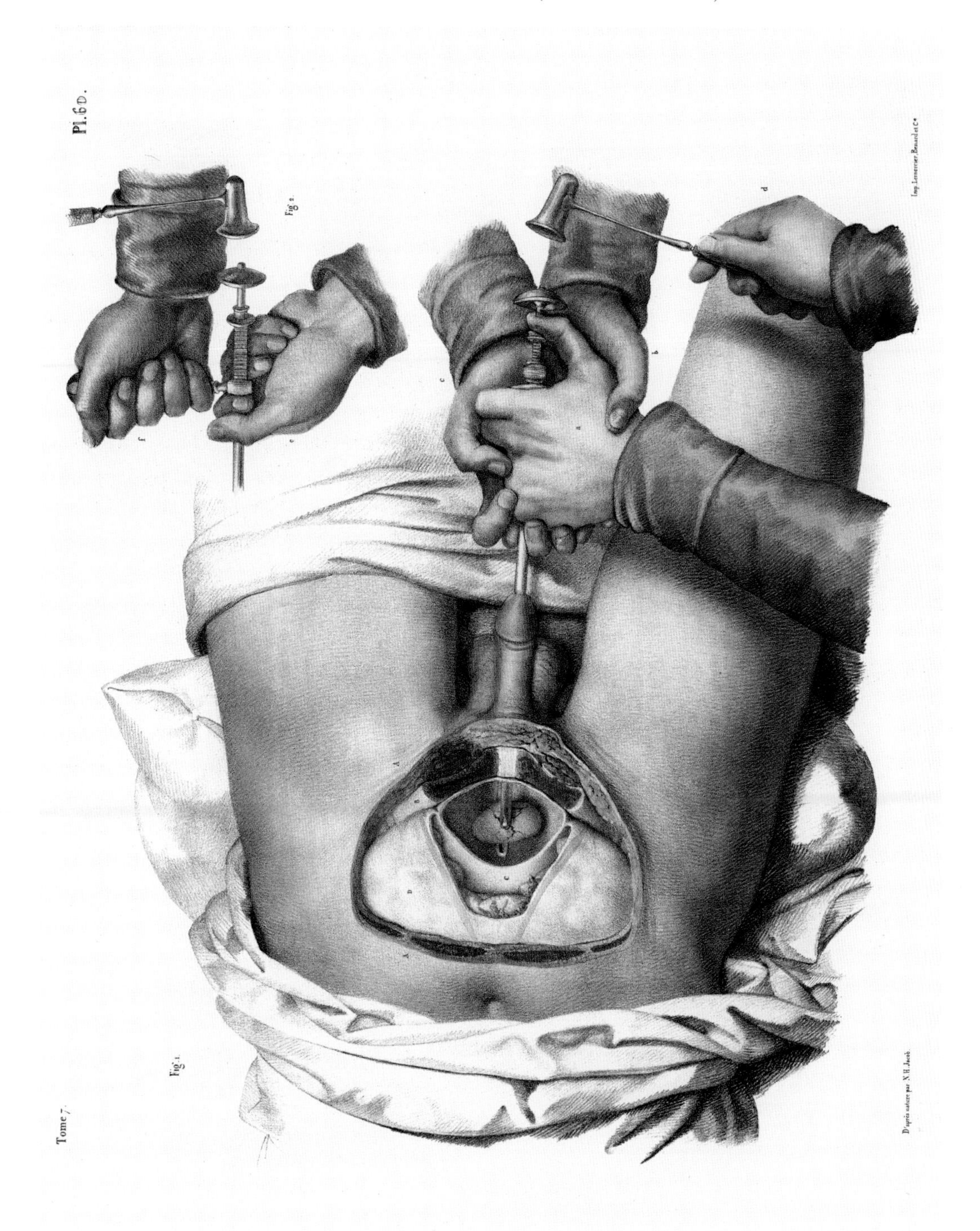

Surgery for bladder stones (lithotripsy)
Chirurgie des calculs de la vessie (lithotritie)
Cirugía de los cálculos vesicales (litotricia)

CHIRURGIA CALCULORUM VESICAE URINARIAE (LITHOTRITIA): INSTRUMENTA CHIRURGICA

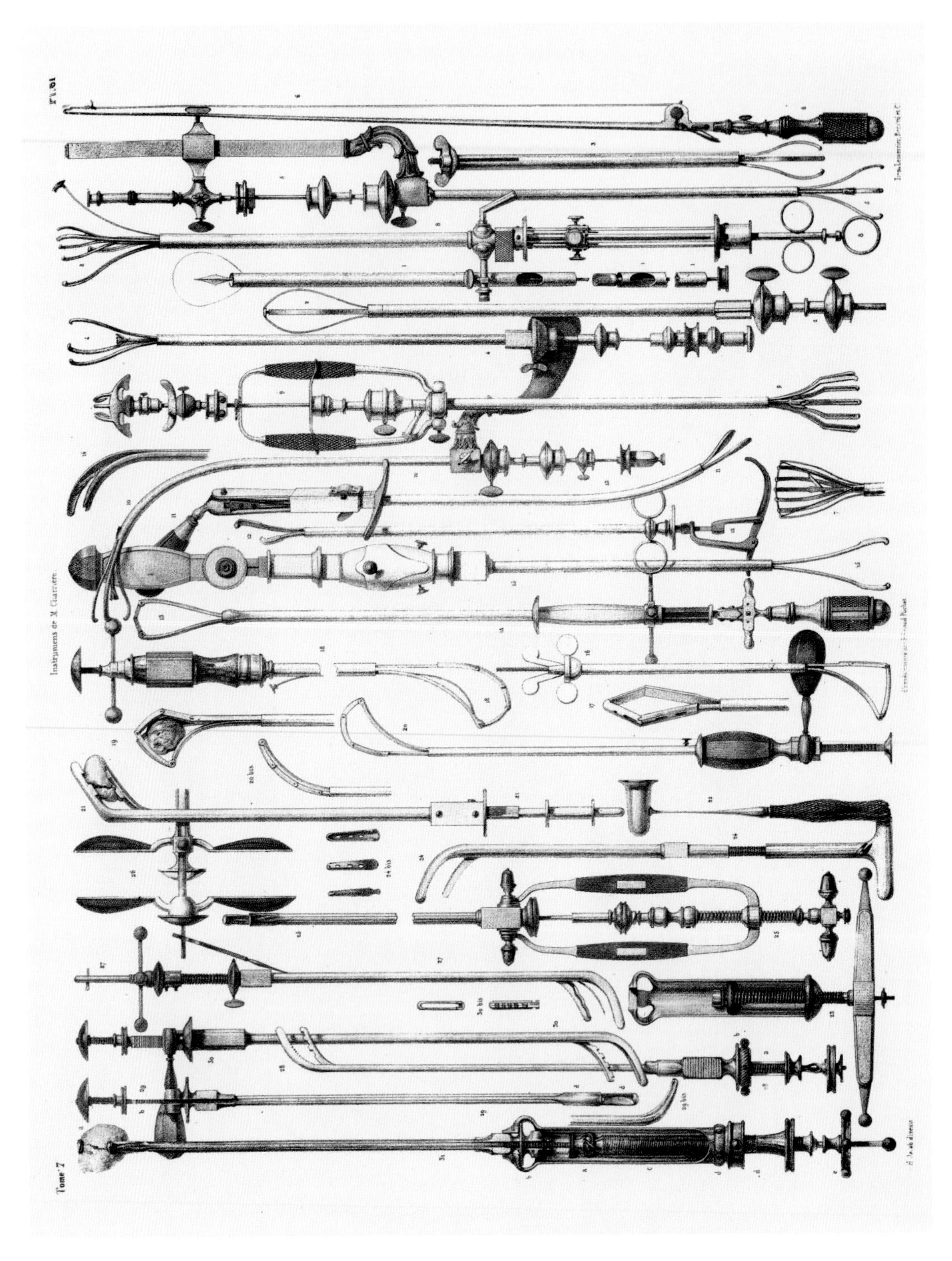

Surgery for bladder stones (lithotripsy): Surgical instruments
Chirurgie des calculs de la vessie (lithotritie) : Instruments chirurgicaux
Cirugía de los cálculos de la vejiga (litotricia): instrumentos quirúrgicos

CHIRURGIA CALCULORUM VESICAE URINARIAE (LITHOTOMIA)

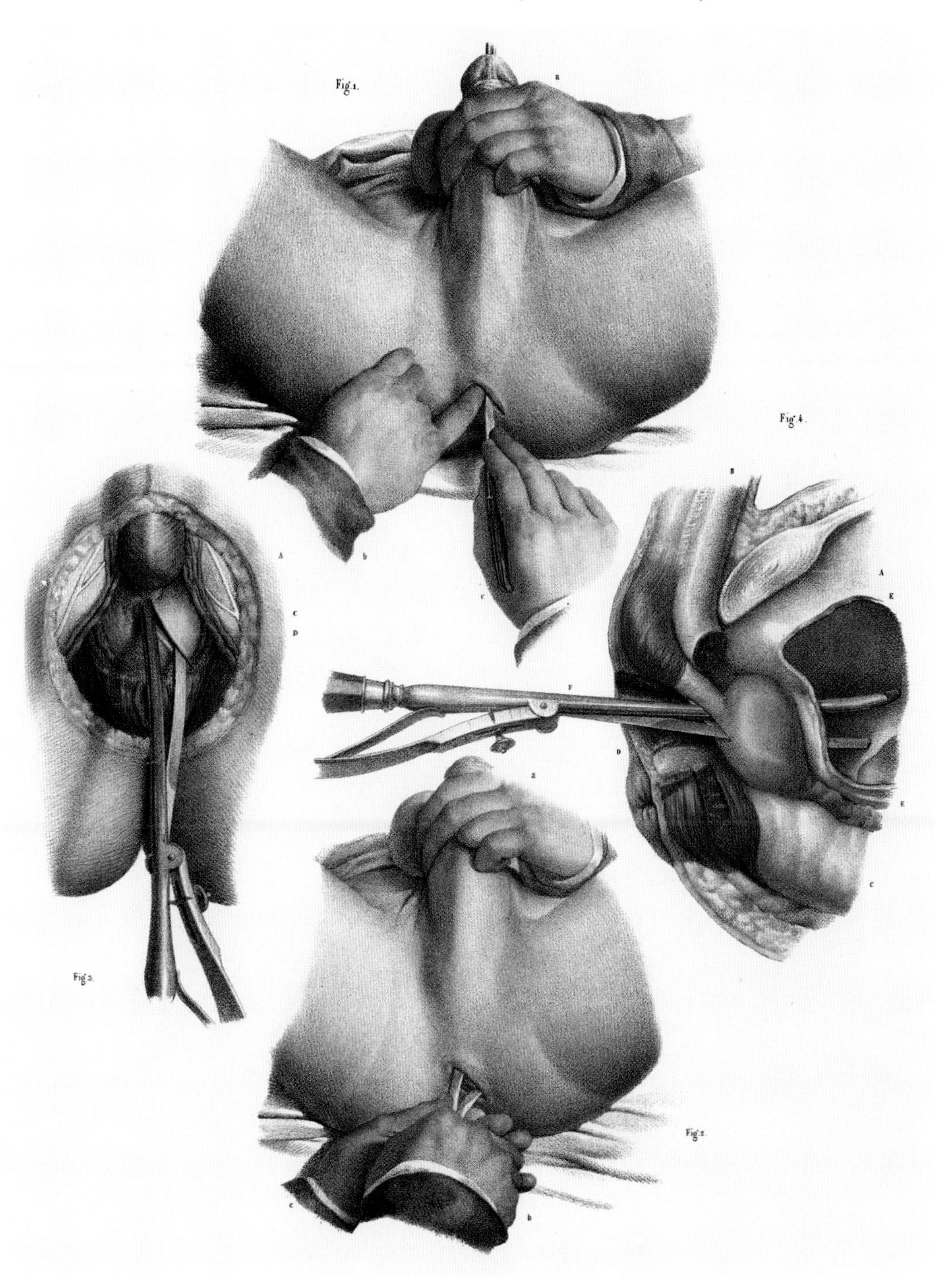

Surgery for bladder stones (lithotomy)
Chirurgie des calculs de la vessie (lithotomie)
Cirugía de los cálculos de la vejiga (litotomía)

CHIRURGIA CALCULORUM VESICAE URINARIAE (LITHOTOMIA)

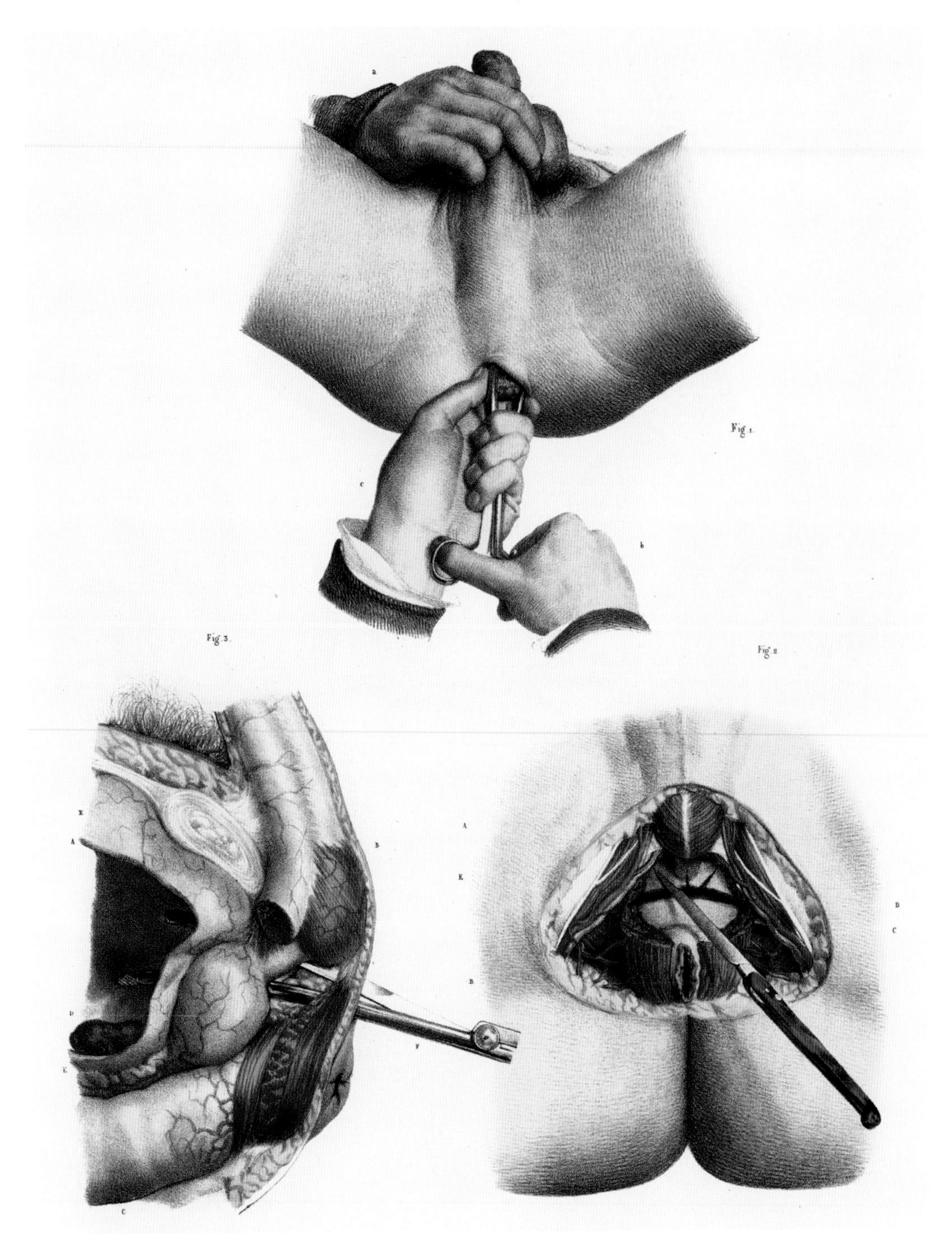

Surgery for bladder stones (lithotomy)
Chirurgie des calculs de la vessie (lithotomie)
Cirugía de los cálculos de la vejiga (litotomía)

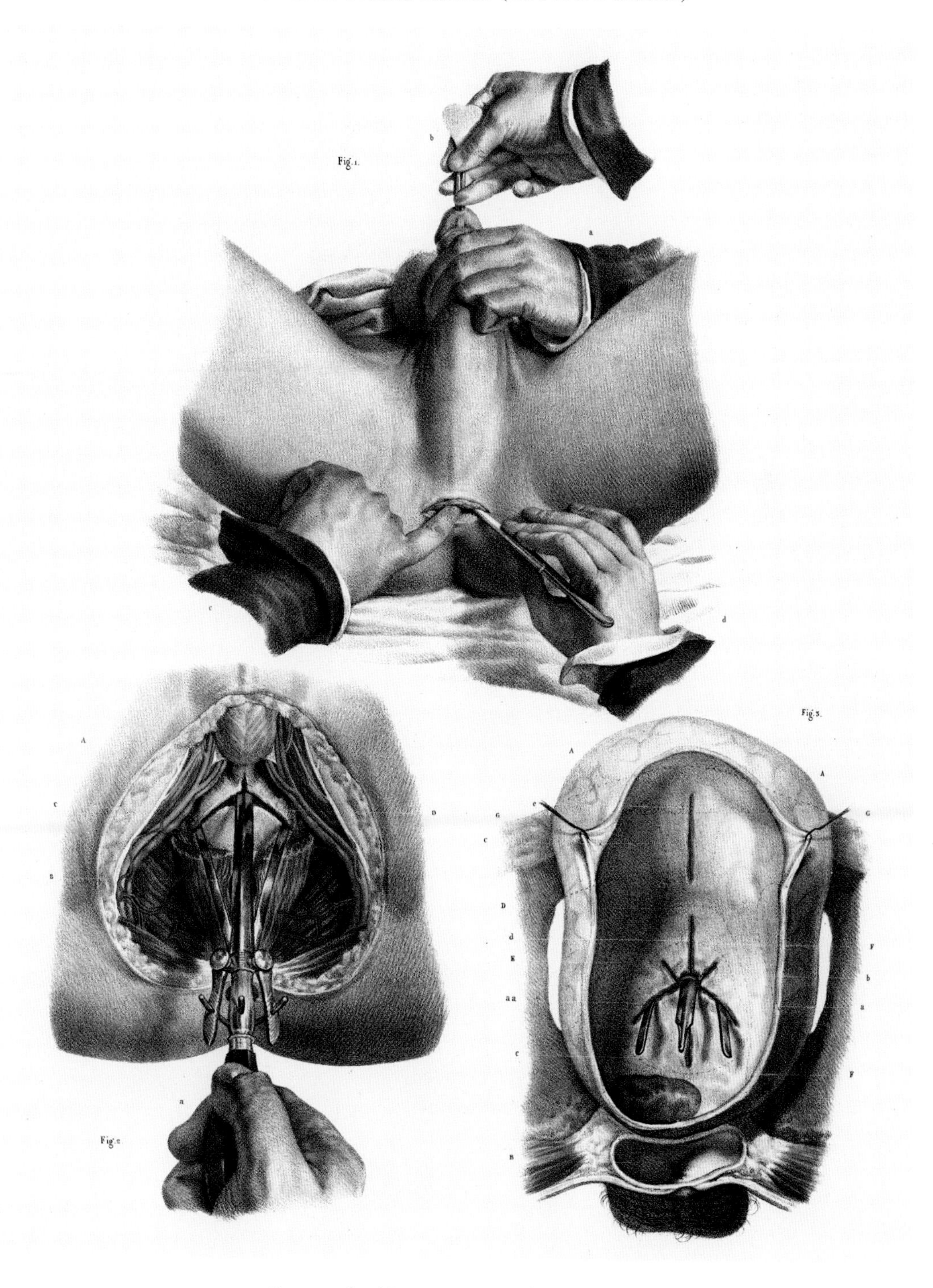

Surgery for bladder stones (lithotomy)
Chirurgie des calculs de la vessie (lithotomie)
Cirugía de los cálculos de la vejiga (litotomía)

CHIRURGIA CALCULORUM VESICAE URINARIAE (LITHOTOMIA)

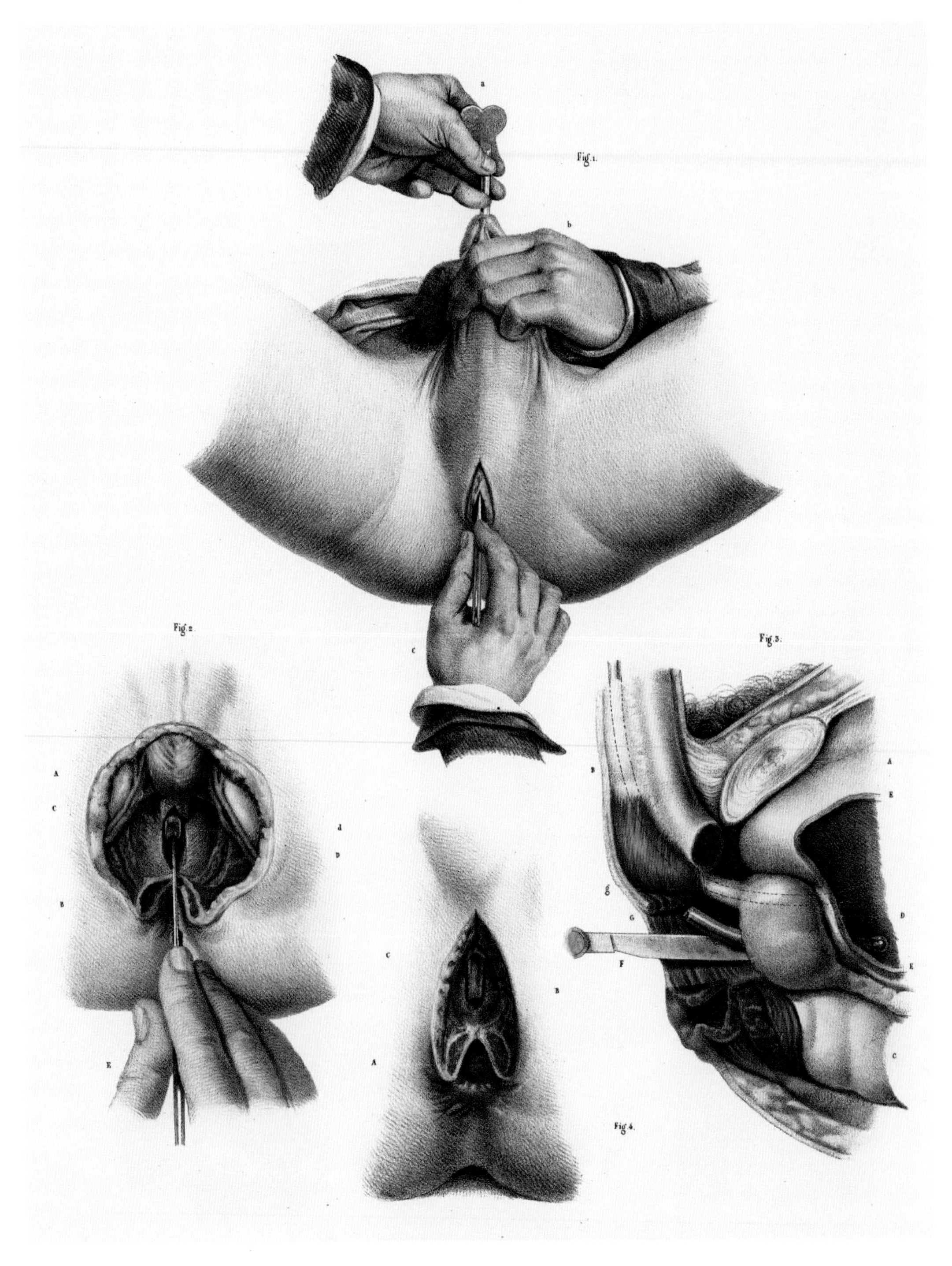

Surgery for bladder stones (lithotomy)
Chirurgie des calculs de la vessie (lithotomie)
Cirugía de los cálculos de la vejiga (litotomía)

CHIRURGIA CALCULORUM VESICAE URINARIAE (LITHOTOMIA)

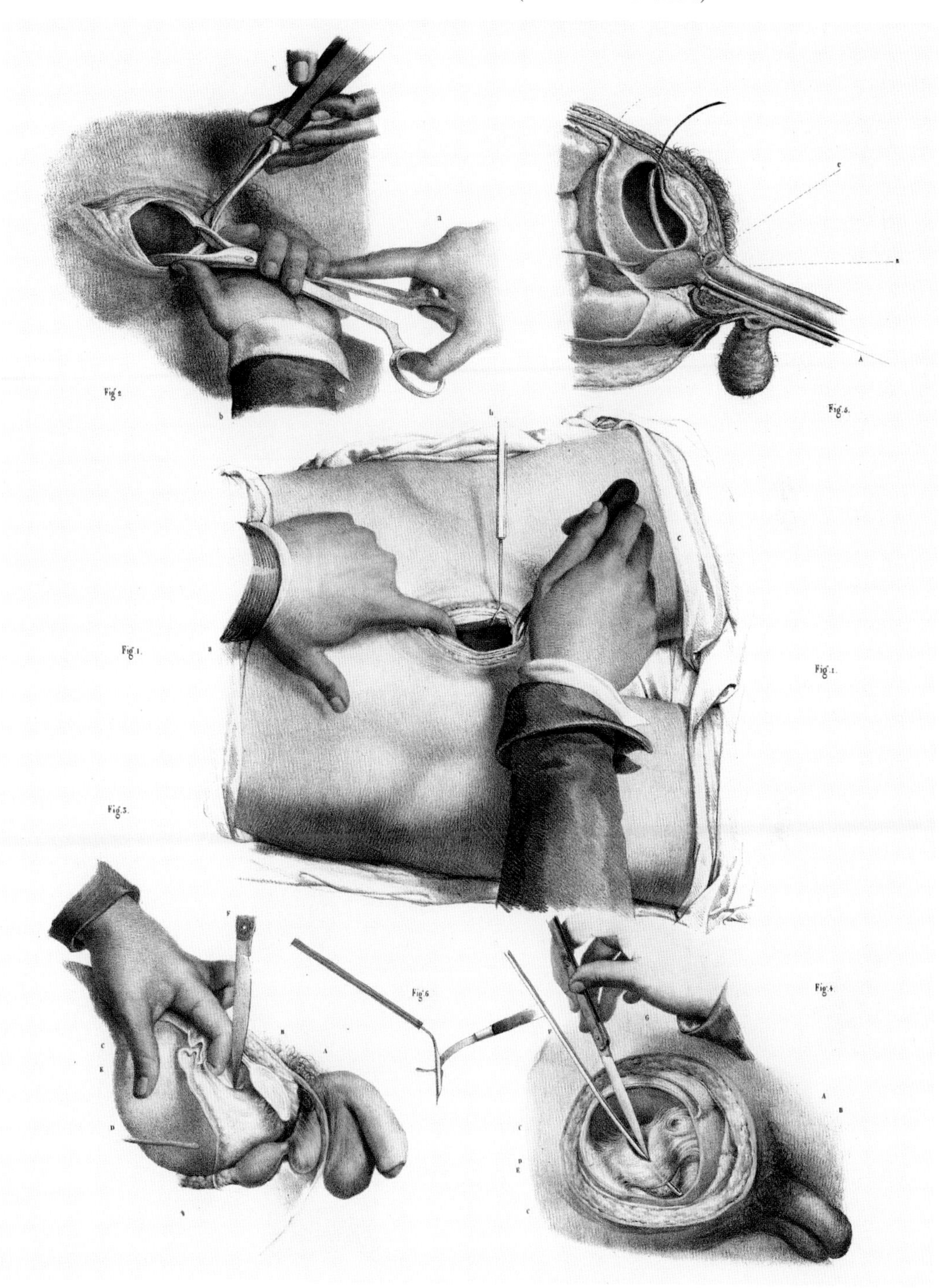

Surgery for bladder stones (lithotomy)
Chirurgie des calculs de la vessie (lithotomie)
Cirugía de los cálculos de la vejiga (litotomía)

CHIRURGIA CALCULORUM VESICAE URINARIAE (LITHOTOMIA)

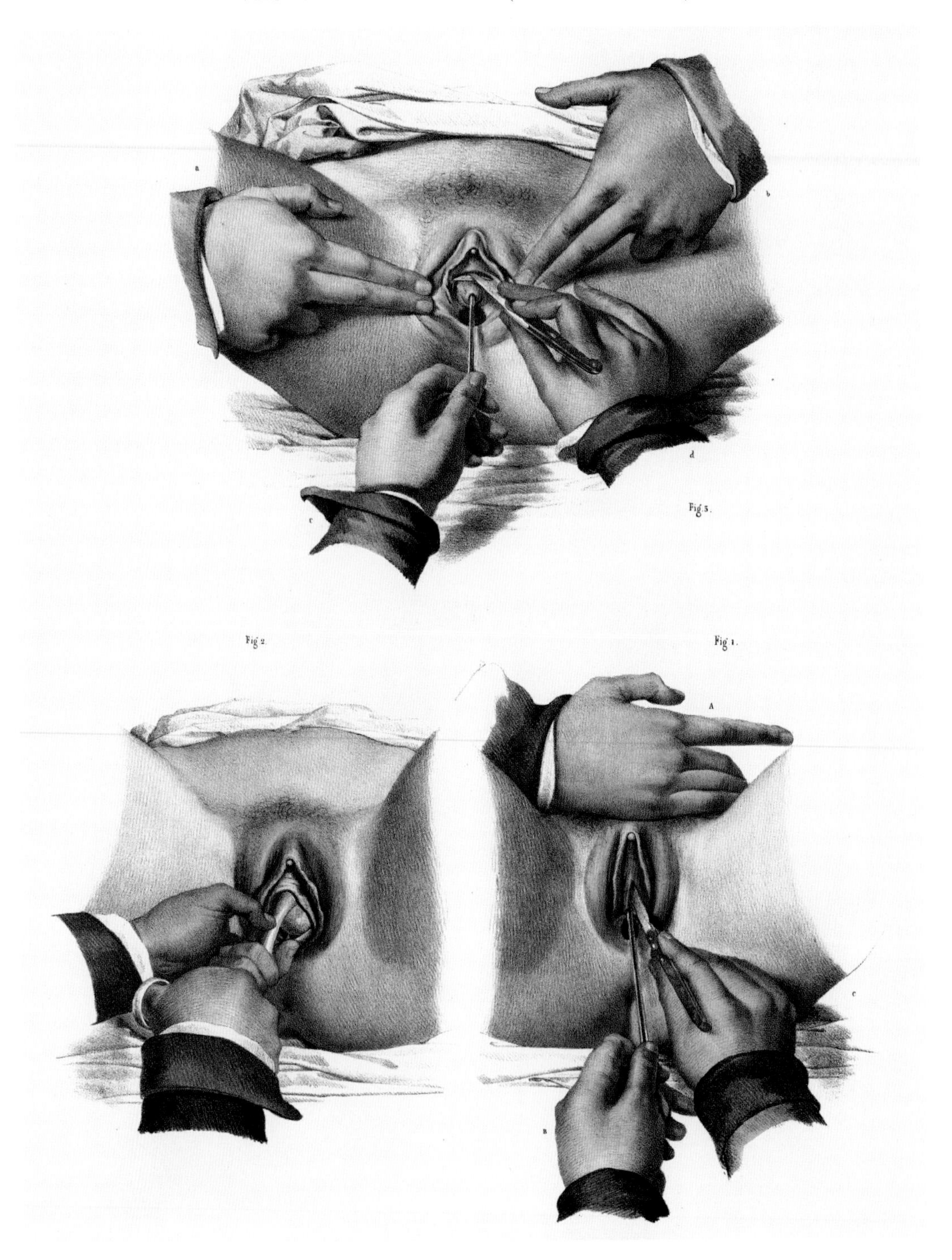

Surgery for bladder stones (lithotomy)
Chirurgie des calculs de la vessie (lithotomie)
Cirugía de los cálculos de la vejiga (litotomía)

CHIRURGIA CALCULORUM VESICAE URINARIAE (LITHOTOMIA): INSTRUMENTA CHIRURGICA

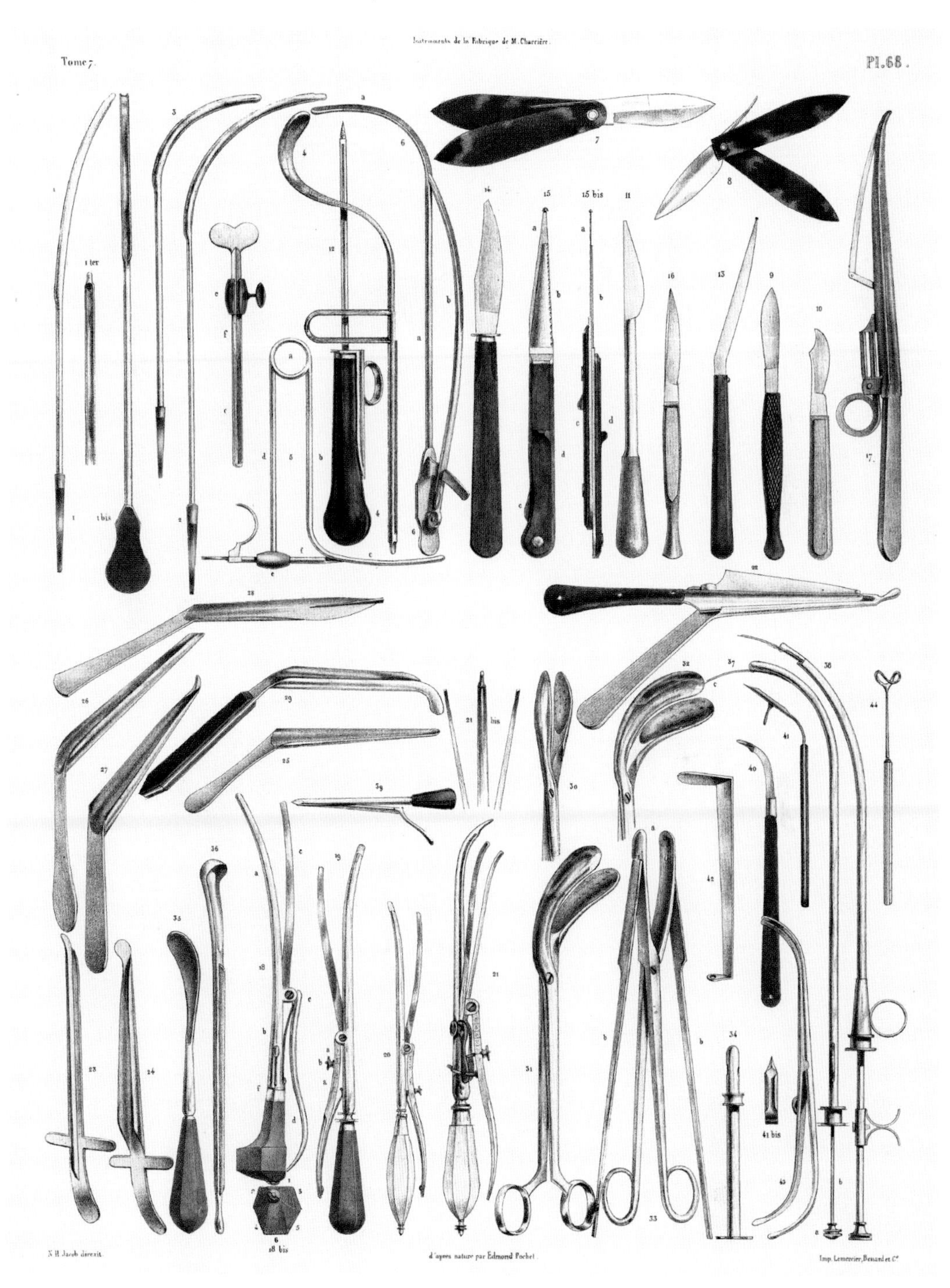

Surgery for bladder stones (lithotomy): Surgical instruments
Chirurgie des calculs de la vessie (lithotomie) : Instruments chirurgicaux
Cirugía de los cálculos de la vejiga (litotomía): instrumentos quirúrgicos

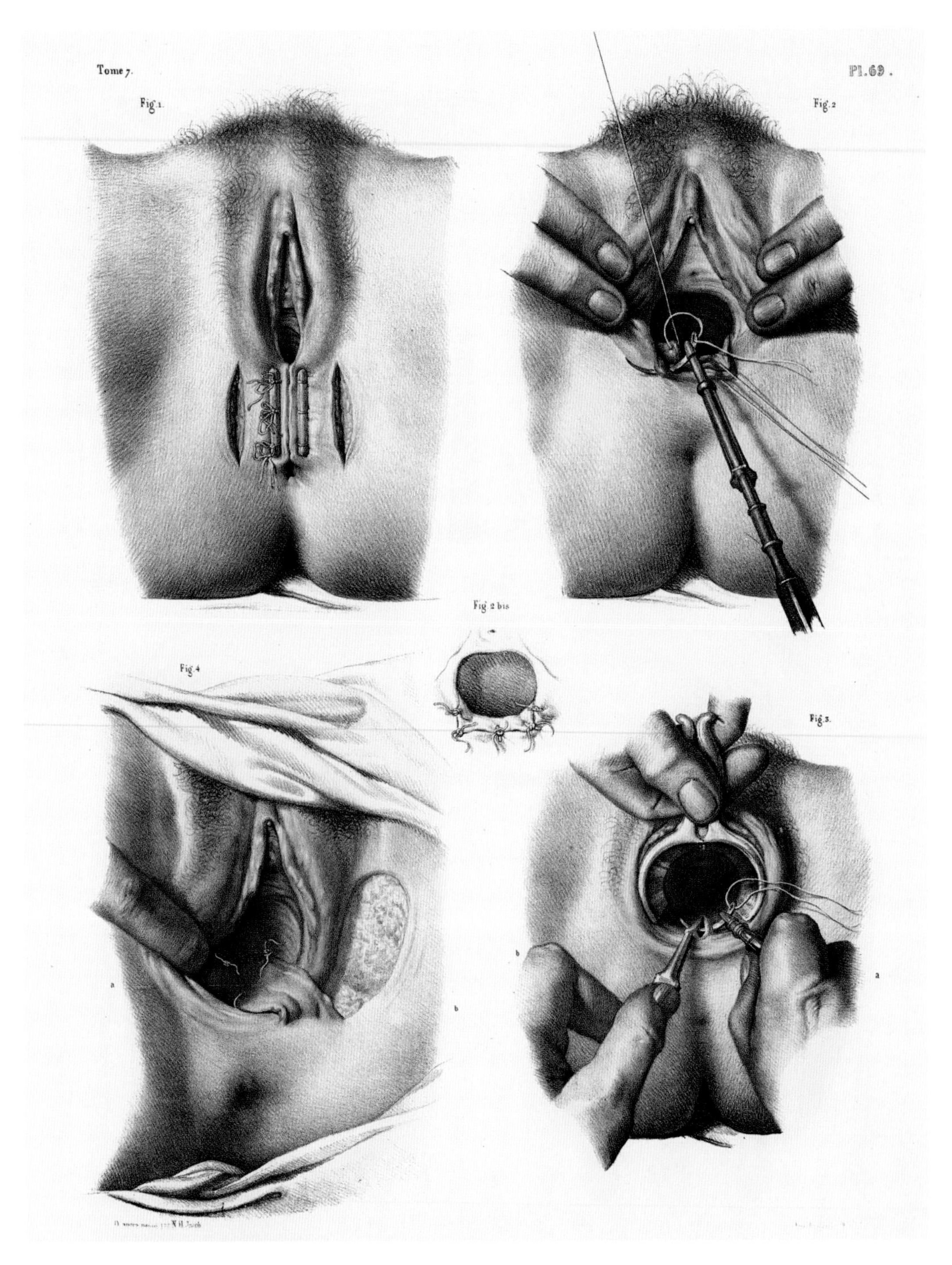

Surgery of the female perineum. Surgery of the vagina
Chirurgie du périnée féminin. Chirurgie du vagin
Cirugía del periné femenino. Cirugía de la vagina

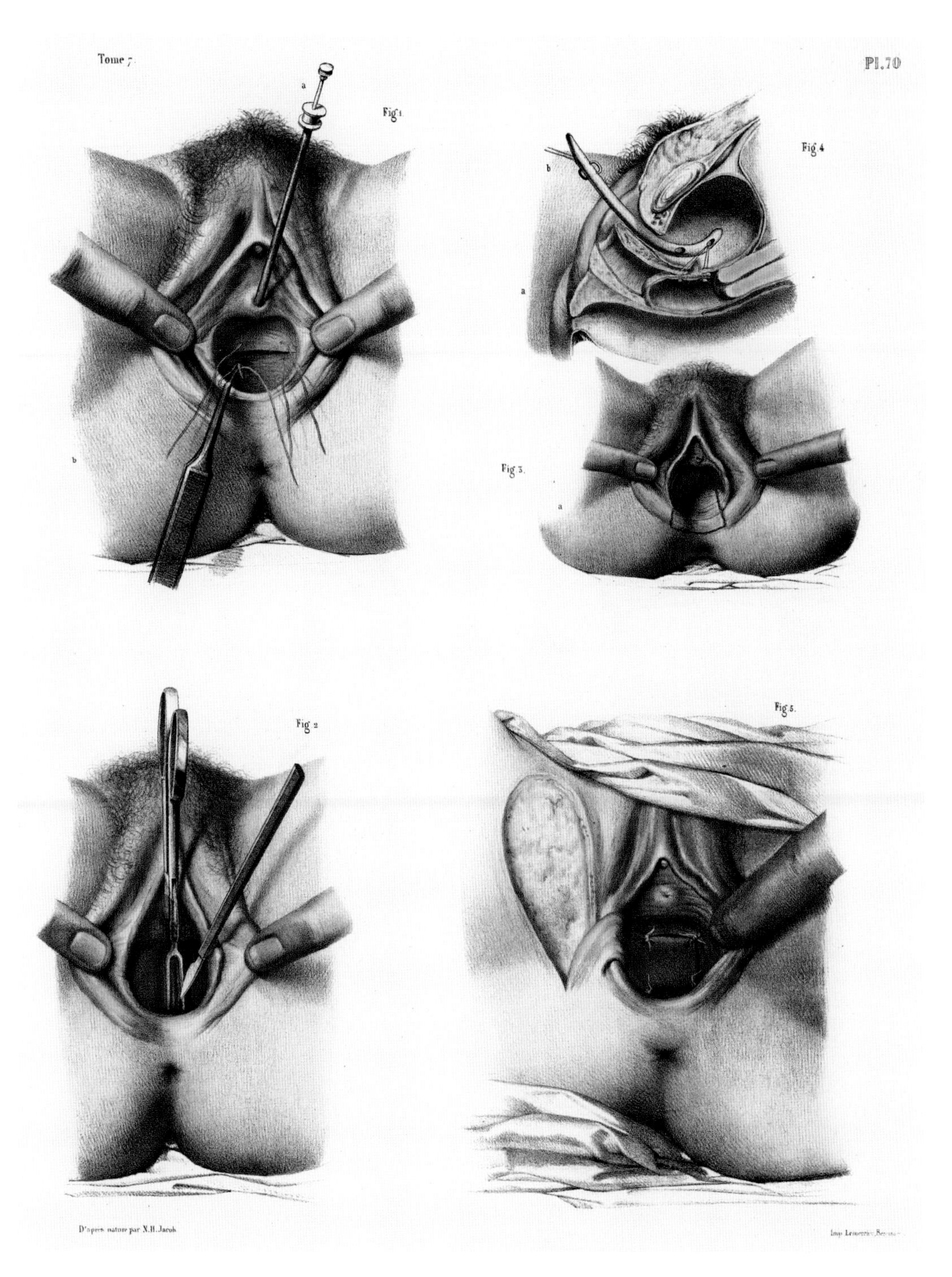

Surgery of the vagina / Chirurgie du vagin / Cirugía de la vagina

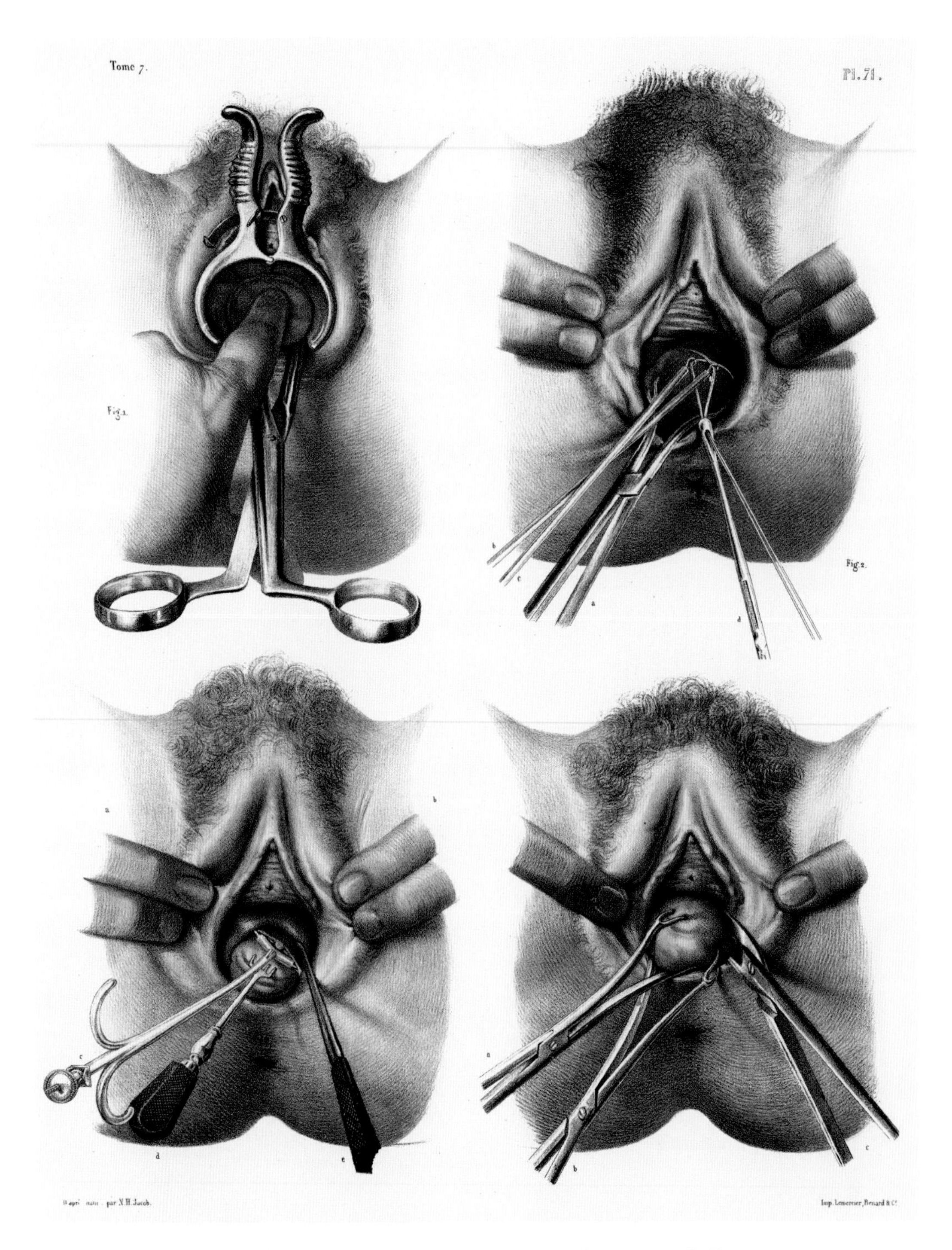

Surgery of the vagina and uterus / Chirurgie du vagin et de l'utérus
Cirugía de la vagina y del útero

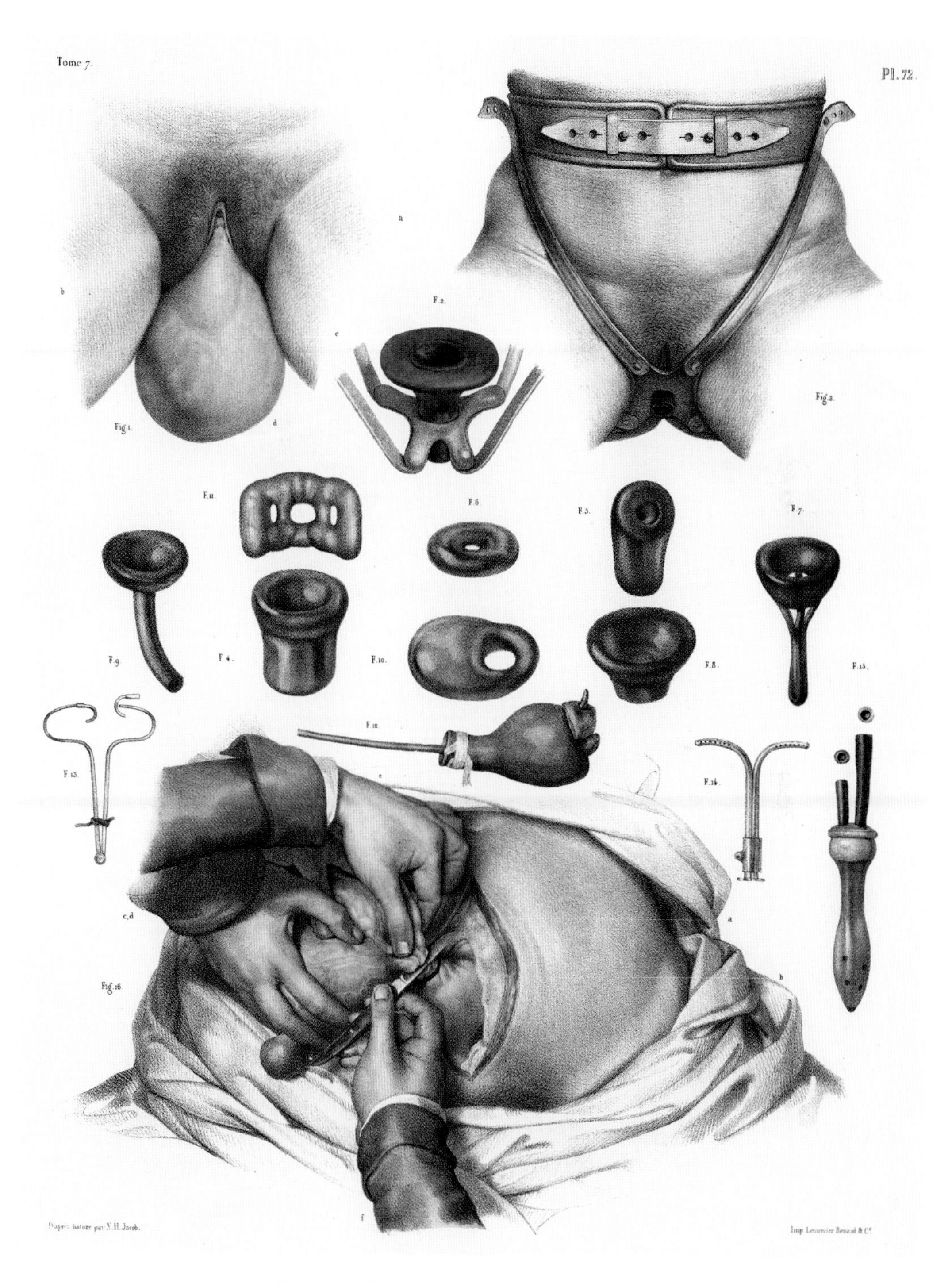

Surgery of the vagina, uterus, and ovaries
Chirurgie du vagin, de l'utérus et des ovaires
Cirugía de la vagina, del útero y de los ovarios

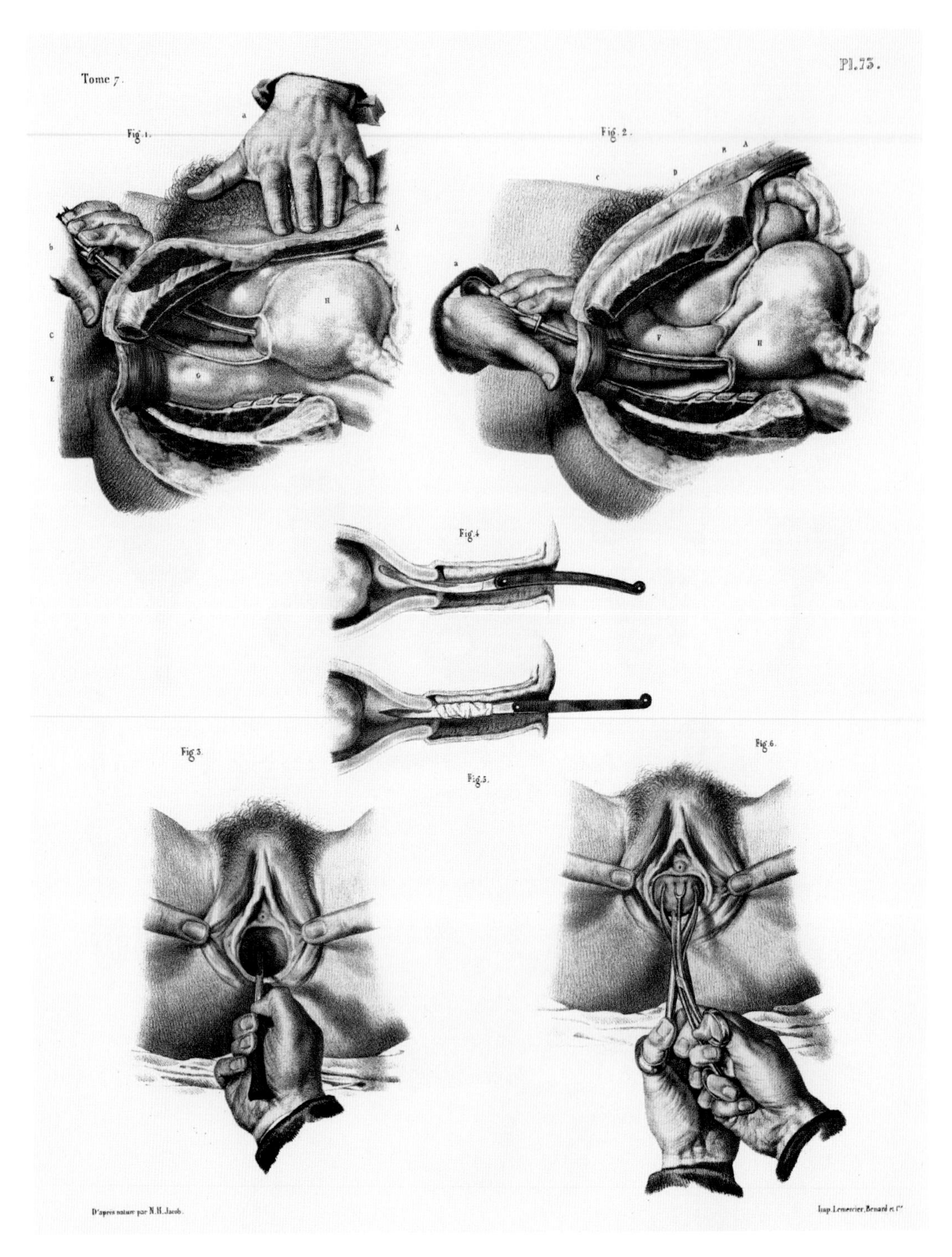

Surgery of the uterus / Chirurgie de l'utérus / Cirugía del útero

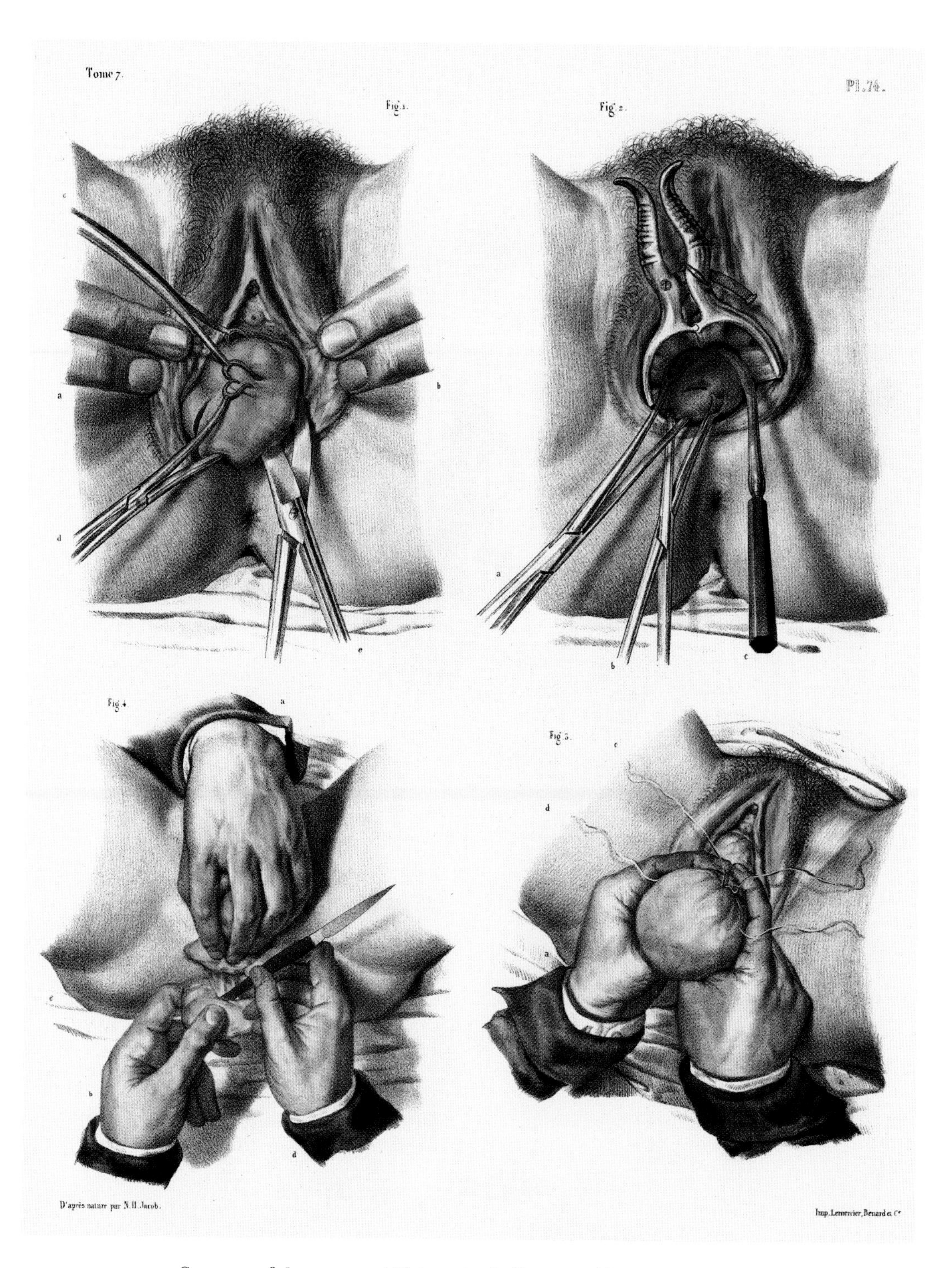

Surgery of the uterus / Chirurgie de l'utérus / Cirugía del útero

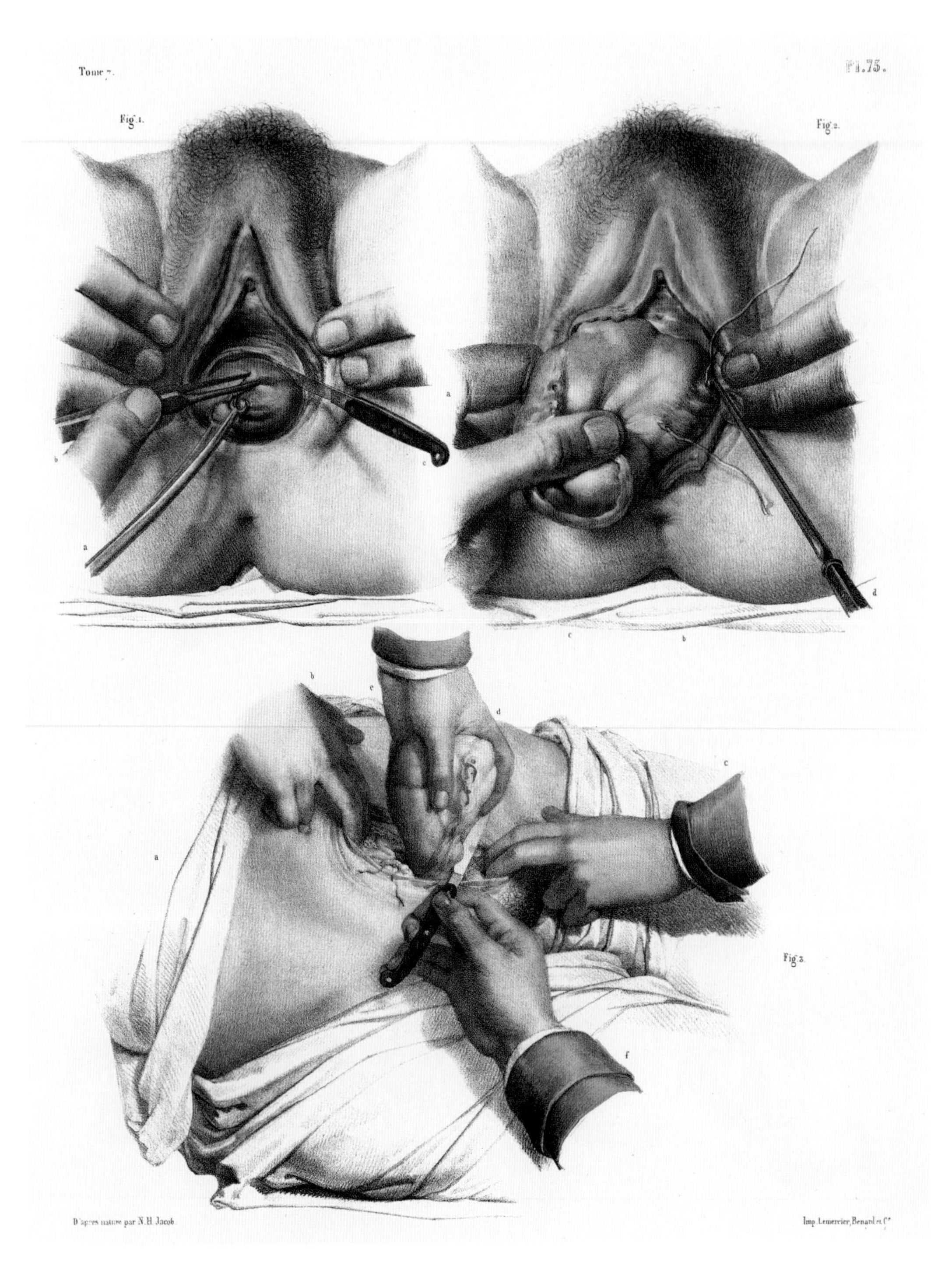

Surgery of the uterus / Chirurgie de l'utérus / Cirugía del útero

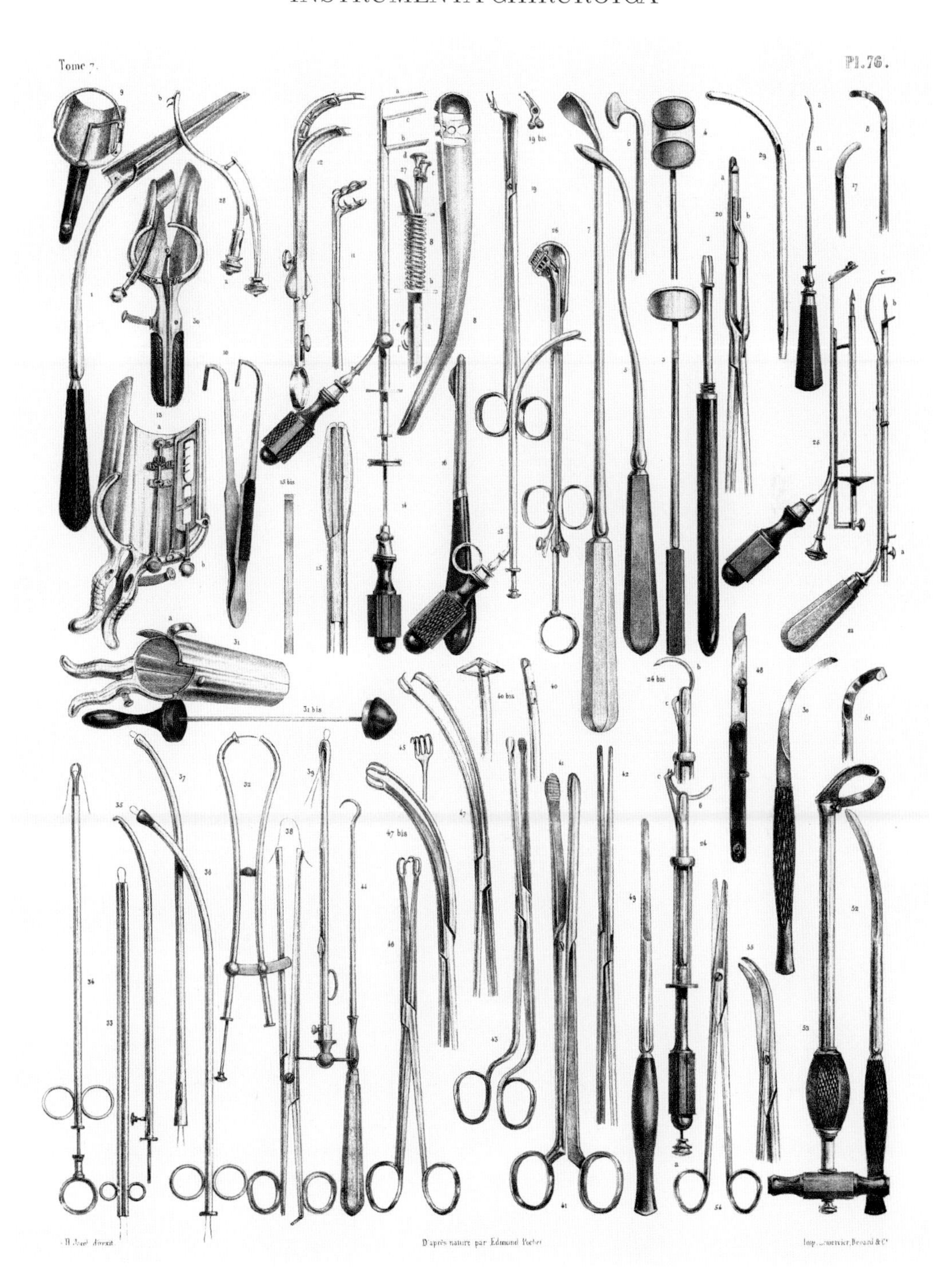

Surgery of the vagina and uterus: Surgical instruments
Chirurgie du vagin et de l'utérus : Instruments chirurgicaux
Cirugía de la vagina y del útero: instrumentos quirúrgicos

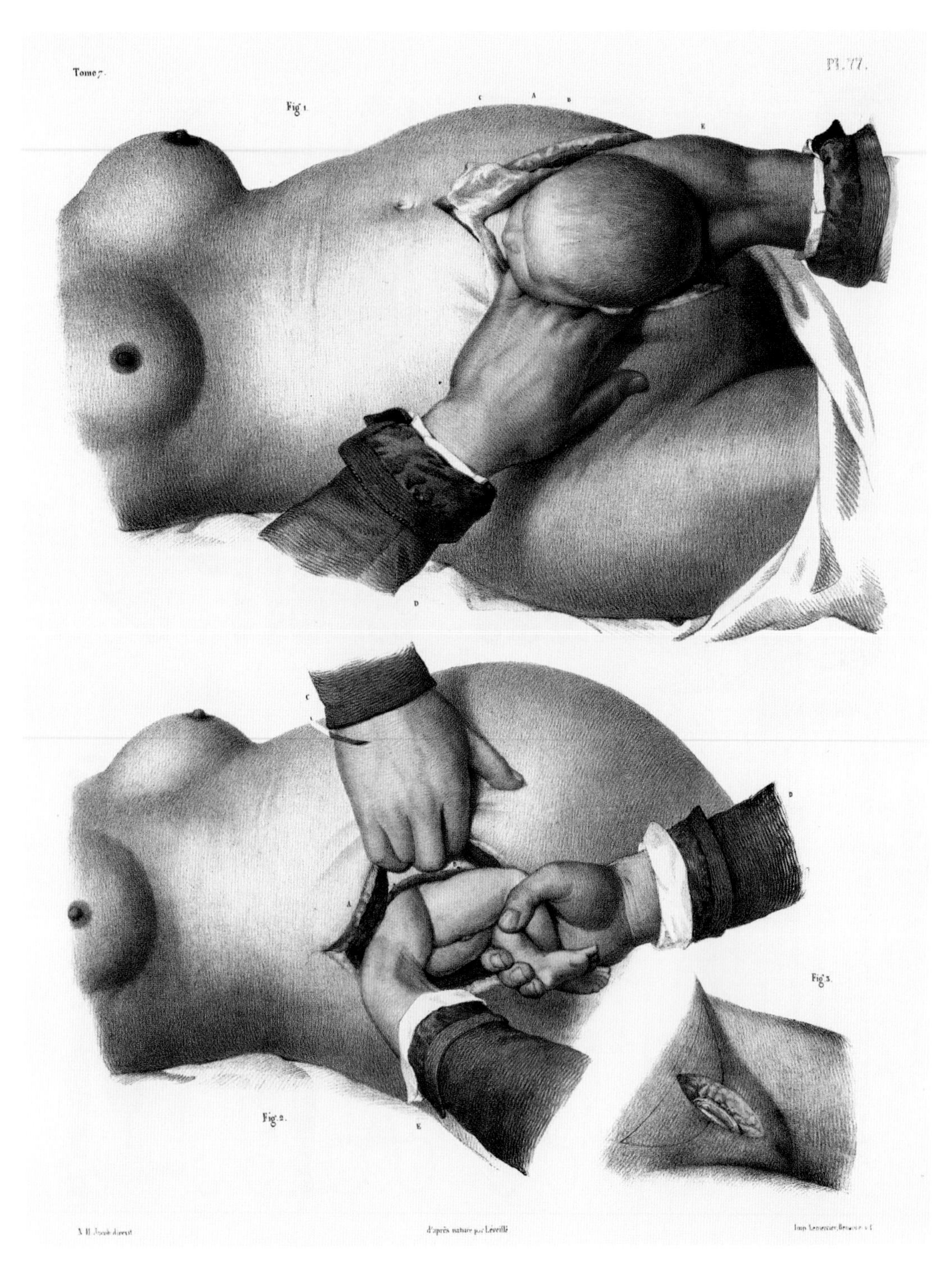

Caesarean section. Symphysiotomy / Césarienne. Symphyséotomie
Cesárea. Sinfisotomía

ANATOMIA CHIRURGICA MUSCULORUM OCULI (STRABISMUS)

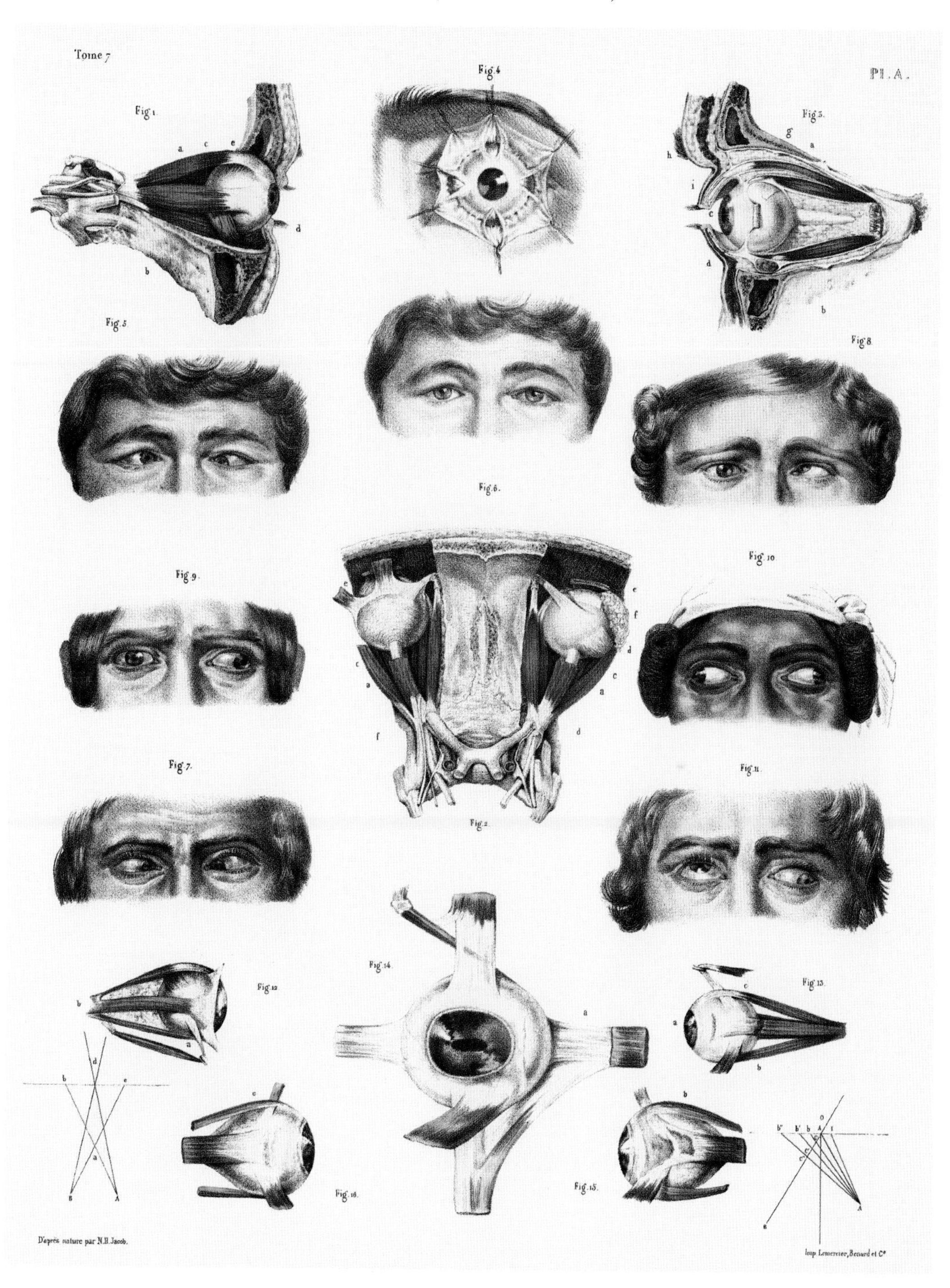

Surgical anatomy of the muscles of the eye (strabismus)
Anatomie chirurgicale des muscles de l'œil (Strabisme)
Anatomía quirúrgica de los músculos oculares (estrabismo)

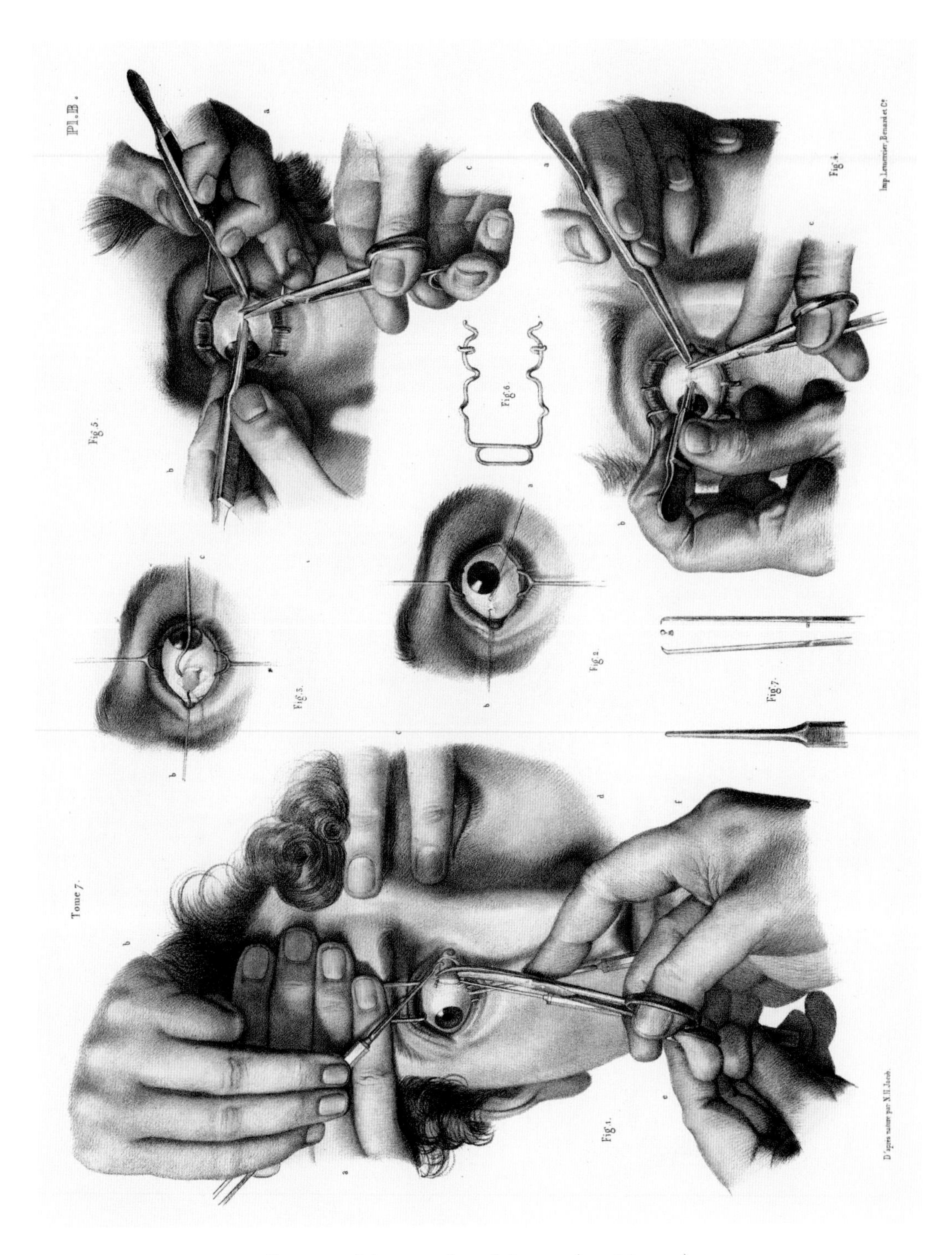

Surgery of the muscles of the eye (strabismus)
Chirurgie des muscles de l'œil (strabisme)
Cirugía de los músculos oculares (estrabismo)

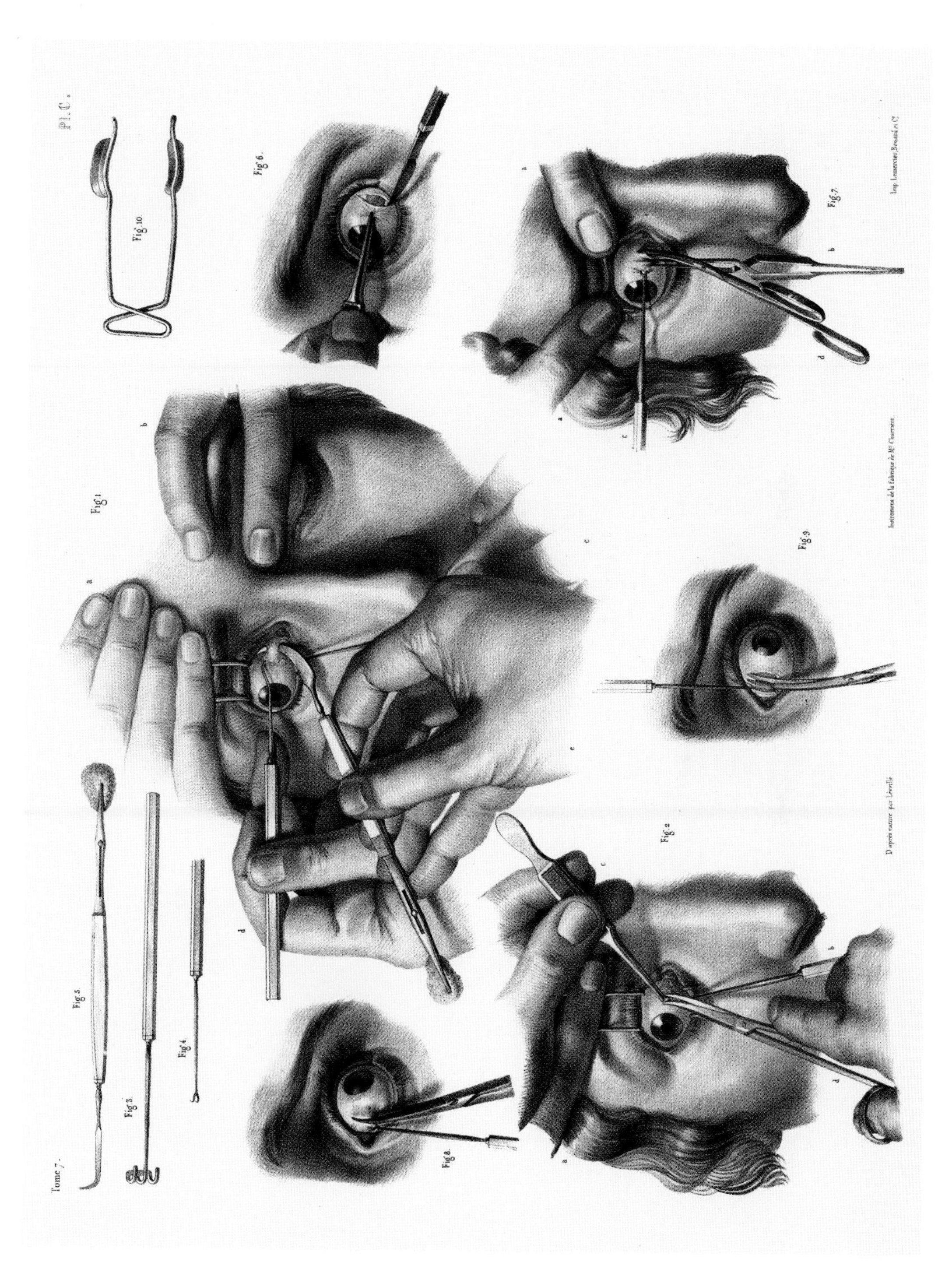

Surgery of the muscles of the eye (strabismus)
Chirurgie des muscles de l'œil (strabisme)
Cirugía de los músculos oculares (estrabismo)

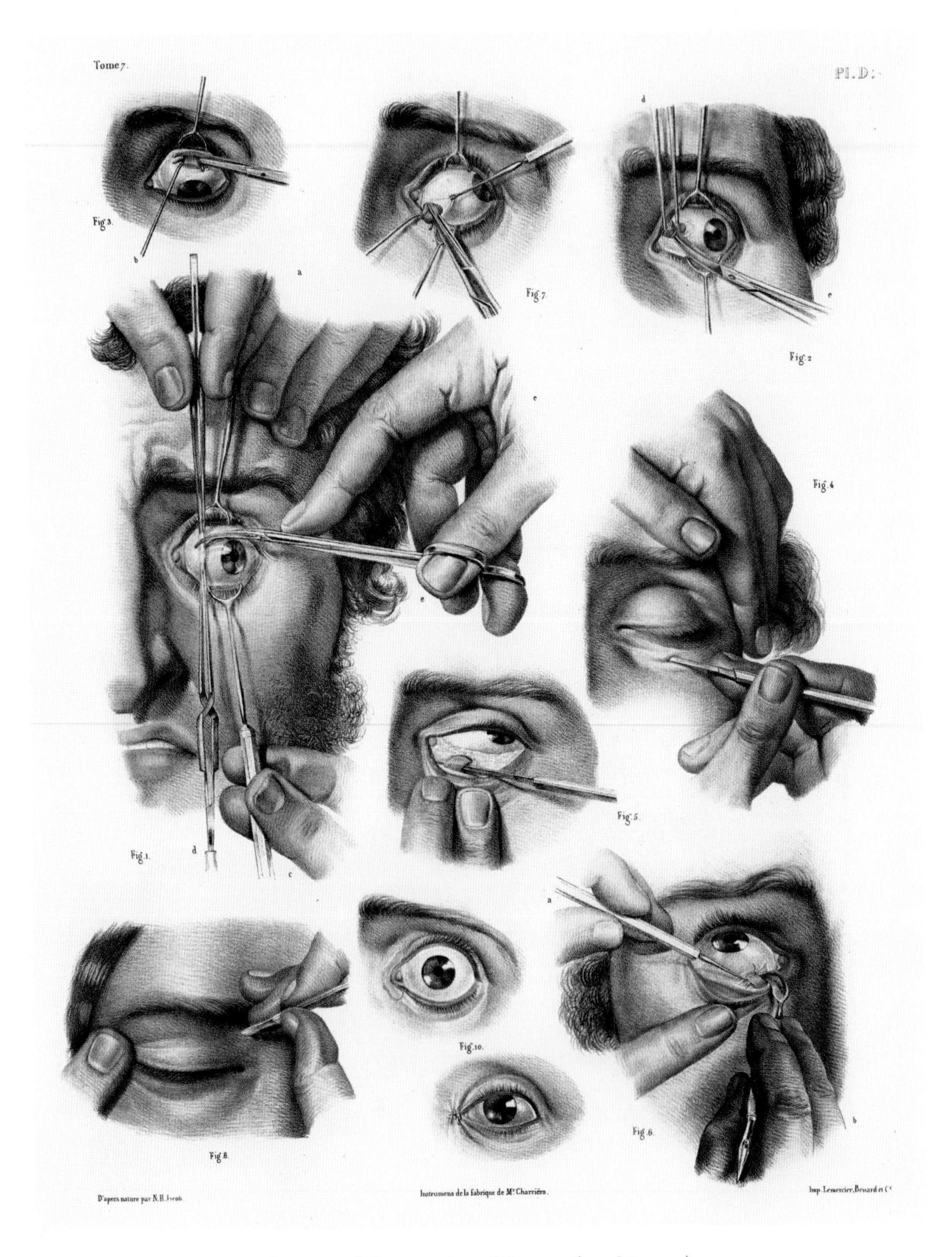

Surgery of the muscles of the eye (strabismus)
Chirurgie des muscles de l'œil (strabisme)
Cirugía de los músculos oculares (estrabismo)

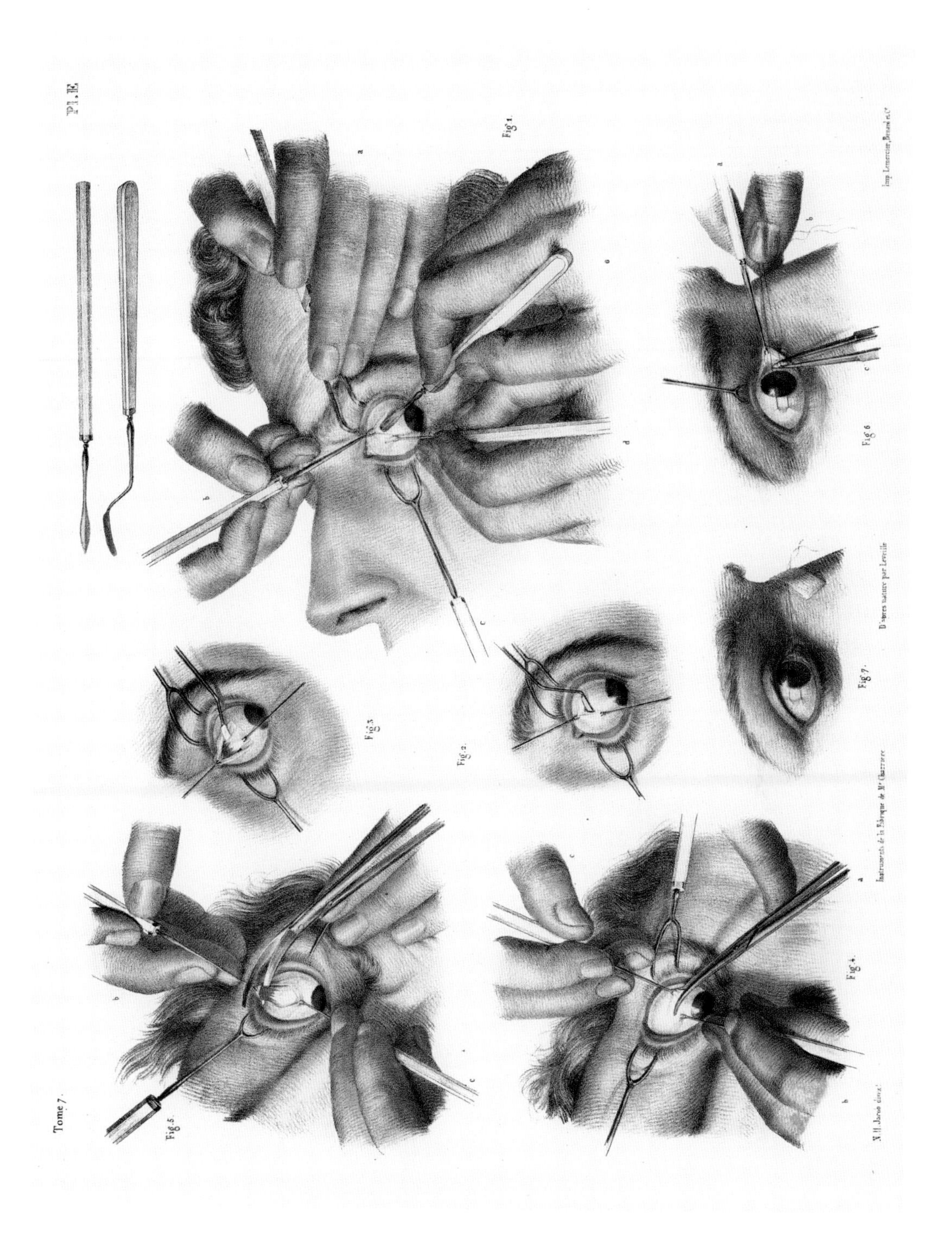

Surgery of the muscles of the eye (strabismus)
Chirurgie des muscles de l'œil (strabisme)
Cirugía de los músculos oculares (estrabismo)

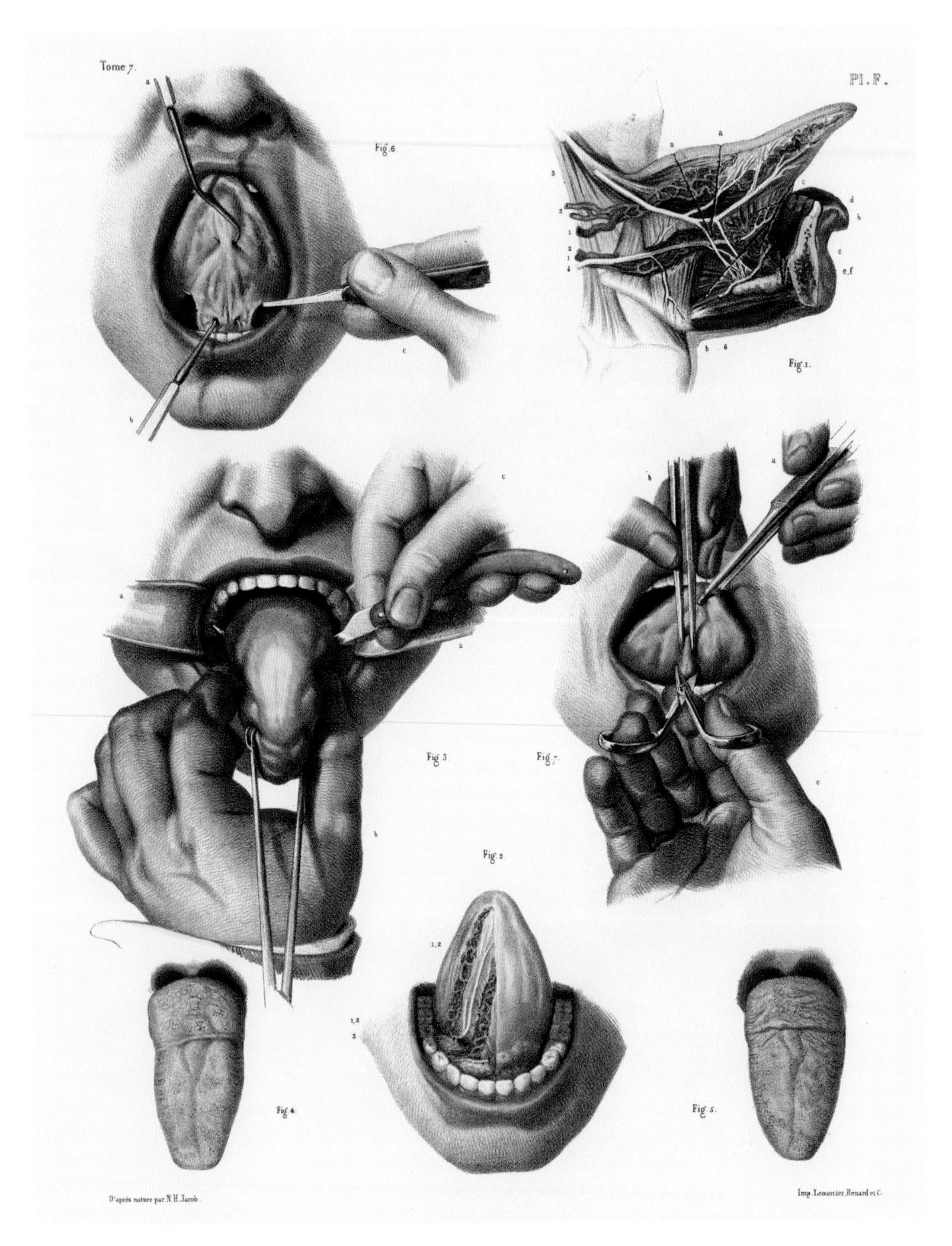

Surgery of distortions of the tongue / Chirurgie des distorsions de la langue
Cirugía de las distorsiones linguales

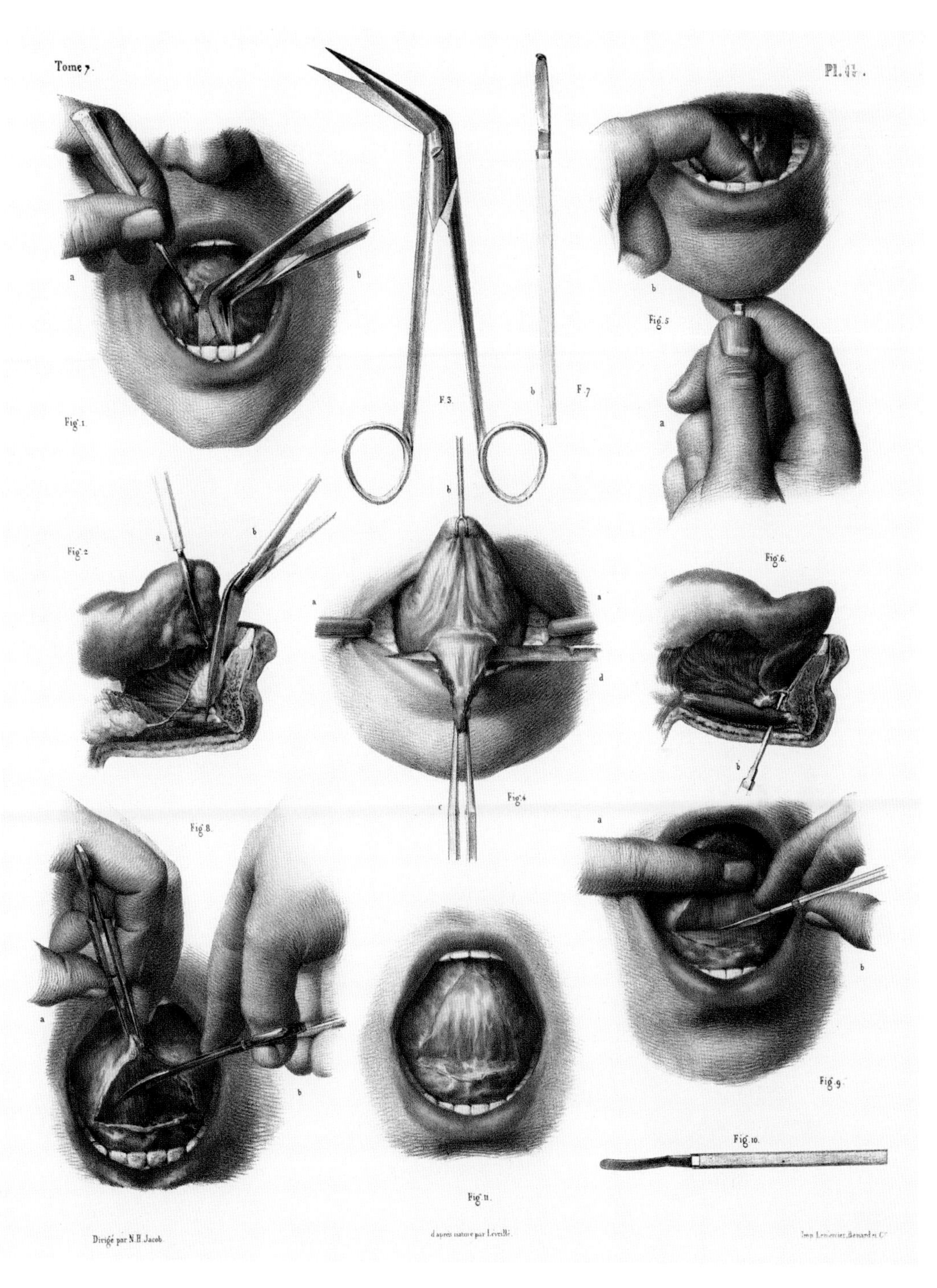

Surgery of distortions of the tongue / Chirurgie des distorsions de la langue
Cirugía de las distorsiones linguales

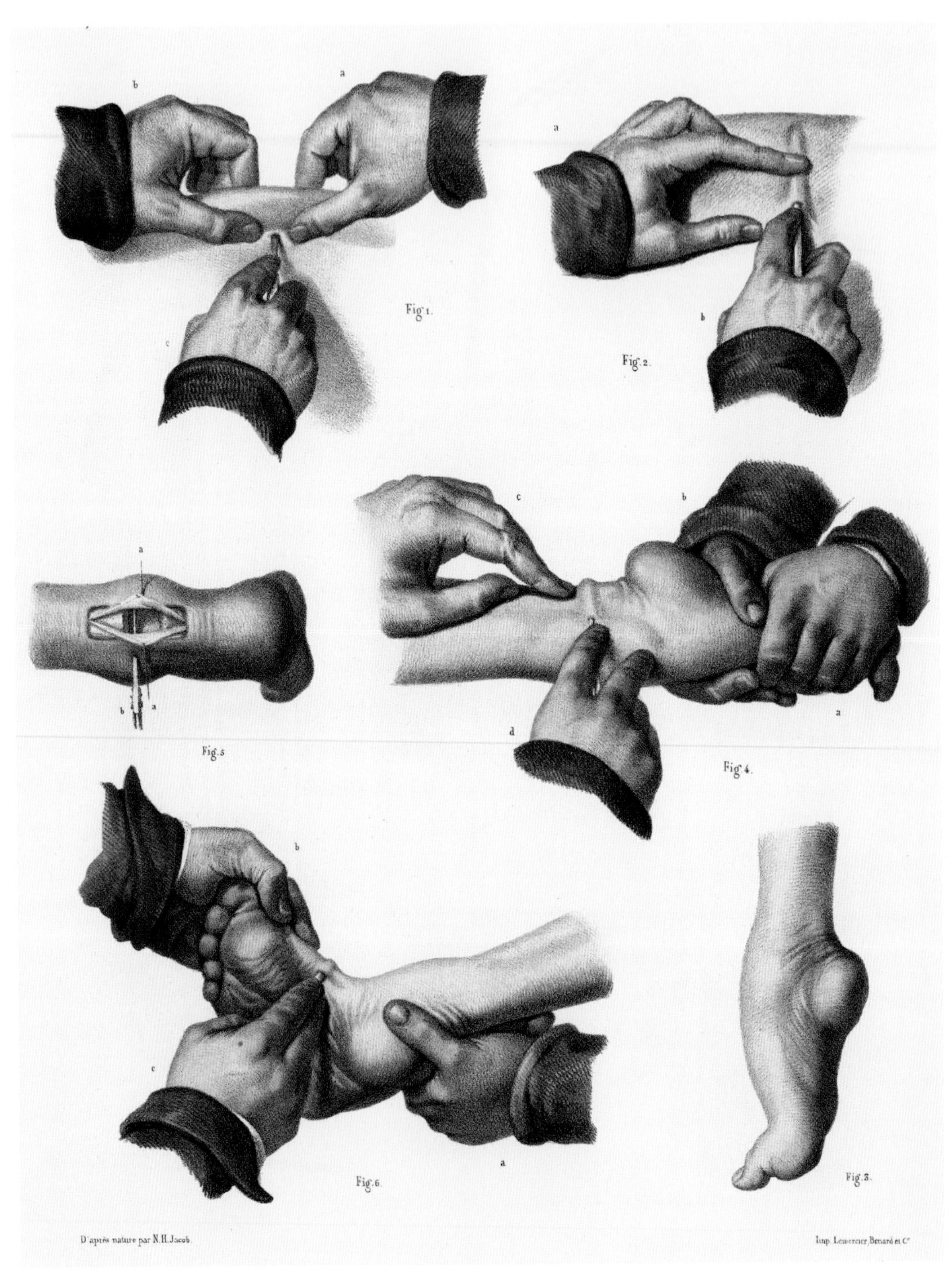

Surgery for deformations of the foot (club feet)
Chirurgie des déformations du pied (pieds bots)
Cirugía de las deformaciones del pie (pies zambos)

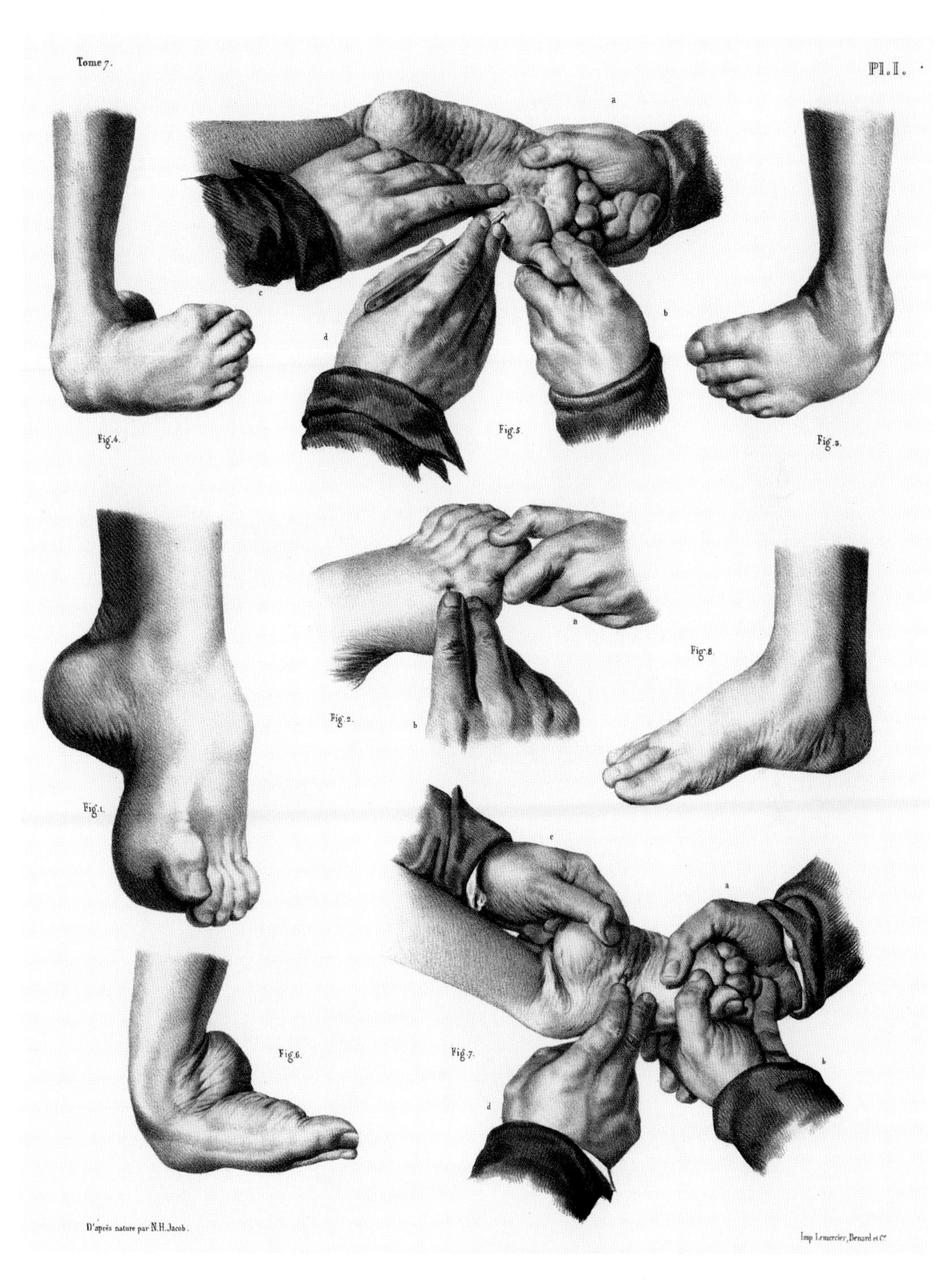

Surgery for deformations of the foot (club feet)
Chirurgie des déformations du pied (pieds bots)
Cirugía de las deformaciones del pie (pies zambos)

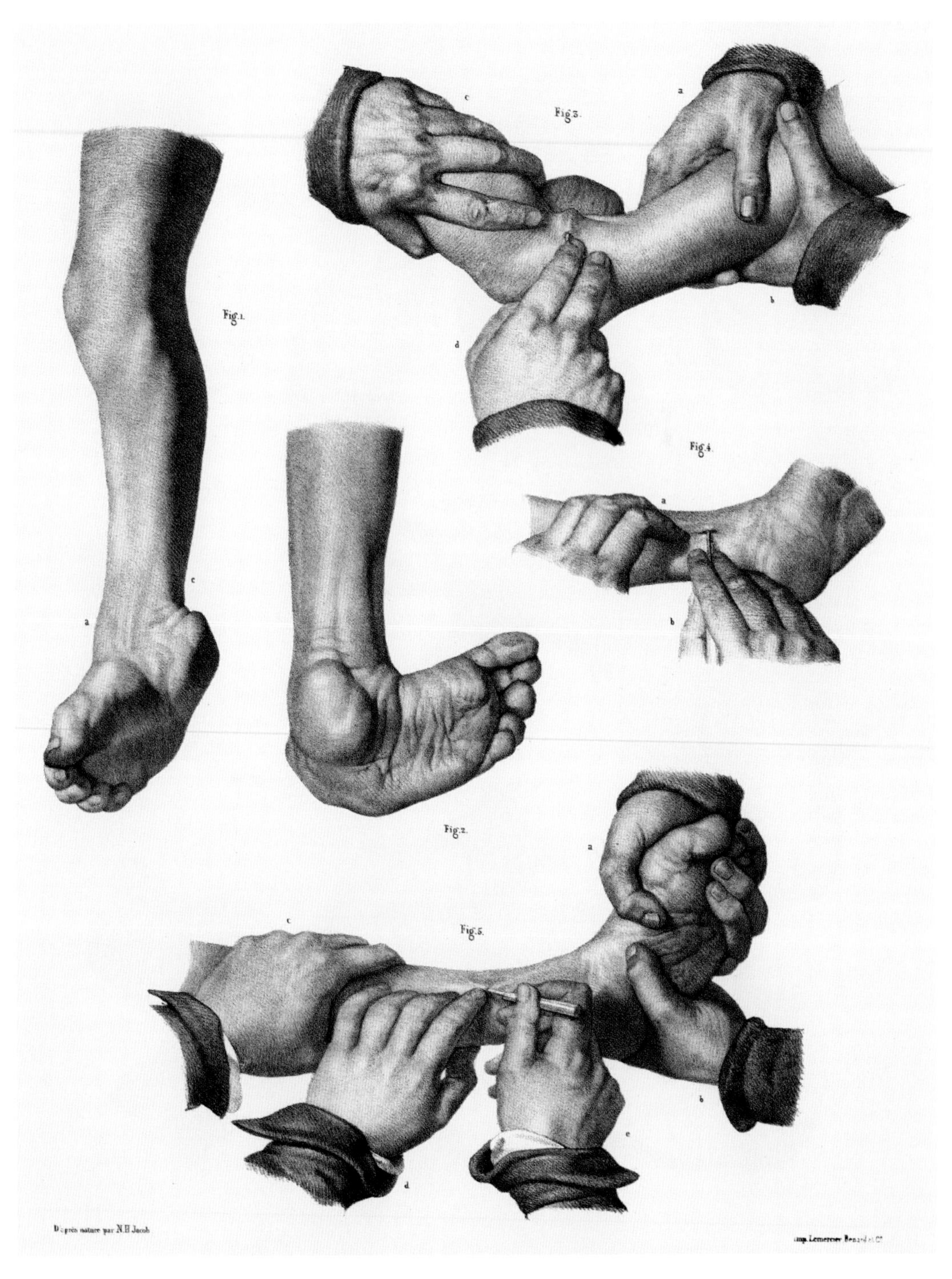

Surgery for deformations of the foot (club feet)
Chirurgie des déformations du pied (pieds bots)
Cirugía de las deformaciones del pie (pies zambos)

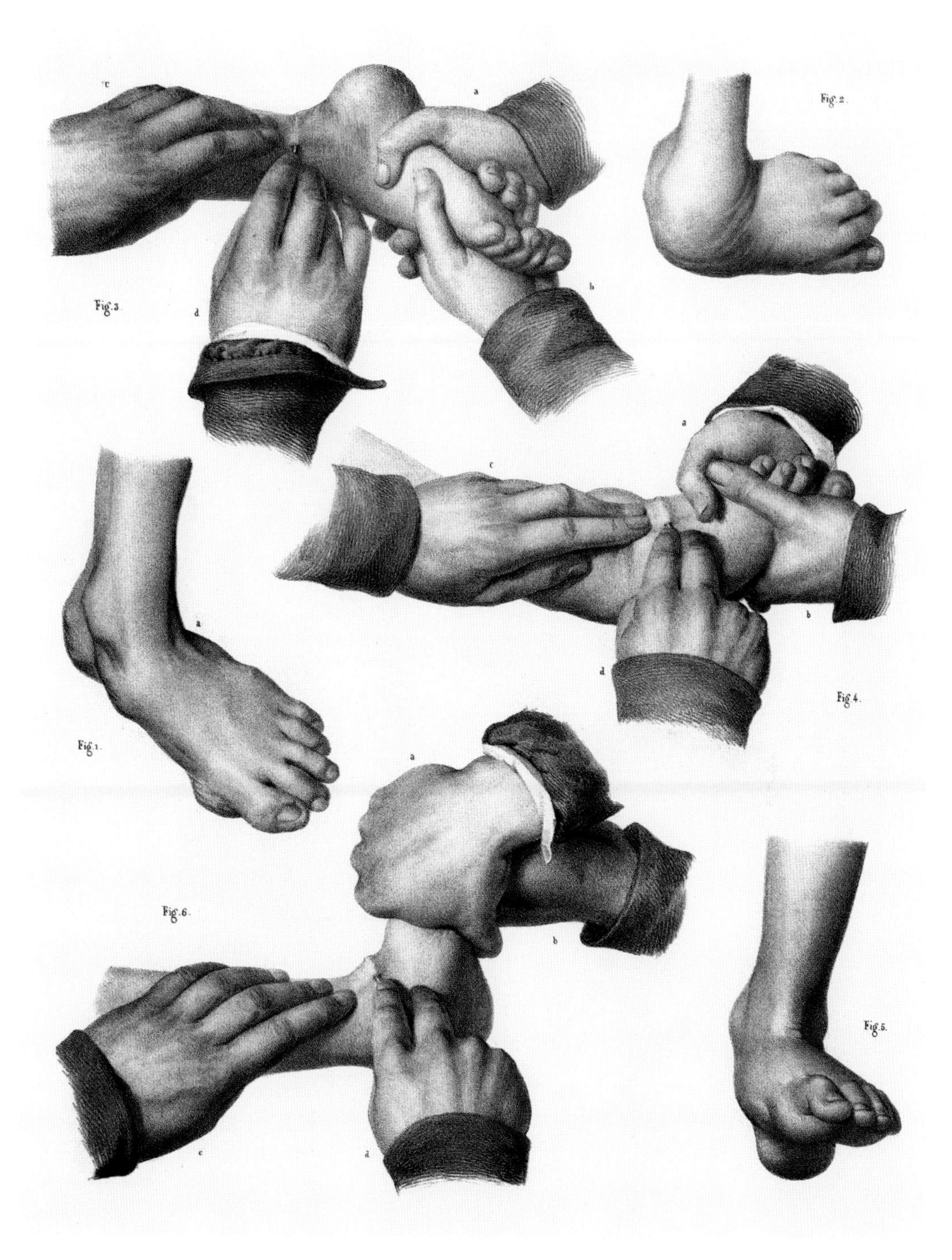

Surgery for deformations of the foot (club feet)
Chirurgie des déformations du pied (pieds bots)
Cirugía de las deformaciones del pie (pies zambos)

SECTIONES TENDINUM (TENOTOMIAE): INSTRUMENTA CHIRURGICA. TENOTOMIAE FEMORIS

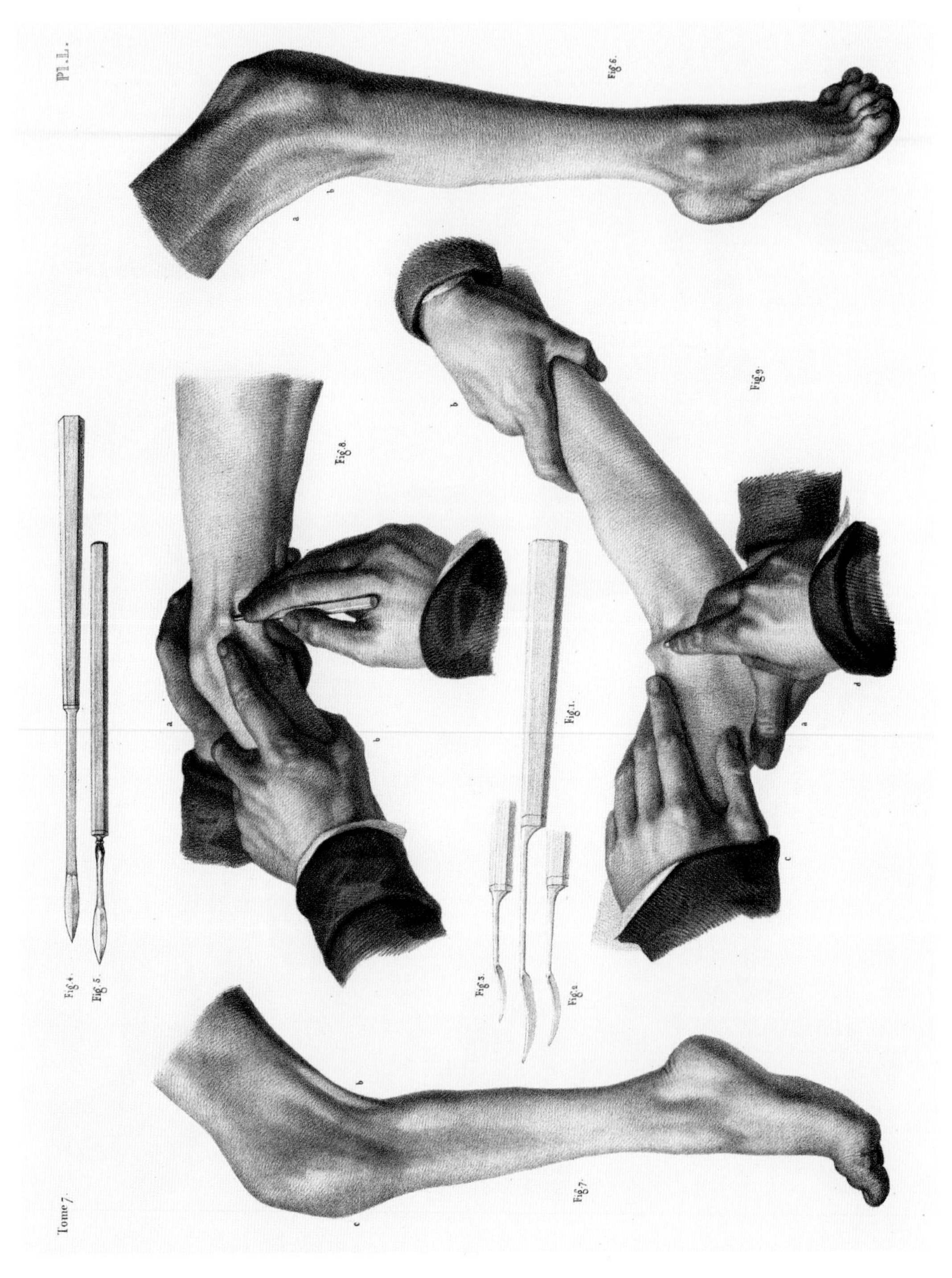

Sections through the tendons (tenotomies): Surgical instruments. Tenotomies of the thigh
Sections tendineuses (ténotomies) : Instruments chirurgicaux. Ténotomies de la cuisse
Secciones tendinosas (tenotomías): instrumentos quirúrgicos. Tenotomías del muslo

CERVICIS RIGORES.
SECTIONES TENDINUM COLLI (TENOTOMIAE)

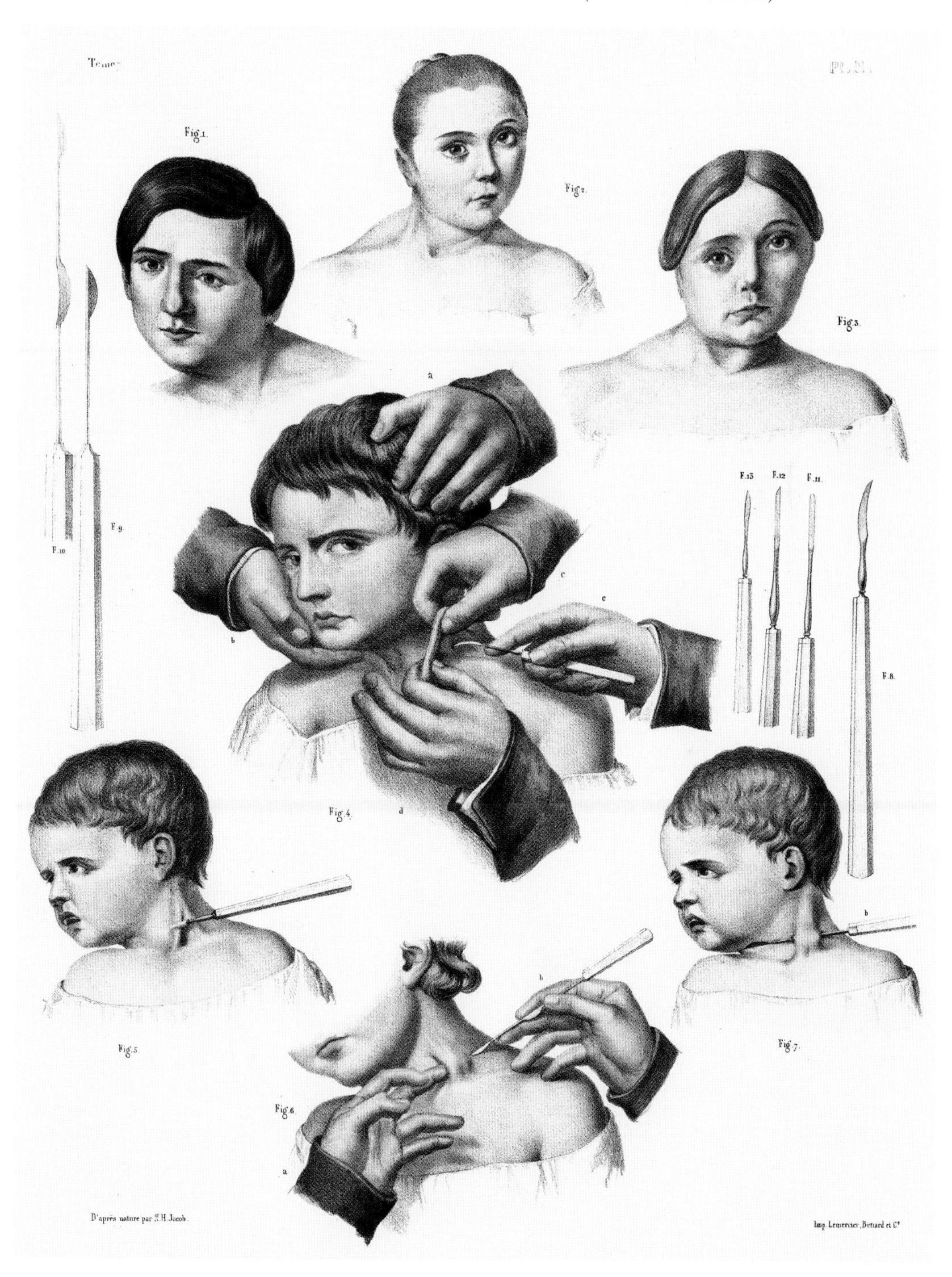

Torticollis. Sections of muscles and tendons of the neck (tenotomies)
Torticolis. Sections musculo-tendineuses du cou (ténotomies)
Tortícolis. Secciones musculotendinosas del cuello (tenotomías)

SECTIONES TENDINUM VARIAE (TENOTOMIAE)

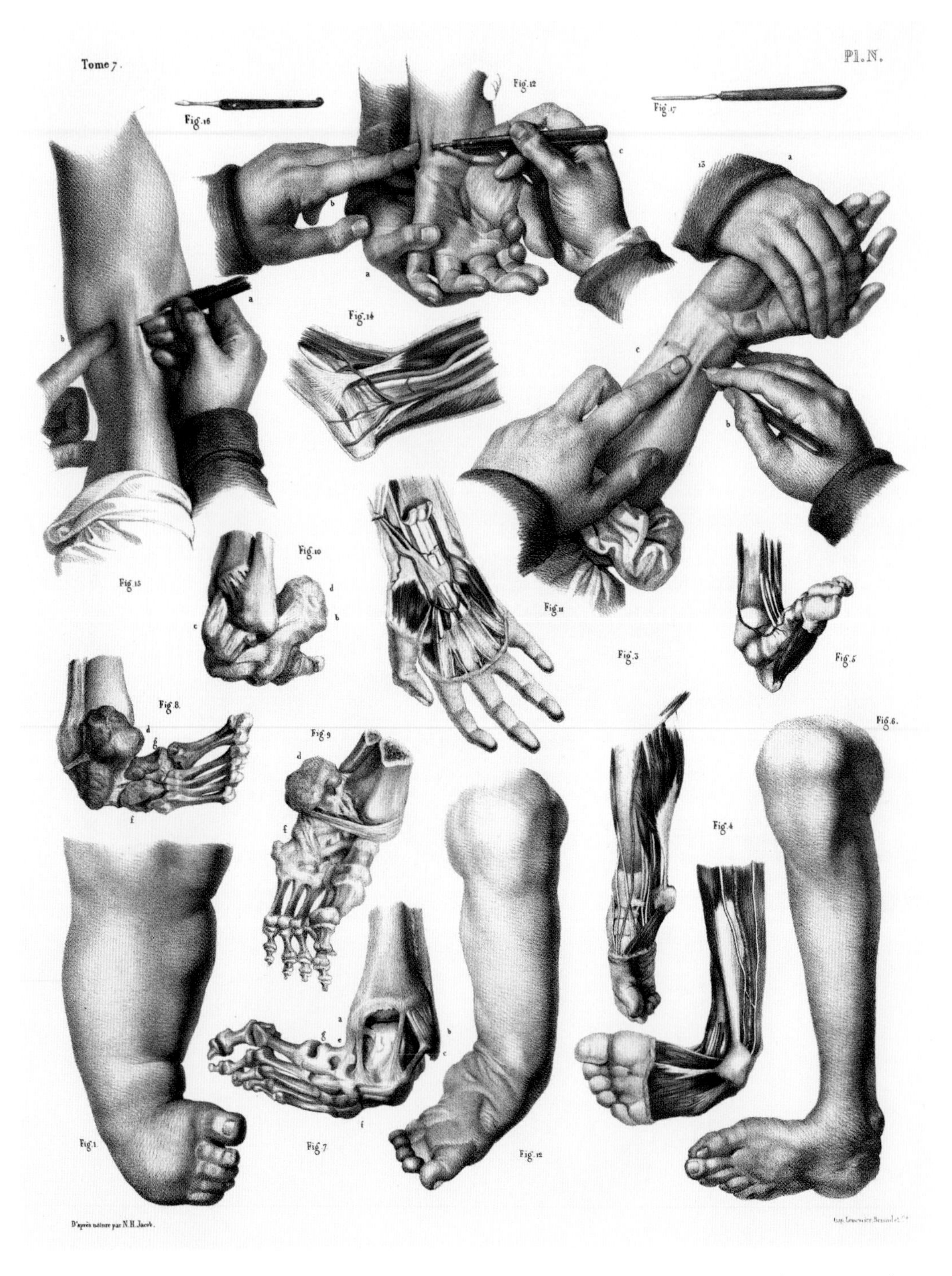

Sections of different tendons (tenotomies) / Sections tendineuses diverses (ténotomies)
Secciones tendinosas diversas (tenotomías)

DEFORMATIONES
COLUMNAE VERTEBRALIS

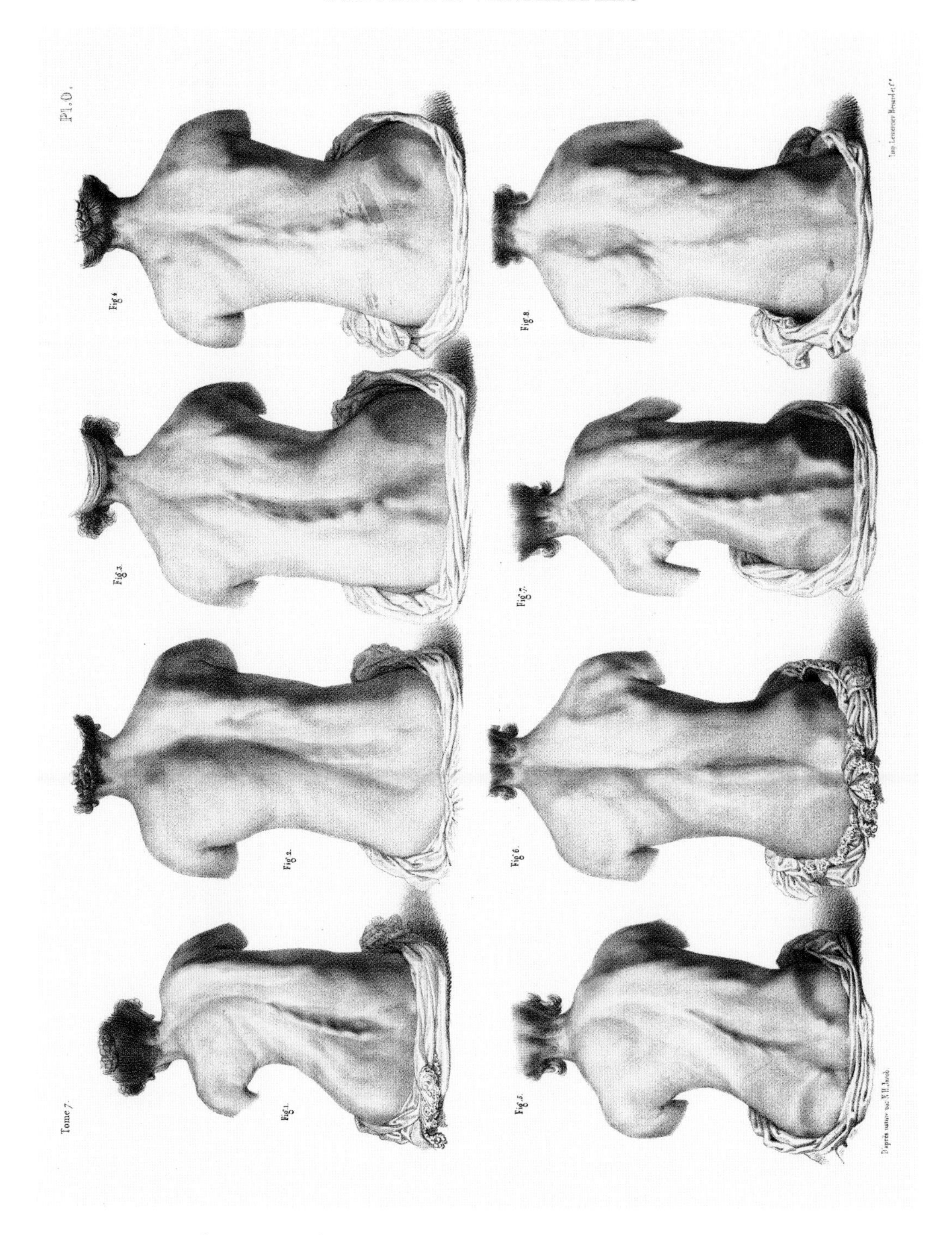

Deformations of the spine / Déformations de la colonne vertébrale
Deformaciones de la columna vertebral

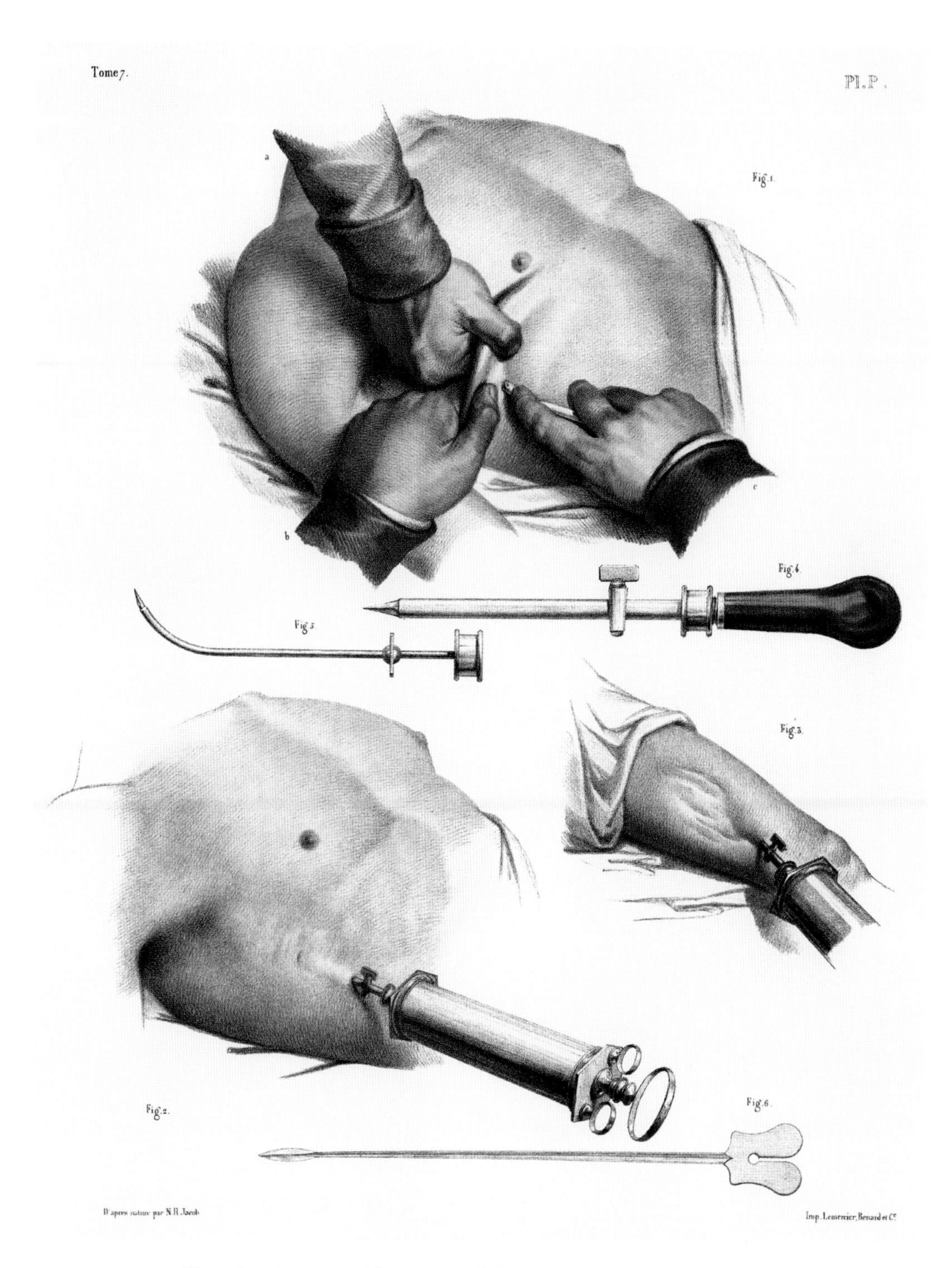

Taps for abscesses / Ponctions d'abcès / Punciones de abscesos

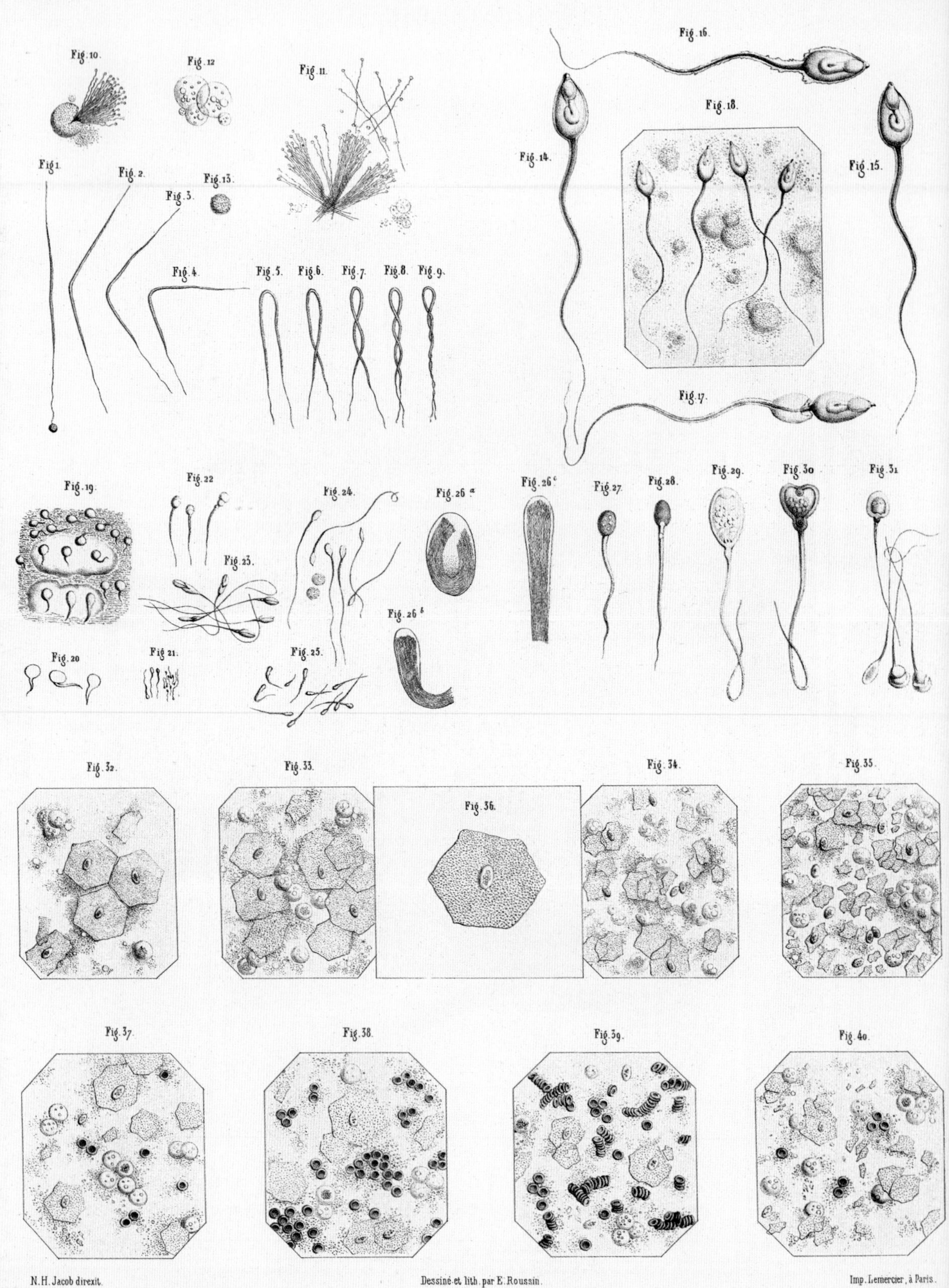

N.H. Jacob direxit. Dessiné et lith. par E. Roussin. Imp. Lemercier, à Paris.

VOL. 8

✠

Embryologia. Anatomia Comparata. Anatomia Microscopia

EMBRYOLOGY.
COMPARATIVE ANATOMY.
MICROSCOPIC ANATOMY

EMBRYOLOGIE.
ANATOMIE COMPAREE.
ANATOMIE MICROSCOPIQUE

EMBRIOLOGÍA.
ANATOMÍA COMPARADA.
ANATOMÍA MICROSCÓPICA

Left page / Ci-contre / Página contigua:
Embryology: Spermatozoids / Embryologie : Spermatozoïdes
Embriología: espermatozoides

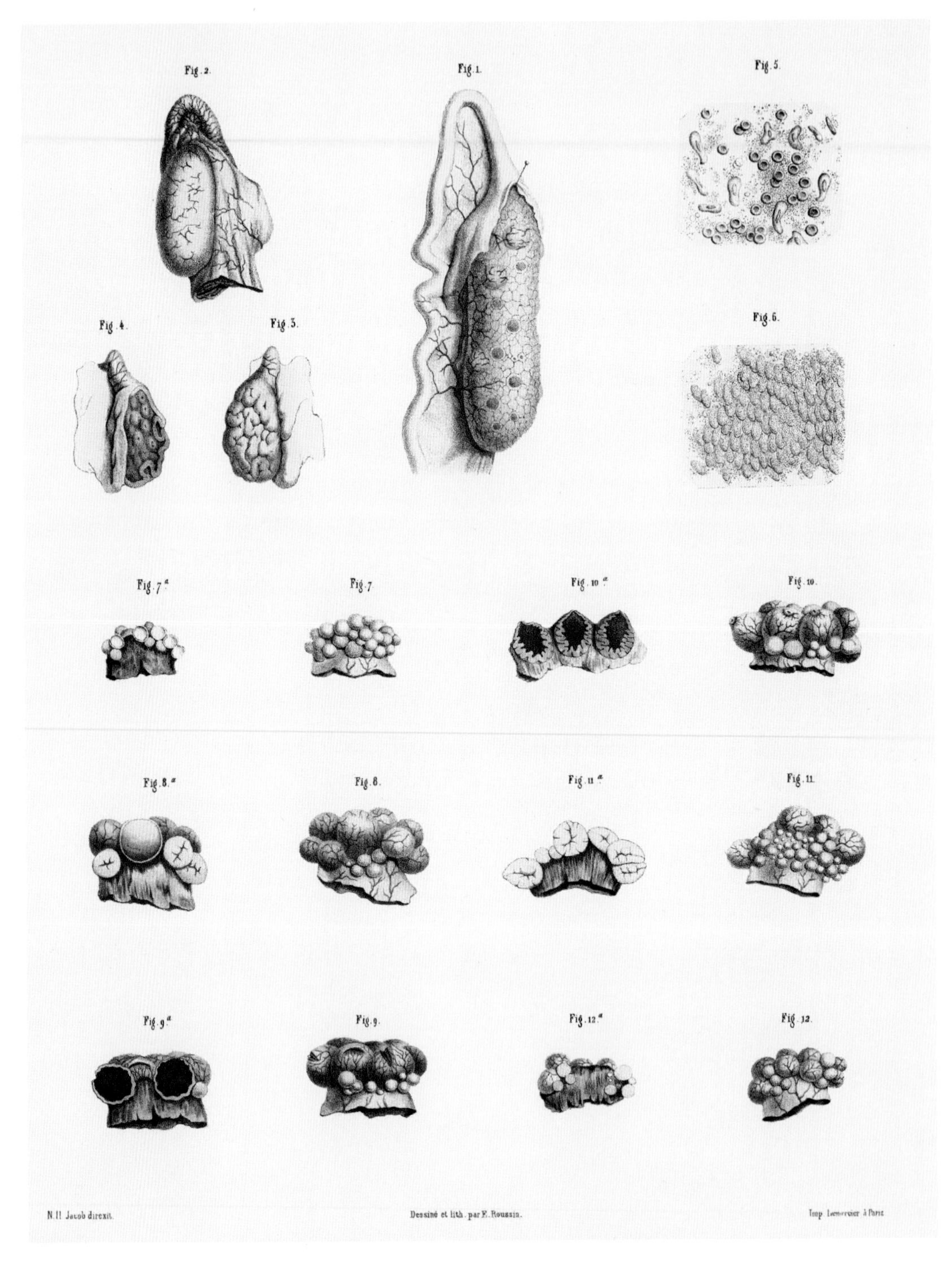

Embryology: Ovary and ovarian follicles
Embryologie : Ovaire et follicules ovariens
Embriología: ovario y folículos ováricos

EMBRYOLOGIA: OVARIUM, FOLLICULI OVARICI, ET OVOCYTUS

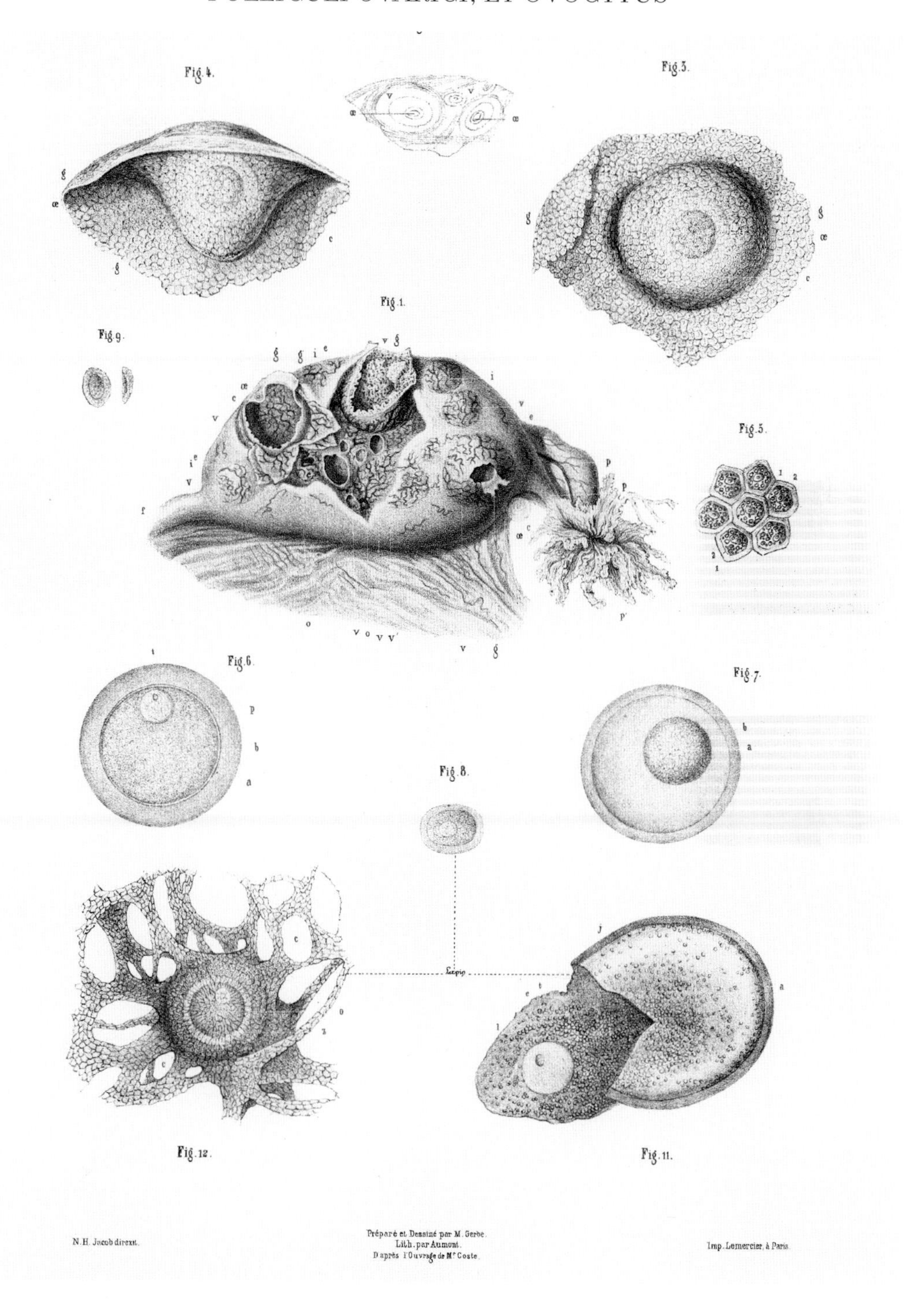

Embryology: Ovary, ovarian follicles, and oocyte
Embryologie : Ovaire, follicules ovariens et ovocyte
Embriología: ovario, folículos ováricos y ovocito

EMBRYOLOGIA: OVOCYTUS, FECUNDATIO, ET FISSIO

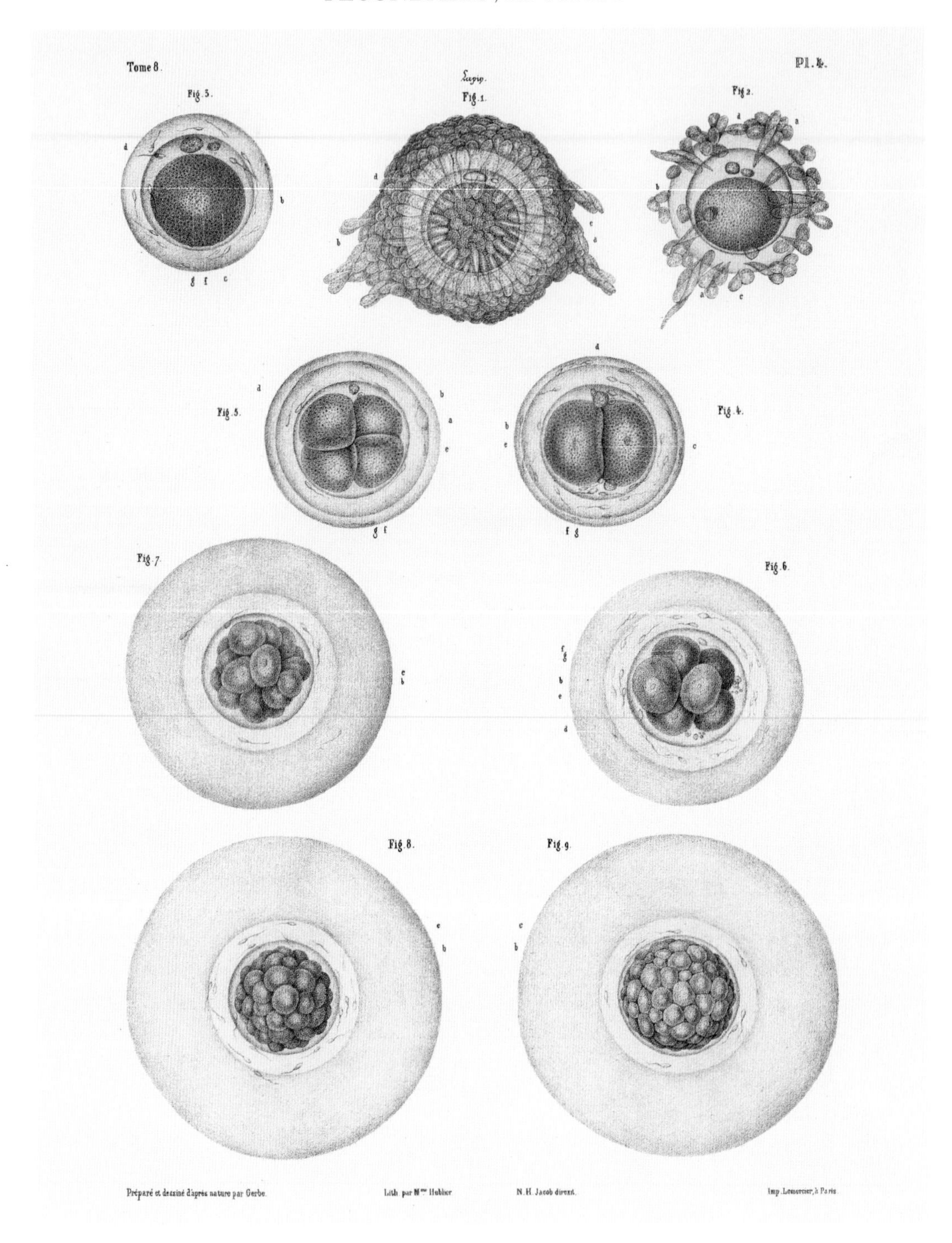

Embryology: Oocyte, fertilisation, and segmentation
Embryologie : Ovocyte, fécondation et segmentation
Embriología: ovocito, fecundación y segmentación

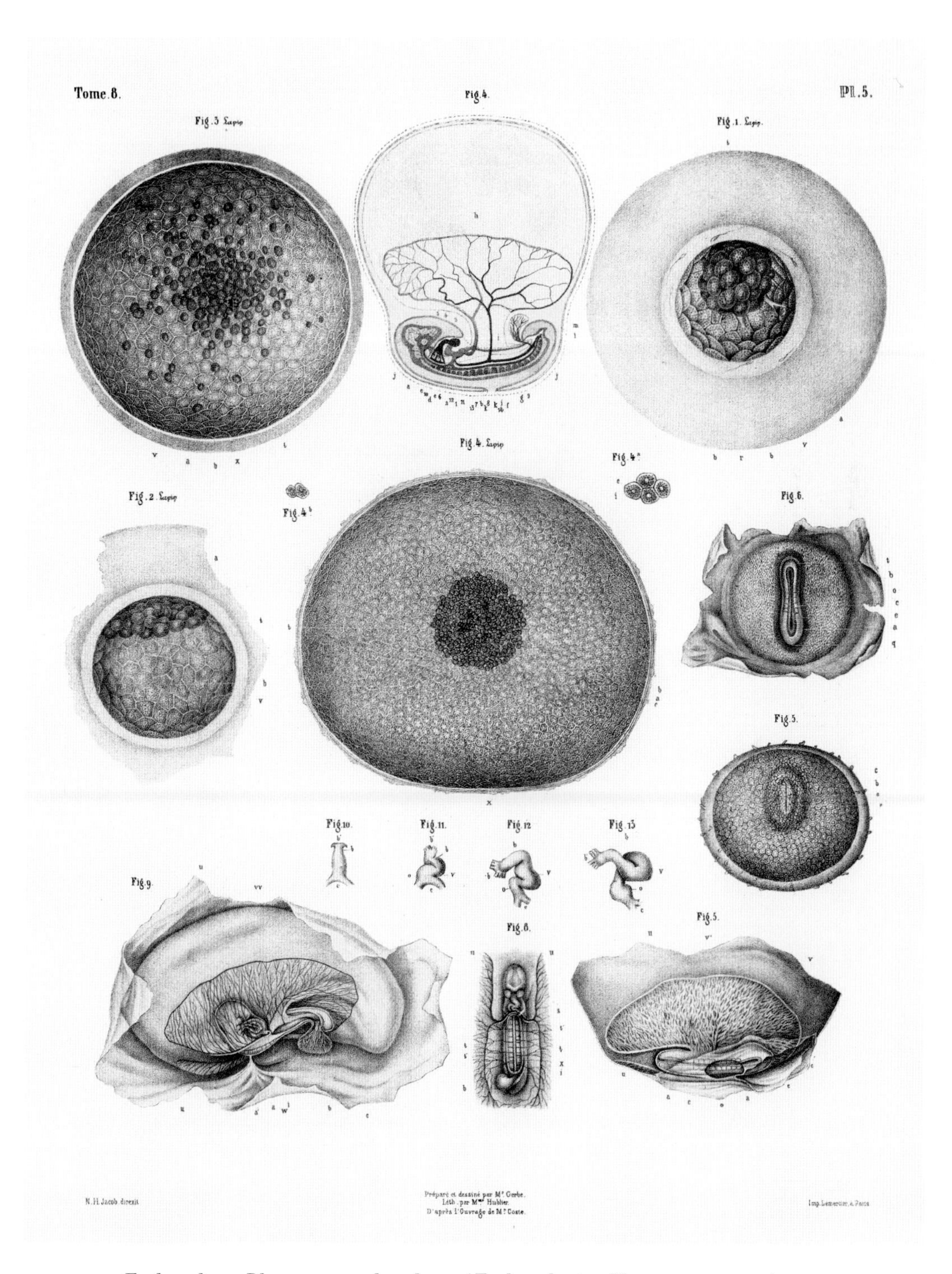

Embryology: Blastocyst and embryo / Embryologie : Blastocyste et embryon
Embriología: blastocisto y embrión

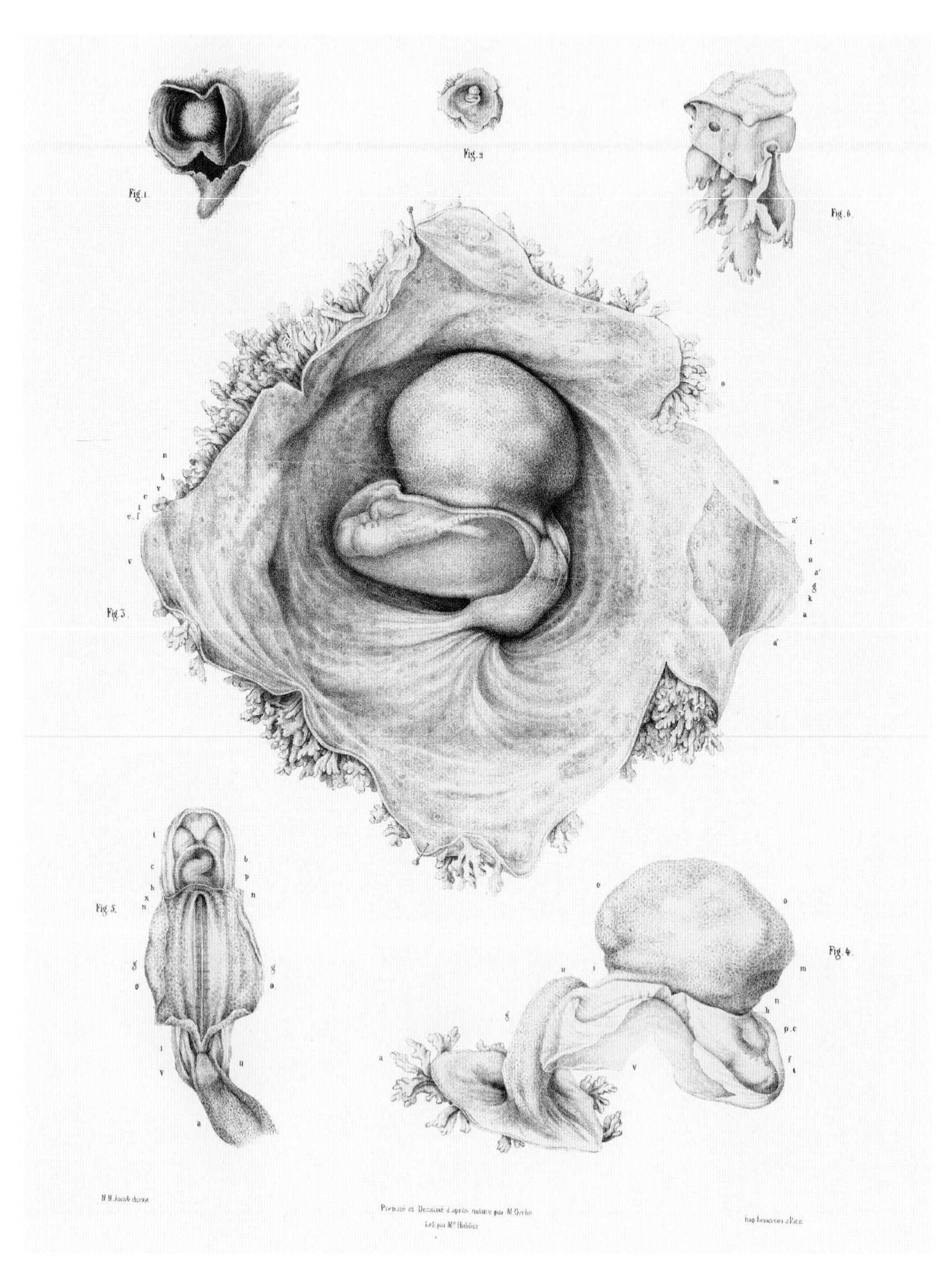

Embryology: Embryo / Embryologie : Embryon / Embriología: embrión

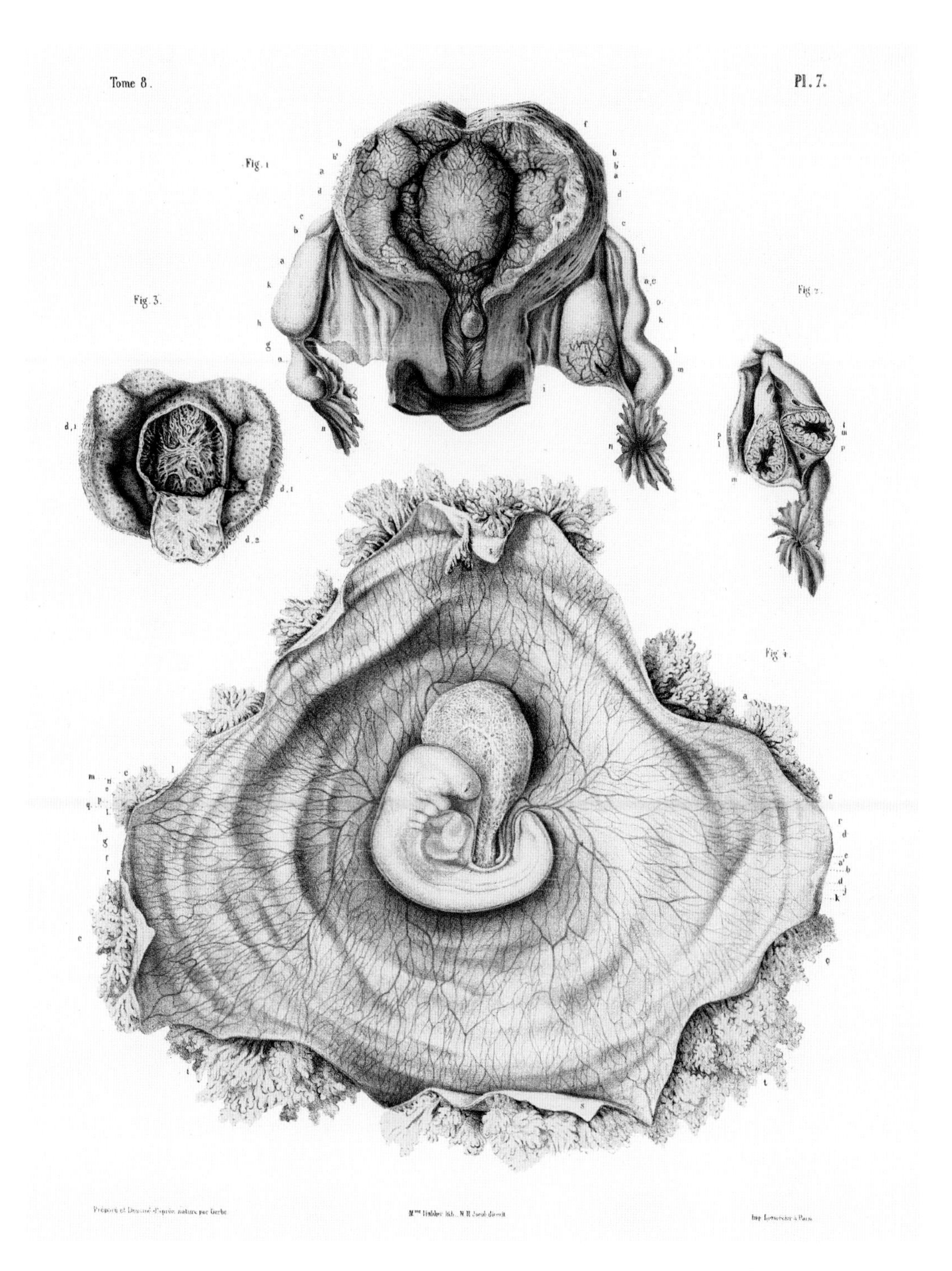

Embryology: Embryo / Embryologie : Embryon / Embriología: embrión

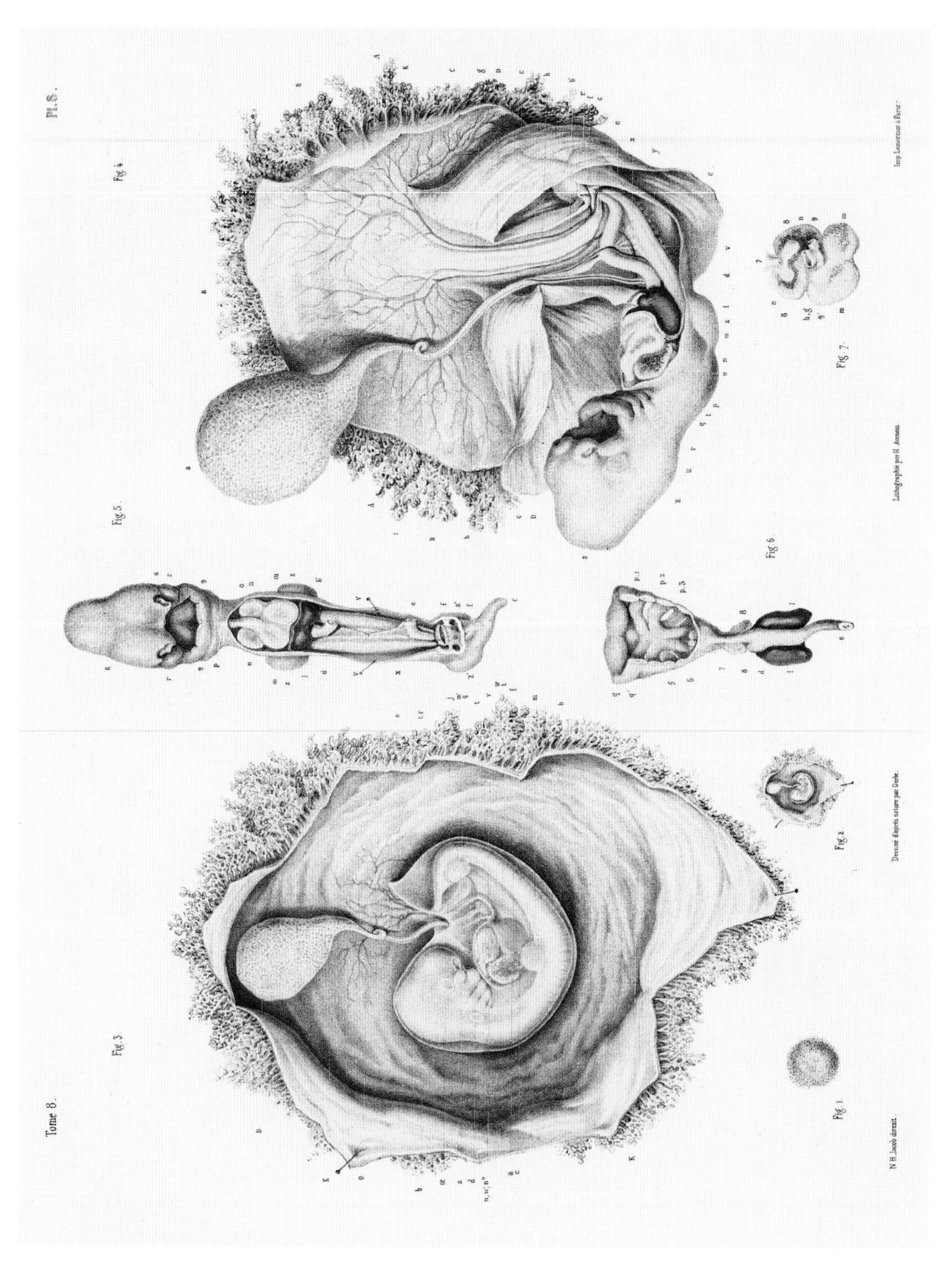

Embryology: Embryo / Embryologie : Embryon / Embriología: embrión

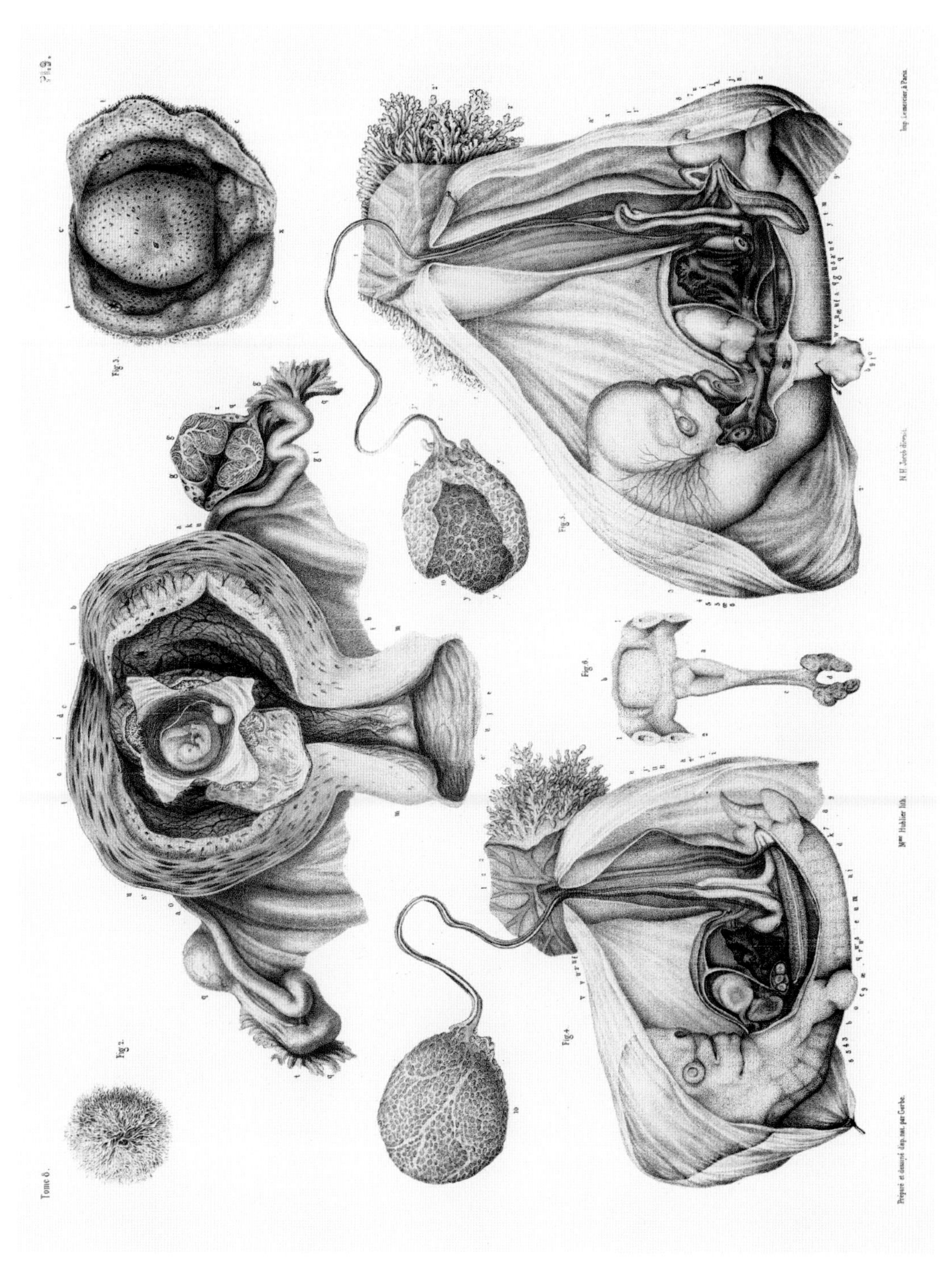

Embryology: Embryo / Embryologie : Embryon / Embriología: embrión

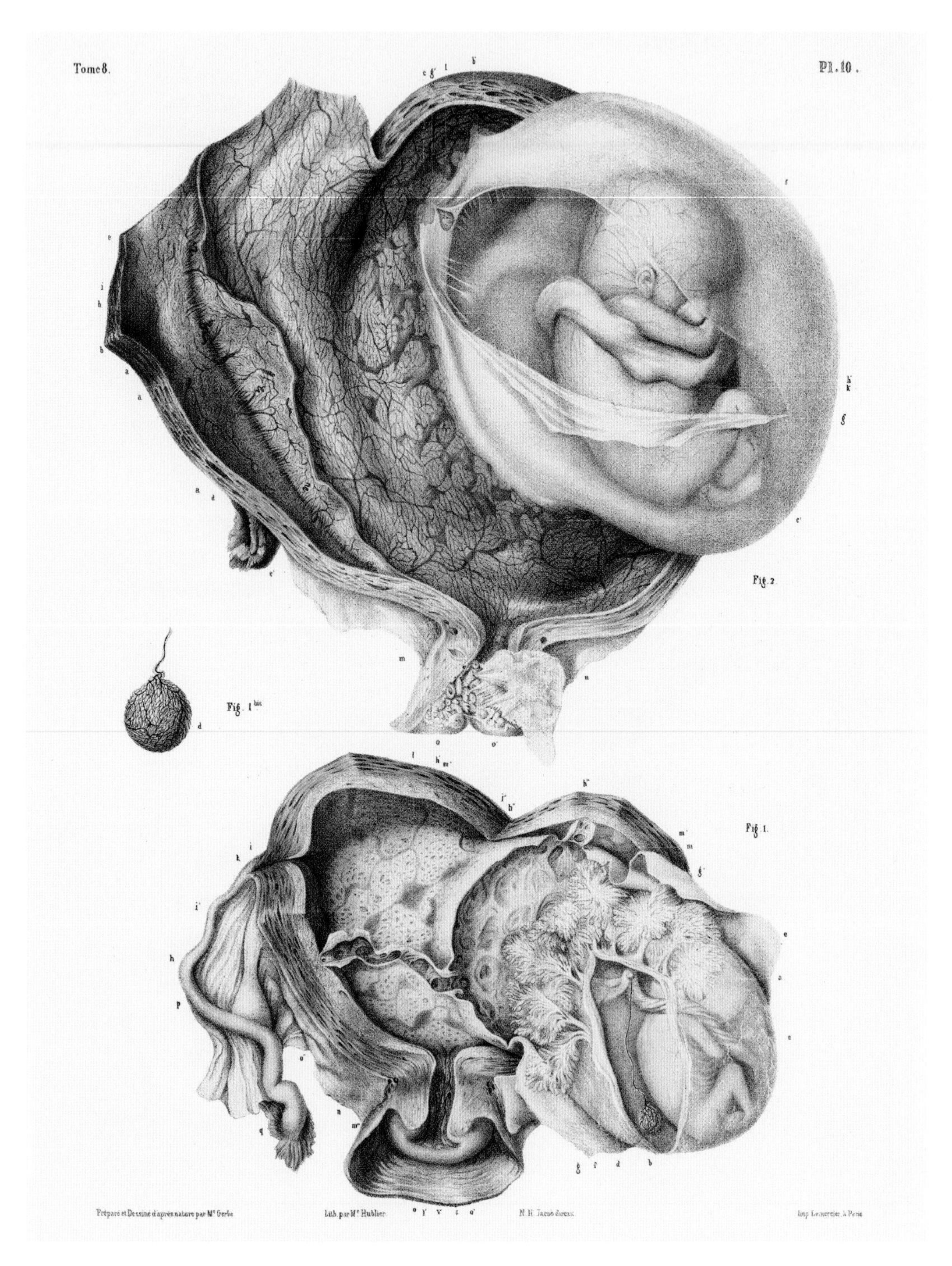

Embryology: Fetus / Embryologie : Fœtus / Embriología: feto

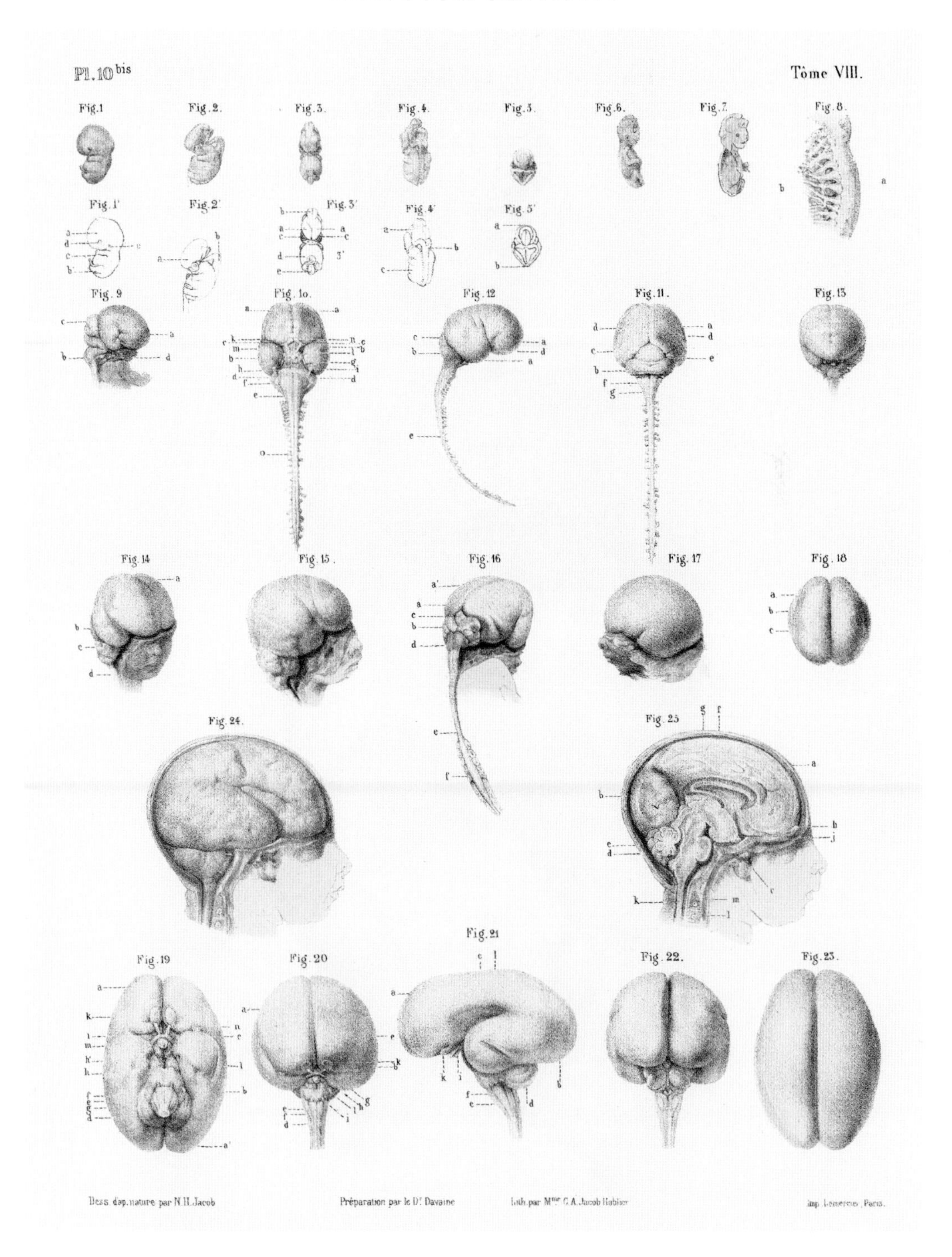

Embryology: Central nervous system / Embryologie : Système nerveux central
Embriología: sistema nervioso central

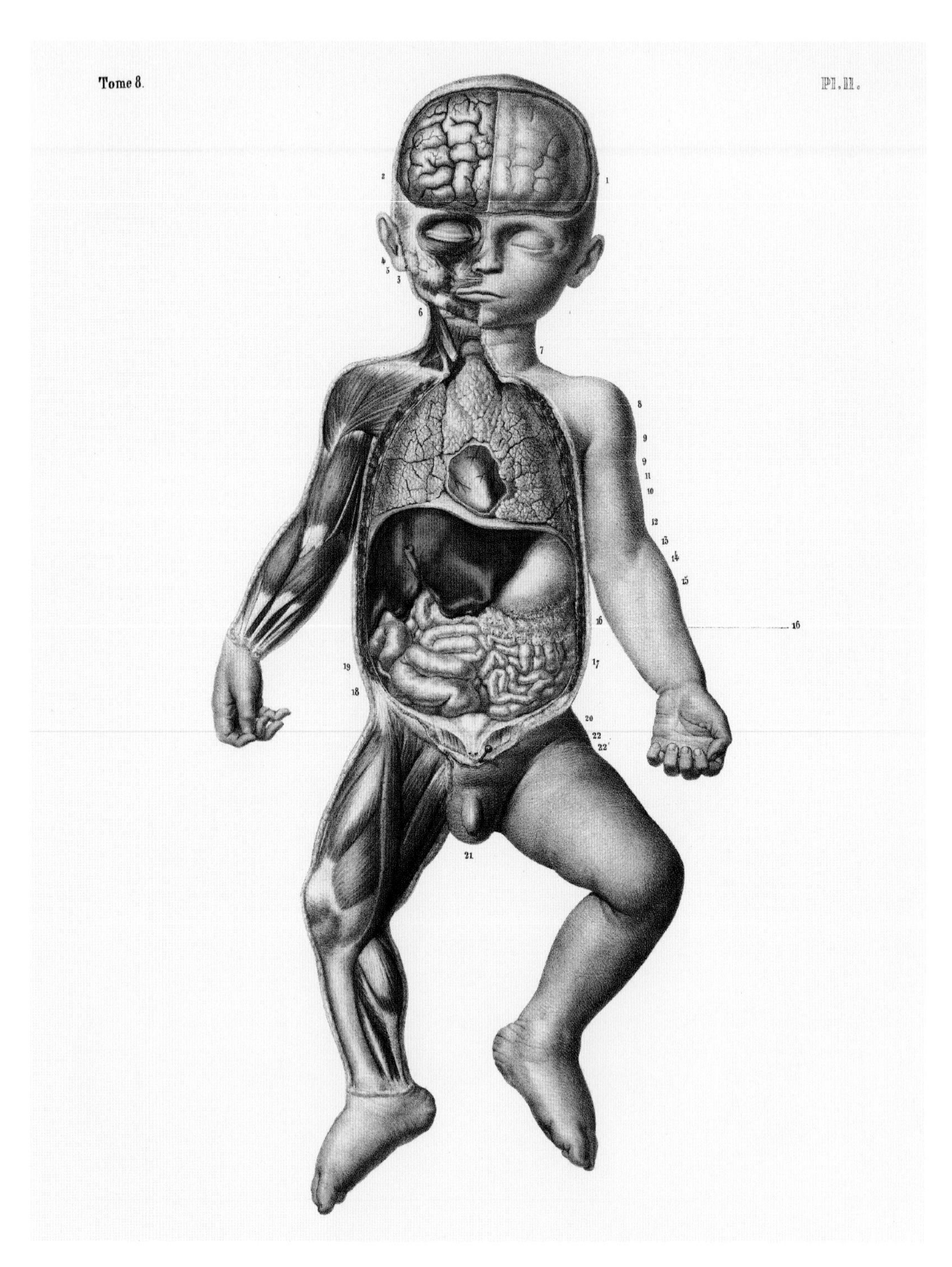

Embryology: Fetus / Embryologie : Fœtus / Embriología: feto

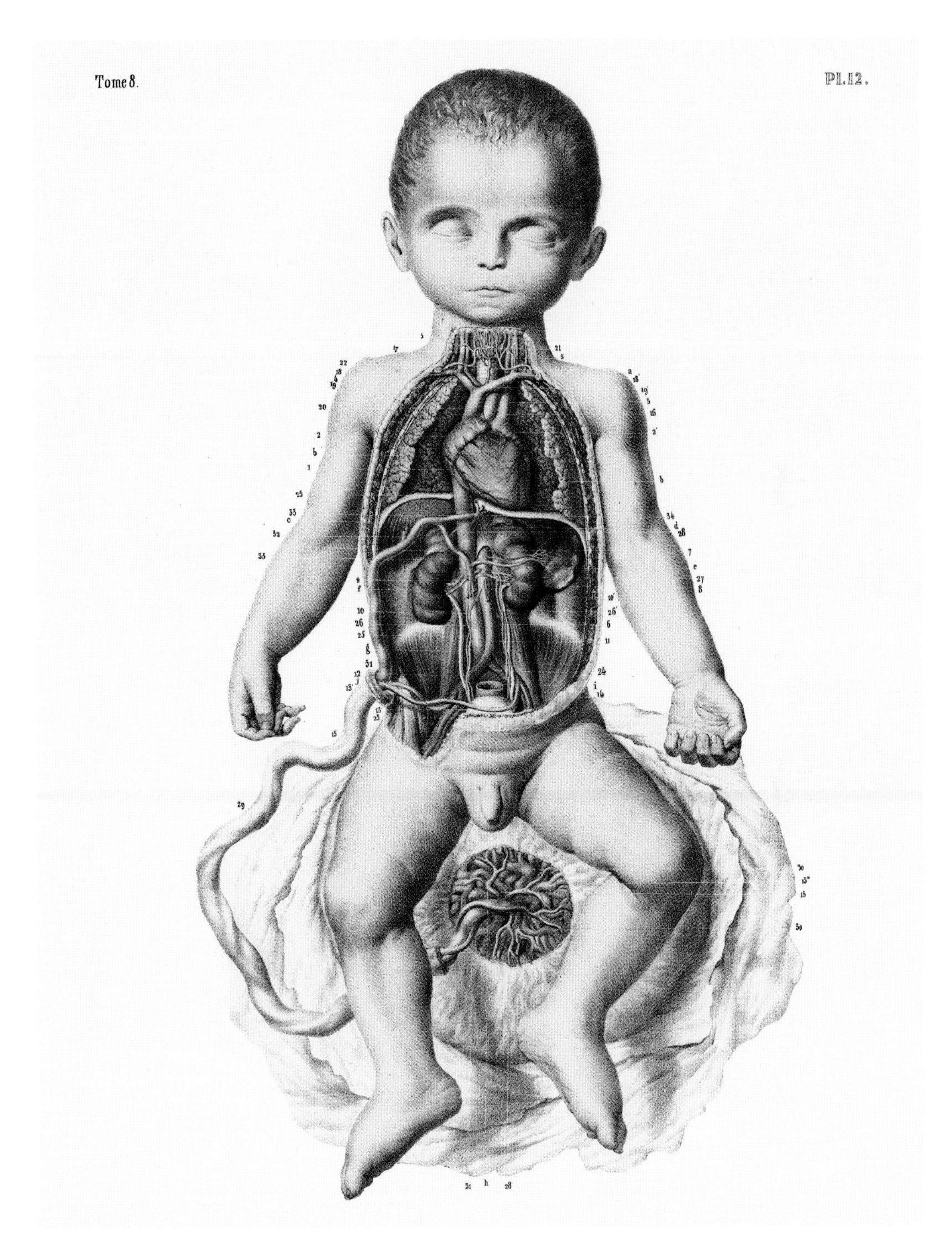

Embryology: Fetus / Embryologie : Fœtus / Embriología: feto

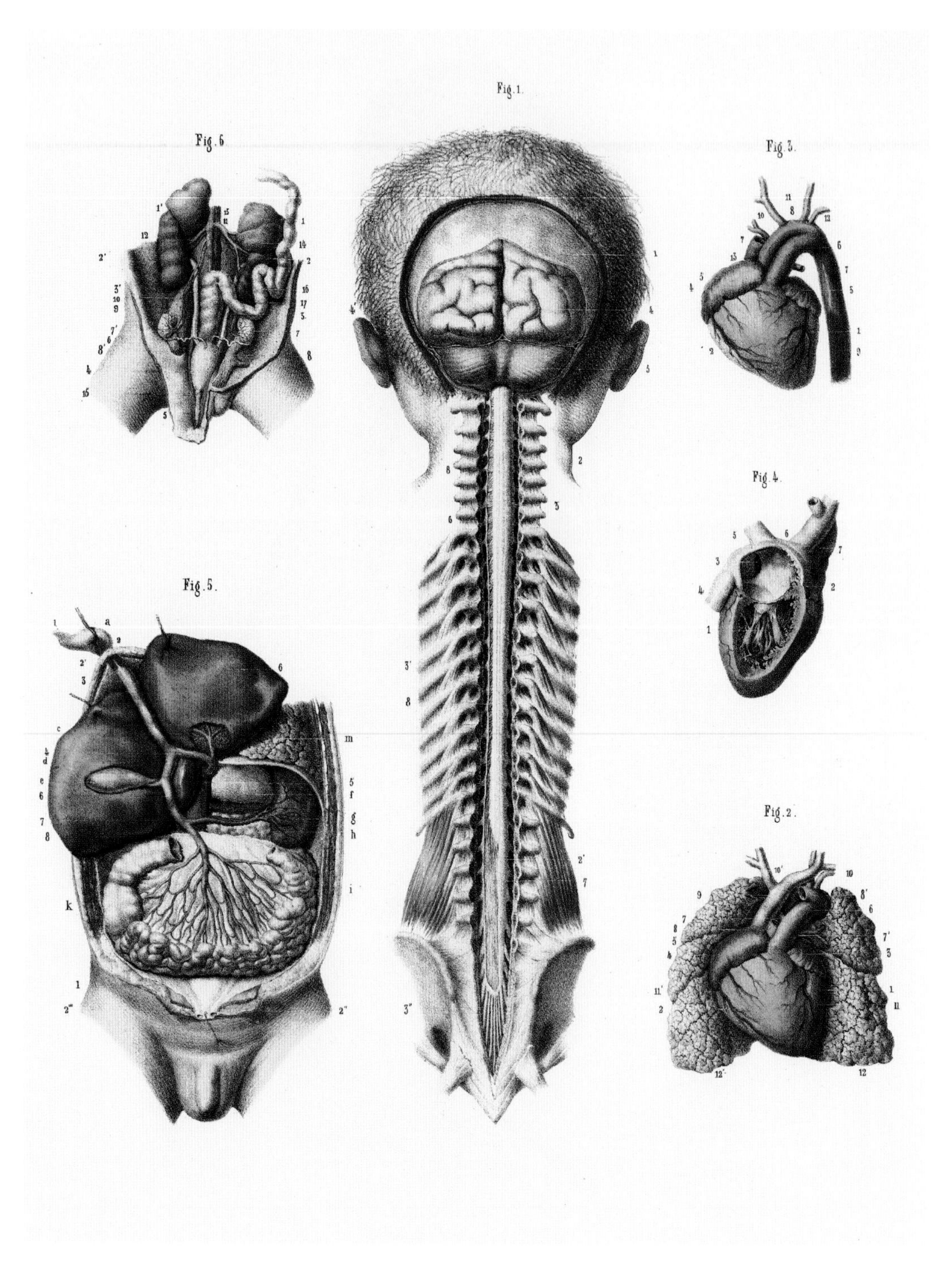

Embryology: Fetus / Embryologie : Fœtus / Embriología: feto

Embryology: Placenta / Embryologie : Placenta / Embriología: placenta

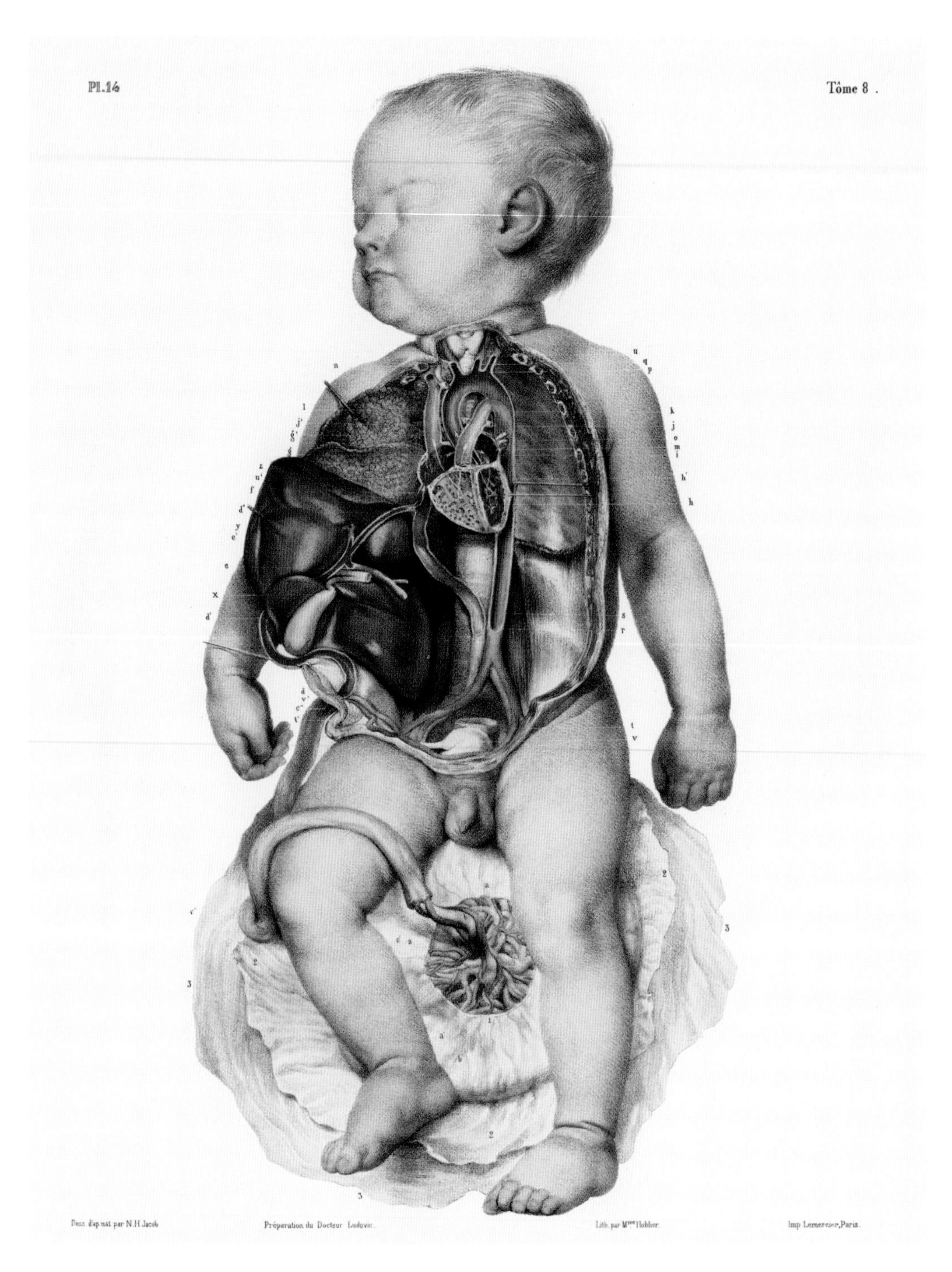

Embryology: Fetus / Embryologie : Fœtus / Embriología: feto

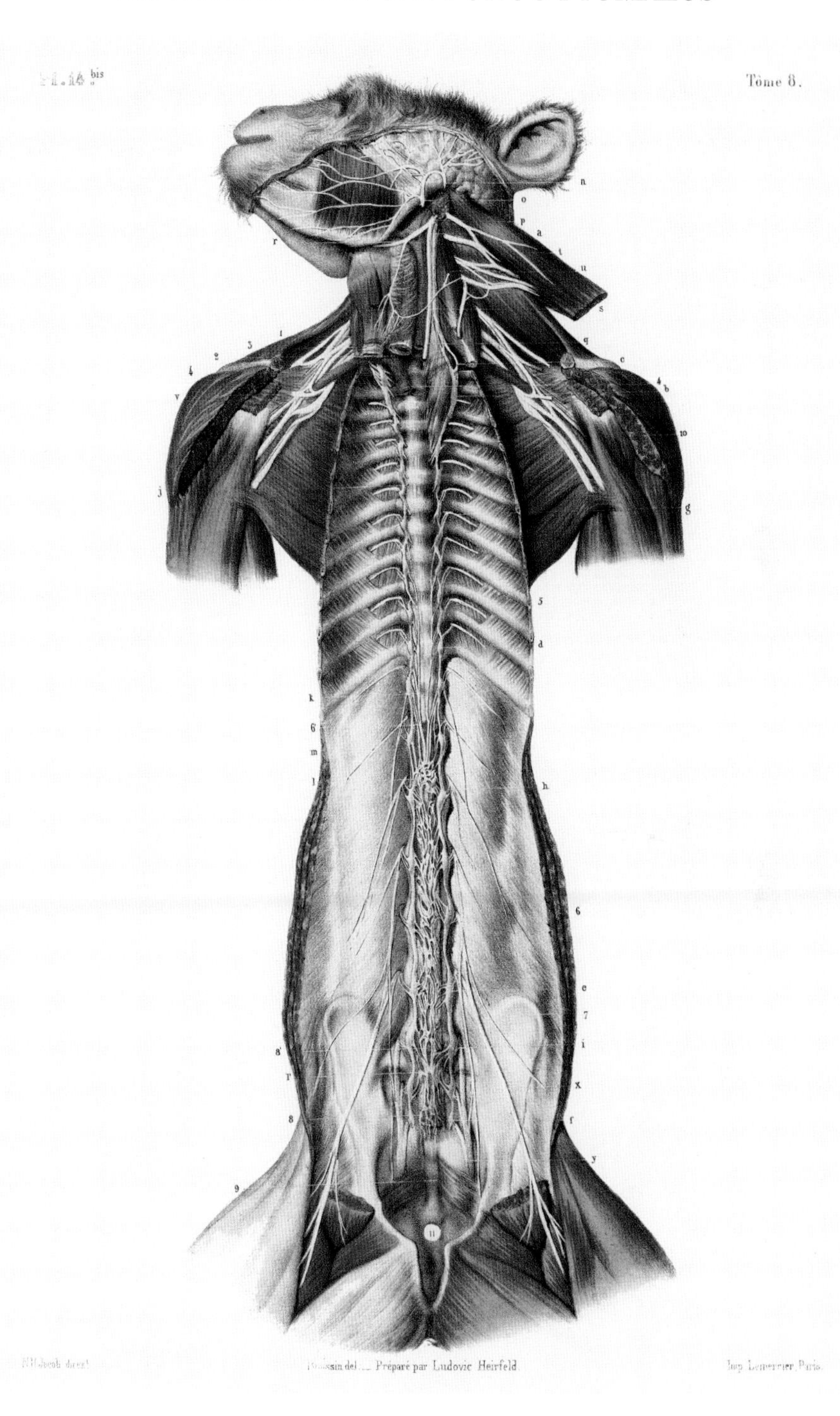

Comparative anatomy of the nervous system: Orang-utan
Anatomie comparée du système nerveux : Orang-outan
Anatomía comparada del sistema nervioso: orangután

ANATOMIA COMPARATA
SYSTEMATIS NERVOSI: PONGO PYGMAEUS

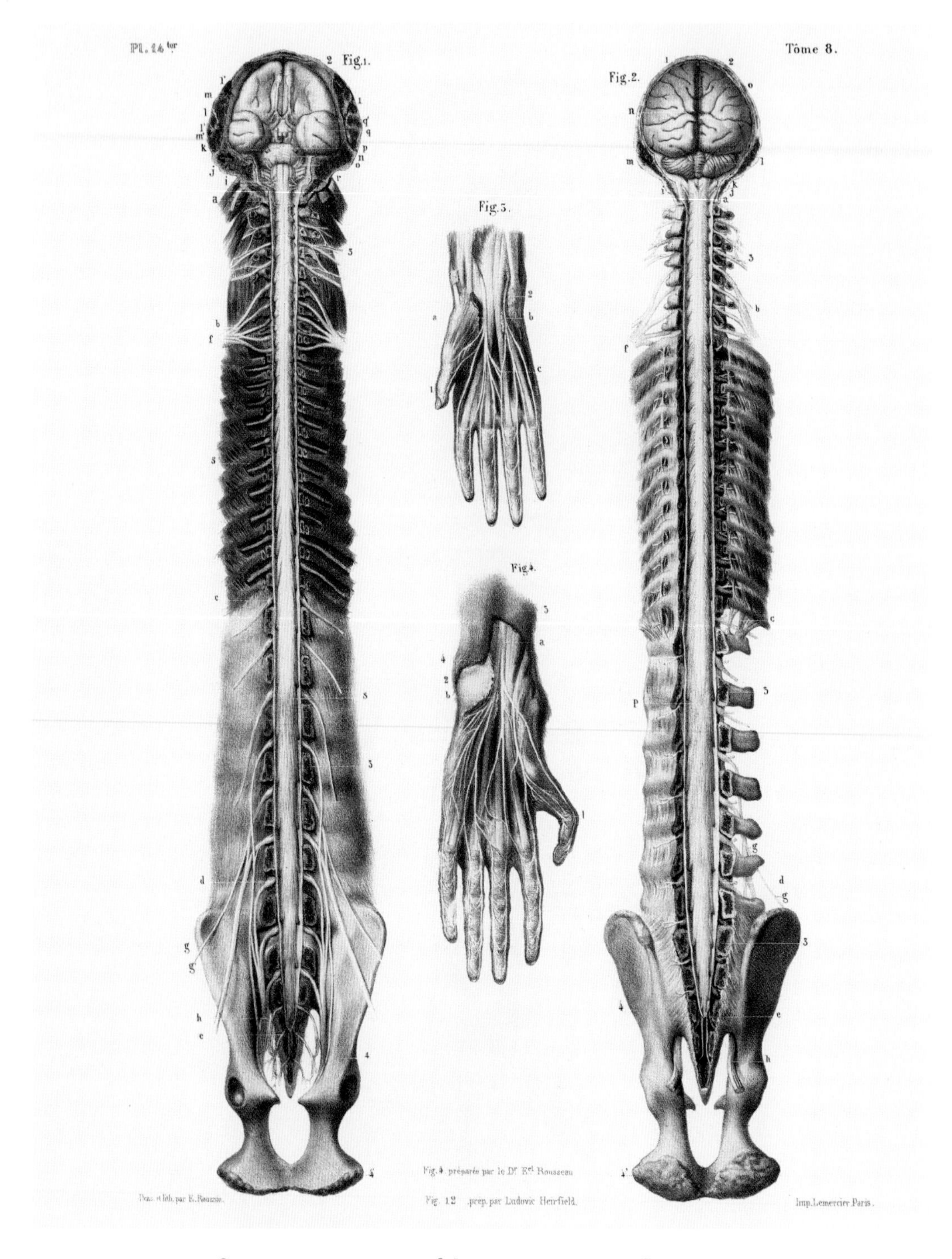

Comparative anatomy of the nervous system: Orang-utan
Anatomie comparée du système nerveux : Orang-outan
Anatomía comparada del sistema nervioso: orangután

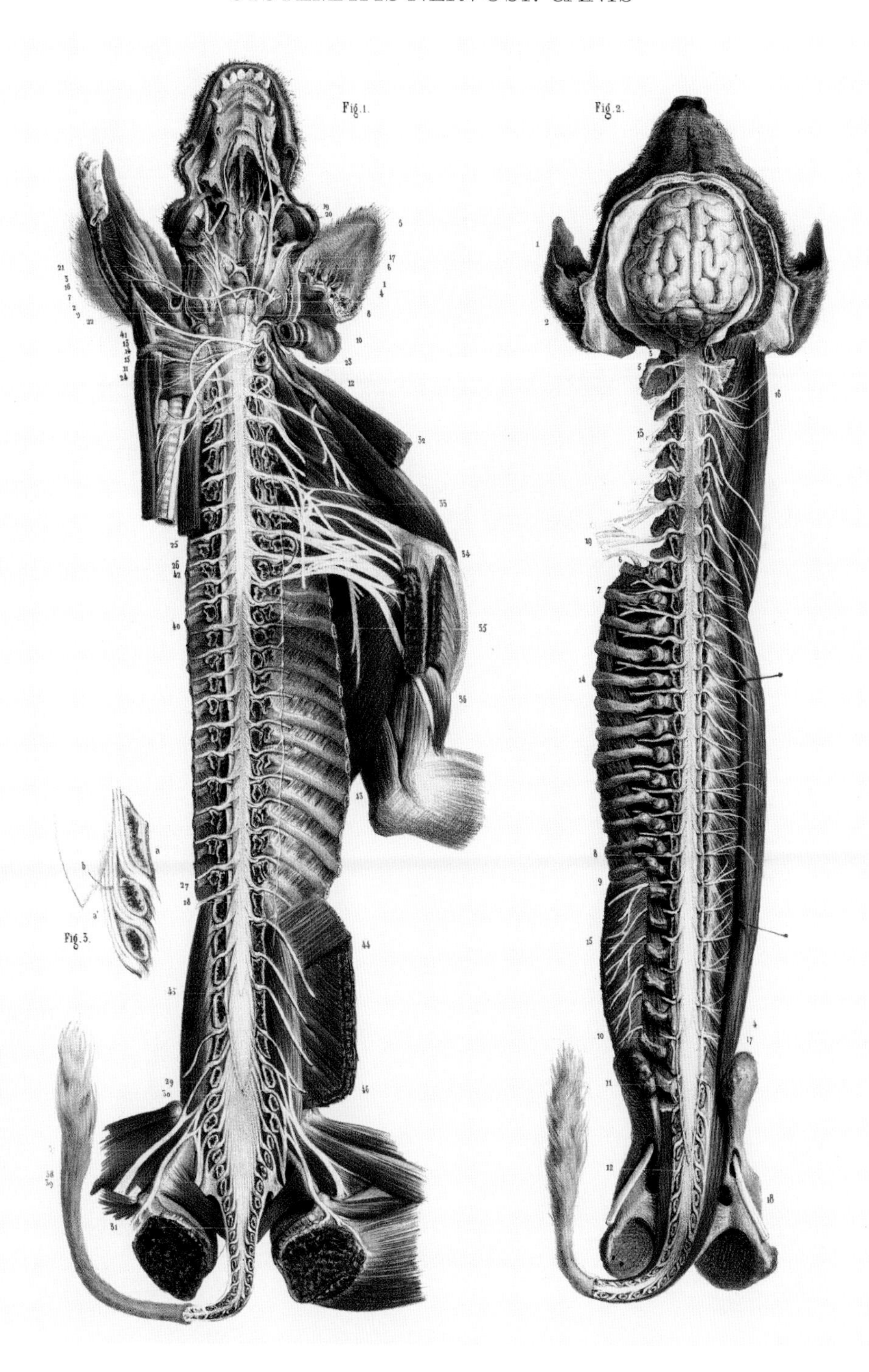

Comparative anatomy of the nervous system: Dog
Anatomie comparée du système nerveux : Chien
Anatomía comparada del sistema nervioso: perro

ANATOMIA COMPARATA
SYSTEMATIS NERVOSI: CATTUS

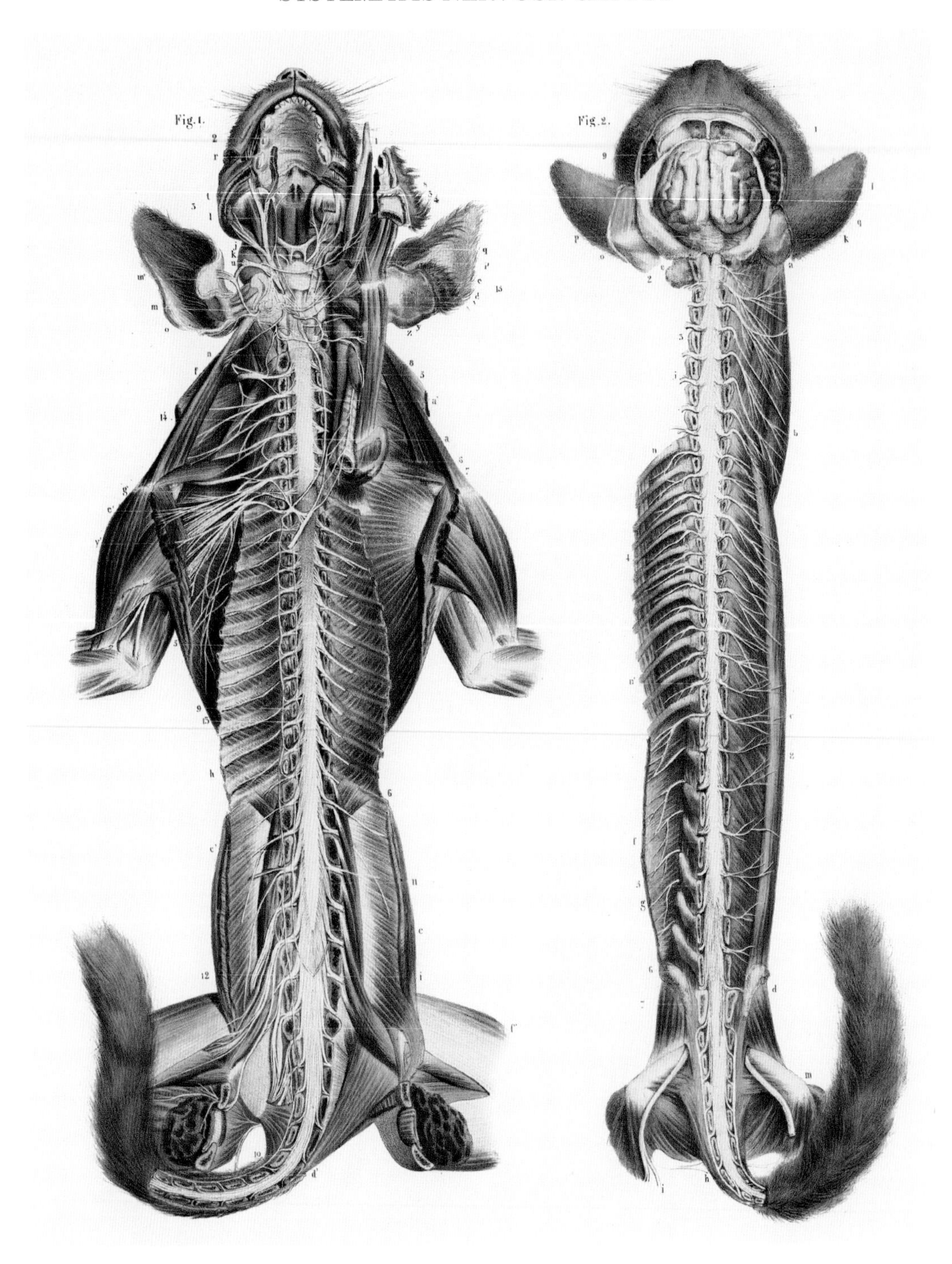

Comparative anatomy of the nervous system: Cat
Anatomie comparée du système nerveux : Chat
Anatomía comparada del sistema nervioso: gato

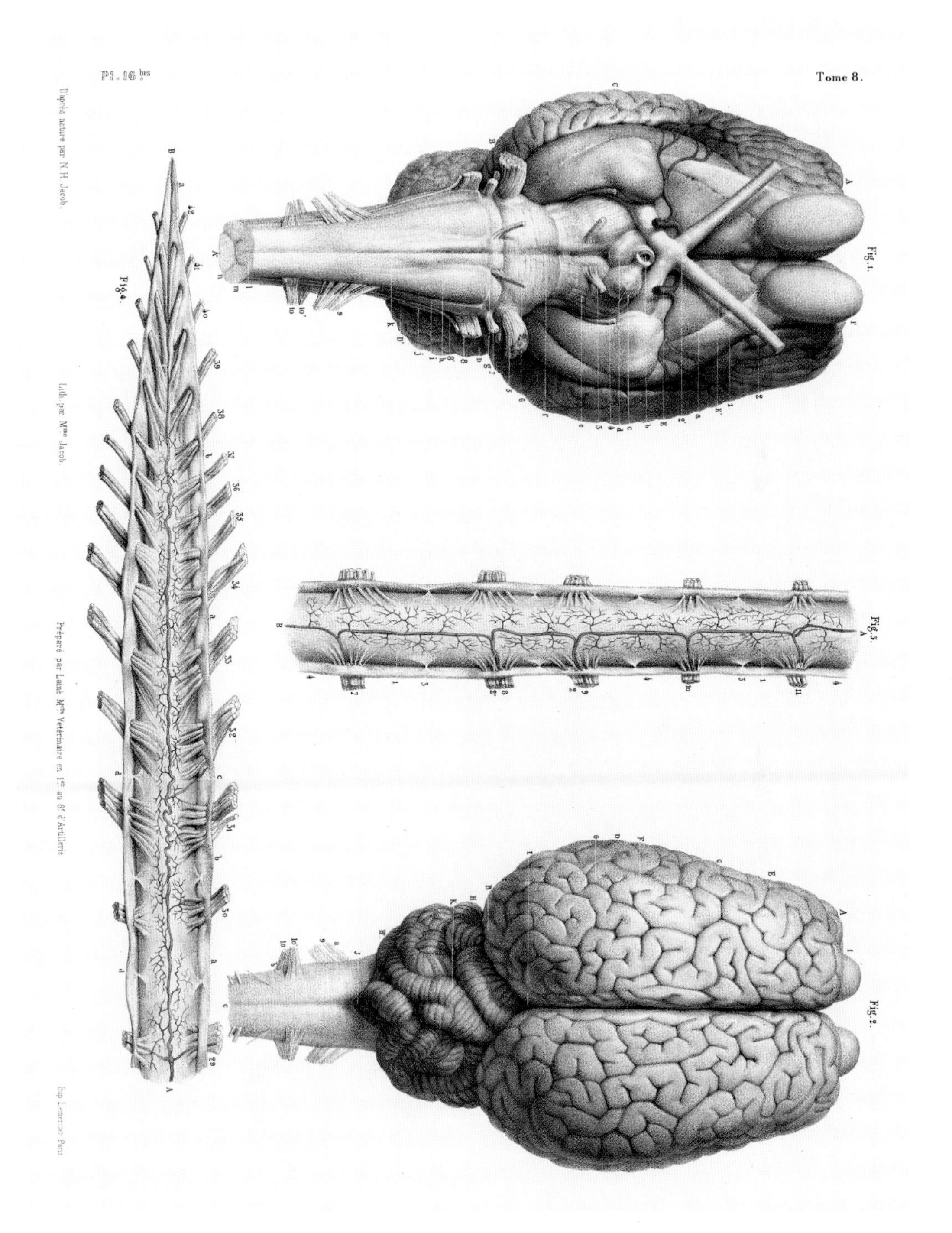

Comparative anatomy of the nervous system: Horse
Anatomie comparée du système nerveux : Cheval
Anatomía comparada del sistema nervioso: caballo

ANATOMIA COMPARATA SYSTEMATIS NERVOSI: EQUUS, CUNICULUS, SCIURUS, ELEPHAS, APER, BOS, ET VERVEX

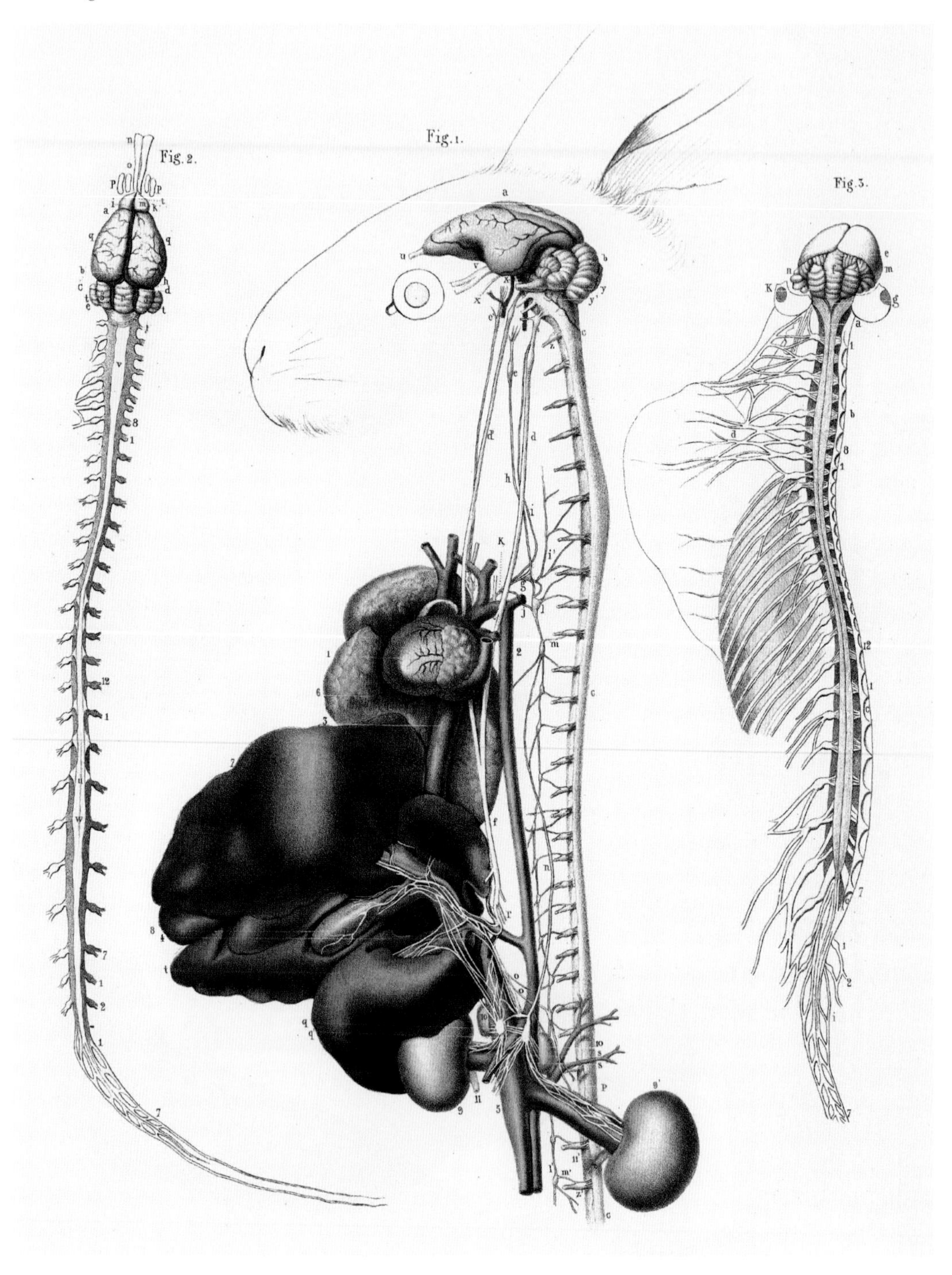

Comparative anatomy of the nervous system: Rabbit and squirrel
Anatomie comparée du système nerveux : Lapin et écureuil
Anatomía comparada del sistema nervioso: conejo y ardilla

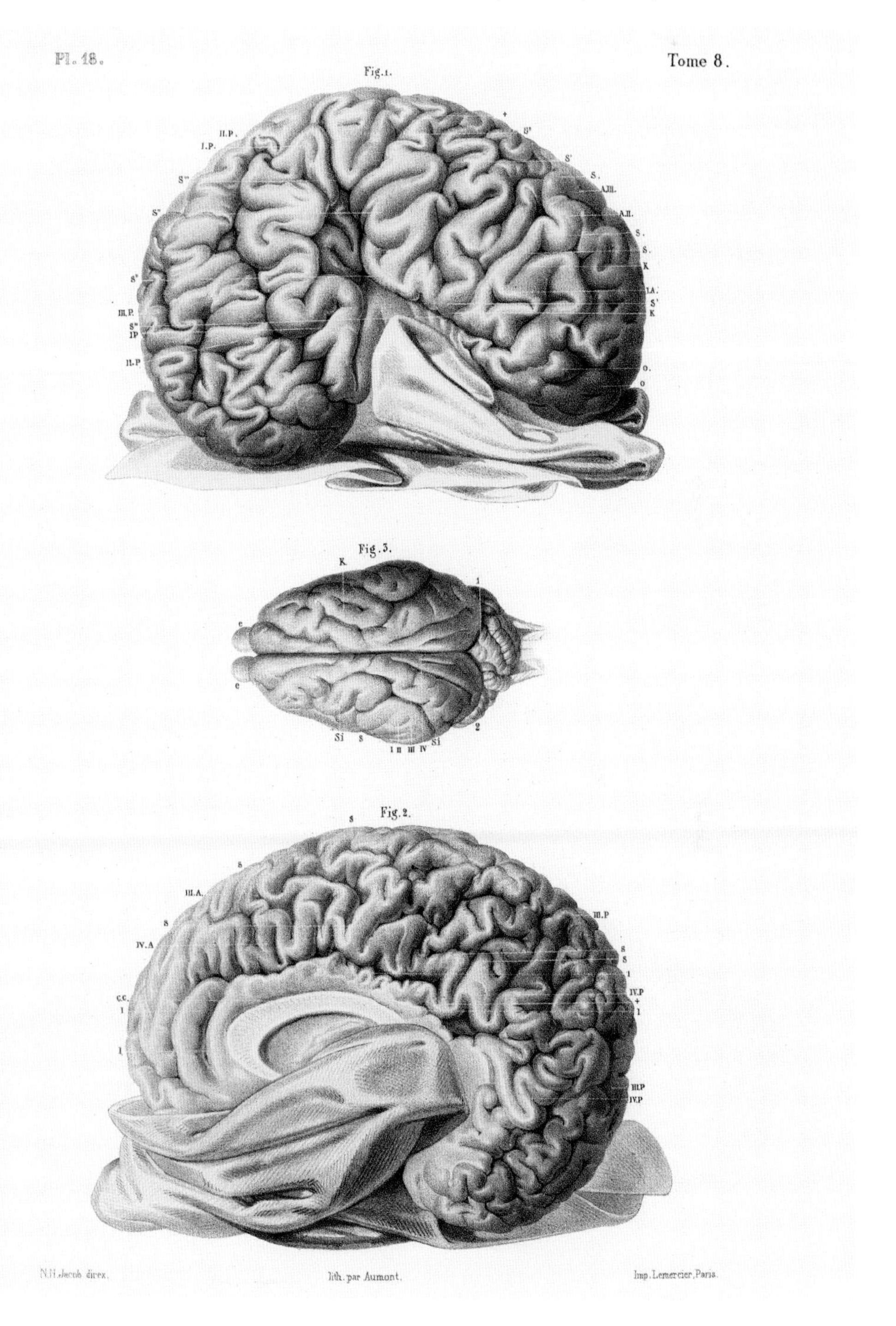

Comparative anatomy of the nervous system: Elephant and wild boar
Anatomie comparée du système nerveux : Eléphant et sanglier
Anatomía comparada del sistema nervioso: elefante y jabalí

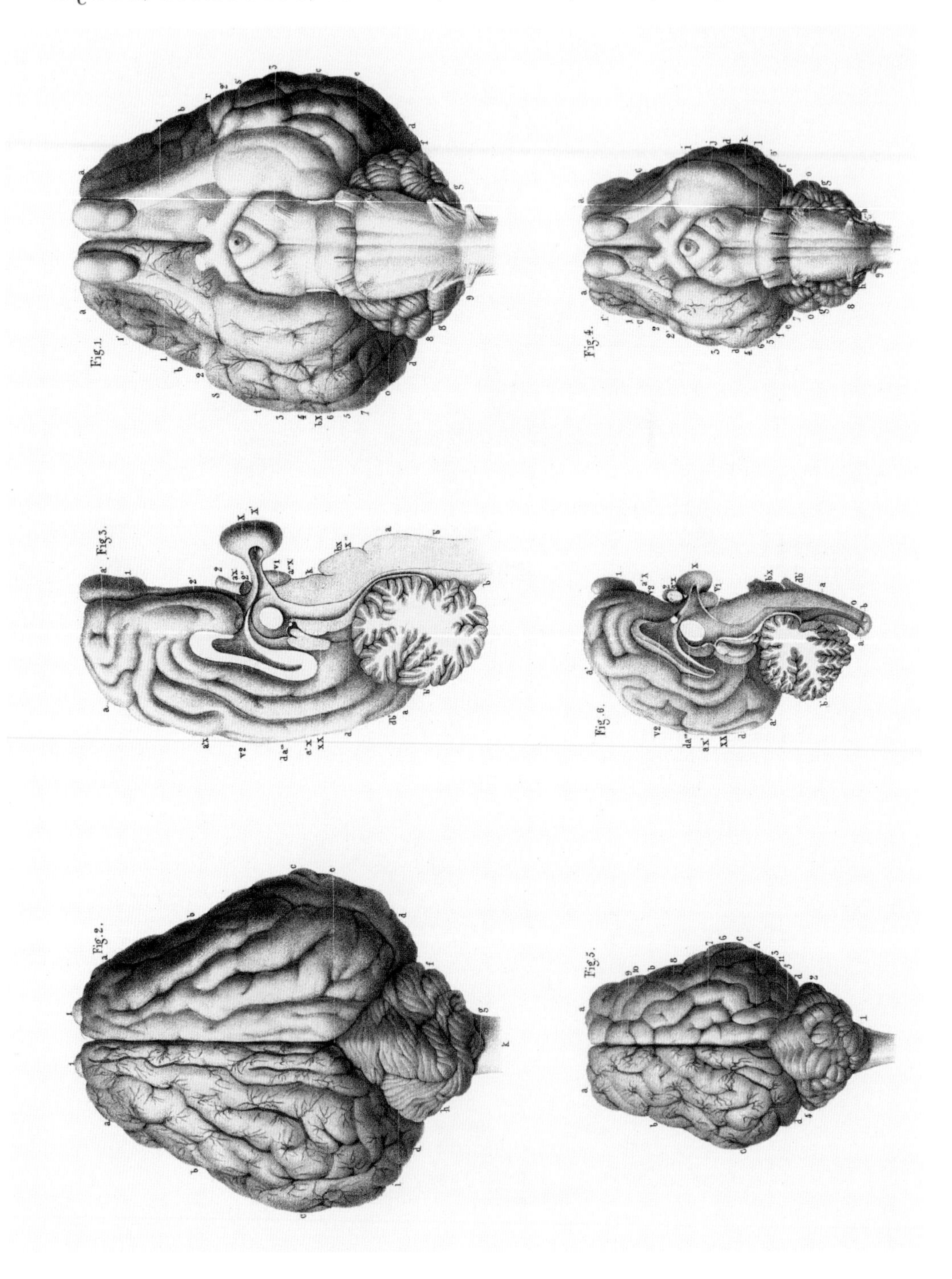

Comparative anatomy of the nervous system: Ox and sheep
Anatomie comparée du système nerveux : Bœuf et mouton
Anatomía comparada del sistema nervioso: buey y carnero

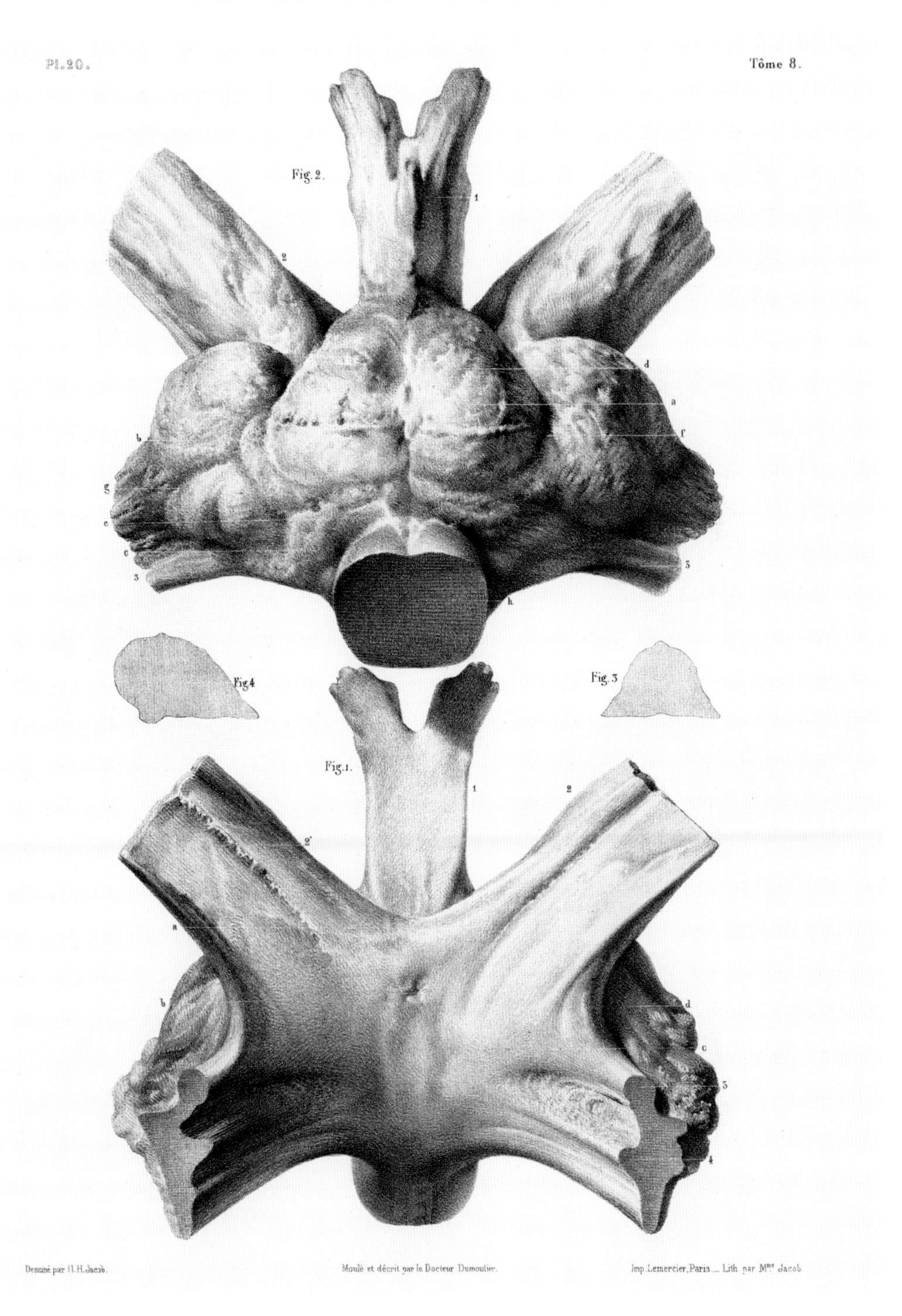

Comparative anatomy of the nervous system: Bowhead whale
Anatomie comparée du système nerveux : Baleine franche
Anatomía comparada del sistema nervioso: ballena franca

ANATOMIA COMPARATA SYSTEMATIS NERVOSI: PHOCA ET PORCULUS MARINUS

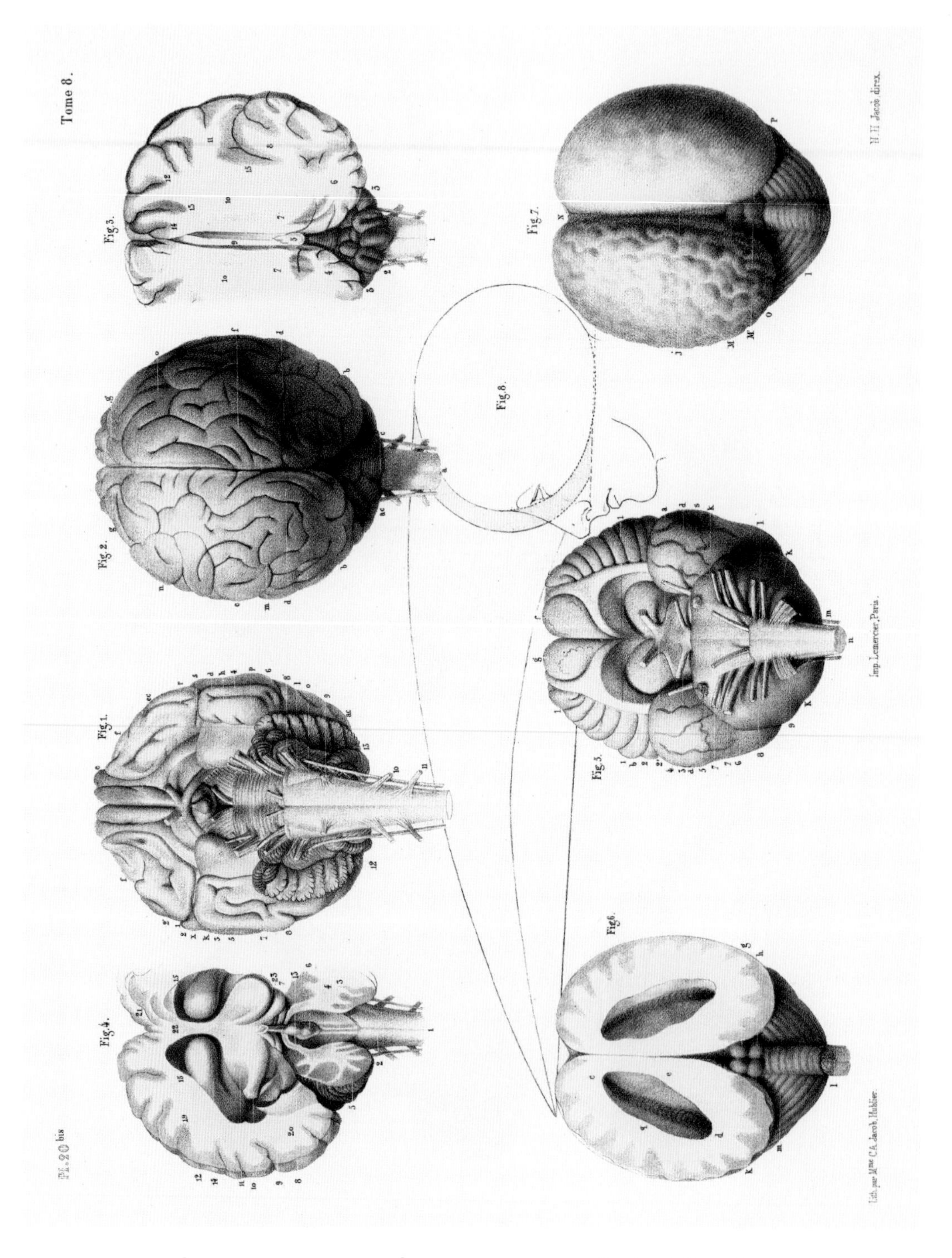

Comparative anatomy of the nervous system: Seal and Porpoise
Anatomie comparée du système nerveux : Phoque et marsouin
Anatomía comparada del sistema nervioso: foca y marsopa

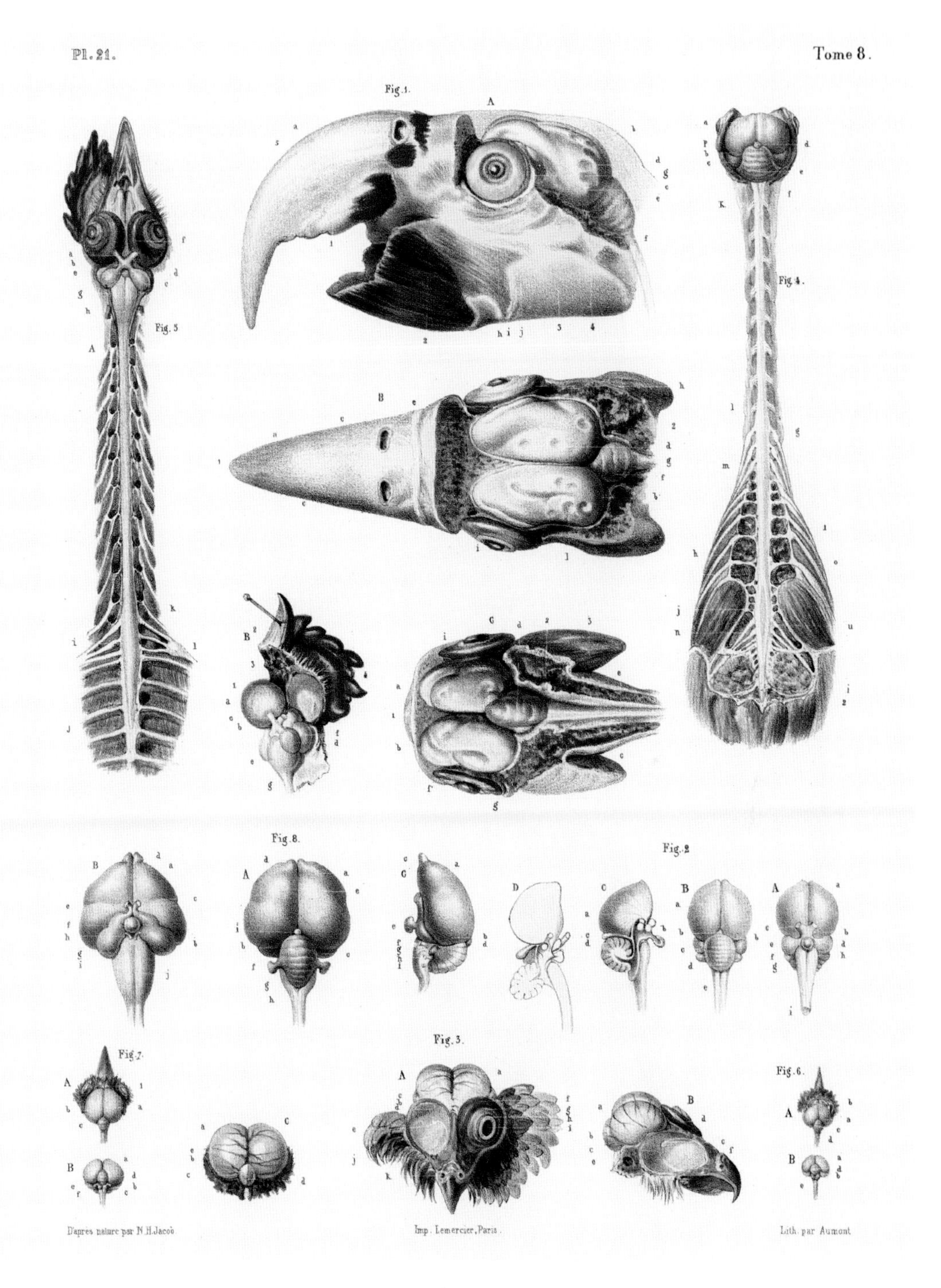

Comparative anatomy of the nervous system: Birds
Anatomie comparée du système nerveux : Oiseaux
Anatomía comparada del sistema nervioso: aves

ANATOMIA COMPARATA
SYSTEMATIS NERVOSI: REPTILIA ET AMPHIBIA

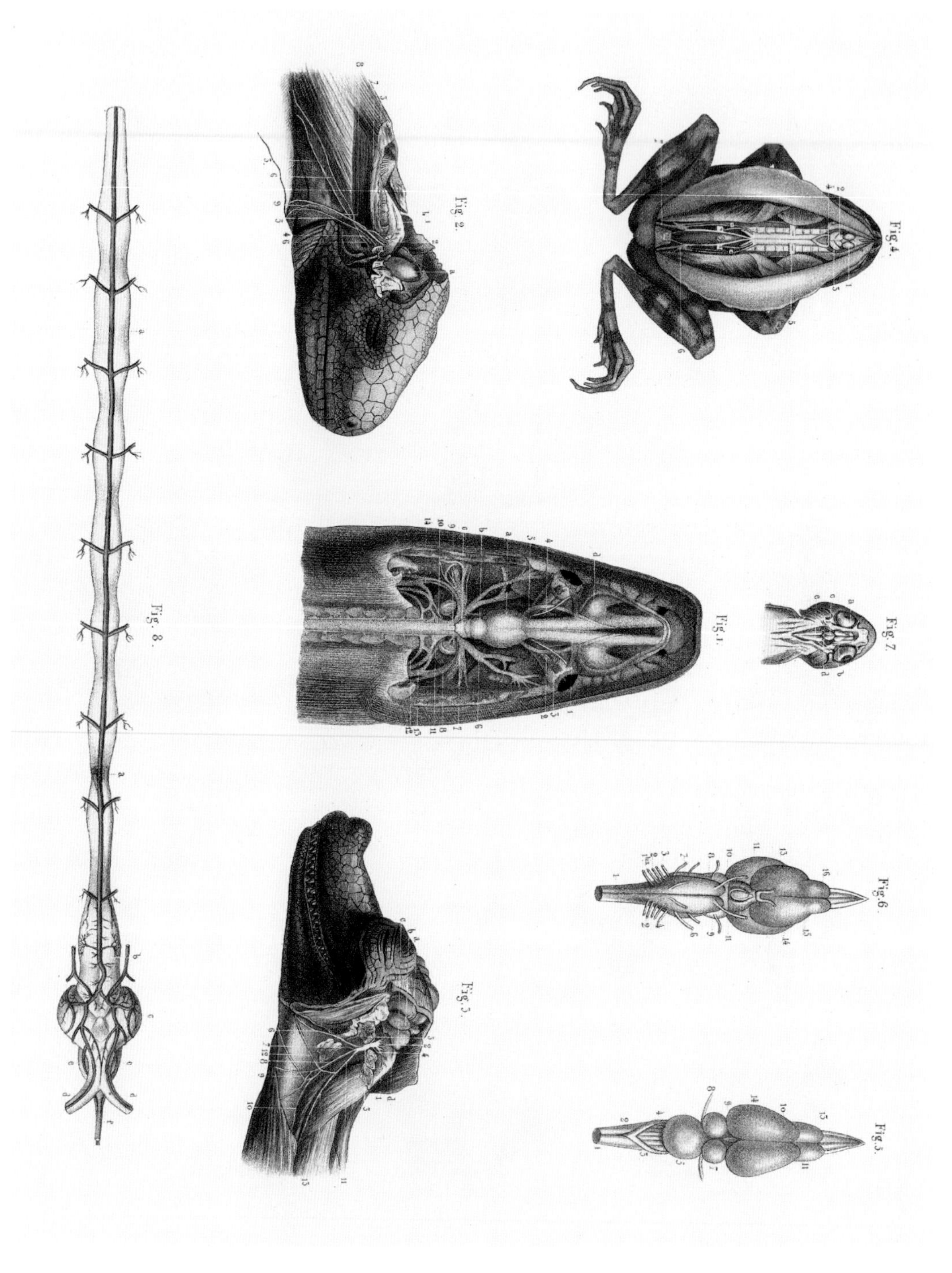

Comparative anatomy of the nervous system: Reptiles and amphibians
Anatomie comparée du système nerveux : Reptiles et amphibiens
Anatomía comparada del sistema nervioso: reptiles y anfibios

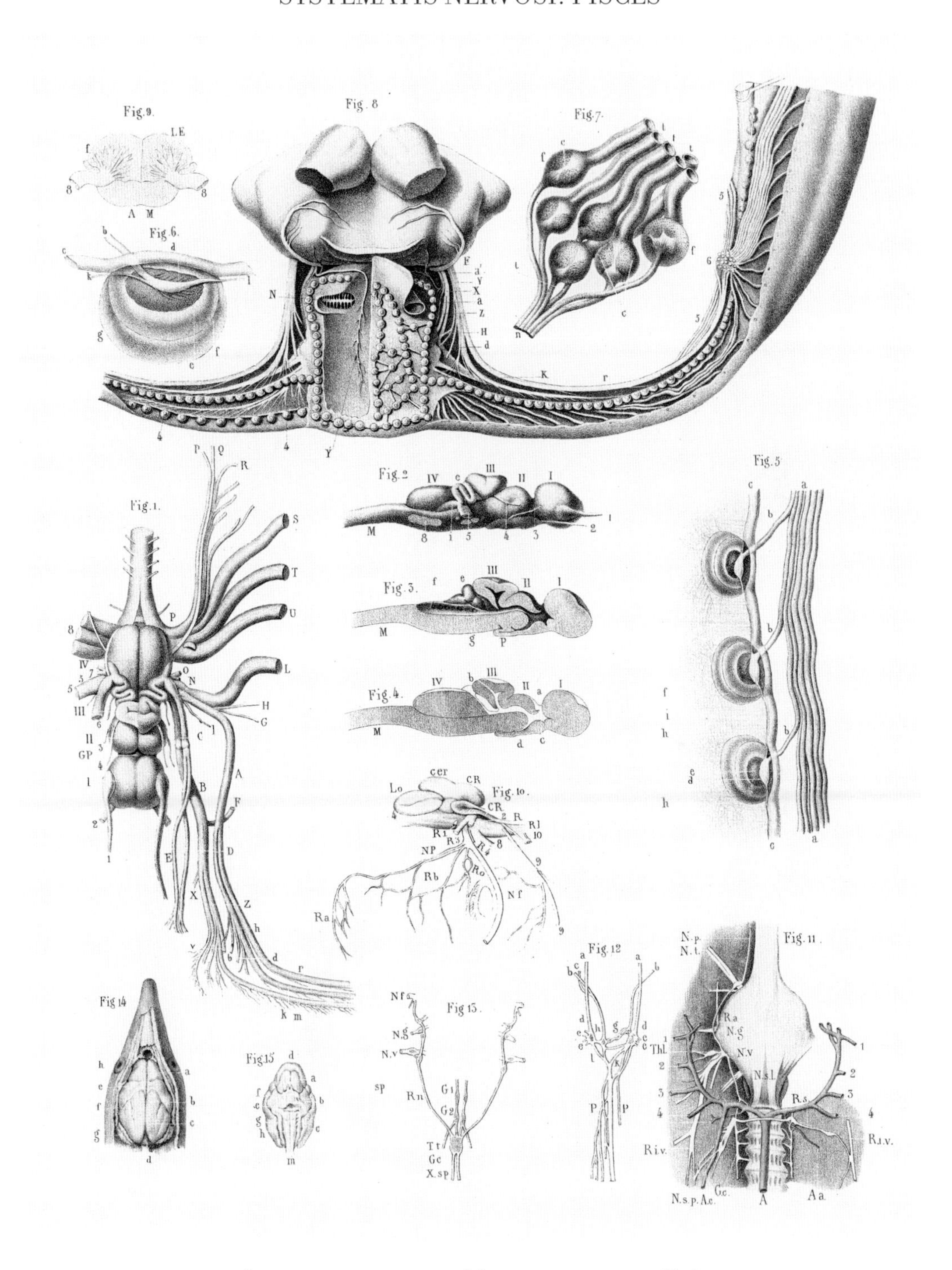

Comparative anatomy of the nervous system: Fish
Anatomie comparée du système nerveux : Poissons
Anatomía comparada del sistema nervioso: peces

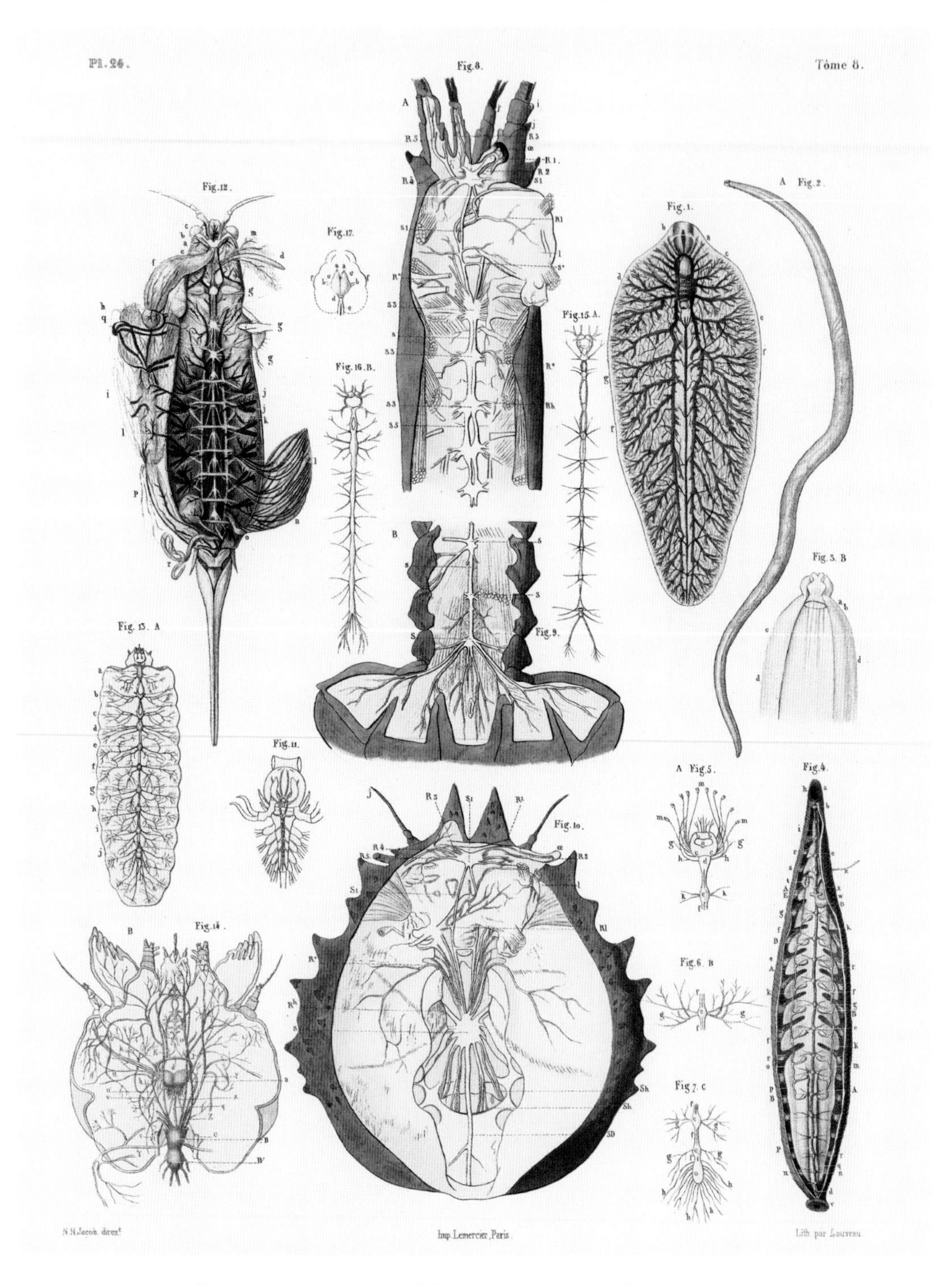

Comparative anatomy of the nervous system: Invertebrates
Anatomie comparée du système nerveux : Invertébrés
Anatomía comparada del sistema nervioso: invertebrados

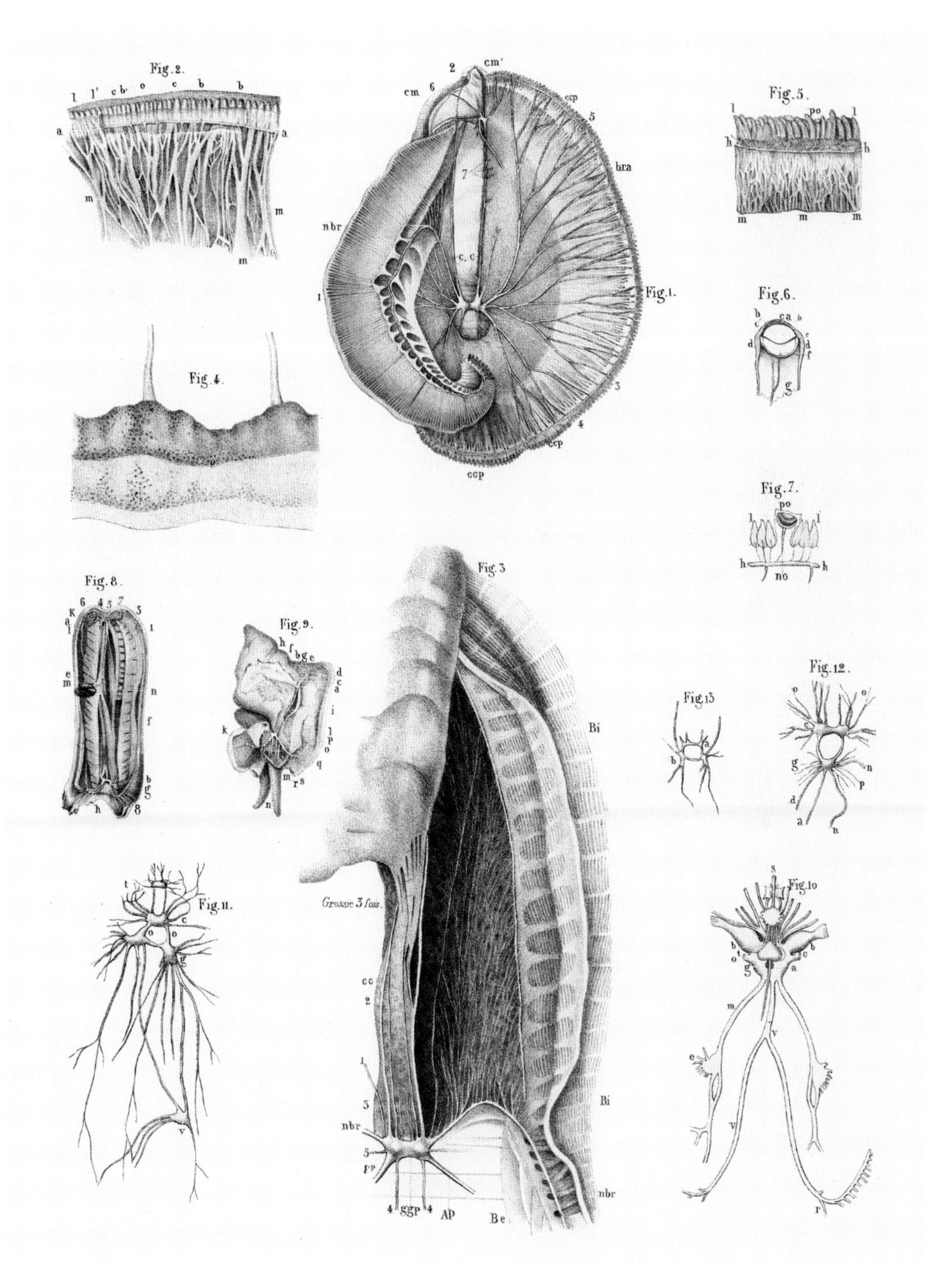

Comparative anatomy of the nervous system: Invertebrates
Anatomie comparée du système nerveux : Invertébrés
Anatomía comparada del sistema nervioso: invertebrados

ANATOMIA MICROSCOPICA: OSSA ET ARTICULATIONES

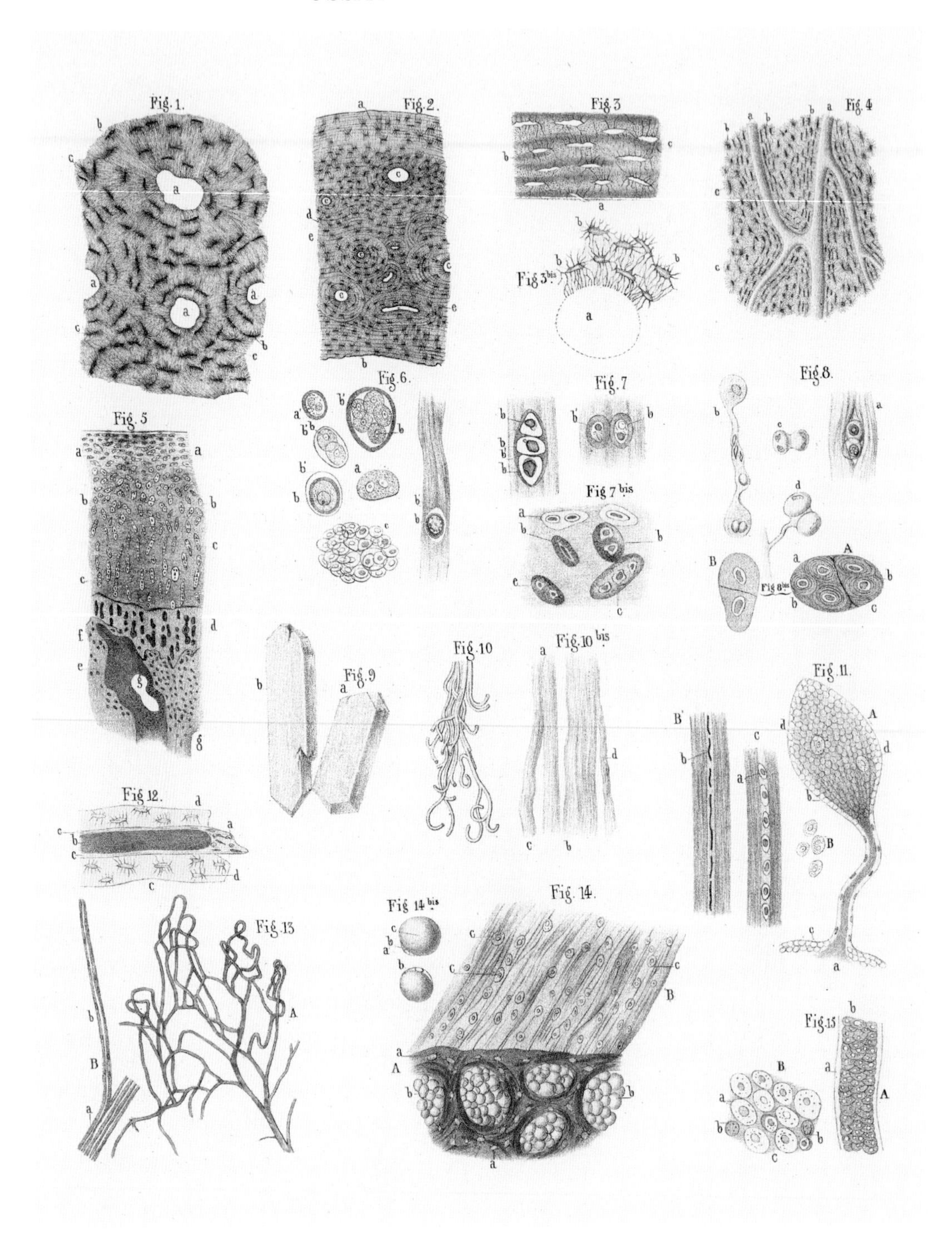

Microscopic anatomy: Bones and joints
Anatomie microscopique : Os et articulations
Anatomía microscópica: huesos y articulaciones

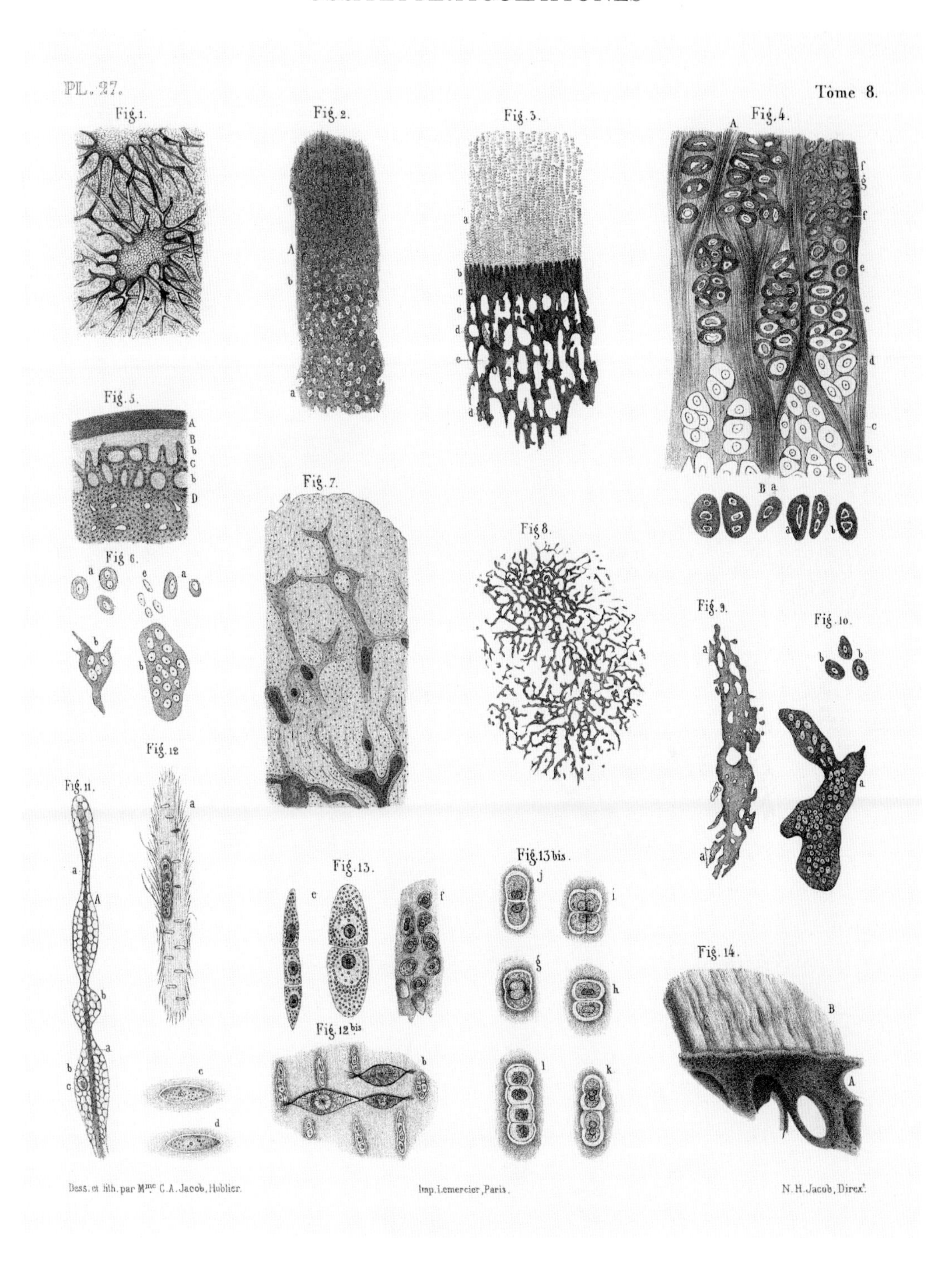

Microscopic anatomy: Bones and joints
Anatomie microscopique : Os et articulations
Anatomía microscópica: huesos y articulaciones

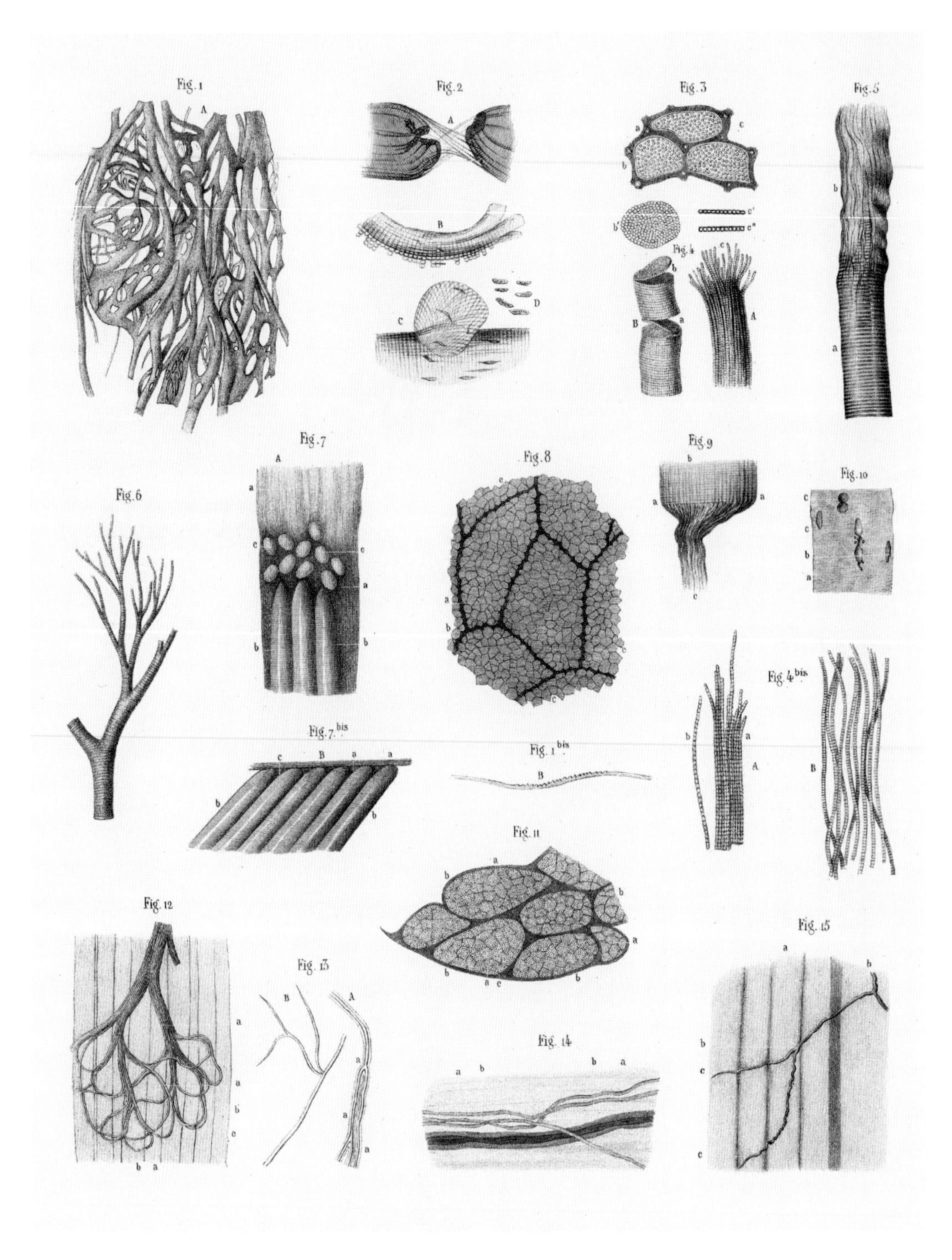

Microscopic anatomy: Muscles and tendons
Anatomie microscopique : Muscles et tendons
Anatomía microscópica: músculos y tendones

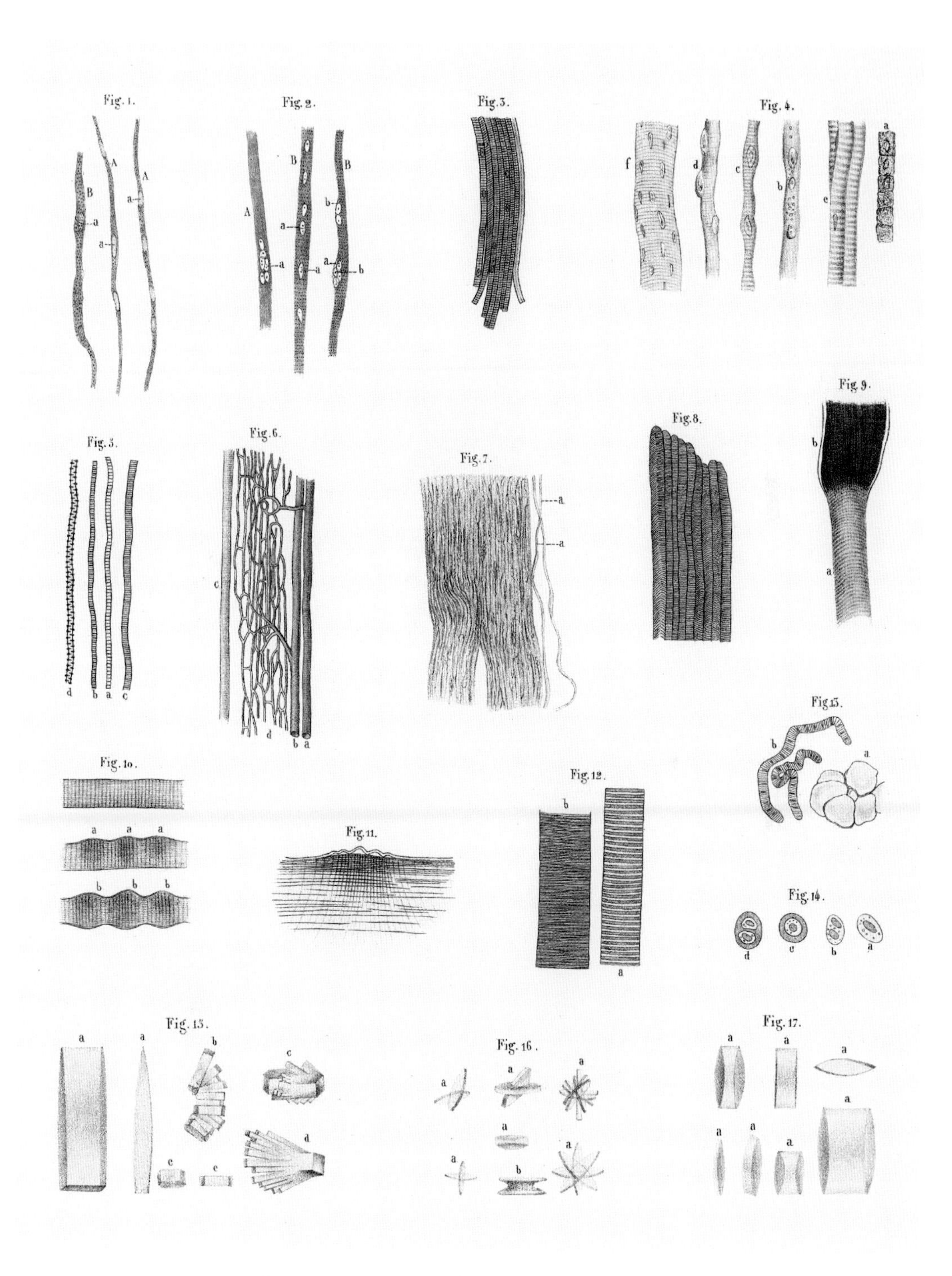

Microscopic anatomy: Muscles and tendons
Anatomie microscopique : Muscles et tendons
Anatomía microscópica: músculos y tendones

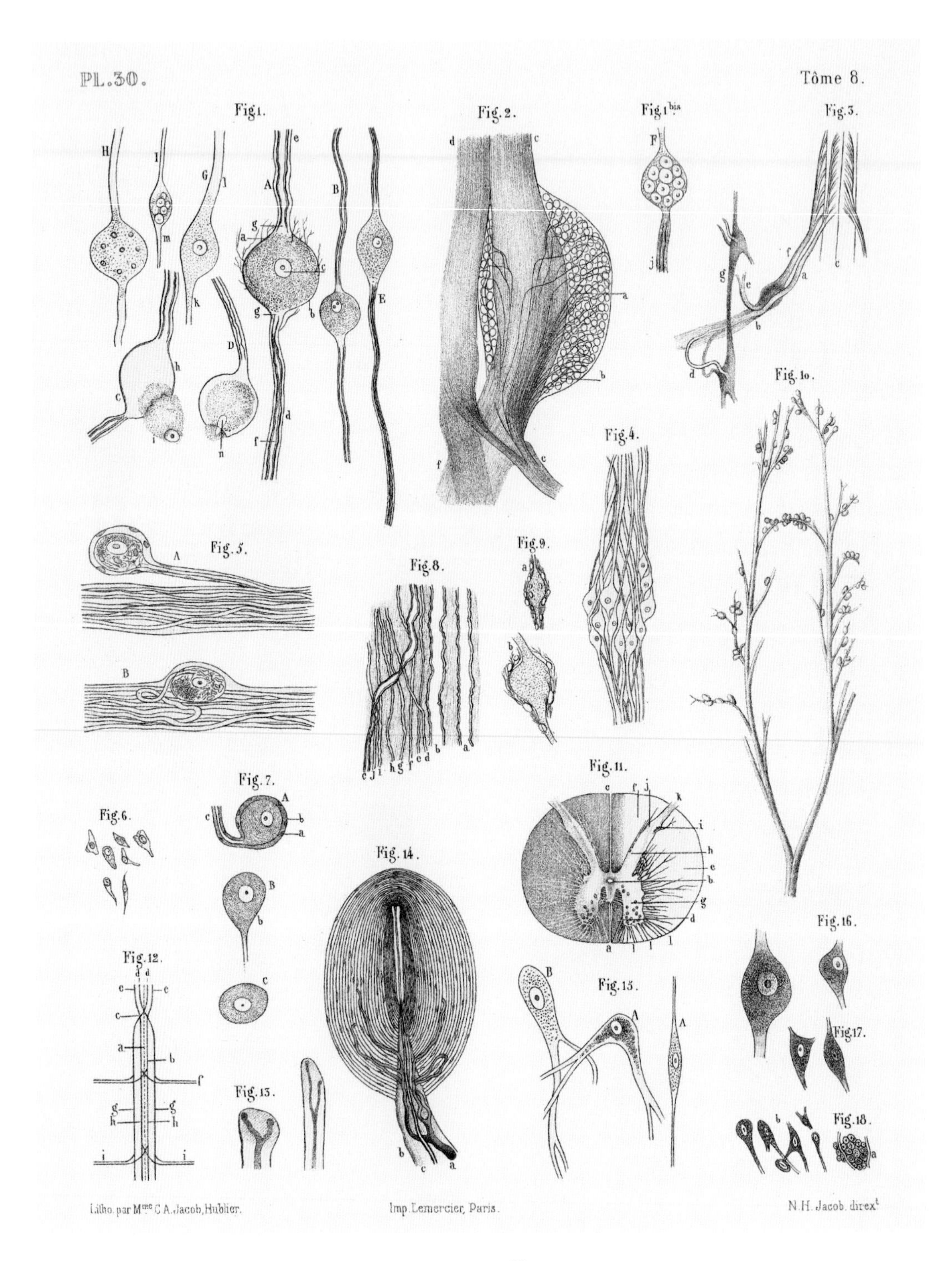

Microscopic anatomy: Nervous system
Anatomie microscopique : Système nerveux
Anatomía microscópica: sistema nervioso

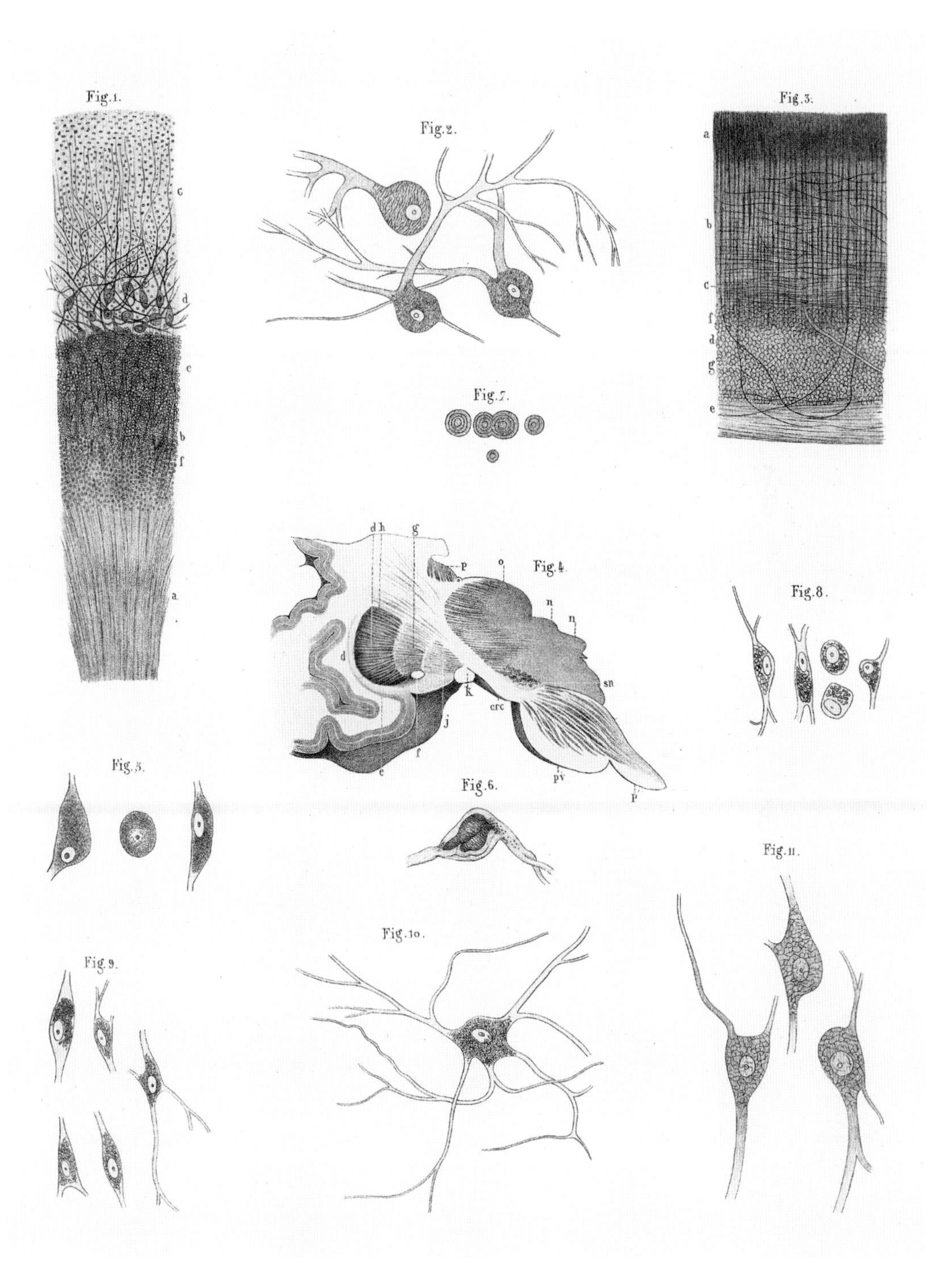

Microscopic anatomy: Nervous system
Anatomie microscopique : Système nerveux
Anatomía microscópica: sistema nervioso

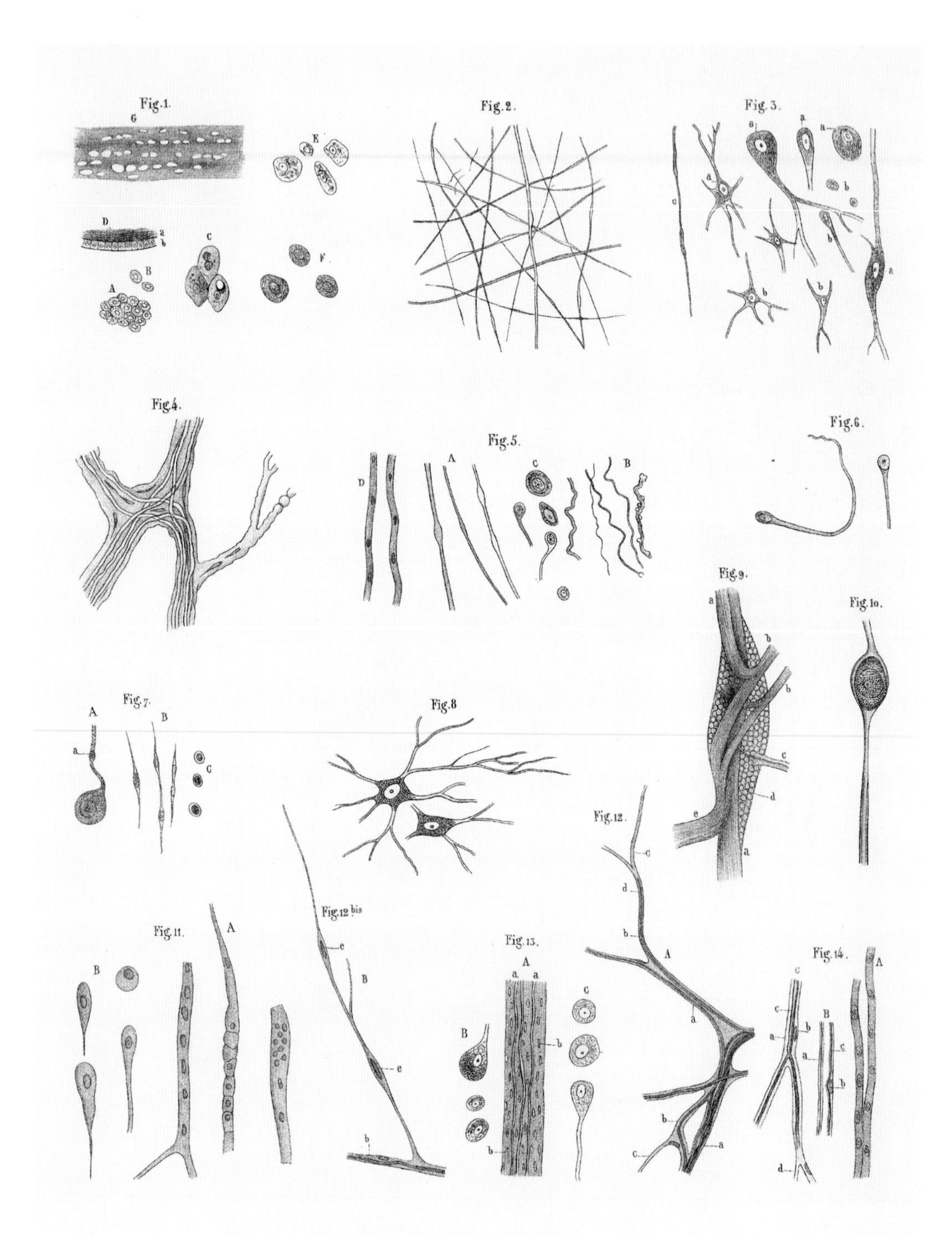

Microscopic anatomy: Nervous system
Anatomie microscopique : Système nerveux
Anatomía microscópica: sistema nervioso

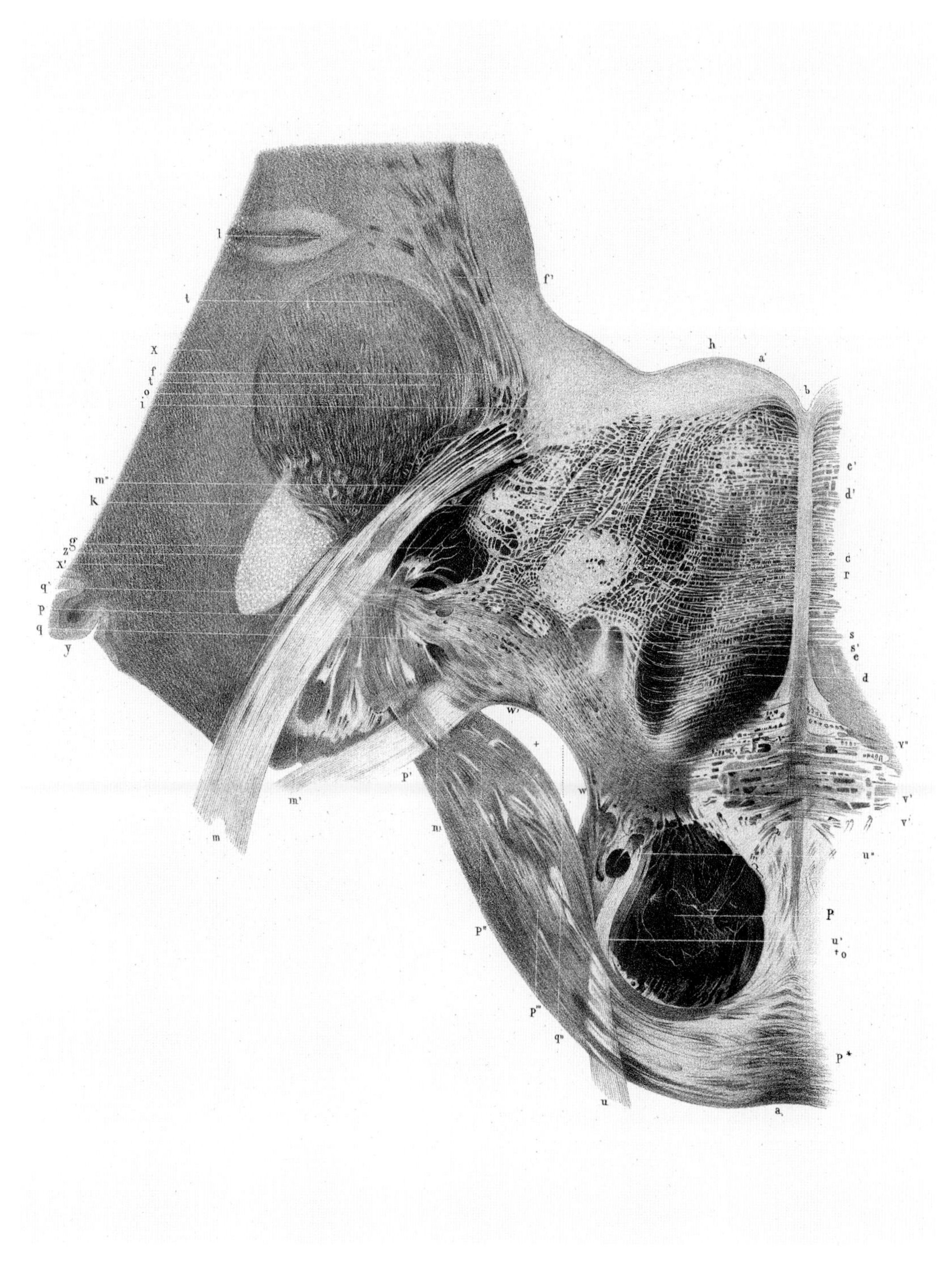

Microscopic anatomy: Nervous system
Anatomie microscopique : Système nerveux
Anatomía microscópica: sistema nervioso

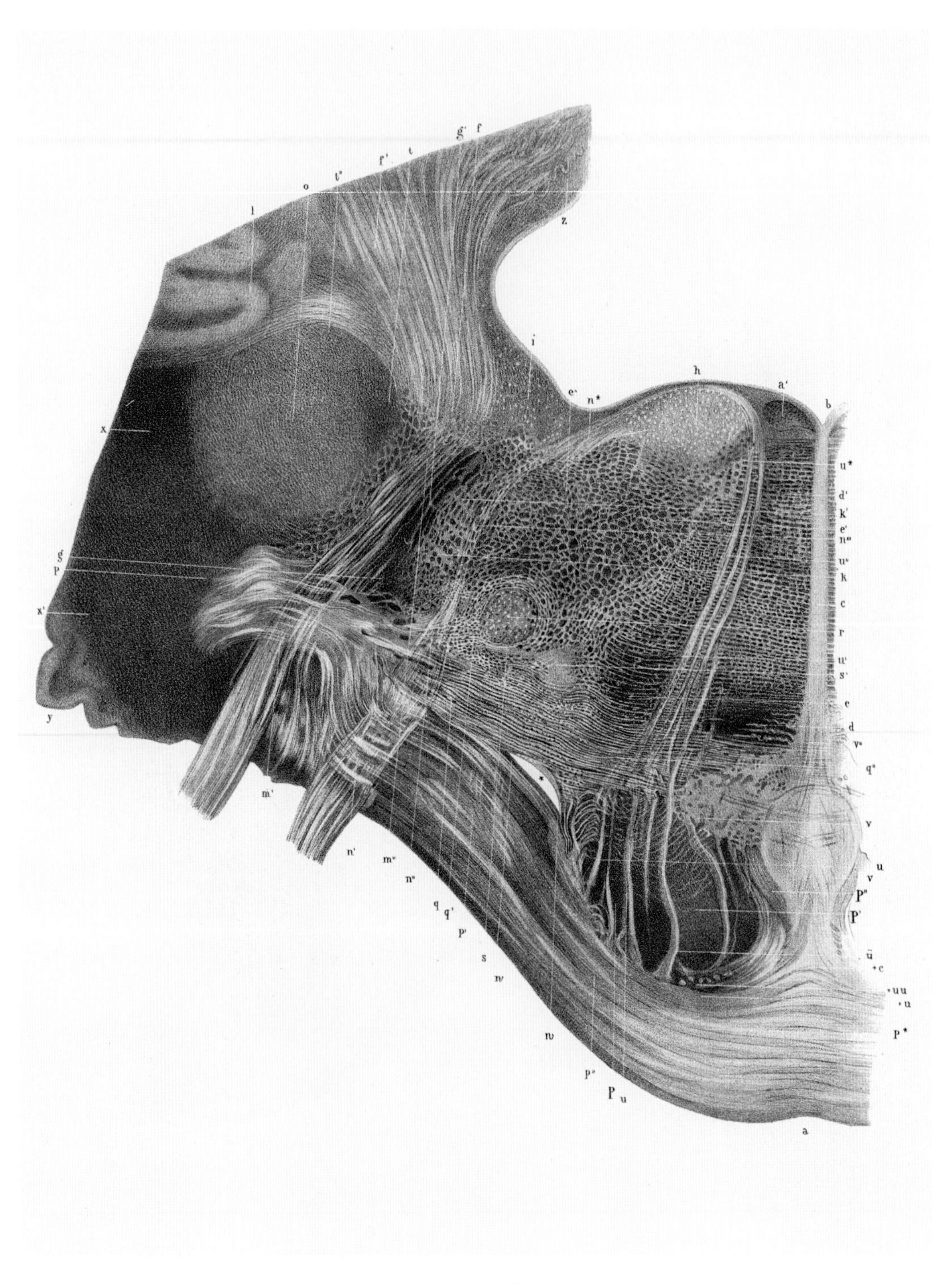

Microscopic anatomy: Nervous system
Anatomie microscopique : Système nerveux
Anatomía microscópica: sistema nervioso

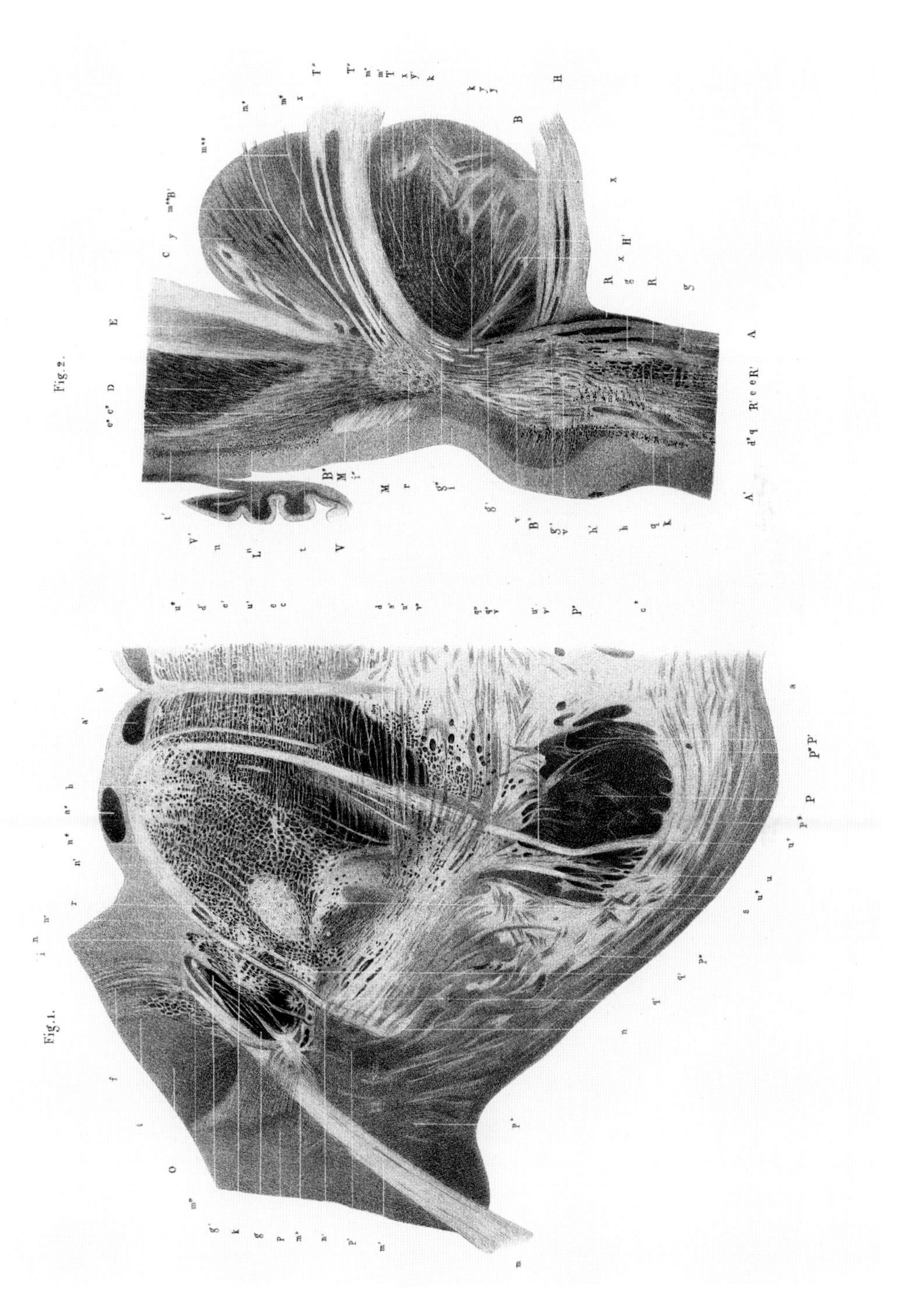

Microscopic anatomy: Nervous system
Anatomie microscopique : Système nerveux
Anatomía microscópica: sistema nervioso

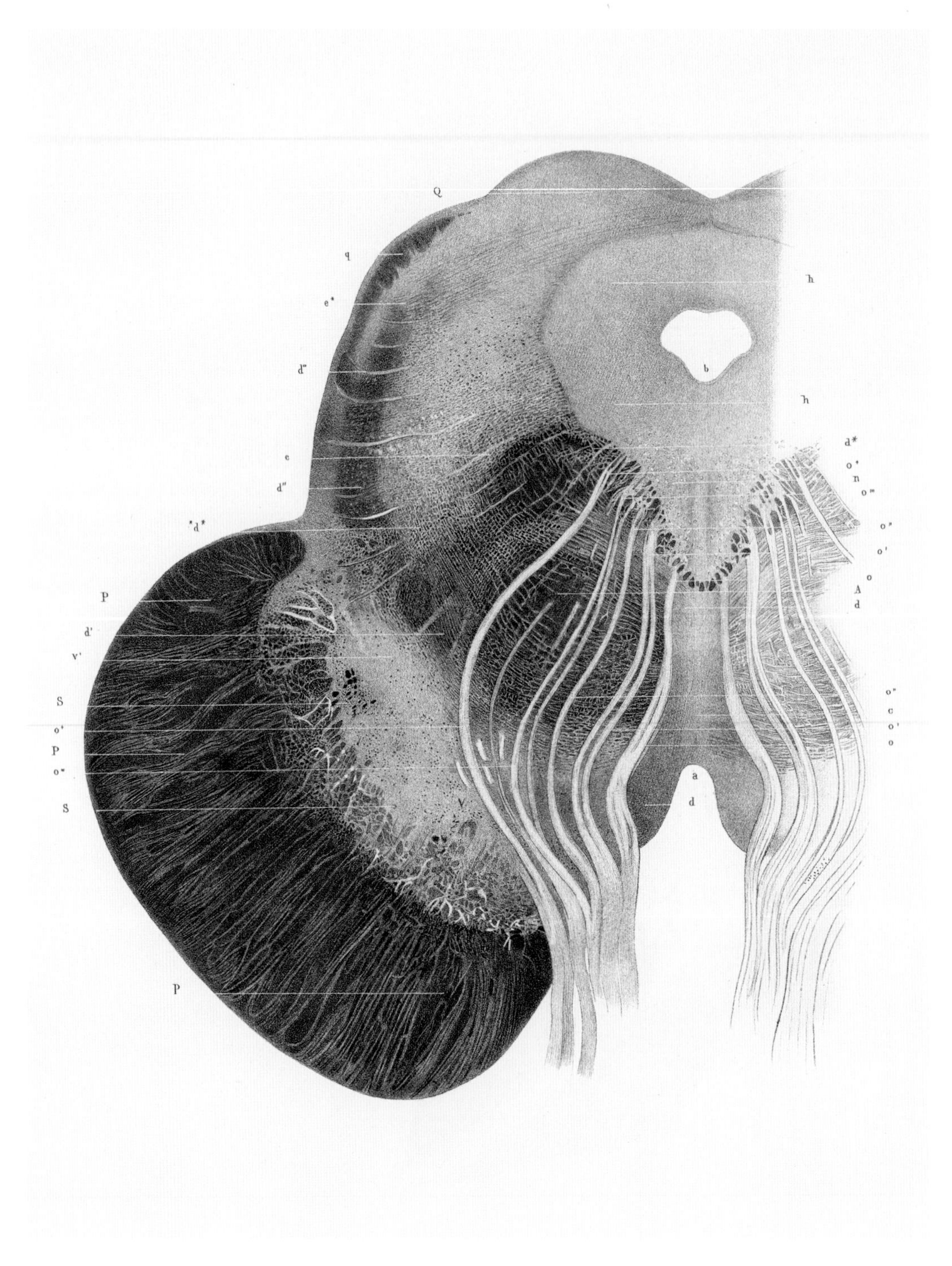

Microscopic anatomy: Nervous system
Anatomie microscopique : Système nerveux
Anatomía microscópica: sistema nervioso

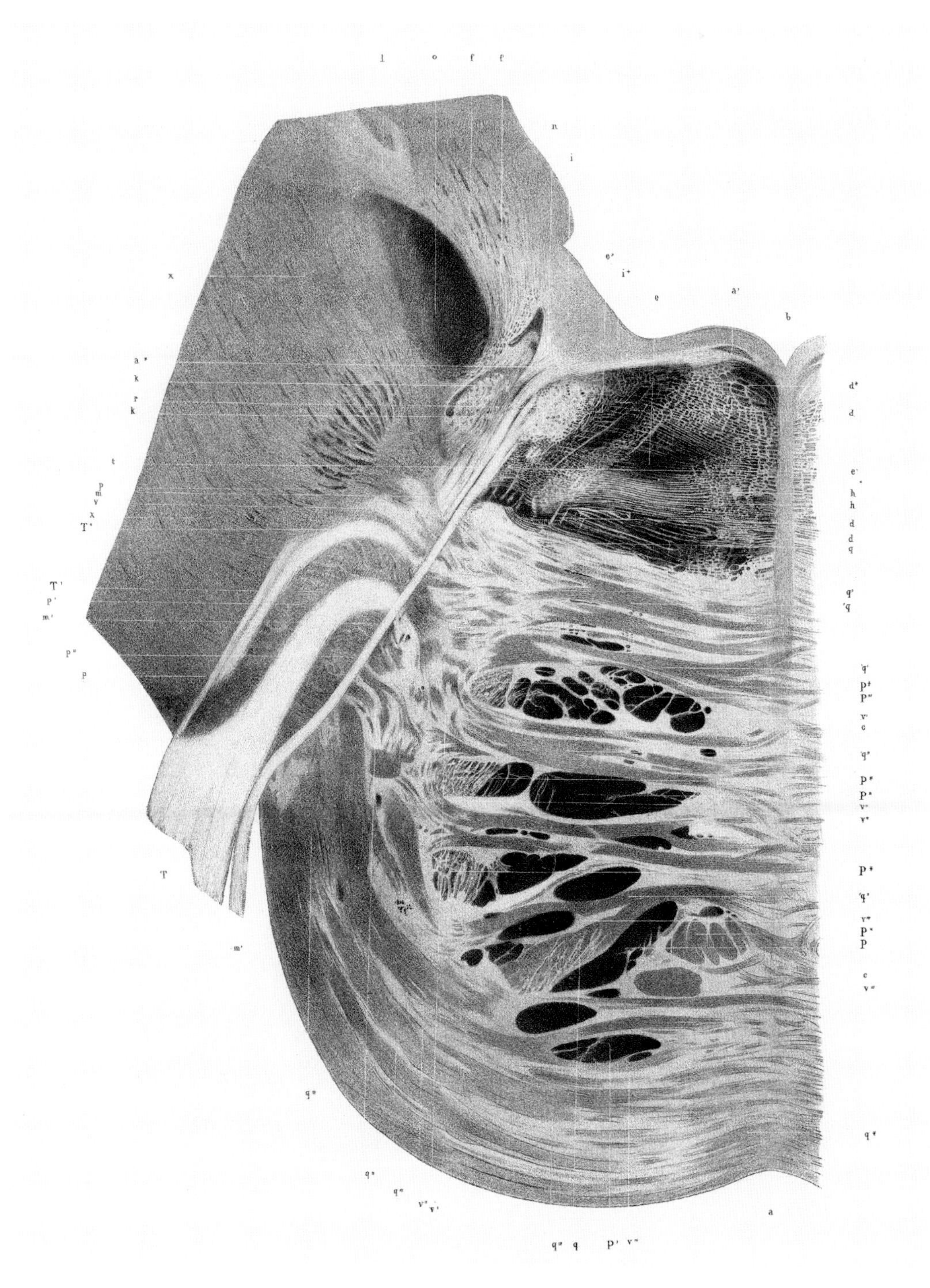

Microscopic anatomy: Nervous system
Anatomie microscopique : Système nerveux
Anatomía microscópica: sistema nervioso

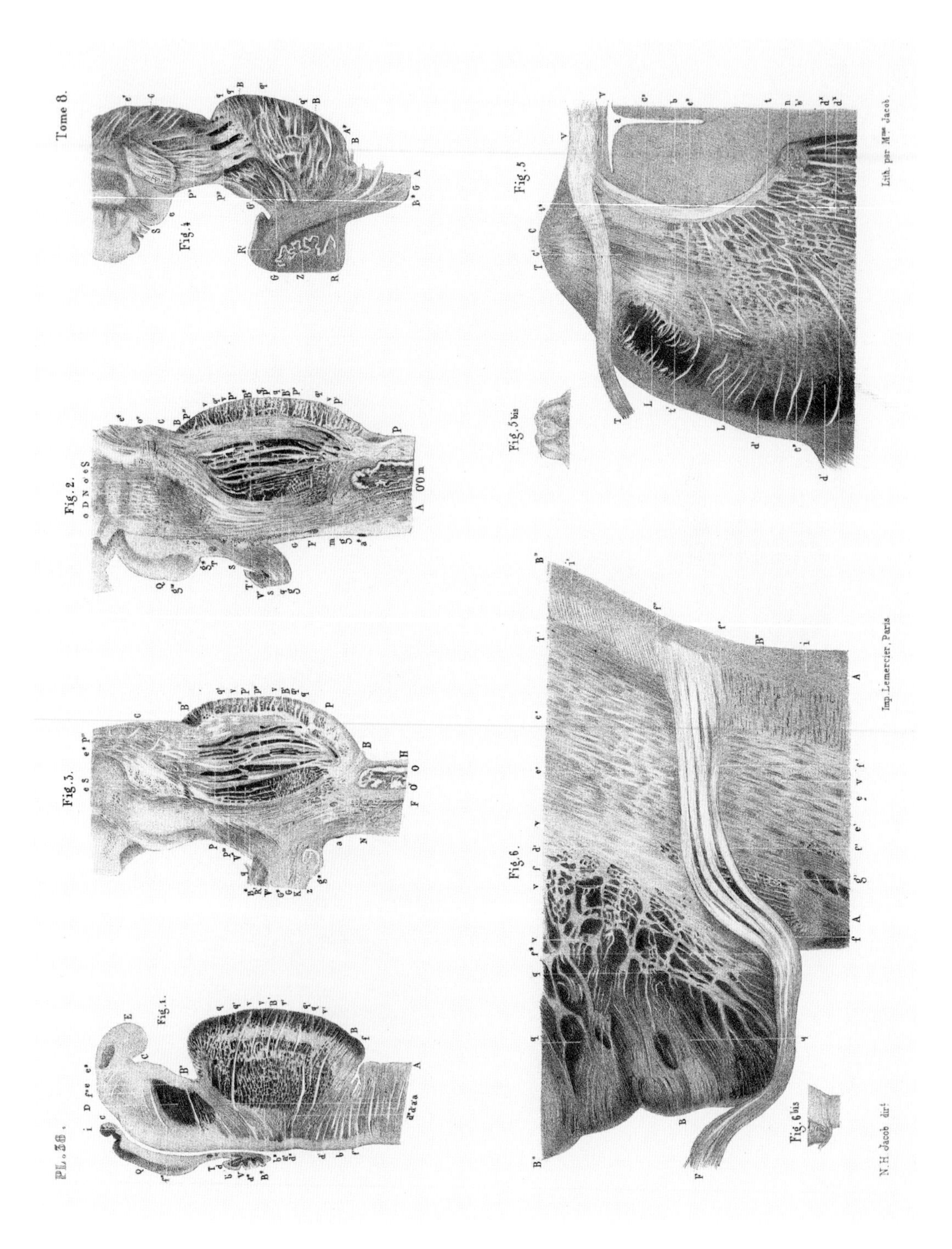

Microscopic anatomy: Nervous system
Anatomie microscopique : Système nerveux
Anatomía microscópica: sistema nervioso

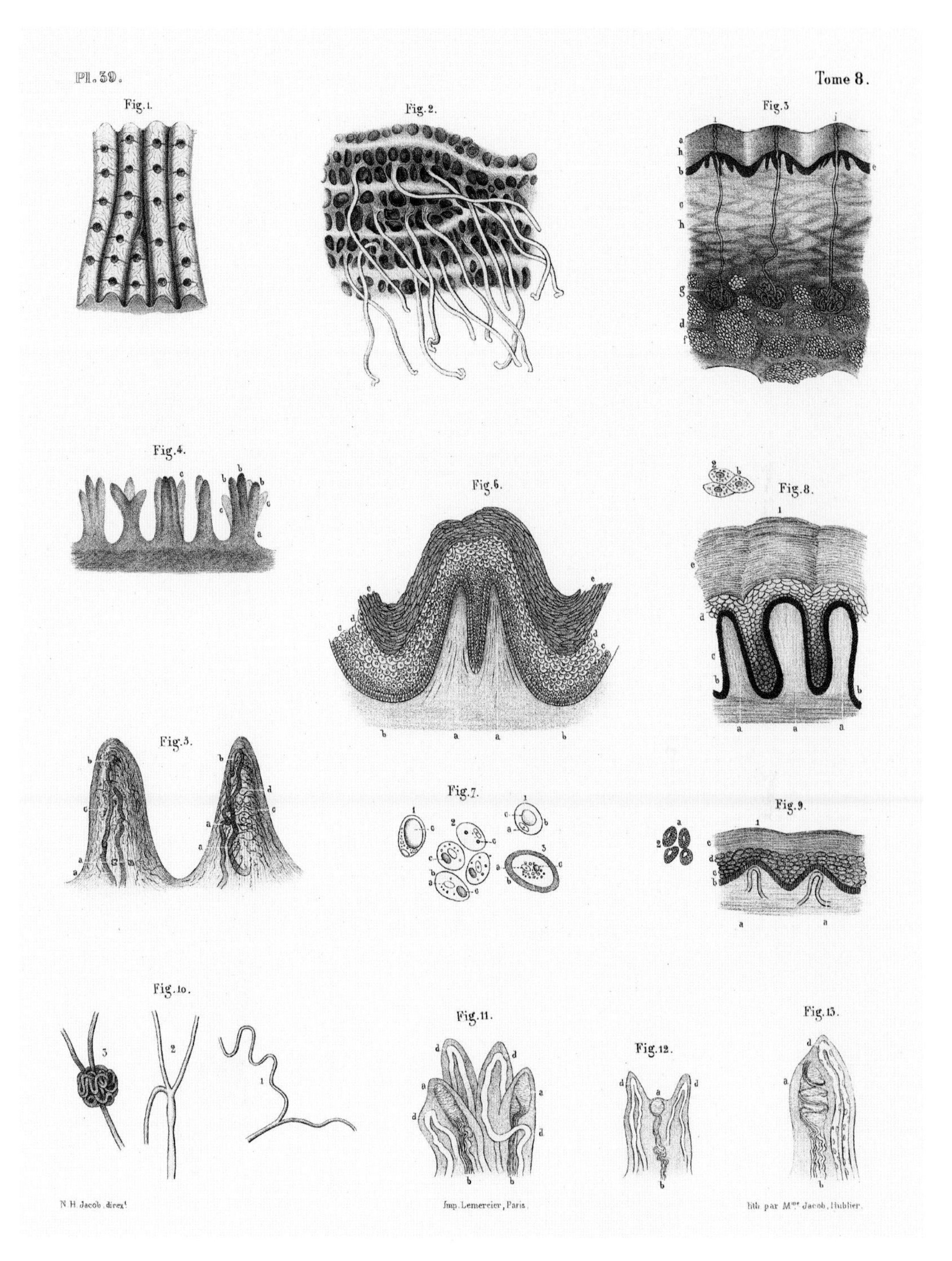

Microscopic anatomy: Skin and appendages
Anatomie microscopique : Peau et phanères
Anatomía microscópica: piel y faneras

ANATOMIA MICROSCOPICA: INTEGUMENTUM COMMUNE

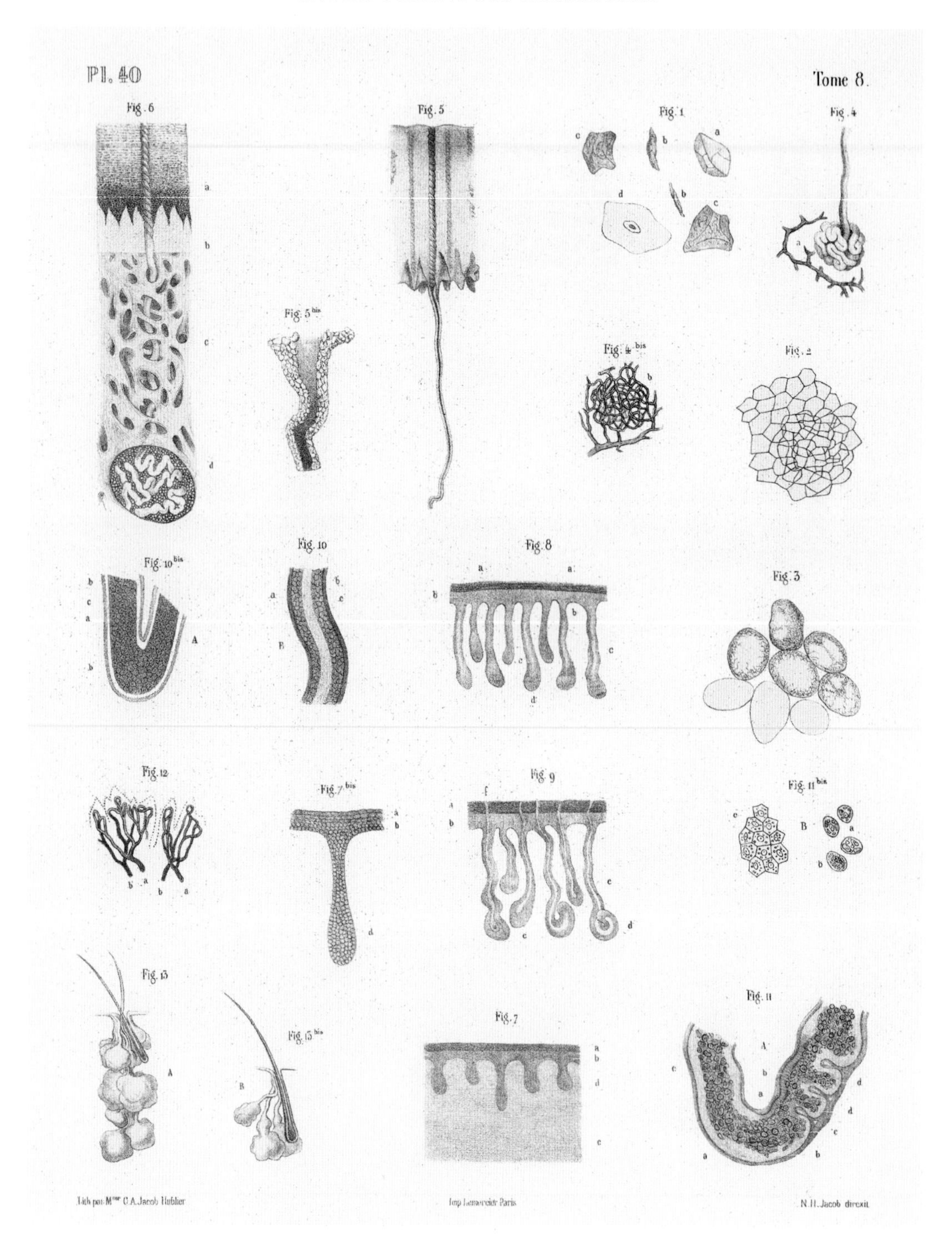

Microscopic anatomy: Skin and appendages
Anatomie microscopique : Peau et phanères
Anatomía microscópica: piel y faneras

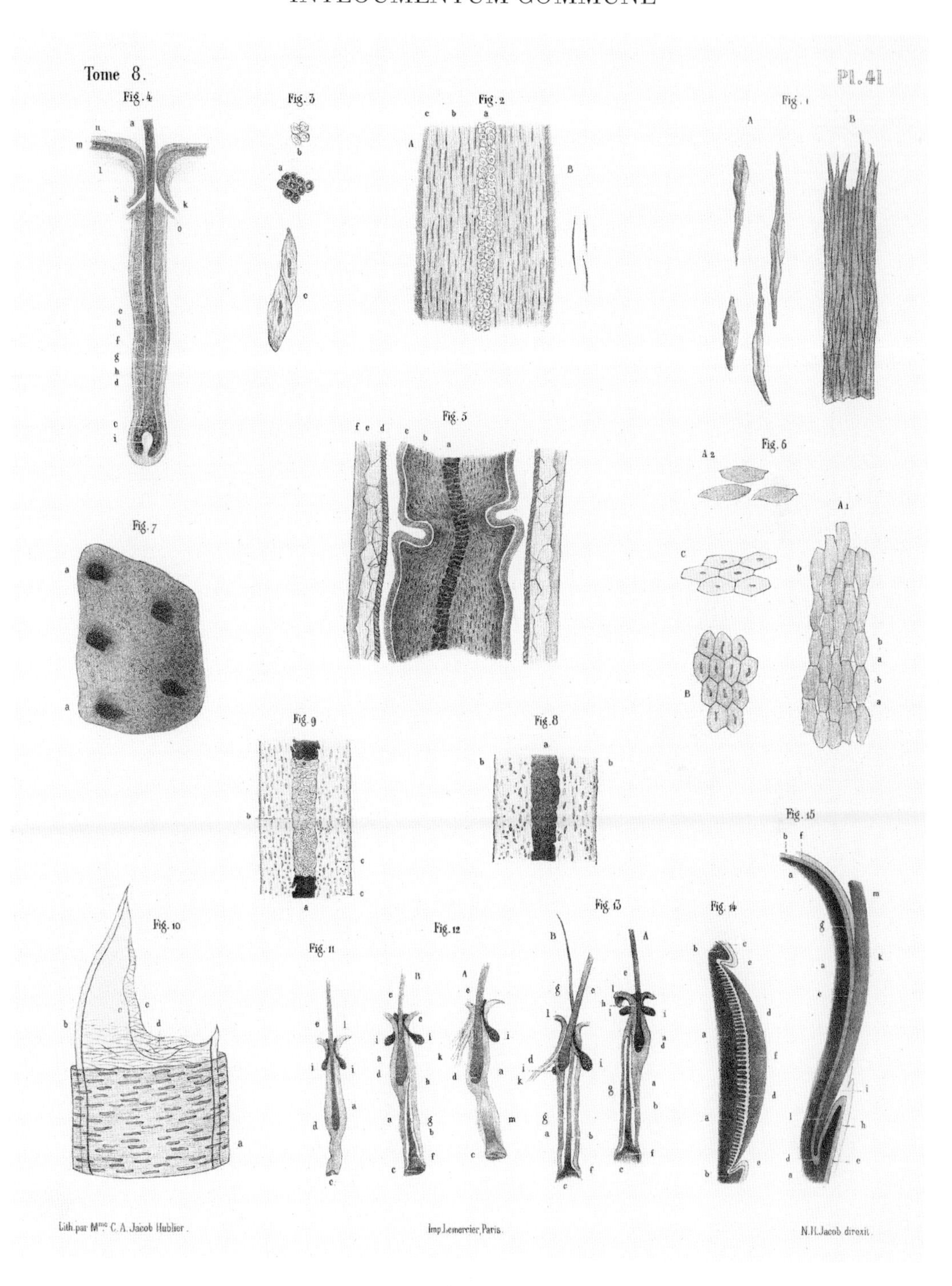

Microscopic anatomy: Skin and appendages
Anatomie microscopique : Peau et phanères
Anatomía microscópica: piel y faneras

ANATOMIA MICROSCOPICA: INTEGUMENTUM COMMUNE

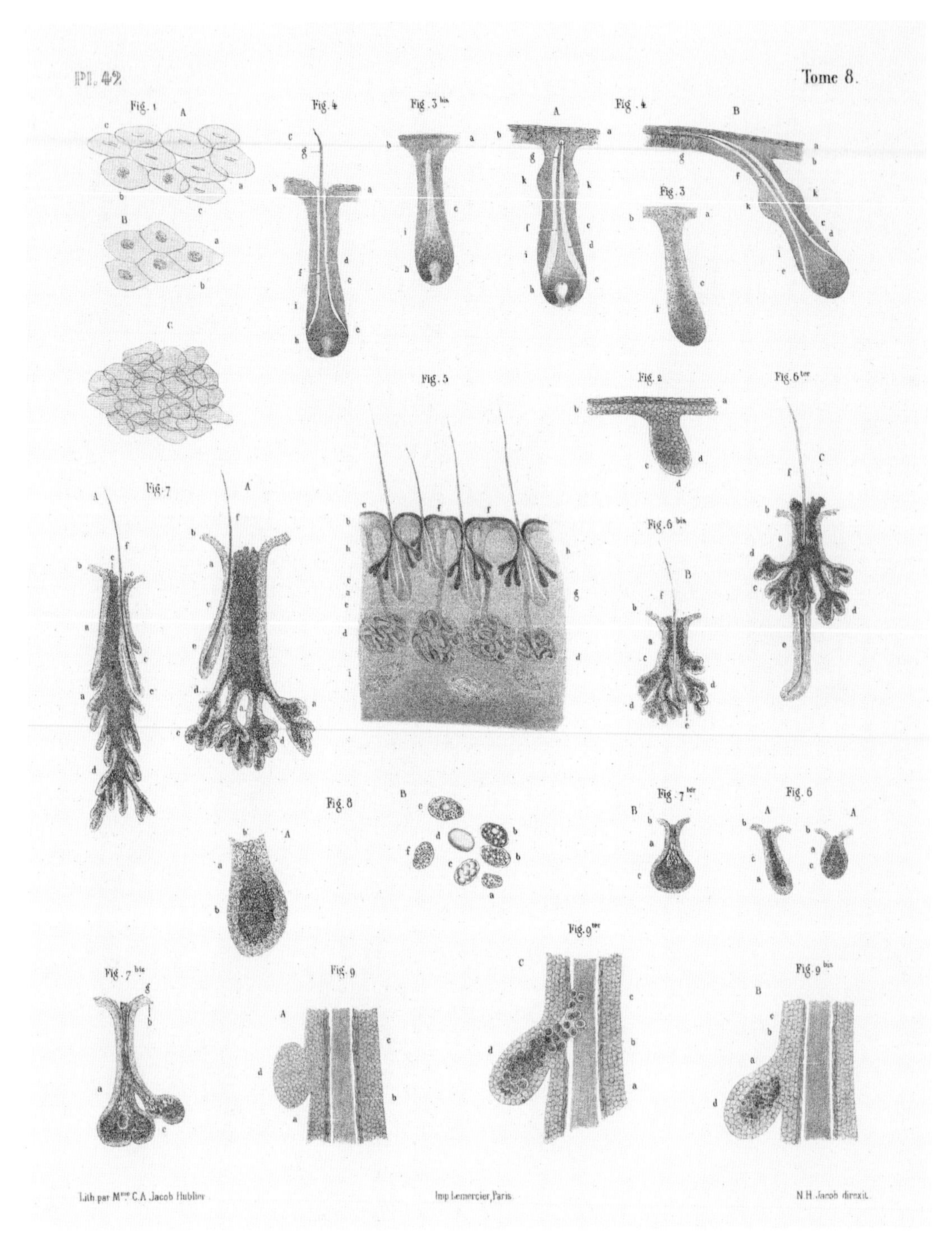

Microscopic anatomy: Skin and appendages
Anatomie microscopique : Peau et phanères
Anatomía microscópica: piel y faneras

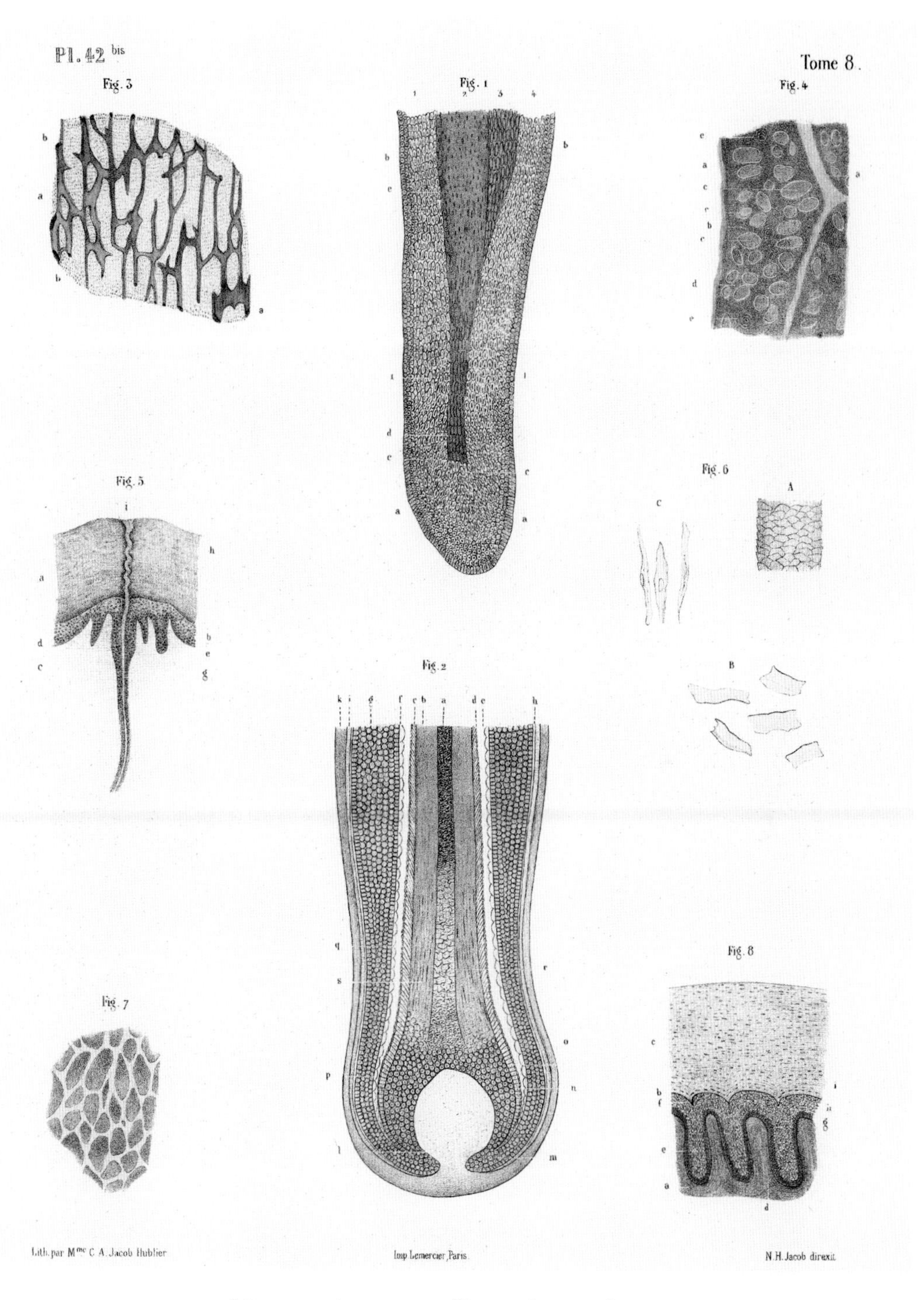

Microscopic anatomy: Skin and appendages
Anatomie microscopique : Peau et phanères
Anatomía microscópica: piel y faneras

ANATOMIA MICROSCOPICA: CAVITAS ORIS ET GLANDULAE SALIVARIAE

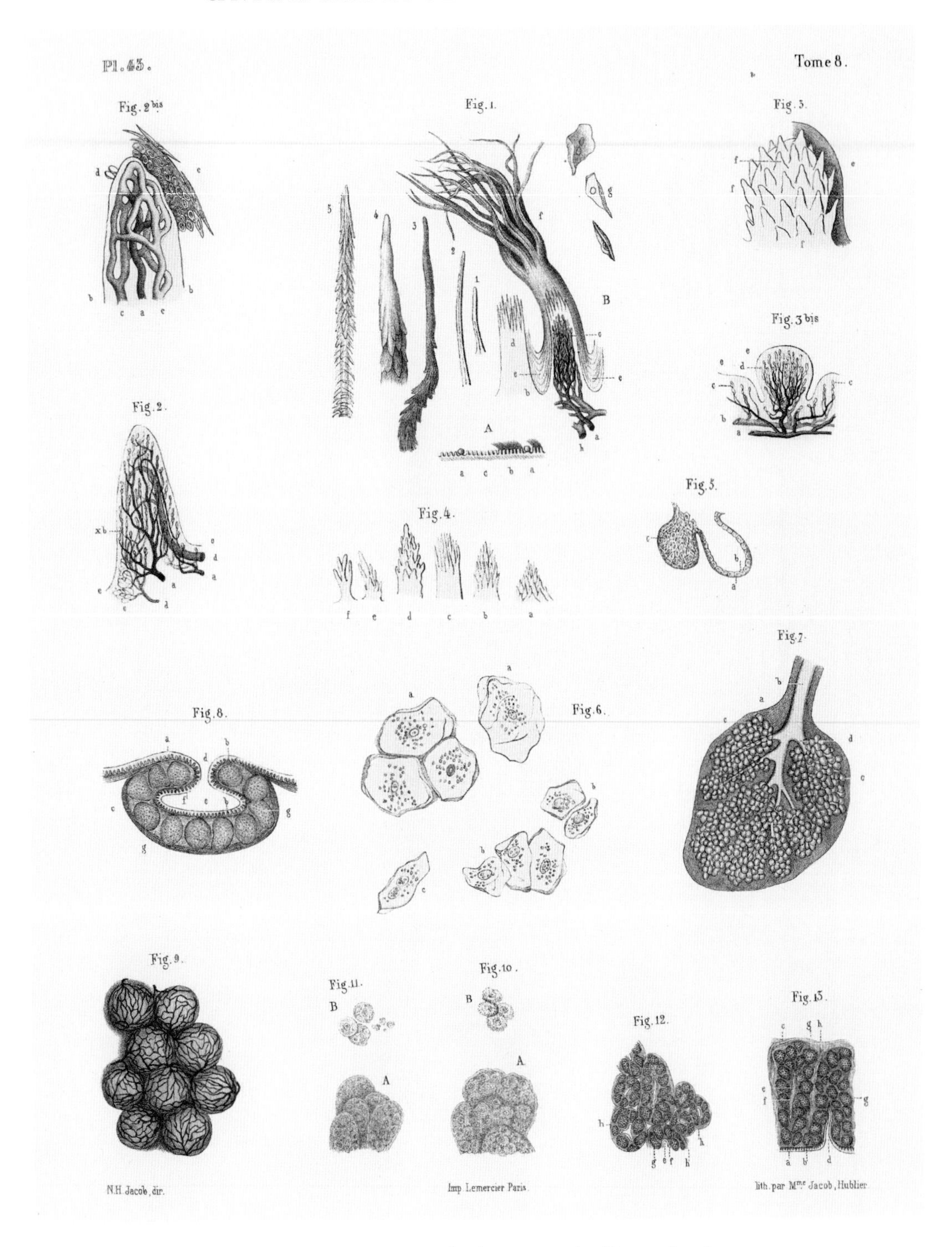

Microscopic anatomy: Oral cavity and salivary glands
Anatomie microscopique : Cavité orale et glandes salivaires
Anatomía microscópica: cavidad bucal y glándulas salivales

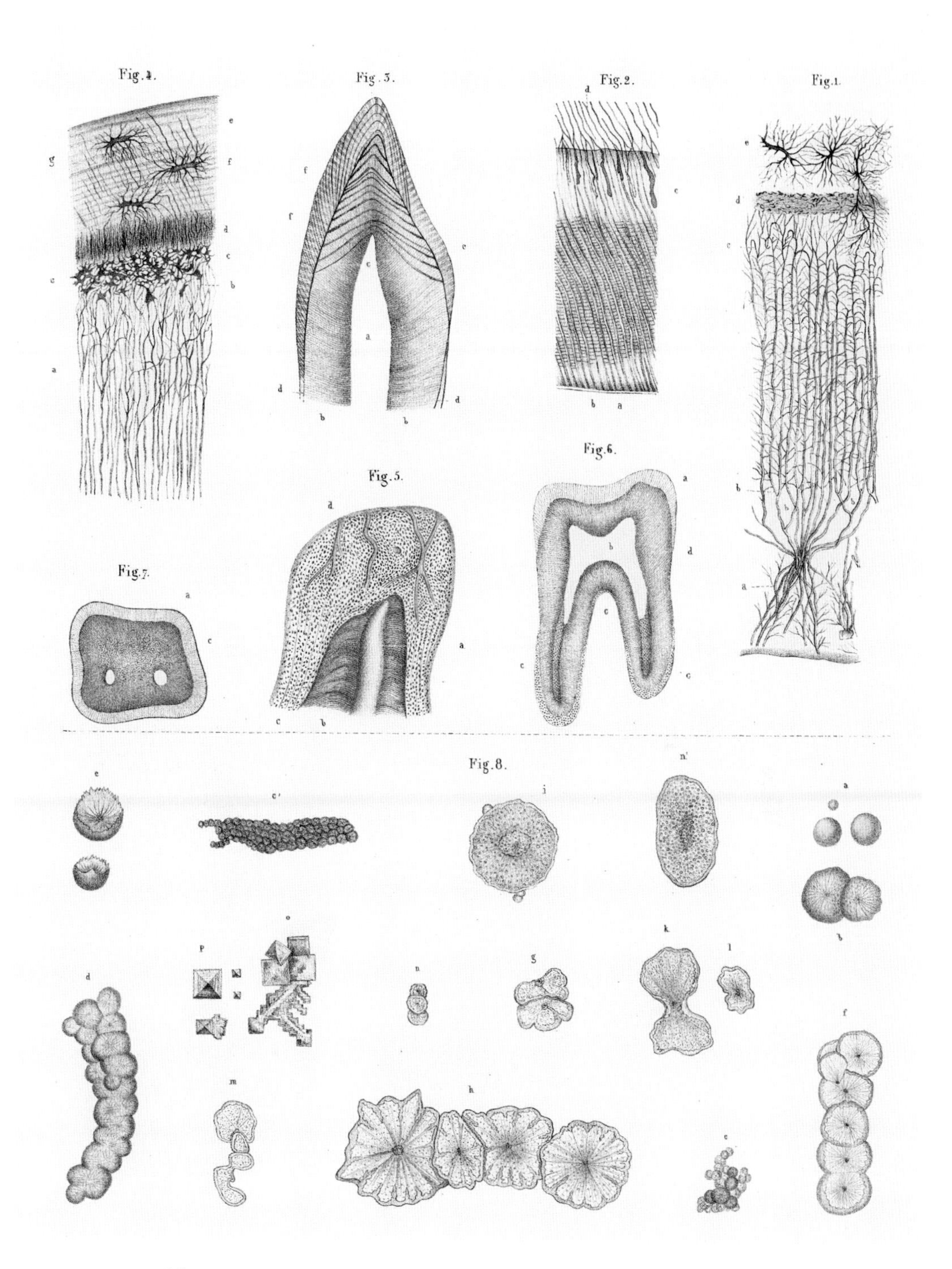

Microscopic anatomy: Teeth / Anatomie microscopique : Dents
Anatomía microscópica: dientes

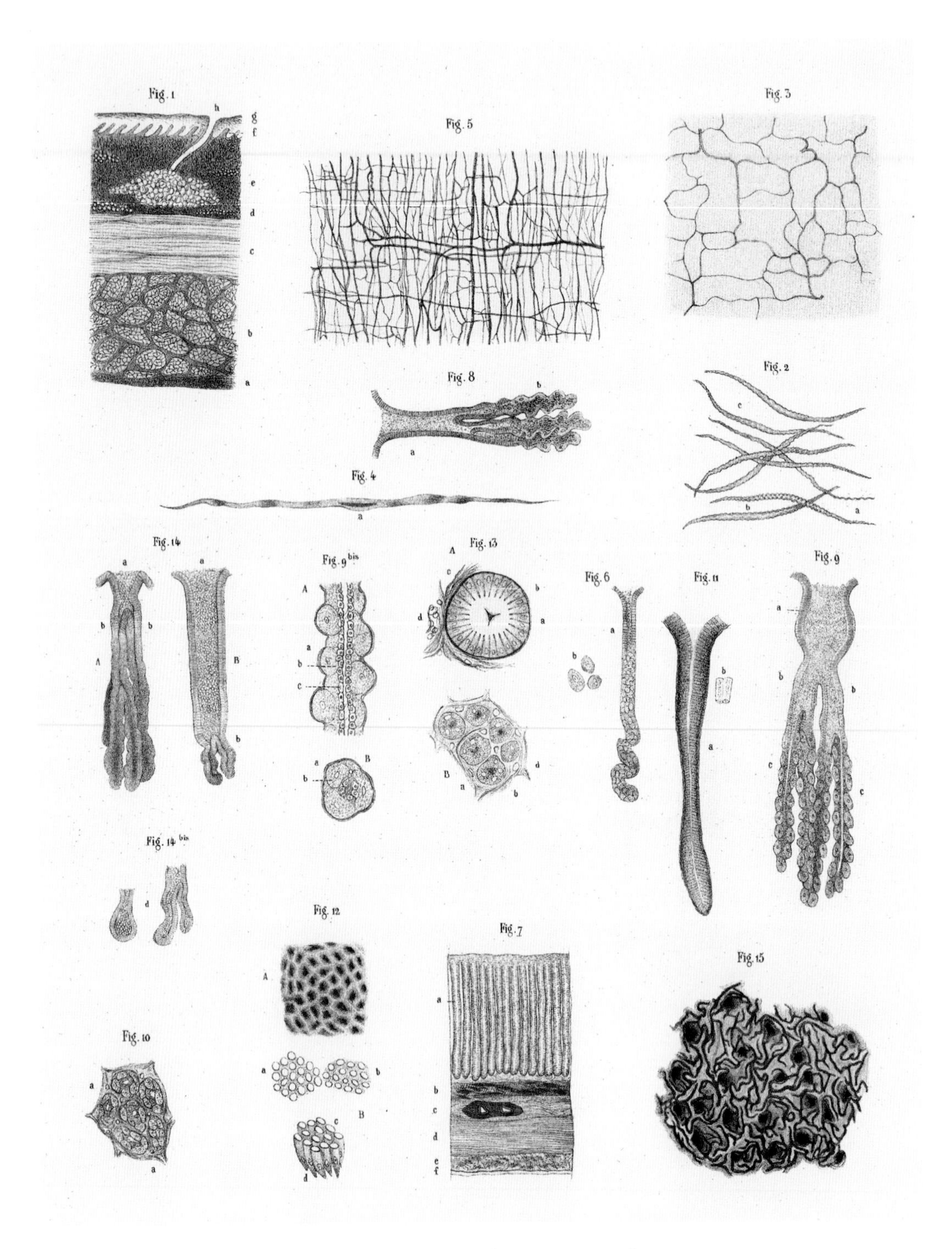

Microscopic anatomy: Gastrointestinal tract
Anatomie microscopique : Tube digestif
Anatomía microscópica: tubo digestivo

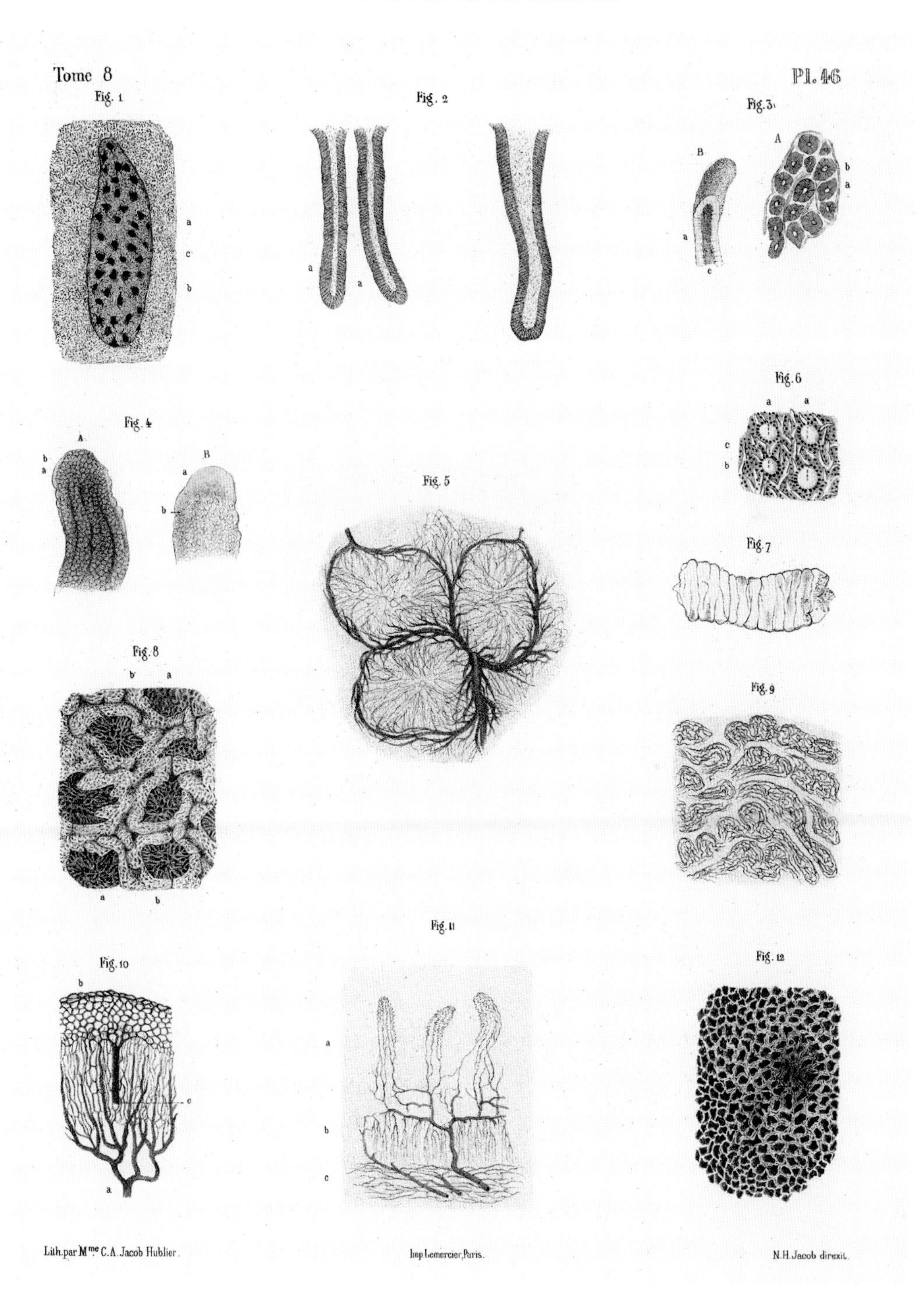

Microscopic anatomy: Gastrointestinal tract
Anatomie microscopique : Tube digestif
Anatomía microscópica: tubo digestivo

ANATOMIA MICROSCOPICA: CANALIS ALIMENTARIUS ET HEPAR

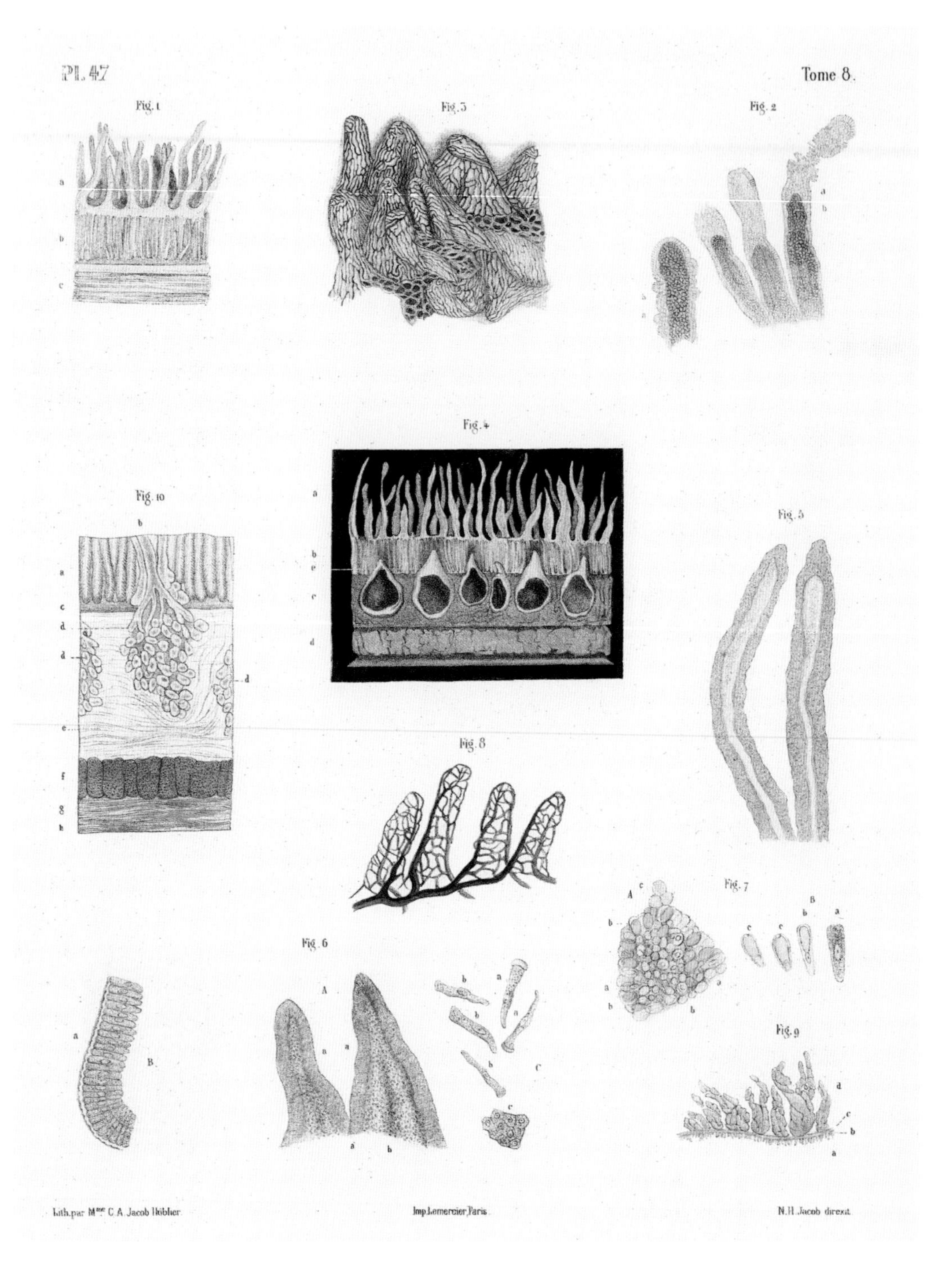

Microscopic anatomy: Gastrointestinal tract
Anatomie microscopique : Tube digestif
Anatomía microscópica: tubo digestivo

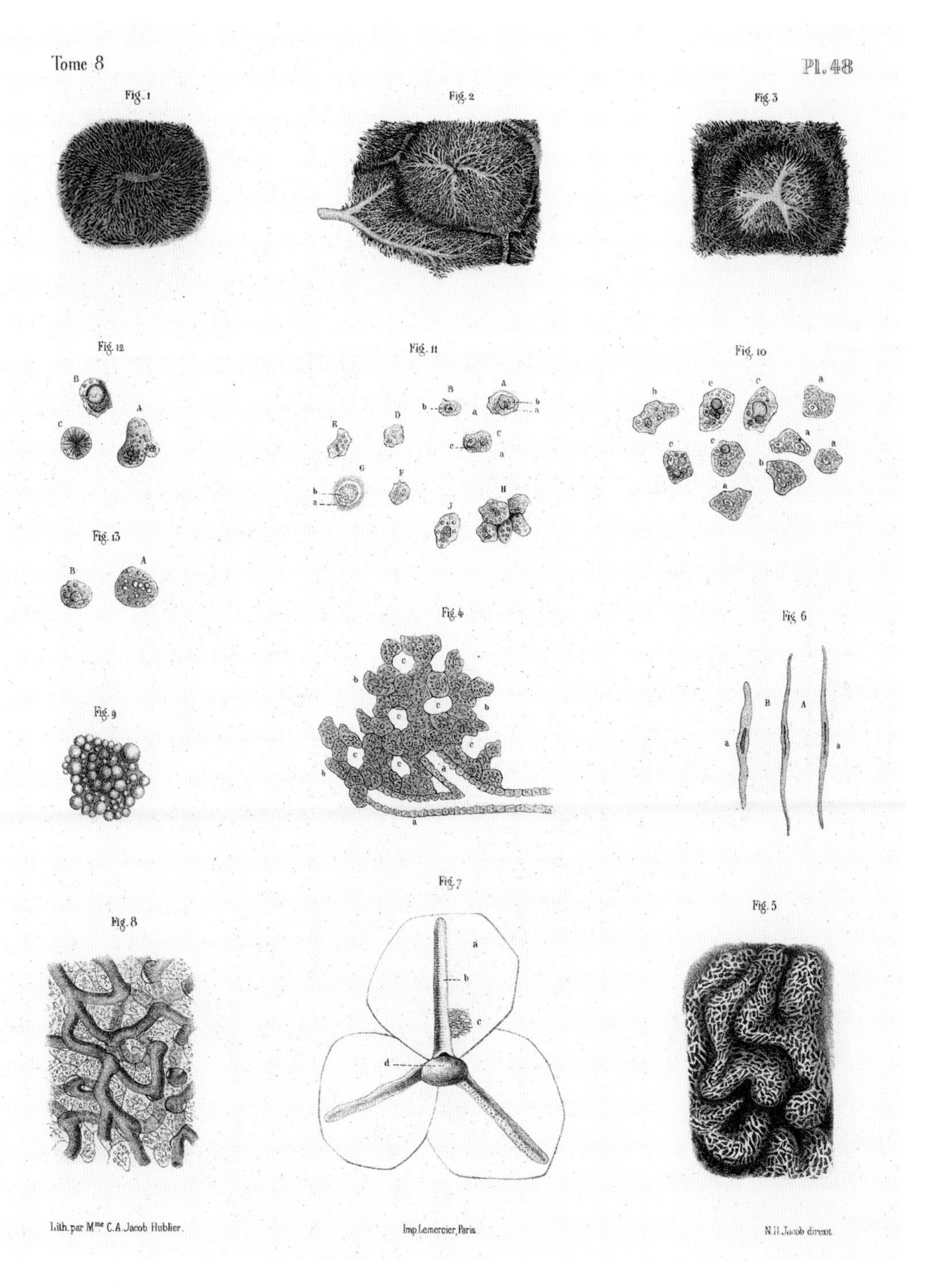

Microscopic anatomy: Liver / Anatomie microscopique : Foie
Anatomía microscópica: hígado

ANATOMIA MICROSCOPICA: CANALIS ALIMENTARIUS ET HEPAR

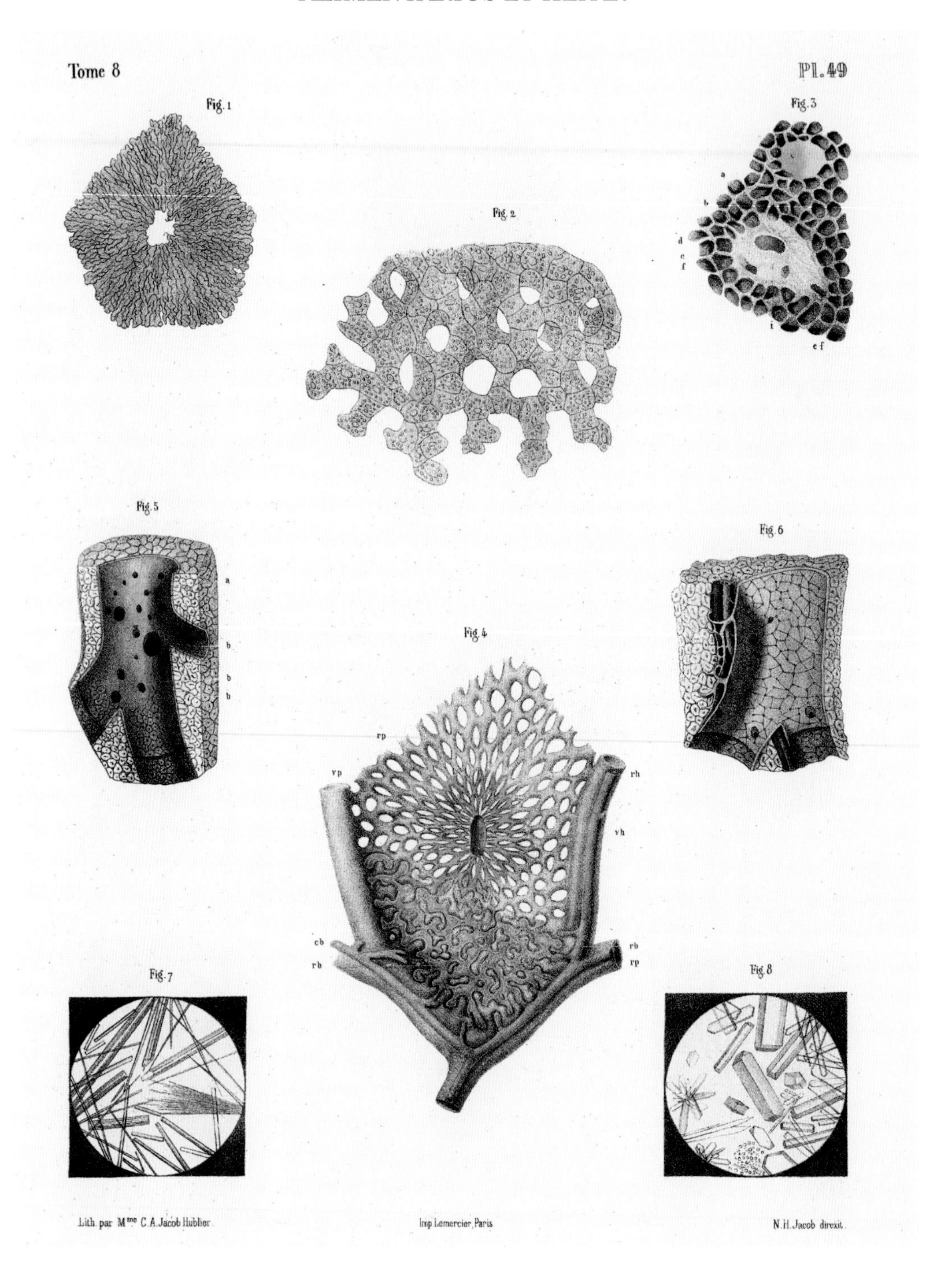

Microscopic anatomy: Liver / Anatomie microscopique : Foie
Anatomía microscópica: hígado

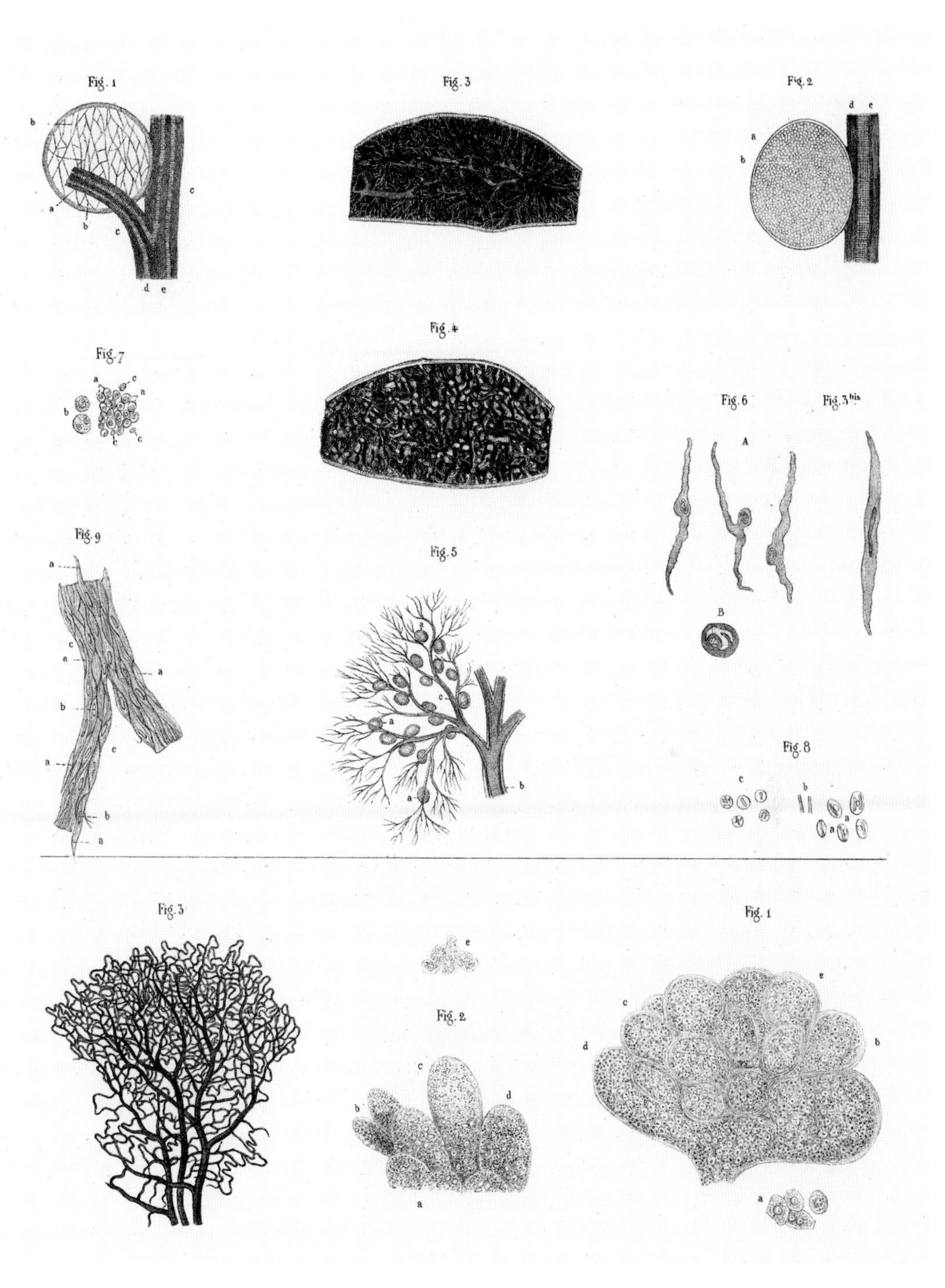

Microscopic anatomy: Spleen and pancreas
Anatomie microscopique : Rate et pancréas
Anatomía microscópica: bazo y páncreas

ANATOMIA MICROSCOPICA: APPARATUS RESPIRATORIUS ET GLANDULA THYROIDEA

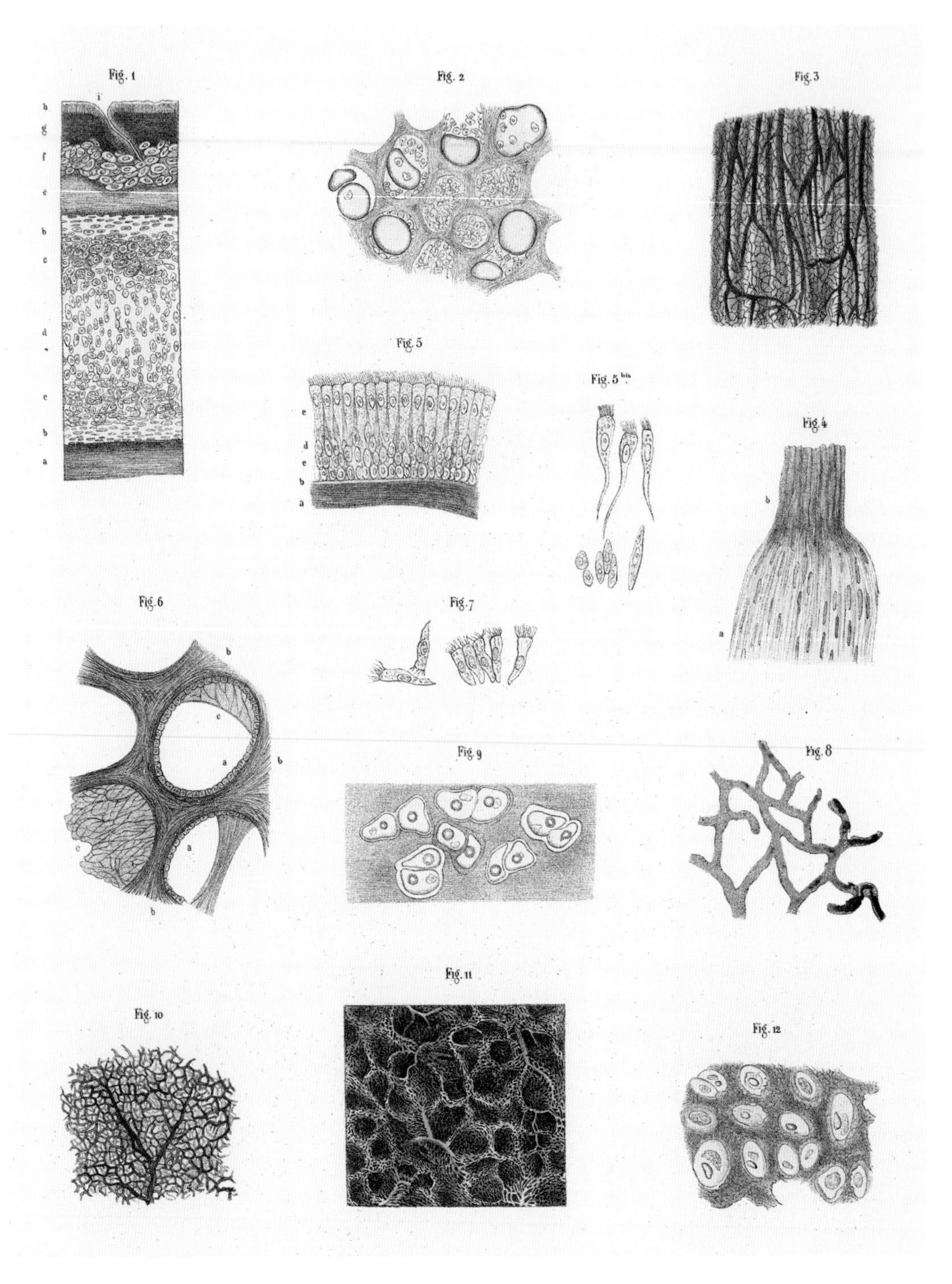

Microscopic anatomy: Respiratory tract and thyroid gland
Anatomie microscopique : Appareil respiratoire et glande thyroïde
Anatomía microscópica: aparato respiratorio y glándula tiroides

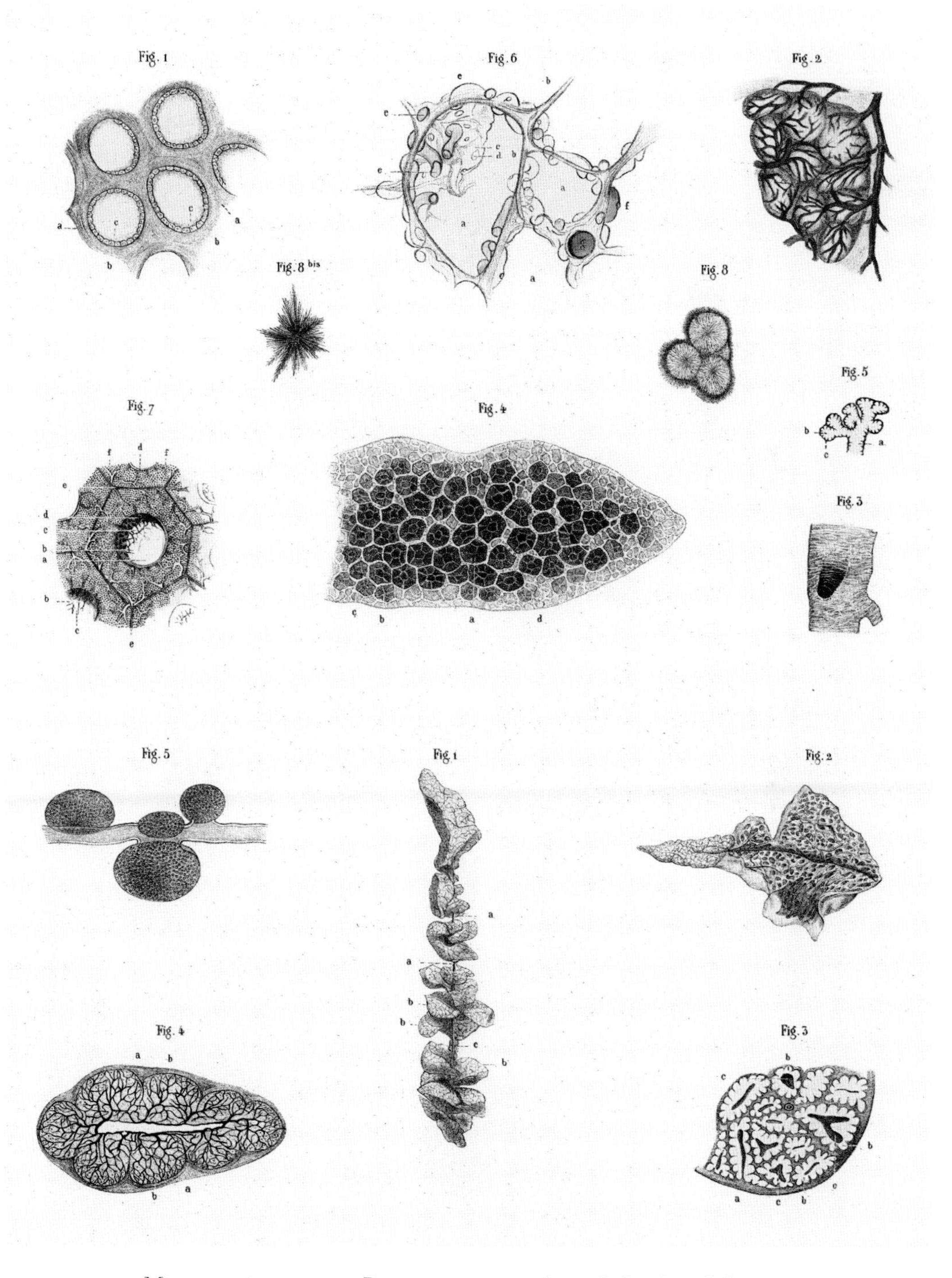

Microscopic anatomy: Respiratory tract, thyroid gland, and thymus
Anatomie microscopique : Appareil respiratoire, glande thyroïde et thymus
Anatomía microscópica: aparato respiratorio, glándula tiroides y timo

ANATOMIA MICROSCOPICA: REN, GLANDULA SUPRARENALIS, ET TESTIS

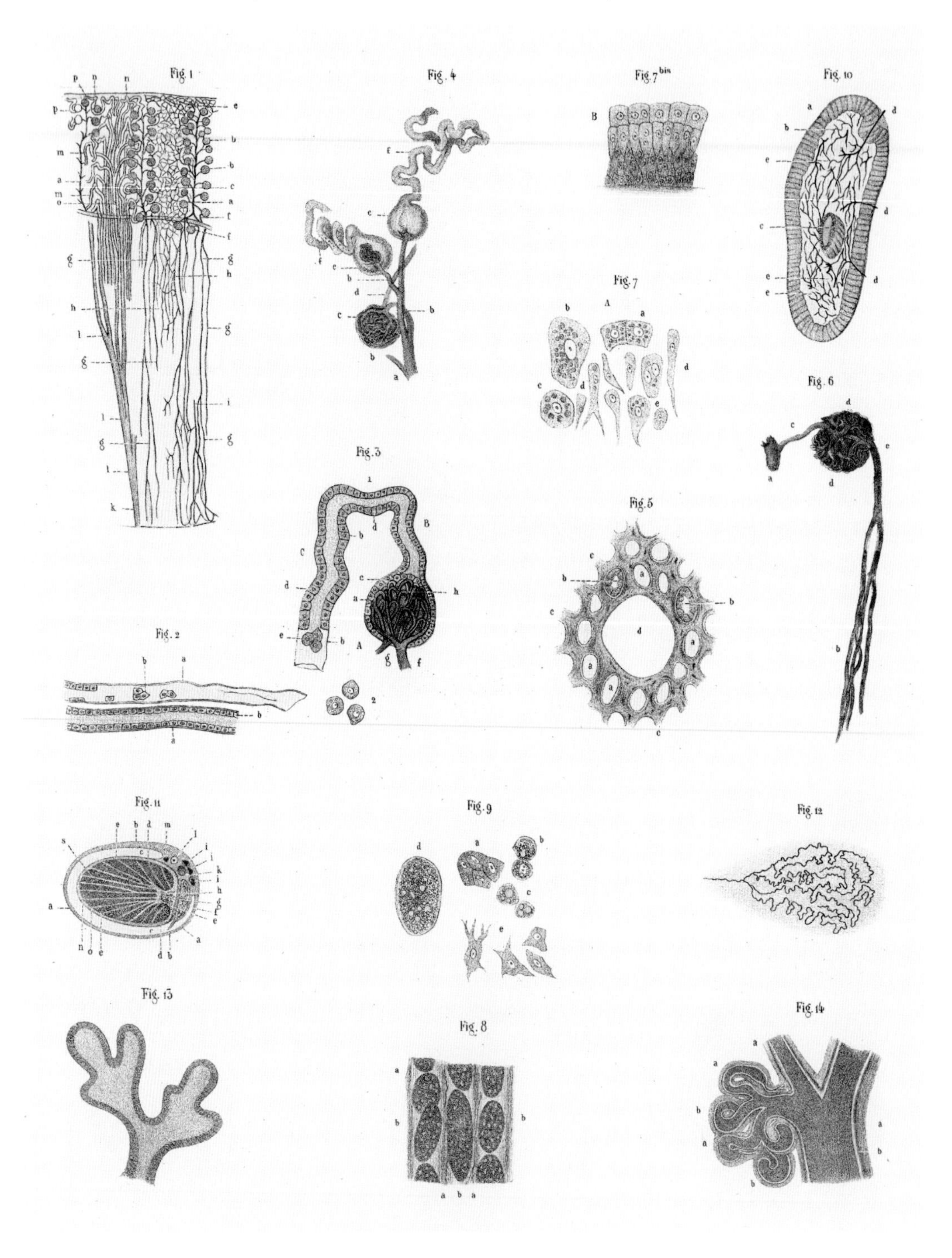

Microscopic anatomy: Kidney, adrenal gland, and testicle
Anatomie microscopique : Rein, glande surrénale et testicule
Anatomía microscópica: riñón, glándula suprarrenal y testículo

ANATOMIA MICROSCOPICA: UTERUS, OVARIUM, ET MAMMA

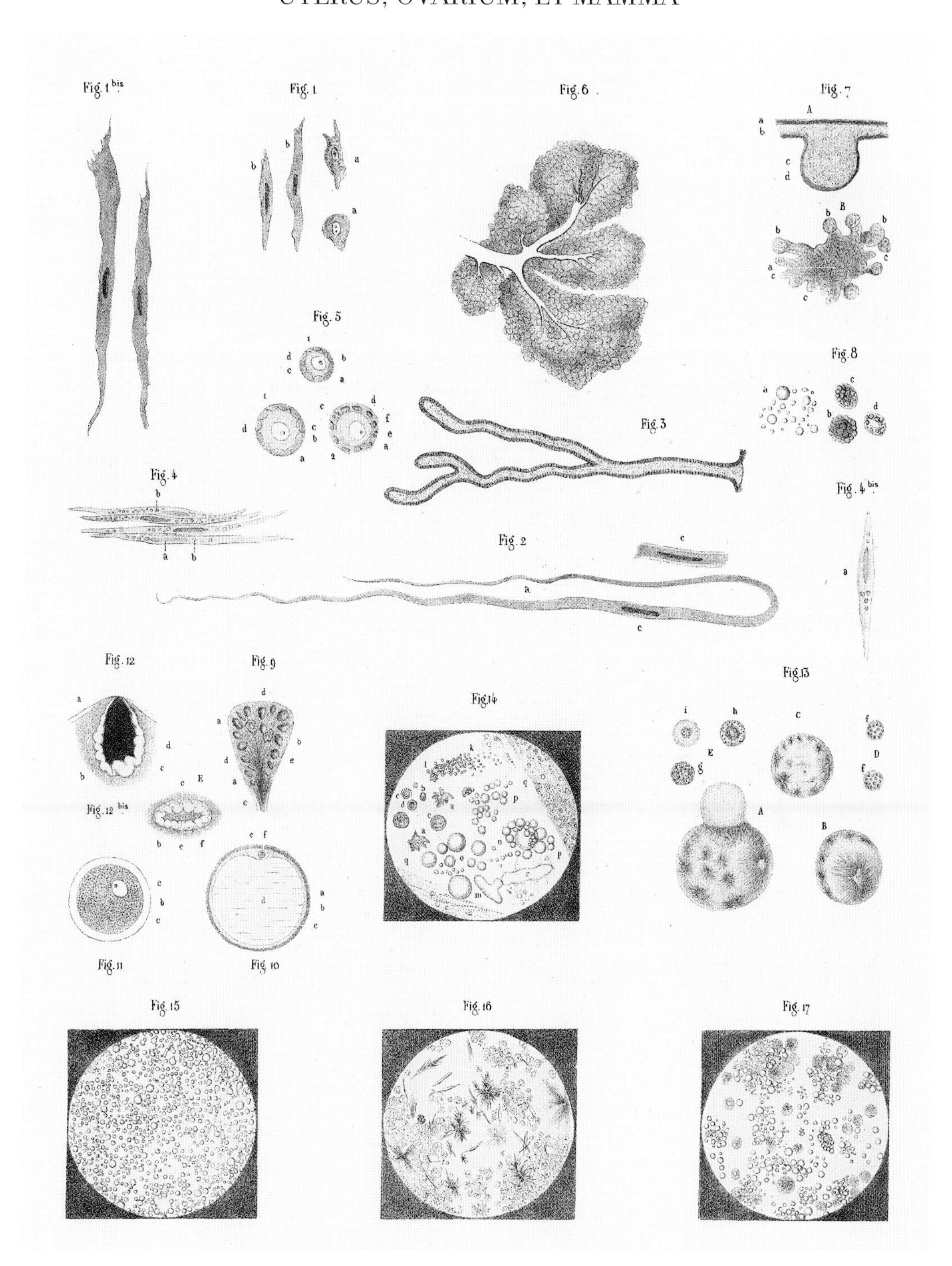

Microscopic anatomy: Uterus, ovary, and breast
Anatomie microscopique : Utérus, ovaire et sein
Anatomía microscópica: útero, ovario y glándula mamaria

ANATOMIA MICROSCOPICA: COR, ARTERIAE, ET VENAE

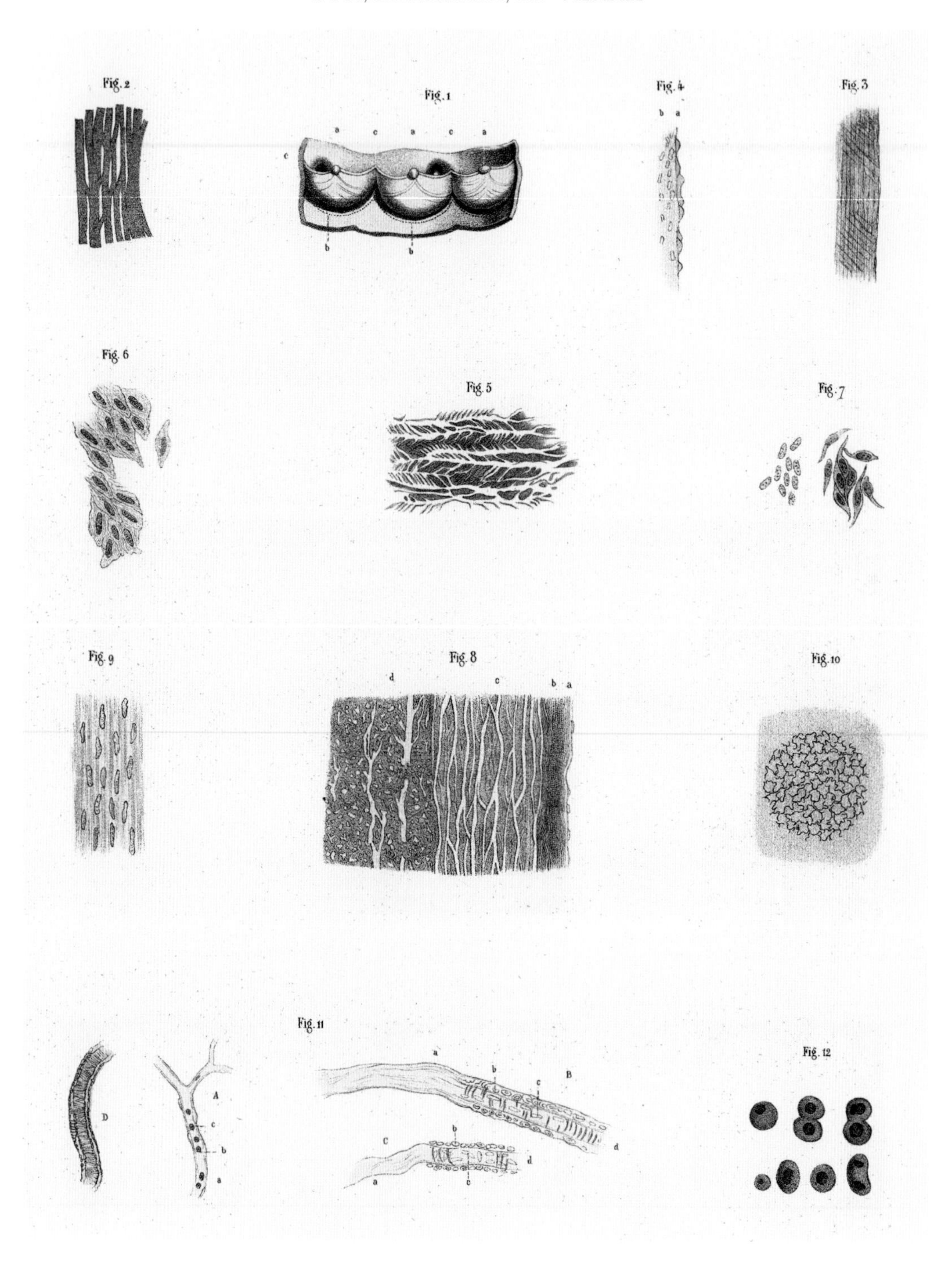

Microscopic anatomy: Heart, arteries, and veins
Anatomie microscopique : Cœur, artères et veines
Anatomía microscópica: corazón, arterias y venas

ANATOMIA MICROSCOPICA:
ARTERIAE ET VENAE

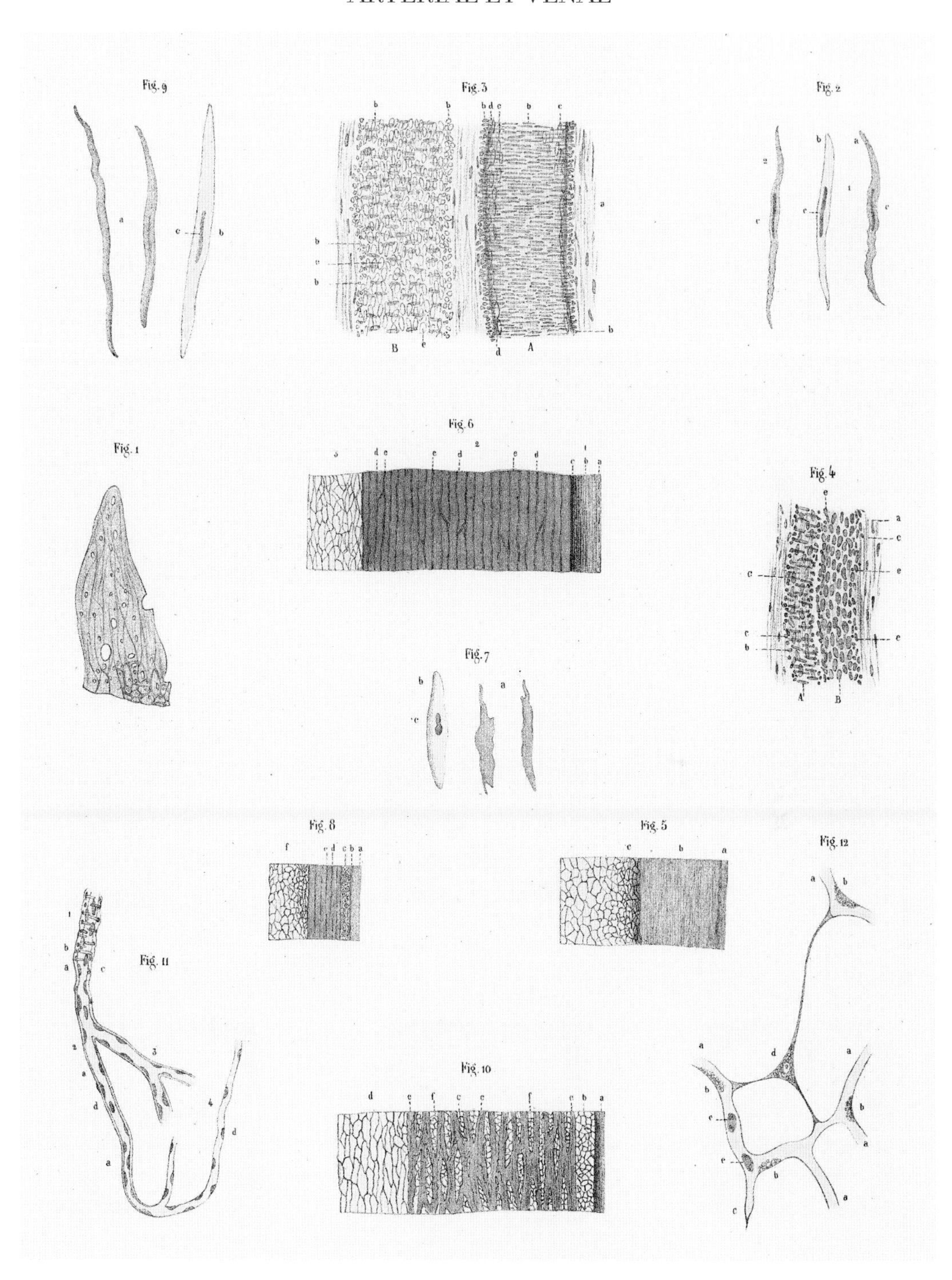

Microscopic anatomy: Arteries and veins
Anatomie microscopique : Artères et veines
Anatomía microscópica: arterias y venas

ANATOMIA MICROSCOPICA: SYSTEMA LYMPHATICUM

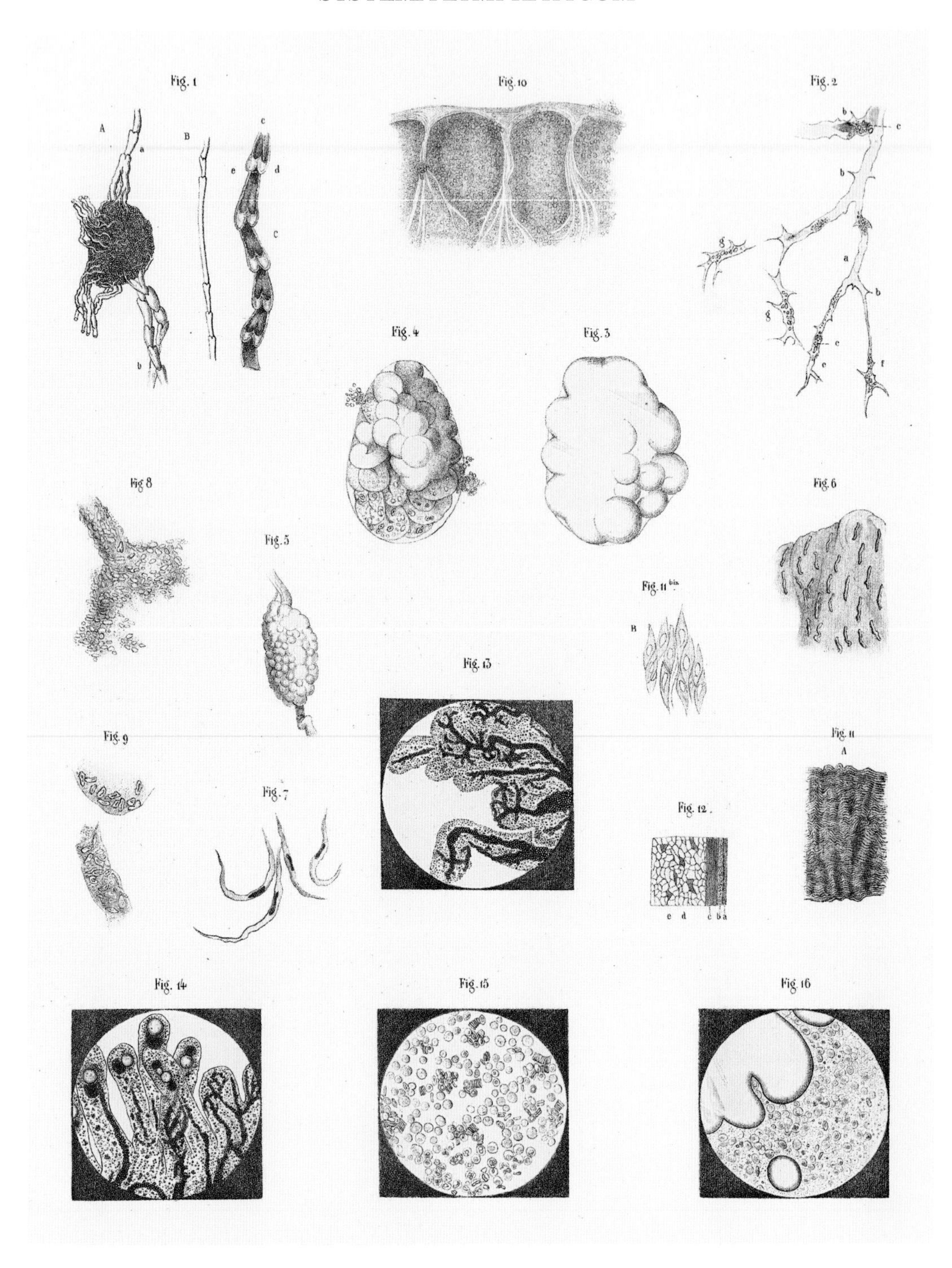

Microscopic anatomy: Lymphatic system
Anatomie microscopique : Système lymphatique
Anatomía microscópica: sistema linfático

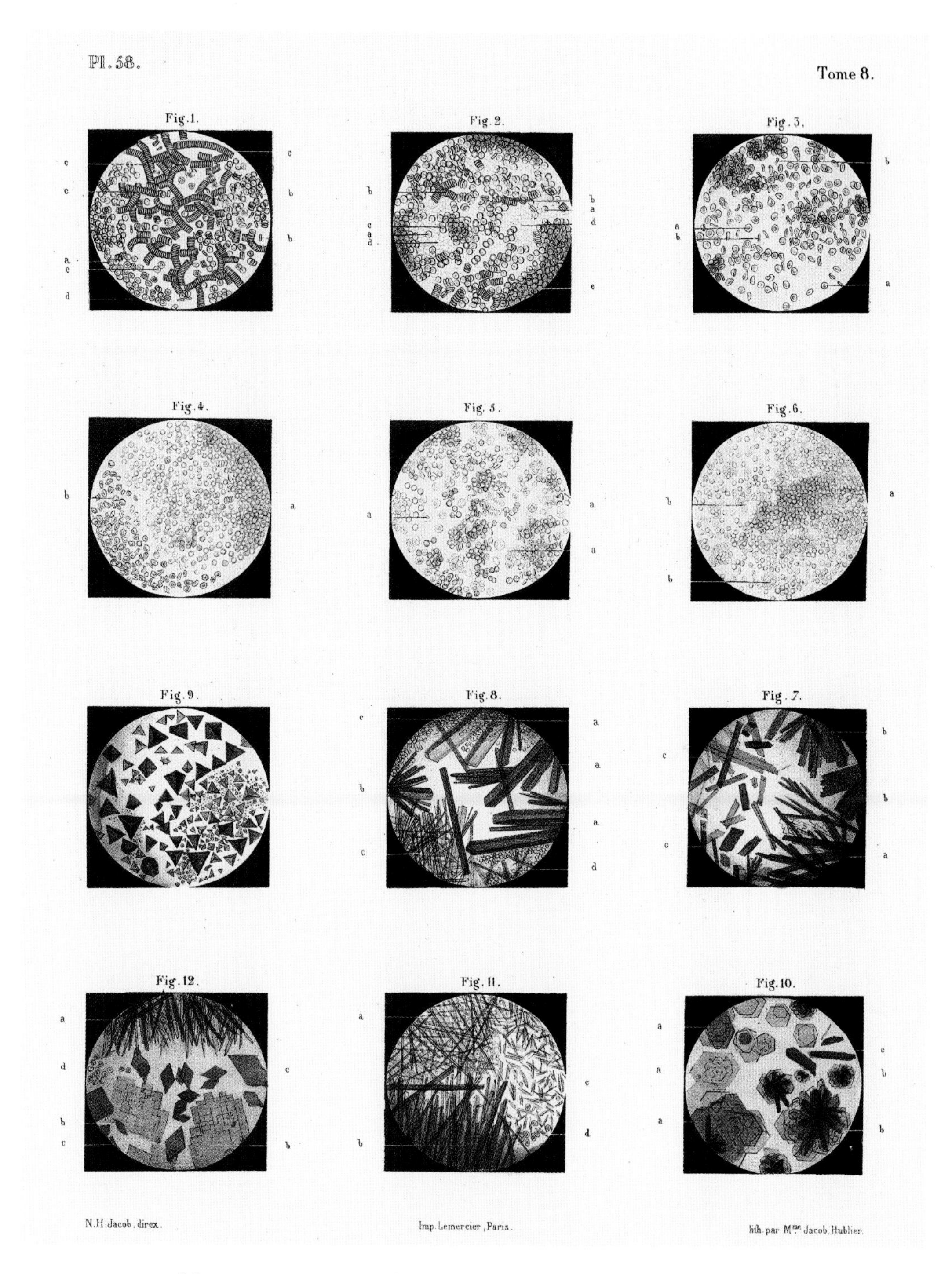

Microscopic anatomy: Blood / Anatomie microscopique : Sang
Anatomía microscópica: sangre

ANATOMIA MICROSCOPICA: OCULUS ET GLANDULA LACRIMALIS

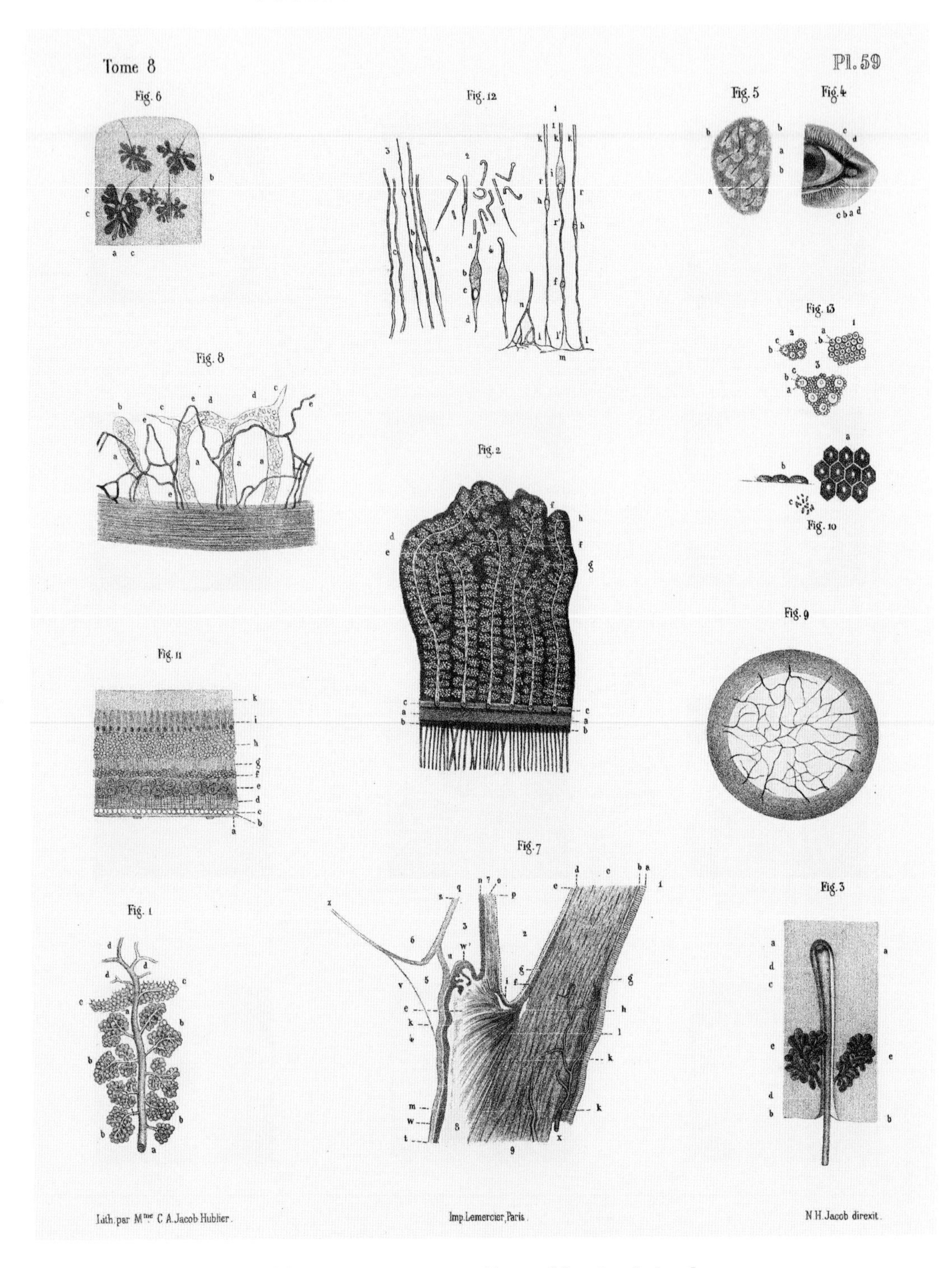

Microscopic anatomy: Eye and lacrimal gland
Anatomie microscopique : Œil et glande lacrymale
Anatomía microscópica: ojo y glándula lagrimal

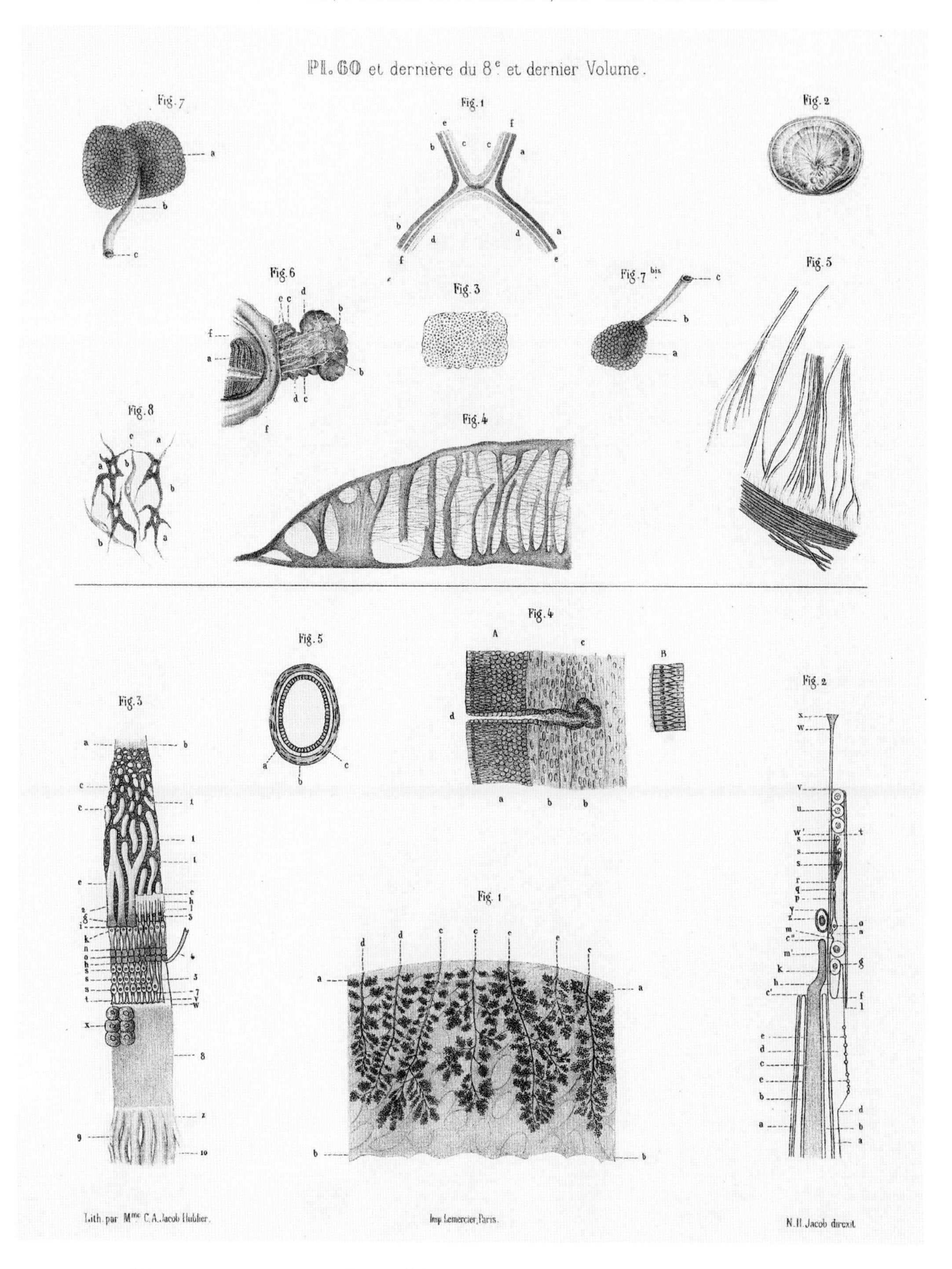

Microscopic anatomy: Eye and lacrimal gland, inner ear, and nasal cavity
Anatomie microscopique : Œil et glande lacrymale, oreille interne et cavité nasale
Anatomía microscópica: ojo y glándula lagrimal, oído interno y cavidad nasal

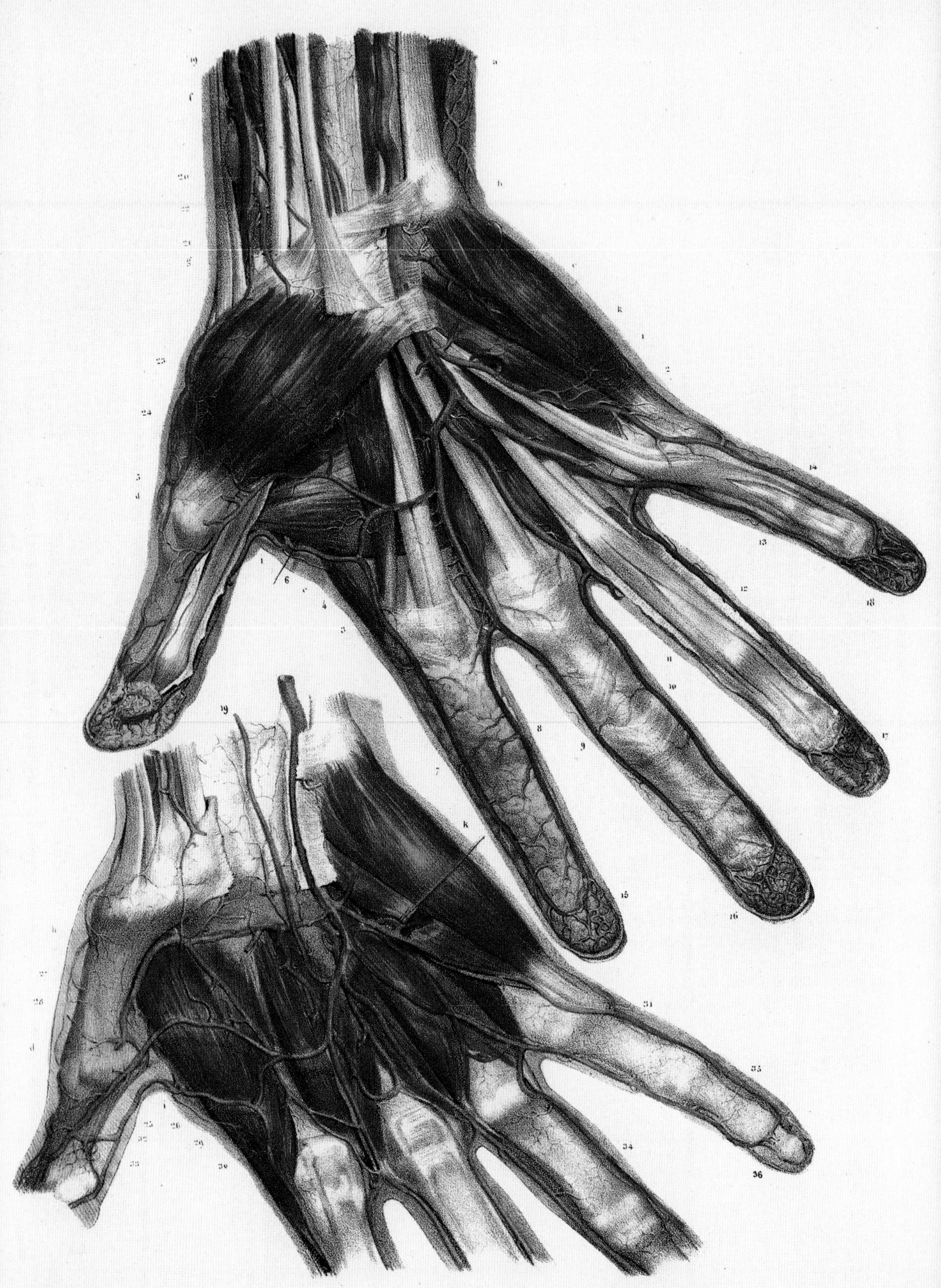

Dessiné d'après nature par N.H. Jacob.

Imprimé par Benard

APPENDIX

Index
Bibliography
Imprint

Left page / page à gauche / Pagina contigua:
Arteries of the hand / Artères de la main / Arterias de la mano

PRIMARY LITERATURE

Publications of J. M. Bourgery

Quelques faits sur l'emploi des ligatures circulaires des membres dans la plupart des maladies périodiques, M. D. thesis, Paris, 1827.

Traité de petite chirurgie, Paris, ed. Rouen, 1829; 2nd French ed.: Paris, G. Baillière ed., 1835; *A treatise on lesser surgery or the minor surgical operations*, New York, 1834; *Die kleinern chirurgischen Operationen und Handgriffe, Handbuch für Wundärzte erster und zweiter Klasse*, Berlin, 1836.

Traité complet de l'anatomie de l'homme comprenant la médecine opératoire par le Docteur J. M. Bourgery avec planches lithographiées d'après nature par N. H. Jacob, Paris, C. A. Delaunay, 1831–1854 (folio, 8 vols., 2108 pp., 725 pl.); 2 nd ed. Paris, ed. L. Guérin., 1866–1871; *The whole anatomy of the human body, with its various practical applications, including a system of operative surgery, by J. M. Bourgery, ...illustrated by lithographic plates drawn from nature by N. H. Jacob*, Paris, ed. C. A. Delaunay, 1833–1837.

Anatomie élémentaire en 20 planches... avec un texte explicatif à part... formant un manuel complet d'anatomie physiologique, Paris, ed. J. B. Baillière, 1834–1835; 2 nd French ed. Paris, ed. Crochard, 1836–1839; *Anfangsgründe der Anatomie in 20 Steindrucktafeln*, Leipzig, 1837.

Note sur les titres de M. Bourgery comme candidat à la chaire d'anthropologie au Muséum d'Histoire Naturelle, Paris, printed by P. Renouard, n. d.

Notice sur les titres de M. Bourgery comme candidat à l'une des deux places vacantes dans la section de médecine et de chirurgie de l'Académie des Sciences, Paris, printed by P. Renouard, 1843.

Les annexes du fœtus et leur développement, Thèse concours professeur chaire anatomie, Paris, printed by P. Renouard, 1846.

Articles:

Comptes-Rendus de l'Académie des Sciences de Paris:

"Anatomie microscopique de la rate dans l'homme et les mammifères" (1842).

"Recherches sur la structure intime des poumons dans l'homme et les mammifères" (1842, vol. 15, pp. 63–65 and 107–109).

"Rapport de la structure anatomique avec la capacité fonctionnelle des poumons dans les deux sexes et à différents âges" (1842–1843, vol. 15, pp. 590–592, and vol. 16, pp. 182–186).

"Sur les masses comparatives que présentent dans l'homme et quelques animaux mammifères les différents organes qui composent le système nerveux" (1844, vol. 19, pp. 603–607).

"Mémoire sur l'extrémité céphalique du grand sympathique dans l'homme et les animaux mammifères" (1845, vol. 20, pp. 1014–1020).

"Mémoire sur les nerfs des membranes séreuses en général" (1845, vol. 21, pp. 566–570).

"Recherche sur la structure intime de la masse musculaire et de la membrane tégumentaire de la langue dans l'homme et les mammifères" (1847, vol. 24, pp. 154–158).

"Mémoire sur le système capillaire circulatoire dit intermédiaire des artères aux veines" and "Deuxième mémoire sur l'appareil capillaire circulatoire" (1848, vol. 27, pp. 261–264 and 378–380).

Gazette Médicale de Paris:

"Mémoire sur la coordination générale et la structure intime de l'appareil nerveux de la langue dans l'homme et les mammifères" (1848).

Illustrations for books, memoirs and articles by N. H. Jacob:

SENEFELDER A., *L'art de la lithographie*, Paris, 1819; frontispiece: *Le génie de la lithographie à la gloire d'A. Senefelder*, and 2 pl.: *Portrait d'Aloys Senefelder, and* Tête d'amazone.

BLANDIN P. F., *Traité d'anatomie topographique des régions du corps humain considérée spécialement dans ses rapports avec la chirurgie & la médecine opératoire*, Paris, 1826; 12 pl. lithographed by N. H. Jacob.

GIRARD J., *Traité des hernies inguinales dans le cheval et autres monodactyles*, Paris, 1827; 7 pl. lithographed by N. H. Jacob.

BOURGERY J. B., *Traité complet de l'anatomie de l'homme...* see publication of J. M. Bourgery.

BOURGERY J. B., *Anatomie élémentaire en 20 planches...* see publication of J. M. Bourgery.

DUPUYTREN G., *Mémoire sur une manière nouvelle de pratiquer l'opération de la pierre*, Paris, 1836; 10 pl. drawn by N. H. Jacob and lithographed by Langlumé.

DOMEYKO I., "Mémoire sur les fossiles secondaires recueillis dans le Chili", *Mémoires de la Société Géologique de France*, 1851, 2nd series, vol. 4; 8 pl. (86 figs.) by N. H. Jacob.

Bulletin de la Société Géologique de France (1855–1857).

SECONDARY LITERATURE

General biographical dictionnaries

BELLIER de la CHAVIGNERIE E. & L. AUVRAY, *Dictionnaire général des artistes de l'école française depuis l'origine des arts du dessin jusqu'à nos jours*, Paris, 1882.

BENEZIT E., *Dictionnaire critique et documentaire des peintres, sculpteurs, dessinateurs et graveurs de tous les temps et de tous les pays*. Nouvelle édition, 14 vols., Paris, 1999.

BERALDI H., *Les graveurs du XIX*e *siècle*, Paris, 1885–1892.

Dictionnaire de biographie française, (Eds. J. Balteau & M. Prévost), 19 vols. (A–L), Paris, 1933–2001.

Dictionnaire encyclopédique des sciences médicales (Ed. A. Dechambre), 100 vols., Paris, 1869–1889.

Dictionnaire Napoléon, (Ed. J. Tulard), Paris, 1987.

DUGNAT G. & P. SANCHEZ, *Dictionnaire des graveurs, illustrateurs et affichistes français et étrangers (1673–1950)*, 5 vols., Dijon, 2001.

GABET C., *Dictionnaire des artistes de l'École française au XIX*e *siècle*, Paris, 1831.

HIRSCH A., E. GURLT & A. WERNICH, *Biographisches Lexikon der hervorragenden Aerzte aller Zeiten und Völker*, 6 vols., 3rd ed., 1962.

HUGUET F., *Les professeurs de la faculté de médecine de Paris. Dictionnaire biographique 1794–1939*, Paris, 1991.

LAROUSSE P., *Grand dictionnaire universel du XIXe siècle*, Paris, 1866–1876.

MANUILA A., L. MANUILA, M. NICOLE & H. LAMBERT, *Dictionnaire français de médecine et de biologie*, 4 vols., Paris, 1970–1975.

NAGLER G. K., *Neues allgemeines Künstler-Lexikon*, 25 vols., 1835–1852.

Nouvelle biographie universelle publiée par MM. Firmin Didot Fr., (Ed. Dr Hoefer), Paris, 1853.

OLRY R., *Dictionary of anatomical eponyms*, Stuttgart, 1995.

Répertoire biographique des membres de l'Académie des Sciences (Institut de France), Paris, 1989.

SACHAILE de la BARRE C., *Les médecins de Paris jugés par leurs œuvres*, Paris, 1845.

SAUR K. G., *Allgemeines Künstler-Lexikon. Die Bildenden Künstler aller Zeiten und Völker*, 43 vols. (A–F), Munich, Leipzig, 1992–2004.

J. M. Bourgery, N. H. Jacob, C. Bernard

BERNARDY F. de, *Eugène de Beauharnais 1781–1824*, Paris, 1973.

DELECLUZE E. J., "Des travaux anatomiques de M. le Docteur Bourgery", *Revue de Paris*, 17, 1840, pp. 208–222.

DELHOUME L., P. HUARD & J. THEODORIDES, "Un cahier de notes inédites de Jean Marc Bourgery", *Histoire des Sciences Médicales*, (special no.), 1959, pp. 103–114.

Eugène de Beauharnais, honneur & fidélité, (ed. A. Pillepich), Paris, 1999.

GRMEK M., *Catalogue des manuscrits de Claude Bernard avec la bibliographie de ses travaux imprimés et des études sur son œuvre*, Paris, 1967.

– *Claude Bernard et la méthode expérimentale*, Geneva, 1973 (and Paris, 1991).

HILDENBRAND R., "Bourgery und Jacob, Hirschfeld und Léveillé – über Meisterwerke der anatomischen Ikonographie zur Blütezeit der Lithographie", *Anatomischer Anzeiger*, 158, 1985, pp. 363–372.

HUBERT N. & A. POUGETOUX, *Châteaux de Malmaison et de Bois-Préau*, Musées napoléoniens de l'Ile d'Aix et de la maison Bonaparte à Ajaccio: catalogue sommaire illustré des peintures et dessins, Paris, 1989, p. 97.

LEGRAND N., "Les dessins originaux de N. H. Jacob ayant servi à lithographier les planches du 'Traité complet de l'anatomie de l'homme' par Bourgery et Jacob. Autres dessins. Portrait inédit de l'impératrice Joséphine", *Bulletin de la Société Française d'Histoire de la Médecine*, 1909, pp. 1–14.

Nineteenth century French drawings, (ed. Hazlitt, Gooden, & Fox), London, 1984.

OLMSTED J. M. D. & E. H. OLMSTED, *Claude Bernard and the Experimental Method in Medicine*, London, 1952.

OMAN C., *Napoleon's Viceroy Eugène de Beauharnais*, London, 1966.

PROCHIANTZ A., *Claude Bernard. La révolution physiologique*, Paris, 1990.

SCHILLER J., *Claude Bernard et les problèmes scientifiques de son temps*, Paris, 1967.

TISSERON L. & de QUINCY, "Notice sur M. le Docteur Bourgery", *Archives des hommes du jour*, April 1846.

History of Anatomy

Anatomie de la couleur: l'invention de l'estampe en couleurs, (ed. F. Rodari), Paris, Lausanne, 1996.

BINET J. L., *Dessins et traités d'anatomie*, Paris, 1980.

BRIDSON G. D. R. & J. J. WHITE, *Plant, animal and anatomical illustrations in art and science: a bibliographical guide from the 16th century to the present day*, Winchester, 1990.

CABANIS E. A., V. DELMAS, M. T. IBA ZIZEN, J. P. LASSAU & R. SABAN, "Le musée Delmas-Orfila-Rouvière", *Les musées de médecine. Histoire, patrimoine et grandes figures de la médecine en France*, Toulouse, 1999, pp. 105–111.

CAZORT M., M. KORNELL & K. B. ROBERTS., *The ingenious machine of nature: four centuries of art and anatomy*, Ottawa, 1996.

CHOULANT L., *Geschichte und Bibliographie der anatomischen Abbildungen nach ihrer Beziehung aus anatomischer Wissenschaft und bildender Kunst*, Leipzig, 1852 (2nd ed., 1945); *History and bibliography of anatomic illustration and its relation to anatomic science and the graphic arts*, Chicago, 1920 (2nd ed., New York, 1962).

CLARKE E. & K. DEWHURST, *An illustrated history of brain function*, Oxford, 1972 (*Histoire illustrée de la fonction cérébrale*, Paris, 1975).

CLOQUET G., *Jules Cloquet. Sa vie, ses œuvres*, Paris, 1910.

CORDIER G., *Paris et les anatomistes au cours de l'histoire*, Paris, 1955.

Colloque "J. B. Baillière et Fils, éditeurs de livres médicaux et scientifiques", (Ed. D. Gourevitch), Paris, 29 January 2005, in press.

CONAN P., C. REGNIER & M. ROUX-DESSARPS, "A propos de l'exposition: Une grande maison d'édition médicale française J. B. Baillière et fils", *Histoire des Sciences Médicales*, 37, 2003, pp. 407–414.

Corps à vif. Art et anatomie, (Ed. D. Petherbridge, C. Ritschard & A. Carlino), Geneva, 1998.

HAHN A. & P. DUMAITRE, *Histoire de la médecine et du livre médical à la lumière des collections de la Bibliothèque de la Faculté de Médecine de Paris*, Paris, 1962.

HERRLINGER R., "Das erste lithographisch illustrierte Lehrbuch der Anatomie", *Sudhoffs Archiv*, 47, 1963, pp. 224–226.

HILDENBRAND R., "Bourgery und Jacob, Hirschfeld und Léveillé – über Meisterwerke der anatomischen Ikonographie zur Blütezeit der Lithographie", *Anatomischer Anzeiger*, 158, 1985, pp. 363–372.

HOUEL M., *Catalogue du musée Orfila*, Paris, 1881.

LE MINOR J. M., "Les 'Nouveaux Éléments d'Anatomie Descriptive' de H. Beaunis et A. Bouchard (1868)", *Histoire des Sciences Médicales*, 29, 1995, pp. 165–174.

– "L'artiste strasbourgeois Émile Schweitzer (1837–1903) et l'illustration anatomique et médicale", *Cahiers Alsaciens d'Archéologie, d'Art et d'Histoire*, 45, 2002, pp. 141–149.

LEMIRE M., *Artistes et mortels*, Paris, 1990.

L'âme au corps: arts et sciences 1793–1993, (Ed. J. Clair), Paris, 1993.

L'illustration anatomique de la Renaissance au siècle des Lumières, (Ed. D. de Montmollin), Neuchâtel, 1998.

MAYOR A. H., *Artists and anatomists*, New York, 1984.

Musées Delmas-Orfila-Rouvière, (*Surgical and Radiologic Anatomy*, 17, suppl. 1), 1995.

PARIENTE L., "La vie et l'œuvre de Jules

Germain Cloquet", *Manuel d'anatomie descriptive du corps humain, nouvelle édition en cinq volumes avec les reproductions des 340 planches lithographiées de l'originale*, Paris, 1998, pp. 11–70.

PUTSCHER M., *Geschichte der medizinischen Abbildung von 1600 bis zur Gegenwart*, Munich, 1972.

RAILLET A. & L. MOULE, *Histoire de l'École d'Alfort*, Paris, 1908.

REGNIER C., "Jean-Baptiste Baillière (1797–1885), l'éditeur visionnaire qui diffusa la médecine française à travers le monde", *Medicographia*, 27, 2005, pp. 1–10.

ROBERTS K. B. & J. D. W. TOMLINSON, *The fabric of the body. European traditions of anatomical illustration*, Oxford, 1992.

SOUSA J. de, "La lithographie dans l'illustration d'anatomie", *Art & Métiers du Livre*, no. 201, Janvier–Février 1977, pp. 19–23.

VENE M., *Ecorchés. L'exploration du corps XIVe–XVIIIe siècle*, Paris, 2001.

WEGNER R. N., *Das Anatomenbildnis. Seine Entwicklung im Zusammenhang mit der anatomischen Abbildung*, Basel, 1939.

WOLF-HEIDEGGER G. & A. M. CETTO, *Die anatomische Sektion in bildlicher Darstellung*, Basel, 1967.

History of Lithography

ADHEMAR J., *L'estampe française: la lithographie en France au XIXe siècle*, Paris, 1944.

La France romantique. Les lithographies de paysage au XIXe siècle, Paris, 1997.

BEGUIN A., *Dictionnaire technique de l'estampe*, Paris, 1998.

BLAND D., *A history of book illustration*, London, 1958.

BOUCHOT H., *La lithographie*, Paris, 1895.

BREGEAUT L., *Manuel complet théorique et pratique du dessinateur et de l'imprimeur lithographe*, Paris, 1927.

BURCH R. M., *Colour printing and colour printers*, London, 1910.

DELMAS B., "Lithographie et lithographes à Paris dans la première moitié du XIXe siècle", *Le livre et l'historien*, Geneva, 1997, pp. 723–742.

ENGELMANN G., *Manuel du dessinateur-lithographe*, Paris, 1822.

– *Rapport sur la chromolithographie, nouveau procédé produisant des lithographies coloriées*, Mulhouse, 1837.

– *Traité théorique et pratique de la lithographie*, Mulhouse, 1835–1840.

GRÄFF W., *Die Einführung der Lithographie in Frankreich: eine kunstgeschichtliche Untersuchung*, Heidelberg, 1906.

HULLMANDEL G., *The art of drawing on stone*, London, 1824 (2nd ed., 1833; 3rd ed., 1835).

LANG L. & J. E. BERSIER, *La lithographie en France*, 3 vols., Mulhouse, 1946–1952.

LARAN J., J. ADHEMAR & J. PRINET, *L'estampe*, 2 vols., Paris, 1959.

LEMERCIER A., *La lithographie française de 1796 à 1896 et les arts qui s'y rattachent s'adressant aux artistes et aux imprimeurs*, Paris, 1896–1898.

LIEURE J., *La lithographie artistique et ses diverses techniques*, Paris, 1939.

MELOT M., "Le texte et l'image", *Histoire de l'édition française. 3. Le temps des éditeurs. Du romantisme à la Belle Epoque*, (Ed. H. J. Martin & R. Chartier Paris, 1985, pp. 287–311.

SENEFELDER A., *Vollständiges Lehrbuch der Steindruckerei*, Munich, 1818 (*L'art de la lithographie*, Paris, 1819; new ed., Paris, 1974).

SHARP R., *The development of chromolithography in the nineteenth century: a brief history of lithography & its association with colour in Germany, France & England over a hundred years*, Manchester, 1962.

SOUSA J. de, *La mémoire lithographique, 200 ans d'images*, Paris, 1998.

TWYMAN M., *Lithography 1800–1850*, London, 1970.

WAGNER C., *Die Geschichte der Lithographie*, Leipzig, 1914.

WEBER W., *Saxa loquuntur, Steine reden. Geschichte der Lithographie*, Heidelberg, Berlin, 1961 (*A history of lithography*, London, 1966; *Histoire de la lithographie*, Paris, 1967).

WINKLER R. A., *Die Frühzeit der deutschen Lithographie. Katalog der Bilddrucke von 1796–1821*, Munich, 1975.

ACKNOWLEDGEMENTS

This edition of J. M. Bourgery's and N. H. Jacob's *Traité* is based on a copy once in the possession of Simon Finch in London and was made possible by the kind permission of the owner.

The original volumes were digitally reproduced by the Digitalisierungs-Zentrum der Staats- und Universitätsbibliothek Göttingen. We wish to thank Martin Liebetruth of GDZ for their kind support. The authors wish to thank in particular Dr Franck Billmann for his reading and corrections of the French manuscript, the English and German translations and the proofs of the work, as well as for his help in composing the Latin titles for the plates. The authors also thank Dr Matthias Rozak, Dr Nicolas Greib and Dr Hervé Schlotterbeck for helping with the composition of the Latin titles for the plates and for their much appreciated support, and Mr Louis Schlaefli, for the reading and the correction of the Latin titles of the work. The authors also thank M. Olivier Gabet, curator at the Musée d'Orsay in Paris, Maître Philippe Plantade, François Rollin, Dr Julien Wolff, and finally Dr. Petra Lamers-Schütze.

REMERCIEMENTS

La présente édition du *Traité* de J. M. Bourgery et N. H. Jacob a été réalisée à partir de l'exemplaire déjà en possession de Simon Finch à Londres et n'aurait pu voir le jour sans l'aimable autorisation de son propriétaire que nous remercions chaleureusement. La numérisation des volumes de l'édition originale a été réalisée par le DigitalisierungsZentrum de la Bibliothèque Universitaire de Göttingen. Nous adressons nos remerciements à M. Martin Liebetruth, du Centre de numérisation.

Les auteurs souhaitent remercier en premier lieu le Dr Franck Billmann pour sa relecture et ses corrections du manuscrit français, des traductions anglaises et allemandes et des épreuves de l'ouvrage, ainsi que pour son aide dans la rédaction de titres latins des planches. Les auteurs remercient également le Dr Matthias Rozak, le Dr Nicolas Greib, et le Dr Hervé Schlotterbeck pour leur aide dans la rédaction de titres latins des planches et leur soutien apprécié, et M. Louis Schlaefli, pour la relecture et la correction des titres latins de l'ouvrage. Les auteurs remercient enfin M. Olivier Gabet, Conservateur au Musée d'Orsay à Paris, Maître Philippe Plantade, M. François Rollin, le Dr Julien Wolff, et enfin Mme le Dr Petra Lamers-Schütze.

AGRADECIMIENTOS

La presente edición del *Traité* de J. M. Bourgery y N. H. Jacob ha sido realizada a partir del ejemplar que obra en posesión de Simon Finch en Londres, sin cuya amable autorización no habría podido publicarse. Por ello, le estamos profundamente agradecidos.

La numeración de los volúmenes de la edición original ha sido realizada por el Digitalisierungs-Zentrum de la Biblioteca Universitaria de Gotinga. Quisiéramos dar las gracias a Martin Liebetruth, del DigitalisierungsZentrum.

Los autores desean agradecer en primer lugar al doctor Franck Billmann su segunda lectura y las correcciones del manuscrito francés, de las traducciones inglesa y alemana, y de las galeradas de la obra, así como su ayuda en la redacción de los títulos latinos de las planchas. Los autores también dan las gracias al doctor Matthias Rozak, al doctor Nicolas Greib y al doctor Hervé Schlotterbeck por su ayuda en la redacción de los títulos latinos de las láminas y su apreciado apoyo, y a Louis Schlaefli, por la segunda lectura y la corrección de los títulos latinos de la obra. Los autores expresan su agradecimiento, por último, a Olivier Gabet, comisario del Musée d'Orsay de París, a Philippe Plantade, a François Rollin, al doctor Julien Wolf y, por último, a la doctora Petra Lamers-Schütze.

ABOUT THE AUTHORS

Jean-Marie Le Minor has been professor of anatomy at the University of Strasburg since 1990, radiologist at the University Hospital in Strasburg, member of the French National Academy of Surgery since 2012, laureate of the French National Academy of Medicine (2003), and officer of the Ordre des Arts et des Lettres (French Ministry of Culture). He is the author of several anatomy and history books and numerous scientific and historical articles.

Henri Sick was professor of anatomy at the University of Strasburg from 1972 to 2003 and director of the Institute of Anatomy from 1994 to 2003. He is an officer of the Ordre des Palmes Académiques (French Ministry of Education) and the author of several books on sectional anatomy, as well as numerous scientific articles.

À PROPOS DES AUTEURS

Jean-Marie Le Minor est professeur d'anatomie à l'Université de Strasbourg depuis 1990, radiologue aux Hôpitaux universitaires de Strasbourg, membre de l'Académie Nationale de Chirurgie depuis 2012, lauréat de l'Académie Nationale de Médecine (Paris, 2003) et officier de l'Ordre des Arts et des Lettres (Ministère de la Culture). Il est l'auteur de plusieurs ouvrages d'anatomie et d'histoire et de nombreux articles scientifiques et historiques.

Henri Sick a été professeur d'anatomie à l'Université de Strasbourg de 1972 à 2003 et directeur de l'Institut d'Anatomie de 1994 à 2003. Officier de l'Ordre des Palmes Académiques (Ministère de l'Éducation Nationale), il a publié plusieurs ouvrages sur l'anatomie sectionnelle ainsi que de nombreux articles scientifiques.

SOBRE LOS AUTORES

Jean-Marie Le Minor ha sido profesor de anatomía en la Universidad de Estrasburgo desde 1990, radiólogo en el Ho spital Universitario de Estrasburgo, miembro de la Academia Nacional de Cirugía de Francia desde 2012, premio de la Academia Nacional de Medicina de Francia (2003), y oficial de la Orden de las Artes y las Letras (Ministerio de Cultura de Francia). También es autor de numerosos libros y artículos sobre anatomía e historia.

Henri Sick fue profesor de anatomía en la Universidad de Estrasburgo de 1972 a 2003 y director del Instituto de Anatomía entre 1994 y 2003. Es oficial de la Orden de las Palmas Académicas (Ministerio de Educación de Francia) y autor de varios libros sobre anatomía seccional, así como de numerosos artículos científicos.

IMPRINT

EACH AND EVERY TASCHEN BOOK PLANTS A SEED! TASCHEN is a carbon neutral publisher. Each year, we offset our annual carbon emissions with carbon credits at the Instituto Terra, a reforestation program in Minas Gerais, Brazil, founded by Lélia and Sebastião Salgado. To find out more about this ecological partnership, please check: www.taschen.com/zerocarbon
Inspiration: unlimited.
Carbon footprint: zero.

To stay informed about TASCHEN and our upcoming titles, please subscribe to our free magazine at www.taschen.com/magazine, follow us on Twitter, Instagram, and Facebook, or e-mail your questions to contact@taschen.com.

Photos in the introduction by Mathieu Bertola, Strassbourg

Hohenzollernring 53, D-50672 Köln
www.taschen.com

Printed in China
ISBN 978-3-8365-7798-4

Front cover / Couverture / Cubierta anterior:
Phrenic nerve / Nerf phrénique / Nervio frénico

Spine / Dos / Lomo:
Encephalon / Encéphale / Encéfalo

Back cover / Quatrième de couverture / Cubierta posterior:
Incisions: Scalpel positions / Incisions : Positions du bistouri / Incisiones: posiciones del bisturí

Original edition: © 2005 TASCHEN GmbH
Project management:
Petra Lamers-Schütze, Cologne
Scientific editing: Nikolaus Hildebrand and Karin Opeker, Freiburg i. Br.
Co-editing: Brigitte Beier, Hamburg
English translation:
Annegret Dahlmann, Cambridge
Spanish translation: Carlos Chacón Zabalza (introduction) and Ignacio Navascués (captions) for LocTeam, S. L., Barcelona
Design: Sense/Net Art Direction, Andy Disl and Birgit Eichwede, Cologne. www.sense-net.de
Production: Horst Neuzner, Cologne

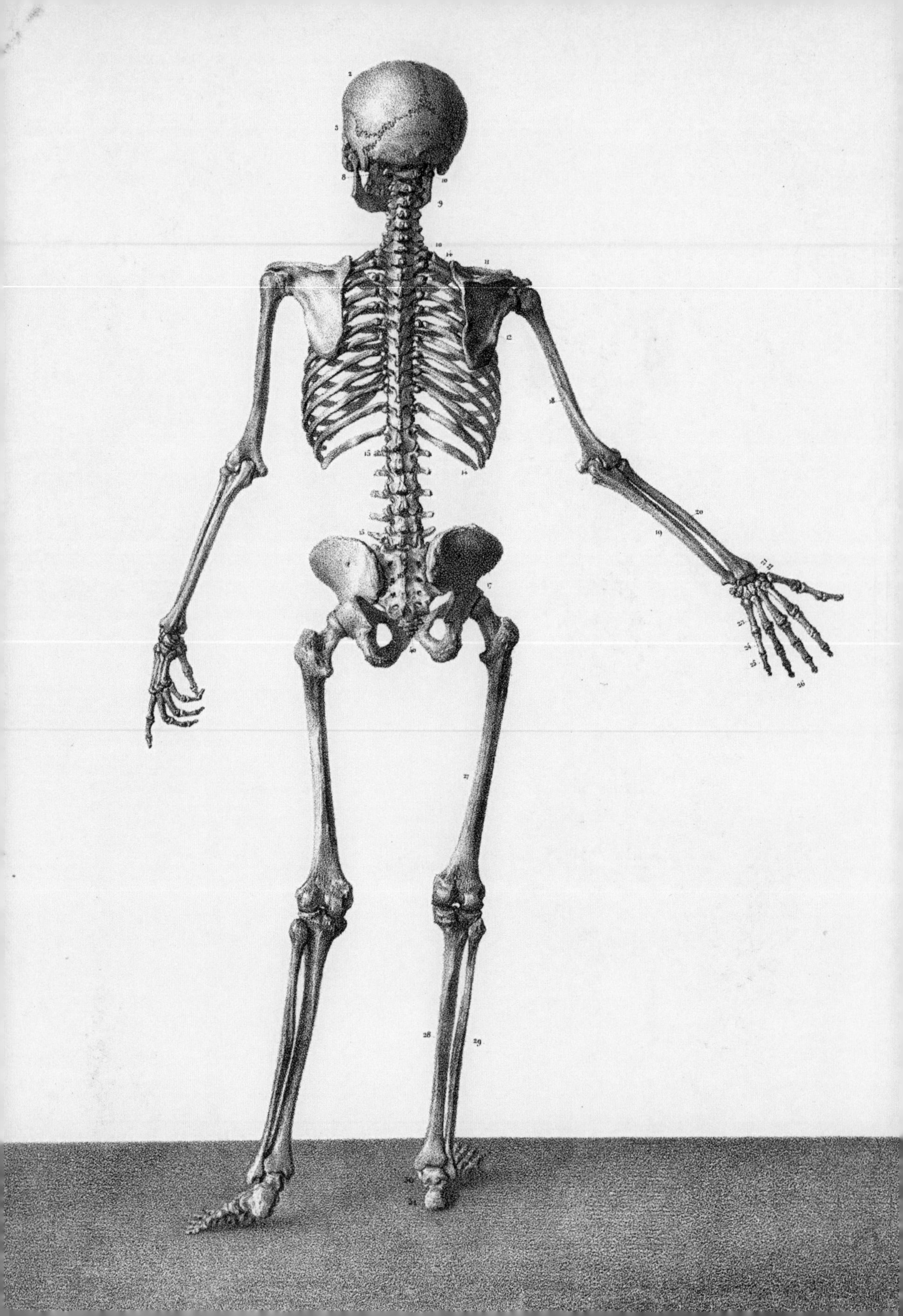